FETAL AND NEONATAL PHYSIOLOGY FOR THE ADVANCED PRACTICE NURSE

Amy J. Jnah, DNP, NNP-BC, is a veteran of the U.S. Navy Nurse Corps, an alumna of the Marquette University School of Nursing (BSN), East Carolina University College of Nursing (MSN), and University of Alabama at Birmingham (DNP). Dr. Jnah is currently an associate professor and director of the neonatal nurse practitioner program at the East Carolina University College of Nursing. She also serves as an assistant professor (adjunct) at the University of North Carolina at Chapel Hill School of Medicine.

Her clinical interests include hyperbilirubinemia, neonatal resuscitation, the transition to extrauterine life, and issues that affect late-preterm infants. Dr. Jnah is a master trainer for the American Academy of Pediatrics Helping Babies Breathe program, and an Instructor-Mentor for the Neonatal Resuscitation Program. Her academic interests include mentoring, role modeling, and the integration of multisensory teaching innovations within distance education.

Dr. Jnah has received numerous awards and honors, which include the Reserve Officer Training Corps academic scholarship (1994–1998), distinguished graduate of the East Carolina University neonatal nurse practitioner program (2007–2008), and East Carolina University Scholar-Teacher of the Year (2017–2018) award. She is an active member of the National Association of Neonatal Nurses (NANN), the National Association of Neonatal Nurse Practitioners (NANNP), and the Academy of Neonatal Nursing (ANN), as well as the Carolinas Association of Neonatal Nurse Practitioners (CANNP).

Andrea N. Trembath, MD, MPH, is a neonatologist and health services researcher at the University of Carolina at Chapel Hill. She is an alumna of the University of Michigan (BS), Wayne State University School of Medicine (MD), and the University of North Carolina School of Public Health (MPH). She completed a combined medicine–pediatrics residency at William Beaumont Hospital/Oakland University before completing her neonatal–perinatal medicine fellowship at the University of North Carolina. She is board certified in both general pediatrics and neonatal–perinatal medicine and is a fellow of the American Academy of Pediatrics. Currently she is an associate professor of pediatrics at the University of North Carolina at Chapel Hill.

Dr. Trembath's research focuses on improving healthcare delivery, clinical decision making, and reducing the health disparities of high-risk women and infants. She has been a member of multiple task forces aimed at reducing infant mortality and has been a maternal–child health consultant for state and governmental agencies.

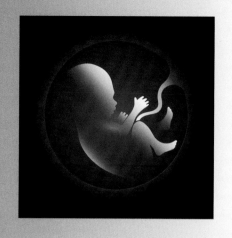

FETAL AND NEONATAL PHYSIOLOGY FOR THE ADVANCED PRACTICE NURSE

Amy J. Jnah, DNP, NNP-BC

Andrea N. Trembath, MD, MPH

EDITORS

SPRINGER PUBLISHING COMPANY

NEW YORK

Springer Publishing Company, LLC
11 West 42nd Street
New York, NY 10036
www.springerpub.com

Acquisitions Editor: Elizabeth Nieginski
Compositor: Diacritech, Chennai

ISBN: 978-0-8261-5731-7
ebook ISBN: 978-0-8261-5745-4
Image Bank ISBN: 978-0-8261-5758-4
Chapter Podcasts ISBN: 978-0-8261-5773-7

Instructor's Materials: Qualified instructors may request supplements by emailing textbook@springerpub.com.
Visit http://connect.springerpub.com/content/book/978-0-8261-5745-4 to access the podcasts.

19 20 21 22 / 5 4 3 2

The author and the publisher of this Work have made every effort to use sources believed to be reliable to provide information that is accurate and compatible with the standards generally accepted at the time of publication. Because medical science is continually advancing, our knowledge base continues to expand. Therefore, as new information becomes available, changes in procedures become necessary. We recommend that the reader always consult current research and specific institutional policies before performing any clinical procedure. The author and publisher shall not be liable for any special, consequential, or exemplary damages resulting, in whole or in part, from the readers' use of, or reliance on, the information contained in this book. The publisher has no responsibility for the persistence or accuracy of URLs for external or third-party Internet websites referred to in this publication and does not guarantee that any content on such websites is, or will remain, accurate or appropriate.

Library of Congress Cataloging-in-Publication Data
Names: Jnah, Amy, editor. | Trembath, Andrea, editor.
Title: Fetal and neonatal physiology for the advanced practice nurse /
    [edited by] Amy J. Jnah, Andrea N. Trembath.
Description: New York, NY: Springer Publishing Company, LLC, [2019] |
    Includes bibliographical references.
Identifiers: LCCN 2018033971| ISBN 9780826157317 | ISBN 9780826157454 (ebook) | ISBN 9780826157737
    (chapter podcasts)
Subjects: | MESH: Fetus—physiology | Infant, Newborn—physiology | Nurses'
    Instruction
Classification: LCC RG610 | NLM WQ 210.5 | DDC 612.6/47—dc23 LC record available at
https://lccn.loc.gov/2018033971

Contact us to receive discount rates on bulk purchases.
We can also customize our books to meet your needs.
For more information please contact: sales@springerpub.com

Publisher's Note: New and used products purchased from third-party sellers are not guaranteed for quality, authenticity, or access to any included digital components.

Printed in the United States of America.

We would like to thank several individuals who made this book possible:

To our spouses – Lieutenant Colonel Eric Jnah and Mr. Bradley Trembath.
Thank you for your unwavering love and support.

To our children – Mya, Ryan, Lauren, and Nicholas.
Mya, thank you for selflessly creating several drawings for this textbook. You remind me, every day, that intrinsic motivation propels students toward their human potential. Ryan, thank you for teaching me to be a creative problem-solver who never gives up. You remind me that learning requires curiosity, and engaging that curiosity achieves lasting learning.
–AJ

Lauren, thank you for your natural curiosity.
You are my spark, who reminds me to think "outside the box" and to always be ready for change.
Nicholas, thank you for teaching me about tenacity.
Your focus and drive keep me working for solutions even when I'm ready to give up.
–AT

To our mothers – Judy Bryniak and Susan Woodruff.
Thank you for introducing us to the Montessori method.

To our contributing-author teams, student artists, and East Carolina University NNP alumni who graciously donated intellectual material from their tenure in the NNP program to this book:
Thank you for faithfully committing your intellectual genius to this project!

CONTENTS

CONTRIBUTORS

Deanna W. Adkins, MD
Division of Pediatric Endocrinology
Duke University Medical Center
Lenox Baker Children's Hospital
Durham, North Carolina

Uduak Akpan, MD
Assistant Professor of Pediatrics–Neonatology
East Carolina University
Brody School of Medicine
Greenville, North Carolina

Sofia Aliaga, MD, MPH
Associate Professor of Pediatrics
Neonatal-Perinatal Medicine
University of North Carolina at Chapel Hill
Chapel Hill, North Carolina

Ana Arias-Oliveras, MSN, CRNP, NNP-BC
Associate Program Director
Neonatal Nurse Practitioner Program
University of Pennsylvania
Philadelphia, Pennsylvania

Melissa S. Bauserman, MD, MPH
Associate Professor of Pediatrics
Neonatal-Perinatal Medicine
University of North Carolina at Chapel Hill
Chapel Hill, North Carolina

Bobby Bellflower, DNSc, APRN, NNP-BC
Associate Professor and Director, Doctor of Nursing
    Practice Program
University of Tennessee Health Sciences Center
    College of Nursing
Memphis, Tennessee

Amy Bieda, PhD, APRN, PNP-BC, NNP-BC
Assistant Professor and Lead Faculty,
    NNP Program
Frances Payne Bolton School of Nursing
Case Western Reserve University
Cleveland, Ohio

Meghan Bjerke, MSN, APRN, NNP-BC
East Carolina University
College of Nursing
Greenville, North Carolina

Stephanie M. Blake, DNP, APRN, NNP-BC
Neonatal Nurse Practitioner
Duke University Medical Center, Division of
    Neonatology
Durham, North Carolina
Adjunct Faculty
Duke University School of Nursing
Durham, North Carolina

Curry Bordelon, DNP, MBA, APRN, NNP-BC,
CPNP-AC
Assistant Professor
University of Alabama at Birmingham
School of Nursing
Birmingham, Alabama

Darlene A. Calhoun, DO
Professor of Pediatrics
University of Central Florida
    College of Medicine
Orlando, Florida
Chief of Neonatology
Nemours Children's Hospital
Orlando, Florida

Leigh Ann Cates-McGlinn, PhD, APRN, NNP-BC, RRT-NPS, CHSE
Clinical Associate Professor
Old Dominion University
NNP Program
Neonatal Nurse Practitioner
Atrium Heath
Charlotte, North Carolina

Terri A. Cavaliere, DNP, APRN, NNP-BC
Clinical Associate Professor
Stony Brook University
School of Nursing
Stony Brook, New York

Rebecca Chuffo Davila, DNP, APRN, NNP-BC, FAANP
Assistant Professor
University of Iowa
Iowa City, Iowa

Rani M. Delaney, DNP, APRN, NNP-BC
Neonatal Nurse Practitioner
North Carolina Children's Hospital
Adjunct Assistant Professor
University of North Carolina at Chapel Hill
Chapel Hill, North Carolina

Bill Diehl-Jones PhD, BScN, RN
Associate Professor
Athabasca University
Children's Hospital Research Institute of Manitoba
Athabasca, Alberta, Canada

Bresney Fanning, MSN, APRN, NNP-BC
Neonatal Nurse Practitioner
Department of Pediatrics
Division of Neonatology and Perinatal Medicine
Medical University of South Carolina
Charleston, South Carolina

Jennifer Fitzgerald, DNP, CRNP, NNP-BC
Neonatal Nurse Practitioner
University of Maryland Medical Systems
Baltimore, Maryland

Debbie Fraser, MN, RNC-NIC
Associate Professor
Athabasca University
Faculty of Health Disciplines
Athabasca, Alberta, Canada

Lauren C. Frazer, MD, PhD
Department of Pediatrics
University of North Carolina at Chapel Hill
Chapel Hill, North Carolina

Carolyn Herrington, PhD, RN, NNP-BC, CLC
Assistant Professor, Clinical
Wayne State University
College of Nursing
Detroit, Michigan

Jacqui Hoffman, DNP, APRN, NNP-BC
Assistant Professor
Rush University
College of Nursing
Chicago, Illinois

Amy J. Jnah, DNP, APRN, NNP-BC
Clinical Associate Professor
Director, Neonatal Nurse Practitioner Concentration
East Carolina University
College of Nursing
Greenville, North Carolina

Mark Kadrofske, MD, PhD, FAAP
Assistant Professor
Michigan State University
East Lansing, Michigan

Amy R. Koehn, PhD, APRN, NNP-BC
Assistant Professor
Neonatal Concentration Coordinator
University of Tennessee
Health Sciences Center
Memphis, Tennessee

Courtney Komar, MSN, APRN, NNP-BC
East Carolina University
College of Nursing
Greenville, North Carolina

Maryellen Lane, BSN, APRN, NNP-BC
Neonatal Nurse Practitioner
North Carolina Children's Hospital
Adjunct Assistant Professor
University of North Carolina at Chapel Hill
Chapel Hill, North Carolina

Molly F. May, MSN, CRNP, NNP-BC
Neonatal Nurse Practitioner
University of Pennsylvania
School of Nursing
Philadelphia, Pennsylvania

Jenna Meredith, MSN, APRN, NNP-BC
Neonatal Nurse Practitioner
Department of Pediatrics
Division of Neonatology and Perinatal Medicine
The MetroHealth System
Cleveland, Ohio

Ryan Moore, MD, FAAP
Clinical Associate Professor of Pediatrics
Co-Medical Director and Chief of Neonatology
East Carolina University
    Brody School of Medicine
Greenville, North Carolina

Leanne Nantais-Smith, PhD, APRN, NNP-BC
Assistant Clinical Professor
College of Nursing
Wayne State University
Detroit, Michigan

Vivek Narendran, MD, MRCP (UK), MBA
Professor of Pediatrics
Children's Hospital of Cincinnati
University of Cincinnati
Cincinnati, Ohio

Desi M. Newberry, DNP, APRN, NNP-BC
Assistant Professor, Clinical
East Carolina University
College of Nursing
Greenville, North Carolina

Erin Orth, MD
Fellow, Neonatal–Perinatal Medicine
North Carolina Children's Hospital
University of North Carolina at Chapel Hill
Chapel Hill, North Carolina

Mary Elaine Patrinos, MD
Assistant Professor of Pediatrics
Case Western Reserve University
Cleveland, Ohio
Neonatologist
Rainbow Babies & Children's Hospital
University Hospitals Cleveland Medical Center
Cleveland, Ohio

Rebecca Rose, MD, MS
Neonatologist
Indiana University School of Medicine
Department of Pediatrics
    Division of Neonatal–Perinatal Medicine
Fishers, Indiana

Lisa Schepper, MSN, APRN, NNP-BC
Adjunct Faculty
University of Indianapolis
Indianapolis, Indiana
Neonatal Nurse Practitioner
Riley Hospital for Children
Indianapolis, Indiana

Elizabeth Sharpe, DNP, APRN, NNP-BC, VA-BC, FAANP
Associate Professor of Clinical Nursing
The Ohio State University
College of Nursing
Columbus, Ohio

Evelyn Stephenson, DNP, APRN, NNP-BC, RNC-NIC, CHSE
Clinical Assistant Professor
Indiana University School of Nursing
Indianapolis, Indiana

Linda Strickland, DNP, MSN, NNP-BC
Coordinator, Neonatal Nurse Practitioner Track
Assistant Professor
University of Indianapolis
Indiana University School of Medicine
Indianapolis, Indiana

Wendy J. Sturtz, MD
Attending Neonatologist
Medical Director, IMPACT
Christiana Care Health System
Newark, Delaware
Assistant Professor of Pediatrics
Thomas Jefferson University Hospital
Philadelphia, Pennsylvania

Mary Terhaar, DNSc, RN, ANEF, FAAN
Garvin Professor & Associate Dean for
    Academic Affairs
Frances Payne Bolton School of Nursing
Case Western Reserve University
Cleveland, Ohio

Nicole Thompson-Bowie, MSN, APRN, NNP-BC, PNP-BC
Neonatal Nurse Practitioner
Jackson Memorial Hospital
Miami, Florida

Paula M. Timoney, DNP, ARNP, NNP-BC
Clinical Associate Professor
Stony Brook University
School of Nursing
Stony Brook, New York

Andrea N. Trembath, MD, MPH
Associate Professor of Pediatrics
Neonatal-Perinatal Medicine
University of North Carolina at Chapel Hill
Chapel Hill, North Carolina

Marty Visscher, PhD, MEd, CPI
Professor
Skin Sciences Program
Children's Hospital of Cincinnati
University of Cincinnati
Cincinnati, Ohio

Melody Norris Waller, PhD, RN
Assistant Professor
RN–BSN Coordinator
University of Tennessee Health Science Center
College of Nursing
Memphis, Tennessee

Aksana Waskosky, DNP, APRN, NNP-BC
Neonatal Nurse Practitioner
University of Indianapolis
Indianapolis, Indiana

Janice L. Wilson, DNP, CRNP, NNP-BC
Assistant Professor
University of Maryland
School of Nursing
Baltimore, Maryland

FOREWORD

Fetal and neonatal physiology is foundational to the care provided by neonatal professionals and creates a framework for how the body works and, in some cases, doesn't work. Understanding physiology provides in-depth knowledge of the mechanical, physical, and biochemical function of humans. The study of what is normal provides the building blocks for identification of what is abnormal. In the field of neonatology, we often concentrate on the pathological and not the physiologic state of normal body function. Without the building blocks of knowledge regarding physiology, it is difficult to understand pathophysiology at the depth that is needed to provide specialized care.

The term *physiology* was introduced by Jean Fernel around 1520, but the work had begun years before. Around 420 BC, Hippocrates, known as the "father of medicine," shared his theory of humors consisting of earth, water, air, and fire. He related these four elements to things like bile, phlegm, and blood. He shifted the religious and magical beliefs of those times to a systematic approach to care, observing clinical signs and making rational conclusions to create a balance. Others built on this theory and in 130–200 AD Galen of Pergamum did the first experiments on the human body. He moved science further with the understanding of a connection among three systems: the brain and nerves, the heart and arteries, and the liver and veins. By the 1800s, the world of physiology began to explode with the study of blood coagulation and inflammation, which led to an understanding of pathophysiology in regard to the human body. This era also brought about the concept of germs and antiseptics. Knowledge continued to expand in the 1900s with an understanding of the cellular environment. In the current age of the Internet, not only is science expanding, but the ability to get new information out to those caring for patients is faster than ever before.

As a nurse practitioner and researcher, I have had a passion for physiology and pathophysiology throughout my entire career. I have used my knowledge of physiology to provide me with a framework to understand and often research the abnormal. My work on secondary surfactant deficiency was based off the understanding that although we could provide surfactant in the early hours of life for premature infants, over time, the body's ability to produce and recycle surfactant might be altered. This would lead the premature infant to continue to be vulnerable to further surfactant deficiencies over time. This might be especially true in cases of chorioamnionitis and other infections in which inflammatory mediators cause more damage. To question the difficulties these vulnerable premature infants were faced with required a strong foundational knowledge of normal physiology of surfactant production and use in the human body. From that foundation, researchers have been able to develop and initiate treatments to meet the needs of these infants when their prematurity prevents what is normal.

As an educator, I have found that students must be able to discuss the physiology before they explain the pathophysiology of the process that is causing the illness or disease. It is in this explanation that they can find the rationale for the pathology and understand the treatment options. Many of the authors of this new volume are faculty at leading universities in the country. In addition to that, many are also past students, colleagues, national leaders, and friends. The dedication of these authors in volunteering their time and resources to provide readers with detailed physiology is evident in each chapter. In the book, the authors discuss the basic principles of placental, fetal, maternal, and neonatal development and physiology. Each system is outlined with a timeline for organ development, developmental physiology, genetics, maternal influences, common problems, and lifetime implications. This book, which has been so well organized by the editors, has been developed as a learning resource for students and provides them with learning tools.

The book is easily understandable and builds core knowledge to further understand disease and dysfunction. In this new age of data, the work on cellular physiology expands our understanding of disease not only at the cellular level, but in the microenvironment that surrounds the cell. Current research is focused on microbial mechanisms of pathogenesis, immune responses, epidemiology, and drugs. Healthcare providers and students are faced with the challenges of keeping up with the "state of the science." Information expands at a rapid pace and challenges the best of us. In 2010, it was estimated that knowledge doubles every 3.5 years; it is estimated that this interval will be down to 73 days by 2020. Knowledge learned in medical and nursing schools is outdated before graduation. Knowledge expands faster than our ability to assimilate and apply it effectively. What is key then is an expectation that providers have a foundational knowledge that they have mastered and on which they build continually. In addition to the rapid change in the evidence, knowledge itself decays over time; it is critical that we remain cognizant of these changes and reeducate ourselves on a continuum. This text is dedicated

to neonatal care and designed for neonatal healthcare providers along a continuum from new learner to expert clinician.

Robin L. Bissinger, PhD, APRN, NNP-BC, FAAN
Executive Director, National Certification Corporation,
Chicago, Illinois

Further Reading

Densen, P. (2011). Challenges and opportunities facing medical education. *American Clinical and Climatological Association, 122,* 48–58. PMID: 21686208

Fullerton, J., & Silverman, M. (2009). Claudius Galen of Pergamum: Authority of medieval medicine. *Clinical Cardiology, 32*(11), E82–E83. doi:10.1002/clc.20388

Wade, N., Piccolino, M., & Simmons, A. (n.d.). Portraits of European neuroscientists: Jean Fernel. Retrieved from https://neuroportraits .eu/portrait/jean-fernel.html

Yapijakis, C. (2009). Hippocrates of Kos, the father of clinical medicine, and Asclepiades of Bithynia, the father of molecular medicine. Review. *in vivo, 23*(4), 507–514. Retrieved from http://iv.iiarjournals.org/content/23/4/507.full

PREFACE

Fetal and Neonatal Physiology for the Advanced Practice Nurse offers a unique framework for the study of human physiology and common diseases that may afflict premature and term infants. The scope, sequence, and construct of each individual chapter is grounded in the Montessori method, which underpins Dr. Jnah's multisensory, active approach to didactic instruction and Dr. Trembath's engaging, clinically relevant teaching methods.

This three-part textbook provides advanced practice nurses with core concepts of fetal and neonatal physiology in a manner that promotes contemplative thinking, understanding, and retention. Therefore, this content is intended to precede the study of clinical diagnostics and management. Part I introduces core concepts, including fetal origins of disease, genetic inheritance patterns, and placental physiology. Part II investigates each major human body system. Part III offers an exploration into the transition to extrauterine life and common challenges facing perinatal and neonatal clinicians.

It is well known that teamwork, communication, and mentoring behaviors are associated with optimal outcomes for individuals and organizations. Therefore, each chapter reflects a purposeful, interprofessional integration of the knowledge of both junior and senior nursing and medical professionals. Most chapter mind maps and other select visuals are the work of aspiring neonatal nurse practitioners, who handpicked challenging concepts and, in consultation with academic faculty, created these graphic learning tools. Blank timelines are included to encourage active annotation during studying, self-directed learning, and the creation of feedback loops with academic or clinical mentors. Qualified instructors may obtain access to an image bank ancillary by emailing textbook@springerpub.com. Audio podcasts offer learners a complementary method for studying common, core phenomena that affect the fetus and newborn. These podcasts, written by neonatal APNs and physicians, mimic breakout teaching moments that occur during daily rounding at academic teaching hospitals. (Please visit http://connect.springerpub.com/content/book/978-0-8261-5745-4 to access the podcasts.) Practical advice from contributing authors offers valuable perspectives and encourages mentoring through the provision of support, trust, encouragement, and hope between novice learners and experienced clinicians. After all, the value of human connection can never be overstated.

Amy J. Jnah
Andrea N. Trembath

LIST OF PODCASTS

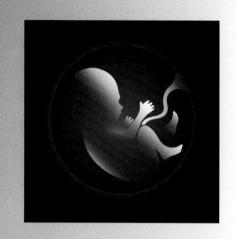

I

BASIC PRINCIPLES OF FETAL AND NEONATAL PHYSIOLOGY

1
INTRODUCTION

Amy J. Jnah and Andrea N. Trembath

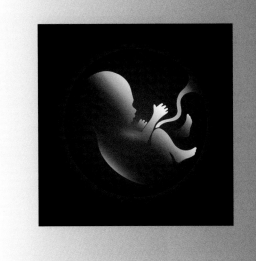

"We cannot create observers by saying 'observe,' but by giving them the power and the means for this observation and these means are procured through education of the senses."

—Maria Montessori

Human anatomy involves the study of body morphology and development. It is one of the first undergraduate courses assigned to all students in the health professions. The study of human anatomy logically precedes, or is partnered with, the study of human physiology. A well-developed foundation in human physiology is key, as this forms the basis for our understanding of pathophysiologic disorders. Unique to the study of the fetus and neonate is the integration of embryologic development. This pairing is essential to connect the genesis of organ systems and structures with environmental influences that may lead to immediate or latent manifestations of disease. As a result, the most critical period is during early pregnancy or, as some suggest, before the woman is even aware of her pregnant state (Almond & Currie, 2011). This approach to the study of fetal and neonatal physiology prepares an emerging advanced practice nurse (APN) for his or her role as a resourceful and informed problem solver, caregiver, and health promoter.

EMBRYOLOGY: THE TIMELINE OF HUMAN DEVELOPMENT

The formation of each human body system involves intricate and carefully sequenced processes. Beginning with the second week postfertilization (postconception), the embryo arises as a rudimentary, dual-layered disc. Its outer layer is composed of epiblast cells, whereas the inner layer contains hypoblast cells. These two layers differentiate during gastrulation, beginning in the third gestational week, into a three-layered organism. The *endoderm* (inner layer) ultimately gives rise to the respiratory, renal, gastrointestinal, and metabolic and endocrine systems. The *mesoderm* (middle layer) gives rise to the future cardiovascular, skeletal, and reproductive systems, as well as muscles and cartilages. Finally, the *ectoderm* (outer layer) gives rise to the central nervous system and the skin. Environmental factors, maternal health conditions, and genetic influences can affect human development at any stage in embryonic or fetal development; environmental and genetic influences can also exert an untoward influence on human development or physiology after birth and across the life span (Figure 1.1).

When reading this textbook, it is important to understand that dating associated with the embryonic and fetal periods of development correspond with the number of days *after* conception. Some authors denote this as "E12" (embryonic period, day 12) or "F75" (fetal period, day 75). Here author teams will provide a concise, systematic overview of human development separated by the embryonic, fetal, and postnatal periods of development, as appropriate. Dating is therefore rendered by "week of gestation" occurring postconception. This offers a realistic review of the progression of human development, by system, and avoids additional clarifying (and occasionally confusing) terminology.

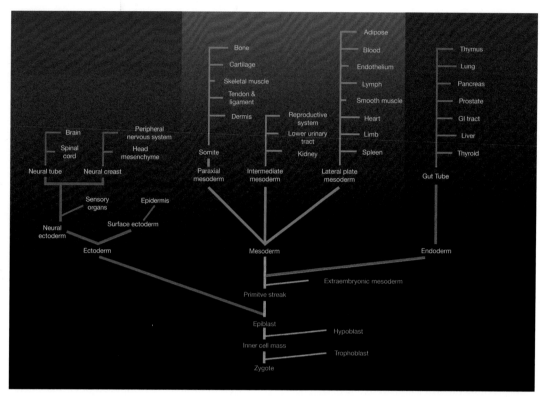

Figure 1.1 Formation of body systems.

Source: LifeMap Sciences, Inc.

DEVELOPMENTAL PHYSIOLOGY

Understanding Normal Function

Broadly speaking, human physiology involves the study of human body function. To be more specific, physiology reflects the synergy of cellular physiology, histophysiology (tissues), and systemic physiology. Primitive physiologic function begins during early fetal development and matures as the fetus grows, develops, and approaches extrauterine life. Some maturational events even occur postnatally; however, experts agree that the intrauterine environment exerts a critical influence upon developmental physiology. Maternal health and genetic factors, as well as the external environment and age of the fetus at birth, can perturb physiologic maturation and function and give rise to structural malformations and pathological disease states.

Maternal Health and Environmental Influences

An intriguing interplay exists among maternal health, genes, the environment, and their influence upon fetal development. The prenatal and postnatal periods are particularly vulnerable times for the developing fetus and neonate, as these time frames mark a period of rapid

TABLE 1.1 Environmental Shocks That Implicate Fetal Metabolic Programming

- Air pollution*
- Anxiety
- Depression
- Drug and alcohol addiction
- Glucocorticoids
- Hypoxia
- Infectious diseases
- Malnutrition
- Stress

*NOTE: Sources of air pollution include automobile exhaust and smoking. Fetal exposure to air pollution has been associated with later reduction in standardized test scores during high school years.

Sources: From Almond, D., & Currie, J. (2011). Killing me softly: The fetal origins hypothesis. *Journal of Economic Perspectives: A Journal of the American Economic Association, 25*(3), 153–172. doi:10.1257/jep.25.3.153; Calkins, K., & Devaskar, S. U. (2011). Fetal origins of adult disease. *Current Problems in Pediatric and Adolescent Health Care, 41*(6), 158–176. doi:10.1016/j.cppeds.2011.01.001; Chay, K. Y., & Greenstone, M. (2003). The impact of air pollution on infant mortality: evidence from geographic variation in pollution shocks induced by a recession. *Quarterly Journal of Economics, 118*(3), 1121–1167. doi:10.1162/00335530360698513

development and plasticity. In other words, any factor may alter fetal development, disrupt normal structural and functional maturation, and program the fetus or neonate for latent development of chronic disease. This concept, known as the Barker hypothesis or "fetal origins of adult disease," describes how metabolic characteristics acquired in utero, secondary to environmental influences, program a fetus to develop latent disease (Almond & Currie, 2011; Barker, Osmond, Kajantie, & Eriksson, 2009; Vaag, Grunnet, Arora, & Brøns, 2012). Ultimately, clinicians must be aware that influences during pregnancy may result in maternal health problems and fetal development, thereby disrupting epigenetic, structural, and functional development (Table 1.1).

Early 20th-century understanding of the placenta positioned this reproductive organ as a barrier to maternally exposed noxious substances. Epidemiologic data later derailed this assumption, proving the placenta to be a selective filter. This data suggested that the maternal-fetal dyad was vulnerable to a host of large-scale environmental influences (Table 1.2). In the 1860s, pregnant women in Finland who suffered during the famine epidemic gave birth to infants who would later display increased fat deposition (females) and hypertension (males and females) as adults. The late-19th-century phylloxera outbreak, pinpointed to vineyards in France, left the offspring of affected pregnant females with decreased stature. The 1920 flu epidemic that occurred in the United States resulted in an increase in intellectual disability and decreased educational attainment among offspring of flu-infected pregnant women. The well-known Dutch Hunger Winter of the 1940s and Chinese famine of the 1960s provoked widespread famine and resultant adult-onset obesity and psychiatric disorders among offspring whose mothers suffered malnutrition. More recent, the troubling opioid, heroin, and alcohol epidemics in the United States are known to leave affected fetuses in a disruptive postnatal state of abstinence; offspring of alcohol-addicted women may be also affected by fetal alcohol syndrome (Almond & Currie, 2011; World Health Organization [WHO], 2018). Other environmental exposures, including prescription

TABLE 1.2 Global Epidemics and Pandemics and Latent Disease (19th to 21st Centuries)

Time Frame (*approximation*)	Epidemic and Pandemic Outbreaks	Known Latent Health Risks
1860	Famine (Finland)	Increased fat deposition (females only) Cardiovascular disease
1890	Phylloxera (France)	Reduced stature (0.5–0.9 centimeters)
1920	Influenza (US)	Intellectual disability Reduced educational attainment[*]
1940	Helsinki	Hypertension Insulin resistance
1940	Hunger Winter (Netherlands)	Obesity Mental health disorders
1950	Heroin (US)	Mental health disorders
1960	Famine (China)	Obesity Mental health disorders
1970	Alcohol (US)	Mental health disorders
2000	Heroin (US)	Intellectual disability Mental health disorders

[*]**NOTE:** *Reduced educational attainment* refers to a reduction in the total number of years that affected individuals dedicate to secondary and postsecondary education compared to their unaffected counterparts.

Sources: From Almond, D., & Currie, J. (2011). Killing me softly: The fetal origins hypothesis. *Journal of Economic Perspectives: A Journal of the American Economic Association, 25*(3), 153–172. doi:10.1257/jep.25.3.153; Baig, U., Belsare, P., Watve, M., & Jog, M. (2011). Can thrifty gene(s) or predictive fetal programming for thriftiness lead to obesity? *Journal of Obesity, 2011*, 1–11. doi:10.1155/2011/861049; Centers for Disease Control and Prevention. (2004). Interim guidelines for the evacuation of infants born to mothers infected with West Nile virus during pregnancy. *Morbidity and Mortality Weekly Report, 53*(7), 154–157 Retrieved from https://www.cdc.gov/mmwr/preview/mmwrhtml/mm5307a4.htm; World Health Organization. (2018). Emergencies preparedness, response: Disease outbreaks by year. Retrieved from http://www.who.int/csr/don/archive/year/en

or illicit drug exposure and exposure to certain viral infections (e.g., influenza), have been linked to learning disabilities and late-onset mental health disorders. Many of these disruptions will be discussed throughout this textbook as a maternal health influence on fetal development.

The most notable environmental influence is maternal malnutrition. Historically, malnutrition occurred secondary to widespread famines. Presently, malnutrition occurs at the individual level and is attributed to maternal body and dietary composition, as well as alterations in uteroplacental blood flow. These alterations in maternal environment are associated with decreased nutrient supply and resultant fetal undernutrition. Decreased nutrient transfer from the mother to the fetus induces a compensatory fetal catabolic state. Concurrently, a redistribution of blood flow occurs that prioritizes nutrient delivery to the brain and away from other vital and developing organs, most notably the kidneys and liver. Stunted renal development may result in low nephron number and value, reducing the capacity for adaptation or compensation for dietary excesses or renal injury (Calkins & Devaskar, 2011). Similarly, stunted hepatic development may result in a reduction of β-cells and insulin secretion. A reduction in maternal glucose transfer causes a reduction in fetal glucose, and, in combination with hepatic development, may result in decreased insulin reactivity, or insulin resistance. These factors increase the risk for latent chronic diseases that rely upon normal metabolic (insulin) reactivity, most notably obesity, type 2 diabetes mellitus (T2DM), dyslipidemia, hypertension, and coronary artery disease, as well as short stature, osteoporosis, and cognitive and behavioral disorders (Barker, 1998; Benyshek, 2007; Calkins & Devaskar, 2011; Gluckman, Hanson, & Buklijas, 2010; Gluckman, Hanson, Buklijas, Low, & Beedle, 2009; Kuzawa, 2007; Kuzawa & Quinn, 2009; Thayer & Kuzawa, 2011).

Fetal undernutrition is commonly correlated with low birth weight (LBW). LBW babies are understood to have stunted growth and development secondary to exposure to an environmental shock. Neel (1962) first introduced a potential relationship between persistent fetal undernutrition and the presence of a "thrifty phenotype." This relationship involved allele-mediated anticipatory fetal programming to "thriftiness" (calorie conservation, increased fat deposition) that manifests during periods of periodic starvation (Vasan & Thomas, 2012). It is suggested that fetuses exposed to undernutrition undergo epigenetic changes (or "switching on") of hypothalamic pathways (methylate or acetylate genes) that control metabolism. This process slows fetal metabolism as a compensatory response to undernutrition. These methylations and acetylations (epigenetic changes) are retained postnatally and, in fact, are passed to offspring. Individuals born possessing the "thrifty gene" are predisposed to a famine-like compensatory response during periods of short-term (less than 8–12 hours) or long-term (more than 12 hours) fasting.

It is interesting to note that LBW and rapid childhood catch-up growth are positively correlated with adult-onset diseases (Calkins & Devaskar, 2011). Infants born small for gestational age (SGA) who undergo rapid catch-up growth between ages 7 and 15, known as *crossing growth percentiles*, incur a 39% greater risk for developing latent T2DM. The disproportionate increase in fatty deposition compared to lean body mass is thought to encourage insulin resistance and later T2DM.

Although the bulk of this textbook focuses on influences that occur during pregnancy and their implications on the human life span, recall that postnatal events can disrupt normal postnatal physiologic maturation. All infants, including healthy, appropriate-for-gestational age (AGA) neonates, are at risk for altered programming and, as a result, altered physiologic maturation and function. Consider, for example, the maturation of the sweat glands. Over the first few years of life, the climate in which the family unit resides essentially programs the functional maturation of the infant's sweat glands; infants living in warmer climates develop an increased number of functional glands compared to those residing in cooler climates, and by age 3 maturation is considered permanent (Barker, 1998). Natural experiments support this hypothesis. For example, Japanese military activities during the mid 20th century (1940–1950) placed soldiers into significantly warmer climates, giving way for a heightened awareness of glandular programming in early life; soldiers who grew up in warmer climates and who developed an increased number of functional sweat glands readily adapted to warmer climates, whereas those who primarily resided in cooler climates did not (Barker, 1998).

Genetic Influences and Inheritance Patterns

Genes are material substances that are passed from parents to their offspring. Structurally, genes are nucleotide sequences of deoxyribonucleic acid (DNA). DNA was discovered by Watson and Crick in 1953 and is found in most human cells. Gene sequences offer cells a transcript that guides the synthesis and secretion of protein molecules. Essentially, human cells extract gene sequences and record and translate them, using the gene's "recipe," into biologically active proteins. These processes modulate human growth, development, and function. This explains why children often resemble their parents, and in some ways, their immediate ancestors.

An understanding of the patterns of inheritance are critical before progressing to the various chapters of this textbook. Numerous resources are available that explain this process. Nonetheless, we will summarize dominant and recessive inheritance patterns here, as they are integral to understanding genetic influences upon the developing fetus and neonate. A list of common genetic terms and their associated definitions are provided in Table 1.3.

Under normal circumstances, there are 46 chromosomes contained within every human cell. These chromosomes are organized into pairs; 50% of each pair is donated from each parent. Twenty-two of the chromosome pairs are numbered and considered "nonsex" alleles, or autosomes; autosomal genes usually produce similar outcomes in males and females. This leaves one pair to function, under normal circumstances, as the sex chromosomes; X-linked sex genes affect males and females differently. In females, despite the presence of two X chromosomes, only one is responsible for modulating gene product. The other X chromosome is subject to X-inactivation.

Autosomal Dominant. *Dominant inheritance* refers to the inheritance of one faulty, or mutated, dominant autosome (1–22) from either parent. In the case of autosomal dominance, the faulty gene copy *dominates* its working gene partner. Therefore, if one parent possesses an autosomal dominant gene defect, each child has a 50% chance of being an affected carrier. Children who do not inherit the abnormal gene will not develop or pass on the disease. In rare circumstances a child may inherit the same dominant faulty gene from both parents and display a severe manifestation of the trait or disease, which in some cases is fatal. Males and females are affected equally. Figure 1.2 describes outcomes based on common parental carrier statuses.

Autosomal Recessive. *Recessive inheritance* refers to the inheritance of a complete pair of faulty recessive autosomes (1–22), one from each parent. Unlike dominant inheritance, offspring must inherit a faulty gene pair to manifest an autosomal recessive disease or trait. Typically, both parents are unaffected carriers. For this reason, pregnant females may choose to undergo prenatal screening for cystic fibrosis carrier status, a common autosomal recessive disease. When both parents are carriers, offspring have a 25% chance of inheriting one faulty gene from each parent and becoming affected by the disease or trait. Males and females are affected equally. Figure 1.3 describes outcomes based on common parental carrier statuses.

X-Linked Dominant Inheritance. *X-linked dominant inheritance* refers to the inheritance of a faulty X chromosome. Among females, the faulty X chromosome "dominates" the normal, working copy of the gene and the disease process or trait manifests. Among males, the lack of a second X chromosome offers no recourse; males with a faulty X chromosome will express the disease process or trait. When the mother is affected by a condition caused by an X-linked dominant gene mutation, there is an

TABLE 1.3 Genetic Terminology

Term	Definition
Autosomes	22 pairs of "nonsex" chromosomes
Deletion	Fracturing of a chromosome in two places with loss of the intervening portion
Gene	Section of DNA that codes for biochemical molecules and proteins
Mosaicism	Abnormal germline (egg/sperm) or somatic (all cells except reproductive cells) cellular divisions resulting in two or more types of cells comprised of varying numbers of chromosomes
Mutation	Faulty gene that alters the protein the gene is supposed to secrete
Sex Chromosomes	X (female) and Y (male)
Translocation	Exchange or rearrangement of chromosomal segments between two nonhomologous chromosomes
Trisomy	Three copies of a chromosome within a somatic or germline cell

Source: From Barrett, J. (2016). *An introduction to genetic association analysis*. London, UK: Henry Stewart Talks.

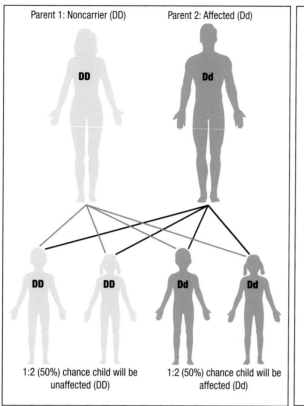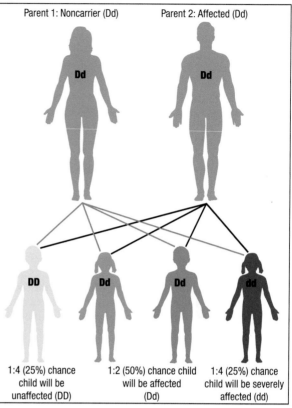

Figure 1.2 Autosomal dominant inheritance. The working gene copy is represented as "D" and the faulty dominant gene copy is represented as "d." When neither parent is a carrier of a dominant faulty gene and they have a child affected by a condition known to be due to autosomal dominant inheritance, the condition is likely the result of a new (de novo) mutation in that gene that occurs for unknown reasons during conception. Rarely, a parent may possess a mutation for the gene.

equal (50%) chance that male and female offspring may, or may not, inherit the X-linked dominant gene mutation. When the father is affected by a condition caused by an X-linked dominant gene mutation, there is a 100% chance he will pass the faulty X chromosome to female offspring; male offspring will be unaffected. Figure 1.4 describes outcomes based on common parental carrier statuses.

X-Linked Recessive Inheritance. *X-linked recessive inheritance* commonly refers to the inheritance of one (in males) or a pair (in females) of faulty X chromosomes. Females who carry one working copy and one faulty copy of the X chromosome are unaffected carriers of the disease or trait. In these circumstances, the working copy of the X chromosome produces sufficient gene product and compensates for the faulty copy and the disease or trait does not manifest. Rarely, females who possess one working and one faulty gene pair express X-inactivation of the working copy of the X chromosome and manifest

the disease or trait. Females who inherit a complete pair of faulty X chromosomes, one from each parent (not shown in Figure 1.5), will be affected by the disease or trait. Among males, the lack of a second X chromosome offers no recourse; males who inherit a faulty X chromosome will express the disease process or trait. Figure 1.5 describes outcomes based upon common parental carrier statuses.

TRANSLATING NORMAL PHYSIOLOGY TO CLINICAL PRACTICE

Generally speaking, clinicians would agree that a healthy newborn is not a customary resident within a neonatal intensive care unit (NICU). Rather, an alteration in normal human physiology led to the development of transient or lifelong disease, which necessitated a NICU admission. Therefore, it is imperative that clinicians gather a working knowledge of common

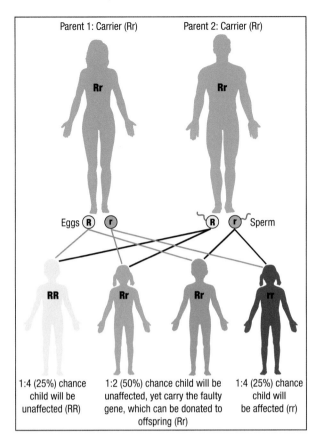

Figure 1.3 Autosomal recessive inheritance. The working gene copy is represented as "R."

problems, their incidence, pathophysiology, common clinical manifestations, and implications across the life span. As such, we offer an integrated approach to the study of fetal and neonatal physiology through the inclusion of "common problems" known to afflict the fetus and neonate and their implications across the life span. Some "not so common" diagnoses are also threaded throughout the textbook, specific to certain body systems. These less common problems, sometimes rare diseases, have been specifically selected to help illustrate important clinical diagnoses that should not be overlooked when generating a differential diagnosis list. This facilitates an almost immediate application of knowledge of normal function to the abnormal and the development of conceptual understanding, which can be later applied in the clinical setting.

Clinicians across the spectrum of expertise, from the emerging novice to esteemed expert, must recognize that *learning is an active process*. This calls for interpersonal collaboration, communication, and the integration of verbal and tactile work. In other words, learning

involves much more than simply watching a tutorial, listening to a didactic lecture, and taking meticulous notes. As such, we offer a multisensory approach to the study of fetal and neonatal physiology, grounded in the principles of adult learning theory. Chapter teams, comprised of obstetric, neonatal, and pediatric nursing and medical professionals, role model a step-by-step learning method through the presentation of fixed content areas within each chapter. For the visual learner, the written text is amply infused with figures and diagrams to lay a foundation. Tables and figures complement written content and offer learners alternative, multisensory tools to make sense of complex phenomenon. In addition, the mind maps for each chapter are another visual approach that reinforces processes and concepts. According to Spencer, Anderson, and Ellis (2013, p. 291), mind maps encourage

radiant thinking…which promotes all aspects of the brain working in synergy, with thought beginning from a central point. The mind map, which is a graphical technique to improve creative thinking and knowledge attainment, utilizes colors, images, codes, and dimensions to amplify and enhance key ideas. This technique augments the visualization of relationships and links between concepts, which aids in information acquisition, data retention, and overall comprehension.

The mind maps, as they are presented in the following chapters, are only a starting point and are meant to spur discussion. We encourage learners to take time to understand why highly successful learners mind map, develop an individual style for mind mapping, and adopt this process as an active learning behavior. This is particularly helpful when studying stepwise processes and feedback loops, as it facilitates the identification of relationships and conceptual understanding. Learners should also consider annotating or customizing the exemplars threaded within most major chapters of this textbook.

In addition, we provide learners with a blank "Timeline of Organ" development (Chapters 3-13). These have been intentionally left blank. Their purpose is to allow learners an opportunity to annotate each timeline and develop a conceptual understading of the stepwise progression of human development, from conception to birth, as well as identify the genesis for common pathologies and implications for future development across the lifespan. Exemplars are provided at the end of this chapter (Figure 1.6), as well as within Chapter 2.

Throughout the textbook, many chapters include podcasts (audio content) that flesh out key concepts, common problems, or offer complementary or interprofessional scholarly discourse. This high-fidelity teaching

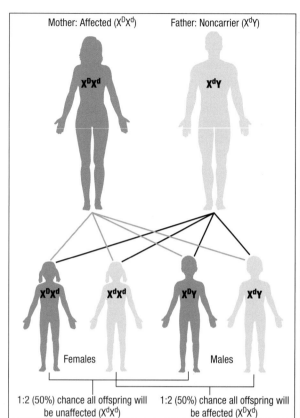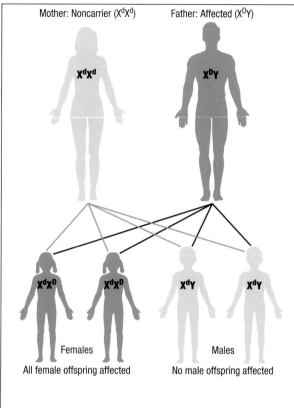

Figure 1.4 X-linked dominant inheritance. The working gene copy is represented as "D" and the faulty gene copy is represented as "d."

method mimics methods used during teaching rounds at academic hospitals and are meant to add yet another layer of depth to the content.

CONCLUSION

Our sincere hope is that students come to understand how they learn best by engaging the written content and multisensory tools offered within this textbook; this is a layered approach to learning that maximizes the use of multiple senses, enhancing knowledge acquisition and retention. Similarly, our hope is that academic and clinical faculty utilize this textbook as a vibrant learning platform for one of the most intimidating graduate-level courses offered within the health sciences. The benefits of activating an interest in human physiology and engaging students in active learning methods are far reaching; direct and memorable teaching and learning experiences, as opposed to the use of secondhand reports and abstract conceptualizations, encourage intellectual curiosity as well as lifelong teaching and learning behaviors.

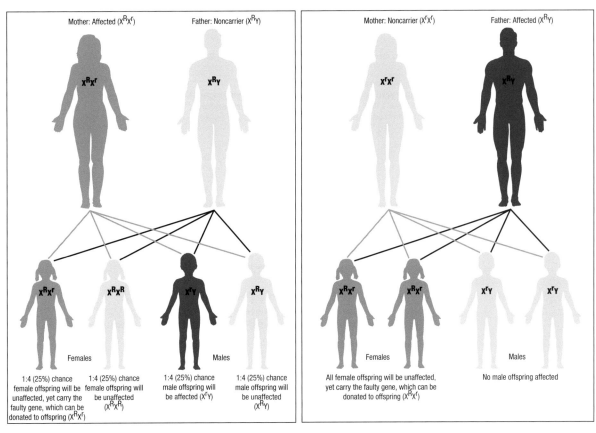

Figure 1.5 X-linked recessive inheritance. The working gene copy is represented as "R" and the faulty gene copy is represented as "r." In rare circumstances, female offspring with X^RX^r inheritance may experience X-inactivation of the working gene copy and thereby manifest the disease or trait.

TIMELINE OF ORGAN DEVELOPMENT OF THE RESPIRATORY SYSTEM

Timeline of **Organ Development**: *The Embryonic Period (Weeks 1–9)*

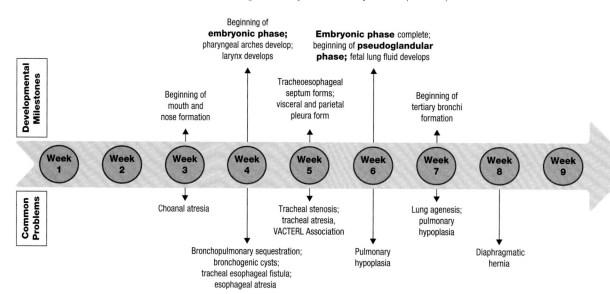

Timeline of **Organ Development**: *The Fetal Period (Weeks 10–21)*

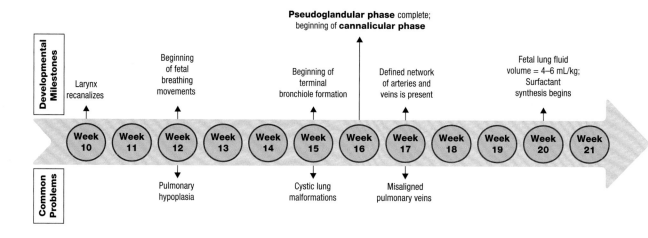

TIMELINE OF ORGAN DEVELOPMENT OF THE RESPIRATORY SYSTEM (cont.)

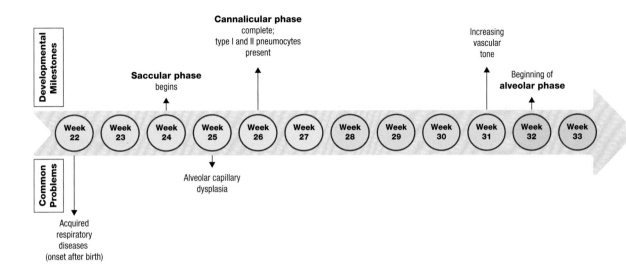

Timeline of **Organ Development**: *The Fetal Period*
(Weeks 22–33)

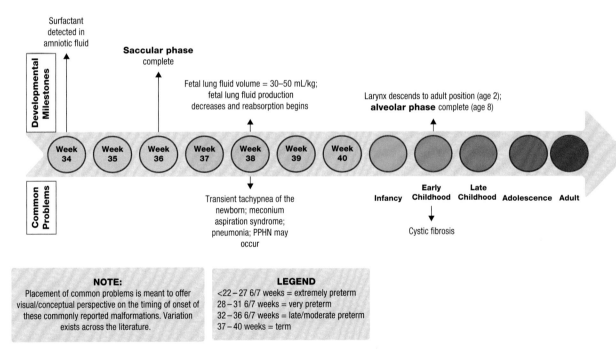

Timeline of **Organ Development**: *The Neonatal Period and Beyond*
(Weeks 34–40; Infancy–Adulthood)

NOTE:
Placement of common problems is meant to offer visual/conceptual perspective on the timing of onset of these commonly reported malformations. Variation exists across the literature.

LEGEND
<22 – 27 6/7 weeks = extremely preterm
28 – 31 6/7 weeks = very preterm
32 – 36 6/7 weeks = late/moderate preterm
37 – 40 weeks = term

Figure 1.6 Timeline of development.

PPHN, persistent pulmonary hypertension of the newborn; VACTERL; vertebral defects, anal atresia, cardiac defects, tracheoesophageal fistula, renal anomalies, and limb abnormalities.

Source: Created by Janice Wilson and Jennifer Fitzgerald

LEARNING TOOLS AND RESOURCES

Advice From the Editors

"I tend to use three sequential strategies when learning new concepts. First, I commit to focused reading, note-taking, and dialogue with experts. Second, I create a color-coded mind map of concepts that I find particularly challenging. This helps me identify and understand relationships. Third, I explain the concept aloud to a trusted mentor. This process encourages the identification of knowledge gaps, self-directed learning, and an empowering (yet humbling) progression from novice to expert.

I encourage you to resist complacency by remaining intellectually curious. Give yourself permission to ask 'why' and seek to understand the answer. Look a challenge in the eye, and wink at it."

– Amy J. Jnah, DNP, APRN, NNP-BC

"Spiral learning is the way I transition new ideas and concepts to mastery. I approach each topic from a distance at first, trying only to get a sense of the overall structure and the relationships between topics. Then I focus more closely on the details of those relationships. In my own learning I use mind maps and auditory resources extensively to dive deeper into content, frequently 'circling back' to content I've already learned to solidify my understanding."

– Andrea N. Trembath, MD, MPH

References

Almond, D., & Currie, J. (2011). Killing me softly: The fetal origins hypothesis. *Journal of Economic Perspectives: A Journal of the American Economic Association, 25*(3), 153–172. doi:10.1257/jep.25.3.153

Baig, U., Belsare, P., Watve, M., & Jog, M. (2011). Can thrifty gene(s) or predictive fetal programming for thriftiness lead to obesity? *Journal of Obesity, 2011*, 1–11. doi:10.1155/2011/861049

Barker, D. J. P. (1998). In utero programming of chronic disease. *Clinical Science, 95*(2), 115–128. doi:10.1042/cs0950115

Barker, D. J. P., Osmond, C., Kajantie, E., & Eriksson, J. G. (2009). Growth and chronic disease: Findings in the Helsinki birth cohort. *Annals of Human Biology, 36*(5), 445–458. doi:10.1080/03014460902980295

Barrett, J. (2016). *An introduction to genetic association analysis.* London, UK: Henry Stewart Talks.

Benyshek, D. C. (2007). The developmental origins of obesity and related health disorders—prenatal and perinatal factors. *Collegium Antropologicum, 31*(1), 11–17.

Calkins, K., & Devaskar, S. U. (2011). Fetal origins of adult disease. *Current Problems in Pediatric and Adolescent Health Care, 41*(6), 158–176. doi:10.1016/j.cppeds.2011.01.001

Centers for Disease Control and Prevention. (2004). Interim guidelines for the evacuation of infants born to mothers infected with West Nile virus during pregnancy. *Morbidity and Mortality Weekly Report, 53*(7), 145–168. Retrieved from https://www.cdc.gov/mmwr/preview/mmwrhtml/mm5307a4.htm

Chay, K. Y., & Greenstone, M. (2003). The impact of air pollution on infant mortality: Evidence from geographic variation in pollution shocks induced by a recession. *Quarterly Journal of Economics, 118*(3), 1121–1167. doi:10.1162/00335530360698513

Gluckman, P. D., Hanson, M. A., & Buklijas, T. (2010). A conceptual framework for the developmental origins of health and disease. *Journal of Developmental Origins of Health and Disease, 1*(1), 6–18. doi:10.1017/S2040174409990171

Gluckman, P. D., Hanson, M. A., Buklijas, T., Low, F. M., & Beedle, A. S. (2009). Epigenetic mechanisms that underpin metabolic and cardiovascular diseases. *Nature Reviews Endocrinology, 5*(7), 401–408. doi:10.1038/nrendo.2009.102

Kuzawa, C. W. (2007). Developmental origins of life history: Growth, productivity, and reproduction. *American Journal of Human Biology, 19*(5), 654–661. doi:10.1002/ajhb.20659

Kuzawa, C. W., & Quinn, E. A. (2009). Developmental origins of adult function and health: Evolutionary hypotheses. *Annual Review of Anthropology, 38*, 131–147. doi:10.1146/annurev-anthro-091908-164350

Neel, J. V. (1962). Diabetes mellitus: A "thrifty" genotype rendered detrimental by "progress"? *American Journal of Human Genetics, 14*, 353–362.

Spencer, J. R., Anderson, K. M., & Ellis, K. K. (2013). Radiant thinking and the use of the mind map in nurse practitioner education. *Journal of Nursing Education, 52*(5), 291–293. doi:10.3928/01484834-20130328-03

Thayer, Z. M., & Kuzawa, C. W. (2011). Biological memories of past environments: Epigenetic pathways to health disparities. *Epigenetics, 6*(7), 798–803. doi:10.4161/epi.6.7.16222

Vaag, A. A., Grunnet, L. G., Arora, G. P., Brøns, C. (2012). The thrifty phenotype hypothesis revisited. *Diabetologia, 55*(8), 2085–2088. doi:10.1007/s00125-012-2589-y

Vasan, S. K., & Thomas, N. (2012). Developmental origins of adult metabolic disease: The Indian scenario, driving toward a unified hypothesis. *Indian Journal of Endocrinology and Metabolism, 16*(4), 493–495. doi:10.4103/2230-8210.97990

World Health Organization. (2018). Emergencies preparedness, response: Disease outbreaks by year. Retrieved from http://www.who.int/csr/don/archive/year/en

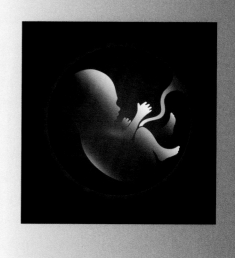

2

PLACENTAL DEVELOPMENT AND FUNCTION

Leanne Nantais-Smith, Carolyn Herrington, and Mark Kadrofske

LEARNING OBJECTIVES

After completing this chapter, the reader should be able to:

1. Discuss the development of individual structures of the placenta.
2. Describe uteroplacental circulation from mother to fetus through the placenta.
3. Identify the major functions of the placenta.
4. Analyze mechanisms involved in nutrient transfer to the fetus across the placenta.
5. Relate altered placental development to abnormal fetal development.
6. Discuss maternal diseases that result in altered placental and fetal development.

INTRODUCTION

The placenta is a feto–maternal organ that develops after ovum fertilization and implantation and provides a connection between the developing fetus and maternal circulation. During the menstrual cycle, follicle-stimulating hormone (FSH) and luteinizing hormone (LH) are released by the anterior pituitary and regulate ovarian follicle development and changes in the uterine mucosa. The mature ovarian follicle ruptures and expels the oocyte (egg) into the fallopian tube, a process called *ovulation*. After ovulation, the remnant follicle becomes the corpus luteum and helps regulate ongoing changes to the uterine mucosa. The uterine mucosa, or endometrium, undergoes growth with proliferation of spiral arteries and glands, all in anticipation of implantation (Figure 2.1). In the absence of oocyte fertilization by a spermatozoon, modification of the spiral arteries and blood flow to the changing endometrium is halted and sloughing of this now unnecessary evolving endometrium is initiated (Cunningham et al., 2014).

If fertilization occurs, changes in the architecture of the endometrium continue and the endometrium becomes the location for the development of the placenta (Cunningham et al., 2014). This unique organ ceases to function and is expelled at the end of pregnancy. This chapter focuses on placental development, whereas later chapters present the fetal phases of development specific to each body system. In addition, alterations in fetal development and disease resulting from developmental abnormalities of the placenta and maternal disease will be discussed.

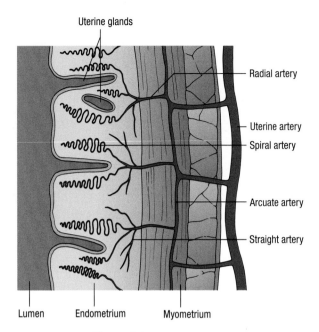

Figure 2.1 Uterine anatomy.

TIMELINE OF PLACENTAL DEVELOPMENT

The timeline highlights the development of major structures of the placenta (*top*) and the fetal and neonatal problems potentially associated with a specific stage of placental development (*bottom*; **Figure 2.2**). The exact timing of events can be variable and subtle differences are described in the literature.

DEVELOPMENTAL PHYSIOLOGY

The first week of human development begins at fertilization, as the oocyte is released into the fallopian tube and fertilized. This results in the formation of the first somatic cell, or zygote. Through the process of mitosis, the zygote grows into an aggregate of somatic cells, while being ushered through the fallopian tube, toward the uterus. Finally, by the end of the first week of development, the zygote matures into a blastocyst, reaches the uterine cavity, and begins implantation into the endometrium (Moore, Persaud, & Torchia, 2016).

Fertilization

At ovulation, the spherical oocyte enters the distal end of the fallopian tube. Subsequent penetration of the ooctye by a spermatozoon induces fertilization. The pronuclei from the oocyte and spermatozoon combine to form the zygote, which carries the genetic material necessary

to create a unique human being (Moore et al., 2016; Sadler, 2015). Over the next 3 days, the zygote undergoes repeated cell divisions. It is propelled through the fallopian tube toward the uterus by a combination of peristalsis and ciliated cells lining the fallopian tube. Nutrients stored within the shell-like glycoprotein (glucose and protein) matrix (zona pellucida) of the oocyte provide the necessary energy to nourish and support the zygote during this time as it migrates and proliferates into a blastocyst (Sadler, 2015). The zona pellucida not only nourishes, but also protects the blastomeres and morula from adhering to the fallopian mucosa and from being rejected by the maternal immune system as it is propelled toward the uterus.

Blastocyst Formation

Throughout its migration, the zygote undergoes cleavage, or a series of cell divisions. This process of mitosis results in the rapid doubling of genetically identical cells, or blastomeres. Blastomeres undergo compaction and realignment, and form into a tight cluster of cells, called the *morula*. The morula (future blastocyst), now a hollow 12- to 16-cell mass, finishes the journey through the fallopian tube and into the uterus (**Figure 2.3**). At this point, the blastomeres begin separation into the inner cell mass and the outer cell mass, which will become the embryoblast and trophoblast, respectively (Moore et al., 2016). Fluid from the uterine cavity also enters the morula, forming a blastocyst cavity that will provide nutrients for continued development. The morula has now evolved into the blastocyst (**Figure 2.4A**).

The blastocyst thereby enters the uterine cavity as its outer zona pellucida undergoes alteration and is shed, removing any physical constraint to future embryonic growth (Sadler, 2015). This permits "hatching" of the blastocyst and its subsequent implantation into the maternal endometrium (**Figure 2.4B**). The embryonic pole, which is the point of contact between the embryoblast and the trophoblast, is the first to implant.

Implantation

At the end of the first week, the blastocyst attaches to the endometrial wall and begins the process of implantation (**Figure 2.5**). The trophoblast cells forming the outer layer of the blastocyst differentiate into the syncytiotrophoblast (the outer trophoblastic cell layer) and the cytotrophoblast (the inner trophoblastic cell layer), eventually becoming the chorionic sac (Sadler, 2015; Velicky, Knöfler, & Pollheimer, 2016). This differentiation sets the stage for the necessary changes in the maternal endometrium and the development of the placental structures (e.g., umbilical cord) that will establish feto–maternal circulation and support the growing embryo/fetus.

Continued expansion of the syncytiotrophoblast (syncytium) is dependent on further proliferation of the cytotrophoblast, as the syncytium is not independently capable of proliferation. The cytotrophoblast begins by penetrating the syncytium, forming a chorionic villus. It thereby migrates deeper into the endometrium to anchor the fetus to the uterine wall (anchoring villi; Sadler, 2015). Cytotrophoblast cells colonize the exterior surfaces of the spiral arteries to facilitate circulatory adaptation (a low-resistance system of flow) to support the rapidly growing fetus (Forbes & Westwood, 2010).

Early in this stage of placental development, as the syncytium grows, lacunar (sunken) spaces begin to form within the syncytium. At the same time, the maternal capillaries in the endometrium dilate to form sinusoids, and maternal blood flows into the lacunar networks (Moore et al., 2016). These lacunar spaces stop growing at about 12 days after fertilization and coalesce to form fused intervillous spaces. In combination with formation

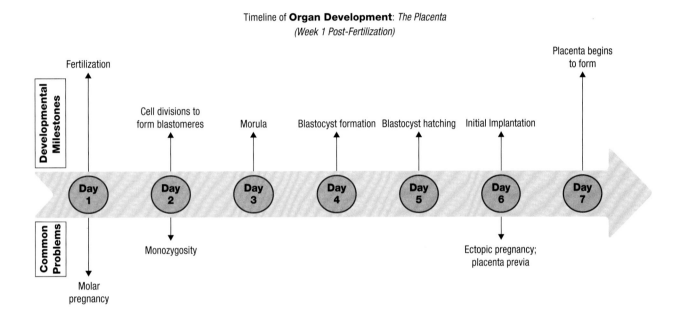

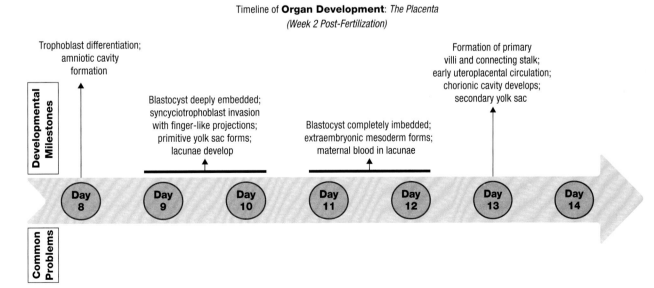

Figure 2.2 Visual timeline.

(*continued*)

Timeline of **Organ Development**: *The Placenta*
(Week 3-8 Post-Fertilization)

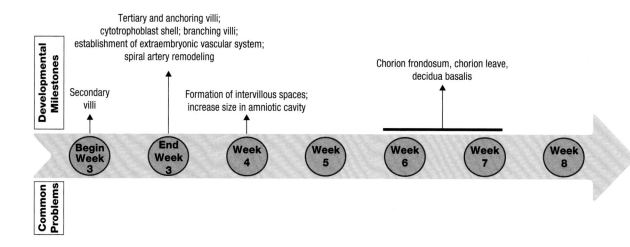

Timeline of **Organ Development**: *The Placenta*
(Fetal Period; Week 9 to delivery)

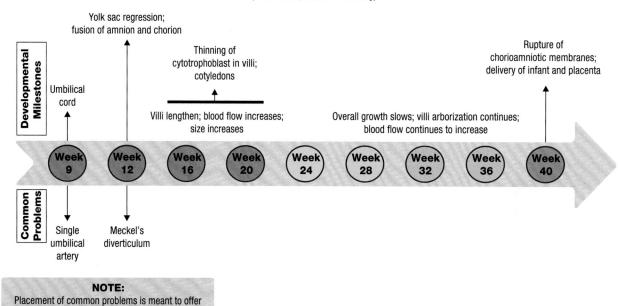

NOTE:
Placement of common problems is meant to offer visual/conceptual perspective on the timing of onset of these commonly reported malformations. Variation exists across the literature.

Note: Amniotic band disruption, intrauterine growth restriction, oligohydramnios, polyhydramnios, and abruptio placenta may arise at variable times

Figure 2.2 Visual timeline.

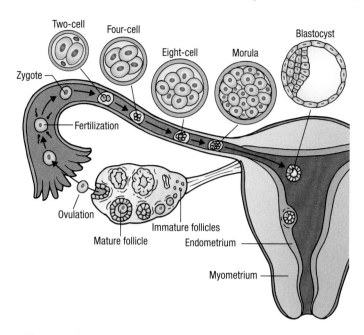

Figure 2.3 From ovulation to blastocyst formation: First, the 2-cell embryo appears approximately 36 hours after fertilization. Twenty-four hours later, the embryo divides into a 4-cell mass. Twelve hours later, the embryo divides into an 8-cell mass, and 6 hours afterward into a 16-cell morula ("mulberry"). Finally, approximately 4 hours after becoming a densely packed morula, the embryo changes into a hollow blastocyst.

NOTE: Failure of ciliated cells to propel the embryo through the fallopian tube and into the uterus results in an ectopic pregnancy.

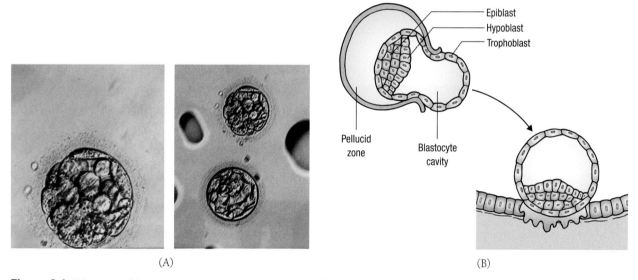

(A)   (B)

Figure 2.4 (A) Human blastocyst. Figure on right is of twins. (B) The anatomic composition of the blastocyst is noteworthy, as its major components differentiate into the future embryo and placenta. The hollow inner portion will fill with fluid and become the embryoblast, or future embryo. The embryoblast will further differentiate into the hypoblast and the epiblast, the origin of all three germ layers of the fetus (endoderm, mesoderm, ectoderm; Moore et al., 2016). The one-cell thick outer layer, or trophoblast, will differentiate into placental structures including the chorionic villi, umbilical cord, and other critical structures such as the fetal membranes (Sadler, 2015).

Source: Erin Broush, MSN, APRN, NNP-BC.

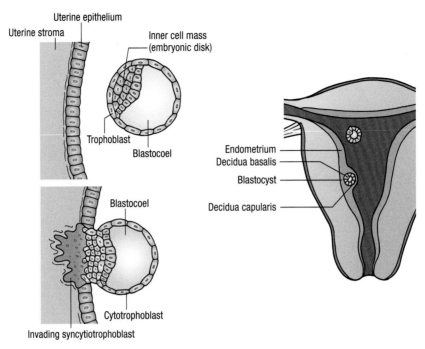

Figure 2.5 Implantation of the blastocyst.

of the villi, early uteroplacental circulation is established (Sadler, 2015).

Next, syncytiotrophoblast cells begin to secrete progesterone and human chorionic gonadotropin (hCG; Kliman, 1999a). hCG prevents degradation of the corpus luteum, which also secretes hormones necessary for maintaining the pregnancy until the placenta can provide sufficient hormones by week 8 of gestation (Cunningham et al., 2014; Moore et al., 2016). Progesterone maintains the thick endometrial lining of the uterus, an environment rich in blood vessels (Cunningham et al., 2014). The syncytiotrophoblasts secrete proteolytic enzymes that lyse the endometrium, such that fingerlike projections can invade the endometrial epithelium. These projections are the chorionic villi. These villi develop into a structure composed of a bilayered epithelium (inner layer of cytotrophobasts and an overlying layer of syncytiotrophoblasts) and will provide the area for future maximal nutrient exchange (Sadler, 2015).

The syncytium adheres to the endometrium and covers the surface of the placenta, positioned for a future role in barrier function. The syncytium will grow as the nutrient demands of the fetus increase during advancing gestation. The syncytiotrophoblast cells have a short life span as they are unable to renew themselves. Therefore, the cytotrophoblast cells drive ongoing cell proliferation and differentiation of the syncytium. Problems with altered rates of cell turnover have been linked to fetal growth

abnormalities (Forbes & Westwood, 2010). The embryoblast orients near the endometrial surface to accommodate correct placement of the future umbilical cord. Finally, by 11 to 12 days postfertilization, the blastocyst is fully implanted into the endometrium.

Development of the Extraembryonic Membranes

During the second week after fertilization, the blastocyst differentiates into various layers that are vital to the embryo's survival. These extraembryonic membranes, which are required to support and protect the growing embryo, include the chorion, amnion, yolk sac, and the allantois.

The Chorion. The chorion represents the outermost layer of the fetal portion of the placenta and is derived from the trophoblast. As the extraembryonic mesoderm penetrates the core of the developing villi, the villi are contiguous with the chorionic plate. Blood vessels develop within the chorionic plate and connect to both the developing umbilical cord and developing blood vessels within the villi, forming the extraembryonic vascular system. The portion of the chorion that interfaces with the decidua capsularis undergoes atrophy and these villi disappear. The chorion fuses with the decidua parietalis and forms the membranous, nonvillus portion of the placenta (Sadler, 2015). This smooth area is called the chorionic laeve. The remaining portion of the chorion will form the villous portion of the placenta.

Chorionic Villi. Recall that the fingerlike projections of the chorionic villi, or chorionic frondosum, are created after the syncytiotrophoblast lyses the endometrial surface. At approximately 13 days after fertilization, primary chorionic villi are formed. These early villi are small and nonvascular, and branch outward from the chorionic plate toward the basal (or maternal) plate (Figure 2.6). Secondary villi develop during week 3 of gestation, increase in size, and contain a core of extraembryonic mesoderm surrounded by the cytotrophoblast; secondary villi cover the entirety of the chorionic sac (Moore et al., 2016). Shortly thereafter, the mesoderm differentiates into capillaries and venules, giving rise to the vascular tertiary villi. The tertiary villi account for the major site of nutrient and waste exchange between maternal and fetal circulations (Sadler, 2015; Wang & Zhao, 2010).

Maternal arteries, which grow from the endometrium and extend into the decidua basalis, deliver pulsatile maternal blood to these intervillous spaces (Figure 2.7). Remodeling of the anatomic configuration of the maternal arteries, along with trophoblast-mediated pressure regulation, lowers resistance to flow into these intervillous spaces and increases volume capacity. This structural adaptation results from alteration of the endothelium and removal of the neurovascular control of the blood vessels (Wang & Zhao, 2010).

The maternal endometrium, or inner layer of the uterine wall, also begins a process of structural change, or decidualization, which supports formation of the placenta and the developing future fetus. Three regions are formed as a result of the decidual process: the decidua basalis, decidua capsularis, and decidua parietalis. The decidua basalis provides a soft vascular bed on which the blastocyst rests, and along with uterine vessels and glands forms the maternal portion of the placenta (Moore et al., 2016). The decidua capsularis lies just above the area of trophoblastic proliferation, initially covers the growing embryo, and disappears with development of the chorion. The decidua parietalis (or vera) supports trophoblastic adhesion and migration (Cunningham et al., 2014; Sadler, 2015).

The decidua basalis (maternal portion of the placenta) extends septa between intervillous spaces resulting in about 15 to 20 subdivisions called *cotyledons* (Sadler, 2015). Each cotyledon is supplied by a maternal arteriole, contains a main stem of a chorionic villus and its branches, receives fetal blood, and contains all of the structures necessary for exchange of oxygen and nutrients between maternal blood and fetal capillaries (Moore et al., 2016). The decidua basalis and its cotyledons comprise the maternal circulation at the level of the placenta, located within the endometrial layer of the uterus. It is important to recognize that neither the maternal nor fetal circulations comingle or innervate one another, but rather communicate via diffusion.

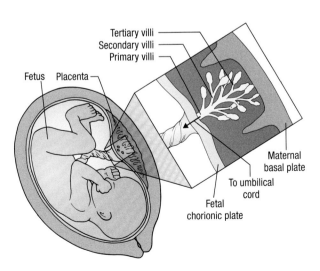

Figure 2.6 Chorionic villi. The chorion is the outermost layer of the fetal portion of the placenta. It arises from the cytotrophoblast layer of the blastocyst and the chorionic plate.

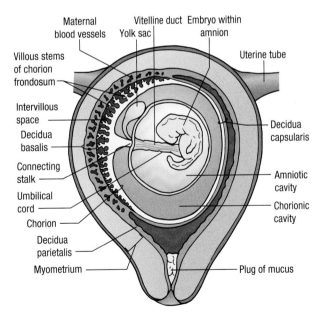

Figure 2.7 Orientation of chorionic structures within the uterus. The image represents the gravid uterus in the second month. The decidua basalis forms the maternal portion of the placenta. The decidua capsularis initially covers the growing embryo and disappears with development of the chorion. The decidua parietalis facilitates trophoblastic adhesion and migration.

The Amnion (and Amniotic Cavity). Early in week 2, a cavity is created in the embryoblast between the embryonic disc and the trophoblast, developing from the upper layer (epiblast) of the embryonic disc. The epiblasts form the floor of the cavity, which later becomes ectoderm, and also gives rise to amnioblasts (Sadler, 2015). These amnion-forming cells create the amniotic membrane, which will cover the developing embryo. The amnion fills with fluid and expands to become the amniotic sac. The fluid volume increases over the next 3 to 4 weeks, and this volume expansion leads to adherence of the amnion to the inner surface of the chorion at about 12 to 14 weeks, forming the amniochorionic membrane (Ahokas & McKinney, 2008; Moore et al., 2016). Composition of the amniotic fluid includes a filtrate of maternal plasma (early on) and then includes urine later once fetal kidney function is established. The function is to provide a neutral thermal environment, as well as a trauma-free environment that allows the fetus to move freely and initiate other acts, including breathing and swallowing. The amniotic fluid cushions the developing fetus, allows for symmetrical growth, and prevents adherence. In addition, amniotic fluid allows for movement of the fetus for development of skeletal structure and participates in development of the lungs and GI system.

The Yolk Sac. While the placenta develops, the yolk sac plays an important role in supporting the developing embryo. During the first week after fertilization, the yolk sac develops and begins to provide nutrition via a primitive vitelline circulation. The yolk sac also plays a role in blood development before the fetal liver takes over, at about week 5 of gestation. The yolk sac is incorporated into the embryo and is involved in development of the trachea, lungs, and bronchi. In addition, it plays a role in development of the gut and sex glands (Pansky, 1982). The yolk sac begins to regress by week 7 of gestation, as the placenta assumes the role of nourishing the developing embryo.

The Allantois (and Umbilical Cord). The umbilical cord provides a connection between the fetus and the placenta and replaces the yolk sac as the source of nutrient delivery. Early in development, a primitive circulation via diffusion is established between the maternal spiral arteries and veins and the blood-filled lacunae. By the third week after fertilization, the umbilical cord develops from remnants of the yolk sac and the allantois. This primitive cord is composed of extraembryonic mesoderm extending from the chorionic plate to the developing embryo (Spurway, Logan, & Pak, 2012).

By week 5 of gestation, the primitive umbilical cord contains two umbilical veins, two umbilical arteries, the allantois, and other rudimentary elements such as the omphaloenteric duct and the umbilical coecum (Sadler, 2015). The umbilical veins arise from the extraembryonic allantois; the second umbilical vein regresses by week 6 of gestation. The umbilical arteries arise initially from the dorsal aorta and, over time, the internal iliac arteries. The allantois arises from the yolk sac and develops into the urachus, which connects the yolk sac and fetal bladder and participates in the removal of waste from the fetal bladder (Moore et al., 2016). The allantois normally regresses by week 8 of gestation and exists as a small and functionally insignificant remnant (urachus) between both umbilical arteries; failed regression can lead to formation of Meckel's diverticulum or a patent urachus. The omphaloenteric duct (vitelline duct or yolk stalk) connects the yolk sac with the rudimentary intestinal tract and disappears by week 10 of gestation. The umbilical coelom, which connects both intraembryonic coelom (pleura, pericardial, and peritoneal spaces) and extraembryonic coelom (yolk sac, amniotic cavity, and chorionic cavity), disappears by week 12 of gestation (Spurway et al., 2012).

The epithelium of the umbilical cord forms by week 12 of gestation and contains two arteries and one vein, both surrounded by Wharton's jelly. Wharton's jelly is formed from mucopolysaccharides, which produce a gelatinous material that protects the umbilical blood vessels (Kliman, 1999b). The umbilical vessels are longer than the cord and twist and spiral within the cord. Length of the umbilical cord depends on fetal movement, with more movement resulting in longer length and decreased movement shorter length (Kliman, 1999b). The cord is usually inserted in the center of the placenta and reaches maximal length by 30 weeks of gestation, with an average length of about 60 cm (Kliman, 1999b). The minimal cord length necessary for safe delivery is approximately 30 cm (Cunningham et al., 2014).

The Fetal Period: The Structurally Formed Placenta

The placenta is fully formed structurally at about week 12 of gestation, though it continues to grow in size until term in order to meet the demands of the growing fetus (Sadler, 2015). The cytotrophoblast layer begins to thin out in order to decrease the distance for diffusion. The fetal part of the placenta, called the *chorionic plate*, contains the amnion, embryonic mesenchyme, and both cell layers (cytotrophoblast and syncytiotrophoblast). The maternal part of the placenta, the decidual plate, contains the decidua basalis, uterine vessels, and glands (Sadler, 2015). At term gestation, the placenta weighs about 500 grams with a diameter of approximately 18 to 25 cm, and 2 to 2.5 cm thickness (Cunningham et al., 2014; Sadler, 2015).

MATERNAL–FETAL CIRCULATION

Now that the structure of the placenta is described, blood flow can be followed from the maternal blood supply through the placenta to the fetus via the umbilical cord and then back to the mother (Figure 2.8). Oxygen-rich blood from the maternal uterine artery is delivered to the uterus, then to the maternal spiral arteries supplying the cotyledons. Maternal blood flows into the intervillous spaces in which the chorionic terminal villi extend. The fetal capillary system in the terminal villi take up contents of the maternal blood by diffusion and transport via the arteriovenous system, deliver it to the branching venules in the chorionic plate, and empty it into the single umbilical vein, which delivers oxygenated blood into the fetal circulation. Fetal circulation has a specialized architecture composed of fetal shunts (ductus venosus, foramen ovale, and ductus arteriosus [DA]) that allow the blood to circulate through the fetus within the context of the placenta, functioning as an organ of respiration, nutrition, and excretion.

The oxygenated blood enters the fetus via the umbilical veins, a portion of the blood enters the portal circulation, and the remaining blood (approximately 50%) flows through the ductus venosus into the inferior vena cava, joining deoxygenated blood returning from perfused organs. Minimal mixing occurs and the oxygenated blood is "preferentially streamed" into the right atrium, through the foramen ovale into the left atrium and ultimately to the aortic arch. From the aortic arch, the blood is distributed to the coronary and cerebral circulations.

Poorly oxygenated blood enters the right atrium from the superior vena cava and passes into the right ventricle and the pulmonary artery. Only about 10% of this blood flows to the lungs to nourish the proliferating pulmonary tissues; the majority of the blood volume is shunted through the DA, due to the high pulmonary vascular resistance, and into the descending aorta and returns to the placenta through the umbilical arteries.

Because only a small amount of blood is returning from the lungs via the pulmonary veins into the left atrium, the level of oxygenated blood sitting in the left atrium is minimally affected. This oxygenated blood in the left atrium flows into the left ventricle and the aorta and is delivered to the head and heart via the carotid and coronary arteries, with the remaining blood continuing down the aorta. This remaining blood is joined by the deoxygenated blood returning from the right ventricle that has shunted through the DA into the aorta. This mixed blood continues through the aorta, eventually drains into the umbilical arteries, and delivers waste products to the mother through the placenta via the chorionic villi to the maternal uterine vein.

In summary, this unique fetal circulation occurs due to the specific architecture of fetal circulation (Martin, Fanaroff, & Walsh, 2015):

1. The ductus venosus shunts blood from the placenta via the umbilical vein into the inferior vena cava.
2. The oxygenated blood from the mother maintains its oxygen level via preferential streaming and bypasses the lungs via the foramen ovale.
3. Poorly oxygenated blood from the right ventricle bypasses the lungs and shunts into the descending aorta via the DA at a point distal to where the highest oxygenated blood has already been delivered to the heart and brain. This blood returns to the placenta through the umbilical arteries.

Other unique compensatory mechanisms that involve gas and nutrient delivery are discussed later in the chapter. The rate of fetal blood flow in the placenta is 500 mL/minute; it is dependent on fetal heart rate and regulated by interaction of blood pressure, fetal right to left shunts, and systemic and pulmonary vascular resistance. The placenta serves as a low-resistance circuit in the fetal circulatory system (Martin et al., 2015).

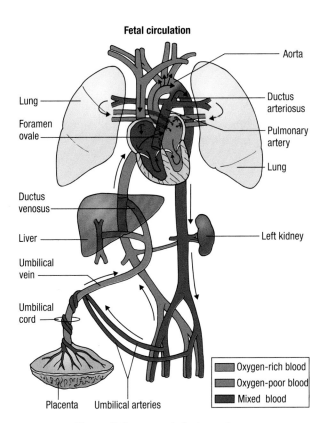

Fetal circulation

Aorta

Lung

Foramen ovale

Ductus arteriosus

Pulmonary artery

Lung

Ductus venosus

Liver

Left kidney

Umbilical vein

Umbilical cord

Placenta   Umbilical arteries

■ Oxygen-rich blood
■ Oxygen-poor blood
■ Mixed blood

Figure 2.8 Maternal–fetal circulation.

Placental Function

The placenta is an organ essential for transfer of nutrients and gases from the mother to the fetus and removal of fetal waste products from the fetus to the mother. The placenta performs four major functions to support growth and development of the fetus. The transport of substances across the placenta increases during the course of gestation due to changes in placental structure (decreased distance between maternal and fetal blood), increased maternal and fetal blood flow, and greater demands of the growing fetus. The gas exchange, nutrition and excretion, immunologic, and endocrine functions will be described in detail later in the chapter.

Remember that the decidua basalis and chorionic villi are the site of communication between the mother and fetus. Maternal and fetal arteries and veins provide delivery of blood to and from mother and fetus. The actual exchange of nutrient uptake and waste exchange occurs via the fetal capillary bed in the terminal villi that are suspended in the intervillous spaces and bathed in maternal blood. How these nutrients are exchanged can be explained by different modes of placental transport.

MODES OF PLACENTAL TRANSPORT

Fick's law (Poirier & Geiger, 2016) essentially states that the rate of diffusion of a gas across a permeable membrane is determined by the chemical nature of the membrane itself, the surface area of the membrane, the partial pressure gradient of the gas across the membrane, and the thickness of the membrane. This type of diffusion is the simplest form of diffusion, known as *passive diffusion*. The same is true of other substances that cross membranes passively, such as electrolytes. Substances will move from an area of higher concentration to an area of lower concentration based on the concentration of the substances on both sides of the membrane, with greater diffusion occurring with increased surface area, thinness of the membrane, and the velocity of the flow or pressure on either side of the membrane. In terms of maternal–fetal diffusion, this relates to the overall surface area of the placenta (which increases over the length of the pregnancy), as well as the surface area of the villi membranes in the intervillous space, maternal uterine artery blood flow velocity, and the concentration of the gases or electrolytes in the maternal blood compared with the fetal blood.

Many other factors affect the transfer of any substance across the placenta, including the pH of both maternal and fetal blood, presence of substance-specific transporters, molecular weight, lipid solubility, protein-binding capacities, and concentration gradients. There are five major processes involved in placental transfer.

Simple Diffusion

Simple diffusion, also called *passive diffusion*, is the simplest pathway across any membrane (Figure 2.9). Simple diffusion is concentration dependent, with substances moving from areas of higher concentration to areas of lower concentration. Diffusion occurs across the lipid membrane of the cell, or through channel proteins. Passage is affected by molecular size, membrane depth, and the degree to which the molecules are water soluble or fat soluble. Not all substances diffuse with the same ease; some easily pass through the cell membranes such as CO_2, whereas others are dependent on significant differences between the level of concentration on both sides of the membrane. In simple diffusion, the direction of the movement is always from an area of higher concentration to an area of lower concentration with movement from mother to fetus favored with higher concentration in maternal blood, and fetal to maternal movement when concentrations are higher in the fetus. In general, smaller, water-soluble molecules pass more readily. Water, electrolytes, oxygen, carbon dioxide, urea, simple amines, creatinine, fatty acids, steroids, fat-soluble vitamins, narcotics, barbiturates, and anesthetics cross by the process of simple diffusion.

Facilitated Diffusion

Facilitated diffusion, unlike simple diffusion, requires the presence of specific proteins that assist the transfer of the

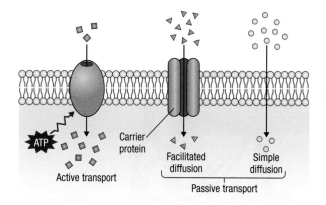

Figure 2.9 Simple diffusion, facilitated diffusion, and active transport. Facilitated diffusion requires the presence of a carrier protein in order for a particle to cross the desired membrane.

ATP, adenosine triphosphate.

substance. Particles cross over a membrane after attaching to a carrier protein. Glucose is transferred via facilitated diffusion with glucose transport proteins assisting in this process.

Active Transport

Active transport is energy dependent as well as transfer protein specific, and results in the transfer of substances against concentration gradients. It is the process used for transfer of most amino acids, potassium, water-soluble vitamins, calcium, phosphate, iron, and iodide. Active transport allows for concentrations of nutrients to be higher in the fetus during critical growth periods.

Endocytosis and Exocytosis

The processes of endocytosis and exocytosis allow for substances to be enveloped or engulfed within a membrane for transport into the cell (endocytosis), or to be removed from a cell (exocytosis; Figure 2.10). These processes are used when substances are too large to be accommodated by simple or facilitated diffusion, or specific carrier proteins are not available. Antibodies are an example of substances that require endocytosis for transfer from maternal circulation to the fetal circulation.

Bulk Flow

Bulk flow may result in large, rapid transfer of substances across the placental membrane resulting from

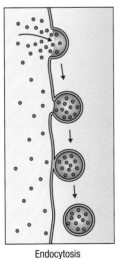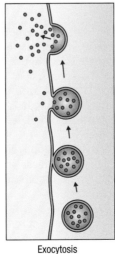

| Endocytosis | Exocytosis |

Figure 2.10 Endocytosis and exocytosis are reverse processes and involve fusion of substances (e.g., antibodies) within the plasma membrane for transport into and out of a cell.

changes in osmotic pressure and hydrostatic forces. When osmotic pressure drops, the bulk movement of water will be in the direction from the higher side to the lower side of the maternal–fetal circuit and results in concomitant electrolyte shifts as well. This process may also include the use of special aqueous pores or water channels.

In addition to these processes for substance transfer, there may be transfer of fetal or maternal blood cells due to tiny capillary breaks within the villus covering, allowing small amounts of maternal blood to enter fetal circulation, and vice versa. Maternal leukocytes, some bacteria, and some viral organisms can also cross the placenta and infect the fetus, but the mechanisms by which these processes occur are unknown.

TRANSPLACENTAL GAS TRANSFER

Gas transfer is by simple diffusion across a 3.5-micron distance between the fetal and maternal circulations. In the case of oxygen, it is transferred down an average concentration gradient of 30 mmHg. Oxygen delivery to the uterus and placenta is from the uterine artery and is delivered to the fetus via the umbilical vein. Fetal hemoglobin has a higher oxygen affinity (P50 = 18–20 mmHg) than adult hemoglobin (P50 = 26.6 mmHg) and this difference assists in the transfer of oxygen from maternal to fetal circulations. Fetal hemoglobin lacks binding sites for 2,3-diphosphoglycerate (DPG), a key regulator of oxygen affinity. High levels of 2,3-DPG in adult red blood cells leads to a right shift (lower affinity) in the oxyhemoglobin saturation curve (OHSC).

Also assisting in oxygen transfer from maternal to fetal circulations is the "double" Bohr effect. This is a significant, albeit small, effect (results in 2%–8% of total transplacental oxygen transfer). The *Bohr effect* refers to the role of carbon dioxide and pH on hemoglobin's affinity for oxygen. High pCO_2 (and lower pH) alters the structure of the hemoglobin molecule and results in lower oxygen affinity and a shift of the OHSC to the right; low pCO_2 (and higher pH) results in higher oxygen affinity and a shift of the OHSC to the left. The *"double" Bohr* refers to this process occurring concurrently in both the maternal and fetal circulations (Figure 2.11). Increased pCO_2 in the maternal intervillous sinuses leads to unloading of oxygen by maternal adult hemoglobin. The subsequent decrease in the pCO_2 on the fetal side leads to an increase in oxygen affinity by the fetal hemoglobin. The double Bohr effect leads to a widening of the difference between the maternal and fetal hemoglobin OHSC for any given pO_2 (Figure 2.12).

Carbon dioxide is removed from the fetus and returned to the maternal circulation via the

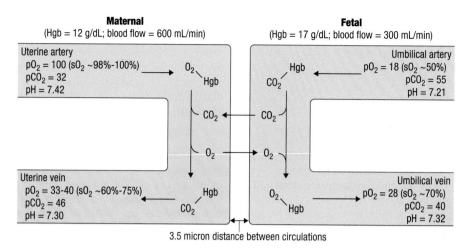

Figure 2.11 Double Bohr effect. [Left] As more carbon dioxide passes into the maternal blood from fetal circulation, the pH and affinity of maternal hemoglobin for oxygen decreases. This prompts displacement of oxygen into the fetal blood. [Right] At the same time, on the fetal side of the placental membrane, there is a decrease in carbon dioxide and this increases the affinity of fetal hemoglobin for oxygen and increased oxygen binding occurs.

Hgb, hemoglobin; pCO_2, partial pressure of carbon dioxide

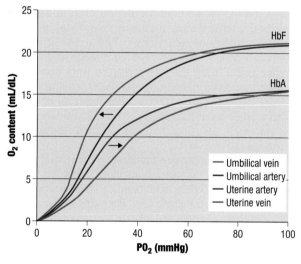

Figure 2.12 Oxyhemoglobin dissociation curve within the placenta.

HbA, adult hemoglobin; HbF, fetal hemoglobin; PO_2, partial pressure of oxygen

umbilical arteries. It is transferred by simple diffusion down a concentration gradient owing to maternal hyperventilation and lowered maternal average pCO_2. Another factor regulating CO_2 transfer is the "double" Haldane effect, which accounts for up to 46% of transplacental CO_2 transfer (**Figure 2.13**). The *Haldane effect* refers to the role of oxygen on hemoglobin affinity to carbon dioxide: higher pO_2 results in a lower capacity for hemoglobin to carry CO_2.

NUTRITION AND EXCRETION

Nutrients, waste products, and drugs are exchanged across the syncytiotrophoblast, passing in both directions—maternal to fetal and fetal to maternal circulation. This exchange occurs through various processes, including simple diffusion, facilitated diffusion, active transport, endocytosis and exocytosis, and bulk flow.

Glucose

The main source of carbohydrate is glucose; it is transported from maternal to fetal circulation by a protein-mediated facilitated diffusion. There are several glucose transporters involved, each with a specific function. The fetus itself produces little glucose during gestation. Normal glucose levels in the fetus are proportional to maternal levels. Fetal glucose levels are approximately 70% to 80% of the maternal glucose levels. Elevated blood glucose in the mother causes elevated blood glucose in the fetus, with subsequent sequelae for the infants of diabetic mothers with poor glucose control.

Amino Acids

Amino acids are transported across the placenta and can be metabolized by the fetus as well. Protein transfer across the placenta is an energy-requiring process that relies on amino acid transporters. Amino acids are higher in the fetal circulation than in maternal circulation.

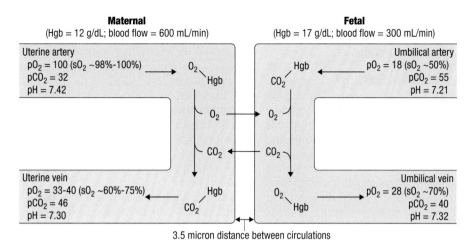

Figure 2.13 Double Haldane effect. [Left] As oxygen is released and passes into the fetal circulation, there is an increase in carbon dioxide affinity by the maternal hemoglobin. [Right] The oxygen that is passed to the fetal circulation results in a decrease in affinity for carbon dioxide by fetal hemoglobin, which enhances release and transfer to the maternal circulation.

Hgb, hemoglobin.

Lipids

Lipids are present in many forms in both maternal and fetal circulation and transport varies based on the form. Free fatty acids and glycerol are transported via simple diffusion or facilitated through fatty acid binding proteins (Gude, Roberts, Kalionis, & King, 2004; Haggarty, 2004). The trophoblast itself can synthesize cholesterol and other fatty acids, but most cholesterol is transported across the placenta from the maternal circulation (Gude et al., 2004).

Water, Ions, Vitamins, and Minerals

Water transport is thought to occur through several processes, including passive transport dependent on hydrostatic and osmotic pressure, and through water channels. Ion transport occurs through several processes as well, dependent on the ion. Sodium and chloride move through passive diffusion with the gradient, but may also be transported by various ion pump mechanisms. Potassium, calcium, and phosphate are actively transported, with levels being higher in fetal circulation than maternal circulation (Gude et al., 2004). This is particularly true in the last trimester when bone accretion activity is highest. Vitamins are transported from mother to fetus via multiple diffusion methods. Vitamin D, vitamin E, vitamin K, and biotin cross via simple diffusion; thiamine, riboflavin, nicotinic acid, and pantothenic acid cross via active transport; and vitamin A, folate, and vitamin C use facilitated transfer (McNanley & Woods, 2008).

In addition to the excretion of carbon dioxide, the placenta also excretes by-products of metabolism that would normally be excreted by the liver and kidneys. Ammonia is converted into uric acid and urea and passively diffuses across the placenta. For the most part, unconjugated bilirubin is thought to be diffused passively although there is some evidence that some unconjugated bilirubin is carrier mediated (Serrano et al., 2002).

IMMUNOLOGIC FUNCTION

One of the most significant immunologic functions of the placenta is its ability to permit implantation and maintenance of the pregnancy itself because the developing fetal tissue is semiallogeneic, having both maternal and paternal proteins. Several factors are involved in protecting the fetal tissues (which include the placenta) from being attacked by the maternal immune system. Human leukocyte antigen G (HLA-G) is a maternally derived antigen responsible for decreasing the maternal immune response to the fetal tissue. Fetal cells also contribute to this process by producing immunosuppressive cytokines, chemokines, and prostaglandins that limit T-lymphocyte proliferation and enhance progesterone production, which helps reduce immune response (Hunt, Petroff, McIntire, & Ober, 2005). The syncytiotrophoblast and cytotrophoblast of the villi within the intervillous space do not produce tissue antigens. This prevents reactions between maternal and fetal blood that are in constant direct contact with the villi (fetal structures). The placenta itself also blocks maternal cytotoxic cells, further enhancing the antigenic mechanisms that promote human reproduction.

Passive immunity to many viruses is passed from mother to fetus by endocytosis. Maternal immunoglobulin G (IgG) antibodies developed in response to prior exposure to viruses, or through prior immunization, are taken up by membrane-bound vesicles and transported across the placenta into fetal circulation. IgG provides immunity for a limited period of time (Gude et al., 2004).

The placenta has several features that offer protection from many viruses and bacteria; however, this protection is limited. The first level of protection is provided by the syncytiotrophoblast itself. There are no intracellular junctions in the placenta, which limits the passage of most bloodborne pathogens. The decidual trophoblast has multiple cellular defenses in the form of macrophages, and natural killer cells that enhance placental elimination of invading pathogens. The final layer of protection is afforded by the basement membrane of the placenta, separating the capillary endothelium and syncytiotrophoblast, which further limits transfer of infectious agents (Robbins & Bakardjiev, 2012). There are, however, pathogens that are known to pass from mother to fetus, including syphilis, rubella, toxoplasmosis, cytomegalovirus, parvovirus B-19, herpes simplex, and mycobacterium tuberculosis, which cause devastating sequelae in the fetus.

The placenta does not offer protection to the fetus from drug transfer. Drugs that cross the placenta most readily are those with low molecular weight that are uncharged and lipophilic and have high levels of unbound drug in maternal circulation. Drugs that cross the placenta include most antibiotics, antivirals, anesthetics, analgesics, cardiovascular drugs, tobacco, caffeine, and alcohol. Very few drugs do not cross the placenta; this group includes heparin and insulin. The mechanisms of transfer follow the processes listed earlier: diffusion, facilitated diffusion, active transport, and endocytosis.

Drug safety in pregnancy is a complex issue and cannot easily be categorized. In 2014 the Food and Drug Administration (FDA) overhauled its recommendations for drugs in pregnancy and lactation, changing from an alphabetical system listing drugs in order of known or suspected fetal risk from small to significant. The FDA now provides a summary of known and suspected risks in narrative form preceding each drug description and includes the molecular weight (FDA, 2014).

ENDOCRINE FUNCTION

The placenta produces hormones that are critical in maintenance of the pregnancy, preparation and coordination of the mother's body to sustain changes in function to support additional metabolic and circulation requirements of pregnancy and lactation, and regulation of fetal growth. This hormonal production begins during the blastocyst stage even before the placenta is formed and implantation has taken place (Garnica & Chan, 1996). The primary site of placental hormone synthesis is the syncytiotrophoblast. These hormones include, but are not limited to, estrogens, progesterone, oxytocin, human chorionic gonadotropin (hCG), human chorionic somatomammotropin (hCS), growth hormones, corticotropin-releasing hormone, human placental lactogen, and insulin-like growth factors.

Some of the hormones initially produced in the placenta are also made in the fetal brain as gestation continues. Placental hormones may remain in the placenta, whereas others cross the placenta to maternal and/or fetal circulation (Pasca & Penn, 2010).

Estrogen, progesterone, and oxytocin work to help maintain the endometrium, suppress gonadotropin secretion, trigger parturition, and have important roles in neuroendocrine processes. Estrogens also stimulate mammary gland development while progesterone stimulates the development of the alveolar tissue within the mammary glands. Lactogen is critical for maternal carbohydrate and lipid metabolism for nutrient availability for the fetus as well as milk production for the infant after birth. Chorionic gonadotropin is critical in maintenance of the corpus luteum, in synchrony with LH in the first few weeks of pregnancy, and also plays a role in suppressing the immune response, preventing rejection of the embryo. Somatomammotropin increases lipolysis in adipose tissue to provide placental energy, sparing glucose for use by the fetus.

GENETIC INFLUENCES ON PLACENTAL DEVELOPMENT

Currently, research on maternal genetic defects that might have a direct effect on the developing placenta is ongoing. Investigation is warranted into the etiology of recurring early pregnancy loss to determine maternal genetic mutations that may predispose a woman to early fetal demise as a direct result of abnormal placental development.

Chronic histiocytic intervillositis (CHIV) of the placenta occurs in less than 1% of pregnancies and is associated with fetal demise and intrauterine growth restriction (IUGR; Freitag, von Kaisenberg, Kreipe, & Hussein, 2013). Histiocytic infiltration and lesions in the intervillous spaces of the placenta characterize CHIV (Boyd & Redline, 2000). Resulting trophoblast degeneration and increased distance between maternal blood and the chorionic villi are suggested causes of IUGR and fetal demise (Freitag et al., 2013). Current investigation includes evaluation of angiogenesis-associated genes from placental tissue (Freitag et al., 2013).

Pregnant women with a mutation in methylenetetrahydrofolate reductase (MTFHR) suffer recurrent miscarriages, develop preeclampsia, and give birth to infants with congenital defects, for example, neural tube defects (Boyd & Redline, 2000; Yaliwal & Desai, 2012). However, it is unclear whether these recurrent miscarriages are directly related to defective placental development. Current understanding of this genetic disease links high homocysteine levels to development of preeclampsia (Noto et al., 2003), but whether this is associated with faulty trophoblast invasion or defects in placental blood vessel development remains unclear. Development of neural tube defects appears to be related to altered folate metabolism due to hyperhomocysteinemia (Yaliwal & Desai, 2012).

Zeltser and Leibel (2011) reviewed studies in which maternal nutrient deprivation may play a role in altering gene expression and ultimately the function of the placenta. These alterations in placental function focus on the impact of the maternal environment on adaptive gene expression and fetal brain development.

As scientific knowledge advances in genetic sequencing, epigenetics, and identification of biomarkers for diagnosis of maternal disease, and from examination of the placenta in early pregnancy losses, we may better understand the direct genetic influences on placental development. Currently, there are known placental developmental abnormalities and maternal illnesses that may not be genetic in nature, but affect fetal development, and these conditions are discussed in the following section.

COMMON DEVELOPMENTAL ABNORMALITIES OF THE PLACENTA AND THEIR EFFECT ON THE FETUS

During the development of the placenta, problems with site of implantation, individual placental structures, or development of placental vasculature can alter the normal structure and function of the placenta. These problems are presented as they occur from fertilization to later in fetal development. These can occur due to maternal illness and can impact the developing fetus or affect the future health of the human being.

Placental Structure: Zygosity and Abnormal Vasculature

The structure of the placenta is determined at the time of fertilization and depends on whether the pregnancy is single or multiple. A twin pregnancy is used here to illustrate differences in placental structure. Monozygotic twins arise from the division of a single ovum after fertilization and can result in a monochorionic or dichorionic placenta and the following possible placental structures: monochorionic–monoamniotic, monochorionic–diamniotic, and dichorionic–diamniotic. Dizygotic twins arise when two ova enclosed within a single follicle are fertilized simultaneously, or when ovulation of two ova from one or both ovaries are independently fertilized. This results in a dichorionic placenta (separate or fused), that is to say, two dichorionic–diamniotic placentas (Cunningham et al., 2014; Sadler, 2015; Figure 2.14).

Improper development of the vasculature in monozygotic twins can lead to placental vascular anastomoses that alter normal blood flow, decreasing blood flow to one fetus and increasing flow to the other fetus. In addition, given the high demands of a pregnancy with more than one fetus, insufficient blood flow may result in restricted

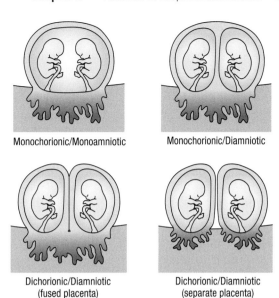

Monochorionic/Monoamniotic   Monochorionic/Diamniotic

Dichorionic/Diamniotic   Dichorionic/Diamniotic
(fused placenta)   (separate placenta)

Figure 2.14 Zygosity.

growth and preterm delivery (Cunningham et al., 2014). Twin-to-twin transfusion syndrome is a disorder of the placenta in which the blood flow is unequal and can occur in up to 15% of monochorionic–diamniotic twin pregnancies (Bliss, Carr, De Paepe, & Luks, 2017). The smaller donor twin pumps blood to the larger recipient twin. The donor twin receives less blood flow, resulting in anemia, oliguria, and thus decreased amniotic fluid (oligohydramnios). Oligohydramnios places the developing fetus at risk for abnormal organ development and compromises cushioning of the developing fetus. The larger donor twin receives an excess of blood resulting in polycythemia and polyuria, and leads to a higher volume of amniotic fluid (polyhydramnios), risk for rupture of the sac, heart failure, and hydrops (Bliss et al., 2017).

Molar Pregnancy

A molar pregnancy, also called *gestational trophoblastic disease*, occurs in 0.1% of pregnancies and results from implantation of a fertilized egg that is not viable. The developing chorionic villi swell and form fluid-filled cysts in the placenta (Cunningham et al., 2014). Although most molar pregnancies are noncancerous growths and result in pregnancy loss, there are malignant forms (Cunningham et al., 2014).

Implantation Errors

Ectopic Pregnancy. An ectopic pregnancy occurs any time the fertilized egg implants in a location other than the uterine endometrium, though most often this occurs in the fallopian tubes (tubal pregnancy). Any conditions that affect the integrity of the tissue in the fallopian tubes, such as inflammation from infection or sexually transmitted diseases, scar tissue, or abnormal tube shape, can lead to improper implantation of the fertilized egg in the tube, where the growing embryo cannot be supported. Ectopic pregnancies may occur in approximately 1% to 2% of first-trimester pregnancies, but can account for 6% to 10% of pregnancy-related deaths (Cunningham et al., 2014; Sadler, 2015). Early detection of a tubal pregnancy allows for laparoscopic surgery, preventing tubal rupture and reduces maternal morbidity. However, there is a risk for subsequent ectopic pregnancies and subsequent unsuccessful pregnancies (Cunningham et al., 2014).

Placenta Accreta. After a normal fertilization, the deep portion of the endometrium does not undergo decidualization and limits trophoblastic invasion beyond the endometrial layer into the maternal myometrium by secreting locally acting factors (Kliman, 1999a). However, in women with previous cesarean sections or in conditions leading to endometrial damage or scarring, the placenta can invade and become inseparable from the uterine wall. Three types of abnormal attachment (accreta) are known. *Placenta accreta*, the most common type of abnormal attachment, occurs when the chorionic villi penetrate deep into the endometrium, but not the myometrium. *Placenta increta* occurs if the chorionic villi invade the myometrium, and *placenta percreta* occurs if the villi invade the muscle layer into the serosal layer or even other organs such as the bladder (Cunningham et al., 2014). At delivery, these conditions create a risk for life-threatening maternal hemorrhage when the placenta does not appropriately separate from the uterine wall (Figure 2.15).

Placenta Previa. Placenta previa results from the improper implantation of the blastocyst close to or overlying the internal os of the uterus. At delivery, as the cervix dilates, risk of hemorrhage threatens the fetus and mother. Delivery route is determined by the severity of the previa and potential hemorrhage. In general, a complete previa describes two conditions: The cervical os is completely or partially covered by the placenta. In the low-lying placenta, the placenta extends to the edge of the cervix, but not over the os (Figure 2.16; Cunningham et al., 2014).

Velamentous Cord Insertion. Velamentous insertion of the cord occurs when the umbilical cord does not insert directly into the middle of the placenta, but instead

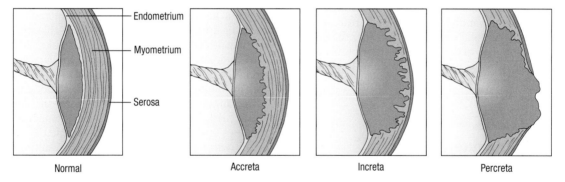

Normal   Accreta   Increta   Percreta

Figure 2.15 Diagram of degrees of abnormal placental infiltration. Placenta accreta is adherent to the myometrium. Placenta increta invades the myometrium. Placenta percreta extends beyond the uterine serosa and may invade any other organ.

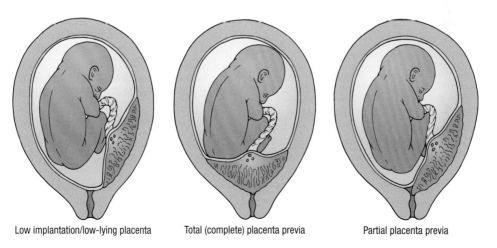

Low implantation/low-lying placenta   Total (complete) placenta previa   Partial placenta previa

Figure 2.16 Placenta previa.

travels to the placenta between the amnion and the chorion. Abnormal cord placement may result from improper implantation of the blastocyst (Wang & Zhao, 2010). The cord is not protected by Wharton's jelly and the vessels are vulnerable to compression and rupture (Figure 2.17; Cunningham et al., 2014; Kliman, 1999b).

Vasa Previa. Vasa previa occurs when the umbilical vessels cross the cervical os. The vessels are vulnerable to tearing as the cervix dilates, which can lead to significant fetal blood loss and fetal mortality (Figure 2.18; Cunningham et al., 2014).

Abnormal Spiral Arteries

If the cytotrophoblast fails to correctly invade the uterus and its vasculature, transformation of the spiral arteries into low resistant circuits does not occur and can lead to

decreased uteroplacental blood flow to the fetus. This developmental abnormality characterizes maternal preeclampsia and can lead to growth restriction of the fetus (Genbacev, DiFederico, McMaster, & Fisher, 1999; Lyall et al., 2001). Pijnenborg, Vercruysse, and Hanssens (2006) underline the need for further research into defining the mechanisms of vessel remodeling and altered hemodynamics and their relationship to preeclampsia and altered placental function.

Yolk Sac

Persistence of the Proximal Yolk Sac. By the end of week 7 of gestation, the small yolk sac, lying between the amnion and chorion, shrinks in size and has no function. Although rare, a persistence of the proximal intra-abdominal portion of the yolk sac leads to Meckel's diverticulum in the ileum in 2% of the population (Pansky, 1982).

Quality and Size of the Yok Sac. Formation of the yolk sac provides early nutrient delivery to the fetus. Cho, Chen, Tai, and Yang (2006) and Moradan and Forouzeshfar (2012) report a relationship between the size and morphology of the yolk sac and early gestation pregnancy loss.

Umbilical Cord Defects

Any compression or knotting of the umbilical cord can compromise normal blood flow to and from the placenta and affect normal function of the placenta. Umbilical cord compression during delivery, a knot in the cord, or a nuchal cord disrupts umbilical blood flow. Cord length can also cause problems; a longer cord may be prone to prolapse, knotting, or twisting; a short cord may limit

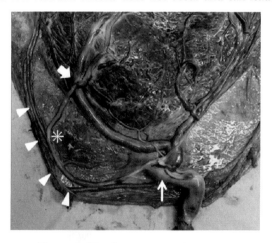

Figure 2.17 Velamentous cord insertion.

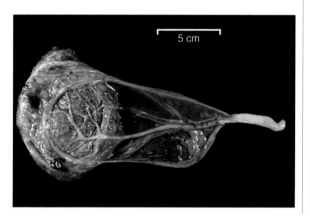

Figure 2.18 Vasa previa.

Source: [Left] Vasa Previa. (2008). *A midwife's muse: Midwifery & childbirth, family.* Retrieved from https://midwifemuse.wordpress.com/2008/02/27/vasa-previa; [Right] Iwahashi, N., Ota, N., Shiro, M., Yagi, S., Minami, S., & Ino, K. (2016). Vasa previa evaluated by noncontrast time-of-flight magnetic resonance angiography. *Taiwanese Journal of Obstetrics & Gynecology, 55*(4), 585–587. doi:10.1016/j.tjog.2016.06.007

sufficient blood volume delivery or tear during delivery (Kliman, 1999b).

Single Umbilical Artery. The normal umbilical cord contains one vein and two arteries. In most cases, there are no associated anomalies. However, in the 1% of infants born with a single umbilical artery, there have been cases of associated cardiovascular anomalies (Kliman, 1999b).

Fusion Failure of the Amnion and Chorion

Failure of the chorion and amnion to fuse by the end of week 12 of gestation has historically been seen as benign. However, researchers are investigating the association between fusion failure and preterm birth or chromosomal abnormalities (Bibbo et al., 2016; Ulm, Ulm, & Bernaschek, 1999).

Amnion (Amniotic Bands)

Rupture of the amniotic sac or accumulation of fluid in the space between the amnion and chorion leading to rupture of the amnion may lead to development of fibrous amniotic bands that can surround any area of the developing fetus, such as arms, legs, and forehead. Depending on the tightness of this banding, development of the affected fetal body area can be limited or totally impeded, leading to malformations or amputations (Sadler, 2015).

Abnormal Amniotic Fluid Volume

Oligohydramnios occurs when there is low volume of amniotic fluid for gestational age (less than 400–500 mL at term). This condition can result from placental insufficiency with diminished placental blood flow, premature rupture of amniochorionic membrane, or fetal renal anomalies (Martin et al., 2015). Any of these conditions can lead to complications in fetal development (such as pulmonary hypoplasia) or defects from lack of protective cushioning and resulting compression (facial defects or structural limb defects).

Polyhydramnios occurs when there is a higher volume of amniotic fluid than normal, usually in excess of 2,000 mL. Etiology includes maternal factors, such as Rh isoimmunization or maternal diabetes, or fetal factors, such as esophageal atresia, which prevents swallowing of amniotic fluid (Martin et al., 2015). Polyhydramnios can lead to premature rupture of membranes or abruptio placentae.

Abruptio Placentae

Premature separation of a normally implanted placenta prior to delivery characterizes abruptio placentae and is a common cause of antepartum bleeding (Martin et al., 2015). With ensuing bleeding, the decidua basalis separates from the placenta and leads to disruption in normal uteroplacental exchange and therefore fetal compromise. Etiology of abruptio placentae includes abdominal trauma and maternal conditions that cause vasoconstriction, such as hypertension or use of tobacco or cocaine (Cunningham et al., 2014). Onset of hemorrhage may lead to preterm labor or, depending on the severity of the hemorrhage, may result in intrauterine fetal demise (Cunningham et al., 2014).

MATERNAL HEALTH INFLUENCES ON PLACENTAL DEVELOPMENT AND FUNCTION

Maternal conditions can alter normal placental implantation and development, disrupt placental blood flow, and affect placental function. As a result, normal growth of the fetus can be affected or fetal diseases can develop. Specific diseases affecting the neonate will be discussed in detail in subsequent chapters specific to body systems.

Forbes and Westwood (2010) have investigated the role of maternal growth factors in the development and function of the placenta. Particular focus is on the levels of maternal growth factors and their role in signaling molecules that might alter cytotrophoblastic proliferation necessary for the growth of the placenta. Any alteration in cytotrophoblast proliferation has the potential to impact normal fetal growth. An increase in cell proliferation might lead to macrosomia, whereas a decrease in cell proliferation, and thus the failure to keep up with the expanding syncytium needed to support the growing fetus, could lead to decreased fetal growth (IUGR; Forbes & Westwood, 2010). Continued investigation into the role of maternal growth factor levels in altered fetal growth could lead to potential treatment in preventing these conditions.

Maternal hypertension, which occurs in up to 10% of pregnancies (Cunningham et al., 2014), is characterized by constriction of maternal blood vessels and can lead to uteroplacental insufficiency, which is the failure of the placenta to deliver sufficient nutrients to the fetus, often as a result of insufficient blood flow to the placenta. Chronic uteroplacental insufficiency is correlated with IUGR and preterm labor (Martin et al., 2015). The type and severity of the maternal hypertensive disorder (gestational diabetes, preeclampsia, eclampsia, or preeclampsia with chronic hypertension) will determine the impact on the health of the mother, placental function, and well-being of the fetus (Cunningham et al., 2014). Investigation into the role of genetic variables that might be involved with the phenotypic expression of preeclampsia is ongoing (Cunningham et al., 2014).

Maternal infection can alter tissue in the fallopian tubes and cause an implantation error. Any condition resulting in villitis, chorioamnionitis, or uterine inflammation can alter normal placental function, impede delivery of blood to the fetus, and result in growth restriction and preterm labor (Martin et al., 2015). Neonatal infection can occur as a result of transmission of infectious agents, such as bacteria and viruses, via the placenta and is discussed in detail in the chapter on neonatal infection.

Overall, diabetes mellitus (DM) affects about 6% to 7% of pregnancies (Buchanan, Xiang, & Page, 2012; Sutton, Han, & Werner, 2017) and includes gestational DM or pregestational DM. The severity of DM can impact the integrity of the maternal vasculature, disrupt normal placental blood flow, and alter normal fetal growth. The placenta is sensitive to hyperglycemia and villus immaturity and necrosis are associated with developmental abnormalities of the placenta (Jarmuzek, Wielgos, & Bomba-Opon, 2015). The surface area of the villi, the diffusion distance between maternal and fetal circulation, and placental metabolic and endocrine functions are affected by both types of DM (Leach, Taylor, & Sciota, 2009; Vambergue & Fajardy, 2011). The type of diabetes, timing of diagnosis, and control of maternal blood glucose levels will determine the effect on the fetus (Buchanan et al., 2012; Sutton et al., 2017; Vambergue & Fajardy, 2011). However, pregestational DM is also associated with major congenital abnormalities of fetal organ systems, as it is present prior to pregnancy and impacts organogenesis early in pregnancy (Sutton et al., 2017). Neonatal hypoglycemia is a common problem in infants born to mothers with pregestational and gestational DM and is associated with maternal glucose control (glucose crosses the placenta) and resulting fetal insulin production (maternal insulin does not cross the placenta). The degree of fetal hyperinsulinemia in response to poorly controlled maternal glucose levels can lead to fetal macrosomia, as insulin is a growth factor. Macrosomia can lead to birth trauma during delivery and/or need for cesarean delivery (Sutton et al., 2017).

EFFECTS OF PLACENTAL FUNCTION ON DEVELOPMENT OF ADULT DISEASE

There is evidence that alterations in maternal health may influence placental development and function (Godfrey, 2002). Alterations in placental development and function, in turn, play a role in "fetal programming," including the development of chronic diseases in the adult. Fetal programming, or fetal adaptation to nutrient alteration across the placenta, occurs when a stimulus evokes an adaptive response in cell structure, tissue perfusion pattern, organ function, or metabolism in the fetus in an effort to minimize short-term deleterious outcomes; this

may predispose the infant to the development of chronic disease in adult life (Godfrey, 2002). In the case of the fetus with reducing nutrient availability, whether due to poor maternal nutrition or placental insufficiency, this response favors perfusion, and thereby oxygen and nutrient delivery to the fetal brain, which limits their availability to the rest of the fetus.

Placental size is one factor that influences the overall efficiency of nutrient delivery to the fetus and there is evidence to support that infants whose placentas were either smaller or larger than normal are at increased risk for adult-onset cardiovascular disease, diabetes, hypertension, and other chronic diseases, including certain cancers (Thornburg & Marshall, 2015). Poor maternal nutrition also impacts fetal growth due to deficiency in available nutrients for placental transfer. In IUGR resulting from placental insufficiency, there is a higher incidence of neurodevelopmental issues as well as increased rates of cardiovascular disease and diabetes in the IUGR infant as an adult (Jansson & Powell, 2006). The mechanisms involved in this relationship continue to be investigated; however, at this time, it appears that placental transport properties for protein and ion diffusion from maternal to fetal circulation are downregulated by the placental insufficiency, perhaps related to oxygenation status (Jansson & Powell, 2006).

Maternal stress increases the level of circulating glucocorticoids. Glucocorticoids pass readily through the placenta and affect the regulation of nutrient delivery and subsequent growth in the fetus at many levels, including cell number and differentiation, organ structure, gene expression, and vascular response (Seckl & Holmes, 2006). High levels of maternal stress have been linked to neurodevelopmental disorders, including increased risk for mental health disorders in childhood and adulthood. The exact mechanism is unclear; current research suggests the effect of stress due to poor nutrition as the most likely etiology (Kinsella & Monk, 2009).

CONCLUSION

A basic understanding of placental structure, development, and function provides the foundation for understanding the role of the placenta in normal fetal development. Examination of the placenta after birth may provide information on the etiology of abnormal fetal development and neonatal disease. Assisted reproductive technology has improved due to an understanding of the blastocyst, leading to implantation techniques that limit the incidence of multiple embryos. Continued investigation into the impact of maternal disease on abnormal placental development and function may lead to early therapeutic interventions that attenuate or eliminate placental abnormalities and ensure normal fetal development.

LEARNING TOOLS AND RESOURCES

Podcast

 Transplacental Gas Transfer

Mark Kadrofske

Discussion Prompts

1. Describe how the exchange of nutrients and waste products occurs when there is no direct communication between the maternal and fetal vasculature.
2. Identify three maternal factors that may be associated with implantation errors or placental insufficiency.
3. Discuss three transport mechanisms involved in the transfer of nutrients across the placenta.

Advice From the Authors

"I am a visual learner. As I read about how the placenta forms, it helps me to look at the figures and get a 'visual image' of what the structure looks like as I am reading the descriptive text. Once I have these visual images, I can follow the timeline and watch a movie in my mind's eye of placental development and the relationship between developmental abnormalities that alter placental function and ultimately affect the growing fetus."

–Leanne Nantais-Smith, PhD, RN, NNP-BC

"I am an intuitive, reflective learner. I learn best by identifying and mastering overall concepts and key theories first. Once I have identified the overall concepts, I reflect on how the subconcepts fit within the overall picture and how these subconcepts relate to one another, or perhaps, how they may relate to other concepts I have already learned."

–Carolyn Herrington, PhD, RN, NNP-BC, CLC

"I often learn difficult concepts, such as placental development or transplacental gas exchange, by drawing diagrams with lines and arrows on which I literally 'connect the dots.' I will also take a diagram, such as the 'mind map,' and fill in the gaps using details from the text. I find this style of learning to be fun and effective."

–Mark Kadrofske, MD, PhD, FAAP

Mind Maps

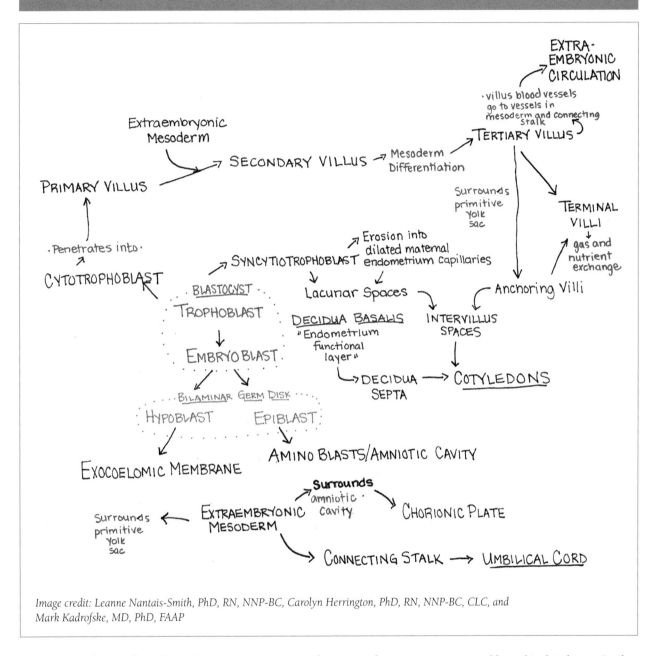

Image credit: Leanne Nantais-Smith, PhD, RN, NNP-BC, Carolyn Herrington, PhD, RN, NNP-BC, CLC, and Mark Kadrofske, MD, PhD, FAAP

Note: This mind map reflects this author team's interpretation of a portion of one or more concepts addressed in this chapter. Readers should regard the mind maps woven throughout this textbook as examples of multi-sensory study tools that can be developed to encourage conceptual understanding. Readers are encouraged to develop their own unique mind maps in consultation with academic faculty or clinical preceptors.

References

Ahokas, R., & McKinney, E. (2008). Development and physiology of the placenta and membranes. *The Global Library of Women's Medicine*. doi:10.3843/GLOWM.10101.

Bibbo, C., Little, S. E., Bsat, J., Botka, K. A., Benson, C. B., & Robinson, J. N. (2016). Chorioamniotic separation found on obstetric ultrasound and perinatal outcomes. *American Journal of Perinatology Reports, 6*, e337–e343. doi:10.1055/s-0036-1593407

Bliss, J. M., Carr, S. R., De Paepe, M. E., & Luks, F. I. (2017). What—and why—the neonatologist should know about twin-to-twin transfusion syndrome. *NeoReviews, 18*(1), e22–e32. doi:10.1542/neo.18-1-e22

Boyd, T. K., & Redline, R. W. (2000). Chronic histiocytic intervillositis: A placental lesion associated with recurrent reproductive loss. *Human Pathology, 31*(11), 1389–1396. doi:10.1016/S0046-8177(00)80009-X

Buchanan, T. A., Xiang, A. H., & Page, K. A. (2012). Gestational diabetes mellitus: Risks and management during and after pregnancy. *Nature Reviews Endocrinology, 8*(11), 639–649. doi:10.1038/nrendo.2012.96

Cho, F.-N., Chen, S.-N., Tai, M.-H., & Yang, T.-L. (2006). The quality and size of yolk sac in early pregnancy loss. *Australian and New Zealand Journal of Obstetrics and Gynaecology, 46*(5), 413–418. doi:10.1111/j.1479-828X.2006.00627.x

Cunningham, F. G., Leveno, K. J., Bloom, S. L., Spong, C. S., Dashe, J. S., Hoffman, B. L., ... Sheffield, J. S. (Eds.). (2014). *Williams obstetrics* (24th ed.). New York, NY: McGraw-Hill.

Food and Drug Administration. (2014). Content and format of labeling for human prescription drug and biological products; requirements for pregnancy and lactation labeling. 21 CFR 201. Retrieved from https://www.federalregister.gov/documents/2014/12/04/2014-28241/content-and-format-of-labeling-for-human-prescription-drug-and-biological-products-requirements-for

Forbes, K., & Westwood, M. (2010). Maternal growth factor regulation of human placental development and fetal growth. *Journal of Endocrinology, 207*, 1–16. doi:10.1677/JOE-10-0174

Freitag, L., von Kaisenberg, C., Kreipe, H., & Hussein. K. (2013). Expression analysis of leukocytic histiocytic intervillositis of the placenta. *International Journal of Clinical and Experimental Pathology, 6*(6), 1103–1111. Retrieved from https://www.ncbi.nlm.nih.gov/pmc/articles/PMC3657363

Garnica, A. D., & Chan, W. (1996). The role of the placenta in fetal nutrition and growth. *Journal of the American College of Nutrition, 15*(3), 206–222. doi:10.1080/07315724.1996.10718591

Genbacev, O., DiFederico, E., McMaster, M., & Fisher, S. (1999). Invasive cytotrophoblast apoptosis in preeclampsia. *Human Reproduction, 14*(Suppl. 2), 59–66. doi:10.1093/humrep/14.suppl_2.59

Godfrey, K. M. (2002). The role of the placenta in fetal programming—A review. *Placenta, 23*(Suppl. A), S20–S27. doi:10.1053/plac.2002.0773

Gude, N. M., Roberts, C. T., Kalionis, B., & King. R. G. (2004). Growth and function of the normal human placenta. *Thrombosis Research, 114*, 397–407. doi:10.1016/j.thromres.2004.06.038

Haggarty, P. (2004). Effect of placental function on fatty acid requirements during pregnancy. *European Journal of Clinical Nutrition, 58*, 1559–1570. doi:10.1038/sj.ejcn.1602016

Hunt, J. S., Petroff, M. G., McIntire, R. H., & Ober, C. (2005). HLA-G and immune tolerance in pregnancy. *Federation of American Societies for Experimental Biology, 19*(7), 681–693. doi:10.1096/fj.04-2078rev

Iwahashi, N., Ota, N., Shiro, M., Yagi, S., Minami, S., & Ino, K. (2016). Vasa previa evaluated by noncontrast time-of-flight magnetic resonance angiography. *Taiwanese Journal of Obstetrics & Gynecology, 55*(4), 585–587. doi:10.1016/j.tjog.2016.06.007

Jansson, T., & Powell, T. L. (2006). Human placental transport in altered fetal growth: Does the placenta function as a nutrient sensor?—A review. *Placenta, 27* (Suppl.), 91–97. doi:10.1016/j.placenta.2005.11.010

Jarmuzek, P., Wielgos, M., & Bomba-Opon, D. (2015). Placental pathologic changes in gestational diabetes mellitus. *Neuro Endocrinology Letters, 36*(2), 101–105. Retrieved from http://nel.edu/userfiles/articlesnew/NEL360215R01.pdf

Kinsella, M. T., & Monk, C. (2009). Impact of maternal stress, depression and anxiety on fetal neurobehavioral development. *Clinical Obstetrics and Gynecology, 52*(3), 425–440. doi:10.1097/GRF.0b013e3181b52df1.

Kliman, H. J. (1999a). From trophoblast to human placenta. In E. Knobil & J. D. Neill (Eds.), *Encyclopedia of reproduction* (pp. 834–846). San Diego, CA: Academic Press.

Kliman, H. J. (1999b). The umbilical cord. In E. Knobil & J. D. Neill (Eds.), *Encyclopedia of reproduction.* (pp 915–923). San Diego, CA: Academic Press.

Leach, L., Taylor, A., & Sciota, F. (2009). Vascular dysfunction in the diabetic placenta: Causes and consequences. *Journal of Anatomy, 215*(1), 69–76. doi:10.1111/j.1469-7580.2009.01098.x

Lyall, F., Bulmer, J. N., Duffie, E., Cousins, F., Theriault, A., & Robson, S. C. (2001). Human trophoblast invasion and spiral artery transformation. *American Journal of Pathology 158*(5), 1713–1721. doi:10.1016/S0002-9440(10)64127-2

Martin, R. J., Fanaroff, A. A., & Walsh, M. C. (Eds.). (2015). *Fanaroff & Martin's neonatal–perinatal medicine: Diseases of the fetus and infant* (10th ed.). Philadelphia, PA: Elsevier Saunders.

McNanley, T., & Woods, J. (2008). Placental physiology. *Global Library of Women's Medicine, 10*(4). doi:10.3843/GLOWM.10195.

Moore, K., Persaud, T. V. N., & Torchia, M. G. (2016). *Before we are born: Essentials of embryology and birth defects* (9th ed.). Philadelphia, PA: Elsevier.

Moradan, S. M., & Forouzeshfar, M. (2012). Are abnormal yolk sac characteristics important factors in abortion rates? *International Journal of Fertility and Sterility, 6*(2), 127–130. Retrieved from http://www.ijfs.ir/library/upload/article/af_246342382744222347242634223733426446234 3Moradan.pdf

Noto, R., Neri, S., Noto, Z., Cilio, D., Abate, G., Noto, P., ... Molino, G. (2003). Hyperhomocyteinemia in preeclampsia is associated to higher risk pressure profiles. *European Review for Medical and Pharmacological Sciences, 7*(3), 81–87. Retrieved from http://www.europeanreview.org/wp/wp-content/uploads/84.pdf

Pansky, B. (1982). *Review of medical embryology*. New York, NY: Macmillan.

Pasca, A. M., & Penn, A. A. (2010). The placenta: The lost neuroendocrine organ. *NeoReviews, 11*(2), e64–e77. doi:10.1542/neo.11-2-e64

Pijnenborg, R., Vercruysse, L., & Hanssens, M. (2006). The uterine spiral arteries in human pregnancy: Facts and controversies. *Placenta, 27*(9-10), 939–958. doi:10.1016/j.placenta.2005.12.006

Poirier, D. R., & Geiger, G. H. (2016). *Transport phenomena in materials processing* (pp. 419–461). Cham, Switzerland: Springer International.

Robbins, J. R., & Bakardjiev, A. I. (2012). Pathogens and the placental fortress. *Current Opinion in Microbiology, 15*(1), 36–43. doi:10.1016/j.mib.2011.11.006

Sadler, T. W. (2015). *Langman's medical embryology* (13th ed.). Philadelphia, PA: Lipincott Williams & Wilkins.

Seckl, J. R., & Holmes, M. C. (2006). Mechanisms of disease: Glucocorticoids, their placental metabolism and fetal "programming" of adult pathophysiology. *Nature Clinical Practice Endocrinology & Metabolism, 3*(6), 479–488. doi:10.1038/ncpendmet0515

Serrano, M. A., Bayón, J. E., Pascolo, L., Tiribelli, C., Ostrow, J. D., Gonzalez-Gallego, J., & Marin, J. J. G. (2002). Evidence for carrier-mediated transport of unconjugated bilirubin across plasma membrane vesicles from human placental trophoblast. *Placenta, 23*(7), 527–535. doi:10.1053/plac.2002.0838

Spurway, J., Logan, P., & Pak, S. (2012). The development, structure and blood flow within the umbilical cord with particular reference to the venous system. *Australasian Journal of Ultrasound in Medicine, 15*(3), 97–102. doi:10.1002/j.2205-0140.2012.tb00013.x

Sutton, D. M., Han, C. S., & Werner, E. F. (2017). Diabetes mellitus in pregnancy. *NeoReviews, 18*(1), e33–e43. doi:10.1542/neo.18-1-e33.

Thornburg, K. L., & Marshall, N. (2015). The placenta is the center of the chronic disease universe. *American Journal of Obstetrics and Gynecology, 213*(4), S14–S20. doi:10.1016/j.ajog.2015.08.030

Ulm, B., Ulm, R., & Bernaschek, G. (1999). Unfused amnion and chorion after 14 weeks gestation: Associated fetal structural and chromosomal abnormalities. *Ultrasound in Obstetrics and Gynecology, 13*, 392–395. doi:10.1046/j.1469-0705.1999.13060392.x

Vambergue, A., & Fajardy, I. (2011). Consequences of gestational and pregestational diabetes on placental function and birth weight. *World Journal of Diabetes, 2*(11), 196–203. doi:10.4239/wjd.v2.i11.196

Vasa Previa. (2008). *A midwife's muse: Midwifery & childbirth, family.* Retrieved from https://midwifemuse.wordpress.com/2008/02/27/vasa-previa

Velicky, P., Knöfler, M., & Pollheimer, J. (2016). Function and control of human invasive trophoblast subtypes: Intrinsic vs. maternal control. *Cell Adhesion & Migration, 10*(1–2), 154–162. doi:10.1080/19336918.2015.1089376

Wang, Y., & Zhao, S. (2010). *Vascular biology of the placenta.* San Rafael, CA: Morgan & Claypool Life Sciences. Retrieved from https://www.ncbi.nlm.nih.gov/books/NBK53254/

Yaliwal, L. V., & Desai, R. M. (2012). Methylenetetrahydrofolate reductase mutations, a genetic cause for familial recurrent neural tube defects. *Indian Journal of Human Genetics, 18*(1), 122–124. doi:10.4103/0971-6866.96680

Zeltser, L., & Leibel, R. (2011). Roles of the placenta in fetal brain development. *Proceedings of the National Academy of Sciences of the United States of America, 108*(38), 15667–15668. doi:10.1073/pnas.1112239108

II

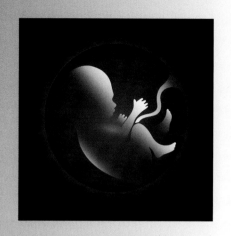

FETAL AND NEONATAL PHYSIOLOGY BY BODY SYSTEM

3

THE NERVOUS SYSTEM

Curry Bordelon, Bresney Fanning, Jenna Meredith, and Amy J. Jnah

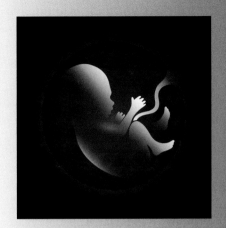

LEARNING OBJECTIVES

After completing this chapter, the reader should be able to:

- Understand normal central nervous system (CNS) development.
- Analyze the physiologic function of the fetal and neonatal CNS.
- Discuss common inherited disorders and their effect on fetal and neonatal CNS development and function.
- Identify maternal health issues that have a potential impact on fetal and postnatal CNS development and function.
- Evaluate common disorders that affect the CNS and their implications across the life span.

INTRODUCTION

The greater nervous system is comprised of the central nervous system (CNS), peripheral nervous system (PNS), somatic and autonomic nervous systems Figure 3.1). It is one of the most complex systems in the human body and communicates with other body systems to maintain physiologic homeostasis. The human brain is a fragile, complicated organ with postnatal function dependent on normal embryologic and fetal development. Alterations in embryologic development, which may occur secondary to environmental factors, genetic factors, or maternal health influences, can lead to the development of structural or functional pathologies, imposing lifelong neurologic consequences. Therefore, we begin this chapter with a review of key milestones in normal CNS development and functional organization.

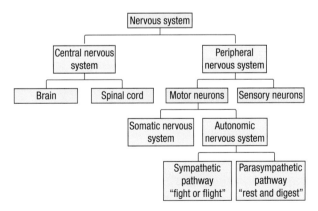

Figure 3.1 The nervous system.

Source: Adapted from Carlson, B. M. (2014). *Human embryology and developmental biology* (5th ed.). Philadelphia, PA: Elsevier/Saunders.

TIMELINE OF ORGAN DEVELOPMENT

Fetal neurologic development is dependent on a series of activities and progressions in specified sequencing, beginning with week 3 of gestation and the production of neurons. The sequential processes are predetermined and crucial to normal fetal neurologic development and function. Postnatally, the brain continues a process of maturation throughout late adolescence. Experts posit that after late adolescence brain differentiation continues across the life span.

The Embryonic Period of Development

Primary Neurulation. Primitive neurulation begins during week 3 of gestation and peaks during week 4 of gestation. This process involves cellular and structural differentiation, resulting in the formation of the neural plate and neural groove and, ultimately, the formation of the neural tube. Cellular differentiation begins with the production of neural stem cells. Epiblast cells travel to the primitive node, a molecular signaling center. This stimulates gene expression within the cells and the production of certain proteins. Although a discussion of the intricacies of each protein is beyond the scope of this textbook, it is important to recognize that they bind to extracellular receptors on the epiblasts and transform them into neural progenitor cells. Neural progenitor cells elicit the formation of the forebrain, hindbrain, and spinal cord as well as neurons and glial cells (Figures 3.2 and 3.3).

The neural tube, the first well-defined neural structure, is formed during the latter end of week 3 of gestation. This begins with neural plate formation, which occurs between days 18 and 22 of gestation. By day 23 of gestation, two ridges flanked by the neural progenitor cells form on either side of the neural plate (Moore, Persaud, & Torchia, 2016). The ridges then rise upward and begin to fold inward on themselves, preparing for fusion. Just prior to fusion, the anterior end of the neural tube differentiates into three distinct pouches (primitive vessels). The first and most anterior of these pouches is the *prosencephalon*, which gives rise to the forebrain. Next is the *mesencephalon*, which gives rise to the midbrain. The third pouch is the *rhombencephalon*, precursor to the hindbrain (Table 3.1, Figure 3.4).

Once the pouches are formed, fusion of the neural tube begins within the medial segment and progresses in a rostrocaudal (head-to-tail) direction. Anterior neural tube fusion is complete by 24 to 25 days of gestation and posterior fusion is complete by 26 to

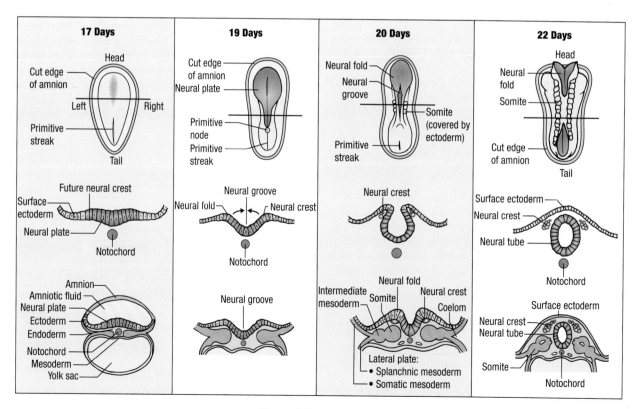

Figure 3.2 Neurulation.

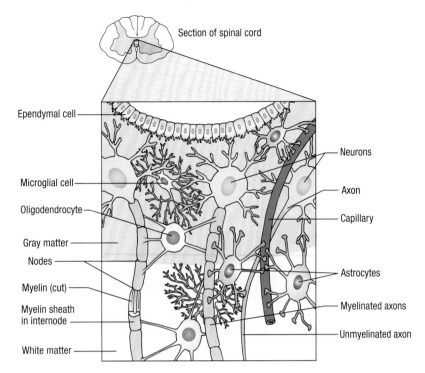

Section of spinal cord

Ependymal cell

Microglial cell

Oligodendrocyte

Gray matter

Nodes

Myelin (cut)

Myelin sheath in internode

White matter

Neurons

Axon

Capillary

Astrocytes

Myelinated axons

Unmyelinated axon

Figure 3.3 Glial cells.

TABLE 3.1 Embryologic-to-Adult Brain Differentiation

Primary Structure	First Division	Second Division	Major Adult Structures & Vessels
Forebrain	Prosencephalon	Telencephalon	• Basal ganglia • Cerebrum • Lateral ventricles • Limbic system
		Diencephalon	• Hypothalamus • Thalamus • Third ventricle
Midbrain	Mesencephalon	Mesencephalon	• Cerebral aqueduct • Cerebral peduncles • Tectum • Tegmentum
Hindbrain	Rhombencephalon	Metencephalon	• Cerebellum • Fourth ventricle (upper portion) • Pons
		Myelencephalon	• Fourth ventricle (lower portion) • Medulla oblongata

Source: Fleiss, B., Stolp, H., Mezger, V., & Gressens, P. (2018). Central nervous system development. In C. A. Gleason & S. E. Juul (Eds.), *Avery's diseases of the newborn* (10th ed., pp. 852-856). Philadelphia, PA: Elsevier.

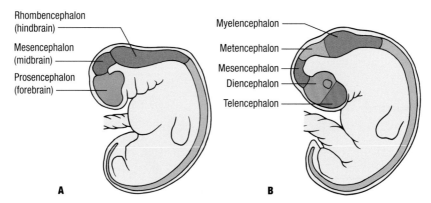

Figure 3.4 (A) Primitive differentiation of the neural tube, prior to fusion, includes the genesis of the prosencephalon, mesencephalon, and rhombencephalon. (B) By week 5 of gestation, the primitive neural tube begins a process of differentiation, which gives rise to five structures: telencephalon, diencephalon, mesencephalon, metencephalon, and myelencephalon.

27 days of gestation. Once fused, the neural progenitor cells reorganize into a layer that lines the interior walls of the hollowed out neural tube (Gressens & Huppi, 2015; Moore et al., 2016; Volpe et al., 2018). In its primitive and fused form, the neural tube closely resembles a drinking straw. This tube undergoes morphologic changes, becoming the ventricular region of the brain. Because the caudal end of the neural tube develops into the spinal cord, failed closure is associated with disorders such as anencephaly, spina bifida, or encephalocele.

Prosencephalic differentiation. Prosencephalic differentiation is arguably one of the most critical processes during early brain formation, as it gives rise to structures that include the adult cortex and subcortical white matter. Prosencephalic differentiation encompasses the formation of most major brain structures. Differentiation begins during week 5 and peaks between weeks 8 and 12 of gestation (Moore et al., 2016). Significant events that occur during this period of peak differentiation are summarized in the text that follows, as a means to connect normal developmental milestones with the development of relatively common neurologic syndromes, defects, and other craniofacial anomalies.

Prosencephalic differentiation can be divided into three phases: *formation, cleavage,* and *development.* Prosencephalic *formation* occurs at the rostral end of the neural tube, between weeks 5 and 8 of gestation. *Cleavage* of the prosencephalon thereby begins (almost immediately) between weeks 5 and 6 of gestation, resulting in the *development* of the diencephalon and telecephalon. The diencephalon gives rise to the thalamus and hypothalamus, whereas the telencephalon gives rise to the cerebellum, basal ganglia, and limbic system (Figure 3.5). Last, midline development occurs between weeks 8 and 12 of gestation. Midline development results in the formation of the chiasmatic, hypothalamic, and commissural

places. These structures contribute to the formation of the corpus callosum, septum pellucidum, optic nerves, and hypothalamus (Gressens & Huppi, 2015; Lee & Mukundan, 2015; Volpe et al., 2018). Failure of normal prosencephalic development between weeks 9 and 12 of gestation is correlated with severe defects, including holoprosencephaly, agenesis of the corpus callosum (ACC), Chiari malformation, septo-optic dysplasia, and facial anomalies (Lee & Mukundan, 2015; Volpe et al., 2018).

Mesencephalic differentiation. The mesencephalon develops during week 5 of gestation and gives rise to midbrain structures, including the tectum, tegmentum, cerebral peduncles, and cerebral aqueduct. This midbrain,

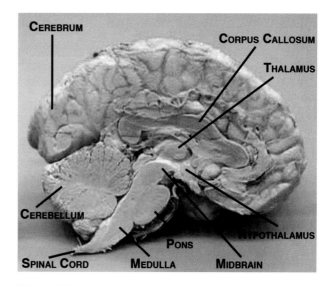

Figure 3.5 The limbic system.

Source: From Bryn Mawr College, 2017. Reprinted with permission.

or communication center between the right and left hemispheres of the brain, is responsible for the perception of visual, auditory, and motor system information. Failure of normal mesencephalic development, which can be a consequence of prematurity or a familial trait, may result in aqueductal stenosis, hydrocephalus, or other obstructive disorders (Patton, 2015; Radoš, Orešković, Radoš, Jurjević, & Klarica, 2014).

Rhombencephalic differentiation. Differentiation of the rhombencephalon begins during week 5 of gestation and results in formation of the hindbrain. The dorsolateral sides of the rhombencephalon rise upward, forming lips. Neural progenitor cells migrate radially and tangentially, giving rise to nuceli, Purkinje cells, and cells of the inner cerebellum. Rhombencephalic differentiation ultimately contributes to formation of hindbrain structures, including the pons, cerebellum, fourth ventricle, and medulla oblongata. Failed differentiation is associated with conditions such as Dandy-Walker syndrome, which is characterized by the following four major defects: (a) partial or complete cerebral agenesis, (b) cystic dilation of the fourth ventricle, (c) hydrocephalus, and (d) an enlarged posterior fossa (Moore et al., 2016; Volpe et al., 2018; Yuskaitis & Pomeroy, 2017).

Vascular Development

During week 3 of gestation, six paired aortic arches provide early blood supply to the developing brain. Shortly after, these primitive vessels undergo a series of modifications. The second pair of branch arteries fuse to form the pharyngeal artery (PA) and the third pair of primitive branch arteries fuse to form the internal carotid arteries (ICA). The ventral side of the PA and ICA fuse, giving rise to the common carotid artery (CCA) and the external carotid artery (ECA). The anterior end of the ICA differentiates into the anterior cerebral artery (ACA), middle cerebral artery (MCA), and the anterior choroidal artery (AChA). The posterior end of the ICA gives rise to the posterior cerebral artery (PCA) and posterior choroidal artery (PChA) (Menshawi, Mohr, & Gutierrez, 2015). These posterior vertebral arteries form the basilar artery, ultimately dividing to become two posterior cerebral arteries. The middle cerebral artery supplies the lateral surface of the cerebrum, the anterior artery supplies the midline of the cerebrum, and the posterior cerebral artery supplies the midtemporal region as well as a large portion of the brainstem. During week 8 of gestation, the left and right ACA join together and form the anterior communicating artery (ACOM), completing the circle of Willis. The circle of Willis thereby provides the necessary blood supply to the brain (Figure 3.6; Menshawi et al., 2015; Takakuwa, Koike, Muranaka, Uwabe, & Yamada, 2016).

Distal cerebral angiogenesis occurs concomitant with the development of the major structures of the brain. Arterial supply to the cerebrum, brainstem, and periventricular regions is established by week 24 of gestation. In the basal ganglia, diencephalon, and germinal matrix, arteriogenesis is complete by week 28 of gestation. Of note, angiogenesis is particularly active among premature infants. Vessels that generate in the germinal matrix, mainly between 24 and 28 weeks of gestation, are affixed with fewer structural support mechanisms (astrocyte end-feet and pericyte capillary coverage). The result is an increasingly fragile vasculature, highly susceptible to hemorrhage. It is evident that the timing of these developmental milestones places prematurely born infants at increased risk for ischemic injury near the ventricles and within the white matter of the brain, as well as hemorrhage within the fragile germinal matrix (Brew, Walker, & Wong, 2014; Fleiss, Stolp, Mezger, & Gressens, 2018).

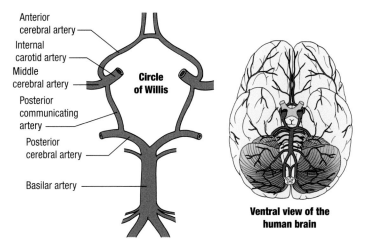

Figure 3.6 Circle of Willis.

Embryologic-to-Fetal Period of Development

The end of the embryonic period (week 8) and beginning of the fetal period (week 9) involves significant morphological brain development. During week 8 of gestation, a longitudinal fissure arises within the prosencephalon and begins a process of subdividing the brain into two distinct and interconnected hemispheres. This fissure continues to proliferate and differentiate, until week 22 of gestation, when development is considered complete (Moore et al., 2016).

Then, the brain begins to transition away from its smooth, primitive morphology. Primary, secondary, and tertiary sulci (invaginations of brain tissue) arise during the fetal period of development. Primary sulci arise between weeks 14 and 26 of gestation, and include the Sylvian, cingulate, parieto-occipital, and calcarine sulci. The central and superior temporal sulci arise beginning during week 20 of gestation, and the superior frontal, precentral, inferior frontal, postcentral, and intraparietal sulci arise during week 25 of gestation. The secondary sulci appear during week 30 of gestation, and tertiary sulci begin developing during week 36 of gestation (Figure 3.7).

Neuronal Proliferation. Neuronal proliferation is critical to normal neurologic function and involves the synthesis of neural progenitor cells and neurons. Although it is true that neural progenitor cell formation begins during gastrulation (week 3 of gestation), the quantity produced is insufficient and devoid of neurons. Proliferation begins during week 8 and peaks between weeks 12 to 16 of gestation. Beginning with week 8 of gestation, asymmetric division of neural progenitor cells produces one neural progenitor cell and one neuron. The neural progenitor cells remain in the ventricular zone, continuing the process of subdivision and synthesis of neurons. Then, the newly synthesized neurons

travel outward from the ventricular zone to the cortical region of the brain (outer layer of the brain), the control center of future behavior, thought, and intellectual capacity. This movement is known as *corticogenesis* and marks the beginning of neuronal migration. This is followed by the synthesis of radial glia, which begins at week 20 of gestation and continues into the postnatal period (Moore et al., 2016; Volpe et al., 2018). Any interruption in neuronal proliferation is associated with microcephaly (Winn, 2017).

Neuronal Migration. Early neuronal migration involves radial migration from the central ventricular zone to the outer neocortex. The outer neocortex (or "new" cortex) is the outermost layer of the brain. Radial migration is the primary mechanism for formation of the cortex and deep nuclear structures, including the basal ganglia, hypothalamus, thalamus, brainstem, cerebellum, and spinal cord (Verklan, 2015; Winn, 2017). However, as the brain continues to grow, the pathways to the cortical plate extend and neurons are not capable of independent migration. One mode for neuronal migration involves the assistance of radial glia. Radial glia extend outward and in a linear fashion, functioning as a durable matrix. Neurons travel across their length as they migrate toward the cortical plate (cortex). A second mode of neuronal migration is coined *tangential migration*. Tangential migration facilitates formation of the basal ganglia, which occurs during cortical neurogenesis. During this process, neurons migrate at *angles* to the radial glia and through the cerebral cortex (Q. Wu et al., 2014).

Neuronal migration to the cerebral cortex begins as early as week 8 of gestation (embryonic period), peaks between weeks 12 and 20 of gestation, and is considered complete by 6 months of gestation (Gressens & Huppi, 2015; Verklan, 2015). At completion, a thin, 3- to 5-mm thick layer of approximately 85 to 100 billion neurons covers the cerebral cortex (Hall, 2016; Stanojevic et al., 2011). These neurons serve an integral role in future postnatal processing of somatosensory stimuli (Brown, Uncapher, Chow, Eberhardt, & Wagner, 2017; Rosenthal & Soto, 2016). Failed neuronal migration, most notably between weeks 14 and 26 of gestation, has been known to lead to a lack of sulcation and resultant lissencephaly, or neuropsychiatric disorders including schizophrenia, autism, and intellectual disability (Moore et al., 2016; Volpe et al., 2018).

Neuronal Organization. Although neuronal migration commences commensurate with their arrival in the cortex and other regions of the brain, peak timing for neuronal organization spans from week 20 of gestation into early childhood (Gressens & Huppi, 2015). Organization is a predecessor to myelination and the establishment of early brain circuitry.

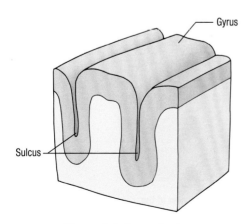

Figure 3.7 Gyri and sulci.

In addition, neuronal organization permits differentiation of grey and white brain matter. Groups of axon fibers become enveloped in myelin, a white-colored, phospholipid substance. These areas of the brain are considered the "white matter." Axons transmit electrochemical information between neurons in the cortex, thalamus, hippocampus, and brainstem. These major centers of the brain, housed within the white matter, control cognition, decision making, emotion, and neurodevelopment (Fields et al., 2014; Leong, Pestilli, Wu, Samanez-Larkin, & Knutson, 2016; Purger, Gibson, & Monje, 2016). The grey matter, which is realistically grey-pink in color, is composed of dendrites, axon *terminals*, and other cell bodies (Wandell, 2016). It is critical for the advanced practice nurse to recognize that neuronal organization is not complete until several years after birth; therefore, infants born prematurely are at an increased risk for altered electrochemical transmission (Verklan & Walden, 2015).

Programmed Cell Death. Neuronal proliferation is a rather overzealous process that results in overproduction of neurons. Therefore, programmed cell death (apoptosis) is necessary to prune between 10% to 50% of unnecessary neurons. Scheduled apoptosis occurs between weeks 28 and 41 of gestation, through the activation of genetic pathways, subsequent synthesis, and secretion of proteolytic enzymes. Proteolytic enzymes act to collapse the nuclear cytoskeleton (as their name suggests) and disassemble the nuclear envelope. This leads to fragmentation of the nuclear DNA and subsequent apoptosis. Apoptosis is a selective event known for targeted pruning, which averts damage to nearby cells (Alberts, 2015; Gressens & Huppi, 2015).

Although programmed cell death is an anticipated, normal physiologic cascade during brain development, it can be activated and exacerbated in a pathophysiologic manner. Specific to the perinatal–neonatal arena, abnormal cell death can be imposed secondary to repetitious use of antenatal corticosteroids, antiepileptic drugs, and postnatal corticosteroid use for the management of pathologies, such as chronic lung disease (CLD). These pathologies are associated with pathophysiologic programmed neuronal cell death within the neocortex and basal ganglia (cortical gray matter). This increases the relative risk for acquired cognitive dysfunction and cerebral palsy (Gressens & Huppi, 2015).

The Postnatal Period

Secondary Neuronal Proliferation, Organization, and Migration. Although the majority of neurogenesis, neuronal and glial proliferation, organization, and migration occur prenatally, a limited amount occurs after birth. Most significant is the process of glial proliferation and migration, which is known to extend into early adulthood and positively contributes to cell regeneration after neuronal injury. This is particularly significant for newborns who suffer brain injuries, including hypoxic–ischemic injury (Jablonska et al., 2016).

Myelination. Myelination begins during week 25 of gestation, peaks after birth, and continues into adulthood (Moore et al., 2016). This process improves motor nerve conduction, which facilitates the postnatal shift from primarily passive to active muscle tone. For that reason, myelination is included here, as an event occurring predominantly after birth.

As previously stated, myelin is a white, fatty substance composed primarily of lipids (80%) and water (20%). Myelin is formed from neural crest derivatives (Schwann cells). Myelination occurs as a result of two active processes: (a) oligodendroglial proliferation with differentiation and (b) myelin deposition. Oligodendroglial progenitor cells increase myelin protein synthesis. The myelin proteins wrap themselves around the neuronal axon fibers (several times), serving as an insulating and all-encompassing protective sheath. This enables efficient transmission and communication of nerve impulses (Verklan & Walden, 2015; Volpe et al., 2018).

Within the PNS, myelination of motor nerve fibers precedes that of somatic nerve fibers. The reverse is true in the CNS. Disorders that impede white matter accumulation include periventricular leukomalacia (PVL), inborn errors of metabolism (amino and organic acidopathies), congenital hypothyroidism, and postnatal undernutrition (Volpe et al., 2018). In addition, neuromotor deficits are reported in infants who suffer hypoxia-related injury, secondary to abnormal myelin composition (Watzlawik et al., 2015).

DEVELOPMENTAL PHYSIOLOGY

The nervous system is a complex network of vessels, structures, cells, and electrochemical impulses. The two major divisions of the nervous system are the CNS and PNS. The PNS is further subdivided into the somatic nervous system (SNS) and ANS. These systems work collaboratively when activated by biochemical, electrical, or sensory inputs.

Physiology of Cerebral Circulation

Cerebral Blood Flow. The cerebral circulation consists of a complex network of intracranial and extracranial arteries and veins. Among healthy infants, children and adults, this neurovascular system autoregulates to maintain a physiologic (homeostatic) cerebral blood flow (CBF) pattern.

This process of autoregulation shields the brain from damage secondary to abrupt increases or decreases in perfusion pressure, which can occur with injuries or illnesses. Neonatal APNs must recognize that premature infants and some critically-ill term infants are unique in their limited ability to autoregulate. These infants present with a variable degree of neurovascular immaturity and potentially abnormal CBF. Therefore, we will define and discuss core concepts related to CBF. This will be followed by a timely discussion of common factors that threaten CBF homeostasis. Last, we will close this section with a review of cerebral autoregulation. For student learners, garnering conceptual understanding of CBF and risk factors associated with abnormal CBF is necessary to attain clinical proficiency with hemodynamic assessments.

Physiologic CBF is contingent upon two major factors: (a) cerebral perfusion pressure and (b) cerebrovascular reactivity (resistance). Cerebral perfusion pressure can be defined as the mathematical difference between arterial pressure and venous pressure. Arterial pressure is measured as the mean arterial pressure and is influenced by gestational age and comorbid conditions. Venous pressure is measured as the pressure within the superior vena cava, reflecting the amount of blood returning to the heart from the head and upper extremities, and is influenced by factors including intracranial pressure or the presence of an outflow obstruction.

As mentioned, physiologic CBF is also contingent upon cerebrovascular reactivity. Cerebrovascular reactivity can be defined as a change in vascular tone and diameter in response to a change in flow dynamics. Vascular tone (of the muscularis layer of the arterioles) is affected by several mediators, including prostanoids, angiotensin, nitric oxide, perivascular nerves, and catecholamines (Brew et al., 2014; Takakuwa et al., 2016). The primary mechanism of action of prostanoids (e.g. PGE 1, PGE2) on the cerebral vasculature is vasodilation. Angiotensin II modulates an increase in cerebrovascular tone. Nitric oxide, released from perivascular nerves, neural cells, and inflammatory cells, (or when administered as a pharmacologic adjunct), acts as a cerebral vasodilator. Perivascular nerves innervate the cerebral arteries and influence constriction and vasodilation. Finally, catecholamines, namely adrenaline and noradrenaline, induce cerebrovascular constriction (Brew et al., 2014; Takakuwa et al., 2016; Vutskits & Wolf, 2014).

Interruptions in CBF homeostasis may occur in fetuses and neonates. This is often the result of one or more of the following factors: (a) incomplete or variant angiogenesis, the (b) factors which affect cerebrovascular dynamics during birth, (c) poor vascular tone, or the (d) presence of cerebrovascular disorders.

First, incomplete or dysregulated angiogenesis is posited to be a contributing factor to alterations in cerebral hemodynamics. *Incomplete angiogenesis may*

occur secondary to aplasia or hypoplasia of the anterior communicating artery (ACOM), posterior communicating segment (P1), and posterior communicating artery (PCOM), or a merger of the right and left communicating arteries (Takakuwa et al., 2016). These vessels normally supply blood and oxygen to major structures including the cerebellum and brainstem. *Dysregulated angiogenesis* may occur secondary to partial or variant up-regulation of pro-angiogenic proteins, which normally stimulate the synthesis of new blood vessels from existing vessels, or as a consequence of injuries that alter or obstruct blood flow, including hypoxia-ischemia and intraventricular hemorrhage. Decreased tortuosity (incomplete curving) of the proximal major cerebral arteries within the circle of Willis, is a common consequence of dysregulated angiogenesis. Abnormal collateral flow patterns emerge and alter intracranial hemodynamics, which encourages aberrant brain development (Raybaud, 2010).

Second, the birth process itself may alter CBF patterns. It is important that neonatal APNs understand that a transient decrease in CBF is understood to occur during the peripartum period. Among premature infants, this transient decrease in CBF, which manifests as low systemic arterial blood pressure, may even fall below the minimum required CBF and threaten neuronal health. Therefore, APNs should recognize the proportional relationship that exists between gestational age and the CBF nadir; lower gestational ages are associated with an increasingly lower CBF nadir after birth. This is likely explained by the incomplete state of angiogenesis demonstrated by increasingly preterm neonates, as this process is not fully complete until week 28 of gestation. As a result of both incomplete angiogenesis and low CBF, perfusion to the periventricular white matter may be impaired and increase the risk for cerebral injury. Within a few days after birth, CBF gradually increases and continues into childhood and adulthood. Of note, perinatal asphyxia is known to exacerbate CBF patterns during the intrapartum period by significantly reducing or ceasing blood flow to the brain. Microvascular dysfunction, cerebral edema, and hypercapnia or hypocapnia, common mechanisms of secondary brain injury after the hypoxic-ischemic injury, may further exacerbate abnormal CBF patterns after birth (Sekhon, Ainslie & Griesdale, 2017). Clearly, both preterm infants, as well as term infants who suffer hypoxic-ischemic injury, are at increased risk for mortality as well as long-term neurologic disability.

APNs also must recognize a paradoxical (inverse) relationship between the CBF nadir that occurs during and after birth, and cerebral oxygen extraction (COE). COE can be defined as the percent of oxygen extracted by brain tissue. It is understood that the transient decrease in CBF exhibited during the immediate postnatal period elicits an increase in cerebral oxygen extraction (COE). This is thought be a compensatory buffer to the transient decrease in CBF. Given the fact that premature infants exhibit a lower nadir compared to term counterparts, it should come as no surprise that the compensatory increase in COE is often higher among premature infants (Brew et al., 2014).

In addition to the risk factors discussed above, poor vascular tone may alter cerebral hemodynamics. Recall that under normal circumstances, cerebral vascular resistance is contingent on resting tone, vessel diameter, and development of the muscularis layer of the arterioles. As angiogenesis occurs in cadence with the formation of the superficial and deep structures of the brain, vascular tone is often reduced or absent among the most immature, deep cerebral vessels. Given this pattern of development, deeper vessels found within the parenchyma are significantly at-risk for shearing, secondary to their pressure-passive state (Bennet, Booth, Drury, Quaedackers, & Gunn, 2012; Brew et al., 2014).

Last, structural cerebrovascular disorders may alter CBF. Examples of diseases that neonatal APNs may encounter in the clinical setting include arteriovenous malformations (e.g. vein of Galen malformation), congenital heart diseases, cerebral venous sinus thrombosis, and even sickle cell disease. Each of these disease processes are associated with abnormal flow velocity and dynamics (Brew et al., 2014; Takakuwa et al., 2016; Wu et al., 2016).

Cerebrovascular Autoregulation. Cerebrovascular autoregulation is a mechanism that maintains homeostatic cerebral perfusion during changes in perfusion pressure. It is also referred to as the *autoregulatory plateau* (Brew et al., 2014). Vascular smooth muscle cell membrane potential adjusts during periods of hypertension and hypotension as a means to regulate arterial tone and maintain homeostatic CBF. This is regarded as a complex feedback system, implicated among term and premature infants by several proposed factors, including the metabolic response pathways, myogenic reflexes, sympathetic nervous system activity, disease, and medications (Back & Miller, 2018; Riera et al., 2014).

Myogenic, metabolic, and sympathetic responses are elicited secondary to changes in vascular wall tension. Vascular endothelial cells mediate compensatory vascular constriction and relaxation through calcium-activated potassium channels. This myogenic response is considered the primary mechanism for autoregulation among premature and term newborns. The metabolic hypothesis posits that either hypertensive states *or* reduced oxygen tension (a) activates a local reflex or (b) stimulates the release of adenosine and subsequent vasodilatory metabolites (nitric oxide and carbon monoxide; Austin, 2012; Brew et al., 2014). Alternatively, activation of the sympathetic nervous system may modulate hypotensive states through the stimulation of perivascular nerves. The metabolic release of metabolites and activation of nitric oxide and carbon monoxide channels are poorly developed in infancy. Their ability to exert a significant effect on vascular reactivity increases with age (Riera et al., 2014).

The Sensory–Somatic System

Somatosensory function involves the receipt and neural processing of sensory information. Neurons within the cerebral cortex and other areas of the brain work collaboratively (in circuits) to transmit information received via afferent (input) pathways and respond via efferent (motor output) pathways. These pathways are either somatic or visceral and involve the cranial nerves. In addition, spinal nerves, which arise from the spinal cord, send sensory information via afferent pathways to the CNS for processing. Therefore, it is essential to briefly digress and recognize the spinal cord as a powerful modulator of somatosensory processing. We will then discuss the cranial nerves, followed by a discussion of somatosensory response pathways.

The Spinal Cord and Nerves. Located in the vertebral canal, the spinal column extends from the brain to the lower portion of the first lumbar vertebrae, and is supported and protected by the vertebral column. Brainstem–spinal cord sensory controls are postulated to be an influential feedback system for sensory processing and motor and autonomic function (Schwaller, Kanellopoulos, & Fitzgerald, 2017).

Recall that there are 31 pairs of spinal nerves connected to the spinal cord, numbered according to the vertebral column from which they emerge. Each spinal nerve (8 cervical, 12 thoracic, 5 lumbar, 5 sacral, and 1 coccygeal) innervates with skin, muscle, or bone. Therefore, the spinal nerves can be sensory, motor, or mixed. Each area of skin (dermatome), muscle, or bone typically innervates with only one spinal nerve (Figure 3.8; Ignatavicius & Workman, 2016; Vanderah, Gould, & Nolte, 2016).

Spinal nerves attach to the spinal cord by a ventral (anterior, motor) root and a dorsal (posterior, sensory) root. Once the nerves exit the intervertebral foramen, they branch out into several directions. This branching mechanism creates complex networks of interconnected nerves, which send electrochemical information to the CNS via afferent (input) pathways for processing and subsequent efferent (output) motor responses. For example, the *cervical plexus* is comprised of a clustering of the anterior (motor) rami spinal nerves, C1–C4 and C5. These nerves innervate the muscles of the neck, shoulders, and parts of the head (Patton, 2015). The *brachial plexus* is a clustering of anterior (motor) rami of the lower cervical nerves and first thoracic nerve, C5–C8 and T1. This plexus innervates the shoulder and entire upper extremity (Schwaller et al., 2017; Vanderah et al., 2016).

For the developing fetus, any disruption in neural tube formation may negatively affect spinal cord development and spinal nerve function, causing later sensory processing dysfunction. Children with spina bifida, for example, often suffer urinary dysfunction, as the lowest spinal nerve modulates bowel and bladder control. Damage to the brachial plexus may be implicated in deliveries resulting in a shoulder dystocia (C5-C6 injury known as Erbs palsy; C8-T1 injury known as Klumpke palsy) and cause motor and respiratory dysfunction (Ignatavicius & Workman, 2016; Patton, 2015; Vanderah et al., 2016).

The Cranial Nerves. No less important are the cranial nerves. These 12 nerves emerge from the brainstem through a small foramen in the cranial cavity (Figure 3.9). Typically, the cranial nerves are organized by their basic function or embryologic origin (Table 3.2). Most cranial nerves control a sensory or motor function. Similar to the spinal nerves, injury to any of the cranial nerves

(CN V–VIII), as well as the first thoracic cranial nerve, may be associated with traumatic deliveries and shoulder dystocia.

Integrated Somatosensory Function: Input, Processing, and Response Systems

Sensory Inputting. Sensory inputs are external stimuli. In the presence of a sensory input, neurons direct electrochemical responses across axons to various areas of the cerebral neocortex and spinal cord for processing. For example, neurons in the spinal cord transmit information across afferent sensory axons secondary to sensory inputs from skin, muscle, or connective tissue receptors. Similarly, thalamic axons (axons residing on neurons located in the thalamus) transmit information about sensation, motor function, and internal physiologic state to the neocortex (Figure 3.10; Boron & Boulpaep, 2017).

Among premature and term infants, sensory inputs produce outputs primarily in the form of body movements and emotions to external stimuli. In children and adults, sensory inputs produce additional outputs, including awareness, cognition, and perception. The nervous system spends the majority of its time processing sensory inputs. Proficiency is essential to maintaining physiologic homeostasis.

Sensory Processing. Sensory integration is an organizational process by which sensory neurons recognize sensory inputs and send appropriate responses across electrochemical circuits. This process involves identification, interpretation, modulation, and organization of stimuli.

The Spinal Cord

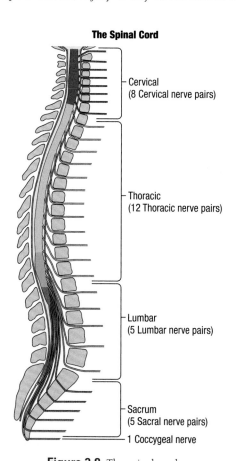

Cervical
(8 Cervical nerve pairs)

Thoracic
(12 Thoracic nerve pairs)

Lumbar
(5 Lumbar nerve pairs)

Sacrum
(5 Sacral nerve pairs)

1 Coccygeal nerve

Figure 3.8 The spinal cord.

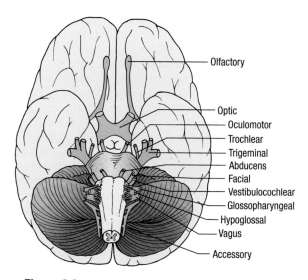

Olfactory

Optic
Oculomotor
Trochlear
Trigeminal
Abducens
Facial
Vestibulocochlear
Glossopharyngeal
Hypoglossal
Vagus

Accessory

Figure 3.9 Anatomic location of the 12 cranial nerves.

TABLE 3.2 The Cranial Nerves

Number	Name	Innervation	Locus of Control
I	Olfactory	S	Olfaction
II	Optic	S	Vision
III	Oculomotor	M	Eye movement, pupillary constriction and accommodation
IV	Trochlear	M	Eye movement
V	Trigeminal	S, M	General sensation, mastication, tympanic membrane tension
VI	Abducens	M	Eye movement
VII	Facial	S, M	Taste, facial movement, tension of ossicles, salivation, lacrimation
VIII	Vestibulocochlear	S	Hearing, proprioception, balance
IX	Glossopharyngeal	S, M	General sensation, chemoreception/baroreception, taste, swallowing, salivation
X	Vagus	S, M	General sensation, chemoreception/baroreception, visceral sensation, parasympathetic control of CVS, respiratory and GI systems
XI	Accessory	M	Head and shoulder movement
XII	Hypoglossal	M	Tongue movement

CVS, cardiovascular system; GI, gastrointestinal; M, motor fiber innervation; S, sensory fiber innervation.

Source: Lee, T. C., & Mukundan, S. (2015). Brainstem and cranial nerves. In T. C. Lee, S. Mukundan, Jr., & F. H. Netter (Eds.), *Netter's correlative imaging: Neuroanatomy* (pp. 175–271). Philadelphia, PA: Elsevier Saunders.

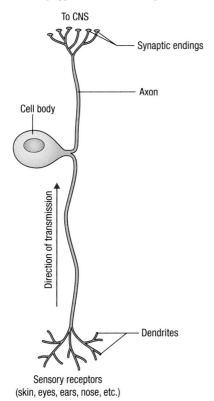

Figure 3.10 Sensory input transmission.

CNS, central nervous system.

Source: Drawing by Mya Jnah.

Electrochemical circuits. Electrochemical communications are critical for sensory processing. Communications primarily travel to and from (and within) the cerebrum. Recall that these communication pathways are established during neuronal migration and organization, which spans the latter portion of fetal development into the postnatal period.

Once neurons migrate to their target areas of the brain, they must become functionally integrated. Functional integration (organization) involves morphological change in the structure of the neuron. A single axon, the fibrous electrochemical signaling pathway, and hundreds of dendrites form at opposing ends of an individual neuron. With the help of a growth cone, the axon elongates (axonal outgrowth) and makes contact and synapses with its target cell. This establishes the electrochemical circuit, allowing transmission of information from the host neuron to the target cell. Dendrites (short, matrix-like pathways) extend off the neuron and function by receiving electrochemical inputs from other neurons (Figure 3.11; Rubenstein & Rakic, 2013; Volpe et al., 2018).

These electrochemical communication tracts connect one part of the brain to another. Three types of communication tracts are known as *projection, association,* and *commissural tracts* (Patton, 2015). Projection tracts are part of the sensory spinothalamic and motor corticospinal tracts. The tracts extend vertically between higher and lower brain structures, transmitting information upward toward the cerebellum and cerebral cortex or downward toward

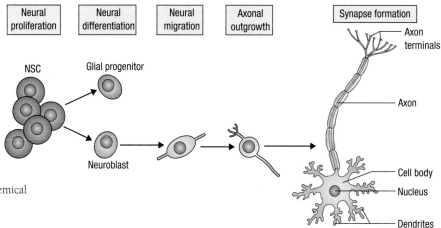

Figure 3.11 Genesis of the electrochemical communication pathway.

NSC, neural stem cell.

motor neurons (Figure 3.12). Association tracts are axon fiber pathways connecting areas of the cerebrum, cerebral cortex, or gyri within the same hemisphere of the brain, linking memory and perception centers. Association tracts vary in length and shape, with some assuming a "U-shaped" appearance. Commissural tracts extend horizontally across hemispheres with many passing directly through the corpus callosum. Therefore, commissural tracts influence motor (e.g., hand–eye coordination), sensory, and cognitive function (Barbas, 2015; Patton, 2015).

Gestational age at birth (degree of prematurity), gender, and maternal education levels are associated with

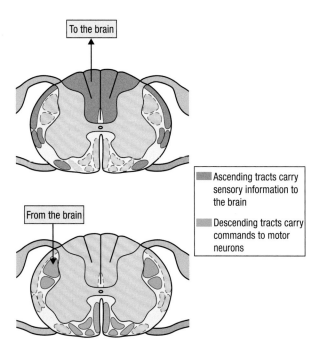

Figure 3.12 Projection electrochemical communication pathways.

reduced proficiency with sensory integration (Pekçetin, Aki, Üstünyurt, & Kayihan, 2016). This is attributed to the fact that limited sensory transmission pathways are evident before week 25 of gestation and progressively develop thereafter. More specific, auditory, proprioceptive, and vestibular sensory hypo-processing deficits are commonly reported among premature infants, with extremely low-birth-weight (ELBW) infants at the highest risk for impairment (Pekçetin et al., 2016). As these pathways mature, additional sensory processing and higher order cognitive functioning are exhibited (Dumont et al., 2017). Perturbing the maturational aspect of sensory processing in the postnatal period, by way of sensory deprivation *or* sensory overload, can negatively affect the developmental physiology and later function of the somatosensory system. This is of great concern among infants born prematurely.

Motor Responses. Motor response involves a physical response to a sensory stimulus and represents development of the CNS. This is regulated by the cerebral cortex (the frontal lobe specifically) by way of the activity from the motor cortex. Upper and lower motor neurons are organized to receive a sensory stimulus from sensory transmission pathways and translate the stimulus into a motor response. This creates a feedback system (feedback loop) that serves to modulate muscle contractions, passive muscle tone, spinal control, and muscle stretch reflexes. The physiology of muscle contraction and relaxation will be discussed later in this chapter (see the "Hypotonia" section of this chapter). Motor function responses to stimuli may be absent or immature among premature infants. Muscular maturation occurs in a caudocephalad direction and increases with advancing gestational age (Table 3.3). In addition, infants who suffer hypoxia-related brain injury may display altered neurosensory and neuromotor responses to provocative events (Gulati, Shubert, Sitaram, Wei, & Jadcherla, 2015).

TABLE 3.3 Timeline of Fetal Motor Development	
Week of Gestation	**Motor Function**
7.5	Spontaneous flexion–extension of vertebral column and sideways bending
9	Spontaneous gross arm, leg, neck, trunk movements (no patterning or sequencing)
10	Twitching movements
11	Harmonious leg movements
12	Hand-to-face movements Rotation of head and torso
13	Reciprocal and harmonious limb movements
14	Leg movements
15	Finger-sucking movements
16	Coordinated limb movements
24	Hand, face, respiratory movements

NOTE: Direction of motor function and tone follow a caudocephalad direction; onset of motor function and tone are approximate.

Sources: Moore, K. L., Persaud, T. V. N., & Torchia, M. G. (2016). *The developing human: Clinically oriented embryology* (10th ed.). Philadelphia, PA: Elsevier; Piontelli, A. (2010). *Development of normal fetal movements: The first 25 weeks of gestation.* Milan, Italy: Springer Verlag; van Merendonk, E. J. J. M., Brouwers, J. J. W. M., De Catte, L., Hasaerts, D., Nijhuis-van der Sanden, M. W. G., & Kerckhofs, E. (2017). Identification of prenatal behavioral patterns of the gross motor movements within the early stages of fetal development. *Infant and Child Development, 26*(5), e1–e15. doi:10.1002/icd.2012.

The Peripheral Nervous System

The PNS, an integrated portion of the CNS and greater nervous system, is composed of sensory and motor neurons (spinal and cranial nerves) and is integral to somatosensory function. To review, the PNS is subdivided into the SNS and ANS.

Somatic Nervous System. The SNS controls all *voluntary* motor responses as well as involuntary reflexes (see the "Motor Responses" section of this chapter).

Autonomic Nervous System. The ANS consists of sensory neurons and motor neurons and regulates *involuntary* responses, including heart rate, vascular tone, smooth muscle contraction, glandular secretion, and digestive motility (Carlson, 2014). The ANS is divided into *sympathetic* and *parasympathetic* pathways. Each pathway is composed of nerves, ganglia, and plexus that conduct impulses away from the brainstem or spinal cord and toward autonomic effectors (Patton, 2015; Powley, 2013).

The *sympathetic pathway* contains adrenergic neurons (axons) that transmit norephinephrine to target structures, including the sweat glands and blood vessels. This pathway is best known for its ability to activate the "fight or flight" response (see Chapter 10).

Alternatively, the *parasympathetic pathway* consists of cholinergic neurons (axons). This pathway elicits "rest and digest" responses. Neurons project through certain cranial nerves (III, VIII, IX, and X) and target the brain, thorax, and abdomen. This allows the parasympathetic pathway to control pupillary sphincter, ciliary muscles, salivary and lacrimal glands, mucus secretion, food ingestion and digestion, musculature of the heart and esophagus, and select structures of the conducting portion of the respiratory system (Powley, 2013).

Enteric Nervous System. The enteric nervous system (ENS) is a complex network of nerves located within the intestinal wall (Patton, 2015). These nerves control visceral effectors, such as endocrine and exocrine cells and smooth muscles.

Neuroprotective Mechanisms

The Skull. The skull is a protective cavity for the brain. Cranial osteogenesis begins during week 4 of gestation. Mesenchyme, or loosely organized tissue, derived from the primitive streak, occipital sclerotomes, and the neural crest proliferate to cover the brain. The lower portion of mesenchyme gives rise to the base of the cranium and the upper portion gives rise to the calvaria (skullcap). Once the primitive skull is formed, it undergoes chondrification (conversion into cartilage). Portions of the skull convert into parachordal cartilage, which gives rise to the temporal bones. Hypophyseal cartilage forms the roof of the orbit, whereas trabecular cartilage gives rise to the ethmoid bone.

Ossification of the mesenchyme begins with week 13 of gestation (Duderstadt, 2014). Once formed, these bones remain independent of one another throughout fetal development and into infancy, permitting continued brain growth. Over time, the cranial bones approximate to form sutures and fontanelles. The cranial sutures include the metopic, lambdoid, coronal, and squamosal sutures (Figure 3.13). The two major fontanelles are the anterior and posterior fontanelles (Table 3.4). Ossification results in the formation of 45 bones; however, after fusion is complete, 22 bones remain (Som & Naidich, 2013). Craniosynostosis occurs due to premature closure and aberrant ossification of any one or more cranial sutures. Craniosynostosis is discussed in greater detail later in this chapter.

Meninges. The meninges are a three-layered protective covering around the brain and spinal cord. The outermost layer of the meninges is the dura mater. The arachnoid matter comprises the middle layer, and pia mater accounts for the innermost layer (Figure 3.14).

Dura Mater. The dura mater is the thickest and most superior layer of the meninges. It is innervated by CN V, IX, X, and XII. The dura mater functions as a protective layer for the brain and spinal cord, and does so by forming several folds (structures) that separate the brain into various cavities. The *falx cerebri* divides the hemispheres of the brain, and the *falx cerebelli* separate the lobes of the cerebellum. The *tentorium cerebelli* divides the cerebrum and cerebellum. In addition these protective and functional divisions, the dura mater also forms into several large pressure-dependent channels, or venous sinuses. These venous sinuses (superior saggital, straight sinus, inferior sinus, and transverse sinus) drain blood from the brain and back to the heart, by way of the internal jugular veins.

Advanced practice nurses should recognize that the anatomic location of the dura, its nerve innervations, and venous sinuses, make it vulnerable to injury, in particular during traumatic operative vaginal deliveries (Vanderah et al., 2016). Hemorrhage may lead to blood sequestrations (accumulation and hematoma) within the (a) epidural space between the dura mater and the skull, or the (b) subdural space between the dura mater and arachnoid mater. This can lead to fluid accumulation and increased intracranial pressure (ICP); subdural hemorrhage can be a life-threatening emergency for a newborn (see Chapter 14).

Arachnoid Mater, subarachnoid space, and pia mater. The middle layer of the meninges, which connects the dura

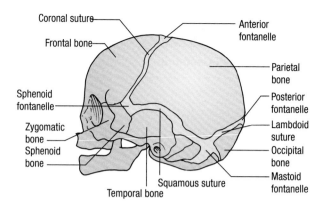

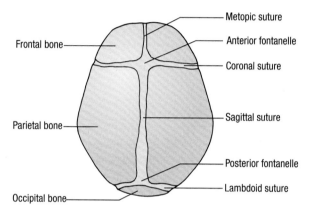

Figure 3.13 The cranial sutures.

TABLE 3.4 Cranial Sutures and Fontanelles

Suture	Closure or Fusion
Metopic	3 months–2 years of age
Lambdoid, sagittal, coronal	40 years of age
Squamosal	40–70 years of age
Fontanelle	**Closure or Fusion**
Posterior	2–3 months of age
Sphenoidal	6 months of age
Mastoid	6–18 months of age
Anterior	18 months–2 years of age

Sources: Schoenwolf, G. C., Bleyl, S. B., Brauer, P. R., & Francis-West, P. H. (2015). *Larsen's human embryology* (5th ed.). Philadelphia, PA: Churchill Livingstone; Verklan, M. T., & Walden, M. (2015). *Core curriculum for neonatal intensive care nursing* (5th ed.). St. Louis, MO: Elsevier;

and pia, is the *arachnoid mater*. Some projections of the arachnoid mater (known as the *arachnoid villi*) protrude into the venous sinuses of the dura. This innervation with the dura permits some cerebrospinal fluid (CSF) that normally travels through the arachnoid mater to traverse the arachnoid villi, enter the venous sinuses, and thereby enter the bloodstream.

Below the arachnoid mater is the *subarachnoid space*. This is regarded as a functionally significant portion of the brain for three important reasons: (a) it stores and circulates CSF and (b) it is innervated by the cranial nerves, and (c) it is generously supplied with blood vessels (Lee & Mukundan, 2015). In fact, the "arachnoid" is coined after the Greek term 'arachne' (spider) and the arachnoid mater is understood to be affixed with a spiderweb-like vasculature.

The *pia* mater is the thinnest, innermost layer of the meninges. It adheres tightly to the surface of the brain and spinal cord (Lee & Mukundan, 2015). The pia merges with the membranous lining of the cerebral ventricles

in order to form choroid plexes. Recall that the choroid plexes are the structures which produce CSF. Disruptions during formation of these structures are associated with neural tube defects, whereas injuries to normally formed structures are often a result of a traumatic birth.

Choroid Plexus and Cerebrospinal Fluid. The choroid plexus is the major site for CSF secretion, second only to the ependymal epithelial cells. CSF protects the CNS while working as a barrier between the vasculature and the tissues of the brain.

CSF is produced by the choroid plexus by an energy-dependent active transport process, reabsorbed by the arachnoid villi, and then directed into the superior sagittal sinus. CSF produced by the choroid sinuses in the lateral ventricles follows a pathway to the third ventricle and then passes through the cerebral aqueduct to the fourth ventricle. From the fourth ventricle, the CSF travels to the subarachnoid spaces. While in the subarachnoid spaces, CSF travels in a rostrocaudal direction toward the arachnoid villi (rostral) and central canal of the spinal cord (caudal; Figure 3.15; Brinker, Stopa, Morrison, & Klinge, 2014; Gressens & Huppi, 2015). Structural defects, such as Chiari malformation, can interrupt normal movement of CSF.

Vertebral Column. The vertebral column is the bony structure that protects the spinal cord. Originally derived from the paraxial mesoderm, the vertebrae begin to form during week 4 of gestation. Sclerotome cells migrate around the spinal cord and notochord to combine with cells on the opposing side of the neural tube. During development, resegmentation occurs when the caudal half of the sclerotome fuses with the cephalic half. This results in the formation of each individual vertebra (Schoenwolf, Bleyl, Brauer, & Francis-West, 2015). Once the vertebrae are

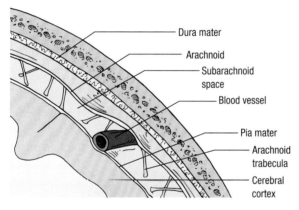

Figure 3.14 The meninges.

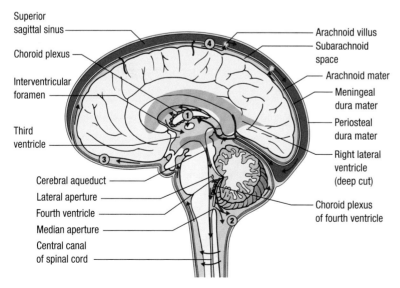

Figure 3.15 Cerebrospinal fluid circulation pathway. Cerebrospinal fluid (CSF) is secreted by the choroid plexus and travels through the lateral ventricles to the third, and then fourth, ventricle. When CSF reaches the subarachnoid spaces it is directed caudally toward the spinal cord and in a rostral direction toward the arachnoid villus, where it is absorbed into the venous sinuses of the dura.

fully formed, the vertebral column consists of 7 cervical, 12 thoracic, and 5 lumbar vertebrae, each separated by an intervertebral disc. The sacrum is comprised of 5 fused vertebrae and 2 coccygeal vertebrae. The 31 spinal nerves (8 cervical, 12 thoracic, 5 lumbar, 5 sacral, and 1 coccygeal), addressed earlier in this chapter, innervate accordingly. There are four curvatures that contribute to posture (Lee & Mukundan, 2015). The 31 spinal nerves (eight cervical, 12 thoracic, five lumbar, five sacral, and one coccygeal) innervate accordingly.

After early infancy, the vertebrae begin to ossify and grow. As such, the initial "C" shape of the spine begins to transition to an "S" shape (lateral view). The thoracic (T) to spinal (S) segment of vertebrae, denoted as T1-S1, is approximately 20 cm in length at birth and 45 cm once mature. T1 to T12 is approximately 12 cm at birth and 27 cm once mature Finally, the lumbar (L) region spans L1 to L5 and is approximately 7.5 cm at birth and 16 cm once mature. Congenitally acquired, rare spinal deformities known to contribute to altered sitting height include scoliosis (lateral "S" curvature), kyphosis (abnormal outward "hunchback" curvature), and lordosis (abnormal inward "swayback" curvature; Canavese & Dimeglio, 2013; Lee & Mukundan, 2015). These deformities are the result of abnormal vertebral development and underdeveloped growth plates, which prevent normal vertical ascent of the spinal column. Early spinal fusion, before the age of 5 years, is often indicated.

Blood–Brain Barrier. Blood–brain barriers (BBB), also termed *neurovascular units*, function to inhibit potentially harmful substances in the bloodstream from entering the cerebral circulation and brain tissue. Although rarely discussed in fetal and neonatal physiology textbooks, five brain barrier interfaces exist as diffusion junctions to control ionic gradients between the blood and the CSF (Saunders, Liddelow, & Dziegielewska, 2012). Therefore, the BBB is a neuroprotective mechanism for the developing fetus and neonate.

The BBB consists of endothelial cells, pericytes, microglia, astrocytes, and a basement membrane. Endothelial cells serve as a physical barrier against paracellular diffusion. These cells reduce permeability through the formation of tight junctions restricting passage of small ions through the barrier. Pericytes, microglia, astrocytes, and basement membrane strengthen endothelial cell junction formation. Although its intricacies are beyond the scope of this book, BBB function is influenced by the Wnt/β-catenin pathway. This pathway upregulates endothelial junction formation and modulates ongoing maintenance of the BBB.

The efficacy of endothelial cells as a barrier to diffusion in the fetus is complex and not well understood. Although previously regarded as "leaky" or "immature," more recent studies indicate the endothelial barrier in the fetus and premature infant is capable of resisting molecules as small as sucrose (Saunders et al., 2012). However, other properties of the BBB mechanism, including the cerebral vasculature and presence of protein transport mechanisms,

may place the fetus and premature infant at risk for injury secondary to developmental and functional immaturity. Recent studies indicate endothelial cells located in the choroid plexus contain receptor/protein-binding molecules that hold a particular affinity for albumin. This mechanism may be associated with protein transfer and, in some cases, transfer of unconjugated bilirubin (bound to albumin) across the BBB and into the CSF. Other efflux transporters may further implicate this pathology; however, additional investigation is necessary before the evidence can be reported with confidence (Saunders et al., 2012, 2014).

GENETIC INFLUENCES

Genomic technologies, including linkage analysis, have been used in recent years to investigate the genome, transcriptome, and epigenome from a whole-genome perspective to better understand the genesis of certain neurologic defects. Several neurologic disorders are hereditary, commonly of Mendelian inheritance, and the result of errors during conception. Some present at birth, whereas others manifest during infancy, childhood, or later into adulthood. We present a discussion of several inherited disorders that implicate the nervous system and manifest within the first 2 years of life. Additional disorders are provided in Table 3.5.

Autosomal Dominant Inherited Disorders

Neurofibromatosis. Neurofibromatosis (NF) is an autosomal dominant genetic disorder affecting the skin, nerves,

TABLE 3.5 Other Inherited Disorders of the Nervous System

- Agenesis of corpus callosum
- Anencephaly
- Apert syndrome (Acrocephalosyndactyly)
- Congenital myotonic dystrophy
- Congenital neonatal myasthenia gravis
- Cri-du-chat
- Crouzon syndrome
- Dandy–Walker malformation
- Fragile X (Martin–Bell syndrome)
- Neurofibromatosis
- Prader–Willi syndrome
- Spina bifida
- Sturge–Weber syndrome
- Trisomy 21 (Down syndrome)
- Werdnig–Hoffman disease (spinal muscular atrophy type 1)

NOTE: A more comprehensive list is provided by the National Institutes of Health, Genetic and Rare Diseases Information Center (GARD); (https://rarediseases.info.nih.gov/diseases/diseases-by-category/17/nervous-system-diseases).

brain, and spinal cord (Abramowicz & Gos, 2014). Neurofibromas (tumors) may grow along nerves throughout the body. NF is classified into two types, NF1 and NF2. NF1 is the most common form of NF and affects one in 3,000 to 4,000 births; no gender prevalence is reported (National Institutes of Health [NIH], 2018c). Mutations in the *NF1* gene are to blame for the development of NF1. *NF1* genes normally modulate the production of neurofibromin, which regulates cellular proliferation and acts as a tumor-suppressing gene. Infants with NF1 may present with café-au-lait spots (six or more), macrocephaly, or seizures. The importance of a comprehensive physical examination during the birth hospitalization, with astute recognition and classification of skin lesions, cannot be understated (see Chapter 12). Learning disabilities occur in up to 50% of children with NF1.

Congenital Myotonic Dystrophy. Congenital myotonic dystrophy (CMD) affects one in every 47,000 births (Campbell, Levin, Siu, Venance, & Jacob, 2013). This is a multisystem genetic disease caused by expansions of a CTG trinucleotide repeat in the dystrophia myotonica gene (DMPK) region (Ho, Cardamone, & Farrar, 2015). Mutations in the *DMPK* gene alter normal cellular proliferation and function, which leads to muscular dystrophy (Muscular Dystrophy Association, n.d.). CMD often manifests within the first hours of life. Typical clinical manifestations include persistent hypotonia, facial diplegia, areflexia, hyporeflexia, or muscle atrophia. Life-span implications include motor deficits, facial weakness, and developmental delays. A 30% to 40% mortality risk during the neonatal period is reported (Echenne & Bassez, 2013).

Autosomal Recessive

Spinal Muscular Atrophy. Spinal muscular atrophy (SMA) is a degenerative disorder that affects anterior horn cells and impacts lower motor neurons. The overall incidence of SMA is one in 6,000 to 10,000 births and Caucasian infants are most commonly affected (NIH, 2018f; Ogino & Wilson, 2004). Mutations in the *SM1, UBA1, CYNC1H1,* and *VAPB* genes implicate SMA. The mutations alter normal genetic modulation of the motor neurons, which leads to failed nerve impulses and altered muscle control. SMA manifests with progressive muscle weakness and atrophy and is classified by type (0–IV; Markowitz, Singh, & Darras, 2012). Type 0 and type I SMA present within the first 6 months of life. Common clinical manifestations include profound hypotonia and facial diplegia. Notable manifestations associated with type 1 SMA, or Werdnig–Hoffman disease, include "frog-leg" posturing, hyporeflexia, and areflexia. Life expectancy is less than 2 years (Markowitz et al., 2012).

Deletion Disorders

Prader–Willi. Prader–Willi syndrome (PWS) affects one in every 15,000 to 30,000 births (Cassidy & Driscoll, 2009; NIH, 2018d). The majority of cases (70%) are the result of a deletion in chromosome 15. Less frequently, two *maternal* copies (uniparent disomy) of chromosome 15 are inherited by affected offspring. Although poorly understood, the deletion of *SNORD116* and *OCA2* genes at chromosome 15 likely implicate the spectrum of findings associated with PWS (NIH, 2018d). Essentially, dysfunction on chromosome 15 alters messenger ribonucleic acid function and the production of proteins necessary for normal cellular function; additional research is necessary to fully explain this relationship. Clinical manifestations observed during the fetal and neonatal period include decreased fetal movement, hypotonia, poor feedings, and failure to thrive. Later manifestations include fair skin, light-colored hair, behavioral problems, and mild to severe intellectual impairment (Cassidy, Schwartz, Miller, & Driscoll, 2012). Prognosis varies due to the spectrum of neurodevelopmental involvement and consistency of care.

Angelman Syndrome. Angelman syndrome affects one in every 12,000 to 24,000 births (Mertz et al., 2013; NIH, 2018a). In most cases, affected infants inherit two defective copies of the *UBE3A* gene, one from each parent. A smaller percentage of cases involve the inheritance of two *paternal* copies (uniparent disomy) of chromosome 15. The genetic basis for this syndrome is poorly understood. Common clinical manifestations include microcephaly and seizures, both of which manifest during early infancy (Lalande & Calciano, 2007; NIH, 2018a; Williams, Driscoll, & Dagli, 2010). Neurodevelopmental deficits are common and become apparent between 6 to 12 months of age.

Chromosomal Disorders

Trisomy 18 (Edwards Syndrome). Trisomy 18 affects one in 5,000 to 8,000 live births; a female prevalence is reported (Chen, 2012; NIH, 2018g). Nearly all (95%) infants are affected by a translocation of genetic material, which yields three copies of chromosome 18 within each cell in the body. Less often, infants may be affected by a mosaicism (partial trisomy) at the long arm of chromosome 18 (Haldeman-Englert, Saitta, & Zackai, 2018). Hallmark clinical manifestations include clenched hands and "rockerbottom" feet, a small and narrow cranium, prominent occiput, and low-set ears. Midline defects may include **v**ertebral defects, **a**nal atresia, **c**ardiac defects (80%), **t**racheo**e**sophageal fistula, **r**enal anomalies, and other **l**imb abnormalities, including club feet (VACTERL). Long-term outcomes vary. Partial to severe forms of trisomy 18 are associated with moderate to severe neurologic deficits and hypotonia. Infants with a mosaicism may express fewer anomalies and have improved neurodevelopmental outcomes (NIH, 2018g). Rarely, trisomy 18 is associated with fatal neural tube defects, such as anencephaly. This is usually the result of a somatic or unbalanced translocation.

Trisomy 21 (Down Syndrome). Trisomy 21 affects one in every 800 births. An increased incidence, estimated at one in 25 to 300 births, is reported among pregnant women over 35 years of age (Moore et al., 2016; NIH, 2018b). Nearly all (94%) infants are affected by a translocation of genetic material, which yields three copies of chromosome 21 within each cell in the body. Less common, infants may be affected by a mosaicism (Haldeman-Englert et al., 2018). Approximately 50% of fetuses with trisomy 21 are spontaneously aborted or stillborn. Hallmark clinical manifestations include microcephaly, congenital heart defects (atrioventricular canal defects, tetralogy of Fallot, and patent ductus arteriosus), brachycephaly, upward-slanted palpebral fissures, epicanthal folds, Brushfield spots, a flattened nasal bridge, prominent tongue, short neck, single palmar crease (indicative of hypotonia in utero), and abnormal digits. Life-span implications include cognitive and intellectual deficits, including difficulty with reasoning, judgment, and emotional lability (Haldeman-Englert et al., 2018; NIH, 2018b).

Trisomy 13 (Patau Syndrome). Trisomy 13 affects an estimated one in 16,000 live births (National Organization for Rare Disorders [NORD], 2018a). Most (80%) infants are affected by a translocation of genetic material, which yields three copies of chromosome 18 within each cell in the body. Mosaicism, associated with reduced disease severity, is associated with approximately 5% of all cases. Less than 5% of fetuses affected by trisomy 13 survive to term; the majority of affected pregnancies result in spontaneous abortion or stillbirth (Haldeman-Englert et al., 2018). Hallmark clinical manifestations include holoprosencephaly (50% of patients), postaxial polydactyly, microcephaly, cardiac and renal anomalies, and microcephaly. Incomplete development of the forebrain, spinal cord abnormalities, hypotonia, and seizures are also reported. Infants affected by a mosaicism may express varying degrees of mental deficit and incur longer survival rates (Haldeman-Englert et al., 2018; NORD, 2018a).

X-Linked Disorders

Agenesis of Corpus Callosum. Agenesis of the corpus callosum (ACC) is a birth defect resulting from failed or partial development of fiber bundles connecting the cerebral hemispheres. ACC affects seven of every 1,000 births and may be an isolated defect or associated with brain malformations, including Chiari malformation, schizencephaly, holoprosencephaly, Anderman syndrome, or Dandy–Walker malformation (NORD, 2018b; Volpe et al., 2018). Females may be concurrently affected by Aicardi syndrome (Govil-Delela, Kumar, Agarwal, & Chugani, 2017). Clinical manifestations include seizures, abnormalities of the spine, developmental delay, and congenital hydrocephalus. Life expectancy is related to extent and severity of associated disorders or abnormalities (NORD, 2018b).

Aqueductal Stenosis. Congenital stenosis of the aqueduct of Sylvius involves a narrowing of the passageway between the third and fourth ventricle, which slows the passage of CSF from the ventricles. This is an X-linked recessive disorder associated with 15% to 60% of all cases of congenital hydrocephalus (Cinalli, Mirone, Spennato, & Nastro, n.d.; Cinalli et al., 2011). Hallmark clinical manifestations include congenital hydrocephalus with or without seizures, hypotonia, and weakness (Pina-Garza, 2013). Long-term outcomes are related to the underlying cause of aqueductal stenosis and associated disorders (Cinalli et al., n.d.).

Fragile X. Fragile X syndrome is the most common cause for mental retardation and affects 1 in every 4,000 to 8,000 births; a male prevalence (2:1) is reported (Raspa, Wheeler, & Riley, 2017). Fragile X syndrome follows an X-linked dominant inheritance pattern and involves mutations in the fragile X mental retardation 1 gene (*FMR1*; Centers for Disease Control and Prevention [CDC], 2018b). Mutations effectively shut off transcription of the *FMR1* gene, which is normally responsible for modulating synapses between axons and target cells. Delayed speech and language development is common and typically identified by age 2. Therefore, common life-span implications include delayed neurocognitive development and behavioral problems. Seizure disorders and macrocephaly have also been reported (CDC, 2018b).

MATERNAL HEALTH INFLUENCES

Stability of the maternal–fetal dyad is critical for the developing fetus. Certain pharmacologic agents, maternal infection, alterations in maternal health, and placental and delivery complications may impact neurologic system development.

Maternal Disease States

Maternal health status is important to a stable fetal growth environment. Neurodevelopmental consequences of maternal disease states, including malnutrition, on the developing fetus may impose lifelong challenges for the affected child. Common maternal disease states that affect the fetal neurodevelopment are summarized in Table 3.6.

It is important to associate stress-response systems with morbidity risks. Maternal disease states activate stress-response systems in the mother. For example, the hypothalamic–pituitary–adrenal (HPA) axis (see Chapter 10) may be activated with certain maternal disease states to preserve homeostasis within the pregnant female's biological environment. Although this normal stress response is helpful to the pregnant female, it can compromise the intrauterine environment and alter or interrupt normal fetal neurodevelopment. For example, placental blood flow may be reduced during maternal stress responses. Recurrent activation of the HPA axis, or the hypothalamic–pituitary–thyroid axis in cases of maternal thyroid disorders, may impose long-lasting, deleterious effects on fetal neurodevelopment and across the life span. As such, maternal health and well-being are of critical importance throughout pregnancy (Vohr, Davis, Wanke, & Krebs, 2017).

TABLE 3.6 Summary of Common Maternal Diseases and Risks to Fetal Neurodevelopment and Childhood Function

Maternal Disease States	Risks
Infections (CMV*, chorioamnionitis)	*Fetal/Neonatal:* Sensorineural hearing loss (CMV), impaired gray matter development (chorioamnionitis) *Childhood:* Cognitive deficits
Inflammatory diseases	*Fetal/Neonatal:* Atypical brain development* *Childhood:* Cognitive deficits
Thyroid disorder	*Fetal/Neonatal:* Craniosynostosis *Childhood:* Attention deficit disorder
Diabetes mellitus	*Fetal/Neonatal:* Atypical brain development* *Childhood:* Language delay, impaired recognition, poor motor development, neuropsychological impairment
Obesity	*Fetal/Neonatal:* Inflammation-mediated atypical brain development* *Childhood:* Cognitive and language deficits
Micronutrient deficiencies (folate, B_{12}, choline, zinc, tryptophan, omega-3 fatty acids, iodine)	*Fetal/Neonatal:* Neural tube defects, atypical brain development*, reduced myelination *Childhood:* Cognitive and language deficits; motor, socioemotional, and behavioral dysfunction*

*NOTE: *Atypical brain development* refers to an interruption of normal embryologic and fetal brain development during neurogenesis (proliferation, migration, organization, or myelination). The correlation between maternal obesity and neurologic dysfunction in childhood may be confounded by sociodemographic factors. CMV is the most common cause for congenital infections; however, the TORCH infections excluded from this table may yield similar neurological consequences on the developing fetus.

CMV, cytomegalovirus; TORCH, *Toxoplasma gondii*, rubella, cytomegalovirus, and herpes simplex.

Source: Gressens, P., & Huppi, P. S. (2015). Intracranial hemorrhage and vascular lesions in the neonate. In R. J. Martin, A. A. Fanaroff, & M. C. Walsh (Eds.), *Fanaroff and Martin's neonatal-perinatal medicine: Diseases of the fetus and infant* (10th ed., pp. 836-853). Philadelphia, PA: Elsevier-Mosby.

Pharmacologic Influences

Sufficient evidence exists related to the potential harmful effect of certain pharmacologic agents on the developing fetus. These substances may have a direct or indirect influence on developing fetal CNS. Direct impact may alter neuronal pathways, receptors, and structures resulting in potential short-term and long-term complications. Indirect impact includes alterations in maternal health and nutrition, intrauterine growth restriction (IUGR), neonatal respiratory depression, hypotonia, apnea, and premature delivery. Clinicians must weigh the risk of maternal and fetal pharmacologic exposure with the benefits of the intended medication. For those mothers using illicit substances, dosing and frequency are commonly inconsistent, providing a greater challenge for diagnosis and management of neonatal abstinence.

Any use of general or regional obstetric analgesia or narcotics should alert the clinician to potential adverse effects to the fetus (as well as the pregnant female). Narcotic analgesics may precipitate maternal hypotension, altered labor pattern, ineffective labor, and drowsiness (Davidson, London, & Ladewig, 2012). This may disrupt CBF patterns and fetal oxygen consumption. Fetal manifestations of obstetric analgesia may include decreased fetal heart rate variability and postnatal respiratory depression. General anesthesia may provoke maternal hypotension, hypertension, tachycardia, vomiting (with possible aspiration), and laryngospasm (Davidson et al., 2012; Palanisamy, 2012). Fetal manifestations of general anesthesia include hypotonia and CNS depression. Regional spinal or epidural anesthesia risks include maternal hypotension, allergic reaction, and prolonged second-stage labor. Potential fetal complications include toxic reaction to maternal dosing, late decelerations, bradycardia, and variability (Tsen, 2011).

Antihypertensive agents are known to readily cross the placenta. These medications may precipitate IUGR, premature labor and delivery, hypoxia, and acidosis (Dekker, 2011; Sibai, 2012). Postnatal manifestations of maternal antihypertensive use include hypotonia, apnea, respiratory depression, and hypotension in the newborn (Dekker, 2011; Sibai, 2012). High-dose maternal antihypertensive therapy is associated with increased risk for neonatal neuromuscular and respiratory depression (Davidson et al., 2012).

Antiseizure medications readily cross the placental barrier and can lead to significant congenital malformations in the developing fetus. There is an approximate threefold increase in risk for major anomalies in the developing fetus when mothers use valproic acid (Valproate) for seizure management (Petersen et al., 2017). The most common risk to the fetus is development of a neural tube defect.

Maternal Substance Abuse

Perinatal substance abuse is a significant issue within the United States. The most commonly abused substances include tobacco, alcohol, cannabinoids, opioids, and cocaine. Polysubstance abuse is common and, in certain cases, can exacerbate manifestations of neonatal abstinence syndrome (NAS). The effects of drug abuse on fetal neurodevelopment include alterations to neurotransmitters and receptors, brain organization, and structural malformations. In addition, certain drugs disrupt the maternal–fetal placental interface, which can cause rapid shifts in fetal CBF and vascular resistance, thereby increasing the risk for brain injury.

Tobacco and Nicotine. Tobacco and nicotine products used during pregnancy include chewing tobacco, rolled cigarettes, e-cigarettes, and nicotine replacement therapies. Approximately 16% of pregnant women report using one or more of these products during early pregnancy, with 8% achieving abstinence (Forray & Foster, 2015). Fetal neurodevelopmental consequences of tobacco or nicotine exposure include observed reductions in cortical gray matter. These findings are observed and reported using cohorts of children exposed to smoking during pregnancy (Chatterton et al., 2017). The pathophysiology of tobacco and nicotine exposure has been investigated using fetal rodent models. Abnormal development of cerebral dendrites and axon-mediated synapses within the cortex are observed. Epigenetic changes in DNA methylation are reported. Therefore, risk factors to the human fetus include cognitive impairment, behavioral issues, and reductions in executive function, which typically manifest in childhood (O'Keeffe, Greene, & Kearney, 2014). Of note, smoking during pregnancy is positively associated with antenatal anxiety and depression and a reduction in maternal–fetal bonding, as well as breastfeeding practices, in the postpartum period (Chatterton et al., 2017; Hernández-Martínez et al., 2017).

Alcohol. An estimated 60% of pregnant women across the world consume alcohol during pregnancy (Vall, Salat-Batlle, & Garcia-Algar, 2015). Alcohol consumption during pregnancy can be categorized as social consumption, moderate, binge, or heavy drinking. *Moderate drinking* is defined as up to one drink per day, *binge drinking* is defined as four or more drinks in about 2 hours, and *heavy drinking* refers to binge drinking on 5 or more days during a 30-day period (National Institute on Alcohol Abuse and Alcoholism [NIAAA], 2017). There is no safe range for alcohol consumption during pregnancy. The American College of Obstetricians and Gynecologists (ACOG) report even moderate drinking during early pregnancy can lead to neurodevelopment sequela (anxiety-like behavior) in offspring (ACOG, 2017; CDC, 2018a; NIAAA, 2017; Rouzer, Cole, Johnson, Varlinskaya, & Diaz, 2017). Impaired oxidative and nonoxidative metabolism of ethanol is one proposed etiology for high circulating levels of ethanol within amniotic fluid (Heller & Burd, 2014). In addition, ethanol is known to impose placental and umbilical cord vasoconstriction and increase fetal–placental vascular resistance. Consequences of fetal exposure to alcohol include speech and language deficits, cognitive and behavior deficits, learning disabilities, hyperactivity, reduced executive functioning, and psychosocial dysfunction in adulthood (O'Keeffe et al., 2014).

Cannabis. Approximately 1 out of every 25 women use marijuana while pregnant (CDC, 2017b). The psychoactive component of cannabis is Δ9-tetrahydrocannabinol (THC). THC can cross the placenta as well as the BBB (CDC, 2017b). In doing so, it may function as a noxious stimulant to the endocannabinoid system, which can interfere with folic acid absorption, cerebral angiogenesis, neuronal proliferation, axon development, and synaptogenesis. In addition, fetal THC exposure disrupts fetal dopamine synthesis by impairing dopamine receptor cell maturation (Jaques et al., 2014; C.-S. Wu, Jew, & Lu, 2011). Prenatal exposure to THC is associated with neonatal tremors, irritability, and an exacerbated startle response. Life-span implications include learning disabilities, impaired higher order executive functions (impulse control, visual memory, and attention span) during school-age years, and neuropsychiatric disorders (drug addiction, schizophrenia, and depression) in older children and adults (Jaques et al., 2014; Volkow, Compton, & Wargo, 2017). Dose–response relationships between THC and fetal neurodevelopment have not been defined to date (Jaques et al., 2014).

Stimulants. Common reported stimulants ingested during pregnancy include cocaine and methamphetamines. Mechanisms by which cocaine and methamphetamines implicate fetal neurodevelopment are poorly understood. Neurologic manifestations of early cocaine use during pregnancy (first trimester) include impaired short-term memory and behavioral issues. Similarly, manifestations of methamphetamine exposure include altered neurodevelopment and behavior issues in childhood (Anand & Campbell-Yeo, 2015).

Opioids. Opioid use involves both opioids as well as heroin. A significant increase in prenatal opioid abuse, from 1.19 to 5.77 per 1,000 live births, was observed between 2000 and 2009 (Forray & Foster, 2015; Patrick et al., 2012). Prenatal opioid and heroin exposure disrupts early cortical brain development, including neurogenesis, proliferation, and migration. These disruptions may negatively affect brain growth and development of the basal ganglia. Early consequences of opioid abuse include NAS. NAS manifests as crying, irritability, poor sleep, increased muscle tone, tremors, skin excoriation, hyperthermia, loose stools, yawning, sweating, nasal stuffiness, and sneezing (D'Apolito, 2014; Stover & Davis, 2015). Isolating life-span implications associated only with maternal opioid abuse are complicated in that polydrug use is often prevalent. Although altered neurodevelopmental outcomes are reported in the literature, clinicians must consider polydrug use as a confounder to linking neurologic outcomes exclusively to prenatal opioid exposure. In addition, the severity of NAS and pharmacologic treatment mechanisms, as well as environmental factors and parenting behaviors, may implicate infant developmental assessments in infancy and childhood (D'Apolito, 2016).

Infectious Disease

Maternal infections during pregnancy can adversely affect the developing fetus in various ways. Complications may include alterations in fetal development (IUGR, microcephaly), premature delivery, alterations in cerebral tissue (intraventricular and intracerebral calcifications), seizures, or long-term neurodevelopmental complications. In many cases, the risk for adverse outcomes is inversely related to the infant's gestational age and age of infectious exposure during pregnancy. Of particular concern are those infectious agents capable of readily crossing the placenta (Neu, Duchon, & Zachariah, 2015). These infectious agents include toxoplasmas, others (syphilis, varicella-zoster, parvovirus B19), rubella, cytomegalovirus (CMV), and herpes (TORCH; Table 3.7). These infectious agents increase the risk for neonatal neurologic sequelae from maternal prenatal infection. In some cases, the neurologic impact is related to the onset of maternal infection during pregnancy.

COMMON PROBLEMS WITH IMPLICATIONS ACROSS THE LIFE SPAN

Disorders of Early Brain Development

Anencephaly. Anencephaly is a lethal disorder of early brain development resulting in incomplete or defective closure of the rostral end of the anterior neural tube. The incidence of anencephaly within the United States is three per every 10,000 live births per year, with females more affected than males (CDC, 2017a). An increased prevalence of anencephaly among Hispanic infants has been reported (Huang & Doherty, 2018).

Risk factors for development of anencephaly include maternal mineral deficits (such as deficiencies in folate, copper, and zinc) and maternal febrile illnesses during the first one third to one half of gestation (Volpe et al., 2018). Recurrence risk ranges from 1.9% to 3% with subsequent pregnancies (Huang & Doherty, 2018; Jones, & Casanelles, 2013). Causes of anencephaly are generally unknown (CDC, 2017a). Genetic and environmental influences appear to impact the development of this disorder (Volpe

TABLE 3.7 Prenatal Infections
Toxoplasmosis (*Toxoplasma gondii*)
Congenital Rubella (German measles)
Cytomegalovirus (CMV)
Herpes simplex virus (HSV)
Congenital syphilis (Treponema pallidium)
Congenital varicella (Varicella zoster virus)
Zika virus

Sources: Elmore, S. A., Jones, J. L., Conrad, P. A., Patton, S., Lindsay, D. S., & Dubey, J. P. (2010). *Toxoplasma gondii*: Epidemiology, feline clinical aspects, and prevention. *Trends in Parasitology, 26*(4), 190–196. doi:10.1016/j.pt.2010.01.009; Neu, N., Duchon, J., & Zachariah, P. (2015). TORCH infections. *Clinical Perinatology, 42*(1), 77–103. doi:10.1016/j.clp.2014.11.001.

et al., 2018). Environmental factors may include toxins, certain medications, and folic acid deficiencies.

The pathogenesis of anencephaly involves closure of the cranial neuropore leading to incomplete brain and skull development. Direct exposure of the hemispheres of the brain to amniotic fluid, as well as prolonged trauma from fetal movement causing brain tissue to interface with the uterine wall, contributes to the development of this neural tube defect (Figure 3.16; Copel, 2018).

Anencephaly manifests as craniorachischisis totalis or myeloschosis. Large portions of the skull (and in some cases, the scalp) are missing. Craniorachischisis totalis involves absent dermal or skeletal coverage of the neural plate. Myeloschosis involves open dermal layer, absent skeletal coverage, and exposed nerve tissue resulting in posterior exposure of the spinal cord. Prominent-appearing eyes, hypertonia, hyperactive reflexes, and myoclonus may be present. Life-span implications include fetal demise, stillbirth, or postnatal death within the first 2 months of life (Huang & Doherty, 2018).

Encephalocele. Encephalocele is a neural tube defect occurring from a failure of rostral neural tube closure during primary neurulation. Incidence rates for encephalocele in the United States are one in 10,000 to 12,200 live births (Huang & Doherty, 2018; Parker et al., 2010). The majority of cases (80%) in the Western hemisphere involve occipital encephaloceles, whereas Eastern countries (Thailand, for example) report a higher incidence of frontal encephaloceles (Copel, 2018). Associated anomalies (microcephaly, cleft lip/palate, hydrocephalus, craniosynostosis, and spina bifida) are seen in 50% of all cases (Huang & Doherty, 2018). Risk factors include previous children with spina bifida or anencephaly, Meckel's

syndrome, Walker–Warburg syndrome, exposure to maternal teratogens, maternal mineral deficits (such as deficiencies in folate, copper, and zinc), and maternal febrile illness during early gestation (Huang & Doherty, 2018; Jones et al., 2013).

The pathogenesis of encephalocele is well understood. Occipital encephaloceles involve one of two possible mechanisms: (a) failed anterior fusion of the neural folds, or (b) herniation of brain tissue outside of the cranial cavity and into a protuberant mass or fluid-filled saclike structure (Figure 3.17). Defects may also occur in the frontal, nasopharyngeal, or parietal regions (Volpe et al., 2018).

Life-span implications are related to location, size, and regional involvement. Intellectual deficits may occur in up to 50% of all cases (Huang & Doherty, 2018). Encephaloceles arising in the occiput are also associated with blindness (Kerr & Huether, 2014).

Spina Bifida. *Spina bifida* refers to incomplete formation, or absence, of the posterior vertebral arch, giving rise to a saclike protuberance at the base of the spinal column. Four forms of spina bifida are reported: (a) occulta (most common), (b) closed neural tube defects, (c) meningocele, and (d) myelomeningocele (Figure 3.18). Spina bifida affects between 1,500 to 2,000 infants each year in the United States. Rates are highest among the Hispanic population (3.8 per 10,000 live births), followed by Caucasian infants (3.09 per 10,000 live births) and African American infants (2.73 per 10,000 live births; CDC, n.d.). The incidence of spina bifida increases to 6.1 to 13.8 per 10,000 live births when associated with trisomy 21 or midline defects, including cleft lip and/or cleft palate (Parker et al., 2010). Risk factors include maternal malnutrition (specifically folic acid deficiencies), diabetes, and certain medications

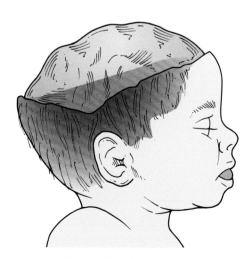

Figure 3.16 Anencephaly.

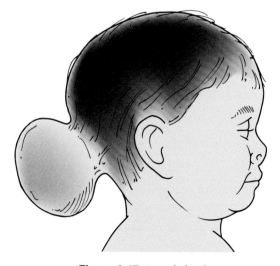

Figure 3.17 Encephalocele.

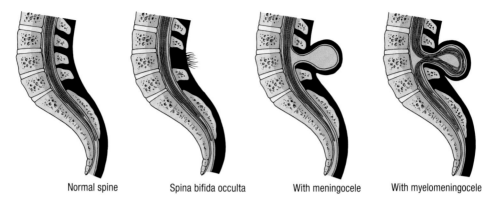

Figure 3.18 Normal spine and types of spina bifida.

such as valproic acid and carbamazepine (ACOG, 2008; NIH, 2018e).

Clinical manifestations vary depending on the extent of tissue involvement and level of the defect. Generally speaking, increased neural tissue involvement and defects involving the cervical or upper thoracic spine are associated with increased morbidity risks. A tuft of hair, dimple, lipoma, or hemangioma located in the lower lumbar region should increase the index of suspicion for spina bifida (Gressens & Huppi, 2015). Infants with an accompanying tethered cord and Chiari malformation may present with hydrocephalus, as 85% to 90% of cases involving thoracolumbar, lumbar, or lumbosacral lesions are associated with obstructed flow of CSF secondary to kinking of the fourth ventricle (Elgamal, 2012).

Spina bifida occulta. Spina bifida occulta occurs in 1.5% to 3% of individuals. This occurs secondary to failed closure of the posterior vertebral laminae, most often during week 4 of gestation, and results in failed fusion of one or more arches of the spine, which forms a spinal cleft (Robinson & Cohen, 2015). The overlying skin remains intact. Life-span implications include altered gait, chronic back pain, bowel and bladder dysfunction, and alterations in spinal alignment (scoliosis).

Meningocele. A meningocele is a saclike dilation of the meninges that results in bulging below the skin. Meningoceles occur equally along the cervical, thoracic, and lumbar spinal regions. The structures (meninges and spinal cord) are normally developed. No neurodevelopmental deficits are reported among infants and children.

Myelomeningocele. Myelomeningocele is a similar saclike dilation comprised of spinal fluid and neural tissue, spinal cord, nerves, or a combination of these neural structures. Up to 80% of all myelomeningoceles occur in the lumbar and lumbosacral regions (Kerr & Huether, 2014; Volpe et al., 2018). Of those that do originate in

these regions, nearly all are associated with Chiari II malformation (Kerr & Huether, 2014). Chiari II malformation involves the downward displacement of the brainstem, medulla, cerebellum, and fourth ventricle through the foramen magnum (Figure 3.19). Chiari II formation is associated with hydrocephalus secondary to obstruction of the fourth ventricle or aqueductal stenosis (Volpe et al., 2018).

Life-span implications of these three variants of spina bifida include altered neurologic function below the level of the defect. Severity is related to the extent and location of the defect, integrity of associated structures, and comorbidities (Volpe et al., 2018). Closure of a meningocele may impose few, if any, long-term complications. Life-span implications of spina bifida occulta include altered gait, chronic back pain, bowel and bladder dysfunction, and alterations in spinal alignment (scoliosis; Volpe et al., 2018). Life-span implications of myelomeningocele include seizures (30% of all affected patients), issues with visual perception and astigmatism, talipes equinovarus (clubfoot), congenital hip dysplasia, and spinal alignment defects (kyphosis and scoliosi; Volpe et al., 2018). In particular, intellectual deficits are also common with the Chiari II malformation.

Congenital Hydrocephalus. Congenital hydrocephalus is known as *distention of the cerebral ventricles* (Figure 3.20; Garne et al., 2010). The incidence of congenital hydrocephalus is approximately 0.48 to 1.1 per 1,000 live births (Tully & Dobyns, 2014). Upwards of 70% of all cases of congenital hydrocephalus are associated with other congenital anomalies, including ACC, Dandy–Walker cysts, and aqueductal stenosis (Volpe et al., 2018).

Risk factors for the development of congenital hydrocephalus include Dandy–Walker malformation, exposure to excessive radiation, maternal malnutrition, maternal infections (such as toxoplasmosis and cytomegalovirus), aqueductal stenosis, congenital fetal cerebral tumors,

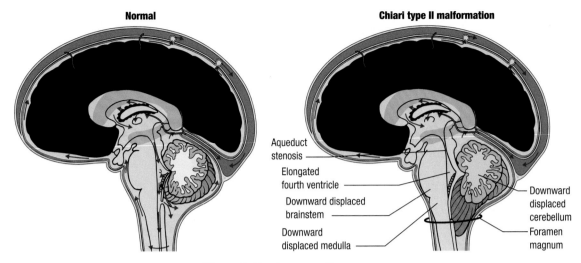

Figure 3.19 Chiari II malformation.

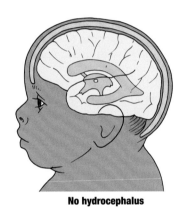

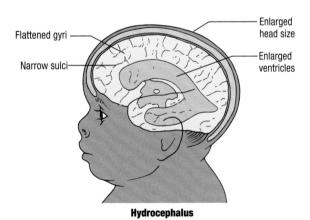

Figure 3.20 Normal infant brain and infant brain with hydrocephalus.

vein of Galen malformation, and intrauterine intraventricular hemorrhage (Garne et al., 2010; NORD, 2018c). Brain tumors, trauma, cysts, thrombi, spina bifida, and arteriovenous malformations are other causes of obstructive hydrocephalus.

The pathogenesis of congenital hydrocephalus relates to inhibition of flow of CSF from the cerebral ventricles (area of production) to the systemic circulation (area of absorption). This is a result of X-linked genetic aberrations or altered physiologic CSF function (McAllister, 2012). Ventriculomegaly and the resultant impedance or obstruction to normal flow of CSF alters the physiologic flow of CSF. In this case, ventriculomegaly creates a structural blockade that reduces flow of CSF through the ventricles, to the arachnoid space and cerebral microvasculature.

Congenital hydrocephalus manifests at birth as a constellation of physical findings. Typically, the anterior and posterior fontanelles are full, enlarged, and possibly bulging; cranial sutures are palpably separated. Frontal bossing may be observed. Scalp veins may be distended and bulging (Volpe et al., 2018). Ocular prominence (bulging) with a staring expression, with or without the sclera visible above the iris (sunset eyes), may be present. A high-pitched cry may accompany increasing intracranial pressure. Other manifestations include lethargy, irritability, poor feeding, and emesis.

Life-span implications correlate with the extent of the disease process, onset of treatment, and other comorbidities. With prompt and adequate neurosurgical evaluation and intervention, 5-year survival rates are more than 80% (Kerr & Huether, 2014). Epilepsy may develop in up to 34% of infants following treatment (Persson, Hagberg, & Uvebrant, 2006). An increased correlation between impairment of cognitive function and degree of hydrocephalus is seen in patients with additional complications (Smith & Buckley, 2012). Increased mortality rates are seen in patients with severe congenital hydrocephalus or progressive disorders such as brain tumors.

Microcephaly. Microcephaly is a disorder of neuronal proliferation involving an abnormal reduction of global brain growth. Cranial head circumference measurements are typically 2 to 3 standard deviations lower in affected infants compared to counterparts of similar gestational age, gender, and ethnicity (Huang & Doherty, 2018; Volpe et al., 2018). The annual incidence within the United States is estimated to be two to 12 babies per 10,000 live births (CDC, 2016). In the United States, microcephaly is often attributed to noninfectious causes, including maternal malnutrition, hypothyroidism, polysubstance abuse, and placental insufficiency. Cases of microcephaly in developing countries are often related to maternal viral infections (Devakumar et al., 2017).

The pathophysiology of microcephaly involves increased apoptosis or reduced growth proliferation. Primary (true) microcephaly involves disruptions during primary neurulation, causing either dysfunction or death of neural progenitor cells. Secondary microcephaly develops during the postnatal period and involves disruptions to neuronal maturation (Devakumar et al., 2017). The cranial vault is within normal limits at birth but fails to grow and develop properly over time. Consideration of the delivery method is essential for an appropriate assessment of cranial size. Vaginal delivery may compress the skull, impose cranial molding, and cause a transient reduction in head circumference. In these cases, the transient cranial deformity resolves within a few days (Ditzenberger & Blackburn, 2014).

Life-span implications are related to underlying cause and comorbidities; the diagnosis does not automatically confer lifelong neurodevelopmental consequences. Infants with mild cases of microcephaly often exhibit minimal long-term neurodevelopmental complications. More severe forms of microcephaly result in moderate to severe long-term neurodevelopmental complications, including seizures, learning disabilities, and physical disabilities (National Birth Defects Prevention Network [NBDPN], 2016).

Disorders of the Cerebral Vasculature Not Related to Birth Injury

Intraventricular Hemorrhage. Intraventricular hemorrhage (IVH) is the collection of blood within the ventricular space. Hemorrhage may occur as a result of insult to the germinal matrix or subependymal portions of the brain. IVH is a common hemorrhagic disorder most frequently reported in premature infants. The incidence is inversely related to gestational age and birth weight. Approximately 3.5% to 4.6% of term infants develop IVH. In comparison, up to 27% of infants born at less than 32 weeks gestation or weighing less than 1,500 grams at birth are diagnosed with IVH (Szpecht, Szymankiewicz, Nowak, & Gadzinowski, 2016). ELBW infants weighing less than 750 grams at birth have a 45% to 60% risk of acquiring IVH (Neil & Inder, 2018; Parsons, Seay, & Jacobson, 2016; Volpe et al., 2018).

Risk factors include gestational age, developmental fragility of germinal matrix vascularity, low birth weight, coagulation disturbances, delivery room resuscitation complications, illness severity, disturbances in CO_2 levels, respiratory distress syndrome, race, infant gender, high-frequency ventilation, and fluctuating CBF (Neil & Inder, 2018; Shankaran et al., 2014; Volpe et al., 2018). Preterm males are at an increased risk for IVH when compared to preterm females (Kent, Wright, & Abdel-Latif, 2012). Preterm infants of Caucasian race with birth weight between 500 to 1,250 grams have a decreased risk for IVH grade II, III, and IV when comparted to other races (Shankaran et al., 2014). The risk for IVH increases with multiple-gestation pregnancies.

The pathogenesis of IVH is well understood and reconciles the aforementioned risk stratifications. Fluctuations in CBF (decreases and increases) elicit IVH, as continuous fluctuations in pressure on the cerebral microvasculature can provoke rupture. Decreased CBF may occur secondary to hypoxia and coagulation disorders. Increased CBF may occur from hypercarbia, hypoglycemia, blood transfusions, rapid use of volume expanders, mechanical ventilation, tracheal suctioning, and scheduled "hands on" care times (Volpe et al., 2018). Optimizing neurologic function among premature infants is tenuous at best, and must be grounded in a clear understanding of human physiology. Strategies used to restore or maintain homeostasis are not without risk.

Consider the effect of respiratory support on CBF. ELBW infants often, if not always, require invasive mechanical ventilation secondary to respiratory distress. The mechanics of ventilation impose fluctuations in CBF. In addition, periods of hypercarbia, hyperoxemia, hypotension, and hypovolemia, which often occur during the first week of life, perturb CBF patterns. Furthermore, the cerebral vasculature is pressure passive at this time, nearly incapable of mounting an adequate protective response to changes in blood flow. This lack of autoregulation, in combination with the other factors listed here, significantly increases the risk for IVH in this subpopulation (Volpe et al., 2018).

The majority of IVHs occurs prior to 72 hours of age. Approximately 50% of IVH cases occur in the first 24 hours of life, 80% occur by 48 hours, and 90% occur by 72 hours of life (Neil & Inder, 2018; Parsons et al., 2016; Volpe et al., 2018). Approximately 20% to 40% exhibit a progressive hemorrhagic insult over the first 3 to 5 days of life. Clinical manifestations include lethargy, apnea, hypotension, thrombocytopenia, and anemia (Neil & Inder, 2018; Volpe et al., 2018). Lethargy, apnea, seizures, or spastic irritability may present in the term infant with IVH.

Severity of IVH is appraised through the use of grading systems. Both systems are presented in Table 3.8. Lifespan implications are associated with severity of IVH and associated comorbidities (de Vries, 2015; Neil & Inder, 2018; Volpe et al., 2018). Using Volpe's classification system, risk thresholds for long-term neurodevelopmental impairment are as follows: Grade I (15%), Grade II (25%), Grade III (50%), and Grade III with parenchymal injury (75%; Volpe et al., 2018).

Intracerebellar Hemorrhage. Intracerebellar hemorrhage (ICH) involves bleeding within the cerebellum. ICH may result from primary bleeding or as a result of the extension of a subarachnoid or IVH into cerebellar tissues. Approximately 2% to 19% of premature infants weighing less than 1,500 grams or less than 32 weeks of gestation develop an ICH (de Vries, 2015; Volpe et al., 2018).

Risk factors include respiratory distress, prematurity, hypoxic birth event, vitamin K deficiency, rapid fluid resuscitation, and complicated instrument-assisted deliveries. The majority of ICH in term infants is related to birth trauma. For preterm infants, birth trauma or intense respiratory management early in the hospital course may contribute to ICH (Volpe et al., 2018).

The pathogenesis of ICH is not fully understood. One of four mechanisms may explain the genesis of an ICH: (a) trauma to the posterior fossa resulting in rupture of the cerebellar bridging veins or the occipital sinuses, (b) venous infarction, (c) primary cerebellar hemisphere or vermis hemorrhages, or (d) supratentorial IVH and subarachnoid hemorrhages (Volpe et al., 2018).

Clinical manifestations of ICH include motor agitation, respiratory compromise, and apnea. These findings may be associated with brainstem compression (Whitelaw, Osredkar, & Thoresen, 2016). Other general symptoms of ICH include bradycardia and lateral eye deviation. Lifespan implications include possible long-term neurodevelopmental deficits (Volpe et al., 2018).

Cerebral Artery Infarction. A cerebral artery infarction (neonatal stroke) is defined as a disturbance in cerebral blood supply. The incidence of neonatal strokes is increasing, likely secondary to increased diagnostic testing methods. Currently, strokes affect one in every 1,600 to 4,000 neonates per year (Bernson-Leung & Rivkin, 2016). A male prevalence is reported and a higher incidence of left-sided infarcts within the middle cerebral artery is observed among term infants (Aa, Benders, Groenendaal, & Vries, 2014; Hielkema & Hadders-Algra, 2016; Volpe et al., 2018).

Risk factors for the development of neonatal stroke are multifactorial. Maternal factors include infection, coagulation disorders, preeclampsia, and drug (cocaine) and tobacco use (Bernson-Leung & Rivkin, 2016). Fetal risk factors include congenital heart disease, congenital infection, coagulation disorders, and difficult deliveries that require mechanical force or involve perinatal asphyxia (Volpe et al., 2018). Postnatal risk factors include systemic or CNS-specific infections, dehydration, congenital

TABLE 3.8 Methods for Classifying Intraventricular Hemorrhage

Grade of IVH	Volpe	Papile
I	Site: Germinal matrix Degree of hemorrhage within ventricle: 0%–10% Ventricular distention? No	Site: Subependymal matrix Degree of hemorrhage within ventricle: N/A Ventricular distention? N/A
II	Site: Lateral ventricle Degree of hemorrhage within ventricle: 10%–50% Ventricular distention? No	Site: Lateral ventricle Degree of hemorrhage within ventricle: <50% Ventricular distention? No
III	Site: Lateral ventricle(s) Degree of hemorrhage within ventricle: >50% Ventricular distention? Yes	Site: Lateral ventricle(s) Degree of hemorrhage within ventricle: >50% Ventricular distention? Yes
IV	N/A	Site: Subependymal matrix or lateral ventricle(s) Degree of hemorrhage within ventricle: any Ventricular distention? Absent or any degree of distention Other: Extension of hemorrhage into parenchyma

NOTE: Dr. Volpe's method argues that bleeding into parenchymal tissue is multifactorial and not exclusive to IVH.

IVH, intraventricular hemorrhage.

Source: Papile, L. A., Burstein, J., Burstein, R., & Koffler, H. (1978). Incidence and evolution of subependymal and intraventricular hemorrhage: A study of infants with birth weights less than 1,500 gm. *Journal of Pediatrics, 92*(4). 529–534. doi:10.1016/S0022-3476(78)80282-0; Volpe, J. J. (2018). *Volpe's neurology of the newborn* (6th ed.). Philadelphia, PA: Elsevier.

heart disease, polycythemia, and coagulation disorders (disseminated intravascular coagulopathy, factor VIII or V deficiency, prothrombin abnormalities; Hielkma & Hadders-Algra, 2016; Sehgal, 2011).

The pathogenesis of cerebral artery infarcts correlates with risk factors. Vascular anomalies, emboli, arterial or venous thrombi, or impaired venous drainage within the periventricular white matter of the brain contribute to the formation of a thrombus and subsequent occlusion and infarct. Congenital heart defects, for example, are often associated with deranged vasculature, which may facilitate the formation of thrombi. Similarly, infections can trigger clotting mechanisms, which increase the risk for thrombi and resultant infarcts. Premature infants often suffer a stroke secondary to impaired venous drainage within periventricular regions (Bernson-Leung & Rivkin, 2016; Hielkma & Hadders-Algra, 2016; Volpe et al., 2018).

Following the vascular injury, a period of oxidative stress and inflammation precedes necrosis of all affected cells. Within the next 24 hours, monocytes enter the affected space, wedge between vascular endothelial cells, and then migrate into subendothelial spaces. Over the following 24 to 48 hours, the monocytes transform into macrophages, ingest oxidized lipids, and transform into larger, "foamy"-looking cells (Figure 3.21). Release of glial fibrillary acidic protein is initiated, which causes astrocyte hypertrophy. Astroglial proliferation is elicited next as a reactive response to inflammation. This disorganized proliferation produces excessive amounts of glial fibrillary cells, which induce tissue reorganization, structural changes, and glial scar formation (Volpe et al., 2018). In fact, astroglial proliferating cells only differentiate into astrocytes, which stunts the repair of injured tissue. Strategies to "loosen" the dense covering of glial fibrillary processes and promote neurulation and synthesis of oligodendrocytes are necessary to encourage healing (Kratzer, Chip, & Vexler, 2014).

The most common clinical manifestations of neonatal hemorrhagic stroke include seizures, hypotonia, focal weakness, apnea, encephalopathy, and poor feeding (Armstrong-Wells, Johnston, Wu, Sidney, & Fullerton, 2009; Bruno et al., 2013; Cole at al., 2017). Life-span implications vary based on underlying pathology and comorbidities. Greater than 50% of infants affected by neonatal stroke display normal neurodevelopment in early childhood and beyond. Refractory seizures have been reported in some cases; however, the data is rather antiquated (de Vries, 2015). Cerebral palsy, intellectual disabilities, hemiparesis, hemisensory impairments, and cognitive dysfunction are other long-term complications (Westmacott, MacGregor, Askalan, & Deveber, 2009). That said, approximately one out of every four premature infants and one out of every three term infants who suffer a stroke will develop an intellectual disability.

Periventricular Leukomalacia. Periventricular leukomalacia (PVL) is a white-matter brain injury characterized by ischemic, necrotic periventricular white matter (Volpe et al., 2018). The incidence of cystic and noncystic PVL is known to be inversely proportional to gestational age; however, sparse publications quantify this relationship. This is likely secondary to variable screening mechanisms and difficulty discerning microscopic lesions with noncystic PVL (Volpe et al., 2018). Generally speaking, cystic PVL affects up to 3% of all living infants (Volpe et al., 2018). Risk factors include prematurity, postnatal age greater than 3 days of life, cardiorespiratory disease, IVH, and infection/inflammation (e.g., maternal–placental infections; Scher, 2013; Volpe et al., 2018).

PVL typically affects regions of white matter dorsal and lateral to the lateral ventricles and around the foramen of Monroe. The vessel most often implicated is the *middle cerebral artery*. The pathogenesis of PVL begins with necrosis (focal or diffuse) followed by gliosis and one of three possible end results: (a) diffuse white matter gliosis without the formation of cysts or scars; (b) cystic PVL (focal or diffuse), which includes the formation of cysts/cavities; or (c) noncystic PVL, which includes microscopic lesions. Cystic focal PVL is more severe, despite being more widespread compared to cystic diffuse PVL (Volpe et al., 2018). The progression pathway for focal cystic PVL is provided in Figure 3.22.

Vascular factors, specifically the anatomic state of the periventricular vessels, contribute to the pathogenesis of PVL. The brains of infants less than 32 weeks of gestation are completing the essential process of angiogenesis, proliferation, and branching of the cerebral vasculature throughout the brain and toward the deeper structures. Immature vessels, as previously described, contain a high number of vulnerable "end zones" and "border zones." These zones are particularly sensitive to changes in CBF and pressure; therefore, they are easily ruptured. From week 32 until term, the cerebral arteries (most notable, the middle cerebral artery) penetrate the brain. Long penetrations target deeper structures and short penetrations target subcortical white matter. This involves the establishment of anastamoses between vessels and elimination of end zones and border zones. Therefore, the relationship between degree of ischemia and permanent injury is directly influenced by the maturational state of the periventricular vessels.

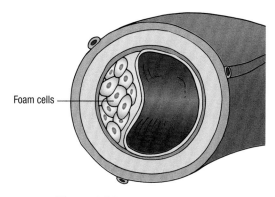

Foam cells

Figure 3.21 Foamy macrophages.

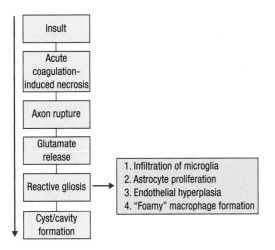

Figure 3.22 Pathogenesis of focal cystic periventricular leukomalacia.

Biochemical factors also contribute to the pathogenesis of PVL. Focal cystic PVL implicates less white matter volume as compared to diffuse cystic PVL. Diffuse cystic PVL as well as noncystic PVL and diffuse gliosis are associated with reduced cellular pathologies. Typical consequences of diffuse cystic PVL, in particular, include ventriculomegaly, reduced preoligodendrocyte formation, and resultant hypomyelination. As such, life-span implications are related to the type of PVL and comorbidities. Infants may experience cognitive and visual impairment; behavioral and attention disorders; and motor deficits, including spastic diplegia. Motor deficits may improve with less severe cases of PVL (Scher, 2013; Volpe et al., 2018).

Disorders of Skull Development

Craniosynostosis. Craniosynostosis (craniostenosis) involves premature closure of one or more cranial sutures. More specific, premature closure of a single suture line (nonsyndromic) or multiple (syndromic) closures may be observed. Although rare, syndromic craniosynostosis may present alongside birth defects and in the absence of a complementary syndrome (Evans, Hing, & Cunningham, 2018). Craniosynostosis occurs in one out of every 2,000 to 2,500 live births with a prevalence reported among males (Cornelissen et al., 2016). Risk factors include fetal tobacco and drug exposure, as well as rickets, idiopathic hypercalcemia, and hypophosphatemia.

Errors within gene-mediated signaling pathways, as well as environmental factors (intrinsic and extrinsic), are root causes for nonsyndromic cases of craniosynostosis (Katsianou, Adamopoulos, Vastardis, & Basdra, 2016). An intricate discussion of gene-mediated factors is beyond the scope of this textbook; however, mutations with the *EphrinA-4*, *FGFR*, and *TWIST-1* genes have been identified. Environmental factors include maternal valproate ingestion, tobacco and drug use, and compression of the developing skull during fetal growth. Regardless of the underlying pathobiology, premature fusion of a suture prevents growth of the affected cranial bones perpendicular to the fused site (Evans et al., 2018). As a result, the brain compensates by growing in alternative directions. Over time, this distorts the shape of the skull and can lead to facial deformities, ocular and auditory malformations, and potential neurodevelopmental impairment (Twigg & Wilkie, 2015).

The most common form of craniosynostosis involves premature closure of the sagittal (midline) suture and is reported in 40% to 55% of all cases; a male prevalence is reported. This type of premature closure leads to elongation of the cranial contour in the anteroposterior direction and commonly manifests as frontal bossing with scaphocephaly (Evans et al., 2018). Premature closure of the coronal suture occurs in 20% to 25% of all cases; lateral expansion of the cranial contour gives rise to a brachycephalic appearance. Mesotopic fusion accounts for 14% of cases. Finally, lambdoid fusion is reported in 3% to 5% of all cases and commonly results in ear displacement as well as an asymmetric skull base (Cornelissen et al., 2016; Evans et al., 2018). Of note, clinicians are to take special precaution to distinguish benign skull deformities from pathologic skull deformities. Positional plagiocephaly is a benign form of cranial contour alteration that occurs secondary to supine positioning at rest (Kerr & Huether, 2014). Cranial contour may be flattened in the occipital or lateral regions of the skull.

Life-span implications are related to number of sutures involved, onset of monitoring and treatment, genetic involvement, and additional comorbidities. Early surgical involvement reduces chronic increased intracranial pressures and reduces the risk for long-term neurologic damage. Custom-molded padded helmets are typically used to reshape the cranial contour of infants affected by positional plagiocephaly (benign). These infants often suffer no long-term neurologic dysfunction.

Neurologic Disorders

Hypotonia. Hypotonia, or "floppy baby syndrome," is the state of low muscle tone or reduced muscle strength. It is a manifestation of diseases or disorders that affect any level of the nervous system. The incidence of hypotonia varies based on the primary, underlying problem. Common etiologies are summarized in Table 3.9.

It is important to understand that hypotonia is not a primary problem. Hypotonia occurs as a consequence of an underlying disorder or disease process. Given the long list of primary problems manifested with hypotonia, and the range of subtle to severe weakness that can be observed among neonates, distinguishing the underlying pathology to blame for the single manifestation of hypotonia (excluding all other manifestations of the primary problem) can be a daunting task.

Clinicians often find themselves asking, "What disruption in homeostasis is causing the baby to present with weakness?" Begin by recognizing that hypotonia occurs due to an injury *above* or *below* the lower motor neuron

(Figure 3.23). Upper motor neurons synapse onto lower motor neurons located in the ventral horn of the spinal cord. Lower motor neurons project from their spinal origins onto muscles (at neuromuscular junctions) to create muscle contraction (motor responses). This gives rise to the sensory–motor feedback system, best explained as it applies to active muscle contraction.

Muscle contraction (active muscle tone) is modulated by way of a feedback loop between upper and lower motor neurons and begins with sensory inputs. Sensory inputs are sent via afferent pathways to the upper motor neurons. Upper motor neurons send efferent communications to alpha motor neurons in the ventral horn of the spinal cord, which elicit muscle contraction. Once adequate contraction is achieved, stretch reflexes become deactivated, completing this feedback loop. Active tone can be assessed with the pull-to-sit maneuver in infants. The infant is slowly pulled up to a sitting position. Under normal circumstances, the elbows will flex and the neck will raise the head (a normal feedback system with muscle contraction). In cases of hypotonia, the head will lag backward during the pull-to-sit and once the infant is in a sitting position, the head will fall forward (altered feedback system with no muscle contraction). Postnatally, muscle cells increase in size, which correlates with progressively increasing muscle strength. Simultaneously, myelination of sensory (afferent) pathways modulates maturation of the motor cortex. The cumulative result is progressive maturation of neuromuscular feedback loops and muscle strength (Verklan & Walden, 2015; Volpe et al., 2018).

Passive tone refers to muscle resistance to passive movements during manipulation; passive tone wanes as active tone increases. Passive motor tone is appraised during the birth hospitalization and remains evident during the first few months of life. Careful assessment of tone can alert the clinician to areas of weakness (hypotonia). Wrist (square window) and knee (popliteal angle) flexibility is an assessment of neuromuscular response to extensor stretch reflex responses and muscle tone of the arms and legs. Similarly, flexor muscle tone at the shoulder is assessed by way of the "scarf sign." Competency of stretch reflexes at the posterior hip flexor muscle are measured by way of the heel-to-ear maneuver. Facial muscle competency is appraised visually. Weakness in the arms, legs, and facial regions informs the location of injury and pathogenesis of neonatal hypotonia. Central injuries occur above the lower motor neuron, whereas anterior horn cell injuries, peripheral nerve injuries, neuromuscular junction injuries, and muscle injuries occur below the lower motor neuron (Verklan & Walden, 2015; Volpe et al., 2018).

TABLE 3.9 Hypotonia as a Manifestation of Common Problems

System	Primary Disease Process
CNS	Hypoxic–ischemic encephalopathy, bilirubin-induced neurologic dysfunction, meningitis, encephalitis, motor neuron lesions, cerebellar lesions and palsies, spinal nerve and muscle disorders
Respiratory	Congenital hypothyroidism, cerebral palsy, teratogenesis
Gastrointestinal	Dehydration, hyperbilirubinemia
Metabolic/Endocrine	Hypoglycemia, hypermagnesemia, inborn errors of metabolism
Immune	Sepsis
Genetic	22q13 deletion syndrome, achondroplasia, CHARGE syndrome, Down syndrome, trisomy 18, trisomy 21, fragile X syndrome, Marfan's syndrome, myotonic dystrophy[*], Noonan syndrome, Prader–Willi syndrome, Smith–Lemli Opitz syndrome, Williams syndrome, Zellweger syndrome
Other	Maternal autoimmune disorders[*]

[*]**NOTE:** Myotonic dystrophy is the most common inherited disorder associated with progressive muscle wasting and weakness. Myasthenia gravis is the most common maternal autoimmune disorder associated with neonatal hypotonia.

CHARGE, coloboma, heart defects, atresia choanae (choanal atresia), growth retardation, genital abnormalities, and ear abnormalities; CNS, central nervous system.

Sources: Bass, N., Lotze, T. E., & Miller, G. (2015). Hypotonia and neuromuscular disease in the neonate. In R. J. Martin, A. A. Fanaroff, & M. C. Walsh (Eds.), *Fanaroff and Martin's neonatal-perinatal medicine: Diseases of the fetus and infant* (10th ed., pp. 950–963). Philadelphia, PA: Elsevier Mosby; Ditzenberger, G. R., & Blackburn, S. T. (2014). Neurologic system. In C. Kenner & J. W. Lott (Eds.), *Comprehensive neonatal nursing care* (5th ed., pp. 393-437). New York, NY: Springer Publishing; Natarajan, N. & Ionita, C. (2018). Neonatal neuromuscular disorders. In C. A. Gleason & S. E. Juul (Eds.), *Avery's diseases of the newborn* (10th ed., pp. 952–960). Philadelphia, PA: Elsevier; Sparks, E. S. (2015). Neonatal hypotonia. *Clinics in Perinatology, 42*(2), 363–371. doi:10.1016/j.clp.2015.02.008; Verklan, M. T., & Walden, M. (2015). *Core curriculum for neonatal intensive care nursing* (5th ed.). St. Louis, MO: Elsevier; Volpe, J. J., Inder, T. E., Darras, B. T., de Vries, L. S., du Plessis, A. J., Neil, J. J., & Perlman, J. M. (2018). *Volpe's neurology of the newborn* (6th ed.). Philadelphia, PA: Saunders Elsevier.

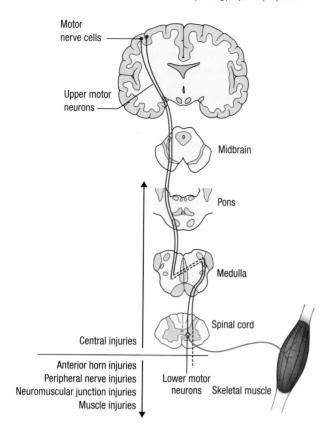

Figure 3.23 Upper and lower motor neurons.

Central hypotonia implies a primary problem within the CNS and may manifest with seizures or hemiparesis. Disorders of the anterior horn cells involve dysfunction of motor neurons and commonly manifest with hypotonia paired with tongue fasciculations and areflexia; sensory system function is unaffected. Peripheral nerve disorders involve a reduction in motor nerve conduction, most often caused by reduced or absent myelination to peripheral nerves; sensory function is absent. Neuromuscular junction disorders involve altered communication (synapses) between motor neurons and skeletal muscle fibers. Muscle disorders impose muscle weakness, as the name suggests (Ahmed, Igbal, & Hussain, 2016; Volpe et al., 2018).

Ultimately, in order to reverse or decrease muscle function, treatment must be directed toward correcting the primary, underlying problem. As such, life-span implications correlate with the primary problem. Hypotonia in tandem with central disorders is associated with neurodevelopmental impairment (Volpe et al., 2018).

Seizures. Neonatal seizures are one of the most commonly observed homeostatic agonists in the neonatal period. Seizures occur in approximately 58 per 100 births (very-low-birth-weight infants) and 1 to 3.5 per 100 live births among term infants (Volpe et al., 2018). Experts caution that incidence rates are merely estimations, as poor interrater reliability, reporting

mechanisms, and hospital settings may affect these rates (Scher, 2015). Major risk factors are summarized in Table 3.10.

Several mechanisms increase the likelihood for seizures and include (a) failed ATP-pump activity, (b) an excess of excitatory neurotransmitters, (c) a deficiency of inhibitory neurotransmitters, or (d) an inherited inborn error of metabolism (Volpe et al., 2018). Failed ATP-pump activity disrupts membrane potential. Excessive amounts of excitatory neurotransmitters provoke increased depolarization. Gamma-aminobutyric acid (GABA), which functions in an exclusive inhibitory capacity in the adult brain, functions in both capacities in the neophyte brain. Furthermore, levels of inhibitory GABA fall short of excitatory GABA levels in the neonatal brain; inhibitory GABA transmitters are also permeable to calcium (Scher, 2015; Volpe et al., 2018).

The pathway evoked during a neonatal seizure, activated to metabolize energy as a means to compensate for energy expenditure, is summarized in Figure 3.24. After reviewing that pathway, it becomes clear that glucose is a significant necessity during a seizure. However, available supply may not match the demand; therefore, insufficient energy metabolism is one mechanism for injury. Other consequences of seizures that are correlated with injury include (a) hypoventilation, (b) hypertension, and (c) increased release of excitatory amino acids (Volpe et al., 2018). Hypoventilation and apnea are commonly observed during prolonged seizures. This causes hypoxia and hypercarbia, which can decrease CBF and provoke injury. Alternatively, hypertension has also been observed, which can increase CBF and increase the risk for IVH with resulting seizures. Excessive release of amino acids (glutamate) serves as a noxious stimulant, similar to the noxious effect that GABA receptors impose preseizure, and may provoke injury.

TABLE 3.10 Risk Factors for Onset of Neonatal Seizures

- Asphyxia
- Benign familial origin
- Congenital brain malformations
- Congenital infections
- Hypocalcemia
- Hypoglycemia
- Inborn errors of metabolism
- Neonatal abstinence syndrome
- Neonatal stroke

Sources: Scher, M. S. (2013). Brain disorders of the fetus and neonate. In A. A. Fanaroff & J. M. Fanaroff (Eds.), *Klaus & Fanaroff's care of the high-risk neonate* (6th ed., pp. 476–524). Philadelphia, PA: Elsevier Mosby; Scher, M. S. (2015). Seizures in neonates. In R. J. Martin, A. A. Fanaroff, & M. C. Walsh (Eds.), *Fanaroff and Martin's neonatal-perinatal medicine: Diseases of the fetus and infant* (10th ed. pp. 927-949). Philadelphia, PA: Elsevier Mosby; Volpe, J. J., Inder, T. E., Darras, B. T., de Vries, L. S., du Plessis, A. J., Neil, J. J., & Perlman, J. M. (2018). *Volpe's neurology of the newborn* (6th ed.). Philadelphia, PA: Saunders Elsevier.

Seizures may be visible yet undetectable on EEG (clinical only), visible and detectable on EEG (electroclinical), or not clinically visible yet detectable on EEG (Tsuchida et al., 2013). The types of seizures that may be observed among neonates include subtle (most common), clonic, myoclonic, and tonic seizures. These seizures may be focal, multifocal, or generalized (Table 3.11). Life-span implications of neonatal seizures are related to the primary problem responsible for precipitating the seizures. Commonly reported

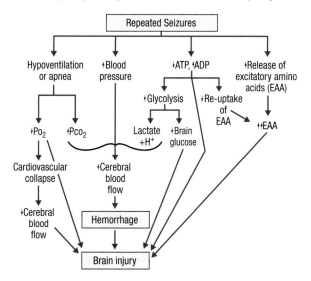

Figure 3.24 Energy metabolism.

Source: Adapted from Volpe, J. J., Inder, T. E., Darras, B. T., de Vries, L. S., du Plessis, A. J., Neil, J. J., & Perlman, J. M. (Eds.). (2018). *Volpe's neurology of the newborn* (6th ed.). Philadelphia, PA: Saunders Elsevier.

consequences include intellectual disability, cerebral palsy, motor deficits, and epilepsy (Scher, 2015; Volpe et al., 2018).

CONCLUSION

The nervous system is one of the most complex and integrated systems in the human body; it communicates with other body systems to maintain physiologic homeostasis. Postnatal neurologic function is largely dependent on a process of systematic and uncomplicated embryologic and fetal development. Environmental and genetic factors, along with maternal health influences, may lead to alterations in embryologic development resulting in lifelong neurologic sequelae. Fetal neurologic development begins with primary neurulation (week 3 of gestation) and continues in sequence with prosencephalic differentiation, neuronal proliferation and migration (complete by 24 weeks), glial proliferation and migration, neuronal organization and migration (complete in early childhood), and neuronal myelination (complete in adulthood). The sequential process is most vulnerable during the first and second trimesters of fetal development; alterations may lead to disorders of early brain development (e.g., anencephaly, encephalocele, spina bifida, congenital hydrocephalus, microcephaly). Cerebral vascular injuries (e.g., intraventricular and ICH, cerebral artery infarction, PVL) may result in a wide range of mild to severe neurodevelopmental short- and long-term complications. Other neurologic complications (e.g., seizures, hypotonia) may further affect long-term prognoses and prove a management challenge for families and healthcare providers following discharge from the neonatal intensive care unit.

TABLE 3.11 Types of Seizures and Associated Clinical Manifestations

Type	Common Clinical Manifestations
Clonic[b]	*Focal:* Rhythmic jerking movements of face, upper/lower extremities (bilateral), or neck/trunk (unilateral) *Multifocal:* Rhythmic jerking movements of two or more body parts *Generalized:* Bilateral and symmetric synchronous movements
Myoclonic[b, c]	*Myoclonic:* Rapid, focal jerking of one or more muscle groups (commonly in upper extremities); may or may not be ictal *Multifocal:* Irregular twitching *Generalized:* Bilateral jerking with flexion of upper limbs
Subtle[a, b]	Lip smacking, fluttering of one or both eyelids, horizontal eye deviation, excessive drooling, episodes of apnea or bradycardia, and abnormal extremity movements (such as stepping, leg rowing, and pedaling motions)
Tonic[b]	*Focal:* Prolonged posturing of one body part (arm, leg, neck, or trunk) *Generalized:* Extension of upper and lower limbs, flexion of upper limb with extension of lower limb

NOTE: [a]These seizures are most common; [b]seizures are clinically evident; [c] these seizures are associated with epilepsy.

Source: Volpe, J. J., Inder, T. E., Darras, B. T., de Vries, L. S., du Plessis, A. J., Neil, J. J., & Perlman, J. M. (2018). *Volpe's neurology of the newborn* (6th ed.). Philadelphia, PA: Saunders Elsevier.

LEARNING TOOLS AND RESOURCES

Podcasts

 Infant Sleep-Wake Pattern

Jenna Meredith and Amy J. Jnah

Discussion Prompts

1. A former 24-week gestation infant, now 6 weeks old, receives a routine cranial ultrasound. Multiple periventricular cysts are noted on coronal view ultrasound imaging, consistent with periventricular leukomalacia (PVL). Explain the relationship between PVL and spastic diplegia, the most common clinical sequela, and the effect upon the infant across the life span.

2. Recent research has shown that the environment in which the premature infant is exposed has influences on growth and development of the nervous system. The current standard of care for neonatal intensive care unit design is the single family room; however, there are many open-bay style NICUs that still exist. Discuss the advantages of the single family room design, and which standard of care practices could be implemented into the open-bay style NICU in order to achieve best neurodevelopmental outcome.

Advice From the Authors

"The neonatal nurse practitioner journey is filled with peaks and valleys. Stay true to your goals and avoid letting the low points stop you. Remember, the journey is a marathon, not a sprint. Pace yourself and use the time to explore your potential."

–Curry Bordelon, DNP, MBA, APRN, NNP-BC, CPNP-AC

"As you make this unique journey to become a neonatal nurse practitioner remember your 'why.' Remember why you began and what it means to you and this special population. When you get discouraged have faith and know that mistakes are necessary for growth and success. I encourage you to persevere through this challenging journey, continue to have a passion for learning, and be confident in who you are and what you will accomplish!"

–Bresney Fanning, MSN, APRN, NNP-BC

"It is the hard work, feeling of success, and ability to help others that makes this career great. Never give up on a dream just because it is hard, or because of the time required to accomplish it."

–Jenna Meredith, MSN, APRN, NNP-BC

"The study of neuroanatomy is incredibly interesting. I suggest that you begin by seeking to understand the process of brain development and anatomic location of each major structure. Then, explore pathways, such as key somatosensory pathways, the major hypothalamic-end organ pathways, and CSF and blood flow pathways. This will help you recognize and understand the pathogenesis of various common diseases. I always encourage learners to go slowly, and draw these structures or concepts on paper. In addition, verbally explain them to other advanced practice nurses while in the hospital setting (test yourself!). Accept the short-term feeling of vulnerability (knowledge gap) as an opportunity for growth!"

–Amy J. Jnah, DNP, APRN, NNP-BC

Mind Maps

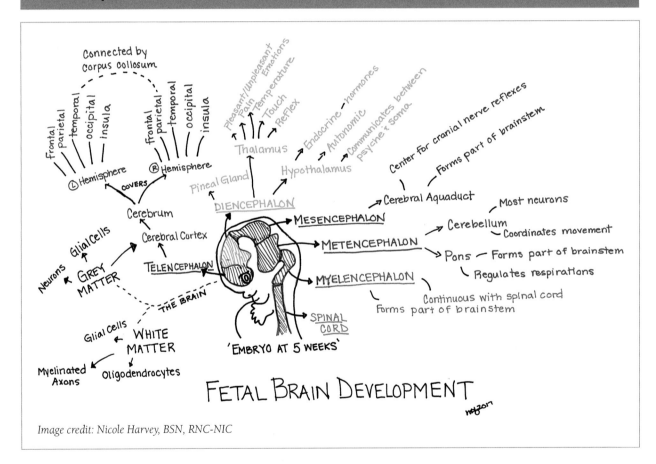

Image credit: Nicole Harvey, BSN, RNC-NIC

Note: This mind map reflects one student's interpretation of a portion of one or more concepts addressed in this chapter. Readers should regard the mind maps woven throughout this textbook as examples of multi-sensory study tools that can be developed to encourage conceptual understanding. Readers are encouraged to develop their own unique mind maps in consultation with academic faculty or clinical preceptors.

TIMELINE OF ORGAN DEVELOPMENT

NOTE:
Placement of common problems is meant to offer visual/conceptual perspective on the timing of onset of these commonly reported malformations. Variation exists across the literature.

LEGEND
<22 – 27 6/7 weeks = extremely preterm
28 – 31 6/7 weeks = very preterm
32 – 36 6/7 weeks = late/moderate preterm
37 – 40 weeks = term

References

Aa, N., Benders, M., Groenendaal, F., & Vries, L. (2014). Neonatal stroke: A review of the current evidence on epidemiology, pathogenesis, diagnostics and therapeutic options. *Acta Paediatrica, 103*(4), 356–364. doi:10.1111/apa.12555

Abramowicz, A., & Gos, M. (2014). Neurofibromin in neurofibromatosis type 1 mutations in NF1 gene as a cause of disease. *Developmental Period Medicine, 18*(3), 297–306. Retrieved from https://www.ncbi.nlm.nih.gov/pubmed/25182393

Ahmed, M. I., Iqbal, M., & Hussain, N. (2016). A structured approach to the assessment of a floppy neonate. *Journal of Pediatric Neurosciences, 11*(1), 2–6. doi:10.4103/1817-1745.181250

Alberts, B. (2015). *Molecular biology of the cell* (6th ed.). New York, NY: Garland Science, Taylor and Francis.

American College of Obstetricians and Gynecologists. (2017). *Neural tube defects* (ACOG Practice Bulletin No. 187). Washington, DC: Author. Retrieved from https://www.acog.org/Resources-And-Publications/Practice-Bulletins-List

Anand, K. J. S., & Campbell-Yeo, M. (2015). Consequences of prenatal opioid use for newborns. *Acta Paediatrica, 104*(11), 1066–1069. doi:10.1111/apa.13121

Armstrong-Wells, J., Johnston, S. C., Wu, Y. W., Sidney, S., & Fullerton, H. J. (2009). Prevalence and predictors of perinatal hemorrhagic stroke: Results from the Kaiser pediatric stroke study. *Pediatrics, 123*(3), 823–828. doi:10.1542/peds.2008-0874

Austin, T. (2012). 104 cerebral autoregulation in the newborn. *Archives of Disease in Childhood, 97*(Suppl. 2), A29. doi:10.1136/archdischild-2012-302724.0104

Back, S. A., & Miller, S. P. (2018). Brain injury in the preterm infant. In C. A. Gleason & S. E. Juul (Eds.), *Avery's diseases of the newborn* (10th ed., pp. 879–896). Philadelphia, PA: Elsevier.

Barbas, H. (2015). General cortical and special prefrontal connections: Principles from structure to function. *Annual Review of Neuroscience, 38*(1), 269–289. doi:10.1146/annurev-neuro-071714-033936

Bass, N., Lotze, T. E., & Miller, G. (2015). Hypotonia and neuromuscular disease in the neonate. In R. J. Martin, A. A. Fanaroff, & M. C. Walsh (Eds.), *Fanaroff and Martin's neonatal-perinatal medicine: Diseases of the fetus and infant* (10th ed., pp. 950–963). Philadelphia, PA: Elsevier Mosby.

Bennet, L., Booth, L. C., Drury, P. P., Quaedackers, J. S., & Gunn, A. J. (2012). Preterm neonatal cardiovascular instability: Does understanding the fetus help evaluate the newborn? *Clinical and Experimental Pharmacology and Physiology, 39*(11), 965–972. doi:10.1111/j.1440-1681.2012.05744.x

Bernson-Leung, M. E., & Rivkin, M. J. (2016). Stroke in neonates and children. *Pediatrics in Review, 37*(11), 463–477. doi:10.1542/pir.2016-0002

Boron, W. F., & Boulpaep, E. L. (2017). *Medical physiology* (3rd ed.). Philadelphia, PA: Elsevier.

Brew, N., Walker, D., & Wong, F. Y. (2014). Cerebral vascular regulation and brain injury in preterm infants. *American Journal of Physiology. Regulatory, Integrative and Comparative Physiology, 306*(11), R773–R786. doi:10.1152/ajpregu.00487.2013

Brinker, T., Stopa, E., Morrison, J., & Klinge, P. (2014). A new look at cerebrospinal fluid circulation. *Fluids and Barriers of the CNS, 11*, 10. doi:10.1186/2045-8118-11-10

Brown, T. I., Uncapher, M. R., Chow, T. E., Eberhardt, J. L., & Wagner, A. D. (2017). Cognitive control, attention, and the other race effect in memory. *PLoS One, 12*(3), e0173579. doi:10.1371/journal.pone.0173579

Bruno, C. J., Beslow, L. A., Witmer, C. M., Vossough, A., Jordan, L. C., Zelonis, S., … Smith, S. E. (2013). Haemorrhagic stroke in term and late preterm neonates. *Archives of Diseases in Childhood, Fetal and Neonatal Edition, 99*(1), F48–F53. doi:10.1136/archdischild-2013-304068

Campbell, C., Levin, S., Siu, V. M., Venance, S., & Jacob, P. (2013). Congenital myotonic dystrophy: Canadian population-based surveillance study. *Journal of Pediatrics, 163*(1), 120–125. doi:10.1016/j.jpeds.2012.12.070

Canavese, F., & Dimeglio, A. (2013). Normal and abnormal spine and thoracic cage development. *World Journal of Orthopedics, 4*(4), 167–174. doi:10.5312/wjo.v4.i4.167

Carlson, B. M. (2014). *Human embryology and developmental biology* (5th ed.). Philadelphia, PA: Elsevier/Saunders.

Cassidy, S. B., & Driscoll, D. J. (2009). Prader–Willi syndrome. *European Journal of Human Genetics, 17*(1), 3–13. doi:10.1038/ejhg.2008.165

Cassidy, S. B., Schwartz, S., Miller, J. L., & Driscoll, D. J. (2012). Prader–Willi syndrome. *Genetics in Medicine, 14*(1), 10–26. doi:10.1038/gim.0b013e31822bead0

Centers for Disease Control and Prevention. (n.d.). Spina bifida: Data and statistics in the United States. Retrieved from https://www.cdc.gov/ncbddd/spinabifida/data.html

Centers for Disease Control and Prevention. (2016). Facts about microcephaly. Retrieved from https://www.cdc.gov/ncbddd/birthdefects/microcephaly.html

Centers for Disease Control and Prevention. (2017a). Facts about anencepaly. Retrieved from https://www.cdc.gov/ncbddd/birthdefects/anencephaly.html#ref

Centers for Disease Control and Prevention. (2017b). Marijuana use and pregnancy. Retrieved from https://www.cdc.gov/healthcommunication/toolstemplates/entertainmented/tips/marijuana-pregnancy.html

Centers for Disease Control and Prevention. (2018a). Alcohol and pregnancy questions and answers. Retrieved from https://www.cdc.gov/ncbddd/fasd/faqs.html

Centers for Disease Control and Prevention. (2018b). Fragile X syndrome (FXS). Retrieved from https://www.cdc.gov/ncbddd/fxs/facts.html

Chatterton, Z., Hartley, B. J., Seok, M., Mendelev, N., Chen, S., Milekic, M., … Haghighi, F. (2017). In utero exposure to maternal smoking is associated with DNA methylation alterations and reduced neuronal content in the developing fetal brain. *Epigenetics & Chromatin, 10*(1), e1–e11. doi:10.1186/s13072-017-0111-y

Chen, H. (2012). *Atlas of genetic diagnosis and counseling* (2nd ed.). New York, NY: Springer Verlag.

Cinalli, G., Mirone, G., Spennato, P., & Nastro, A. (n.d.). Aqueductal stenosis in children. Retrieved from https://www.ispn.guide/hydrocephalus-and-other-anomalies-of-csf-circulation-in-children/aqueductal-stenosis-in-children-homepage

Cinalli, G., Spennato, P., Nastro, A., Aliberti, F., Trischitta, V., Ruggiero, C., … Cianciulli, E. (2011). Hydrocephalus in aqueductal stenosis. *Childs Nervous System, 27*(10), 1621–1642. doi:10.1007/s00381-011-1546-2

Cole, L., Dewey, D., Letourneau, N., Kaplan, B. J., Chaput, K., Gallagher, C., …Kirton, A. (2017). Clinical characteristics, risk factors, and outcomes associated with neonatal hemorrhagic stroke: a population-based case-control study. *JAMA*

Pediatrics, 171(3), 230–238. doi:10.1001/jamapediatrics.2016.4151

Copel, J. (2018). *Obstetric imaging: Fetal diagnosis and care E-book* (2nd ed.). Philadelphia, PA: Elsevier.

Cornelissen, M., Ottelander, B., Rizopoulos, D., van der Hulst, R., Mink van der Molen, A. M., van der Horst, C., … Mathijssen, I. (2016). Increase of prevalence of craniosynostosis. *Journal of Cranio-Maxillofacial Surgery, 44*(9), 1273–1279. doi:10.1016/j.jcms.2016.07.007

D'Apolito, K. C. (2014). Assessing neonates for neonatal abstinence: Are you reliable? *Journal of Perinatal & Neonatal Nursing, 28*(3), 220–231. doi:10.1097/JPN.0000000000000056

D'Apolito, K. (2016). Neonatal abstinence syndrome: A growing problem. *Neonatal Network, 35*(5), 263–264. doi:10.1891/0730-0832.35.5.263

Davidson, M. R., London, M. L., & Ladewig, P. A. (2012). *Olds' maternal–newborn nursing & women's health across the lifespan* (9th ed.). Upper Saddle River, NJ: Pearson.

Dekker, G. (2011). Hypertension. In D. James, P. Steer, C. Weiner, & B. Gonik (Eds.), *High risk pregnancy: Management options* (4th ed.). St. Louis, MO: Elsevier.

Devakumar, D., Bamford, A., Ferreira, M. U., Broad, J. M., Rosch, R. E., Groce, N., … & Abubakar, I. (2017). Infectious causes of microcephaly: Epidemiology, pathogenesis, diagnosis, and management. *Lancet Infectious Diseases, 18*(1), e1–e13. doi:10.1016/S1473-3099(17)30398-5

de Vries, L. S. (2015). Intracranial hemorrhage and vascular lesions in the neonate. In R. J. Martin, A. A. Fanaroff, & M. C. Walsh (Eds.), *Fanaroff and Martin's neonatal–perinatal medicine: Diseases of the fetus and infant* (10th ed., pp. 886–903). Philadelphia, PA: Elsevier Mosby.

Ditzenberger, G. R., & Blackburn, S. T. (2014). Neurologic system. In C. Kenner & J. W. Lott (Eds.), *Comprehensive neonatal nursing care* (5th ed., pp. 393–437). New York, NY: Springer Publishing.

Duderstadt, K. (2014). *Pediatric physical examination* (2nd ed.). St. Louis, MO: Elsevier.

Dumont, V., Bulla, J., Bessot, N., Gonidec, J., Zabalia, M., Guillois, B., & Roche-Labarbe, N. (2017). The manual orienting response habituation to repeated tactile stimuli in preterm neonates: Discrimination of stimulus locations and interstimulus intervals. *Developmental Psychobiology, 59*(5), 590–602. doi:10.1002/dev.21526

Echenne, B., & Bassaz, G. (2013). Congenital and infantile myotonic dystrophy. *Handbook of Clinical Neurology, 113*, 1387–1393. doi:10.1016/B978-0-444-59565-2.00009-5

Elgamal, E. A. (2012). Natural history of hydrocephalus in children with spinal open neural tube defect. *Surgical Neurology International, 3*, 112. doi:10.4103/2152-7806.101801

Evans, K. N., Hing, A. V., & Cunningham, M. L. (2018). Craniofacial malformations. In C. A. Gleason & S. E. Juul (Eds.), *Avery's diseases of the newborn* (10th ed., pp. 1417–1437). Philadelphia, PA: Elsevier.

Fields, R. D., Araque, A., Johansen-Berg, H., Lim, S., Lynch, G., Nave, K., … Wake, H. (2014). Glial biology in learning and cognition. *Neuroscientist, 20*(5), 426–431. doi:10.1177/1073858413504465

Fleiss, B., Stolp, H., Mezger, V., & Gressens, P. (2018). Central nervous system development. In C. A. Gleason & S. E. Juul (Eds.), *Avery's diseases of the newborn* (10th ed., pp. 852–856). Philadelphia, PA: Elsevier.

Forray, A., & Foster, D. (2015). Substance use in the perinatal period. *Current Psychiatry Reports, 17*(11), 1–11. doi:10.1007/s11920-015-0626-5

Garne, E., Loane, M., Addor, M. C., Boyd, P. A., Barisic, I., & Dolk, H. (2010). Congenital hydrocephalus—Prevalence, prenatal diagnosis and outcome of pregnancy in four European regions. *European Journal of Paediatric Neurology, 14*(2), 150–155. doi:10.1016/j.ejpn.2009.03.005

Govil-Dalela, T., Kumar, A., Agarwal, R., & Chugani, H. T. (2017). Agenesis of the corpus callosum and Aicardi syndrome: A neuroimaging and clinical comparison. *Pediatric Neurology, 68*, 44–48. doi:10.1016/j.pediatrneurol.2016.12.002

Gressens, P., & Huppi, P. S. (2015). Intracranial hemorrhage and vascular lesions in the neonate. In R. J. Martin, A. A. Fanaroff, & M. C. Walsh (Eds.), *Fanaroff and Martin's neonatal–perinatal medicine: Diseases of the fetus and infant* (10th ed., pp. 836–853). Philadelphia, PA: Elsevier Mosby.

Gulati, I. K., Shubert, T. R., Sitaram, S., Wei, L., & Jadcherla, S. R. (2015). Effects of birth asphyxia on the modulation of pharyngeal provocation-induced adaptive reflexes. *American Journal of Physiology. Gastrointestinal and Liver Physiology, 309*(8), G662–G669. doi:10.1152/ajpgi.00204.2015

Haldeman-Englert, C. R., Saitta, S. C., & Zackai, E. H. (2018). Chromosome disorders. In C. A. Gleason & S. E. Juul (Eds.), *Avery's diseases of the newborn* (10th ed., pp. 211–223). Philadelphia, PA: Elsevier.

Hall, J. E. (2016). *Guyton and Hall textbook of medical physiology* (13th ed.). Philadelphia, PA: Elsevier.

Heller, M., & Burd, L. (2014). Review of ethanol dispersion, distribution, and elimination from the fetal compartment. *Birth Defects Research Part A: Clinical and Molecular Teratology, 100*(4), 277–283. doi:10.1002/bdra.23232

Hernández-Martínez, C., Voltas Moreso, N., Ribot Serra, B., Arija Val, V., Escribano Macías, J., & Canals Sans, J. (2017). Effects of prenatal nicotine exposure on infant language development: A cohort follow up study. *Maternal and Child Health Journal, 21*(4), 734–744. doi:10.1007/s10995-016-2158-y

Hielkema, T., & Hadders-Algra, M. (2016). Motor and cognitive outcome after specific early lesions of the brain—A systematic review. *Developmental Medicine and Child Neurology, 58*(Suppl. 4), 46–52. doi:10.1111/dmcn.13047

Ho, G., Cardamone, M., & Farrar, M. (2015). Congenital and childhood myotonic dystrophy: Current aspects of disease and future directions. *World Journal of Clinical Pediatrics, 4*(4), 66–80. doi:10.5409/wjcp.v4.i4.66

Huang, S. B., & Doherty, D. (2018). Congenital malformations of the central nervous system. In C. A. Gleason & S. E. Juul (Eds.), *Avery's diseases of the newborn* (10th ed., pp. 857–878). Philadelphia, PA: Elsevier.

Ignatavicius, D. D., & Workman, M. L. (2016). *Medical–surgical nursing patient centered collaborative care* (8th ed., Vol. 2). St. Louis, MO: Elsevier.

Jablonska, B., Gierdalski, M., Chew, L., Hawley, T., Catron, M., Lichauco, A., … Gallo, V. (2016). Sirt1 regulates glial progenitor proliferation and regeneration in white matter after neonatal brain injury. *Nature Communications, 7*, 13866. doi:10.1038/ncomms13866

Jaques, S. C., Kingsbury, A., Henshcke, P., Chomchai, C., Clews, S., Falconer, J., … Oei, J. L. (2014). Cannabis, the pregnant woman and her child: Weeding out the myths. *Journal of Perinatology: Official Journal of the California Perinatal Association, 34*(6), 417–424. doi:10.1038/jp.2013.180

Jones, K. L., Jones, M. C., & Casanelles, M. D. C. (2013). *Smith's recognizable patterns of human malformation* (7th ed.). Philadelphia, PA: Elsevier Saunders.

Katsianou, M. A., Adamopoulos, C., Vastardis, H., & Basdra, E. K. (2016). Signaling mechanisms implicated in cranial sutures pathophysiology: Craniosynostosis. *BBA Clinical, 6*, 165–176. doi:10.1016/j.bbacli.2016.04.006

Kent, A. L., Wright, I. M., & Abdel-Latif, M. E. (2012). Mortality and adverse neurologic outcomes are greater in preterm male infants. *Pediatrics, 129*(1). 124–131. doi:10.1542/peds.2011-1578

Kerr, L. M., & Huether, S. E. (2014). Alterations of neurologic function in children. In K. L. McCance & S. E. Huether (Eds.), *Pathophysiology: The biologic basis for disease in adults and children* (7th ed., pp. 660–680). St. Louis, MO: Elsevier.

Kratzer, I., Chip, S., & Vexler, Z. S. (2014). Barrier mechanisms in neonatal stroke. *Frontiers in Neuroscience, 8*, 359. doi:10.3389/fnins.2014.00359

Lalande, M., & Calciano, M. A. (2007). Molecular epigenetics of Angelman syndrome. *Cellular and Molecular Life Science, 64*(7-8), 947–960. doi:10.1007/s00018-007-6460-0

Lee, T. C., & Mukundan, S., Jr. (2015). Brainstem and cranial nerves. In T. C. Lee, S. Mukundan, Jr., & F. H. Netter (Eds.), *Netter's correlative imaging: Neuroanatomy* (pp. 175–271). Philadelphia, PA: Elsevier Saunders.

Leong, J. K., Pestilli, F., Wu, C. C., Samanez-Larkin, G. R., & Knutson, B. (2016). White-matter tract connecting anterior insula to nucleus accumbens correlates with reduced preference for positively skewed gambles. *Neuron, 89*(1), 63–69. doi:10.1016/j.neuron.2015.12.015

Markowitz, J. A., Singh, P., & Darras, B. T. (2012). Spinal muscular atrophy: A clinical and research update. *Pediatric Neurology, 46*(1), 1–12. doi:10.1016/j.pediatrneurol.2011.09.001

McAllister, J. P. (2012). Pathophysiology of congenital and neonatal hydrocephalus. *Seminars in Fetal & Neonatal Medicine, 17*(5), 285. doi:10.1016/j.siny.2012.06.004

ZMertz, L. G., Christensen, R., Vogel, I., Hertz, J. M., Nielsen, K. B., Gronskov, K., & Ostergaard, J. R. (2013). Angelman syndrome in Denmark. Birth incidence, genetic findings, and age at diagnosis. *American Journal of Medical Genetics. Part A, 161A*(9), 2197–2203. doi:10.1002/ajmg.a.36058

Moore, K. L., Persaud, T. V. N., & Torchia, M. G. (2016). *The developing human: Clinically oriented embryology* (10th ed.). Philadelphia, PA: Elsevier.

Muscular Dystrophy Association. (n.d.). Spinal muscle atrophy. Retrieved from https://www.mda.org/disease/spinal-muscular-atrophy

Natarajan, N., & Ionita, C. (2018). Neonatal neuromuscular disorders. In C. A. Gleason & S. E. Juul (Eds.), *Avery's diseases of the newborn* (10th ed., pp. 952–960). Philadelphia, PA: Elsevier.

National Birth Defects Prevention Network. (2016). Congenital microcephaly. Retrieved from https://www.nbdpn.org/docs/NBDPN_Case_Definition_-_Surveillance_Microcephaly_2016Feb28_Final_DRAFT.pdf

National Institute on Alcohol Abuse and Alcoholism. (2017). Alcohol & your health. Retrieved from https://www.niaaa.nih.gov/alcohol-health

National Institutes of Health. (2018a). Genetics home reference: Angelman syndrome. Retrieved from https://ghr.nlm.nih.gov/condition/angelman-syndrome#statistics

National Institutes of Health. (2018b). Genetics home reference: Down syndrome. Retrieved from https://ghr.nlm.nih.gov/condition/down-syndrome#statistics

National Institutes of Health. (2018c). Genetics home reference: Neurofibromatosis type 1. Retrieved from https://ghr.nlm.nih.gov/condition/neurofibromatosis-type-1#sourcesforpage

National Institutes of Health. (2018d). Genetics home reference: Prader–Willi syndrome. Retrieved from https://ghr.nlm.nih.gov/condition/prader-willi-syndrome

National Institutes of Health. (2018e). Genetics home reference: Spina bifida. Retrieved from https://ghr.nlm.nih.gov/condition/spina-bifida

National Institutes of Health. (2018f). Genetics home reference: Spinal muscle atrophy. Retrieved from https://ghr.nlm.nih.gov/condition/spinal-muscular-atrophy#statistics

National Institutes of Health. (2018g). Genetics home reference: Trisomy 18. Retrieved from https://ghr.nlm.nih.gov/condition/trisomy-18#statistics

National Organization for Rare Disorders. (2018a). Trisomy 13 syndrome. Retrieved from https://rarediseases.org/rare-diseases/trisomy-13-syndrome/#references

National Organization for Rare Disorders. (2018b). Agenesis of corpus callosum. Retrieved from https://rarediseases.org/rare-diseases/agenesis-of-corpus-callosum

National Organization for Rare Disorders. (2018c). Dandy–Walker malformation. Retrieved from https://rarediseases.org/rare-diseases/dandy-walker-malformation

Neil, J. J., & Inder, T. E. (2018). Neonatal neuroimaging. In C. A. Gleason & S. E. Juul (Eds.), *Avery's diseases of the newborn* (10th ed., pp. 922–951). Philadelphia, PA: Elsevier.

Neu, N., Duchon, J., & Zachariah, P. (2015). TORCH infections. *Clinical Perinatology, 42*(1), 77–103. doi:10.1016/j.clp.2014.11.001

Ogino, S., & Wilson, R. B. (2004). Spinal muscular atrophy: Molecular genetics and diagnostics. *Expert Review of Molecular Diagnostics, 4*(1), 15–29. doi:10.1586/14737159.4.1.15

O'Keeffe, L. M., Greene, R. A., & Kearney, P. M. (2014). The effect of moderate gestational alcohol consumption during pregnancy on speech and language outcomes in children: A systematic review. *Systematic Reviews, 3*(1), 1–11. doi:10.1186/2046-4053-3-1

Palanisamy, A. (2012). Maternal anesthesia and fetal neurodevelopment. *International Journal of Obstetric Anesthesia, 21*(2), 152–162. doi:10.1016/j.ijoa.2012.01.005

Papile, L.-A., Burstein, J., Burstein, R., & Koffler, H. (1978). Incidence and evolution of subependymal and intraventricular hemorrhage: A study of infants with birth weights less than 1,500 gm. *Journal of Pediatrics, 92*(4). 529–534. doi:10.1016/S0022-3476(78)80282-0

Parker, S. E., Mai, C. T., Canfield, M. A., Rickard, R., Wang, Y., Meyer, R. E., … Correa, A. (2010). Updated National Birth Prevalence estimates for selected birth defects in the United States, 2004–2006. *Birth Defects, Research and Clinical Molecular Teratology, 88*(12), 1008–1016. doi:10.1002/bdra.20735

Parsons, J. A, Seay, A. R., & Jacobson, M. (2016). Neurologic disorders. In S. L. Gardner, B. S. Carter, M. Enzman-Hines, & J. A. Hernandez (Eds.), *Merenstein & Gardner's handbook of neonatal intensive care* (7th ed. pp. 727–762). St. Louis, MO: Elsevier Saunders.

Patrick, S. W., Schumacher, R. E., Benneyworth, B. D., Krans, E. E., McAllister, J. M., & Davis, M. M. (2012). Neonatal abstinence syndrome and associated health care expenditures: United States, 2000–2009. *Journal of the American Medical Association, 307*(18), 1934–1940. doi:10.1001/jama.2012.3951

Patton, K. (2015). *Anatomy and physiology* (9th ed.). St. Louis, MO: Elsevier.

Pekçetin, S., Aki, E., Üstünyurt, Z., & Kayihan, H. (2016). The efficiency of sensory integration interventions in preterm infants. *Perceptual and Motor Skills, 123*(2), 411–423. doi:10.1177/0031512516662895

Persson, E.-K., Hagberg, G., & Uvebrant, P. (2006). Disabilities in children with hydrocephalus—A population-based study of children aged between four and twelve years. *Neuropediatrics, 37*(6), 330–336. doi:10.1055/s-2007-964868

Petersen, I., Collings, S. L., McCrea, R. L., Nazareth, I., Osborn, D. P., Cowen, P. J., & Sammon, C. J. (2017). Antiepileptic drugs prescribed in pregnancy and prevalence of major congenital malformations: Comparative prevalence studies. *Clinical Epidemiology, 9*, 95–103. doi:10.2147/CLEP.S11833

Pina-Garza, J. E. (2013). *Fenichel's clinical pediatric neurology* (7th ed.). New York, NY: Elsevier.

Piontelli, A. (2010). *Development of normal fetal movements: The first 25 weeks of gestation.* Milan, Italy: Springer Verlag.

Powley, T. L. (2013). Central control of autonomic functions: Organization of the autonomic nervous system. In L. R. Squire (Ed.), *Fundamental neuroscience* (4th ed., pp. 729–747). Boston, MA: Elsevier/Academic Press.

Purger, D., Gibson, E. M., & Monje, M. (2016). Myelin plasticity in the central nervous system. *Neuropharmacology, 110*, 563–573. doi:10.1016/j.neuropharm.2015.08.001

Radoš, M., Orešković, D., Radoš, M., Jurjević, I., & Klarica, M. (2014). Long lasting near-obstruction stenosis of mesencephalic aqueduct without development of hydrocephalus—Case report. *Croatian Medical Journal, 55*(4), 394–398. doi:10.3325/cmj.2014.55.394

Raspa, M., Wheeler, A. C., & Riley, C. (2017). Public health literature review of fragile X syndrome. *Pediatrics, 139* (Suppl. 3), S153–S171. doi:10.1542/peds.2016-1159C

Raybaud, C. (Ed.), Normal and abnormal embryology and development of the intracranial vascular system. *Neurosurgery Clinics of North America, 21*(3), 399–426. doi:10.1016/j.nec.2010.03.011

Riera, J., Cabañas, F., Serrano, J. J., Bravo, M. C., López-Ortego, P., Sánchez, L., … Pellicer, A. (2014). New time-frequency method for cerebral autoregulation in newborns: Predictive capacity for clinical outcomes. *Journal of Pediatrics, 165*(5), 897–902.e1. doi:10.1016/j.jpeds.2014.06.008

Robinson, S., & Cohen, A. R. (2015). Myelomeningocele and related neural tube defects. In R. J. Martin, A. A. Fanaroff, & M. C. Walsh (Eds.), *Fanaroff and Martin's neonatal–perinatal medicine: Diseases of the fetus and infant* (10th ed., pp. 990–992). Philadelphia, PA: Elsevier Mosby.

Rosenthal, C. R., & Soto, D. (2016). The anatomy of nonconscious recognition memory. *Trends in Neurosciences, 39*(11), 707–711. doi:10.1016/j.tins.2016.09.005

Rouzer, S. K., Cole, J. M., Johnson, J. M., Varlinskaya, E. I., & Diaz, M. R. (2017). Moderate maternal alcohol exposure on gestational day 12 impacts anxiety-like behavior in offspring. *Frontiers in Behavioral Neuroscience, 11*(183), 1–13. doi:10.3389/fnbeh.2017.00183

Rubenstein, J., & Rakic, P. (Eds.). (2013). *Cellular migration and formation of neuronal connections: Comprehensive developmental neuroscience.* New York, NY: Academic Press.

Saunders, N. R., Dreifuss, J.-J., Dziegielewska, K. M., Johansson, P. A., Habgood, M. D., Møllgård, K., & Bauer, H.-C. (2014). The rights and wrongs of blood–brain barrier permeability studies: A walk through 100 years of history. *Frontiers in Neuroscience, 8*, 404. doi:10.3389/fnins.2014.00404

Saunders, N. R., Liddelow, S. A., & Dziegielewska, K. M. (2012). Barrier mechanisms in the developing brain. *Frontiers in Pharmacology, 3*, 46. doi:10.3389/fphar.2012.00046

Scher, M. S. (2013). Brain disorders of the fetus and neonate. In A. A. Fanaroff & J. M. Fanaroff (Eds.), *Klaus & Fanaroff's care of the high-risk neonate* (6th ed,, pp. 476–524). Philadelphia, PA: Elsevier Mosby.

Scher, M. S. (2015). Seizures in neonates. In R. J. Martin, A. A. Fanaroff, & M. C. Walsh (Eds.), *Fanaroff and Martin's neonatal-perinatal medicine: Diseases of the fetus and infant* (10th ed., pp. 927–949). Philadelphia, PA: Elsevier Mosby.

Schoenwolf, G. C., Bleyl, S. B., Brauer, P. R., & Francis-West, P. H. (2015). *Larsen's human embryology* (5th ed.). Philadelphia, PA: Churchill Livingstone.

Schwaller, F., Kanellopoulos, A. H., & Fitzgerald, M. (2017). The developmental emergence of differential brainstem serotonergic control of the sensory spinal cord. *Scientific Reports, 7*, 1. doi:10.1038/s41598-017-02509-2

Sehgal, A. (2011). Perinatal stroke: A case-based review. *European Journal of Pediatrics, 171*(2), 225–234. doi:10.1007/s00431-011-1509-3

Sekhon, M. S., Ainslie, P. N., & Griesdale, D. E. (2017). Clinical pathophysiology of hypoxic ischemic brain injury after cardiac arrest: a "two-hit" model. *Critical care (London, England), 21*(1), 90. doi:10.1186/s13054-017-1670-9

Shankaran, S., Lin, A., Maller-Kesselman, J., Zhang, H., O'Shea, T. M., Bada, H. S.,…Ment, L. R. (2014). Maternal race, demography, and health care disparities impact risk for intraventricular hemorrhage in preterm neonates. *Journal of Pediatrics, 164*(5), 1005–1011. doi:10.1016/j.jpeds.2014.01.036

Sibai, B. M. (2012). Hypertension. In S. G. Gabbe, J. R. Niebyl, & J. L. Simpson (Eds.), *Obstetrics: Normal and problem pregnancies* (6th ed., pp. 661–705). Philadelphia, PA: Elsevier.

Smith, A. D., & Buckley, M. G. (2012). Spatial navigational impairments in hydrocephalus. *Cognitive Process, 13*(Suppl. 1): 329–332. doi:10.1007/s10339-0120505-5

Som, P. M., & Naidich, T. P. (2013). Development of the skull base and calvarium: An overview of the progression from mesenchyme to chondrification to ossification. *Neurographics, 3*(4), 169–184. doi:10.3174/ng.4130069

Sparks, E. S. (2015). Neonatal hypotonia. *Clinics in Perinatology, 42*(2), 363–371. doi:10.1016/j.clp.2015.02.008

Stanojevic, M., Kurjak, A., Salihagić-Kadić, A., Vasilj, O, Miskovic, B., Shaddad, A. N., … Tomasović, S. (2011). Neurobehavioral continuity from fetus to neonate. *Journal of Perinatal Medicine, 39*(2), 171–177. doi:10.1515/JPM.2011.004

Stover, M. W., & Davis, J. M. (2015). Opioids in pregnancy and neonatal abstinence syndrome. *Seminars in Perinatology, 39*(7), 561–565. doi:10.1053/j.semperi.2015.08.013

Szpecht, D., Szymankiewicz, M., Nowak, I., & Gadzinowski, J. (2016). Intraventricular hemorrhage in neonates born before 32 weeks of gestation—Retrospective analysis of risk factors. *Child's Nervous System, 32*, 1399–1404. doi:10.1007/s00381-016-3127-x

Takakuwa, T., Koike, T., Muranaka, T., Uwabe, C., & Yamada, S. (2016). Formation of the circle of Willis during human embryonic development. *Congenital Anomalies, 56*(5), 233. doi:10.1111/cga.1216

Tsen, L. R. (2011). Neuraxial analgesia and anesthesia in obstetrics. In D. James, P. Steer, C. Weiner, & B. Gonik (Eds.), *High risk pregnancy: Management options* (4th ed., pp. 1211–1229). St. Louis, MO: Elsevier Saunders.

Tsuchida, T. N., Wusthoff, C. F., Shellhaas, R. A., Abend, N. S., Hahn, C. D., Sullivan, J. E., … Clancy, R. R. (2013). American Clinical Neurophysiology Society standardized EEG terminology and categorization for the description of continuous EEG monitoring in neonates: Report of the American Clinical Neurophysiology Society critical care monitoring committee. *Journal of Clinical Neurophysiology, 30*(2), 161-173. doi:10.1097/WNP.0b013e3182872b24

Tully, H. M., & Dobyns, W. B. (2014). Infantile hydrocephalus: A review of epidemiology, classification and causes. *European Journal of Medical Genetics, 57*(8), 359–368. doi:10.1016/j.ejmg.2014.06.002

Twigg, S. R. F., & Wilkie, A. O. M. (2015). A genetic-pathophysiological framework for craniosynostosis. *American Journal of Human Genetics, 97*(3), 359–377. doi:10.1016/j.ajhg.2015.07.006

Vall, O., Salat-Batlle, J., & Garcia-Algar, O. (2015). Alcohol consumption during pregnancy and adverse neurodevelopmental outcomes. *Journal of Epidemiology and Community Health, 69*(10), 927–929. doi:10.1136/jech-2014-203938

van Merendonk, E. J. J. M., Brouwers, J. J. W. M., De Catte, L., Hasaerts, D., Nijhuis-van der Sanden, M. W. G., & Kerckhofs, E. (2017). Identification of prenatal behavioral patterns of the gross motor movements within the early stages of fetal development. *Infant and Child Development, 26*(5), e1–15. doi:10.1002/icd.2012

Vanderah, T. W., Gould, D. J., & Nolte, J. (2016). *Nolte's the human brain: An introduction to its functional anatomy* (7th ed.). Philadelphia, PA: Elsevier.

Verklan, M. T. (2015). Neurologic disorders. In M. T. Verklan & M. Walden (Eds.), *Core curriculum for neonatal intensive care nursing* (5th ed., pp. 734–766). St. Louis, MO: Elsevier Saunders.

Verklan, M. T., & Walden, M. (2015). *Core curriculum for neonatal intensive care nursing* (5th ed.). St. Louis, MO: Elsevier.

Vohr, B. R., Davis, E. P., Wanke, C. A., & Krebs, N. F. (2017). Neurodevelopment: The impact of nutrition and inflammation during preconception and pregnancy in low-resource settings. *Pediatrics, 139*(Suppl. 1), S38–S49. doi:10.1542/peds.2016-2828F

Volkow, N. D., Compton, W. M., & Wargo, E. M. (2017). The risks of marijuana use during pregnancy. *Journal of the American Medical Association, 317*(2), 129–130. doi:10.1001/jama.2016.18612

Volpe, J. J., Inder, T. E., Darras, B. T., de Vries, L. S., du Plessis, A. J., Neil, J. J., & Perlman, J. M. (2018). *Volpe's neurology of the newborn* (6th ed.). Philadelphia, PA: Saunders Elsevier.

Vutskits, L., & Wolf, A. (2014). Cerebral blood flow in the neonate. *Pediatric Anesthesia, 24*(1), 22–29. doi:10.1111/pan.12307

Wandell, B. A. (2016). Clarifying human white matter. *Annual Review of Neuroscience, 39*(1), 103–128. doi:10.1146/annurev-neuro-070815-013815

Watzlawik, J. O., Kahoud, R. J., O'Toole, R. J., White, K. A. M., Ogden, A. R., Painter, M. M., … Rodriguez, M. (2015). Abbreviated exposure to hypoxia is sufficient to induce CNS dysmyelination, modulate spinal motor neuron composition, and impair motor development in neonatal mice. *PLoS One, 10*(5), 1–24. doi:10.1371/journal.pone.0128007

Westmacott, R., MacGregor, D., Askalan, R., & deVeber, G. (2009). Late emergence of cognitive deficits after unilateral neonatal stroke. *Stroke, 40*(6), 2012–2019. doi:10.1161/STROKEAHA.108.533976

Whitelaw, A., Osredkar, D., & Thoresen, M. (2016). Neurological and neuromuscular disorders. In M. G. MacDonald & M. M. K. Seshia (Eds.), *Neonatology: Pathophysiology and management of the newborn* (6th ed.). Philadelphia, PA: Lippincott Williams & Wilkins.

Williams, C. A., Driscoll, D. J., & Dagli, A. I. (2010). Clinical and genetic aspects of Angelman syndrome. *Genetics in Medicine, 12*(7), 385–395. doi:10.1097/GIM.0b013e3181def138

Winn, H. R. (2017). *Youmans and Winn neurological surgery* (7th ed.). Philadelphia, PA: Elsevier.

Wu, C., Honarmand, A. R., Schnell, S., Kuhn, R., Schoeneman, S. E., Ansari, S. A., Carr, J., Markl, M., … Shaibani, A. (2016). Age-Related Changes of Normal Cerebral and Cardiac Blood Flow in Children and Adults Aged 7 Months to 61 Years. *Journal of the American Heart Association, 5*(1), e002657. doi:10.1161/JAHA.115.002657

Wu, C.-S., Jew, C. P., & Lu, H.-C. (2011). Lasting impacts of prenatal cannabis exposure and the role of endogenous cannabinoids in the developing brain. *Future Neurology, 6*(4), 459–480.

Wu, Q., Liu, J., Fang, A., Li, R., Bai, Y., Kriegstein, A. R., & Wang, S. (2014). The dynamics of neuronal migration. *Advances in Experimental Medicine and Biology, 800*, 25–36. doi:10.1007/978-94-007-7667-6_2

Yuskaitis, C. J., & Pomeroy, S. L. (2017). Development of the nervous system. In R. J. Polin, S. H. Abman, D. H. Rowtich, & W. W. Fox (Eds.), *Fetal and neonatal physiology* (5th ed., pp. 1294–1313). Philadelphia, PA: Elsevier.

4

THE RESPIRATORY SYSTEM

Janice L. Wilson and Jennifer Fitzgerald

LEARNING OBJECTIVES

After completing this chapter, the reader should be able to:

- Understand normal respiratory organ development.
- Analyze the physiologic function of the fetal and postnatal respiratory systems.
- Discuss common inherited disorders and their effect on fetal and neonatal respiratory system development and function.
- Identify maternal health conditions that have a potential impact on fetal and postnatal respiratory system development and function.
- Evaluate common disorders that affect the respiratory system and their implications across the life span.

INTRODUCTION

Respiratory morbidities are some of the most common challenges facing neonatal healthcare providers, and they can have a lasting impact beyond infancy into childhood and adult life. This chapter will discuss lung morphogenesis, the genetic drivers of lung development, fetal and neonatal lung function, common neonatal lung disorders, and long-term sequelae of neonatal lung disease.

TIMELINE OF ORGAN DEVELOPMENT

The respiratory system is one of the most complex of all organ systems. Structural development of the pulmonary system is well understood; however, the processes that drive the regulation of lung morphogenesis are less refined. Studies in mice have assisted in the process of generating new knowledge related to human lung morphogenesis.

The respiratory system is anatomically divided into separate entities: the upper respiratory tract (nose and nasal cavity, pharynx, and larynx) and the lower respiratory tract (trachea, bronchi, and lungs). Therefore, a review of embryologic development could progress in an anatomically minded fashion, organized by each supporting structure. However, the respiratory system does not develop in this manner. Rather, development occurs across gestation, from the early embryonic period through early adulthood. This normal progression is described using five phases of sequential development: the embryonic, pseudoglandular, canalicular, saccular, and alveolar phases (Figure 4.1). Therefore, our review of the developing respiratory system will use this approach, which offers rising clinicians an opportunity to make connections between timing of normal and aberrant development from early embryologic development to birth, and identify the effect of interrupted development (premature birth) on postnatal respiratory function.

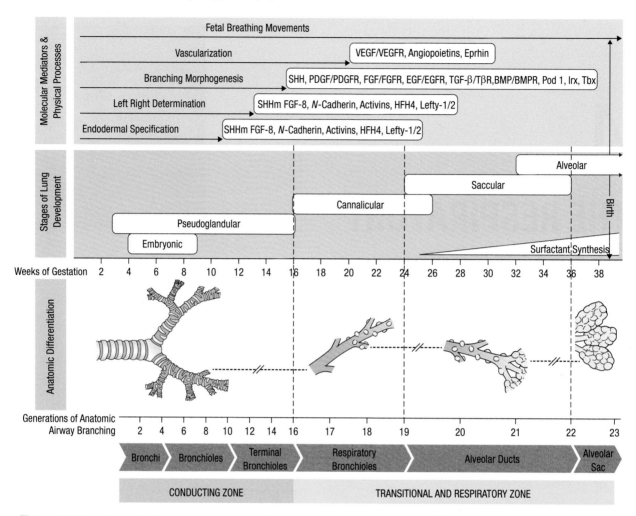

Figure 4.1 Five phases of pulmonary development. Morphogenic development is mediated by molecular mediators (transcription factors, polypeptides) and physical processes (fetal breathing movements). Like the systemic and pulmonary circulations, as the lungs progress through generations of branching, the number of branches increases yet their diameter and length progressively decrease. Airflow velocity decreases as air reaches the most distal bronchioles. Respiratory function is possible beginning at 22 to 23 weeks of gestation.

BMP, bone morphogenetic proteins; BMPR, bone morphogenetic protein receptor; FGF, fibroblast growth factor; FGFR, fibroblast growth factor receptor; HFH4, forkhead homologue hepatocyte nuclear family protein; Irx, Iroquois-complex homeobox family members; Lefty-1/2, genes that help determine left-right determination; PDGF, platelet derived growth factor; PDGFR, platelet derived growth factor receptor; Pod-1, basic helix-loop-helix proteins; SHH, sonic hedgehog; Tbx, Tbox family proteins; TGF-β, transforming growth factor-β; TβR, transforming growth factor-β activating receptor; TGF-β receptor; VEGF, vascular endothelial growth factor; VEGFR, vascular endothelial growth factor receptor

Sources: Adapted from Copland, I., & Post, M. (2004). Lung development and fetal lung growth. *Paediatric Respiratory Reviews, 5,* (Suppl. 1), S259-S264. doi:10.1016/S1526-0542(04)90049-8; Wu, S. (2012). Molecular bases for lung development, injury, and repair. In E. Bancalari & R. A. Polin (Eds.), *The newborn lung: Neonatology questions and controversies* (2nd ed., pp. 3–16) Philadelphia, PA: Elsevier Saunders.

Embryonic Phase

Respiratory development begins with formation of the lung bud, or laryngotracheal (respiratory) diverticulum, during week 4 of gestation (Moore, Persaud, & Torchia, 2016; Sadler, 2015). The formation of the bud is facilitated by increases in retinoic acid (RA) levels, synthesized from the nearby mesoderm, which trigger the upregulation of transcription factor TBX4. TBX4 initiates the formation (and later growth and differentiation) of the lung bud, and later facilitates formation of the diaphragm (Moore et al., 2016; Sadler, 2015).

The lung bud undergoes a process of elongation. As it stretches, it invaginates into a network of embryonic connective tissue (splanchnic mesenchyme) within the mesoderm (Sadler, 2015; Whitsett, Wert, & Weaver, 2015). This prompts proliferation of the bud, from a single primitive bud into one composed of two outpouchings. The bud thereby grows laterally, into the pericardioperitoneal canals that will give rise to pleural cavities during later development (Moore et al., 2016). Now that invagination is complete, an intricate process of folding ensues, resulting in formation of the tracheoesophageal septum. This occurs during week 5 of gestation. As the septum proliferates, it divides the foregut into two separate entities: (a) the trachea and (b) the esophagus (Moore et al., 2016). Failed septation is associated with tracheoesophageal communications, or fistulas.

Next, the trachea begins to lengthen in a cephalocaudal fashion along its vertical axis, forming rudimentary right and left bronchi. Over time, the right main bronchus will grow slightly longer than the left, a pragmatic development to accommodate the superior, middle, and inferior lobes on that right side (Moore et al., 2016). Lengthening continues, and the right and left primary bronchi give rise to secondary bronchi, which thereby give rise to lower lobar, segmental, and intrasegmental branches. These branches then further divide into rudimentary upper, middle, and lower lobes (right side), and upper and lower lobes (left side). These lobar bronchi and rudimentary lung branches continue an intricate process of subdivision and branching throughout the greater portion of fetal development.

Cartilaginous plates form from the surrounding splanchnic mesenchyme and become the bronchial smooth muscle and connective tissue, as well as the pulmonary connective tissue and capillaries. In addition, cartilaginous tracheal rings and lobar airways form. This occurs between weeks 5 and 7 of gestation. In total, this early embryonic period of lung development establishes the anatomic framework, which enables a myriad of maturational developments seen across the remaining pseudoglandular, canalicular, saccular, and alveolar stages of development.

Pseudoglandular Phase

The pseudoglandular phase, which occurs between weeks 6 and 16 of gestation, involves continued, intricate airway branching (Moore et al., 2016). Segmental airways form by week 6 of gestation and subsegmental bronchi are noted by week 7 of gestation (Kallapur & Jobe, 2015). It is interesting to note that the bronchi arise from epithelial buds that are surrounded by mesenchyme. This gives the immature lung a "glandular-like" appearance and explains the label "pseudoglandular" for this phase (Moore et al., 2016).

The tips of the epithelial buds also give rise to all of the other diverse types of cells found in the developing bronchi and bronchioles. Cartilage appears between weeks 9 and 10 of gestation. Ciliated cells (responsible for the development of cilia that move debris within the airways), goblet cells (responsible for mucus production), and basal cells (responsible for the formation of a barrier against environmental damage) arise during week 13 of gestation (Kallapur & Jobe, 2015; Universities of Fribourg, Lausanne, & Bern, Switzerland, 2006). Simple columnar cells begin to accumulate within the lining of the terminal bronchioles between weeks 12 and 13 of gestation. These cells will participate in respiration and gas exchange, once fully formed (Moore et al., 2016). By the end of the pseudoglandular period, all the major components of the lung are formed, with the exception of structures involved in gas exchange (Moore et al., 2016).

Canalicular Phase

The canalicular phase of development begins during the final week of the pseudoglandular phase, and extends between weeks 16 and 26 of gestation (Moore et al., 2016). The terminal bronchioles continue to give rise to respiratory bronchioles, whereas the pulmonary vasculature continues to rapidly proliferate (Moore et al., 2016; Wu, 2012). By week 20, primitive type I pneumocytes, the primary structural cell of the alveolus, are observed. Concurrently, lamellar bodies, surfactant storage repositories, appear within primitive type II alveolar cells. During week 24 of gestation, the acini, a berry-like clustering of cells at the distal ends of respiratory bronchioles, develop. These give rise to primitive alveolar ducts and saccules (Moore et al., 2016). In addition, capillaries derived from the mesenchyme form and surround the acini. This marks the establishment of the primitive air-fluid interface for future gas exchange.

Saccular Phase

The saccular phase occurs between weeks 24 and 36 of gestation (Moore et al., 2016). Sparse clusters of thin-walled saccules appear at the ends of the distal respiratory bronchioles and form primitive alveolar ducts (Wu, 2012). Ridges form along the walls of the ducts and form crests comprised of elastin and muscle tissue. As they proliferate, the ridges develop indentations, which give rise to cup-shaped alveolar sacs (Whitsett & Xu, 2016). As more alveolar sacs develop, the barrier between the epithelium and the endothelium stretches and thins, permitting the exchange of oxygen and carbon dioxide. This establishes the primitive air–fluid interface (Moore et al., 2016).

By week 26 of gestation, type I and type II pneumocytes are present in the distal airways. Type I pneumocytes modulate gas exchange, whereas type II pneumocytes are responsible for the synthesis and secretion of surfactant. Surfactant synthesis and secretion begins, and as a result, surfactant accumulates along the interior walls of the alveolar sacs. Over time, as surfactant synthesis and secretion increases, surface tension (also known as collapsing pressure) along the alveolus decreases. This keeps the alveolar sacs expanded and capable of air exchange. Failed secretion of surfactant, by way of premature birth or a genetically inherited type of surfactant deficiency, can precipitate respiratory distress syndrome and, in some cases, death.

Alveolar Phase

The alveolar phase of development begins at approximately week 32 of gestation and extends into early childhood (age 8; Moore et al., 2016). This stage marks a shift in lung capability from secretory organ to one capable of gas exchange. Saccular septation, or secondary septation, begins at the end of each respiratory bronchiole. This process of septation permits the formation of larger clusters of primordial alveolar sacs. Throughout the third trimester, these sacs produce increasing amounts of surfactant and transitions the fetal lungs away from exclusive dependence upon the placenta, to a state of readiness for independent postnatal gas exchange.

At birth (term gestation), the majority of alveoli (95%) are immature (primordial). These primordial alveoli are uniquely capable of stimulating the production of additional primitive alveoli, which allow for continued alveolar expansion and maturation after birth and through early childhood. Children are considered fully affixed with mature alveoli, incapable of regeneration, by age 8; any pathological issues incurred during fetal or postnatal life may alter alveolar development and increase the risk for chronic respiratory problems (Moore et al., 2016).

Development of the Pulmonary Vasculature

The pulmonary vasculature initially appears within the splanchnic mesenchyme during the embryonic phase, in tandem with proliferation of lung buds. This vascular plexus forms from the sixth aortic arch and moves caudally toward the developing lung bud (Sadler, 2015). Shortly thereafter, circulatory networks arise, modulated by the processes of angiogenesis, vasculogenesis, and fusion. Angiogenesis prompts vascular proliferation from preexisting vessels. Vasculogenesis results in the formation of blood vessels from angioblasts and endothelial precursor cells (Wu, 2012). The fusion of the distal and proximal vessels completes the framework for this circulatory network. Though not definitive, it is likely that angiogenic and vasculogenic processes are responsible for both proximal and distal blood vessel development (Wu, 2012).

Vascular development is influenced by three families of growth factors: vascular endothelial growth factor (VEGF), angiopoietin, and the Ephrin (Eph) families (Alvira, 2016; Baker & Abman, 2015; Le Cras & Rabinovitch, 2016). The *VEGF signaling system* has been implicated in the early stages of vasculogenesis and may play an important role in later angiogenesis, vascular maintenance, and survival during the adult years (Le Cras & Rabinovitch, 2016). The *angiopoietin system* appears to be critical for the successful remodeling and stabilization of embryonic vessels and may facilitate blood vessel responsiveness to VEGF (Alvira, 2016; Baker & Abman, 2015; Le Cras & Rabinovitch, 2016). The *Eph family of growth factors* influence vascular proliferation in the latter stages of pulmonary vascular development (Le Cras & Rabinovitch, 2016). Additional factors involved in

vascular development include factors found in the extracellular matrix (fibronectin laminin, type IV collagen) as well as platelet-derived growth factor (PDGF).

Over time, the pulmonary vasculature differentiates into the pulmonary and bronchial vascular systems. The pulmonary vascular system is responsible for directing blood into the alveolar capillary network for oxygenation, and likewise responsible for directing blood out of the network through the pulmonary veins and into heart (Wu, 2012). The bronchial vascular system is responsible for supplying oxygen and nutrients to portions of the lungs not directly involved in gas exchange, including the bronchial walls and perihilar regions (Wu, 2012).

The Pharyngeal Apparatus

Pharyngeal Arches. Before discussing the development of the facial region, which is particularly significant to both respiratory and gastrointestinal function (see Chapter 6), a review of their derivatives is indicated. The six pharyngeal arches, also known as *branchial arches*, arise during week 4 of gestation. Each arch is initially composed of mesenchyme from two of the primitive germ layers, the endoderm and ectoderm. They remain relatively static until innervated by neural crest cells, after which the arches begin increasing in size. The six arches and their major skeletal derivatives are provided in Table 4.1.

Pharyngeal Pouches. While the pharyngeal gut proliferates, the aforementioned brachial and pharyngeal arches become separated by brachial and pharyngeal clefts and form four pharyngeal pouches (Sadler, 2015). The first pouch gives rise to the middle ear, tympanic membrane, and Eustachian tube. The second pouch forms tonsils and lymph nodes. The third pouch gives rise to the thymus and inferior parathyroid gland, whereas the fourth pouch develops into the superior parathyroid glands and the parafollicular cells of the thyroid (Schoenwolf, Bleyl, Brauer, & Francis-West, 2015).

Other Structures That Influence Respiratory Development and Function

Nose and Nasal Cavity. The nose develops concurrent with facial development. Two genes, *SHH* and *FGF-8*, modulate this process (Moore et al., 2016). During week 4 of gestation, the first pair of pharygneal arches give rise to five facial prominences. The frontonasal prominence gives rise to the forehead, nasal bridge, and septum. The maxillary prominence gives rise to the cheeks and lateral portion of the upper lip. The medial nasal prominence forms the philtrum of the upper lip, crest, and tip of the nose, while the lateral nasal prominence forms the alae (sides of the nose). Finally, the mandibular prominence forms the lower lip (Sadler, 2015).

Specific to nasal development, nasal placodes (embryonic structures that give rise to the nose) appear during

TABLE 4.1. The Pharyngeal Arches			
Pharyngeal Arch	Cranial Nerve Innervation	Primary Muscular Function	Skeletal Derivatives
1	V	Mastication	• Maxilla • Mandible • Incus • Malleus of middle ear • Meckel's cartilage • Tympanic ring
2	VII	Facial expression	• Stapes • Temporal styloid process • Hyoid
3	IX	Swallowing, elevation of larynx and pharynx	• Inferior parathyroid glands • Thymus
4	X	Pharyngeal and laryngeal muscle function	• Superior parathyroid glands • Epiglottis cartilage
6	X	Pharyngeal and laryngeal muscle function	• Cricoid cartilage • Arytenoid cartilages • Comiculate cartilage • Cuneiform cartilages

NOTE: The fifth pharyngeal arch is considered a rudimentary structure and regresses early in fetal development. The stylopharyngeus muscle is an internal muscle of the pharynx.

week 5 of gestation and invaginate, under the influence of platelet-derived growth factor PDGF) alpha polypeptide, to form nasal pits. In doing so, the placodes create a ridge of tissue surrounding each nasal pit, which forms nasal prominences (similar to facial prominences). The nasal prominences fuse with the maxillary prominences to form the nose, while the nasal pits mature into nasal sinuses. Of note, as the maxillary and nasal prominences fuse, a groove forms on either side of the developing nose, into the nasolacrimal duct and nasolacrimal sac. As the nasal pits continue to develop, an oronasal membrane (primary choana) separates each nasal pit from the primitive oral cavity (Sadler, 2015). The choana resides on each side of midline, behind the primary palate. During week 7 of gestation, the oronasal membrane ruptures, bringing the nasal and oral cavities into communication. As development continues, the secondary palate forms and separates the oral and nasal cavities. With these developments, the choana shifts to a definitive position, at the junction of the nasal cavity and pharynx (nasopharynx).

Errors in nasal development, in particular those which encourage anatomical closure of the posterior choanae, can lead to choanal atresia. Impaired RA downregulation of FGF-8 may explain the emergence of this relatively rare disease (Kwong, 2015). In addition, failed development of the secondary palate may give rise to cleft palate, offering a continuous communication between the nasal and oral passages.

The Larynx. Larynx development begins during week 4 of gestation, at the cranial end of the laryngotracheal tube, from the fourth and sixth pairs of pharyngeal pouches. Rapid cellular proliferation and differentiation between weeks 4 and 9 of gestation initially occludes the larynx; however, later organization during week 10 of gestation allows for recanalization and room for vocal cord development (Moore et al., 2016). The larynx initially assumes a high anatomic position during fetal and postnatal development. This allows the epiglottis to establish contact with the soft palate and create a functional separation between the respiratory and digestive tracts. This early positioning explains the obligatory nasal-breathing pattern common to newborns. In addition, clinicians should note that this functional separation encourages postnatal oral feeding proficiency (coordination) by deterring aspiration (Moore et al., 2016). Normal descent of the larynx to its adult position is complete by 2 years of age, whereby infants switch from nasal to oral breathing as their primary mode of respiration.

Pleural Development. As the lungs develop within the mesenchyme, they develop two layers of pleura, or serous membranes (Moore et al., 2016). This begins during week 5 of gestation, with both layers of pleura (parietal and visceral) established by week 6 of gestation (Moore et al., 2016). The parietal pleura develops as a single layer of mesothelial cells supported by connective tissue and lines the thoracic wall and diaphragm. This serves as the outer membrane and, as a result, maintains direct communication with intercostal arteries and lymphatic vessels, as well as the intercostal and phrenic nerves. The visceral pleura covers the lungs and extends into each fissure while maintaining direct communication with the bronchial circulation. The pleural cavity is a space that forms between the two pleurae described earlier. This space is separated from the peritoneal cavity by a pleuroperitoneal membrane (Universities of Fribourg, Lausanne, & Bern, Switzerland, 2006). The pleural cavity is a hollowed out, yet narrow space composed of pleural fluid. During respiration, the pleurae should smoothly glide along each other's exterior surface. Any accumulation of air into the pleural space, which may occur due to changes in the elasticity of the thoracic wall or lungs, may cause a pneumothorax.

Diaphragm. Diaphragm development in rodent models suggests multiple gene involvement, but that process is not as clear in humans. Many of the genes implicated play a critical role in lung morphogenesis, and studies in humans suggest an abnormality in the RA pathway (Ameis, Khoshgoo, & Keijzer, 2017).

The diaphragm develops from four separate embryonic structures: the septum transversum, the pleuroperitoneal membranes, the dorsal esophageal mesentery, and the body wall. The septum transversum first appears as a thick mesodermal layer and develops into an incomplete wall that forms between the thoracic and abdominal cavities (Moore et al., 2016). The septum transversum most likely supplies the scaffolding for the continued development of the diaphragm (Ameis et al., 2017). Large openings in the septum on both sides of the esophagus remain and become the pericardioperitoneal canals. The septum fuses with the dorsal mesentery of the esophagus and the pleuroperitoneal membranes (Moore et al., 2016). This process of fusion creates the primitive diaphragm. As the lungs and pleural cavities grow, they extend into the body walls, and the body wall tissue separates into an internal and an external layer. The internal layer becomes the peripheral parts of the diaphragm, and the external layer becomes part of the abdominal wall (Moore et al., 2016).

Surfactant Development

Surfactant is first seen in fetal lung fluid at the end of the canalicular phase of development, and increases significantly across the last 2 weeks of gestation. Surfactant is critical to normal alveolar stabilization and function. Its synthesis and secretion are modulated by type II pneumocytes and involves the breakdown, clearance, reuptake, and reprocessing of its phospholipid and protein components (Whitsett et al., 2015).

Surfactant is primarily composed of phospholipids (80%), proteins (10%), and fats (10%; Figure 4.2; Kallapur & Jobe, 2015; Weaver, Nogee, & Jobe, 2016;

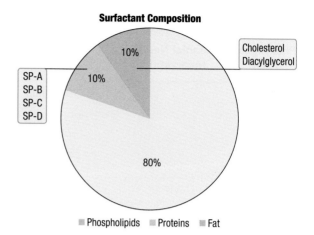

Figure 4.2 Surfactant composition.

SP, surfactant protein.

Whitsett et al., 2015). Numerous different phospholipids account for the majority of surfactant's composition; however, we will highlight three significant phospholipids in this discussion. Phosphatidylcholine (PC) is the major phospholipid in surfactant, accounting for 80% of all phosopholipids contained within surfactant molecules. The second most prevalent phospholipid is phosphatidylglycerol (PG). PG contributes to maintaining the stability of the alveolar membrane and holds a role in the immune response (Agassandian & Mallampalli, 2013; Kültürsay, Uygur, & Yalaz, 2014). Dipalmitoylphosphatidylcholine (DPPC) is the primary surface-active phospholipid and is directly responsible for reducing surface tension (Kallapur & Jobe, 2015; Whitsett et al., 2015).

Four proteins, namely, surfactant proteins (SP) A, B, C, and D (SP-A, SP-B, SP-C, SP-D), contribute to the composition of surfactant molecules. SP-B and SP-C are hydrophobic and important for the disbursement of surfactant within the alveolus. SP-B is critical for the formation of the lamellar bodies within the type II pneumocyte, and because of this, deficiencies in SP-B synthesis and secretion will lead to abnormal SP-C processing. The remaining two surfactant proteins, SP-A and SP-D, are important for the function of the host defense immune system. SP-A activates macrophages within the alveolus. SP-D binds to specific lipid and carbohydrate structures on the cell wall of invading bacteria, virus, fungi, and protozoa (Whitsett et al., 2015). See Table 4.2 for a summary of specific surfactant protein functions. Of note, neonates with gene mutations affecting SP-B production manifest with severe respiratory distress syndrome that often progresses to death unless lung transplantation is performed (this will be discussed later in the chapter; Whitsett et al., 2015). This type of surfactant deficiency is extremely rare.

The synthesis, secretion, metabolism, and recycling of surfactant is slower in newborns, especially preterm neonates, given the decreased number and relative immaturity

TABLE 4.2. Surfactant Proteins: Overview and Availability		
Surfactant Protein Type	**Overview of Function**	**Available in Commercial Surfactant Preparations**
SP-A	Regulator of lung inflammation; binds to bacterial and viral pathogens; facilitates phagocytosis and clearance of surfactant	No
SP-B	Facilitates lipid absorption and reduction in surface tension along with SP-C; complete SP-B deficiency leads to respiratory failure and death	Yes
SP-C	Works in conjunction with SP-B to facilitate lipid absorption and decreasing surface tension	Yes
SP-D	Regulator of lung inflammation; binds to bacterial and viral pathogens; facilitates phagocytosis and clearance of pathogens	No

SP, surfactant proteins.

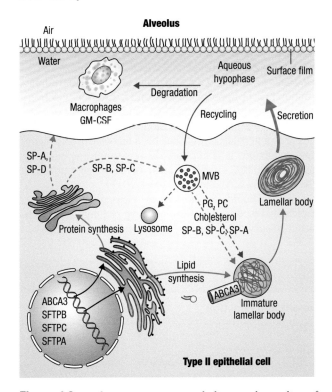

Figure 4.3 Synthesis, secretion, metabolism, and recycling of surfactant.

GM-CSF, granulocyte-macrophage colony-stimulating factor; MVB, multivesicular bodies; PC, phosphatidylcholine; PG, prostaglandin; SP, surfactant protein

of alveoli and type II pneumocytes (Figure 4.3; Akella & Desphande, 2013; Kallapur & Jobe, 2015; Weaver et al., 2016; Whitsett et al., 2015). Nearly all components of surfactant are synthesized and secreted from lamellar bodies (LB), small vesicles found within the type II pneumocytes. LB secrete surfactant upon stimulation, which may occur by way of several biochemical and mechanical signaling pathways. The most common signaling pathway is mechanical stretch. Stretching of the type II pneumocytes activates the synthesis and secretion of surfactant. Phospholipids, SP-B, and SP-C are thereby delivered to the LB, packaged with surfactant phospholipids, and subsequently excreted into the alveoli, forming the tension-reducing bioactive film. The surfactant molecules are thereby metabolized and degraded by alveolar macrophages or taken up by the type II cell for recycling (Whitsett et al., 2015).

Surfactant Function

Surfactant functions by (a) lowering surface tension at the air–liquid interface, (b) disrupting the biological lipid membrane and serving as antimicrobial agents, and (c) modulating the innate immune response (see Chapter 9). Surfactant synthesis, secretion, and metabolism, as well as the recycling of surfactant, are slower in newborns compared to older children and adults. A low surface tension is critical to prevent alveolar collapse during expiration. Yet, attractive forces found at the air–liquid interface favor increased surface tension, also known as *increased collapsing pressure*. Further complicating matters is the fact that alveoli have a natural tendency to collapse because of their spherical shape and small size. Fortunately, the chemical composition of surfactant, specifically its high concentration of DPPC, work to resist (and even lower) the surface tension.

DPPC forms a cohesive bioactive film within the alveoli. One end of the DPPC molecule is hydrophilic, allowing it to dissolve in water and attach in a perpendicular fashion to the alveolar wall. The opposite or hydrophobic end protrudes into the alveolus. The hydrophobic ends of the DPPC molecules crowd together during expiration, which opposes surface tension and holds the alveoli open (Han & Mallampalli, 2015).

While consistently lowering surface tension, surfactant also serves in an antimicrobial capacity. The aforementioned SP-A and SP-D modulate this role by degrading bacteria and clearing them from the distal airways. In fact, new data suggests that these surfactant proteins may offer effective antimicrobial defenses against early-onset sepsis pathogens, including Group B *Streptococcus* (GBS) and *Escherichia coli*, as well as late-onset sepsis pathogens, including *Klebsiella spp.* and *Enterobacter spp.* (Han & Mallampalli, 2015). Likewise, infants with deficient SP-A or SP-D proteins may suffer insufficient phagocytosis and clearance of pathogens.

Last, surfactant plays a role in the innate immune response. In this capacity, surfactant protects infants from pathogens prior to a directed immune response and then participates in the directed immune response. Upregulation of SP-A and SP-D by alveolar epithelial type II pneumocytes is observed when foreign agents, such as dust or pollen, enter the airways. This upregulation functions to stunt allergic reactions by inhibiting the proliferation of lymphocytes and decreasing the allergic histamine response. Children with asthma commonly suffer from deficient SP-A- and SP-D-modulated immune responses (Han & Mallampalli, 2015).

Fetal Lung Mechanics

Fetal Breathing Movements. Fetal breathing movements (FBMs) are essential to pulmonary growth and development (Kallapur & Kotecha, 2016; te Pas & Hooper, 2016). FBMs strengthen the diaphragm and respiratory accessory muscles, facilitate lung growth and differentiation, and facilitate development of the neural control of the respiratory center (Malleske, 2015). Observed episodes of FBM are cyclical and typically occur over a 20- to 30-minute period. They alternate with apnea and appear to coincide with sleep cycles (Malleske, 2015). Peripheral chemoreceptors facilitate FBM in the normal lung through the response to oxygen and carbon dioxide levels. This mimics their function after birth.

Fetal exposure to central nervous system depressants, stimulants, and hypoxia negatively affect fetal lung function. A summary of common licit and illicit drugs and their effect on fetal respiratory function is provided in Table 4.3 (Malleske, 2015). Routine prenatal and intrapartum fetal monitoring assists in the assessment of vascular blood flow and is essential to ensure fetal well-being (Malleske, 2015).

The Role of Antenatal Steroids. Discussions focused on antenatal and postnatal diagnosis and treatment mechanisms are largely beyond the scope of this textbook. However, antenatal steroids exert a significant effect on fetal lung development and postnatal physiologic function. These factors elevate the significance of this topic and warrant its inclusion in this chapter.

The administration of antenatal corticosteroids is one of the most significant prenatal therapies used in light of threatened premature labor and delivery to improve neonatal outcomes. Based on extensive research and meta-analyses, the American College of Obstetricians and Gynecologists (ACOG, 2016) recommends the antenatal administration of a single course of antenatal steroids to women who are threatening preterm delivery between 24 0/7 weeks and 33 6/7 weeks gestation. ACOG also suggests that steroid administration may be appropriate for women threatening delivery at 23 0/7 weeks or between 34 0/7 and 36 6/7 weeks gestation (ACOG, 2016). The provision of at least one complete course of antenatal steroids has been associated with significant reductions in respiratory distress syndrome, necrotizing enterocolitis, intraventricular hemorrhage, and death (Roberts, Brown, Medley, & Dalziel, 2017).

Glucocorticoids are hormones released by the adrenal glands in response to stimulation of the hypothalamic–pituitary–adrenal (HPA) axis, as a means to respond to

TABLE 4.3. Effects of Licit and Illicit Drug Use on Fetal Lung Development and Function

Drug Category	Risks to Lung Development and Function
Depressant	↑ Fetal growth restriction ↑ Teratogenic effects
Opioid	↑ Risk of premature birth: insufficient surfactant and immature lung development ↑ Risk of placental abruption: alterations in surfactant function due to asphyxia ↑ Fetal growth restriction
Stimulant	↑ Risk of premature birth ↑ Risk of placental abruption ↑ Fetal growth restriction ↓ Alveolarization

NOTE: Premature birth is associated with immature lung development and insufficient surfactant production. Placental abruption is associated with alterations in surfactant function due to hypoxia. Fetal growth restriction may negatively restrict lung development.

a stressor and reestablish homeostasis (see Chapter 10; Oakley & Cidlowski, 2013). The ligand-dependent family of transcription factors, known as *glucocorticoid receptors (GR)*, are present on target cells throughout the body (Maeda, 2007). They mediate the effects of corticosteroids (glucocorticoids).

Corticosteroids have a pleiotropic impact on neonatal lung function, most notable through the stimulation of alveolar thinning, enlargement of the air spaces, and increased surfactant production (Jobe, Kallapur, & Kramer, 2012). Corticosteroids also facilitate an increase in antioxidant production and beta-receptor expression as well as the reabsorption of fetal lung fluid (Riley, Boozer, & King, 2011; Wapner, 2013). Increased antioxidant production is important in countering the effects associated with increased oxidative stress commonly seen with the transition to an oxygen-rich environment. An increase in beta-receptor expression leads to bronchial smooth muscle relaxation and increased surfactant production.

Fetal Lung Fluid and Clearance

Fetal lung fluid is an important factor in structural and functional development of the respiratory system. Beginning as early as week 6 of gestation, fetal lung fluid develops from active chloride (Cl⁻) secretion by epithelial cells. These cells fill the alveolar lumen and encourage its spatial expansion (Katz, Bentur, & Elias, 2011). The volume of fetal lung fluid increases throughout the first half of pregnancy, from approximately 4 mL/kg to 6 mL/kg of body weight at 20 weeks of gestation to 30 mL/kg to 50 mL/kg at term, before it progressively decreases in preparation for birth.

Fetal lung fluid prepares the lungs for extrauterine life. It accomplishes this by creating a distending pressure within the lungs, of approximately 1 mmHg to 2 mmHg. This "trains" the fetal lungs to resist the natural recoil of the chest wall (Kallapur & Kotecha, 2016). The lung fluid moves up the respiratory tract with a small amount escaping the trachea during fetal breathing movements (FBM), and is either swallowed or expelled into the amniotic fluid volume (Gao & Raj, 2010; te Pas & Hooper, 2016).

Fetal lung fluid production begins to slow as the neonate approaches term. This is a logical transition, as the neonatal lungs need to quickly shift from a fluid-filled to air-filled cavity. In preparation for life outside of the womb, the lungs transition from active fluid (Cl⁻) secretion to fluid (Na⁺) absorption (Katz et al., 2011). Catecholamine surges that occur with the onset of labor, in addition to activity from type II pneumocytes, enhance the transition from Cl⁻ secretion to Na⁺ absorption (Katz et al., 2011). Type II cells modulate the active transport of Na⁺ across the lung epithelium and into the interstitial space, where it is functionally reabsorbed (Hillman, Kallapur, & Jobe, 2012). This reabsorption is a two-step process: (a) Na⁺ is passively absorbed into the cellular membrane through epithelial Na⁺ channels (ENaC), and (b) Na⁺ is actively excreted into the interstitial space, where it can be absorbed by the pulmonary vasculature and lymphatic systems (Figure 4.4; Hillman et al., 2012). Failed reabsorption of fetal lung fluid increases the risk for retained fetal lung fluid, which manifests as transient tachypnea of the newborn.

Cardiopulmonary Changes at Birth

With advancing gestational age, fetal pulmonary vascular tone increases. This encourages high pulmonary vascular resistance (PVR) and low pulmonary blood flow; recall that less than 20% of cardiac output reaches the lungs during fetal development (Gao & Raj, 2010). Explanations for this phenomenon include the active (in utero) secretion of fluid into the alveolar spaces combined with increased

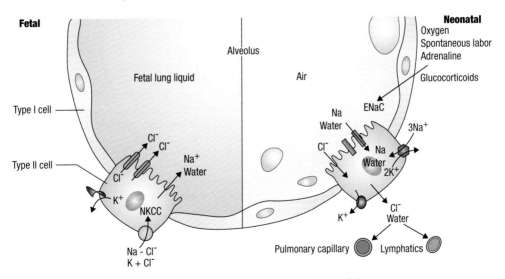

Figure 4.4 Fetal and neonatal lung fluid secretion and absorption.

ENaC, epithelial sodium channel; NKCC, Na⁺-K⁺-Cl⁻ cotransporter.

hydrostatic pressure, which promotes lung distention and compression of the pulmonary vasculature (Gao & Raj, 2010; Hillman et al., 2012). As the fetus approaches term, vasomotor tone becomes more reactive, a necessary adaptation in preparation for extrauterine life (Gao & Raj, 2010).

In the meantime, the placenta continues to modulate gas exchange until birth occurs. Recall that oxygenated blood leaves the placenta and travels to the fetus via the umbilical vein, with most of the blood shunting past the hepatic circulation via the ductus venosus, and into the right atrium. This oxygenated blood mixes with blood returning to the right atrium and shunts across the foramen ovale into the left atrium, where it mixes with the small volume of blood returning from the lungs via the pulmonary veins, into the left ventricle, then out the aorta to the body. Blood returning to the right atrium via the superior vena cava travels primarily to the right ventricle, then out the pulmonary artery and either shunts across the ductus arteriosus, rejoining the blood flow in the aorta, or travels on to the lungs providing nutrients to the developing lung tissue (Figure 4.5). The transition to extrauterine life requires prompt changes within a narrow time frame. Blood flow must change from the aforementioned parallel circulation to one that flows in series (right heart side flowing into the left heart side following a series of steps). In addition, fetal lung fluid secretion must slow.

Fortunately, catecholamines and glucocorticoid release during labor stimulates the release of epithelial Na⁺ channels, which prompt the elimination of lung fluid from the alveoli before and following the first postnatal breath (Gao & Raj, 2010; Guglani, Lakshminrusimha, & Ryan, 2008; Hillman et al., 2012). Clamping of the umbilical cord and the first postnatal breath promote the neonatal lung to primary modulator of oxygenation. The alveoli expand with each subsequent breath and the distending pressure that once compressed the pulmonary vasculature abates (Gao & Raj, 2010). PVR begins to fall, and systemic vascular resistance (SVR) increases (see Chapters 5 and 14; Van Woudenberg, Willis, & Rubarth, 2012). These processes activate the critical air–fluid interface, which under normal circumstances causes a temporary increase in surface tension and elastic recoil (te Pas & Hooper, 2016). Surfactant secretion is critical in these moments, essential to the continuation of a normal extrauterine transition; deficiencies are associated with respiratory distress. Synthesis and secretion of surfactant modulate alveolar stability, or functional residual capacity, and decrease surface tension (collapsing pressure). Over time, chest wall rigidity increases in opposition to lung recoil, allowing the neonatal lung to tolerate greater negative intrapleural pressures while maintaining lung inflation (te Pas & Hooper, 2016).

With the rising postnatal SVR and falling PVR, functional fetal shunts are no longer necessary and the foramen ovale closes. Blood flow returning from the body to the heart is directed from the right ventricle into the pulmonary artery to the lungs. With the postnatal decline of circulating prostaglandins (PGE2), increased elimination of PGE2 by the lungs, increased arterial oxygenation, and decreased vascular tone in the ductus, the ductus arteriosus (DA) constricts; this marks the process of functional closure of the DA (Katheria & Finer, 2018).

Vasoactive properties, activated by the shearing stress of pulmonary vasodilatation, lead to further reductions in PVR (Gao & Raj, 2010). These properties, synthesized in the endothelium of the pulmonary vasculature, include endogenous nitric oxide (EDNO), prostacyclin (PGI2), prostaglandin E2 (PGE2), endothelin-1 (ET-1), and platelet-activating factor (PAF). EDNO, mediated by cyclic guanosine monophosphate (cGMP), stimulates pulmonary vasodilatation. The prostanoids (PGI2 and PGE2) provide control of vasodilatation, a process modulated by the cAMP pathway (Gao & Raj, 2010). Postnatal ET-1 activity at ET_B receptors promotes vasodilation (Gao & Raj, 2010). Due to increased oxygen levels, PAF levels decrease following delivery and contribute to vasodilation of the pulmonary blood vessels post-delivery (Figure 4.6; Gao & Raj, 2010). In the healthy newborn adapting to extrauterine life, these changes happen rather seamlessly. Failed transition may manifest as respiratory diseases or persistent pulmonary hypertension.

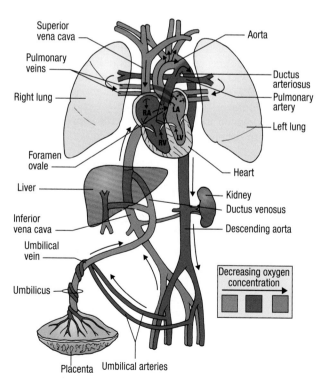

Figure 4.5 Newborn transition to extrauterine life.

LA, left atrium; LV, left ventricle; RA, right atrium; RV, right ventricle.

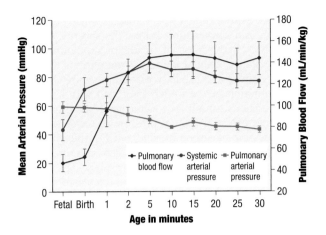

Figure 4.6 Changes in pulmonary blood flow through transition to neonatal life

Source: Adapted from Nair, J., & Lakshminrusimha, S. (2014). Update on PPHN: Mechanisms and treatment. *Seminars in Perinatology, 38,* 78–91. doi:10.1053/j.semperi.2013.11.004

Postnatal Lung Mechanics

The biochemical changes noted previously are critical to postnatal survival. In addition, mechanical changes, albeit more gradual, must occur. Recall that the anatomy and mechanics of the neonatal thorax differ from that of the adult and older child. The neonatal chest is more cylindrical than the elliptical shape of the adult thorax. The ribs

have a more horizontal orientation in comparison to the oblique orientation seen in adults; this results in a relative shortening of the intercostal muscles (Keszler & Abubakar, 2017). As a result, neonates are less able to elevate their rib cage during inspiration and increase intrathoracic volume (Keszler & Abubakar, 2017). The combination of the horizontal nature of the newborn diaphragm and the compliant chest wall results in an inward movement of the lower ribs during inspiration. Maturation of the intercostal muscles and establishment of mature lung compliance progresses across infancy, childhood, and into adulthood. See Table 4.4 for additional definitions of neonatal pulmonary mechanics.

Postnatal Gas Exchange. Following birth, the neonate transitions, over the first 3 to 6 months of life, to the production of adult hemoglobin (HgA); concurrent increases in 2,3-DPG production are also observed. Recall that HgA has a decreased affinity for oxygen, meaning that less oxygen will remain bound to hemoglobin in the lungs as more is released to the tissues. As such, this gradual postnatal transition from HgF to HgA is associated with reduced oxygen affinity and rightward shift of the oxyhemoglobin dissociation curve (ODC). Hemoglobin readily releases oxygen in an effort to ensure adequate tissue oxygenation, as oxygen demand is increased after birth (McNamara & El-Khuffash, 2017). Postnatal blood transfusions can cause shifts in the ODC (right shift secondary to loss of HgF and

TABLE 4.4. Pulmonary Mechanics/Lung Measurement Definitions

Mechanic	Definition
Tidal volume (TV or VT)	Amount of gas moved during one normal inspiration and expiration
Functional residual capacity (FRC)	Volume of gas left in lung after a normal expiration
Residual volume	Minimum lung volume possible—air left in lung after maximum expiration
Vital capacity	Maximum amount of air that can be moved
Total lung capacity	Total amount of volume present in the lung
Inspiratory capacity	Maximum volume of air that can be inspired after a normal expiration
Inspiratory reserve volume	Additional amount of air that can be inspired after a normal inspiration
Expiratory reserve volume	Additional amount of air that can be expired after a normal expiration
Minute volume	Combination of tidal volume and respiratory rate
Anatomic dead space	Part of airway where no gas exchange occurs (trachea, bronchi, etc.)
Physiologic dead space	Alveoli that is ventilated but under- or not perfused

increased acquisition of HgA), as well as alterations in pH, 2,3 DPG levels, and body temperature. Refer to Figure 4.7 to associate increases or decreases in these factors with corresponding shifts in oxygen affinity (McNamara & El-Khuffash, 2017).

Ventilation and Perfusion. Gas exchange is dependent on matching of ventilation and perfusion, referred to as *V (ventilation)/Q (perfusion) matching* (V/Q ratio). The V/Q ratio is a description of the balance between ventilation (airflow at the alveoli) and perfusion (blood flow entering the lungs). In that sense, the V/Q is a reflection of alveolar ventilation divided by cardiac output. If part of the lung is ventilated but not perfused, or perfused but not ventilated, a V/Q mismatch occurs. This leads to either hypoxemia or hypercarbia (Keszler & Abubakar, 2017).

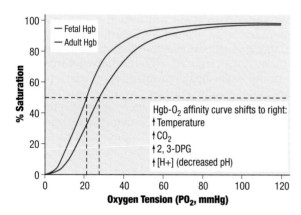

Figure 4.7 Postnatal oxygen dissociation curve.

CO_2, carbon dioxide; Hgb, hemoglobin; O_2, oxygen; PO_2, partial pressure of oxygen; 2, 3-DPG, 2, 3-disphosohoglyceric acid.

Source: Adapted from Ohls, R. K. (2011). Core concepts: The biology of hemoglobin. *NeoReviews, 12*(1), e29–e38. doi:10.1542/neo.12-1-e29

Acid–Base Status. Blood gas evaluation is used to assess ventilation and oxygenation status, the severity of lung disease, the effectiveness of treatment modalities, and acid–base status. Arterial blood gas sampling is the gold standard; venous and capillary gas sampling are clinically useful methodologies and often associated with less invasive and noxious stimuli. The elements of blood gas analysis include pH, pO_2 (partial pressure of oxygen), pCO_2 (partial pressure of carbon dioxide), HCO_3^- (bicarbonate), base excess or base deficit, and oxygen saturation. The pH, pO_2, and pCO_2 are directly measured. The HCO_3^- and base deficit/base excess values are calculated and not directly measured. Depending on the blood gas analyzer used, the oxygen saturation can be directly measured or calculated. Table 4.5 presents normal ranges for blood gas components.

Neonatal Pulmonary Function. Pulmonary function can be assessed, in part, through visual observation. Although a discussion of the pulmonary examination is beyond the scope of this textbook, clinicians should understand that respiratory rate, retractions, nasal flaring, grunting, and cyanosis are invaluable in the identification of abnormal pulmonary function or pulmonary mechanics. Hypoventilation leads to decreases in alveolar minute ventilation, whereas tachypnea yields low tidal volume. Retractions may suggest low lung compliance, obstruction, or atelectasis. Nasal flaring is a compensatory mechanism used to reduce airway resistance and total lung resistance. Grunting is a compensatory attempt to maintain functional residual capacity and maximize the partial pressure of oxygen; infants exhale against a closed or partially closed glottis. Central cyanosis, detected by the examination of the lips, tongue, and oral mucosa, suggests hypoxia. The value of the integrated physical assessment, as a critical component of identifying and diagnosing pulmonary dysfunction, cannot be understated.

TABLE 4.5 Blood Gas Components

Value	Normal Range
pH	**7.25–7.45**
pO_2	**55–95 mmHg**
pCO_2	**27–45 mmHg**
HCO_3^-	**17–24 mmol/L**
BD/BE	**–5/+5**
Oxygen saturation	**88%–95%**

BD, base deficit; BE, base excess; HCO_3^-, bicarbonate; pCO_2, partial pressure of carbon dioxide; pO_2, partial pressure of oxygen.

GENETIC INFLUENCES

A myriad of genetically linked respiratory disorders can manifest in the neonatal period, or later into childhood and early adulthood. Although a discussion of all genetically linked respiratory disorders is beyond the scope of this textbook, we present two rare surfactant deficiencies that manifest within the first 2 years of life. In addition, we discuss cystic fibrosis (CF), a common genetic disorder that affects respiratory function. Additional inherited disorders affecting the respiratory system are provided in Table 4.6.

Hereditary Surfactant B Deficiency

Hereditary SP-B deficiency is a rare autosomal recessive disease that affects one in every 1 million births (National Institutes of Health [NIH], 2018d). Mutations in the *SFPTB* gene located on chromosome 2 cause a reduction in SP-B protein production (Marinicak & Lomas, 2017; Whitsett et al., 2015). Recall that SP-B stimulates the formation of lamellar bodies within the type II pneumocytes and the synthesis and secretion of surfactant (Whitsett et al., 2015). Deficient SP-B is thereby associated with decreased surfactant production, alveolar collapse, and respiratory distress or failure. Infants manifest the disease process within the first 12 to 24 hours of life. This disease is associated with a high mortality risk; most infants do not survive beyond the first 3 to 6 months of life (Marinicak & Lomas, 2017; NIH, 2018d; Whitsett et al., 2015).

Hereditary Surfactant C Deficiency

SP-C deficiency is an autosomal dominant disorder that involves mutations in the *SFTPC* gene. The *SFTPC* gene, located on chromosome 8 (8p21), is responsible for SP-C production (Whitsett et al., 2015). SP-C facilitates lipid recruitment and spreading of the surfactant film within the alveoli. The most severe SFTPC mutations manifest with severe respiratory failure, usually within the first few days of life. Less severe mutations have been associated with progressive interstitial lung disease, which manifests in infancy, as well as idiopathic pulmonary fibrosis in adults (Whitsett et al., 2015).

Cystic Fibrosis

CF is the most common autosomal recessive disorder diagnosed during infancy (Bajaj & Gross, 2015). The incidence varies by ethnicity. One in every 2,500 to 3,500 Caucasian infants are affected, whereas the disease is less commonly diagnosed among African American (1/17,000) and Asian (1/31,000) races (NIH, 2018b).

CF occurs due to mutations in the cystic fibrosis transmembrane conductance regulator (*CFTR*) gene (Marinicak & Lomas, 2017). The *CFTR* gene, located on the long arm of chromosome 7, is responsible for the production of the CFTR protein (Marinicak & Lomas, 2017). CFTR protein regulates ion and water balance at the epithelial membrane located in the lung, gastrointestinal tract, pancreas, sweat glands, and genitourinary system (Terlizzi et al., 2018). Deficient protein concentrations permit the formation of abnormally thick mucosal secretions, which impairs respiratory function.

The hallmark clinical manifestation is meconium ileus, which affects 10% to 20% of newborns with CF (Parry, 2015). Manifestations during infancy and childhood include varying degrees of cough and respiratory disease. Older infants commonly develop a chronic cough, copious thick sputum production, and are considered at risk for pneumonia. In the most severe of cases, respiratory failure secondary to bronchiectasis and lung scarring occurs (Spoonhower & Davis, 2016).

Due to newborn metabolic screening tests, most individuals with CF are identified by age 3. Patients who have some functioning CFTR protein have better outcomes than those who do not (Spoonhower & Davis, 2016). Fifty percent of all deaths occur before 30 years of age; however, the current life expectancy was just recently expanded through age 43 (Cystic Fibrosis Foundation, n.d.).

MATERNAL HEALTH INFLUENCES

Maternal health status impacts all aspects of fetal and neonatal growth and development, including respiratory development and maturation. High-fat diets, maternal obesity, and maternal infections are positively associated with stunted or impaired fetal respiratory development. These common maternal health influences will be explored; their implications on the developing fetus emphasize the importance of performing comprehensive analysis of the maternal health history. Other maternal conditions that implicate surfactant synthesis are summarized in Table 4.7.

Components of a healthy diet are a frequent topic of conversation between obstetrician and mother during all stages

---

TABLE 4.6. Other Inherited Disorders That Affect the Respiratory System

Disease Process

- Neurofibromatosis (NF1)/von Recklinghausen's disease
- Tuberous sclerosis
- Crouzon's disease
- Apert syndrome
- ABCA3 transporter disorder
- Gaucher disease
- Smith–Lemli–Opitz disorder

NOTE: A more comprehensive list is provided by the National Institute of Health, Genetic and Rare Diseases Information Center (GARD).

TABLE 4.7. Other Maternal Conditions Which Affect Surfactant Production

Disease Process	Increased	Decreased
Cardiovascular disease (maternal)	X	
Cesarean section		X
Chorioamnionitis	X	
Chronic hypertension (maternal)	X	
Diabetes (maternal)		X
Pregnancy-induced hypertension	X	
Prolonged rupture of membranes	X	

of pregnancy. Research into the composition of a healthy diet has included a focus on high-fat diets, vitamins, docosahexaenoic acid (DHA), and folic acid supplementation. Specific to fetal respiratory development, a high-fat diet has been linked to impaired respiratory system development (Mayor et al., 2015). Risks include increased maternal glucose and insulin levels, placental insufficiency, fetal growth restriction (FGR), impaired fetal lung development, and a placental inflammatory response (Mayor et al., 2015). Vitamin D supplementation has shown mixed results in humans for prevention or treatment of RDS despite animal study data that demonstrates a stimulation of alveolar type II cell maturation and improved alveolarization of the fetal lung (Lykkedegn, Sorenson, Beck-Nielsen, & Christesen, 2015). DHA supplementation is linked to the respiratory system development secondary to its impact on the inflammatory response. It mediates the inflammatory response, thereby decreasing the damage done by inflammatory cytokines (Valentine, 2012).

Approximately 30% to 66% of women of childbearing age (18–44) are overweight (BMI 25–30) or obese (BMI >30; Britt et al., 2013; March of Dimes, n.d.). Metabolic syndrome (visceral obesity, dyslipidemia, hypertension, and hyperglycemia) among pregnant women has been linked to elevations in proinflammatory cytokines and an increase in wheezing/asthma of their offspring (Britt et al., 2013). Maternal diabetes or hyperglycemia results in hyperinsulinemia in the fetus, which in turn delays the functional maturation of the lungs and prolongs the time in which a neonate is at risk for respiratory distress syndrome (RDS; Britt et al., 2013). Macrosomia in the fetus born to a mother with diabetes increases the risk for birth trauma, asphyxia, cesarean section, and delayed reabsorption of fetal lung fluid.

Fetal growth restriction (FGR), or intrauterine growth restriction (IUGR), has been linked to early and long-term pulmonary consequences that result from impaired nutrient and oxygen delivery to the fetus. Fetal growth, or estimated fetal weight (EFW) that is less than the tenth percentile expected for the gestational age, defines IUGR. The incidence of IUGR is 5% to 12% of all pregnancies, both preterm and term gestation (Britt et al., 2013). Not all small-for-gestational-age (SGA) fetuses will be IUGR. Newer epidemiologic research recommendations indicate that although population-based growth curves are helpful, when assessing an SGA fetus, the growth curve should be customized, accounting for fetal gender, maternal age, weight, height, and parity (Figueras & Gardosi, 2011). SGA fetuses who are growing normally along their customized growth curves do not have the same long-term health concerns seen with those who are failing to grow along their customized growth curves (Figueras & Gardosi, 2011). Many pathologies are associated with the development of IUGR in the fetus. Fetal (chromosomal anomalies, congenital infections), maternal (hypertension, smoking, drug exposure), and placental problems are linked to growth restriction. Respiratory system dysfunction affecting the IUGR fetus includes the development of fewer alveoli, thickened alveolar septation, and abnormal vascular development (Pike, Pillow, & Lucas, 2012).

Maternal infections and development of chorioamnionitis increasingly account for preterm deliveries, especially with decreasing gestational age (Westover & Moss, 2012). Maternal chorioamnionitis is characterized by inflammation within the fetal membranes and is associated with the presence of a maternal fever (>38°C) along with two of the following: maternal tachycardia, fetal tachycardia, uterine tenderness, foul-smelling amniotic fluid, and maternal leukocytosis (Britt et al., 2013). In addition to the effects of preterm delivery on the developing lung, inflammation has both detrimental and beneficial effects. The benefits are the increase in production of endogenous surfactant that results in a decrease in observed RDS. The increase in inflammatory cytokines, the decrease in alveolarization/vascularization, and the increase in alveolar size impact long-term lung development. This includes an increase in the risk of bronchopulmonary dysplasia (BPD; Britt et al., 2013; Kunzmann, Collins, Kuypers, & Kramer, 2013; Westover & Moss, 2012).

COMMON PROBLEMS WITH IMPLICATIONS ACROSS THE LIFE SPAN

Multiple etiologies and overlapping factors contribute to neonatal respiratory distress. For learning purposes, we present two categories of respiratory diseases: (a) congenital or development problems and (b) acquired diseases.

The incidence, manifestations, pathophysiology, and life-span implications of the more common disease processes will be discussed next.

Congenital and Developmental Problems

There is no single standardized classification system to describe respiratory problems attributed to congenital or developmental causes (Biyyam, Chapman, Ferguson, Deutsch, & Dighe, 2010; Fowler & Gould, 2015). Many lung abnormalities occur early in fetal life and are related to genetic causes, whereas others may be related to in utero events that impact the developing lung. Prenatal fetal imaging is critical to the early identification of these lesions to counsel parents adequately and to guide appropriate management strategies. Although many of these disorders can be diagnosed prenatally, some do present later in childhood or adulthood.

Pulmonary Hypoplasia. Pulmonary hypoplasia is a rare disorder and has been estimated to occur in nine to 11 out of 10,000 live births (Triebwasser & Treadwell, 2017). Pulmonary hypoplasia is one part of a triad of pulmonary abnormalities known as *pulmonary underdevelopment complex*; pulmonary aplasia and pulmonary atresia complete the triad. With pulmonary hypoplasia, the lung is incompletely developed. This results in a decreased number of lung cells, airways, alveoli, and their corresponding pulmonary vasculature, which severely limits gas exchange (Crowley, 2015; Triebwasser & Treadwell, 2017).

Pulmonary hypoplasia can be primary or secondary. Primary hypoplasia is most likely due to inappropriate lung-bud development as a result of abnormal expression of growth factors and transcription factors (Hsu et al., 2012). Secondary pulmonary hypoplasia is more common and results from processes that impede normal lung development. Common pathologic processes that contribute to secondary pulmonary hypoplasia include:

- *Oligohydramnios*: Lung fluid and lung fluid exchange facilitate fetal lung expansion. With diminished fluid, adequate lung growth does not occur (Cotton, 2017). Renal anomalies (decreased urine production), early amniotic fluid loss as with early membrane rupture, placental abnormalities, and intrauterine growth restriction can all contribute to decreased lung fluid.
- *Lung compression from space-occupying lesions*: Lung compression and inadequate thoracic space for lung growth can result in hypoplasia (Triebwasser & Treadwell, 2017). Congenital diaphragmatic hernia, cystic lung lesions, congenital heart disease with cardiomegaly, and decreased pulmonary blood flow can contribute to lung compression.
- *Decreased fetal breathing movements*: Normal diaphragm movement is essential for normal lung growth. Central or

peripheral nervous system disorders or lesions, as well as musculoskeletal disorders, can contribute to decreased fetal breathing (Crowley, 2015; Hsu et al., 2012).

At birth, infants with hypoplasia often present with respiratory failure, severe respiratory distress, hypoxia, and reduced lung volume by x-ray, and they can require significant amounts of respiratory support. Respiratory distress is further complicated by the presence of persistent pulmonary hypertension and the development of pneumothoraces.

Survival and prognosis are dependent on the severity, extent, and cause of the hypoplasia. The timing of the disruption of lung growth and development predict the severity of the disease. The earlier the disruption, the more severe the disease. Mortality is high, and those who survive often develop chronic lung disease or bronchopulmonary dysplasia, which will be discussed later in the chapter. Patients with chronic lung disease have a higher incidence of both upper and lower respiratory tract infections (Crowley, 2015; Hsu et al., 2012). It is not uncommon for those children who survive the early newborn period to require oxygen therapy and/or prolonged ventilatory support.

Congenital Diaphragmatic Hernia. Congenital diaphragmatic hernia (CDH) is a developmental defect of the diaphragm that permits the abnormal migration of abdominal contents into the thoracic cavity. CDH is estimated to occur in one of every 2,500 births (NIH, 2018a). Herniation can occur on the left or right side of the diaphragm, as well as centrally. Defects most often occur in the posterior and lateral orientations (Bochdalek hernia) with the left-sided defect being the most prevalent (85%–90%; Chandrasekharan et al., 2017; Kumar, 2015). Anterior, or Morgagni hernias, occur less frequently; central hernias are rare (Chandrasekharan et al., 2017). Bilateral hernias and diaphragmatic agenesis are usually fatal.

The defect can occur in isolation, or in conjunction with other congenital anomalies—heart, genitourinary, chromosomal, gastrointestinal, and musculoskeletal (Chandrasekharan et al., 2017; Crowley, 2015; Kumar, 2015)—as well as in conjunction with trisomy syndromes (Stark et al., 2015). Abdominal contents compress the lung, which affects normal growth and results in pulmonary hypoplasia. Pulmonary hypoplasia can be unilateral or bilateral but is most severe on the side of the hernia (ipsilatera; Register, Jnah, & Newberry, 2016).

CDH is most likely a multifactorial disease and results from some of the same genetic factors that drive lung and diaphragm development. Abnormalities in the retinoic acid pathway have been implicated in the disorder (Ameis et al., 2017; Chandrasekharan et al., 2017; Kumar, 2015). The size of the herniation, severity of the pulmonary hypoplasia, severity of the PPHN, presence (or absence) of liver in the thoracic cavity, and the presence of other anomalies influence the severity of the CDH and associated mortality risk (Chandrasekharan et al., 2017; Kumar, 2015).

In the most severe cases, infants present at birth with significant respiratory distress and respiratory insufficiency. Most develop persistent pulmonary hypertension a short time after birth. Less severe forms may present with mild respiratory symptoms, or with symptoms that develop later within the newborn period or even later in life (Register et al., 2016). Among affected neonates, breath sounds are often diminished on the affected side with a shift in prominence of heart sounds to the opposite (contralateral) side. Chest radiographs will demonstrate bowel contents in the thoracic cavity on the ipsilateral side with mediastinal shift to the contralateral side.

Pulmonary function in CDH patients may remain abnormal through childhood and into adult life. Pulmonary function is predictably worse in those patients with significant pulmonary hypoplasia and prolonged ventilatory support (Danzer et al., 2012; Pantich et al., 2014). Obstructive airway disease, bronchospasm, pulmonary hypertension, and pneumonia are common reasons for hospital readmission within the first few years of life (Danzer et al., 2012; Register et al., 2016). The anatomy of the CDH defect, particularly if the defect is large, contributes to gastroesophageal reflux (GER) that can persist into adulthood. GER, feeding difficulties, and oral aversions contribute to poor growth, which can require gastrostomy placement to ensure adequate nutritional intake (Danzer et al., 2012). The incidence of

hearing loss and neurodevelopmental delays is higher in this population, and they impact patients across the life span. Overall, CDH outcomes are improved when infants deliver at tertiary care centers with access to multidisciplinary collaborative expertise. CDH patient registries help to identify best practices and enable the use of large data sets across multiple sites for CDH research (Lally & Skarsgard, 2017).

Congenital Cystic Lung Lesions. Cystic lung malformations are a collection of developmental lung lesions that include congenital pulmonary airway malformation (CPAM), bronchopulmonary sequestration (BPS), bronchogenic cyst (BC), and congenital lobar emphysema (CLE; Table 4.8; Chowdhury & Chakraborty, 2015; Crowley, 2015; Durell & Lakhoo, 2014). Congenital cystic lesions are estimated to occur in one in 10,000 to 35,000 births; BPS is extremely rare and no itemized incidence is reported (Durell and Lakhoo, 2014). These lesions are usually identified during the antenatal period and are assumed to have a common embryonic/fetal origin. Some more rarely present during infancy, childhood, or adulthood and are commonly associated with other congenital anomalies.

The pathogenesis for this family of lung lesions is poorly understood. The onset of aberrant development seems to occur during the pseudoglandular period of lung development (Sfakianaki & Copel, 2012). Pathogenic theories include failed lung bud and branching morphogenesis, triggered by abnormal gene expression and abnormal transcription factor expression, airway obstruction, and

TABLE 4.8. Congenital Cystic Lung Lesions

Disease Process	Systemic Blood Supply?	Tracheobronchial Connection?	Malignancy Risk
Bronchogenic cyst	No	No [a]	Yes
Bronchopulmonary sequestration—ELS	Yes [b] (*aorta*)	No	No
Bronchopulmonary sequestration—ILS	Yes [b] (*aorta*)	No	Yes
Congenital lobar emphysema	No	No	No
Congenital pulmonary airway malformation	No (*pulmonary vessels*)	Yes	Yes (Type 1 & 4)

ELS, extralobar sequestration; ILS, intralobar sequestration.

[a] Most bronchogenic cysts do not communicate with the airway. Rarely, a patent connection exists that increases the likelihood for infection.

[b] Systemic blood supply to bronchopulmonary sequestrations is derived from anomalous vessels originating from the aorta.

Source: Polin, R. A., Abman, S. H., Rowitch, D. H., Benitz, W. E., & Fox, W. W. (2017). *Fetal and neonatal physiology* (5th ed.). Philadelphia, PA: Elsevier.

metaplasia and dysplasia of otherwise normal tissues (Chowdhury & Chakraborty, 2015; Correia-Pinto, Gonzaga, Huang, & Rottier, 2010; David, Lamas-Pinheiro, & Henriques-Coelho, 2016; Fowler & Gould, 2015).

Congenital pulmonary airway malformation. Congenital pulmonary airway malformation (CPAM), formerly known as *congenital cystic adenomatoid malformation (CCAM)*, accounts for the majority (95%) of all congenital cystic lung lesions (Wert, 2017). CPAM is classified into one of five types (0–4), based on Stocker's most current classification system (Stocker, 2009). *Type 0* is the rarest and most severe with all lobes of the lung frequently involved. The defect arises from the trachea or bronchus and is associated with other anomalies (cardiovascular, renal) and pulmonary hypoplasia (Biyyam et al., 2010; David et al., 2016, Sfakianaki & Copel, 2012). *Type I* lesions are bronchiole or bronchiolar in origin and are the *most common* type of CPAM. When the lesions are large, they can lead to pulmonary hypoplasia and hydrops. This type of lesion may regress as pregnancy advances. There is an increased risk of bronchioalveolar carcinoma with these lesions (Biyyam et al., 2010; Crowley, 2015; David et al., 2016, Sfakianaki & Copel, 2012). *Type II* is bronchiolar in origin with smaller and more evenly distributed cysts than those in type I. They often occur in association with other congenital anomalies (renal, cardiovascular, diaphragmatic hernia, and extrapulmonary sequestration). If the associated congenital anomalies are severe, the outcome will be poor (Biyyam et al., 2010; Crowley, 2015; David et al., 2016; Sfakianaki & Copel, 2012). *Type III* has a bronchiolar–alveolar duct origin also known as *adenomatoid type* (Biyyam et al., 2010). Multiple cysts appear as a solid mass and infants with this lesion have a higher likelihood of developing hydrops and pulmonary hypoplasia. These cysts do not regress with advancing pregnancy, and the outcome is directly related to the severity of pulmonary hypoplasia. *Type IV* lesions are distal acinar in origin (Biyyam et al., 2010) and consist of large air-filled cysts in the lung periphery; surgical resection leads to a good prognosis (Crowley, 2015).

The specific pathogenesis of CPAM is poorly understood. It appears that the cysts arise within the bronchiolar region. Therefore, CPAM likely involves malformations of the distal pulmonary bronchioles and lung parenchyma. More specific, type I to III CPAM is associated with failed branching during the pseudoglandular stage of pulmonary development, whereas type IV CPAM is associated with malformations that arise during the canalicular and saccular stages (Wert, 2017).

Up to 50% of all neonates with CCAM present as well-appearing newborns. Respiratory distress, when present, can range from mild to severe and can manifest any time from birth to adulthood. The most common comorbidity associated with CCAM is pulmonary hypoplasia (Crowley, 2015).

Life-span implications include postsurgical complications as well as cough, fever, and recurrent infections in later childhood. There is an increased risk for postoperative complications with emergency surgery when compared to elective surgery (Sfakianaki & Copel, 2012). Few long-term follow-up reports are available, but there is a small risk of malignancy later in life, most notable with type I and type IV lesions (Casagrande & Pederiva, 2016).

Bronchopulmonary sequestration. BPS are masses of dysplastic pulmonary tissue that do not connect to the tracheobronchial tree. An anomalous systemic arterial supply, commonly from the thoracic or abdominal aorta, communicates with the BPS (Hong, Yu, Tang, Liu, & Xia, 2017; Polin Abman, Rowitch, & Benitz, 2017). The majority (80%) of all BPS are nonfunctional parenchymal lesions. Two types of BPS are reported, intralobar sequestrations (ILS) or extralobar sequestrations (ELS). ILS lesions are 4 times more common than ELS lesions; 98% of all ILS occur within the lower lobes and most often within the left lung. ILS malformations are enveloped by and connected to normal lung tissue, whereas ELS lesions are completely separate from the lung and covered in their own pleura. ELS lesions may also be extrathoracic (Biyyam et al., 2010; Sfakianaki & Copel, 2012).

The pathogenesis of BPS remains unclear. The most widely accepted explanation dates back to Pryce's (1946) seminal work. Nonfunctioning lung tissue is thought to arise from the primitive foregut. During week 4 of gestation, capillaries formerly connecting the dorsal aorta and lung bud normally regress, separate, and are absorbed. Failed absorption results in the formation of an anomalous vasculature, which over time disrupts normal lung development and displaces the embryonic lung tissue into separate parts. This results in the formation of either an ILS or ELS (Hong et al., 2017).

Clinical manifestations in the immediate postnatal period include respiratory distress and congestive heart failure. Large lesions are associated with pulmonary hypoplasia. BPS may be associated with congenital diaphragmatic hernia, which also manifests as severe respiratory distress in the immediate postnatal period. More common, this lesion goes unnoticed in infancy and is discovered later into childhood secondary to cough, fever, dyspnea, hemoptysis, or congestive heart failure. Due to their location, an ELS lesion may be mistaken for an adrenal mass.

Life-span implications of BPS include high-output cardiac failure, hemoptysis, blood loss, or hemothorax. Patients with ILS lesions are at higher risk for malignancy risk later in childhood and adulthood (Casagrande & Pederiva, 2016). Latent ILS is associated with obstruction of the lower, posterior basal segments of the bronchus secondary to repetitive episodes of necrotizing pneumonia (Hong et al., 2017).

Bronchogenic cyst. Bronchogenic cysts, also known as *duplications of the foregut*, are one of the most common cysts found within the middle mediastinum (Wert, 2017). The majority (67%) of lesions are most often found in the mediastinal area. Other locations include the lung parenchyma (33%), pleura, and the diaphragm; these cysts may communicate with the normal airways (Chowdhury & Chakraborty, 2015; Wert, 2017). A paucity of recent literature exists that presents current epidemiologic trends, likely due to the rare status of this type of lung lesion.

Similar to other cystic lung lesions, the pathogenesis of bronchogenic cysts is poorly understood. The paucity of literature specific to this diagnosis adds to the mystery surrounding its genesis during early development. Experts posit that bronchogenic cysts are derived from the primitive foregut and occur secondary to abnormal ventral budding of the tracheobronchial tree. These single-chambered cysts commonly present as smooth-appearing, spherical, and noncalcified masses containing clear fluid or, less often, blood or air (Sarper, Ayten, Golbasi, Demircan, & Isin, 2003).

Clinical manifestations include stridor, wheezing, dysphagia, and dyspnea, caused by compression of the trachea, bronchi, and esophagus. Recurrent infection is reported with bronchogenic cysts found within the parenchyma. Typically, cough, fever, and recurrent infection are commonly reported in infancy and early childhood. Chest pain and dysphagia are the most common complaints reported among newly diagnosed adults.

After surgical correction, few long-term sequelae are reported. Complete resection significantly reduces malignancy risk (Casagrande & Pederiva, 2016; Chowdhury & Chakraborty, 2015). Lesions may regenerate if incompletely resected.

Congenital lobar emphysema/congenital lobar overinflation. Congenital lobar emphysema (CLE), also known as *lobar overinflation*, involves hyperinflation of one or more of the pulmonary lobes with corresponding marked distention of the alveoli. The etiology is thought to be due to disruptions in bronchopulmonary development secondary to abnormal interactions between embryonic endodermal and mesodermal lung components.

Intrinsic causes include dysplastic bronchial cartilage, thick plug-like mucus, extensive mucosal proliferation, bronchial torsion, and bronchial atresia. Extrinsic causes include compression of the bronchi, abnormal cardiopulmonary vasculature, and infection. The result is air trapping with subsequent overdistention (Olutoye, Coleman, Hubbard, & Adzick, 2000). If the lesion is large enough, mediastinal shift and compression of surrounding

structures may occur (Chowdhury & Chakraborty, 2015; Durell & Lakhoo, 2014).

Infants typically present with varying symptoms of respiratory distress; larger lesions are associated with acute respiratory distress (Durell & Lakhoo, 2014). Sparse outcome data on the life-long sequelae of CLE exists. When grouped with other congenital pulmonary malformations, wheezing and increased infection rates persist through early childhood, but improve with age (Calzolari et al., 2016). Therefore, outcomes and prognosis appear to be good with excision of the abnormality.

Tracheoesophageal Fistula. Tracheoesophageal fistula (TEF), although not a pulmonary disorder, is an abnormality that can result in significant respiratory distress. Esophageal atresia (EA) is often part of the defect, and therefore the defect is often labeled as EA/TEF. EA/TEF is an anomaly of the foregut and is estimated to occur in 1 out of every 3,000 to 5,000 births in the United States (NIH, 2018c). This congenital anomaly arises during week 4 of gestation due to an abnormal connection between the trachea and the esophagus. The etiology of EA/TEF is thought to be multifactorial. Genetically induced abnormalities in branching of the primitive lung bud and poorly understood environmental and epigenetic influences are likely causes in the development of the abnormality (Sadreameli & McGrath-Morrow, 2016).

EA/TEF may occur in isolation or with other genetic or other congenital malformations. Its most common association is with the VACTERL spectrum (vertebral anomalies, anal atresia, cardiac defects, tracheoesophageal defects, renal anomalies and limb anomalies). Genetic associations commonly involve the CHARGE spectrum (coloboma, heart defects, choanal atresia, retardation of growth/development, genital/urinary defects, ear anomalies), Feingold syndrome, and Opitz syndrome. EA/TEF is also reported among infants diagnosed with trisomy 18 and 21 (Sadreameli & McGrath-Morrow, 2016).

The five major types of EA/TEF and significant clinical manifestations are provided in Table 4.9. Rarely, esophageal stenosis is observed. In these cases, no esophageal atresia or fistulous connection to the trachea exists (Sadreameli & McGrath-Morrow, 2016; Wert, 2017).

Life-span implications are optimal with isolated defects. Infants with low birth weight and associated cardiac defects incur increased mortality risk (Javia, Harris, & Fuller, 2016; Parry, 2015). Long-term respiratory complications include wheezing, asthma, pneumonia, and abnormal pulmonary function tests (Sadreameli & McGrath-Morrow, 2016). Esophageal dysfunction, esophageal strictures, fistula recurrence, dysphagia, and reflux are reported after surgical correction. Dysphagia may persist into adulthood (Sadreameli & McGrath-Morrow, 2016).

TABLE 4.9. Five Classifications of Esophageal Atresia/Tracheoesophageal Fstula

Incidence	Types	Clinical Manifestations	Image
8%	"A": Isolated esophageal atresia with no tracheal communication	• Scaphoid abdomen • Hypersalivation	
1%	"B": Upper pouch fistula	• Scaphoid abdomen • Hypersalivation with possible entry into lungs	
85%	"C": Esophageal atresia (upper pouch) with distal TEF just above carina	• Distended abdomen • Hypersalivation • Reflux of gastric secretions into lungs	
1%	"D": Double TEF, separate attachments with upper and lower esophagus	• Distended abdomen • Hypersalivation into lungs • Reflux of gastric secretions into lungs	
4%	"E": Isolated TEF ("H" type)	• Asymptomatic • Coughing with feedings • Aspiration pneumonia	

TEF, tracheoesophageal fistula.

Acquired Respiratory Problems

As previously discussed in this chapter, the stages of lung development and maturation impact the severity and type of respiratory distress that a neonate can experience following delivery. The following sections discuss some of the respiratory challenges a neonate may experience after birth as he or she begins to transition to extrauterine life.

Respiratory Distress Syndrome. Survival among premature neonates has improved with the advancements made in neonatal care and the understanding of disease processes affecting them. Over the past 50 years, our knowledge of physiologic changes that lead to RDS has grown, resulting in developments that have improved neonatal outcomes, leading to new challenges and opportunities for continued research and advancement. Gestational age at the time of delivery is inversely related to survival, with the highest morbidity and mortality rates noted for those neonates born at extremely preterm gestational ages (22 to 24 weeks of gestation), with RDS listed as the leading cause of mortality and morbidity among premature neonates (Patel et al., 2015; Stevens, Blennow, Meyers, & Soll, 2007). Risk factors for RDS are summarized in Table 4.10.

Gestational age at the time of delivery impacts the severity of RDS and response to treatments, both antenatal and neonatal. Confounding variables, such as chorioamnionitis, prolonged rupture of membranes, need for resuscitation at delivery, and early mechanical ventilation impacts recovery from RDS. Extremely preterm neonates born between 22 to 25 weeks of gestation are subject to interrupted

canalicular development; primitive gas exchange units do not resemble or function as mature alveoli.

The pathogenesis of RDS involves surfactant deficiency. Surfactant deficiencies have been demonstrated in disease processes that lead to inadequate or insufficient production of surfactant by the type II pneumocyte, damage to the lung epithelium, or result in breakdown or inactivation of surfactant. Surfactant deficiency disables the ability to maintain adequate alveolar expansion through permissive persistence of high surface tension and decreased functional residual capacity (FRC). Atelectatic alveoli result in ventilation to perfusion mismatch resulting in cyanosis, impaired O_2/CO_2 exchange, acidosis, and increased pulmonary pressures, which delay a normal adaptation to extrauterine life (Figure 4.8; Locci, Fanos, Gerosa, & Faa, 2014).

Early clinical manifestations of RDS include increased work of breathing: retractions, grunting, cyanosis, tachypnea, nasal flaring, and apnea (Jackson, 2018). In these circumstances, the neonate has a limited ability to combat alveolar collapse. Nasal flaring (inspiratory volume) and grunting (end-expiratory volume) often follow; these are two compensatory mechanisms aimed to increase lung volume, stabilize FRC, and improve gas exchange (Hillman et al., 2012; Jackson, 2018). For neonates who are unable to maintain an adequate FRC, fluid movement across the cell membrane occurs with each reinflation of the alveoli. This repeated fluid movement has been linked to epithelial damage, inflammation, and acute lung injury (Hillman et al., 2012). Due to the relative compliance of the chest wall in premature infants, retractions (intercostal, subcostal, and sternal) are seen with increased exertion leading to exhaustion and apnea (Jackson, 2018). Repeated efforts by the neonate to

TABLE 4.10. Risk Factors for RDS

Risk Factors

- Prematurity
- Prematurity without antenatal steroid administration
- Cesarean section without trial of labor
- Caucasian race
- Male gender
- Perinatal asphyxia
- Infant of a diabetic mother

RDS, respiratory distress syndrome.

Sources: Jackson, J. C. (2018). Respiratory disorders in the preterm infant. In C. A. Gleason & S. E. Juul (Eds.), *Avery's diseases of the newborn* (10th ed., pp. 653–667). Philadelphia, PA: Elsevier; Kallapur; S. G., & Jobe, A. H. (2015). Lung development andmaturation. In R. J. Martin & A. A. Fanaroff (Eds.), *Fanaroff and Martin's neonatal–perinatal medicine: Diseases of the fetus and infant* (10th ed., pp. 1042–1048). Philadelphia, PA: Elsevier.

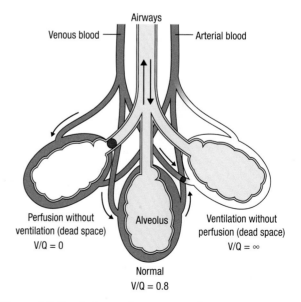

Figure 4.8 Ventilation-perfusion mismatching.

V/Q, ventilation-perfusion ratio.

reestablish lung inflation, or ventilation efforts that lead to alveolar overdistension, cause repeated shearing stress on the alveoli. Evidence suggests that damage occurs when ventilating neonates at either low lung volumes or at higher volumes, leading to overdistension. As a result, an influx of plasma debris into the alveolar space causes a subsequent breakdown of available surfactant (Jackson, 2018; Locci et al., 2014).

Alveolar debris, also known as *hyaline membrane*, prevents oxygenation and ventilation and, if left untreated, will cause the neonate to progress to severe acidosis, apnea, and cardiovascular collapse (Locci et al., 2014). Supportive therapy is frequently needed to stabilize the alveoli, which improves phagocytic function from pulmonary macrophages. The resulting breakdown of debris, removal of edema, and repair of the damaged epithelium leads to improved lung function (Jackson, 2018; Locci et al., 2014). Neonates progressing through the phases of RDS may worsen over the first 24 to 48 hours of life before experiencing diuresis associated with improving lung function (Jackson, 2018).

Radiographic findings and laboratory findings are noteworthy. A reticulogranular ("ground-glass") appearance and air bronchograms of the larger branching airways with low lung volumes are typically noted on radiographic images. This classic appearance is a result of atelectatic alveoli alternating with alveolar distension in addition to alveolar and interstitial edema (Figure 4.9; Jackson, 2018). Laboratory manifestations of mild RDS include hypoxemia with mild hypercapnea. With worsening RDS, a respiratory acidosis is noted with or without metabolic acidosis.

Life-span implications of RDS are often determined by the severity of the disease, the timing of disease presentation, existing congenital anomalies, and any additional comorbidities. Prolonged, difficult, or repeated endotracheal intubations may lead to tracheobronchomalacia (congenital weakness of conducting airways), subglottic stenosis, and small airway disease. All of these comorbidities are associated with architectural damage to lung parenchyma (Zhang, Zhang, & Zhao, 2016). The relative risk for accruing any of the aforementioned upper airway traumas increases with each day an infant is intubated, most notable after 7 *days* of invasive therapy (Zhang et al., 2016).

Despite gentle ventilation modalities, lung injury (secondary to respiratory support) further contributes to structural lung changes resulting in chronic lung disease (CLD) or BPD; hence, BPD is not a disease of prematurity alone. High levels of oxygen and significant respiratory support may be required to sustain adequate ventilation and oxygenation for some neonates. Exposure to positive-pressure ventilation and inspired oxygen has been demonstrated to result in the presence of inflammatory cytokines resulting in an abnormal repair of the epithelium, persistent inflammation, and remodeling of the lung endothelium, all of which are seen in BPD (Abman, Bancalari, & Jobe, 2017; Hillman et al., 2012).

Neonates with RDS, especially those who further develop BPD, will most likely require multiple hospital readmissions and a higher utilization of healthcare services, both of which are costly (Nortiz et al., 2017). Families of these children are challenged financially as well as emotionally in managing their care.

Bronchopulmonary Dysplasia. Following the first description of BPD by Dr. Northway and colleagues in 1967, much has changed in the definition, development, and treatment of this most common form of pediatric chronic lung disease. The first patients with a diagnosis of BPD were premature neonates with a birth weight greater than 1,000 grams who underwent prolonged positive-pressure ventilation with high concentrations of inspired oxygen culminating in respiratory failure with radiographic and histopathologic changes (Sosenko & Bancalari, 2012). The damage seen in the lungs of these neonates included smooth muscle hypertrophy, neutrophilic inflammation, parenchymal fibrosis, and airway damage (Trembath & Laughon, 2012). Since the original description of BPD, many advancements (antenatal steroids, improved ventilation techniques, surfactant replacement therapy) have improved outcomes and survival of neonates once thought to be born at the cusp of viability (Abman et al., 2017; Bancalari & Jain, 2017; Sosenko & Bancalari, 2012; Trembath & Laughon, 2012).

Between 15% and 50% of neonates weighing less than 1,500 grams are affected by BPD (Gao & Raj, 2010; Sosenko & Bancalari, 2012). The incidence of BPD is increasing among neonates born at extremely premature gestational ages due to increased survivability (Keller & Ballard, 2018). The incidence of BPD varies widely across the literature, in part due to historic challenges to accurately defining BPD within the neonatal population. The definition of BPD has changed over the years and

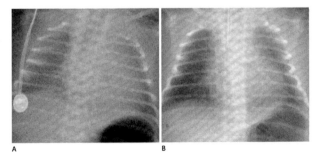

A   B

Figure 4.9 Respiratory distress syndrome. Air bronchograms and reticulogranular patterns are evident throughout the lung fields in images A and B.

Source: Respiratory distress of the newborn [image]. (2015). In *Wikimedia Commons.* Retrieved from https://commons.wikimedia.org/wiki/File:Respiratory_distress_of_the_newborn.jpg

TABLE 4.11. Severity-Based Definitions of BPD			
Gestational Age at Birth	**Mild BPD**	**Moderate BPD**	**Severe BPD**
<32 weeks	Room air at 36 weeks PMA or discharge	<30% oxygen at 36 weeks PMA or discharge	≥30% oxygen and/or positive pressure at 36 weeks PMA
≥ 32 weeks	Room air by 56 days postnatal age or discharge	<30% oxygen at 56 days postnatal age or discharge	≥30% oxygen and/or positive pressure at 56 days postnatal age or discharge

BPD, bronchopulmonary dysplasia; PMA, postmenstrual age.

Source: Trembath, A. N., & Laughon, M. M. (2012). Predictors of bronchopulmonary dysplasia. *Clinics in Perinatology, 39*(3), 585–601. doi:10.1016/j.clp.2012.06.014

the most recent revisions offer succinct classifications for disease severity (Table 4.11). Susceptible infants are those born prematurely (low birth weight and extremely low birth weight) who possess a genetic predisposition to altered lung development or function, or fetuses subject to asphyxia or infection.

Prenatal risk factors for BPD include prematurity and maternal chorioamnionitis. In the context of relative risk for postnatal BPD development, prematurity is defined as birth between 26 and 30 weeks of gestation. Some studies link chorioamnionitis with an increased risk for premature birth, as well as postnatal respiratory distress, BPD, and even perinatal death. On the contrary, chorioamnionitis has also been linked to increased lung maturation and a decreased incidence of postnatal respiratory distress (Paul, Zook, Mackley, & Locke, 2010). Regardless, chorioamnionitis is known to increase the likelihood of premature birth, which unequivocally increases the risk for altered anatomic and physiologic pulmonary development and chronic disease. Postnatal risk factors for BPD include prolonged ventilation, oxidative stress, and nosocomial infections (Metcalfe, Lisonkova, Sabr, Stritzke, & Joseph, 2017; Rook et al., 2014; Sosenko & Bancalari, 2012; Trembath & Laughon, 2012). Oxidative damage occurs with exposure to high oxygen concentrations as well as with fluctuations between hyperoxia and hypoxia and arrested alveolarization and vascular development (Madurga, Mizikova, Ruiz-Camp, & Morty, 2013; Sosenko & Bancalari, 2012).

The pathogenesis of the "new" BPD is attributed to alveolar hypoplasia and dysmorphic pulmonary circulation (Abman et al., 2017; Keller & Ballard, 2018; Sosenko & Bancalari, 2012; Trembath & Laughon, 2012). Four stages summarize the development of BPD (Figure 4.10). The first stage involves selection of a vulnerable host. Second, acute lung injury occurs, often secondary to surfactant deficiency, barotrauma, inflammation, or infection. Acute lung injury involves an interruption of the normal anatomic canalicular and saccular (alveolar) development. An influx of chemotactic and chemokinetic factors into

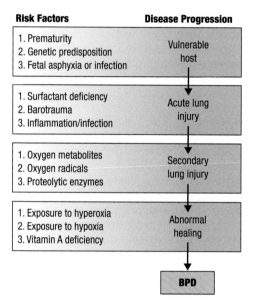

Figure 4.10 Pathogenesis of BPD.

BPD, bronchopulmonary dysplasia.

respiratory secretions is noted, which recruit inflammatory cells (including neutrophils, macrophages, and proinflammatory cytokines) into the pulmonary tissues. Neutrophil invasion occurs often after just minutes of artificial respiratory therapy. Neutrophils adhere to the pulmonary tissues and vascular system and release various proteolytic enzymes as well as oxygen metabolites and radicals. This marks the second stage of lung injury, which permits deranged architectural changes at the alveolar–capillary interface and parenchymal damage. Thickening of what should be a very thin, easily accessed alveolar–capillary interface disrupts gas exchange. Once parenchymal and vascular damage has occurred, further exposure to hyperoxic or hypoxic states promotes abnormal healing. Vitamin A deficiency is common. Vitamin A deficiency is known to reduce healing capacity; upregulation

TABLE 4.12. Characteristics of "New" Bronchopulmonary Dysplasia

Contemporary Clinical Management Strategies

- Antenatal steroid exposure
- Exogenous surfactant administration
- Reduced exposure to positive-pressure ventilation
- Reduced exposure to supplemental oxygen

Contemporary Histological Changes[a]

- Diffuse disease
- Reduced hyperinflation
- Reduced alveoli and capillaries
- Minimal fibrosis

[a]Histologic changes observed among animal models.

Source: Trembath, A. N., & Laughon, M. M. (2012). Predictors of bronchopulmonary dysplasia. *Clinics in Perinatology, 39*(3), 585–601. doi:10.1016/j.clp.2012.06.014

of genes that modulate fetal lung development and surfactant formation is reduced, resulting in stunted growth. It is interesting to note that contemporary and noninvasive respiratory management strategies are not necessarily positively linked to reduced rates of BPD. Recent reports indicated that premature infants who display little early evidence of RDS and who require minimal respiratory support still remain at risk for chronic respiratory disease or BPD (Table 4.12). Further investigation of this phenomenon is indicated.

Life-span implications of BPD include abnormal pulmonary function, asthma with increased bronchodilator use, persistent wheezing, airflow obstruction, chronic obstructive pulmonary disease, and altered neurodevelopment (Islam, Keller, Aschner, Hartet, & Moore, 2015). Altered neurodevelopment may include cerebral palsy, developmental delay, or cognitive and behavioral disorders. Hearing and vision deficits are also reported. Among adults, consequences of BPD include wheezing, and chronic obstructive pulmonary disease with radiologic evidence of emphysema (correlated with moderate to severe BPD diagnosis); these individuals often require long-term subspecialty follow-up for pulmonary dysfunction (Islam et al., 2015).

Neonatal Pneumonia. Pneumonia is the primary cause for infectious disease-related deaths among children across the globe, accounting for 16% of all deaths among children younger than 5 years (World Health Organization, 2016). Neonatal pneumonia is classified into four major categories based on routes of transmission: transplacental (congenital), intrauterine, intrapartum, and postnatal (MacDonald & Seshia, 2016; Wilson, Nizet, Maldonado, Remington, & Klein, 2016). A summary of associated pathogens by timing and mode of infection is provided

in Table 4.13. The fetus and neonate are particularly vulnerable to pneumonia. Risk factors include prematurity, immature innate and adaptive immune function, injury to the respiratory epithelium, and gastrointestinal reflux.

The pathogenesis of pneumonia varies based on timing of infection. Asphyxia, intrauterine infection, or a combination of both factors are responsible for congenitally acquired pneumonia. Pathogens colonizing the vaginal canal vertically ascend the birth canal and, once rupture of membranes occurs, traverse the cervix, infiltrate the chorioamniotic membrane, and enter and contaminate the amniotic fluid (Figure 4.11). The fetus aspirates the amniotic fluid, contaminated with maternal leukocytes, amniotic debris, and pathogens. Similarly, pneumonia acquired during the intrapartum period involves aspiration of pathogens colonizing the vaginal canal. Postnatal infection typically stems from infiltration of pathogens, often at injured regions of the respiratory tract, from sources that include contaminated equipment or caregivers.

Clinical manifestations of pneumonia overlap with RDS and meconium aspiration syndrome (MAS), making the process of clinical, laboratory, and radiographic correlation necessary to distinguish among these disease processes. Pneumonia may manifest with temperature instability, apnea, tachycardia or bradycardia, increased and potentially discolored respiratory secretions, oxygen desaturations, and escalating demand for respiratory support. Laboratory derangements commonly include neutropenia with bandemia. Common radiographic evidence of pneumonia includes pleural effusion, reticulonodular densities (similar to reticulogranular densities observed with RDS), or patchy and asymmetric infiltrates with areas of hyperaeration (similar to MAS).

Life-span implications vary depending on the pathogen, severity of illness, and recurrence. Prolonged

TABLE 4.13. Types of Pneumonia That Affect the Fetus and Neonate

Mode of Infection	Definition	Onset of Infection	Common Pathogens
Transplacental (*Congenital*)	• Ascending (vertical) infection of chorioamniotic membrane *or* • Transplacental (blood borne) maternal–fetal infection	• During fetal development	• Cytomegalovirus • Herpes simplex virus • *L. monocytogenes* • *T. gondii* • *T. pallidum*
Early onset	• Ascending (vertical) infection of chorioamniotic membrane and amniotic fluid **or** • Infection during birth due to contact with pathogens lining birth canal	• At birth or during first week of postnatal life	• Group B *Streptococcus* • *Escherichia coli* • *Klebsiella* • *C. trachomatis*
Late onset	• Infection acquired from human-to-human contact or exposure to contaminated equipment	• After first week of postnatal life	• Group B *Streptococcus* • *Escherichia coli* • *Klebsiella* • *Pseudomonas*

NOTE: List of pathogens limited to common exemplars and is therefore not all inclusive.

Sources: Hooven, T. A., & Polin, R. A. (2017). Pneumonia. *Seminars in Fetal and Neonatal Medicine, 22*(4), 206–213. doi:10.1016/j.siny.2017.03.002; Wilson, C. B., Nizet, V., Maldonado, Y. A., Remington, J. S., & Klein, J. O. (2016). *Remington and Klein's infectious diseases of the fetus and newborn infant* (8th ed.). Philadelphia, PA: Elsevier/Saunders.

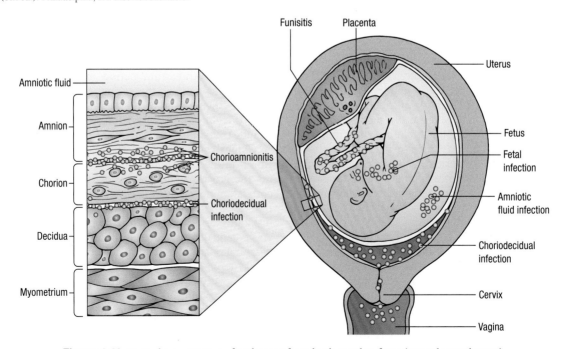

Figure 4.11 Vertical transmission of pathogens from birth canal to fetus (transplacental route).

exposure to broad-spectrum antibiotics increases the risk for chronic drug resistance as well as hearing deficits.

Transient Tachypnea of the Newborn. Transient tachypnea of the newborn (TTN) occurs in approximately 3% to 5% of all near-term or term neonates and results in prolonged hospitalizations for neonates, who are frequently admitted to neonatal intensive care units (NICUs) when compared to uncomplicated deliveries (Kassab, Khriesat, & Anabrees, 2015; Parker & Kinsella, 2018). Risk factors for TTN include male gender, prematurity, maternal diabetes, fetal macrosomia, and birth by cesarean section without a trial of labor (Kassab et al., 2015; Parker & Kinsella, 2018).

The pathogenesis of TTN begins during the transition to extrauterine life. As described earlier in this chapter, successful transition involves the clearance of fetal lung fluid from the pulmonary bed. The reabsorption of fetal lung fluid normally occurs via transport of Na^+ through ENa channels. Failed reabsorption of fetal lung fluid leads to tachypnea and delayed transition to extrauterine life (Crowley, 2015; Parker & Kinsella, 2018). Elective cesarean delivery is associated with reduced endogenous catecholamine secretion and stunted resorption of fetal lung fluid.

Clinical manifestations of TTN include respiratory rates higher than 60 breaths per minute often accompanied by cyanosis, retractions, and grunting. Radiographic findings include mild hyperinflation with increased perihilar markings and fluid trapped within fissures of one or both lungs. Significant laboratory findings may include elevated inflammatory markers.

TTN is considered a diagnosis of exclusion, as the manifestations described previously overlap with other respiratory diseases. The neonatal clinician must rule out more significant causes for tachypnea before settling on the diagnosis of TTN, as delays in treatment of congenital cardiac or pulmonary disease processes may confer deleterious consequences for the newborn and family unit. Life-span implications are associated with any associated defects or disease process; TTN is self-limiting and typically resolves within the first 72 to 96 hours of life.

Meconium Aspiration Syndrome (MAS). Meconium, a complex mixture of bile acids, vernix, hair, epithelial cells, mucus, and blood, is first seen in the fetal ileum between 10 to 16 weeks gestation (Stenson & Smith, 2012; Whitsett, Rice, Pryhuber, & Wert 2016). Meconium is not normally excreted during fetal development and the birth process; its release is a response to hypoxic/ischemic stress (Gien & Kinsella, 2017; Parker & Kinsella, 2018). The frequency of neonates born through meconium-stained amniotic fluid (MSAF) increases with advancing gestational age. Approximately 5% to 10% of all liveborn infants pass meconium in utero; approximately 1.5% of those infants who stool in utero go on to aspirate meconium (Gien & Kinsella, 2017; Parker & Kinsella, 2018). Abnormal fetal heart rate tracings (tachycardia and bradycardia) or evidence of chorioamnionitis/funisitis have been identified as predictive indicators for neonates at a higher risk for developing MAS and increase the likelihood of a poor perinatal outcome (Lee et al., 2016; Whitsett et al., 2016).

The impetus for meconium passage in term and post-term neonates is, therefore, attributed to fetal hypoxic/ischemic stress with advancing maturation of intestinal peristalsis. Fetal hypoxia has long been understood to increase the incidence of fetal passage of meconium in utero. Any mechanism which reduces blood flow through the umbilical cord stresses the fetus and induces vagal stimulation. Increased parasympathetic tone increases intestinal peristalsis and relaxation of the anal sphincter, which permits the passage of meconium in utero (Whitsett et al., 2016).

Aspiration of meconium into the trachea and lungs can result in several pathological changes to the lung parenchyma. The pathophysiology of MAS is multi-focal and includes a ball-valve effect of obstruction by particulate meconium in the distal airways of the lung, inactivation of surfactant, and development of pneumonitis. Alveolar overdistension and gas trapping caused by meconium particles blocking the distal airways during expiration increases the risk of air leaks and may result in an increased anterior-to-posterior diameter, or barrel-chest appearance (Stenson & Smith, 2012; Whitsett et al., 2016). Cholesterol and bile acids found in meconium have been demonstrated to inactivate pulmonary surfactant in the lung and impair its performance (Lopez-Rodriguez, Echaide, Cruz, Taeusch, & Perez-Gil, 2011; Perez-Gil & Weaver, 2010). Damage to the type II pneumocyte can lead to further dysfunctions in the production, recycling, and secretion of surfactant (Stenson & Smith, 2012). A chemical pneumonitis, or inflammatory response, further causes damage to the lung epithelium resulting in pulmonary vasoconstriction, alveolar edema, and imbalances of the vasoactive properties (ET-1, NO, PGI2) needed to establish a successful transition to extrauterine life (Lee et al., 2016; Whitsett et al., 2016). Pulmonary vasoconstriction raises PVR over SVR, which encourages a postnatal right to left shunting across the foramen ovale and clinically observed hypoxemia (Figure 4.12).

The clinical presentation of a neonate with MAS is variable but frequently includes worsening respiratory distress with cyanosis (Stenson & Smith, 2012). Respiratory symptoms include cyanosis, tachypnea, grunting, and a prolonged expiratory phase (Whitsett et al., 2016). Severely affected neonates may manifest with air leak syndrome or persistent pulmonary hypertension. Meconium staining to the skin, umbilical cord, or nail beds may be evident.

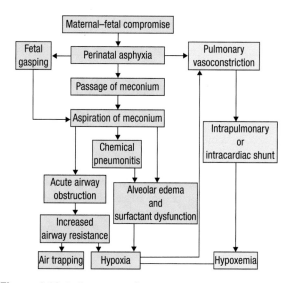

Figure 4.12 Pathogenesis of meconium aspiration syndrome.

Source: Adapted from MacDonald, M. G., Mullett, M. D., & Seshia, M. M. K. (Eds.). (2005). *Avery's neonatology: Pathophysiology and management of the newborn* (6th ed). Philadelphia, PA: Lippincott Williams & Wilkins.

Radiographic findings of neonates with MAS include course, diffuse, and heterogeneous infiltrates with areas of hyperaeration (similar to TTN). Overinflation often displaces the left and right diaphragm to the 10th and 11th ribs.

There is a wide range of possible long-term outcomes which are contingent upon the severity of injury incurred during the disease process and recovery phase; outcomes include progression to BPD. Pharmacologic adjuncts used during management of the disease process may increase the risk for abstinence and other neurodevelopmental consequences.

Persistent Pulmonary Hypertension of the Newborn. Persistent pulmonary hypertension of the newborn (PPHN) involves circulatory maladaptation or maldevelopment, which leads to a failed intrauterine to extrauterine transition and pulmonary arterial hypertension (Simonneau et al., 2013). As many as two of every 1,000 infants develop PPHN. Of infants who present with primary respiratory failure, mild PPHN is associated with 10% of all cases, while moderate to severe PPHN is associated with 2% to 6% of all cases (Lakshminrusimha & Steinhorn, 2017; Steinhorn, 2013). Common risk factors for primary, or *maladaptive*, PPHN include MAS, RDS, sepsis, pneumonia, and perinatal asphyxia (Lakshminrusimha & Steinhorn, 2017). Common risk factors for *maldevelopmental, Karotkin, Keszler, & Suresh PPHN* include congenital heart disease, congenital diaphragmatic hernia (CDH), and pulmonary hypoplasia.

The pathogenesis of primary PPHN focuses on deranged pulmonary vascular structure, reactivity, and right ventricular responses to high afterload. Less frequently, PPHN is the result of increased pulmonary blood flow or left ventricular dysfunction, causing an increase in capillary wedge pressures. Physiologically, increased pulmonary vasoconstriction raises PVR above that of SVR. This elevated PVR discourages blood flow through the right ventricle and pulmonary system, shunting the blood in a right-to-left direction across the foramen ovale and through the ductus arteriosus. The ventilation-perfusion mismatch (V/Q) leads to hypoxemia. In these situations, a discordance in pulse oximetry readings, with elevated preductal oxygen saturations compared to those obtained at a postductal location, is common.

Chronic pulmonary hypertension, also known as *pulmonary hypertension of infancy*, is commonly considered a comorbidity of other primary pulmonary diseases and manifests as altered pulmonary vascular development. New evidence also suggests that this pulmonary vascular maldevelopment may occur during early angiogenesis, secondary to interactions between environmental (in utero), epigenetic factors, and disrupted signaling pathways. These dysfunctional interactions lead to abnormal pulmonary vascular growth, which in turn contributes to narrowing of pulmonary vessel diameter, reduced compliance, and a noted reduction in available alveolar surface area for gas exchange (Abman, Baker, Gien, Mourani, & Galambos, 2014; Lakshminrusimha & Steinhorn, 2017).

Chronic PPHN is associated with increased mortality as well as increased healthcare costs during infancy. Among children, exercise intolerance, respiratory infections, and respiratory compromise are reported. Pulmonary arterial hypertension is common among affected adults (Lakshminrusimha & Steinhorn, 2017; Mourani & Abman, 2013; Naumberg et al., 2015).

Pulmonary Air Leaks. Air leaks include a spectrum of disorders that involve alveolar rupture and collapse with subsequent air leak into the interstitium or pleural spaces (Table 4.14). Pneumothorax, the most commonly identified air leak among newborns, affects approximately 2% to 10% of premature infants with a birth weight up to 1,500 grams (Figure 4.13; Goldsmith, Karotkin, Keszler, & Suresh, 2017). Air leak is associated with symptomatic respiratory distress in 0.05% to 0.07% of affected newborns (Duong et al., 2014; Whitsett et al., 2016). The most common etiology for air leak syndrome is supraphysiologic respiratory support by way of mechanical respiratory support devices. Additional risk factors for air leaks are summarized in Table 4.15.

Secondary to the pressures needed to establish pulmonary function following delivery, air leaks occur more often in the neonatal period than at any other time of life. The pathogenesis involves leakage of air from an overdistended and subsequently ruptured alveolus into the

TABLE 4.14. Common Types of Pulmonary Air Leak

Type	Location of Air Accumulation
• Pneumothorax	• Thorax
• Pneumomediastinum	• Mediastinum
• Pneumopericardium	• Pericardial space
• Pneumoperitoneum	• Peritoneum
• Pulmonary interstitial emphysema	• Interstitium
• Subcutaneous emphysema	• Subcutaneous tissue

Source: Whitsett, J. A., Rice, W. R., Pryhuber, G. S., & Wert, S. E. (2016). Acute respiratory disorders. In M. G. MacDonald & M. M. K. Seshia (Eds.), *Avery's neonatology: Pathophysiology and management of the newborn* (7th ed., pp. 397–415). Baltimore, MD: Wolters Kluwer.

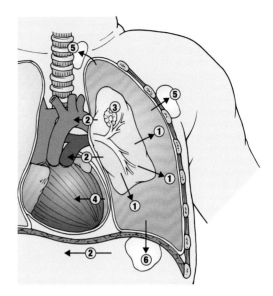

Figure 4.14 Air accumulation by type of air leak. 1, pneumothorax; 2, pneumomediastinum; 3, pulmonary interstitial emphysema; 4, pneumopericardium; 5, subcutaneous emphysema; 6, pneumoperitoneum. Arrows: directions of air leaks.

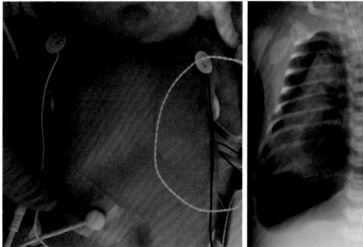
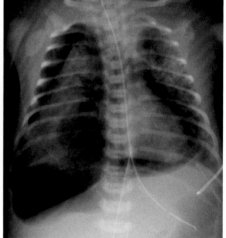

Figure 4.13 Right pneumothorax.

TABLE 4.15. Common Risk Factors for Air Leak

Disease Processes	Procedural	Management
• Prematurity (< 28 weeks *or* >36 weeks of gestation) • Pulmonary hypoplasia • Respiratory distress syndrome • Amniotic fluid aspiration • Infection	• Endotracheal intubation • Endotracheal suctioning • Needle thoracentesis	• ↑ Peak inspiratory pressures • ↑ Peak end-expiratory pressure • ↑ Tidal volume • ↑ Mean arterial pressures • Prolonged inspiratory time (>0.5 seconds)

Source: Duong, H. H., Mirea, L., Shah, P. S., Yange, J., Lee, S. K., & Sankaran, K. (2014). Pneumothorax in neonates: Trends, predictors, and outcomes. *Journal of Neonatal and Perinatal Medicine, 7*, 29–38. doi:10.3233/NPM-1473813

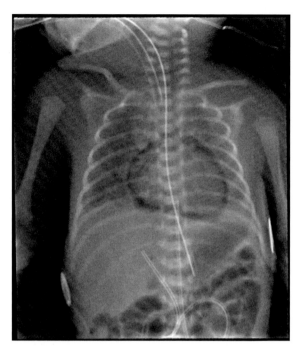

Figure 4.15 Pneumopericardium.

perivascular and tracheobronchial tree (Figure 4.14). The air either may remain trapped in the interstitium or track into the mediastinal spaces or pleural space (Whitsett et al., 2016).

Clinical manifestations may include respiratory distress, grunting, tachypnea, retractions, and cyanosis with increased severity of symptoms noted when large air leaks result in lung collapse and mediastinal shift (Whitsett et al., 2016). Tension pneumothoraces are associated with decreased breath sounds on the affected side, an increased anterior–posterior diameter on the affected side, and the potential for acute hypotension and cardiovascular collapse if left uncorrected. Like tension pneumothoraces, a significant pneumopericardium may impose excessive pressure upon the heart and manifest as with acute hemodynamic decompensation and cardiac tamponade (Figure 4.15). Radiographic findings aid in the differentiation of air leaks. For example, radiographic evidence of a pneumothorax includes an area of hyperlucency without superimposed pulmonary vascular markings. Radiographic evidence of a pneumo-mediastinum yields elevation of the thymic lobes, often called a *spinnaker sail sign* (Jeng, Lee, Tsao, & Soong, 2012).

Neonates who develop air leaks are at an increased risk of death and disability, with mortality rates greater than 50% for premature neonates who develop pulmonary interstitial emphysema.

CONCLUSION

One of the most common reasons for admission to the NICU is respiratory dysfunction. The test of successful mastery of the understanding of respiratory development and function is the ability of providers to explain the complex concepts to the parents and families of infants under their care.

ACKNOWLEDGMENT

The authors would like to thank Dr. Juan Ruiz for his support in the development of this chapter.

LEARNING TOOLS AND RESOURCES

Podcast

 Surfactant, Surface Tension, and LaPlace

Janice L. Wilson and Jennifer Fitzgerald

Discussion Prompts

1. Identify the major developmental milestones that occur during the major stages of lung development. At which stage is the lung considered viable and how might maternal health influences implicate normal lung development?

2. Discuss the short-term and long-term complications associated with pneumothorax, persistent pulmonary hypertension, and chronic lung disease.

3. Discuss the role of the neonatal nurse practitioner in counseling the family of an extremely low birth-weight infant, now 32 weeks postnatal age, who requires >30% oxygen by nasal cannula. What resources are available that offer predictive ability for risk for bronchopulmonary dysplasia?

Advice From the Authors

"As one of the most common reasons for admission to the Neonatal Intensive Care Unit, the care of fragile neonates very often centers around respiratory dysfunction. The successful mastery of understanding complex neonatal respiratory development and function is often measured by the passing of a test or by presenting your patient(s) to the satisfaction of the healthcare team on rounds. While these milestones are important, the ability to explain intricate concepts to the families of the children you care for is the true metric of success. I challenge you to take that family-centered approach to learning as you read this chapter."

–Jennifer Fitzgerald, DNP, CRNP, NNP-BC

"The learning and understanding of fetal/neonatal anatomy and physiology should be an integral part of linking the care provided to infants at the bedside with the fundamental scientific concepts and principles presented in this chapter and in this book. The goal of learning should go beyond the memorization of specific details in order to pass a test or to pass a certification exam. Understanding physiology in general (and in this instance respiratory physiology specifically) allows students of all levels to build a framework that facilitates an individualized approach to diagnosis, management, and care. You may find it useful to jot down a list of key points for each section of the chapter and go back to those key points when you need to review specific content. When you enter the clinical arena, ask yourself questions about the patient at the bedside. For example, WHAT physiologic mechanisms explain WHY an infant might have an increase in respiratory effort or work of breathing? If you develop a better understanding of the WHAT and the WHY you will have a better understanding of HOW to care for newborns."

–Janice L. Wilson, DNP, CRNP, NNP-BC

Mind Maps

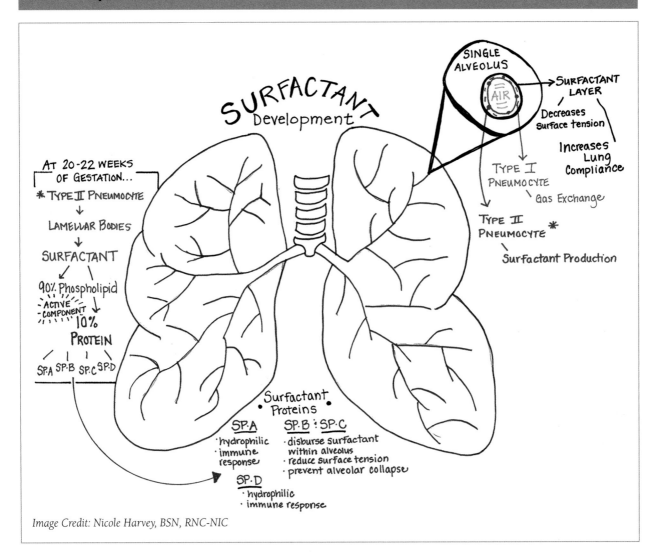

Image Credit: Nicole Harvey, BSN, RNC-NIC

Note: This mind map reflects one student's interpretation of a portion of one or more concepts addressed in this chapter. Readers should regard the mind maps woven throughout this textbook as examples of multi-sensory study tools that can be developed to encourage conceptual understanding. Readers are encouraged to develop their own unique mind maps in consultation with academic faculty or clinical preceptors.

TIMELINE OF ORGAN DEVELOPMENT

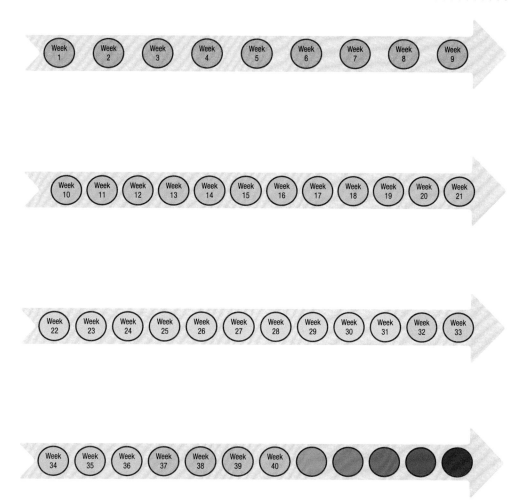

NOTE:
Placement of common problems is meant to offer visual/conceptual perspective on the timing of onset of these commonly reported malformations. Variation exists across the literature.

LEGEND
<22 – 27 6/7 weeks = extremely preterm
28 – 31 6/7 weeks = very preterm
32 – 36 6/7 weeks = late/moderate preterm
37 – 40 weeks = term

References

Abman, S. H., Baker, C., Gien, J., Mourani, P., & Galambos, P. (2014). The Robyn Barst Memorial lecture: Differences between the fetal, newborn, and adult pulmonary circulations: Relevance for age-specific therapies. *Pulmonary Circulation, 4*(3), 424–440. doi:10.1086/677371

Abman, S. H., Bancalari, E., & Jobe, A. (2017). The evolution of bronchopulmonary dysplasia after 50 years. *American Journal of Respiratory and Critical Care Medicine, 195*(4), 421–424. doi:10.1164/rccm.201611-2386ED

Agassandian, M., & Mallampalli, R. K. (2013). Surfactant phospholipid metabolism. *Biochimica et Biophysica Acta, 1831*(3), 612–625. doi:10.1016/j.bbalip.2012.09.010

Akella, A., & Desphande, S. B. (2013). Pulmonary surfactants and their role in pathophysiology of lung disorders. *Indian Journal of Experimental Biology, 51*(1), 5–22.

Alvira, C. M. (2016). Aberrant pulmonary vascular growth and remodeling in bronchopulmonary dysplasia. *Frontiers in Medicine, 3*(21), 1–14. doi:10.3389/fmed.2016.00021

Ameis, S., Khoshgoo, H., & Keijzer, R. (2017). Abnormal lung development in congenital diaphragmatic hernia. *Seminars in Pediatric Surgery, 26*, 123–128. doi:10.1053/j.sempedsurg.2017.04.011

American College of Obstetricians and Gynecologists. (2016). Committee opinion no. 677: Antenatal corticosteroid therapy for lung maturity. *Obstetrics and Gynecology, 128*, e187–e194. doi:10.1097/AOG.0000000000001715

Bajaj, K., & Gross, S. J. (2015). Aspects of perinatal disease and prenatal diagnosis. In R. J. Martin & A. A. Fanaroff (Eds.), *Fanaroff and Martin's neonatal–perinatal medicine: Diseases of the fetus and infant* (10th ed., pp. 130–138). Philadelphia. PA: Elsevier.

Baker, C. D., & Abman, S. H. (2015). Impaired pulmonary vascular development in bronchopulmonary dysplasia. *Neonatology, 107*(4), 344–351. doi:10.1159/000381129

Bancalari, E. H., & Jain, D. (2017). Pathophysiology of bronchopulmonary dysplasia. In R. A. Polin, S. H. Abman, D. H. Rowitch, W. E. Benitz, & W. W. Fox (Eds.), *Fetal and neonatal physiology* (5th ed., pp. 1625–1631). Philadelphia, PA: Elsevier.

Biyyam, D. R., Chapman, T., Ferguson, M. R., Deutsch, G., & Dighe, M. K. (2010). Congenital lung abnormalities: Embryologic features, prenatal diagnosis, and postnatal radiologic–pathologic correlation. *RadioGraphics, 30*(6), 1721–1739. doi:10.1148/rg.306105508

Britt, R. D., Jr., Faksh, A., Vogel, E., Martin, R. J., Pabelick, C. M., & Prakash, Y. S. (2013). Perinatal factors in neonatal and pediatric lung diseases. *Expert Review of Respiratory Medicine, 7*(5), 515–531. doi:10.1586/17476348.2013.838020

Calzolari, F., Braguglia, A., Valfrè, L., Dotta, A., Bagolan, P., & Morini, F. (2016). Outcome of infants operated on for congenital pulmonary malformations. *Pediatric Pulmonology, 51*, 1367–1372. doi:10.1002/ppul.23472

Casagrande, A., & Pederiva, F. (2016). Association between congenital lung malformations and lung tumors in children and adults: A systemic review. *Journal of Thoracic Oncology, 11*(11), 1837–1845. doi:10.1016/j.jtho.2016.06.023

Chandrasekharan, P. K., Rawat, M., Madappa, R., Rothstein, D. H., & Lakshminrusimha, S. (2017). Congenital diaphragmatic hernia: A review. *Maternal Health, Neonatology and Perinatology, 3*(6), 1–16. doi:10.1186/s40748-017-0045-1

Chowdhury, M. M., & Chakraborty, S. (2015). Imaging of congenital lung malformations. *Seminars in Pediatric Surgery, 24*, 168–175. doi:10.1053/j.sempedsurg.2015.02.001

Copland, I., & Post, M. (2004). Lung development and fetal lung growth. *Paediatric Respiratory Reviews, 5*(Suppl. 1), S259–S264. doi:10.1016/S1526-0542(04)90049-8

Correia-Pinta, J., Gonzaga, S., Huang, Y., & Rottier, R. (2010). Congenital lung lesions—Underlying molecular mechanisms. *Seminars in Pediatric Surgery, 19*, 171–179. doi:10.1053/j.sempedsurg.2010.03.003

Cotton, M. C. (2017). Pulmonary hypoplasia. *Seminars in Fetal and Neonatal Medicine, 22*, 250–255. doi:10.1016/j.siny.2017.06.004

Crowley, A. (2015). Neonatal respiratory disorders. In R. J. Martin, A. A. Fanaroff, & M. C. Walsh (Eds.), *Fanaroff and Martin's neonatal–perinatal medicine: Diseases of the fetus and infant* (10th ed., pp. 1113–1136). Philadelphia, PA: Elsevier/Saunders.

Cystic Fibrosis Foundation. (n.d.). Understanding changes in life expectancy. Retrieved from https://www.cff.org/Research/Researcher-Resources/Patient-Registry/2016-Patient-Registry-Reports

Danzer, E., Zarnow, D., Gerdes, M., D'Agostino, J. A., Siegle, J., Bebbington, M. W., ... Hedrick, H. L. (2012). Abnormal brain development and maturation on magnetic resonance imaging in survivors of severe congenital diaphragmatic hernia. *Journal of Pediatric Surgery, 47*(3), 453–461. doi:10.1016/j.jpedsurg.2011.10.002

David, M., Lamas-Pinheiro, R., & Henriques-Coelho, T. (2016). Prenatal and postnatal management of congenital pulmonary airway malformation. *Neonatology, 110*, 101–115. doi:10.1159/00044894

Duong, H. H., Mirea, L., Shah, P. S., Yange, J., Lee, S. K., & Sankaran, K. (2014). Pneumothorax in neonates: Trends, predictors, and outcomes. *Journal of Neonatal and Perinatal Medicine, 7*, 29–38. doi:10.3233/NPM-1473813

Durell, J., & Lakhoo, K. (2014). Congenital cystic lesions of the lung. *Early Human Development, 90*, 935–939. doi:10.1016/j.earlhumdev.2014.09.014

Figueras, F., & Gardosi, J. (2011). Intrauterine growth restriction: New concepts in antenatal surveillance, diagnosis, and management. *American Journal of Obstetrics and Gynecology, 204*(4), 288–300. doi:10.1016/j.ajog.2010.08.055

Fowler, D. J., & Gould, S. J. (2015). The pathology of congenital lung lesions. *Seminars in Pediatric Surgery, 24*(4), 176–182. doi:10.1053/j.sempedsurg.2015.02.002

Gao, Y., & Raj, J. U. (2010). Regulation of the pulmonary circulation in the fetus and newborn. *Physiology Review, 90*, 1291–1335. doi:10.1152/physrev.00032.2009

Gien, J., & Kinsella, J. P. (2017). Pathophysiology of meconium aspiration syndrome. In R. A. Polin, S. H. Abman, D. H. Rowitch, W. E. Benitz, & W. W. Fox (Eds.), *Fetal and neonatal physiology* (5th ed., pp. 1619–1624). Philadelphia, PA: Elsevier.

Goldsmith, J. P., Karotkin, E. H., Keszler, M., & Suresh, G. K. (Eds.). (2017). *Assisted ventilation of the neonate: An evidence-based approach to newborn respiratory care* (6th ed.). Philadelphia, PA: Elsevier.

Guglani, L., Lakshminrusimha, S., & Ryan, R. M. (2008). Transient tachypnea of the newborn. *Pediatrics in Review, 29*, e59–e65. doi:10.1542/pir.29-11-e59

Han, S., & Mallampalli, R. K. (2015). The acute respiratory distress syndrome: From mechanism to translation. *Journal of Immunology, 194*(3), 855–860. doi:10.4049/jimmunol.1402513

Hillman, N., Kallapur, S. G., & Jobe, A. (2012). Physiology of transition from intrauterine to extrauterine life.

Clinics in Perinatology, 39(4), 769–783. doi:10.1016/j.clp.2012.09.009

Hong, C., Yu, G., Tang, J., Liu, Q., & Xia, B. (2017). Risk analysis and outcomes of bronchopulmonary sequestrations. *Pediatric Surgery International, 33*(9), 971–975. doi:10.1007/s00383-017-4097-0

Hooven, T. A., & Polin, R. A. (2017). Pneumonia. *Seminars in Fetal and Neonatal Medicine, 22*(4), 206–213. doi:10.1016/j.siny.2017.03.002

Hsu, J., Lee, Y., Lin, C., Li, F., Jeng, M., Soong, W., … Tang, R. (2012). Primary congenital pulmonary hypoplasia of a neonate. *Journal of the Chinese Medical Association, 75,* 87–90. doi:10.1016/j.jcma.2011.12.004

Islam, J. Y., Keller, R. L., Aschner, J. L., Hartet, T. V., & Moore, P. E. (2015). Understanding the short- and long-term respiratory outcomes of prematurity and bronchopulmonary dysplasia. *American Journal of Respiratory and Critical Care Medicine, 192*(2), 134–156. doi:10.1164/rccm.201412-2142PP

Jackson, J. C. (2018). Respiratory disorders in the preterm infant. In C. A. Gleason & S. E. Juul (Eds.), *Avery's diseases of the newborn* (10th ed., pp. 653–667). Philadelphia, PA: Elsevier.

Javia, L., Harris, M. A., & Fuller, S. (2016). Rings, slings, and other tracheal disorders in the neonate. *Seminars in Fetal & Neonatal Medicine, 21,* 277–284. doi:10.1016/j.siny.2016.03.005

Jeng, M., Lee, Y., Tsao, P., & Soong, W. (2012). Neonatal air leak syndrome and the role of high-frequency ventilation in its prevention. *Journal of the Chinese Medical Association, 75,* 551–559. doi:10.1016/j.jcma.2012.08.001

Jobe, A. H., Kallapur, S. G., & Kramer, B. W. (2012). Perinatal events and their influence on lung development and function. In E. Bancalari & R. A. Polin (Eds.), *The newborn lung: Neonatology questions and controversies* (2nd ed., pp. 57–90). Philadelphia, PA: Elsevier Saunders.

Kallapur, S. G., & Jobe, A. H. (2015). Lung development and maturation. In R. J. Martin & A. A. Fanaroff (Eds.), *Fanaroff and Martin's neonatal–perinatal medicine: Diseases of the fetus and infant* (10th ed., pp. 1042–1048). Philadelphia, PA: Elsevier.

Kallapur, S. G., & Kotecha, S. (2016). Perinatal modifiers of lung structure and function. In A. Jobe, J. Whitsett, & S. Abman (Eds.), *Fetal and neonatal lung development: Clinical correlates and technologies for the future* (pp. 187–206). New York, NY: Cambridge University Press.

Kassab, M., Khriesat, W. M., & Anabrees, J. (2015). Diuretics for transient tachypnoea of the newborn. *Cochrane Database of Systematic Reviews, 2015*(11), CD003064. doi:10.1002/14651858.CD003064.pub3

Katheria, A., & Finer, N. N. (2018). Newborn resuscitation. In C. A. Gleason & S. E. Juul (Eds.), *Avery's diseases of the newborn* (10th ed., pp. 273-288). Philadelphia, PA: Elsevier.

Katz, C., Bentur, L., & Elias, N. (2011). Clinical implication of fetal lung fluid balance in the perinatal period. *Journal of Perinatology, 31,* 230–235. doi:10.1038/jp.2010.134

Keller, R. L., & Ballard, R. A. (2018). Bronchopulmonary dysplasia. In C. A. Gleason & S. E. Juul (Eds.), *Avery's diseases of the newborn* (10th ed., pp. 678–694). Philadelphia, PA: Elsevier.

Keszler, M., & Abubakar, K. (2017). Physiologic principles. In J. P. Goldsmith, E. H. Karotkin, M. Keszler, & G. K. Suresh (Eds.), *Assisted ventilation of the neonate* (6th ed., pp. 8–30). Philadelphia, PA: Elsevier Saunders.

Kültürsay, N., Uygur, Ö., & Yalaz, M. (2014). The use of surfactant in the neonatal period-the known aspects, those still under research and those which need to be investigated further. *Turkish Archives of Pediatrics/Türk Pediatri Arşivi, 49*(1), 1–12. doi:10.5152/tpa.2014.963

Kumar, V. H. S. (2015). Current concepts in the management of congenital diaphragmatic hernia in infants. *Indian Journal of Surgery, 77*(4), 313–321. doi:10.1007/s12262-015-1286-8

Kunzmann, S., Collins, J. J. P., Kuypers, E., & Kramer, B. (2013). Thrown off balance: The effect of antenatal inflammation on the developing lung and immune system. *American Journal of Obstetrics and Gynecology, 208*(6), 429–437. doi:10.1016/j.ajog.2013.01.008

Kwong, K. W. (2015). Current updates on choanal atresia. *Frontiers in Pediatrics, 3*(52), 1–7. doi:10.3389/fped.2015.0052

Lakshminrusimha, S., & Steinhorn, R. H. (2017). Pathophysiology of persistent pulmonary hypertension of the newborn. In R. A. Polin, S. H. Abman, D. H. Rowtich, W. E. Benitz, & W. W. Fox. (Eds.), *Fetal and neonatal physiology* (5th ed., pp. 1576–1588). Philadelphia, PA: Elsevier.

Lally, P. A., & Skarsgard, E. D. (2017). Congenital diaphragmatic hernia: The role of multi-institutional collaboration and patient registries in supporting best practice. *Seminars in Pediatric Surgery, 26,* 129-135. doi:10.1053/j,sempeds.2017.04.004

Le Cras, T. D., & Rabinovitch, M. (2016). Pulmonary vascular development. In A. Jobe, J. Whitsett, & S. Abman (Eds.), *Fetal and neonatal lung development: Clinical correlates and technologies for the future* (pp. 34–57). New York, NY: Cambridge University Press.

Lee, J., Romero, R., Lee, K. A., Kim, E. N., Korzeniewski, S. J., Chaemsaithong, P., & Yoon, B. Y. (2016). Meconium aspiration syndrome: A role for fetal systemic inflammation. *American Journal of Obstetrics and Gynecology, 214*(3), 366.e1–366.e9. doi:10.1016/j.ajog.2015.10.009

Locci, G., Fanos, V., Gerosa, C., & Faa, G. (2014). Hyaline membrane disease (HMD): The role of the perinatal pathologist. *Journal of Pediatric and Neonatal Individualized Medicine, 3*(2), e030255. doi:10.7363/030255

Lopez-Rodriguez, E., Echaide, M., Cruz, A., Taeusch, W., & Perez-Gil, J. (2011). Meconium impairs pulmonary surfactant by a combined action of cholesterol and bile acids. *Biophysical Journal, 100,* 646–655. doi:10.1016/j.bpj.2010.12.3715

Lykkedegn, S., Sorenson, G. L., Beck-Nielsen, S. S., & Christesen, H. T. (2015). The impact of vitamin D on fetal and neonatal lung maturation: A systematic review. *American Journal of Physiology—Lung Cellular and Molecular Physiology, 308,* L587–L602. doi:10.1152/ajplung.00117.2014

MacDonald, M. G., Mullett, M. D., & Seshia, M. M. K. (Eds.). (2005). *Avery's neonatology: Pathophysiology and management of the newborn* (6th ed). Philadelphia, PA: Lippincott Williams & Wilkins.

MacDonald, M. G., & Seshia, M. M. K. (2016). *Avery's neonatology: Pathophysiology and management of the newborn* (7th ed.). Philadelphia, PA: Wolters Kluwer.

Madurga, A., Mizíková, I., Ruiz-Camp, J., & Morty, R. E. (2013). Recent advances in late lung development and the pathogenesis of bronchopulmonary dysplasia. *American Journal of Physiology— Lung Cellular and Molecular Physiology, 305*(12), L893–L905. doi:10.1152/ajplung.00267.2013

Maeda, H. (2007). Supramolecular chemistry of acyclic oligopyrroles. *European Journal of Organic Chemistry, 2007*(32), 5313–5325. doi:10.1002/ejoc.200700382

Malleske, D. (2015). Book review: *Advances in fetal and neonatal physiology. American Journal of Human Biology, 27*(5), 739–740. doi:10.1002/ajhb.22768

March of Dimes. (n.d.). Peristats. Retrieved from http://www.marchofdimes.org/Peristats/ViewSubtopic.aspx?reg=99&top=17&stop=350&lev=1&slev=1&obj=1

Marinicak, S. J., & Lomas, D. A. (2017). Inherited pulmonary disorders. In *Encyclopedia of Life Sciences*. Chichester, UK: John Wiley. doi:10.1002/9780470015902.a0005517.pub3

Mayor, R. S., Finch, K. E., Zehr, J., Morselli, E., Neinast, M. D., Frank, A. P., ... Clegg, D. J. (2015). Maternal high-fat diet is associated with impaired fetal lung development. *American Journal of Physiology—Lung Cellular and Molecular Physiology*, *309*(4), L360–L368. doi:10.1152/ajplung.00105.2015

McNamara, P. J., & El-Khuffash, A. (2017). Oxygen transport and delivery. In R. A. Polin, S. H. Abman, D. H. Rowtich, W. E. Benitz, & W. W. Fox. (Eds.), *Fetal and neonatal physiology* (5th ed., pp. 724–737). Philadelphia, PA: Elsevier.

Metcalfe, A., Lisonkova, S., Sabr, Y., Stritzke, A., & Joseph, K. (2017). Neonatal respiratory morbidity following exposure to chorioamnionitis. *BMC Pediatrics*, *17*(1), 1–7. doi:10.1186/s12887-017-0878-9

Moore, K. L., Persaud, T. V. N., & Torchia, M. G. (Eds.). (2016). *The developing human: Clinically oriented embryology* (10th ed.). Philadelphia, PA: Elsevier.

Mourani, P., & Abman, S. H. (2013). Pulmonary vascular disease in bronchopulmonary dysplasia: Pulmonary hypertension and beyond. *Pulmonology*, *25*, 329–337. doi:10.1097/MOP.0b013e328360a3f6

Nair, J., & Lakshminrusimha, S. (2014). Update on PPHN: Mechanisms and treatment. *Seminars in Perinatology*, *38*, 78–91. doi:10.1053/j.semperi.2013.11.004

National Institutes of Health. (2018a). Genetic home reference: Congenital diaphragmatic hernia. Retrieved from https://ghr.nlm.nih.gov/condition/congenital-diaphragmatic-hernia#statistics

National Institutes of Health. (2018b). Genetic home reference: Cystic fibrosis. Retrieved from https://ghr.nlm.nih.gov/condition/cystic-fibrosis#statistics

National Institutes of Health. (2018c). Genetic home reference: Esophageal atresia/tracheoesophageal fistula. Retrieved from https://ghr.nlm.nih.gov/condition/esophageal-atresia-tracheoesophageal-fistula

National Institutes of Health. (2018d). Genetics home reference: Surfactant dysfunction. Retrieved from https://ghr.nlm.nih.gov/condition/surfactant-dysfunction#statistics

Naumberg, E., Axelson, I., Huber, D., & Soderstrom, L. (2015). Some neonatal risk factors for adult pulmonary arterial hypertension remain unknown. *Foundation Acta Paediatrica*, *104*, 1104–1108. doi:10.1111/apa.13205

Noritz, G., Madden, M., Roldan, D., Wheeler, T. A., Conkol, K, Brilli, R. J., ... Gleeson, S. (2017). A population intervention to improve outcomes in children with medical complexity. *Pediatrics*, *139*(1), e20153076. doi:10.1542/peds.2015-3076

Oakley, R. H., & Cidlowski, J. A. (2013). The biology of the glucocorticoid receptor: New signaling mechanisms in health and disease. *Journal of Allergy and Clinical Immunology*, *132*(5), 1033–1044. doi:10.1016/j.jaci.2013.09.007

Ohls, R. K. (2011). Core concepts: The biology of hemoglobin. *NeoReviews* 12(1), e29–e38. doi:10.1542/neo.12-1-e29

Olutoye, O., Coleman, B., Hubbard, A. M., & Adzick, N. S. (2000). Prenatal diagnosis and management of congenital lobar emphysema. *Journal of Pediatric Surgery*, *35*, 792–795. doi:10.1053/jpsu.2000.6084

Pantich, H. B., Weiner, D. J., Feng, R., Perez, M. R., Healy, F., McDonough, J. M., ... Hedrick, H. L. (2014). Lung function over the first 3 years of life in children with congenital diaphragmatic hernia. *Pediatric Pulmonology*, *50*(9), 896–907. doi:10.1002/ppul.23082

Parker, T. A., & Kinsella, J. P. (2018). Respiratory disorders in the term infant. In C. A. Gleason & S. E. Juul (Eds.), *Avery's diseases of the newborn* (10th ed., pp. 668–677). Philadelphia, PA: Elsevier.

Parry, R. L. (2015). Selected gastrointestinal anomalies in neonates. In R. J. Martin, A. A. Fanaroff, & M. C. Wals (Eds.), *Fanaroff and Martin's neonatal–perinatal medicine: Diseases of the fetus and infant* (10th ed., pp. 1395–1400). Philadelphia, PA: Elsevier.

Patel, R. M., Kandefer, S., Walsh, M. C., Bell, E. F., Carlo, W. A., Laptook, A. R., ... Stoll, B. J. (2015). Causes and timing of death in extremely premature infants from 2000 through 2011. *New England Journal of Medicine*, *372*, 331–340. doi:10.1056/NEJMoa1403489

Paul, D. A., Zook, K., Mackley, A., & Locke, R. G. (2010). Reduced mortality and increased BPD with histological chorioamnionitis and leukocytosis in very-low-birth-weight infants. *Journal of Perinatology*, *30*, 58–62. doi:10.1038/jp.2009.113

Perez-Gil, J., & Weaver, T. E. (2010). Pulmonary surfactant pathophysiology: Current models and open questions. *Physiology*, *25*, 132–141. doi:10.1152/physiol.00006.2010

Pike, K., Pillow, J., & Lucas, J. S. (2012). Long term respiratory consequences of intrauterine growth restriction. *Seminars in Fetal and Neonatal Medicine*, *17*(2), 92–98. doi:10.1016/j.siny.2012.01.003

Polin, R. A., Abman, S. H., Rowitch, D. H., Benitz, W. E., & Fox, W. W. (2017). *Fetal and neonatal physiology* (5th ed.). Philadelphia, PA: Elsevier.

Pryce, D. M. (1946). Lower accessory pulmonary artery with intralobar sequestration of lung: A report of seven cases. *Journal of Pathology and Bacteriology*, *58*(3), 457–467. doi:10.1002/path.1700580316

Register, C. H., Jnah, A. J., & Newberry, D. (2016). Congenital diaphragmatic hernia: Interprofessional care of the neonate and family grounded in Swanson's theory of caring. *Neonatal Network*, *35*(6), 381–390. doi:10.1891/0730-0832.35.6.381

Respiratory distress of the newborn [image]. (2015). *In Wikimedia Commons*. Retrieved from https://commons.wikimedia.org/wiki/File:Respiratory_distress_of_the_newborn.jpg

Riley, C. A., Boozer, K., & King, T. L. (2011). Antenatal corticosteroids at the beginning of the 21st century. *Journal of Midwifery and Women's Health*, *56*, 591–597. doi:10.1111/j.1542-2011.2011.00119.x

Roberts, D., Brown, J., Medley, N., & Dalziel, S. R. (2017). Antenatal corticosteroids for accelerating fetal lung maturation for women at risk of preterm birth (Review). *Cochrane Database of Systematic Reviews*, *2017*(3) 1–266. doi:10.1002/14651858.CD004454.pub3

Rook, D., Schierbeek, H., Vento, M., Vlaardingerbroek, H., van der Eijk, A. C., Longini, M., ... Vermeulen, M. J. (2014). Resuscitation of preterm infants with different inspired oxygen fractions. *Journal of Pediatrics*, *164*(6), 1322–1326.e3. doi:10.1016/j.jpeds.2014.02.019

Sadler, T. W. (2015). *Langman's medical embryology* (13th ed.). Philadelphia, PA: Wolters Kluwer Health.

Sadreameli, S. C., & McGrath-Morrow, S. A. (2016). Respiratory care of infants and children with congenital trachea-oesophageal fistula and oesophageal atresia. *Paediatric Respiratory Reviews,* *17,* 16–23. doi:10.1016/j.prrv.2015.02.005

Sarper, A., Ayten, A., Golbasi, I., Demircan, A., & Isin, E. (2003). Bronchogenic cyst. *Texas Heart Institute Journal,* *30*(2), 105–108.

Schoenwolf, G. C., Bleyl, S. B., Brauer, P. R., & Francis-West, P. H. (2015). *Larsen's human embryology* (5th ed.). Philadelphia, PA: Churchill Livingstone.

Sfakianaki, A. K., & Copel, J. A. (2012). Congenital cystic lesions of the lung: Congenital cystic adenomatoid malformation and bronchopulmonary sequestration. *Reviews in Obstetrics & Gynecology,* *5*(2), 85–93. doi:10.3909/riog0183a

Simonneau, G., Gatzoulis, M. A., Adatia, I., Celermajer, D., Denton, C., Ghofrani, A., … Souza, R. (2013). Updated clinical classification of pulmonary hypertension. *Journal of the American College of Cardiology,* *62*(25 Suppl.), D34–D41. doi:10.1016/j.jacc.2013.10.029

Sosenko, I. R. S., & Bancalari, E. (2012). New developments in the pathogenesis and prevention of bronchopulmonary dysplasia. In E. Bancalari & R. A. Polin (Eds.), *The newborn lung: Neonatology questions and controversies* (2nd ed., pp. 57–90). Philadelphia, PA: Elsevier Saunders.

Spoonhower, K. A., & Davis, P. B. (2016). Epidemiology of cystic fibrosis. *Clinics in Chest Medicine,* *37*(1), 1–8. doi:10.1016/j.ccm.2015.10.002

Stark, Z. , Behrsin, J., Burgess, T., Ritchie, A., Yeung, A., Tan, T. Y., … Patel, N. (2015). SNP microarray abnormalities in a cohort of 28 infants with congenital diaphragmatic hernia. *American Journal of Medical Genetics, Part A,* *167*(10), 2319–2326. doi:10.1002/ajmg.a.37177

Steinhorn, R. H. (2013). Diagnosis and treatment of pulmonary hypertension in infancy. *Early Human Development,* *89,* 865–874. doi:10.1016/j.earlhumdev.2013.09.012

Stenson, B. J., & Smith, C. L. (2012). Management of meconium aspiration syndrome. *Paediatric Child Health,* *22*(12), 532–535. doi:10.1016/j.jnn.2015.05.002

Stevens, T. P., Blennow, M., Meyers, E. H., & Soll, R. (2007). Early surfactant administration with brief ventilation vs. selective surfactant and continued mechanical ventilation for preterm infants with or at risk for respiratory distress syndrome (Review). *Cochrane Database of Systematic Reviews,* *2007*(4), 1–32. doi:10.1002/14651858.CD003063.pub3

Stocker, J. T. (2009). Cystic lung disease in infants and children. *Fetal and Pediatric Pathology,* *28*(4), 155–184. doi:10.1080/15513810902984095

te Pas, A. B., & Hooper, S. (2016). Initiation of breathing at birth. In A. Jobe, J. Whitsett, & S. Abman (Eds.), *Fetal and neonatal lung development: Clinical correlates and technologies for the future* (pp. 164–186). New York, NY: Cambridge University Press.

Terlizzi, V., DiLullo, A. M., Comegna, M., Centrone, C., Pelo, E., Castaldo, G., … Braggion, C. (2018). SFTR is a new CFTR mutation typical of patients originally from Tuscany region in Italy. *Italian Journal of Pediatrics,* *44*(2), 1–7. doi:10.1186/s13052-017-0443-z

Trembath, A., & Laughon, M. M. (2012). Predictors of bronchopulmonary dysplasia. *Clinics in Perinatology,* *39*(3), 585–601. doi:10.1016/j.clp.2012.06.014

Triebwasser, J. E., & Treadwell, M. C. (2017). Prenatal prediction of pulmonary hypoplasia. *Seminars in Fetal and Neonatal Medicine,* *22,* 245–249. doi:10.1016/j.siny.2017.03.001

Universities of Fribourg, Lausanne, & Bern, Switzerland, (2006). Universities of Fribourg, Lausanne & Bern Switzerland. Retrieved from http://www.embryology.ch/genericpages/moduleorganoen.html

Valentine, C. J. (2012). Maternal dietary DHA supplementation to improve inflammatory outcomes in the preterm infant. *Advances in Nutrition: An International Review,* *3,* 370–376. doi:10.3945/an.111.001248

Van Woudenberg, C. D., Willis, C. A., & Rubarth, L. B. (2012). Newborn transition to extrauterine life. *Neonatal Network,* *31*(5), 317–322. doi:10.1891/0730-0832.31.5.317

Wapner, R. J. (2013). Antenatal corticosteroids for periviable birth. *Seminars in Perinatology,* *37,* 410–413. doi:10.1053/j.semperi.2013.06.024

Weaver, T. E., Nogee, L. M., & Jobe, A. H. (2016). Surfactant during lung development. In A. Jobe, J. Whitsett, & S. Abman (Eds.), *Fetal and neonatal lung development: Clinical correlates and technologies for the future* (pp. 141–163). New York, NY: Cambridge University Press.

Wert, S. (2017). Congenital pulmonary airway malformation. In R. A. Polin, S. H. Abman, D. H. Rowitch, W. E. Benitz, & W. W. Fox (Eds.), *Fetal and neonatal physiology* (5th ed., pp. 627–641). Philadelphia, PA: Elsevier.

Westover, A. J., & Moss, T. J. (2012). Effects of intrauterine infection or inflammation on fetal lung development. *Clinical and Experimental Pharmacology and Physiology,* *39*(9), 824–830. doi:10.1111/j.1440-1681.2012.05742.x

Whitsett, J. A., Rice, W. R., Pryhuber, G. S., & Wert, S. E. (2016). Acute respiratory disorders. In M. G. MacDonald & M. M. K. Seshia (Eds.), *Avery's neonatology: Pathophysiology and management of the newborn* (7th ed., pp. 397–415). Baltimore, MD: Wolters Kluwer.

Whitsett, J. A., Wert, S. E., & Weaver, T. E. (2015). Diseases of pulmonary surfactant homeostasis. *Annual Review of Pathology,* *24,* 371–393. doi:10.1146/annurev-path-012513-104644

Whitsett, J. A., & Xu, Y. (2016). Transcriptional mechanisms regulating pulmonary epithelial maturation: A systems biology approach. In A. Jobe, J. Whitsett, & S. Abman (Eds.), *Fetal and neonatal lung development: Clinical correlates and technologies for the future* (pp. 58–76). New York, NY: Cambridge University Press.

Wilson, C. B., Nizet, V., Maldonado, Y. A., Remington, J. S., & Klein, J. O. (Eds.). (2016). *Remington and Klein's infectious diseases of the fetus and newborn infant* (8th ed.). Philadelphia, PA: Elsevier/Saunders.

World Health Organization. (2016). Pneumonia. Retrieved from http://www.who.int/mediacentre/factsheets/fs331/en

Wu, S. (2012). Molecular bases for lung development, injury, and repair. In E. Bancalari & R. A Polin (Eds.), *The newborn lung: Neonatology questions and controversies* (2nd ed., pp. 3–16). Philadelphia, PA: Elsevier.

Zhang, H., Zhang, J., & Zhao, S. (2016). Airway damage of prematurity: The impact of prolonged intubation, ventilation, and chronic lung disease. *Seminars in Fetal & Neonatal Medicine,* *21,* 246–253. doi:10.1016/j.siny.2016.04.001

5

THE CARDIOVASCULAR SYSTEM

Jacqui Hoffman, Nicole Thompson-Bowie, and Amy J. Jnah

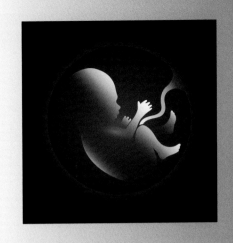

LEARNING OBJECTIVES

After completing this chapter, the reader should be able to:

- Understand normal cardiovascular system development.
- Analyze the physiologic function of the fetal and neonatal cardiovascular system.
- Discuss common inherited disorders and their effect on fetal and neonatal cardiovascular system development and function.
- Identify maternal health issues that have a potential impact on fetal and postnatal cardiovascular system development and function.
- Evaluate common disorders that affect the cardiovascular system and their implications across the life span.

INTRODUCTION

Congenital heart defects (CHDs) are defined as cardiovascular malformations of the structure of the heart or great vessels that are present at birth (Bouma & Mulder, 2017). CHDs are the most common type of congenital anomaly observed among neonates, and affect approximately 1% of all live-born infants in the United States (Abqari et al., 2016; Centers for Disease Control and Prevention [CDC], 2018a). Among developing countries, CHDs account for 4.2% of stillbirths and deaths during the first 28 days of life (neonatal period; CDC, 2018a). Globally, CHDs are the leading cause of infant mortality (Rosa, Rosa, Zen, & Paskulin, 2013).

Any deviations in the normal development of the heart, which may be the result of genetic, environmental, or multifactorial influences during embryologic and fetal development, can cause a CHD. CHDs lead to acyanotic, cyanotic, or obstructive blood flow patterns. Although over 120 different types of CHD are reported, ranging from mild to major malformations, the more common defects that implicate the fetus and neonate are discussed in this chapter (Box 5.1).

Clinicians must be adept at differentiating between benign and life-threatening CHDs. Certain CHDs are associated with significant morbidity and mortality risks, substantial healthcare costs, and the need for lifelong care, especially when left undiagnosed during the early postnatal period. These factors may impose substantial emotional and socioeconomic challenges on patients and families (Fahed, Gelb, Seidman, & Seidman, 2013). Graduate-level and continuing nursing and medical education, in addition to recent quality-improvement efforts, have improved prenatal and postnatal recognition of CHDs and narrowed the gaps among identification, diagnosis, and initiation of medical care. As a result of these ongoing

BOX 5.1

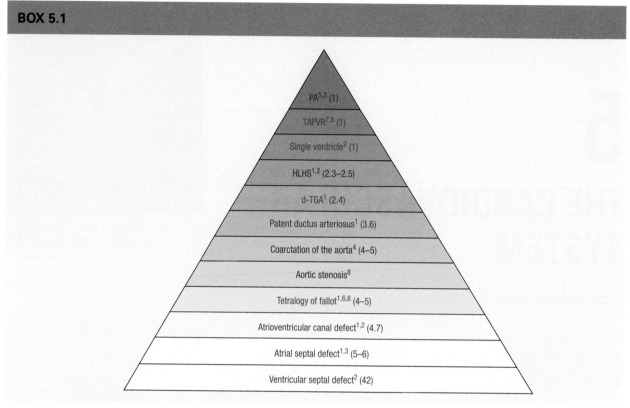

NOTES: Number in parentheses reflects number per 10,000 live births. Red font signifies acyanotic CHDs; blue font signifies cyanotic CHDs; and purple font signifies obstructive CHDs

CHD, congenital heart defect; d-TGA, dextro-transposition of the great arteries; HLHS, hypoplastic left heart syndrome; PA, pulmonary atresia; TAPVR, total anomalous pulmonary venous return.

[1] Bjornard & Riehke-Colarusso, 2013

[2] Centers for Disease Control and Prevention. (2016). Facts about hypoplastic left heart syndrome. Retrieved from https://www.cdc.gov/ncbddd/heart-defects/hlhs.html

[3] Centers for Disease Control and Prevention. (2018b). Facts about atrial septal defect. Retrieved from https://www.cdc.gov/ncbddd/heartdefects/atrialseptaldefect.html

[4] Centers for Disease Control and Prevention. (2018c). Facts about coarctation of the aorta. Retrieved from https://www.cdc.gov/ncbddd/heartdefects/coarctationofaorta.html

[5] Centers for Disease Control and Prevention. (2018e). Facts about pulmonary atresia. Retrieved from https://www.cdc.gov/ncbddd/heartdefects/pulmonaryatresia.html

[6] Centers for Disease Control and Prevention. (2018f). Facts about tetralogy of Fallot. Retrieved from https://www.cdc.gov/ncbddd/heartdefects/tetralogyoffallot.html

[7] Centers for Disease Control and Prevention. (2018g). Facts about total anomalous pulmonary venous return or TAPVR. Retrieved from https://www.cdc.gov/ncbddd/heartdefects/tapvr.html

[8] Fahed, A., Gelb, B., Seidman, J., & Seidman, C. (2013). Genetics of congenital heart disease: The glass half empty. Circulation Research: Journal of the American Heart Association, 112, 707–720. doi:10.1161/CIRCRESAHA.112.300853

and concerted efforts among clinicians, approximately 90% of all U.S.-born infants with a CHD will celebrate their 18th birthday (Bouma & Mulder, 2017; Congenital Heart Public Health Consortium [CHPHC], 2012).

TIMELINE OF ORGAN DEVELOPMENT

The heart is the first organ to reach functional status within the developing fetus. This is necessary, as simple diffusion of oxygen and nutrients across the placenta cannot singlehandedly and adequately nourish the rapidly proliferating embryo (Moore, Persaud, & Torchia, 2016). In fact, early heart function is a stimulus for maturation of other organ systems, namely, the hematologic system, by way of the movement of primitive and definitive red blood cells throughout the body (see Chapter 7).

From the early period of gastrulation through week 8 of gestation, the heart undergoes complex morphogenetic changes and differentiates into three distinct portions: the mesothelium (outer lining), endothelium (inner lining), and myocardium (muscle layer). First, a linear heart, or "primary" myocardium, forms. Second, a specialized ventricular chamber myocardium develops at the ventral surface of the linear heart tube. Concurrently, the left and right atrial myocardium form more caudally on the laterodorsal surfaces. Heart looping thereby occurs, aligning these primordial chambers. As a result, five distinct regions form: (a) truncus arteriosus, (b) bulbus cordis, (c) primitive ventricle, (d) primitive atrium, and (e) sinus venosus. Blood cells cluster to form into blood islands (see Chapter 7), which form the vasculature. These and other significant changes in cardiac development continue up to the end of the embryonic period, at 10 weeks of gestation. In the text that follows, we describe the major phases of embryologic development as separate events; however, it is important to understand that most morphological changes overlap.

Primordial Heart Tube

The primordial heart and vascular system begin to form during the period of gastrulation, between days 16 to 18 of gestation (Baldwin & Dees, 2012; Oostra & Moorman, 2009; Ransom & Srivastava, 2007). Progenitor cells migrate from the endoderm, specifically tasked with forming a cardiogenic crest within the splanchnic mesoderm. The primary heart tube arises from this splanchnic mesoderm as a crescent-shaped formation at the cranial border of the mesoderm (Baldwin & Dees, 2012; England, 1996; Oostra & Moorman, 2009). This region becomes the cardiogenic region of the developing embryo.

By day 19, angiogenic cells cluster and form two primitive endocardial tubes. Each individual tube develops synchronously on either side of the cardiogenic region. During week 3 of gestation, both tubes begin migrating toward one another and merge together in a cranial–caudal fashion. By day 22 of gestation, the tubes fuse and form one primordial heart tube (Figure 5.1; Gittenberger-de Groot, Bartelings, Poelmann, Haak, & Jongbloed, 2013; Goble, Yeh, von Alvensleben, & Panchangam, 2016). The inner aspect of the tube forms the endocardium. The outer aspect of the tube forms the myocardium, or muscular wall of the heart (England, 1996; Fineman & Clyman, 2004). Both the endocardium and myocardium become separated by *cardiac jelly*, an extracellular matrix. At this point in development, the heart tube is bilaterally symmetrical, appearing as an inverted Y, anchored in place by arterial trunks (cranial end) and venous channels (caudal end). By day 23 of gestation, the heart can beat and pump blood (Moore et al., 2016). Now, the heart is ready for looping and further differentiation.

Cardiac Looping

Soon after cardiac contractions (heartbeats) begin, asymmetric dextral looping of the primitive heart ensues. This process precedes the transformation of the single heart tube into a four-chamber heart (Taber, 2006). Growth at the cranial and caudal ends of the primitive heart tube encourage stretching or elongation of the tube. Concurrently, the dorsal mesocardium bends ventrally and to the right; this process is known as *cardiac looping* (dextro- or D-looping; Figure 5.2). Looping enables the initial positioning of the primitive heart, formation and alignment of cardiac chambers, development of accurate septation, alignment of the outflow tracts, and valvular morphogenesis (Brennan & Young, 2001). Once cardiac looping is complete, the primitive circulatory pattern is established.

Chamber Formation

Around the middle of week 4 of embryonic development, septation or partitioning of the primitive ventricle, atrium, and atrioventricular canal begins. Throughout this process, the heart is remarkably capable of pumping blood, in an ebb and flow (or wavelike) fashion. Blood is received from the vitelline vein, common cardinal vein, and the umbilical vein, by way of the sinus venosus, and is propelled cranially toward the truncus arteriosus. By week 10 of gestation, the cardinal vein disappears, leaving only the left atrium and coronary sinus. Quickly, the primitive heart undergoes morphological changes, or dilations, along its anteroposterior axis, which facilitate unidirectional flow of blood through the evolving heart chambers. Both the right and left ventricles thereby emerge simultaneously, partitioned by the atrioventricular canal (Figure 5.3).

Atrial Partitioning. Toward the end of week 4 of gestation, the endocardium proliferates, producing dorsal and ventral bulges in the wall of the atrioventricular aperture. These bulges are invaded by mesenchymal cells, causing inward proliferation of the endocardial cushions. During week 5 of gestation, the endocardial cushions approach each other and fuse, dividing the atrium

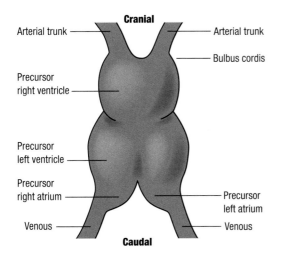

Figure 5.1 The primordial heart tube.

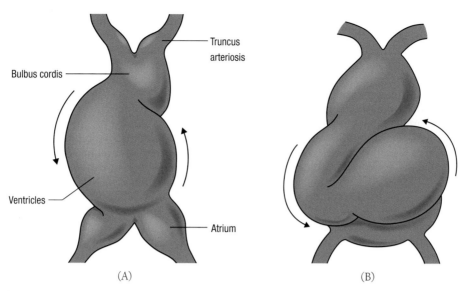

(A)   (B)

Figure 5.2 Cardiac looping. (A) Initial phase of cardiac looping. Note that the right side of the heart rotates in a leftward direction, while the left side of the heart twists in a rightward direction. (B) Continued cardiac looping. Note that the ventricles begin to take shape at the caudal end of the tube (ventral plane), while the atria form at the cranial end of the tube (dorsal plane).

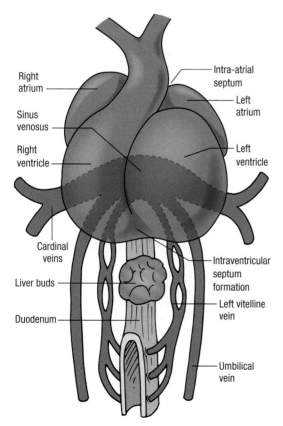

Figure 5.3 Chamber formation.

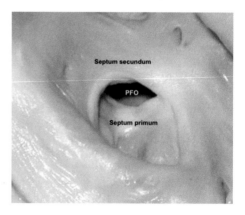

Figure 5.4 Patent foramen ovale (PFO). The caudal membranous septum primum approaches the cranial muscular septum secundum, thereby closing the PFO. The PFO accounts for up to 95% of all right-to-left shunts.

Source: Meier, B., Frank, B., Wahl, A., & Diener, H. C. (2012). Secondary stroke prevention: Patent foramen ovale, aortic plaque, and carotid stenosis. *European Heart Journal, 33*(6), 705–713. doi: 10.1093/eurheartj/ehr443

intra-atrial septum grows toward the fused endocardial cushions. This proliferation works to constrict, and eventually close, a foramen left between the atrial chambers, known as the *foramen primum*. A new foramen emerges as the foramen primum closes, toward the cranial end of the intraatrial septum. A fold of atrial myocardium (*septum secundum*) begins migrating toward this second atrial foramen (*foramen secundum*) and forms its dorsal roof. This series of morphological changes forms the foramen ovale (**Figure 5.4**). The septum primum functions as a type of membranous flutter valve covering the dorsal end of the *foramen ovale*, permitting *right-to-left* shunting of blood

and ventricle into two separate cavities (Anderson, Webb, Brown, Lamers, & Moorman, 2003). Simultaneously, a rapidly proliferating muscular ridge grows from the intraventricular septum toward the base of the heart, and the

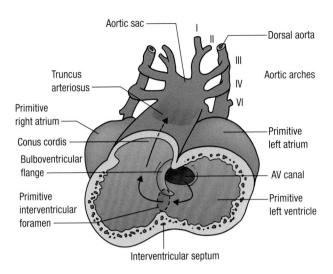

Aortic sac — I

Dorsal aorta

II

Truncus — III
arteriosus

Aortic arches

IV

VI

Primitive
right atrium —

Primitive
left atrium

Conus cordis —

Bulboventricular
flange —

AV canal

Primitive
interventricular
foramen —

Primitive
left ventricle

Interventricular septum

Figure 5.5 Ventricular bulging and partitioning.

AV, atrioventricular.

from the right atrium to the left atrium, throughout fetal development (Anderson et al., 2003).

Ventricular Partitioning. Consider that the stem (caudal end) of the formerly Y-shaped primitive heart tube served as the primary site for the ventricular cavity. As mentioned previously, blood would enter this cavity and travel cranially toward the outflow tract. Once cardiac looping begins, during the fourth week of gestation, the

early ventricular cavity evolves to the right of the midline. As looping continues, the ventricular cavity is pulled to a midline position, where bulging occurs at the point of D-looping. Bulging leads to the formation of each ventricle, whose dimensions quickly grow and exceed the nearby atrial cavity. The left ventricle arises to the left of the intraventricular groove, whereas the right ventricle, or bulbar cordis region, arises to the right of the interventricular foramen (Figure 5.5). In its primitive form, the conjoined left and right ventricle share a communication channel with the primitive truncus arteriosus (Anderson et al., 2003).

Formation of the Aortic Arches

During week 4 of gestation, the superior end of the primitive truncus arteriosus gives rise to the aortic arches. Aortic arches I and II regress, whereas III, IV, and VI go on to form functional anatomic structures. However, if the right dorsal arch persists instead of the left, a right-sided aortic arch results. If the right dorsal aorta involutes proximal to the seventh intersegmented artery, an aberrant right subclavian artery results. If both dorsal aortae persist, a double aortic arch results.

Between weeks 6 and 8 of gestational development, the aortic arches are transformed into the adult arterial arrangement of the carotid, subclavian, and pulmonary arteries. A summary of the aortic arches and their primary function during embryogenesis is provided in Table 5.1. (See also Figure 5.6.)

TABLE 5.1 Embryologic Timeline and Function of the Aortic Arches

Aortic Arches (Pairs)	Week of Gestation When Structure Appears	Regression	Function
I	4 (early)	Yes	Give rise to the maxillary artery; contributes to formation of external carotid artery.
II	4 (midweek)	Yes	Give rise to stapedial and hyoid arteries.
III	4 (end of week)	No	Give rise to common carotid and proximal portions of internal carotid arteries.
IV	4 (end of week)	No	Right side: Proximal portion of right subclavian artery. Left side: Persists as arch of aorta, giving rise to the left subclavian artery.
V	5 (early)	Yes	Rudimentary vessels; no derivatives; does not develop in 50% of embryos.
VI	5 (midweek)	Partial	Give rise to right and left pulmonary arteries. Right side: Complete regression after formation of right pulmonary artery. Left side: Proximal portion persists as proximal segment of left pulmonary artery; distal portion paired with dorsal aorta to form *ductus arteriosus*. After birth, functional closure of ductus arteriosus leaves *ligamentum arteriosum*.

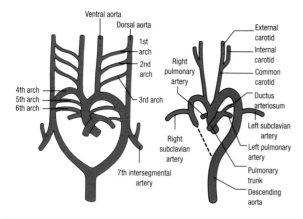

Figure 5.6 The aortic arches.

Partitioning of the Truncus Arteriosus

Beginning during week 4 of gestation, a miraculous spiraling process occurs that bifurcates the truncus arteriosus and gives rise to the pulmonary artery and aorta. What once was a one-directional, single caudo–cranial heart tube becomes a bifurcated tunnel, capable of funneling deoxygenated blood to the lungs (pulmonary artery) and oxygenated blood back to the heart and out to the body (aorta). Spiraling begins with the formation of tissue ridges at the cranial end of the truncus arteriosus. The ridges matriculate into endocardial tissue and complete a 180-degree spiral down the truncus arteriosus toward the superior end of the intraventricular septum. Fusion of the ridges results in formation of the *aortic–pulmonary septum*, which bifurcates the truncus arteriosus into two separate pathways (Figure 5.7).

DEVELOPMENTAL PHYSIOLOGY

Even in its most immature, primitive form, the heart begins its tireless work of supplying other developing body systems with blood flow to nourish growing tissues. Blood flow provides physiological signals essential for the development of the blood vessels. Physiologic feedback shapes the growing network of vessels through chemical signals, such as hypoxia and nutritional requirements, and mechanical stimuli derived from the blood flow, such as shear stress.

Several events are required for the initiation of blood flow and include the formation of the initial vascular network formed by anastomoses between blood vessels, blood vessel endothelial lumen development, the initiation of heart contractions, and the entry of red blood cells (erythrocytes) into the circulation (Jones, 2011). The maturation of cardiac muscle cells, ion channels, and action potentials are necessary in order for the developing heart to mature into a competent organ capable of generating the necessary stroke volume and cardiac output to support life outside the womb. This section of the textbook will begin with a review of core principles of cardiovascular function.

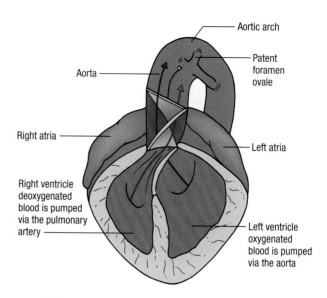

Figure 5.7 Partitioning of the truncus arteriosus.

Cardiac Muscle Tissue

The cardiac conduction system develops from the myocardium and transforms into a specialized electrical wiring network responsible for the initiation and coordination of the heartbeat (Jongbloed et al., 2012). In that sense, it is important to recognize the major role of the myocardium with regard to cardiac conduction. We will begin with a focused review of the anatomy of the cardiac muscle cell, or cardiomyocyte. This will be followed by a review of noteworthy ion channels and exchanges. These conversations are an appropriate predecessor to a later investigation into the cardiomyopathies. Next, we will review action potentials and associated, relevant ion channels.

Cardiac Muscle Cells. *Cardiomyocytes* are muscle cells located within the heart. These cells are covered by a thin cytoskeleton of sarcoplasmic reticulum (the sarcolemma). This cytoskeleton offers structural support as well as a means for mechanical and chemical signaling within and between cardiomyoctes. The interior of the cardiomyocyte is comprised of *sarcomeres*, repeating and interconnected functional units of striated muscle (Figure 5.8). Sarcomeres are comprised of actin (thin) and myosin (thick) filaments, which yield the striated appearance of these cardiac muscle cells. The actin filaments contain regulatory proteins, namely cardiac troponins and α-tropomyosin, which regulate the interaction between the contractile proteins (actin and myosin). The myosin filaments contain myosin-binding proteins (Polin, Abman, Rowitch, Benitz, & Fox, 2017).

The healthy human heart contains more than two to three billion cardiomyocytes. Within each individual cardiomyocyte is repeating chains of as many as 10,000

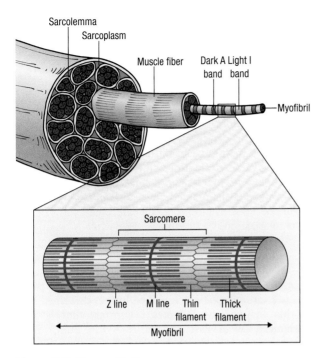

Figure 5.8 The myofibril.

NOTES: The I-band contains the thin filaments. The A-band marks the center area of overlap between the thin and thick filaments. The Z-line denotes the attachment zone of two neighboring sarcomeres. Thin filaments attach to each side of the Z-line.

3-micrometer long sarcomeres. These sarcomeres form end-to-end attachments, which yield *myofibrils,* or contractile threads of myofilament fibers. The arrangement of these fibers, in their parallel orientation, gives the heart its striated, muscular appearance. The end-to-end attachment is facilitated by *intercalated disks.* Intercalated disks are comprised of three types of cells, known as (a) adherens junctions (anchoring cells), (b) desmosomes (binding cells), and (c) gap junctions (conducting cells that permit the movement of ions and cardiac depolarization across the individual cardiomyocytes; Polin et al., 2017). Any genetic mutations that alter the composition of the intercalated disks can lead to the development of a cardiomyopathy.

A cytoskeleton, also known as a *sarcolemma* or *sarcoplasmic reticulum*, covers each myofibril. This cytoskeleton is comprised of numerous filaments, which directly influence both mechanical and chemical signaling that occurs within heart muscle. A discussion of each type of filament is beyond the scope of this chapter; however, a few influential filaments will be summarized. Desmin is one particular filament, located at the Z-line. Desmin links adjacent Z-lines of sarcomeres to one another. In addition, γ-actin, another noteworthy microfilament, links sarcomeres to costameres. *Costameres* are the perpendicularly oriented structural components that connect myofibrils to the sarcolemma at the Z-line and

within the I-band, and transmit force. In that manner, costameres serve a mechanical role by transducing force from one myofibril to another, mainly in a perpendicular direction. To a lesser extent, costameres transduce force longitudinally across sarcomeres, until the end of a myofibril is reached. Therefore, genetic mutations that alter the proteins which comprise costameres increase the likelihood for altered mechanical signaling, and the development of a cardiomyopathy (Peter, Cheng, Ross, Knowlton, & Chen, 2011).

Cardiac Electrophysiology

Ion Channels. Chemical signaling between cardiomyocytes, also known as *excitation-contraction coupling,* occurs by way of three ion channels: (a) Ca^{2+}-ATPase pump, (b) sodium-calcium (Na^+-Ca^{2+}) exchanger, and the (c) sodium-potassium-adenosine triphosphate (Na^+-K^+-ATPase) pump. Ca^{2+} is an excitatory ion, which initially resides within the extracellular space and then enters the sarcomere through its exterior sarcoplasmic reticulum (sarcolemma). Upon entry, Ca^{2+} binds with troponin (specifically, troponin-C), which encourages binding of actin and myosin. This binding elicits a contraction of thin and thick filaments at the Z-line (I-band area) and shortening of the sarcomere. Practically speaking, this contractile movement causes pressure to increase within the ventricles of the heart (systole) and the subsequent ejection of blood. Therefore, it is proper to associate intracellular Ca^{2+} levels, and the strength of calcium binding, with contractile force during systole. Likewise, appropriate levels of ATP and tropomyosin, which unbind Ca^{2+} from troponin and relax the heart muscle, as well as sodium ions through the Na^+-Ca^{2+} exchanger, are necessary to lower Ca^{2+} levels during diastole, in order to permit refilling of the ventricles (Eisner, Caldwell, Kistamás, & Trafford, 2017). When the Na^+- Ca^{2+} exchanger is activated within the sarcolemma, three Na^+ ions enter the cell in exchange for the export of one Ca^{2+} back to the extracellular compartment. As such, intracellular Na^+ (or Na^+ located within the muscle, skin, subcutaneous tissue, or red blood cells) increases. Therefore, any pre-existing, elevated intracellular Na^+ level may limit the efficacy of this pump and efflux of Ca^{2+} during diastole. This may increase Ca^{2+} sparks during diastole, which over time can lead to contractile dysfunction, or a cardiomyopathy (Ottolia, Torres, Bridge, Philipson, & Goldhaber, 2013).

Last, let's consider the Na^+-K^+-ATPase pump. Recall that electrochemical forces normally push K^+ into the extracellular space and Na^+ into the intracellular compartment during resting conditions. Action potentials exaggerate this process. In order to maintain normal intracellular concentrations of Na^+ and K^+, the Na^+-K^+-ATPase pump is utilized. Similar to the aforementioned ion channels, this pump is also located within the sarcolemma. When the Na^+-K^+-ATPase pump is activated, three Na^+ ions are removed from the cell and pushed to the extracellular compartment, while two K⁺ ions are pushed into the cell. Therefore, infants subject to potassium losses secondary to diuretic therapy (i.e., aldosterone antagonists) may exhibit reduced Na⁺-K⁺-ATPase pump activity. On the contrary, infants receiving angiotensin-converting enzyme (ACE) inhibitors may exhibit increased Na⁺-K⁺-ATPase pump activity, and resultant biochemical imbalances which negatively affect cardiovascular function. Clearly, a functional disturbance of these ion channels could explain arrhythmias commonly observed with cardiomyopathies, primarily a dilated cardiomyopathy.

In summary, all components needed for muscle contraction are contained within the sarcomere. Once a muscle is excited by a neuron, calcium (Ca^+) is released from the sarcoplasmic reticulum. Calcium binds with troponin, at the I-band. This causes the sarcomere to shorten, which likewise shortens the I-band. A high-energy attachment occurs between actin and myosin proteins. The end result is a power stroke, whereby myosin pulls the filaments toward the middle of the sarcomere; a muscle contraction occurs. After contraction, adenosine triphosphate (ATP) binds to myosin, which encourages the release of calcium from troponin, relaxation/expansion of the sarcomere, and detachment of myosin from actin. Myosin thereby returns to its high-energy state, in preparation for another muscle contraction. This is termed a *cross-bridge cycle*. Both Na^+/ Ca^{2+} exchanges and the (c) Na⁺-K⁺-ATPase pump are activated, as needed, to maintain normal ion concentrations throughout systole and diastole.

Action Potentials. When extracellular potassium (K⁺) levels are within a normal range (approximately 135–145 mEq/L) and intracellular K⁺ levels are within a normal range (approximately 4 mEq/L), the voltage within the atrial and ventricular myocytes (intracellular voltage), as well as Purkinje fibers, is considered to be at equilibrium, at approximately −90 millivolts (mV). A cardiac action potential occurs when the intracellular voltage becomes less negative, causing ion fluctuations (chemical and electrical potentials) across channels in the sarcolemma of the cardiomyocyte, and ultimately atrial-to-ventricular contraction. Chemical potentials explain the movement of an ion across its selective concentration gradient. Electrical potentials explain the movement of ions away from those with a similar electrical charge. This process is best described as a series of five phases.

The action potential begins with *phase 0*, within the sarcolemma, or sarcoplasmic reticulum. Cell membrane permeability to potassium decreases and sodium channels open. This causes intracellular voltage to become less negative (i.e., −90 mV to +10 mV), which elicits rapid cellular depolarization. Fast Na⁺ channels open, permitting the influx of Na⁺ into the cell. Once the voltage increases from −90 mV to −40 mV, calcium (Ca^{2+}) channels open and a small amount of Ca^{2+} travels across its concentration gradient. Once the voltage reaches 0 mV, the time-dependent, fast Na⁺ channels close. *Phase 1* marks a state of partial

repolarization, secondary to closure of the sodium ion channels, a subsequent decrease in sodium ion exchanges across the cell membrane, and temporary reversal of voltage change back toward the negative. This also causes the voltage to change from a negative to positive charge, to approximately +10 mV. As a result, K⁺ channels open and K⁺ is permitted to leave the cell. As extracellular K⁺ levels increase, the intracellular voltage decreases in a negative direction. This drives the voltage back to approximately 0 mV. This marks the beginning of *Phase 2*—a plateau phase. Ca^{2+} and K⁺ continue to enter and leave the cell, respectively, yet in a balanced state (electrical potential). The voltage is maintained close to 0 mV. Thereafter, a period of repolarization occurs. *Phase 3* marks this period of repolarization. Ca^{2+} channels close while K⁺ continues to exit the cell. This creates an imbalanced exchange of ions and drives the voltage in a negative direction, back toward its resting state of −90 mV. In order to prevent excessive ionic shifts, which could occur during phase 3, three ion pumps (which will be further described later in this chapter) are activated. These are the Na^+-Ca^{2+} exchanger, Ca^{2+}-ATPase, and Na⁺-K⁺-ATPase pump. *Phase 4* thereby begins with this resting state, as ion pumps and exchangers are closed while a slow, persistent leak of K⁺ out of the cell occurs. This helps maintain the voltage of −90 mV, as the cell waits for the next stimulus (action potential; Figure 5.9).

Cardiac Conduction Pathways

The three main components of the cardiac conduction system are (1) the sinoatrial (SA) node, (2) the atrioventricular (AV) node, and (3) the bundle of His (Figure 5.10). These three major parts work collaboratively as the electrical switchboard that modulates the movement of action potentials and coordination of ventricular contractions (Dobrzynski et al., 2013). In order to recognize and understand the genesis for abnormal electrical conduction, one must understand the anatomic arrangement of the conduction system in a healthy heart. Therefore, this section of the chapter reviews the normal transmission of electrical currents, from the sinoatrial node, to atrioventricular node and His-Purkinje system.

Sinoatrial Node. In the early developing heart, the atrium and ventricle muscle layers are continuous. The primordial pacemaker is initially located in the caudal portion of the left heart tube. After development of the sinus venosus myocardium, which occurs during week 5 of development, the SA node is recognizable as a tadpole-shaped structure. The "head" of the SA node is located at the border of the superior caval vein and the right atrium, and the "tail" is located along the terminal crest (Dobrzynski et al., 2013; Jongbloed et al., 2012).

Once mature, the SA node functions as the pacemaker for the heart. Cardiac action potential is initiated here and follows a pathway ending in contraction of heart muscle (also known as a heartbeat). Current research supports that the electrical activity initiated in the SA node is a result of expression of ion channels, gap junction proteins that are responsible for electrical coupling between myocytes, and calcium-handling proteins (Dobrzynski et al., 2013).

Atrioventricular Node. Cells from the left wall of the sinus venosus are incorporated into the interatrial septum; these cells are combined with cells from the atrioventricular canal region forming the AV node and the bundle of His. The AV node is located at the right side of the base of

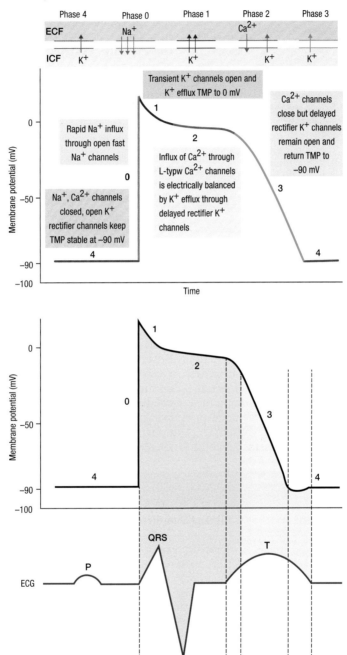

Figure 5.9 Typical action potential of a ventricular myocyte with associated ion currents.

NOTE: This figure is limited to a visual depiction of the status of electrical conduction during the ventricular action potential. During this time, the atria are refilling. More broadly, learners should recognize that the P wave reflects the start of the cardiac action potential cycle and atrial depolarization (not depicted here). As the action potential moves from the SA node to the AV node, isoelectric conduction occurs. The QRS interval reflects time needed for ventricular depolarization (depicted here; phases 0-2), and the QT interval represents the time needed for ventricular repolarization (depicted here; phases 3-4).

ECF, extracellular fluid; ICF, intracellular fluid; TMP, transmembrane potential.

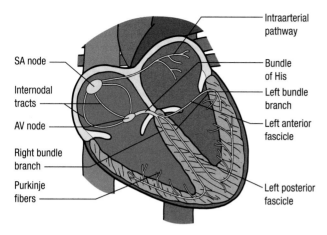

SA node

Internodal tracts

AV node

Right bundle branch

Purkinje fibers

Intraarterial pathway

Bundle of His

Left bundle branch

Left anterior fascicle

Left posterior fascicle

Figure 5.10 The conduction system. The SA node is the pacemaker that initiates electrical activity. The electrical activity is then transmitted to the AV node and onto the His-Purkinje system. The end result is a ventricular contraction (heartbeat).

AV, atrioventricular; SA, sinoatrial.

the atrial septum in the triangle of Koch, superior to the tricuspid valve, and acts as the electrical bridge from the atria to the ventricles.

The AV node innervates the ventricular septum. It permits a frequency-dependent delay, or refractory period in the cardiac action potential (initiated at the SA node). This normal delay allows atrial systole to take place and permits complete filling of the ventricles prior to ventricular systole. This highly coordinated series of events offers protection from atrial tachycardia by limiting the number of action potentials sent from the SA node to the AV node (ventricles; Boyett, 2009; Dobrzynski et al., 2013; Jongbloed et al., 2012). In some cases, the SA node

may fail to initiate an electrical impulse. In these circumstances, the AV node can take over as a secondary pacemaker, although the pacemaker activity of the AV node is slower than the SA node (Dobrzynski et al., 2013; Hund, Smith, Makara, & Mohler, 2014). Maturation of the AV node continues into early childhood (Jongbloed et al., 2012).

His-Purkinje System. The bundle of His is comprised of right and left bundle branches and the Purkinje fibers; this network is commonly referred to as the His-Purkinje system. An electrical impulse from the AV node continues down the thin myocardial fibers arising from a common bundle (the bundle of His), which is located on top of the ventricular septum. In contrast to the SA and AV nodes, the His-Purkinje system is derived from working cardiomyocytes that differentiated early in gestation (Bakker, Christoffels, & Moorman, 2010; Hund et al., 2014). The fibers of the bundle split into right and left bundle branches that are distributed throughout the ventricular myocardium. The bundle branches terminate into the Purkinje fibers, a complex network of cardiac muscle cells extending from the bundle branches that are specialized for conduction and are responsible for synchronous activation of the ventricular myocardium to ensure that the ventricular muscles simultaneously contract (Jongbloed et al., 2012). In the event of heart block, the His-Purkinje system acts as a secondary ventricular pacemaker, once again at an even slower and less robust rate (Boyett, 2009; Dobrzynski et al., 2013).

Clearly, alterations in the normal development of the heart may increase the risk for disturbed electrical conduction. For infants, this may range from benign occurrences, such as isolated premature atrial contractions, to life-threatening rhythms including supraventricular tachycardia or atrial fibrillation (Table 5.2).

TABLE 5.2 Cardiac Conduction System Abnormalities

Electrical Conduction Abnormality	Clinical Significance
SA node dysfunction or "sick sinus syndrome"	Sinus bradycardia Sinus arrest/sinus pause Sinus node exit block Alternating atrial bradyarrhythmias/tachyarrhythmias
AV node dysfunction	AV node reentrant tachycardia Atrial fibrillation Heart block (first, second, and third degree)
His–Purkinje system dysfunction	Bundle branch reentry ventricular tachycardia Bundle branch block Fascicular tachycardia Torsade de pointes arrhythmia Ventricular tachycardia

AV, atrioventricular; SA, sinoatrial.

This aberrant electrical activity may be the result of fluid and electrolyte imbalances or malpositioned central venous catheters, a risk associated with prematurity and critical illness. A mind map, which practically associates common electrolyte abnormalities and abnormal electrocardiographic findings, is provided at the end of this chapter to aid in the application of core principles to common electrical disturbances observed within the neonatal population.

Primordial Cardiovascular Physiology

In the human embryo, the presence of primordial cardiac contractions have been detected as early as week 5 of gestation, at an average rate of 100 beats per minute (BPM). This heartbeat increases as fetal development progresses (Hagen-Ansert, 2018). Cardiac systolic and diastolic function, blood flow, stroke volume, and cardiac output also increase over time. This early function is essential to normal structural cardiovascular development; alterations in these processes will lead to abnormal functional or structural defects. It is important to understand differences between fetal blood flow patterns and postnatal circulation. Neonatal advanced practice nurses are often challenged to identify and stabilize infants with CHD during the peripartum period, in particular, those which depend upon ductal patency.

The Embryonic Period. While anatomic development begins during week 2 of gestation, physiologic function begins between weeks 5 and 6 of gestation. This begins on approximately day 23 of gestation, as a series of "ebb and flow" peristaltic movements, and over time changes to a one-directional blood flow (Acharya, Gui, Cnota, Huhta, & Wloch, 2016; Ashworth, 2013; Martin et al., 2015, Fanaroff, & Walsh, 2015). Recall that three major paired veins communicate with the primitive heart during the embryonic period and supply the heart with blood flow. These veins include the (1) two umbilical veins, (2) vitelline veins, and (3) common cardinal veins. They drain blood into the heart through the sinus venosus, a cavity which communicates with the primitive atrial cavity. A brief digression, to review pertinent anatomy, is an appropriate predecessor to a review of primordial blood flow.

Two umbilical veins deliver oxygenated blood from the chorionic villi to the sinus venosus and into the heart. However, shortly after primitive blood flow begins, the right umbilical vein becomes obliterated, atrophies, and disappears. The left umbilical vein anastomoses with the ductus venosus in the liver, enabling incoming blood from the placenta to proceed directly to the heart without traversing the vascular networks of the liver. This facilitates the "first pass" effect observed when maternally ingested medications cross the placenta and enter the fetal circulation, only to bypass the metabolic center (liver) and travel directly to the heart and onto the systemic circulation.

Deoxygenated blood (from the peripheral tissues) enters the sinus venosus by way of the vitelline veins and cardinal veins. By approximately week 6 of gestation, the vitelline veins (and duct) regress, leaving the paired cardinal veins to continue to transport venous return from the periphery back to the sinus venosus and into the heart. As the heart matures, the left cardinal vein and leftmost portion of the sinus venosus form the coronary sinus. The coronary sinus receives venous return from the coronary system. The right cardinal vein and rightmost portion of the sinus venosus merge and form the superior vena cava (SVC; Ashworth, 2013). The SVC receives venous return from the head, neck, arms, and chest. By week 8 of gestation, the SVC drains blood as in the adult. A summary of the embryonic function of the primitive vessels and their final adult structure is provided in Table 5.3.

TABLE 5.3 Blood Vessels' Embryonic Function and Final Mature Structure

Vein	Primitive Function	Final Adult Structure
Right vitelline vein	Returns poorly oxygenated blood from the umbilical vein	Terminal part of the inferior vena cava
Left vitelline vein	Returns poorly oxygenated blood from the umbilical vein	Regresses
Right anterior *and* common cardinal veins	Drainage system	Superior vena cava
Left common cardinal vein	Drainage system	Tributary of the coronary sinus
Right umbilical vein	Carries oxygenated blood from the chorionic sac (placenta) to the sinus venosus (embryo)	Regresses
Left umbilical vein	Carries oxygenated blood from the chorionic sac (placenta) to the sinus venosus (embryo)	Ligamentum venosum

Recall that as blood enters the sinus venosus, the blood flows through the primordial heart in an "ebb and flow" peristaltic pattern. Blood flows forward, down the vessels, during systole and flows backward, up the vessels, during diastole. As cardiac looping ensues, the atria assume the role of interim pacemaker and early function of the conduction system can be appreciated. Thereafter, the sinus venosus takes on a dual role of blood reservoir and pacemaker; increasingly coordinated conduction and blood flow patterns are thereby observed. However, since smooth muscles located within the sinus venosus have not differentiated, the myocardium is unable to dynamically regulate the diameter of vessel lumens to maintain equilibrium.

Let's consider the pattern of blood flow through the primordial heart, once the primitive conduction system is established. As blood passes through the sinus venosus it enters the atrial cavity. An increased propagation of electrical impulses (action potentials) is observed as blood enters this atrial cavity, which encourages conduction velocity. This mimics the function of the mature SA node. From here, the blood is pushed to the atrioventricular canal, a region comprised with strong, circular connective fibers, yet a significantly slower conduction velocity. This delays the conduction of impulses from the atria to the ventricular myocardium, similar to the function of the mature AV node. Likewise, this slows the conduction velocity from the atria to the ventricles. Once the blood reaches the ventricles, a faster electrical impulse propagation is observed. This mimics the function of the mature His-Purkinje system. In fact, during embryologic development, cardiomyocytes within the ventricles are rapidly differentiating to offer optimal contractility, electrical conduction (ion channel maturation), and energy metabolism. This prepares the ventricles for the role of primary pumping chamber. Contractions within the ventricles move the blood into the conotruncal region (outflow tract) and out to the body (Sedmera & McQuinn, 2008).

The Fetal Period. The fetal period of development marks maturation of the conduction system, which is generally reported as fully mature by week 12 of gestation. Action potentials predictably arise within the SA node and travel to the AV node and His-Purkinje system. This elicits a pattern of serial, rapid atrial and ventricular contractions that facilitate blood flow through the heart. It is at this point that the electrocardiogram begins to resemble that of a mature heart (Acharya et al., 2016; Christoffels, Smits, Kispert & Moorman, 2009).

The following content incorporates content from Chapters 2 and 4 and offers readers an intentional spiraling of core curricular concepts. Here, we describe the parallel cardiovascular circuits present during fetal development. Essentially, the right and left ventricles supply the fetal organ systems through combined ventricular output. This differs from postnatal and adult function, due to structural (anatomic) differences as well as mechanisms by which the fetus increases cardiac output.

The fetal circulation is characterized by two parallel circuits that permit mixing of oxygenated and deoxygenated blood at the atrial and great vessel levels via three intracardiac and extracardiac shunts. These shunts, which permit fetal survival despite the presence of a complex CHD, include the ductus arteriosus (extracardiac), foramen ovale (intracardiac), and ductus venosus (extracardiac). Blood flow is influenced by the high-resistance pulmonary circuit and the low-resistance systemic circuit. Approximately 40% to 50% of fetal cardiac output is received by the placenta, which serves as the major site for gas exchange during fetal development (Bensley, De Matteo, Harding, & Black, 2016).

Recall that during fetal development, the exchange of oxygen, carbon dioxide, nutrients, and waste materials occurs at the placenta. The two umbilical arteries bring the fetal blood to the placenta. This blood circulates through the capillaries of the chorionic villi, where gas exchange takes place. Blood rich in oxygen and nutrients leaves the placenta returning via a single umbilical vein to the fetus. This blood traverses the portal circulation; an average of 30% to 70% of blood bypasses the portal veins and is shunted across the ductus venosus and to the inferior vena cava (R. J. Martin et al., 2015). Normally, flow across the ductus venosus is phasic and anterograde; abnormal flow patterns may suggest possible fetal stress as the fetus attempts to ensure oxygenation of the heart and the brain (Kiserud, 2005; Mari, Deter, & Uerpairojkit, 1996).

The oxygenated blood traversing the inferior vena cava enters the right atrium, where it is divided into two streams by the crista dividens; the majority of flow travels across the foramen ovale and into the left atrium, where it mixes with blood returning from the pulmonary venous system. This oxygen-rich blood passes through the mitral valve, enters the left ventricle, and is thereby pumped out the ascending aorta and toward the developing brain and upper extremities (Figure 5.11). The remainder of the blood flow, travels down the descending aorta (systemic circulation) delivers oxygen to the systemic circulation and becomes progressively deoxygenated, in the process, and then enters either of two umbilical arteries that branch from the internal iliac arteries in order to return to the placenta (Figure 5.10; Mäkikallio, Jouppila, & Rasanen, 2005). This poorly oxygenated blood travels back to the placenta for uptake of oxygen molecules. Normally, flow across the aortic isthmus is both systolic and diastolic as well as anterograde; flow that is retrograde reflects fetal distress and is a mechanism for preserving cerebral perfusion (Mäkikallio, Jouppila, & Räsänen, 2003).

Deoxygenated blood from the IVC and hepatic vein mix with venous return from the SVC (D Iyer & Ikemba, 2012). This mixed blood is directed toward the tricuspid valve and right ventricle. Blood flowing to the right ventricle enters the pulmonary trunk, with 90% to 95% shunted across the patent ductus arteriosus (PDA) and

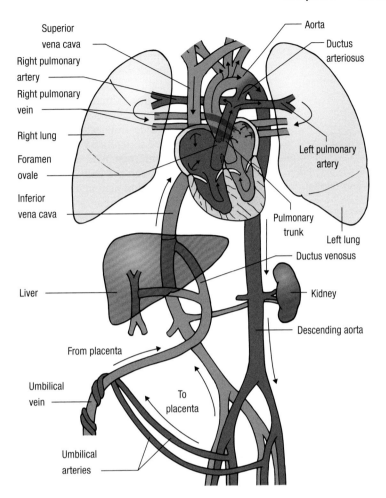

Figure 5.11 Fetal circulation.

thereby bypassing the pulmonary circulation; this is due to high pulmonary vascular resistance (PVR; Bensley et al., 2016). The ductus arteriosus is a wide muscular vessel connecting the pulmonary arterial trunk to the descending aorta; the ductus is approximately the same size as the pulmonary artery and the descending aorta in the fetus. Blood flow shunted across the PDA goes out the descending aorta to the systemic circulation and then returns to the placenta.

Fetal Cardiovascular Physiology

Fetal cardiovascular physiology involves the coordinated activities of two parallel circuits. Essentially, the right and left ventricles supply the fetal organ systems through combined ventricular output. This differs from postnatal and adult function, due to structural (anatomic) differences as well as mechanisms by which the fetus increases cardiac output.

Myocardial Function. Recall that cardiac output equals the heart rate multiplied by the stroke volume

(CO = HR × SV). Stroke volume is the amount of blood that is squeezed from the heart with each heartbeat, and this volume is contingent upon preload, afterload, and cardiac contractility (Dyer & Ikemba, 2012). Preload reflects the amount of blood in the ventricles before ("pre") a heartbeat. Afterload is the pressure that the heart must overcome *after* filling in order to contract and thereby eject blood. Last, contractility is the innate ability of the heart to generate force in order to contract.

The Frank–Starling mechanism offers the ideal foundation for distinguishing differences in myocardial function between fetuses and adults. This mechanism states that increased pressure within the atria during filling (preload) will cause an increase in stroke volume. This is true among adults; however, the fetus has a narrow capacity to increase stroke volume in the face of increased preload. In fact, the fetus typically reaches a peak SV of 4 to 5 mmHg compared to adults, who may compensate by increasing SV to 16 to 18 mmHg in the face of increased preload (Figure 5.12; Dyer & Ikemba, 2012).

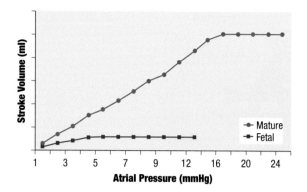

Figure 5.12 Frank–Starling mechanism (fetal versus adult stroke volume capacity).

Source: Adapted from Dyer, A., & Ikemba, C. (2012). Core concepts. *NeoReviews, 13*(10), e583–e589. doi:10.1542/neo.13-10-e583

Several factors may explain this functional immaturity. Decreased contractile proteins within the myocardium, inefficient myocardial calcium uptake, as well as limited passive ventricular filling capacity during diastole help explain why the fetus is seemingly incapable of modulating increases in cardiac output in light of increasing atrial pressure. In addition, spatial constraints imposed by nearby organs (lungs) may limit the heart's ability to effectively contract. Last, cholinergic nerves derived from the vagus nerve (not adrenergic receptors) primarily drive changes in the fetal heart rate. Therefore, the heart rate changes based on vagal stimuli. Later in infancy and adulthood, adrenergic receptors (specifically, beta-1-adrenergic receptors) exert a meaningful effect on the heart by increasing the force and rate of myocardial contraction, thereby increasing cardiac output.

Effects of Congenital Heart Defects on the Fetus. Before progressing to a discussion of transitional and postnatal cardiovascular physiology, it is prudent to consider the effect that CHDs exert on the developing fetus. Normally, left ventricular output traverses the ascending aorta and primarily supplies the head and brain, coronary circulation, and upper extremities. Blood exiting the pulmonary vessels traverses the ductus arteriosus and aortic isthmus and travels through the descending aorta in order to supply the lower extremities. Certain structural defects derange this flow pattern, which may alter oxygenation to various organs as well as alter venous pressure (Rudolph, 2010).

Consider the implications with pulmonary atresia (PA), tricuspid atresia, and tetralogy of Fallot (TOF). These structural defects alter blood flow patterns in utero. Blood flow through the pulmonary artery is obliterated or reduced, and as such, blood is primarily diverted across the foramen ovale and into the left ventricle. Left ventricular output is increased, which, over time, stretches the diameter of the ascending aorta and aortic isthmus. In

contrast, hypoplastic left heart syndrome (HLHS) imposes increased workload on the right heart. Right ventricular pressure increases as this ventricle assumes full responsibility for providing ventricular output. Blood flow traverses the pulmonary artery to the engorged pulmonary vasculature, ductus arteriosus, and across the aortic isthmus; little (if any) flow is ejected from the left heart. Retrograde flow patterns across the aortic isthmus are required to redirect output to the brain, coronary circulation, and upper extremities (Rudolph, 2010).

Although the fetus can compensate for aberrant structural development in utero, prolonged intrauterine cardiopulmonary compensation in combination with removal of the placental circuit can provoke rapid postnatal decompensation. An understanding of normal transitional cardiovascular physiology is essential to develop fluency with linking fetal cardiovascular physiology and postnatal manifestations of CHDs.

Transitional Cardiovascular Physiology at Birth

The cardiac and pulmonary systems undergo drastic changes at birth in response to respirations and loss of the placenta, from parallel circuits to one circuit that operates in series (Bensley et al., 2016). The abrupt cessation of placental blood flow leads to an accumulation of carbon dioxide and decrease in oxygen saturation, which stimulates the onset of postnatal breathing. The first postnatal breath inflates the lungs and increases partial pressures of oxygen in the arterial blood (PaO_2). This modulates the postnatal decrease in pulmonary vascular resistance (PVR) and the increase in pulmonary blood flow; flow increases from an average of 35 mL/kg/min to approximately 160 to 200 mL/kg/min (Flanagan, Yeager, & Weindling, 2016). At this time, 90% of blood flow is redirected to the lungs and the lungs assume the primary role of gas exchange. In addition, the release of vasodilators and endothelial-derived releasing factors occurs, further decreasing PVR and aiding in the redirection of blood flow through the pulmonary circuit.

Closure of the Fetal Shunts. Postnatal cardiovascular function does not depend on fetal shunts. In fact, these shunts must functionally close during the immediate postnatal period in order for the cardiopulmonary circuit to properly transition to extrauterine life; permanent anatomic closure can occur later without inducing pathological problems. To summarize this key concept, functional closure of the intracardiac and extracardiac shunts precedes anatomic closure. On occasion, shunts may functionally close and later reopen; shunts have the ability to intermittently close and reopen before anatomic closure occurs. This may result in transient, functional, and, occasionally, hemodynamically significant murmurs, which are more common among premature infants.

As placental circulation ceases, there is a drop in pressure within the inferior vena cava and right atrium. Pulmonary venous return increases and left atrial pressure exceeds right atrial pressure. These changes lead to the functional closure of the foramen ovale (R. J.Martin et al., 2015). On the contrary, a patent foramen ovale (PFO) may persist among neonates with pulmonary stenosis or other defects associated with increased right atrial pressure. Permanent anatomic closure of the foramen ovale is typically achieved by 2.5 years of age.

Among term infants, functional closure of the PDA is usually noted within the first 3 days after birth (Hines, 2013; R. J. Martin et al., 2015; Verklan & Walden, 2015). Closure occurs as a result of increasing arterial oxygenation saturations amid decreasing PVR, as well as decreased responsiveness to naturally synthesized prostaglandins (see Chapter 4). In fact, functional closure occurs in approximately 50% of term infants by 24 hours of life and 90% by 48 hours of life (Clyman, Couto, & Murphy, 2012). Respiratory distress syndrome, septicemia, excessive fluid administration, furosemide therapy, phototherapy, and prematurity encourage delayed functional closure of the PDA. Anatomic closure is typically noted by 2 to 3 months of life; the remnant of the PDA is thereby labeled the *ligamentum arteriosum* (Clyman et al., 2012).

Within the first minute of life, umbilical blood flow drops to less than 20% of fetal values. During this time, the diameter of the umbilical arteries and veins decreases significantly. This leads to functional closure of the umbilical vessels. Fibrous proliferation occurs within 2 to 3 months, which completely obliterates both vessels.

Next, functional closure of the ductus venosus occurs shortly after birth. This occurs once the parallel circuitry disappears; blood flow from the placenta through the umbilical vein and ductus venosus ceases. Anatomic closure is completed by 2 months of age. The remnant of the ductus venosus is thereby labeled the *ligamentum venosum*. Spasm with prompt closure of the ductus venosus can be particularly problematic when postnatal umbilical venous access is necessary, especially in cases of CHD that require intravenous prostaglandin administration to maintain ductal integrity. Prompt closure may prevent cannulation with umbilical venous catheters.

Postnatal Cardiovascular Physiology

Postnatal Blood Flow. Here we offer intentional cycling of curriculum from Chapter 4, with a particular focus on blood flow patterns after birth. After birth, blood flows in series through the heart and lungs as an organized pattern of flow distinctly different from the parallel pattern observed during fetal development. Deoxygenated blood from the lower body and upper body is returned to the heart via the inferior vena cava and superior vena cava. Blood enters the right atrium and is directed through the trileaflet tricuspid valve and into the right ventricle. From the right ventricle, blood flows through the trileaflet

semilunar pulmonary valve and into the main pulmonary artery. The main pulmonary artery thereby splits into the right and left pulmonary arteries and blood is diverted to either side for oxygenation within either lung.

Oxygenated blood leaves the lungs by way of four pulmonary veins. These four pulmonary veins innervate with the left atrium. Blood thereby flows from the left atrium, through the bileaflet mitral valve, and into the left ventricle, the cavity solely responsible for generating postnatal cardiac output. The left ventricle thrusts the blood through the aortic valve, where some of the cardiac output enters the ascending aorta and is distributed through the three branches of the aorta and to the brain; the remaining cardiac output is diverted in a downward direction through the descending aorta and to the distal organs and tissues (Everett & Lim, 2007; Verklan & Walden, 2015).

Postnatal Cardiovascular Function. The normal postnatal decrease in pulmonary arterial pressure, in combination with the expected rise in systemic arterial pressure, exerts a major impact on myocardial function (Bensley et al., 2016). Similar to fetal myocardial function, ventricular preload and afterload, myocardial contractility, and heart rate all influence cardiac output after birth and across the life span. The major difference between fetal and postnatal myocardial function is the ability to increase cardiac output with increasing atrial pressures (preload).

Ventricular preload. Recall that ventricular preload is a measure of end-diastolic volume in the neonate and is influenced by many factors, including circulating blood volume, myocardial relaxation and compliance, contractility, and afterload (Noori, Stavroudis, & Seri, 2012). After birth, left ventricular filling and stroke volume improve once PVR decreases below systemic vascular resistance (SVR). In addition, increased end-diastolic pressure leads to increased myocardial fiber length and improved contractility. This results in increased stroke volume and a resultant increase in cardiac output.

Ventricular afterload. Recall that ventricular afterload is the myocardial force that pumps blood out of the ventricles during the ejection period (Noori et al., 2012). It is inversely proportional to contractility and, as such, as afterload increases, contractility decreases. The normal postnatal fall in PVR causes a decrease in right ventricular afterload. Over time, right ventricular end-diastolic pressures decrease as ventricular filling is optimized. The end result is improved cardiac compliance and ventricular ejection (Artman, Mahoney, & Teitel, 2011).

Myocardial contractility. Myocardial contractility is dependent on the force of the cardiac contraction, preload, inotropy, and afterload. It is immature among fetuses and neonates; reduced cellular and structural organization and decreased compliance is noted, leaving the heart less responsive to volume demands. The lack of noncontractile proteins leaves the myocardium stiff and less compliant, with little reserve to increase contractility. Therefore, in order to increase cardiac output, the heart rate increases (Artman et al., 2011; Hines, 2013; Noori et al., 2012).

Immediately after birth, clamping of the umbilical cord removes the low resistance placenta and SVR increases. This abrupt increase in SVR can stress the immature myocardium and lead to transient dysfunction, which manifests as (transient) tricuspid regurgitation. The result is decreased left ventricular cardiac output and reduced systemic blood flow. The resultant low systemic blood flow usually resolves within 24 to 36 hours after birth (Noori et al., 2012). In addition, decreased myocardial contractility may be observed in the presence of acidosis, hypercarbia, and hypoxia. These conditions alter cellular permeability and the effectiveness of the sodium–potassium (Na^+-K^+) pump.

Heart rate. With maturation of the parasympathetic system, resting heart rate in the neonate decreases. Any event that provokes catecholamine release, parasympathetic stimulation, or parasympathetic withdrawal will manifest with tachycardia. In the preterm infant, tachycardia is related to sympathetic nervous system control of cardiac function.

GENETIC INFLUENCES

Genetic (syndromic) and environmental influences are capable of altering structural and functional development of the heart. Although 80% of CHDs are not associated with genetic syndromes and occur sporadically, the remaining 20% of cases are positively associated with Mendelian and chromosomal syndromes and can manifest with critical CHDs (Chung, Boskovski, Brueckner, Anyane-Yeboa, & Gupta, 2012; Miller, Riehle-Colarusso, Siffel, Frías, & Correa, 2011). Changes in chromosome number (aneuploidy), or rearrangement of chromosomal material from one chromosome to another (translocation), or loss of chromosomal material (deletions) may be at fault for altering embryonic development of the heart. Here we present common chromosomal aneuploidy, associations, and sporadic genetic malformations that involve aberrant heart development or function. In addition, a summary of rare single gene disorders, which involve the formation of common CHDs, are summarized in Table 5.4.

Chromosomal Aneuploidy Influences

Chromosomal aneuploidy was the first reported genetic basis for syndromic CHDs and currently accounts for the largest percentage of identifiable, syndromic CHDs (Muntean, Toğãnel, & Benedek, 2017). The most common aneuploidy disorders with associated CHDs include trisomy 13, 18, and 21, as well as Turner syndrome (Table 5.5; Bouma & Mulder, 2017).

Trisomy 13. Trisomy 13 results from a translocation of genetic material, resulting in the presence of three copies of chromosome 13 in each cell in the body. It affects an estimated one in 16,000 live births (National Organization for Rare Disorders [NORD], 2007). Nearly 80% of infants with trisomy 13 have three complete copies of chromosome 13. Less than 5% of fetuses affected by trisomy 13 survive to term; the majority of affected pregnancies result in spontaneous abortion or stillbirth (Gleason & Juul, 2018). Complex CHDs are noted in up to 64% of live-born neonates; hallmark defects include conotruncal defects, septal defects, and valvular anomalies (Muntean et al., 2017).

Trisomy 18. Trisomy 18 (Edwards syndrome) commonly results from a translocation of genetic material, causing three copies of chromosome 18 in each cell in the body. Nearly 95% of infants with trisomy 18 have three complete copies of chromosome 18, and 5% are affected by a mosaicism (partial trisomy) of most of the long arm of chromosome 18 (Gleason & Juul, 2018). The incidence of Edwards syndrome is one in 5,000 to 8,000 live births; a female prevalence is reported (H. Chen, 2012; National Institute of Health [NIH], 2018b). CHD is noted in up to 83% of live-born neonates with this chromosomal disorder; hallmark defects include septal and polyvalvular dysplasia (Muntean et al., 2017).

Trisomy 21. Trisomy 21 commonly results from placement of three copies of chromosome 21 on each cell; the majority (94%) of infants with trisomy 21 have three complete copies of chromosome 21, whereas 2% may present with a mosaicism (Gleason & Juul, 2018). This syndrome affects one in 800 births; an increased incidence, estimated at one in 25 to 300 births, is reported among pregnant women over the age of 35 years of age (Moore et al., 2016; NIH, 2018d). Approximately 44% of infants with trisomy 21 are affected by a CHD; hallmark defects include atrioventricular and ventricular septal defects (VSDs). Atrioventricular defects are more common among females and those of Caucasian race (Muntean et al., 2017).

Turner Syndrome. Turner syndrome is a result of loss of one X chromosome (most common) or structural abnormalities to one X chromosome affecting the normal course of development before and after birth only in females. A large number of affected fetuses spontaneously abort or are stillborn. Incidence in live-born neonates is about one per 2,500 (NIH, 2018e). CHDs are noted in about 38% of 45, XO live-born neonates. The most common associated CHDs involve left-sided cardiac structures; most notable are aortic arch and valve abnormalities (Muntean et al., 2017).

TABLE 5.4 Single-Gene Mutation Syndromes Associated with Congenital Heart Defects

Gene Mutation Syndromes	Common Associated Congenital Heart Defects
Noonan syndrome (AD)	Septal defects (e.g., ASD) **Valvular anomalies** (e.g., PS) Cardiomyopathy
Alagille syndrome (AD)	Right-sided heart defects (e.g., **peripheral or valvular pulmonary stenosis**, **TOF**) Coarctation of the aorta
Holt–Oram syndrome (AD)	**Septal defects** (e.g., ASD, VSD) **PDA** **Left ventricular outflow tract defects** (e.g., HLHS) Atrioventricular conduction delays
CHARGE syndrome (AD)	Conotruncal defects (e.g., TOF, DORV) Aortic arch anomalies
Smith–Lemli–Opitz syndrome (AR)	**Septal defects** (e.g., ASD, VSD) **Left ventricular outflow tract defects** (i.e., HLHS) PDA

NOTE: Defects in bold type denote common CHD associations reported in the literature.

AD, autosomal dominant; AR, autosomal recessive; ASD, atrial septal defect; CHD, congenital heart defect; DORV, double outlet right ventricle; HLHS, hypoplastic left heart syndrome; PDA, patent ductus arteriosus; PS, pulmonary stenosis; TOF, tetralogy of Fallot; VSD, ventricular septal defect.

Sources: From Chung, W., Boskovski, M. T., Brueckner, M., Anyane-Yeboa, K., & Gupta, P. (2012). The genetics of fetal and neonatal cardiovascular disease.. In C. S. Kleinman & I. Seri (Eds.), *Hemodynamics and cardiology: Neonatology questions and controversies* (2nd ed. , pp. 343–376). Philadelphia, PA: Elsevier Saunders; Corrigan, N., Brazil, D., & McAuliffe, F. (2009). Fetal cardiac effects of maternal hyperglycemia during pregnancy. *Birth Defects Research (Part A): Clinical and Molecular Teratology, 85,* 523–530; Muntean, I., Toganel, R., & Benedek, T. (2017). Genetics of congenital heart disease: Past and present. *Biochemical Genetics, 55,* 105–123. doi:10.1007/s10528-016-9780-7; Ornoy, A., Reece, E., Pavlinkova, G., Kappen, C., & Miller, R. (2015). Effect of maternal diabetes on the embryo, fetus, and children: Congenital anomalies, genetic and epigenetic changes and developmental outcomes. *Birth Defects Research. Part C, Embryo Today, 105*(1), 53–72 doi:10.1002/bdrc.21090.

Chromosomal Deletion Influences

Deletion of a small, discrete chromosomal region may yield a CHD. The most common deletion syndromes are 22q11.2 (DiGeorge), 11q23 (Jacobsen syndrome), or 7p11.23 microdeletion (Williams syndrome; Table 5.6).

DiGeorge Syndrome. DiGeorge syndrome is the most frequent deletion syndrome and involves the loss of chromosomal material on the long arm of chromosome 22 (22q11.2). This syndrome affects one in every 4,000 live births (Muntean et al., 2017; Ransom & Srivastava, 2007). CHDs are noted in up to 80% of liveborn infants; conotruncal anomalies are the most commonly reported CHDs (Muntean et al., 2017).

Jacobsen Syndrome. Jacobsen syndrome is a rare disorder characterized by deletions at the end of the long arm of chromosome 11 (11q23). Jacobsen syndrome occurs in approximately one in every 100,000 live-born neonates (NIH, 2018c). Normal function of 11q23 is critical for the development of the brain, face, and heart (Muntean et al.,

2017). VSD, left heart obstructive malformations, valvular defects, coarctation of the aorta, or hypoplastic left heart syndrome are reported in up to 56% of all affected infants. The most common CHDs are VSD and left heart obstructive defects (Muntean et al., 2017).

Williams Syndrome. Williams syndrome is a microdeletion syndrome involving the loss of genetic material from the short arm of chromosome 7. This syndrome affects roughly one in every 7,500 to 10,000 infants (NIH, 2018g). The loss of the chromosomal material results in marked variability of clinical presentation, including facial, skeletal, renal, and heart anomalies. CHDs are reported in up to 82% of all affected infants; supravalvular aortic stenosis and pulmonary stenosis are the two most commonly reported CHDs (Muntean et al., 2017).

Sporadic Malformation Syndromes

Many cardiac malformations occur as part of a constellation, or association, of defects. Two common

TABLE 5.5 Chromosomal Aneuploidy Syndrome Associated with Congenital Heart Defects

Chromosomal Abnormality	Common Associated Congenital Heart Defects
Trisomy 13	**Septal defects** (e.g., VSD, ASD) Conotruncal defects (e.g., TOF, DORV) PDA Valvular anomalies
Trisomy 18	Septal defects (e.g., VSD, ASD) Conotruncal defects Polyvalvular dysplasia
Trisomy 21	**Septal defects** (e.g., VSD) **Atrioventricular** (e.g., complete AVSD, partial AVSD) Conotruncal defects (e.g., TOF, DORV) PDA
Turner syndrome	**Valvular anomalies** (e.g., bicuspid aortic valve, aortic stenosis, mitral valve defect) **Coarctation of the aorta** Left ventricular outflow tract defects (e.g., HLHS) Aortic dissection

NOTE: Defects in bold type denote common CHD associations reported in the literature.

ASD, atrial septal defect; AVSD, atrioventricular septal defect; CHD, congenital heart defect; DORV, double outlet right ventricle; HLHS, hypoplastic left heart syndrome; PDA, patent ductus arteriosus; TOF, tetralogy of Fallot; VSD, ventricular septal defect.

Sources: From Chung, W., Boskovski, M. T., Brueckner, M., Anyane-Yeboa, K., & Gupta, P. (2012). The genetics of fetal and neonatal cardiovascular disease. In C. S. Kleinman & I. Seri (Eds.), *Hemodynamics and cardiology: Neonatology questions and controversies* (2nd ed. , pp. 343–376). Philadelphia, PA: Elsevier Saunders; Corrigan, N., Brazil, D., & McAuliffe, F. (2009). Fetal cardiac effects of maternal hyperglycemia during pregnancy. *Birth Defects Research (Part A): Clinical and Molecular Teratology, 85,* 523–530. doi:10.1002/bdra.20567; Muntean, I., Togănel, R., & Benedek, T. (2017). Genetics of congenital heart disease: Past and present. *Biochemical Genetics, 55,* 105–123. doi:10.1007/s10528-016-9780-7; Ornoy, A., Reece, E., Pavlinkova, G., Kappen, C., & Miller, R. (2015). Effect of maternal diabetes on the embryo, fetus, and children: Congenital anomalies, genetic and epigenetic changes and developmental outcomes. *Birth Defects Research. Part C, Embryo Today, 105*(1), 53–72. doi:10.1002/bdrc.21090

TABLE 5.6 Chromosomal Deletion Syndromes Associated with Congenital Heart Defects

Chromosomal Deletion Syndromes	Common Associated Congenital Heart Defects
DiGeorge (22q11.2)	**Conotruncal defects** (e.g., interrupted aortic arch type B, truncus arteriosus, TOF, TGA) Septal defects (e.g., perimembranous VSD)
Jacobsen syndrome (11q23)	Left ventricular outflow tract defects (e.g., **HLHS**) Septal defects (e.g., VSD) Coarctation of the aorta
Williams syndrome (7p11.23 microdeletion)	Valvular anomalies (e.g., **supravalvular aortic stenosis,** supravalvular pulmonary stenosis) **Peripheral pulmonary stenosis**

NOTE: Defects in bold type denote common CHD associations reported in the literature.

CHD, congenital heart disease; HLHS, hypoplastic left heart syndrome; TGA, transposition of the great arteries; TOF, tetralogy of Fallot; VSD, ventricular septal defect.

Sources: From Chung, W., Boskovski, M. T., Brueckner, M., Anyane-Yeboa, K., & Gupta, P. (2012). The genetics of fetal and neonatal cardiovascular disease. In C. S. Kleinman & I. Seri (Eds.), *Hemodynamics and cardiology: Neonatology questions and controversies* (2nd ed. , pp. 343–376). Philadelphia, PA: Elsevier Saunders; Corrigan, N., Brazil, D., & McAuliffe, F. (2009). Fetal cardiac effects of maternal hyperglycemia during pregnancy. *Birth Defects Research (Part A): Clinical and Molecular Teratology, 85,* 523–530. doi:10.1002/bdra.20567; Muntean, I., Togănel, R., & Benedek, T. (2017). Genetics of congenital heart disease: Past and present. *Biochemical Genetics, 55,* 105–123. doi:10.1007/s10528-016-9780-7; Ornoy, A., Reece, E., Pavlinkova, G., Kappen, C., & Miller, R. (2015). Effect of maternal diabetes on the embryo, fetus, and children: Congenital anomalies, genetic and epigenetic changes and developmental outcomes. *Birth Defects Research. Part C, Embryo Today, 105*(1), 53–72 doi:10.1002/bdrc.21090.

associations that manifest with multiple anomalies are the VACTERL association and Beckwith–Wiedemann syndrome (BWS).

VACTERL Association. VACTERL association is a combination of multiple anomalies involving **v**ertebral defects, **a**nal atresia, **c**ongenital heart defects, **t**racheoesophageal fistulas (TEF), **r**enal abnormalities, and **l**imb defects. The incidence has been estimated to be between one in 10,000 to 40,000 live births (NIH, 2018f). The majority of cases occur sporadically (Brosens et al., 2013). Cardiac malformations are reported in approximately 40% to 80% of neonates affected by the VACTERL association (Cunningham et al., 2013). Commonly reported malformations range from clinically insignificant CHDs, including VSDs and atrial septal defects (ASDs), to clinically significant, complex congenital heart malformations requiring surgical interventions and continuing care across the life span (Brosens et al., 2013; Y. Chen et al., 2016; Cunningham et al., 2013; Solomon et al, 2014).

Beckwith–Wiedemann Syndrome. BWS is one of the most commonly described overgrowth disorders. BWS affects one in every 13,700 infants (worldwide). Over time, these infants exhibit abnormally accelerated and often asymmetrical tissue growth (NIH, 2018a). Although classic manifestations include macroglossia and abdominal wall defects, cardiac anomalies are reported in approximately 20% of confirmed cases of BWS (Mussa et al., 2016). Hallmark manifestations include mild cardiomegaly, PDA, and PFO. Rare findings include Long QT syndrome (Mussa et al., 2016; Shuman, Beckwith, & Weksberg 2016). Continuing care across the life span is indicated. Affected children are at risk for developing cancerous and noncancerous tumors, including hepatoblastoma, nephroblastoma (Wilms tumor) and pancreatoblastoma, which typically manifest during early to late childhood (Edmondson & Kalish, 2015).

MATERNAL HEALTH INFLUENCES

Maternal exposures to environmental toxins, such as pesticides, certain medications (sodium valproate, retinoic acid, lithium), or substances, including ethanol, cocaine, and other licit and illicit drugs, can exert a teratogenic effect on fetal cardiovascular development (Table 5.7; Bouma & Mulder, 2017; Fahed et al., 2013; Mone, Gillman, Miller, Herman, & Lipshultz, 2004). In cocaine-exposed fetuses, it is felt that this substance has direct toxic effects on fetal myocytes. Similar findings are also noted in fetal alcohol syndrome; variability appears to be based on time- and dose-dependent exposure (Muralidharan, Sarmah, Zhou, & Marrs, 2013; Yang et al.,

2015). In aggregate, these environmental toxin exposures account for approximately 2% of all CHDs (Brennan & Young, 2001).

Maternal health influences associated with an increased risk of CHDs include advanced maternal age, viral infections during the first trimester of pregnancy (rubella, cytomegalovirus, coxsackie virus), a history of previous spontaneous abortions or stillbirths, maternal diabetes, and other illness, such as systemic lupus erythematosus (SLE; Abqari et al., 2016; Bouma & Mulder, 2017; Miller et al., 2011; Yazigi et al., 2017).

Advanced Maternal Age

A 20% increased risk of CHD is conferred upon offspring born to mothers 35 years of age or older. More specific, conotruncal defects, left ventricular outflow track obstructions, right ventricular outflow tract defects, atrioventricular septal defects (AVSDs), and VSDs are commonly associated with advanced maternal age and pregnancy (Miller et al., 2011).

Maternal Systemic Lupus Erythematosus

Presence of anti-Ro or anti-La antibodies resulting from SLE places the fetus at risk for heart block. There is transplacental passage of the antibodies associated with SLE, with resultant antibody and complement deposition in the fetal myocardium, leading to inflammation, calcification, necrosis, and fibrosis of the conducting tissue (Zahka, 2011). Cardiovascular damage secondary to heart block is evident between 16 and 30 weeks of gestation, and as gestation advances, fetal conduction defects often worsen and increase the risk for hydrops fetalis and congestive heart failure (Mone et al., 2004; Zahka, 2011).

Maternal Diabetes Mellitus

Type 1 or type 2 diabetes mellitus before pregnancy (pregestational), with poorly controlled maternal hyperglycemia before conception and during the first trimester, is associated with a fivefold higher risk for congenital cardiovascular malformations compared to the general population. Cardiac defects occur in roughly 8.5% of cases of pregestational diabetes, which is approximately tenfold higher than the incidence of CHDs in the general population (Corrigan, Brazil, & McAuliffe, 2009; Ornoy, Reece, Pavlinkova, Kappen, & Miller, 2015). High levels of maternal glycosylated hemoglobin (HbA1c) and hyperglycemia during the critical periods of early embryonic development appear to be teratogenic; abnormal migration of neural crest cells occurs and leads to conotruncal malformations (Corrigan et al., 2009). The most common CHDs associated with pregestational diabetes include atrioventricular

TABLE 5.7 Environmental Toxins and Maternal Health Influences Associated with Congenital Heart Defects

Exposure	Common Associated Congenital Heart Defects
Maternal rubella infection	Septal defects (e.g., VSD, ASD) **PDA** Persistent pulmonary stenosis
Maternal lupus	**Heart block** Cardiomyopathy
Maternal diabetes mellitus	Septal defects (e.g., VSD) Conotruncal defects (e.g., TGA, TOF) HLHS Cardiomyopathy Dextrocardia
Alcohol	**Septal defects** (e.g., VSD, ASD) PDA Conotruncal defects
Fetal amphetamine exposure	Septal defects (e.g., VSD, ASD) PDA TGA
Fetal cocaine exposure	**Septal defects (e.g., VSD)** Intracardiac conduction abnormalities
Fetal indomethacin exposure	Premature closure of PDA
Fetal lithium exposure	Septal defects (e.g., ASD) **Ebstein anomaly** RVOT TA
Fetal progesterone exposure	Septal defects (e.g., VSD) Conotruncal defects (e.g., TGA, TOF)
Fetal hydantoin syndrome	Septal defect PDA Valve stenosis
Fetal warfarin syndrome	PDA PPS

NOTE: Defects in bold type denote common CHD association reported in the literature.
ASD, atrial septal defect; HLHS, hypoplastic left heart syndrome; PDA, patent ductus arteriosus; PPS, peripheral pulmonic stenosis; RVOT, right ventricular outflow tract; TA, truncus arteriosus; TGA, transposition of the great arteries; TOF, tetralogy of Fallot; VSD, ventricular septal defect.

Sources: From Mone, S., Gillman, M., Miller, T., Herman, E., & Lipshultz, S. (2004). Effects of environmental exposures on the cardiovascular system: Prenatal period through adolescence. *Pediatrics, 113*(Suppl. 3), 1058–1069 Retrieved from http://pediatrics.aappublications.org/content/113/Supplement_3/1058..info; Patorno, E., Huybrechts, K. F., Bateman, B. T., Cohen, J. M., Desai, R. J., Mogun, H., ... Hernandez-Diaz, S. (2017). Lithium use in pregnancy and the risk of cardiac malformations. New England Journal of Medicine, 376(23), 2245–2254. doi:10.1056/NEJMoa1612222; Yazigi, A., De Pecoulas, A., Vauloup-Fellous, C., Grangeot-Keros, L., Ayoubi, J.-M., & Picone, O. (2017). Fetal and neonatal abnormalities due to congenital rubella syndrome: A review of literature. *Journal of Maternal–Fetal & Neonatal Medicine, 30*(3), 274–278 doi:10.3109/14767058.2016.1169526.

canal defects, dextro-transposition of the great arteries (D-TGA), aortic stenosis, PA, dextrocardia, and conotruncal defects (Ornoy et al., 2015). The fetal heart is also at risk for the development of hypertrophic cardiomyopathy, most commonly seen during the second and third trimester. It has been suggested that the hypertrophy is a result of fetal hyperinsulinism leading to proliferation and hypertrophy of cardiac myocytes triggered by increased proteins and fat synthesis. Maternal hyperglycemia can also alter the embryonic epigenome and impact latent gene expression and regulation among offspring; a higher incidence of latent diabetes and cardiovascular disease is reported among exposed fetuses (Ornoy et al., 2015).

COMMON PROBLEMS WITH IMPLICATIONS ACROSS THE LIFE SPAN

Before beginning a conversation focused on the abnormal, it is always beneficial to establish a firm understanding of the normal. As such, Figure 5.13 provides a visual summary of normal heart anatomy and blood flow. This can be used to compare with the following common congenital heart lesions.

Cyanotic Heart Defects

Cyanotic heart defects are a group of congenital malformations that lead to low circulating blood oxygen levels. CHDs identified during the postnatal period account for 15% of all types of CHD and 33% of all life-threatening types of CHD diagnosed among individuals of all ages (Reller, Strickland, Riehle-Colarusso, Mahle, & Correa, 2008). These types of defects involve the systemic recirculation of desaturated venous blood, which occurs by one of two common mechanisms: (a) mixing of deoxygenated and oxygenated blood at the atrial, ventricular, or ductal level; or (b) a structural diversion redirecting deoxygenated blood returning to the heart away from the lungs and back to the systemic circulation. This shunting of blood from right to left results in hypoxemia, low arterial saturations, and cyanosis.

Transposition of the Great Arteries. Transposition of the great arteries (TGA) is *the most common cyanotic heart defect that manifests during the neonatal period*. The prevalence of TGA in the United States is estimated to be one in every 3,300 live births (CDC, 2018d). Within the United States, TGA accounts for 3% of all CHDs, and further accounts for 20% of all cyanotic heart defects (CDC, 2018d). A 1.8:1 male-to-female preponderance is reported and fetuses exposed to pregestational maternal diabetes mellitus are considered at higher risk for developing TGA (Flanagan et al., 2016). TGA most likely occurs secondary to an abnormality in conotruncal development that happens between weeks 4 and 5 of gestation (Kirby, 2002). Two types of TGA are known: (a) dextro-transposition (D-TGA) and (b) levo-transposition (L-TGA). D-TGA *is the most common type of TGA*.

Dextro-transposition. With D-TGA, the heart tube loops to the right during organogenesis, yielding normal ventricular orientation and great vessel formation, but the aorta and pulmonary artery fail to rotate, resulting in reversal of these two vessels. The aorta ultimately arises from the right ventricle and the pulmonary artery arises from the left ventricle (CDC, 2018d; R. J. Martin et al., 2015). This transposition of the two great vessels results in two independent and parallel circulations (Figure 5.14).

The first circuit involves the persistent recirculation of deoxygenated blood from the right atrium to the right ventricle through the aorta and out to the systemic circulation. The second circuit involves the recirculation of oxygenated blood from the pulmonary veins to the left atrium, left ventricle, and pulmonary artery; blood enters this circuit by way of the patent ductus arteriosus

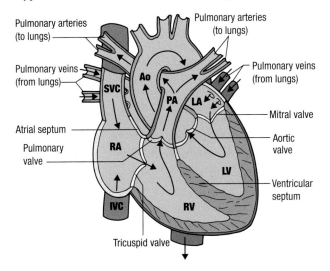

Figure 5.13 Normal heart anatomy. Arrows reflect blood flow pattern.

Ao, aorta; IVC, inferior vena cava; LA, left atrium; LV, left ventricle; PA, pulmonary artery; RA, right atrium; RV, right ventricle; SVC, superior vena cava.

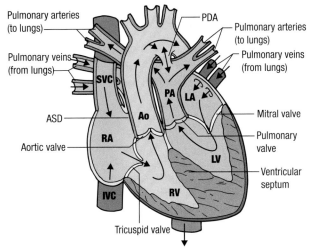

Figure 5.14 Dextro-transposition of the great arteries. Arrows reflect the parallel blood flow pattern.

Ao, aorta; ASD, atrial septal defect; IVC, inferior vena cava; LA, left atrium; LV, left ventricle; PA, pulmonary artery; PDA, patent ductus arteriosus; RA, right atrium; RV, right ventricle; SVC, superior vena cava.

(R. J.Martin et al., 2015; Moore et al., 2016). This type of circulation is incompatible with life; therefore, early identification is critical to establishing an open communication between the two parallel circuits by way of an atrial septal defect (ASD), VSD, or PDA (Moore et al., 2016).

Affected neonates manifest with cyanosis at or within a few hours after birth. Due to increased right ventricular pressure and close proximity of the mitral valve, bowing of the ventricular septum occurs, which causes an outflow obstruction at the aortic inlet. Infants require a PDA to perfuse the pulmonary circuit and facilitate uptake of oxygen. This blood is returned to the heart by way of a left-to-right shunting across the foramen ovale. Infants with a patent ventricular septum (a VSD) benefit from a greater opportunity for mixing of deoxygenated and oxygenated blood, which often results in better arterial oxygenation. Large VSD may increase the risk for pulmonary overcirculation and increase the risk for CHF.

Life-span implications include a 95% survival rate at 15 to 25 years following discharge status after the arterial switch procedure (Khairy et al., 2013). Children with repaired D-TGA often have functional limitations on exercise capacities. Neurodevelopmental delays have also been reported. Continuing care across the life span is indicated.

Levo-transposition. L-TGA is also referred to as *congenitally corrected TGA* because the systemic deoxygenated venous blood returns to the pulmonary circulation and oxygenated pulmonary venous blood returns to the systemic circulation, yet the heart tube is abnormally rotated to the left. Isolated L-TGA is extremely rare; this defect usually presents with other cardiac malformations. Despite the rarity of this CHD, we present a concise overview of L-TGA such that clinicians can discern the differences between both forms of transposition.

In L-TGA, the aorta lies anterior and to the left of the pulmonary artery. The right atrium connects through the mitral valve to a left ventricle that is positioned in a rightward and anterior manner. The left ventricle empties into an outflow tract that leads posteriorly through the pulmonary valve and into the pulmonary artery and to the lungs. Blood then enters the left atrium and empties through the tricuspid valve and into the right ventricle; the right ventricular outflow is anterior, emptying through the aortic valve into the ascending aorta, which is anterior and leftward, pumping pulmonary venous blood outward to the body. These defects lead to misplacement of the cardiac conduction system, which increases the risk for varying degrees of heart block. In addition, positioning of coronary arteries is reversed, with the right coronary artery supplying the anterior descending branch.

L-transposition rarely exists without other major cardiac anomalies, which determine the outcome. The physiologic problems seen with L-transposition are directly related to the associated defects. The neonate may be asymptomatic after birth. In some cases, significant tricuspid insufficiency and systemic ventricular dysfunction can occur. Cyanosis can be present if there is an accompanying VSD and pulmonary stenosis (Everett & Lim, 2007).

Long-term sequelae for patients with L-TGA are dependent on the other cardiac malformations associated with it. Mortality risk after early surgical correction is low; however, the long-term prognosis is poor. Progressively worsening right ventricular dysfunction is common, which precedes heart failure (Rutledge et al., 2002). Continuing care is mandatory.

Tetralogy of Fallot. TOF is *the most common congenital cyanotic defect that manifests during infancy.* TOF is associated with a prevalence of approximately four to five per every 10,000 live births within the United States (CDC, 2018f). This defect accounts for about 7% to 10% of cases of CHD and is one of the most common congenital heart lesions that requires surgical intervention within the first year of life (R. J. Martin et al., 2015; Polin et al., 2017). TOF occurs equally in males and females. Approximately 80% of cases are sporadic; the remaining 20% of cases of TOF have associated risk factors, including maternal pregestational diabetes mellitus; advanced maternal age; family history of CHD; fetal exposure to medications, including valproate, amantadine, and Coumadin; trisomy 21; prune belly syndrome; CHARGE (**c**oloboma of the eye, **h**eart defects, **a**tresia of the choanae, **r**etardation of **g**rowth and development, and **e**ar abnormalities and deafness) syndrome; as well as pyloric stenosis; renal agenesis; hypospadias; and polydactyly (Nies & Brenner, 2013; Simeone et al., 2016).

TOF involves a constellation of four anatomic findings: (a) pulmonary artery stenosis, (b) VSD, (c) overriding aorta, and (d) right ventricular hypertrophy (Figure 5.15; Swamy, Bharadwaj, Varadarajan, & Pai, 2015). The major defect is the right ventricular outflow obstruction, which limits pulmonary blood flow and impedes adequate oxygenation. Pulmonary stenosis results in right ventricular outflow obstruction, which leads to right ventricular hypertrophy. This leads to increased ventricular pressure and causes the perimembranous portion of the ventricular septum to rupture, yielding the large VSD of the conal septum. Furthermore, the aorta is enlarged and displaced to the right, straddling the ventricular septum, which permits aortic uptake of blood from both ventricles. The resultant right ventricular hypertrophy and upward tilting of the left ventricular axis yields the classic "boot-shaped" cardiac silhouette on radiographic studies.

Infants will manifest with either "blue" or "pink" TOF; few cases involve TOF with balanced pulmonary stenosis. Severe pulmonary stenosis is associated with *blue* TOF and is responsible for the audible murmur heard during early disease states. Blood is preferentially shunted in a right-to-left direction across the VSD; patients will present with varying degrees of cyanosis, which is contingent

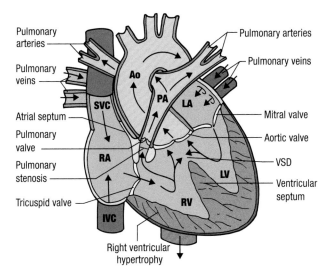

Figure 5.15 Tetralogy of Fallot. Arrows reflect the abnormal blood flow pattern.

Ao, aorta; IVC, inferior vena cava; LA, left atrium; LV, left ventricle; PA, pulmonary artery; RA, right atrium; RV, right ventricle; SVC, superior vena cava; VSD, ventricular septal defect.

upon the severity of the outflow tract obstruction and patency of the ductus arteriosus.

Pink tetralogy involves minimal ventricular outflow obstruction, no significant directional shunt across the VSD, and, likewise, no cyanosis. The disease process may remain subclinical for years, even into adulthood. In between the aforementioned blue and pink extremes are cases of TOF with *balanced pulmonary stenosis*. In these circumstances, equivocal pressures protect the pulmonary arteries from overcirculation and reactive pulmonary hypertension. The main and central pulmonary arteries are typically small or hypoplastic in contrast to the aorta, which is comparatively larger. The amount of right ventricular outflow obstruction is proportionate to the degree to which the aorta overrides the ventricular septum.

Infants with blue TOF may manifest with paroxysmal hypercyanotic episodes, also known as *tet spells*. This leads to increased pulmonary stenosis and reduced blood flow to the pulmonary artery. As a result, increased right-to-left shunting occurs with an acute reduction in the oxygen content of the blood. With severe hypoxemia, a switch from aerobic to anaerobic metabolism occurs and leads to lactic and metabolic acidosis. These hypercyanotic episodes can be fatal if left untreated. Parents must receive ongoing education on mechanisms to reverse tet spells.

Survival is estimated at greater than 93% among patients who undergo corrective procedures; uncorrected TOF is associated with 50% mortality risk in early childhood (Park, Lee, Lim, Kim, & Kim, 2010). Continuing care is needed for patients with TOF. Lifespan implications include a risk for atrial reentrant

tachycardia (30%), ventricular arrhythmias (10%), and sudden cardiac death (0.2%) as a result of scarring at the right ventricular incision site (Hoffman, 2017; Villafañe et al., 2013). Pulmonary valve regurgitation predisposes patients to ventricular dilatation. As the right ventricular dilatation progresses, tricuspid valve regurgitation occurs, which encourages right atrial enlargement. The constellation of these factors increases the risk for the ventricular and atrial arrhythmias described earlier. Affected adults are at increased risk for aortic dilation, likely related to increased aortic blood flow observed prior to surgical correction (McRae, 2015a). Reports indicate that affected women who undergo surgical correction can safely tolerate pregnancy and the birth process (Park et al., 2010).

Total Anomalous Pulmonary Venous Return. Total anomalous pulmonary venous return (TAPVR) involves abnormal drainage of all pulmonary venous blood into the systemic venous system (Crispi & Martinez, 2018). TAPVR is the fifth most common cause of cyanotic CHD, with an estimated incidence of one per every 10,000 live births (CDC, 2018g). Risk factors include heterotaxy syndromes, which include asplenia and polysplenia.

Four types of TAPVR are known: supracardiac, cardiac, infracardiac, and mixed (Figure 5.16). Supracardiac TAPVR is the most common type, accounting for 44%

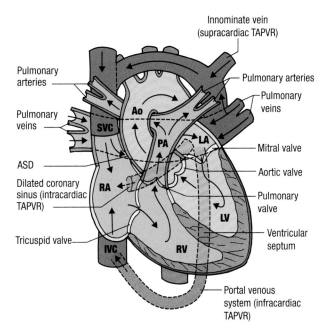

Figure 5.16 Total anomalous pulmonary venous return. Image depicts anatomy with supracardiac, intracardiac, and infracardiac TAPVR. Arrows reflect the abnormal blood flow pattern.

Ao, aorta; ASD, atrial septal defect; IVC, inferior vena cava; LA, left atrium; LV, left ventricle; PA, pulmonary artery; RA, right atrium; RV, right ventricle; SVC, superior vena cava; TAPVR, total anomalous pulmonary venous return.

of all cases of TAPVR (Jaramillo, Hernandez, Garzón, Sánchez Herrera, & Velasco Morales, 2017). Supracardiac TAPVR involves movement of pulmonary venous drainage to a common pulmonary venous channel located behind the left atrium. This pulmonary venous channel drains into the brachiocephalic vein (Jaramillo et al., 2017; B. J. Martin, Karamlou, & Tabbutt, 2016).

Infracardiac TAPVR accounts for 26% of all cases (Jaramillo et al., 2017). All pulmonary veins drain into a common pulmonary vein behind the left atrium where the pulmonary venous blood passes inferiorly through the diaphragm and into the inferior vena cava, portal venous system, or hepatic veins (B. J. Martin et al., 2016). In order to reenter the heart, this blood must pass through the portal vein and ductus venosus to the inferior vena cava and back to the right atrium. Infracardiac TAPVR is often associated with obstruction to flow at the diaphragm or ductus venosus; the portal system is often unable to tolerate cardiac output, which often leads to significant pulmonary venous congestion.

Cardiac TAPVR accounts for 21% of all reported cases (Jaramillo et al., 2017). In these cases, all pulmonary veins drain into a common pulmonary venous channel, which then drains into the right atrium, or more commonly, into the coronary sinus (Jaramillo et al., 2017; B. J. Martin et al., 2016).

The mixed type of TAPVR accounts for 9% of all cases of TAPVR (Jaramillo et al., 2017). Mixed TAPVR involves situations in which the pulmonary venous system drains into two or more locations. For example, left pulmonary veins may pass through the innominate vein, by way of a supracardiac route, whereas the right pulmonary veins drain directly into the right atrium by way of an infracardiac route.

All types of TAPVR involve a degree of obstruction to blood flow at certain anatomic locations; obstruction is most common with infracardiac TAPVR (78%; Jaramillo et al., 2017). Obstruction may occur secondary to compression from adjacent structures, or occur within the pulmonary venous system. Severe obstruction is associated with respiratory distress and cyanosis during the neonatal period and is considered a surgical emergency (B. J. Martin et al., 2016).

Early mortality, defined as death within 30 days of surgical correction, is less than 10% (St. Louis et al., 2012). In fact, surgical correction is associated with 5-year survivability of 97% and 85% survivability to adolescence; pulmonary vein stenosis (5%–19%), pulmonary hypertension, and pulmonary venous obstruction are the most common postsurgical complications (Jaramillo et al., 2017). Life-span implications include neurocognitive delays and cardiac arrhythmias. In the absence of residual pulmonary vein stenosis or pulmonary hypertension, exercise capacity is normal among children with repaired TAPVR (St. Louis et al., 2012). Continuing care is warranted. Patients who progress into adulthood often develop pulmonary vascular disease.

The Single Ventricle. Single-ventricle defects involve the presence of one ventricular chamber, or one large and functionally dominant ventricle with a rudimentary or hypoplastic opposing ventricle. Common single-ventricle defects include tricuspid atresia, hypoplastic left heart syndrome, double outlet left ventricle, and double outlet right ventricle. Less frequent, atrioventricular canal defects and PA may manifest as single-ventricle defects.

Recall that during early embryonic development, the atrioventricular canal opens into the ventricular portion of the primitive heart tube and later becomes the left ventricle. Blood passes to the bulbus cordis from the ventricular portion of the primitive heart tube, contributing to right ventricle development. The arterial trunk arises from the bulbus cordis, later becoming the aorta and main pulmonary artery. With an interventricular septation defect or arrest in development, a double-inlet single left ventricle with a rudimentary right ventricle forms.

The most common type of single ventricle is a single left ventricle with L-transposition of the great arteries. In these circumstances, the aorta arises from a very small, leftward-leaning right ventricle. The pulmonary artery arises posteriorly and the mitral valve is located on the right side of the heart, whereas the tricuspid valve is located to the left. The degree of pulmonary stenosis or amount of PVR determines the amount of pulmonary blood flow and the clinical presentation after delivery. If there is no pulmonary stenosis and pulmonary venous resistance decreases, CHF will develop. When PA is present, the neonate is dependent on a right-to-left shunt through the PDA in order to maintain systemic cardiac output. The degree of cyanosis is thereby determined by the amount of pulmonary blood flow supplied by the collateral circulation.

Life-span implications are associated with venous hypertension and include esophageal varices, liver fibrosis or cirrhosis, protein-losing enteropathy from the intestine, leg varicosities, and pleural effusions. Sinus node dysfunction, intraatrial reentry tachycardia, and ventricular tachycardia are arrhythmias reported among patients treated with the Fontan procedure. The right atrium to pulmonary artery Fontan connection increases the risk for postsurgical right atrial thrombi as well as pulmonary emboli, which is due to passive blood flow and subsequent right atrial enlargement (McRae, 2015b).

Acyanotic Heart Defects

Unlike cyanotic heart defects, which present with clinical symptoms in the first day of life, acyanotic defects may go undetected. Acyanotic heart defects may become clinically apparent days to weeks after birth. As PVR decreases during the postnatal period, increased left-to-right shunting occurs, resulting in increased pulmonary blood flow. Shunting at the atrial level results in right ventricular overload, whereas shunting at the ventricular or great vessel level results in left ventricular overload (Backer, Eltayeb, Mongé, Mazwi, & Costello, 2016). Common acyanotic congenital cardiac defects described here include VSD, ASD, atrioventricular canal (AVC), and PDA.

Ventricular Septal Defect. VSDs are the most common CHD diagnosed during the first year of life and occur in approximately 50% to 60% of infants affected by CHDs (Puri, Allen, & Qureshi, 2017). VSD often presents as an isolated defect, or may occur in combination with other CHDs, including AVC, TOF, and occasionally D-TGA.

The anatomical defect is caused by abnormal ventricular septation. Single or multiple openings at various locations within the ventricular septum result (Moore et al., 2016). As a consequence, oxygenated blood mixes with deoxygenated blood during fetal and postnatal development. Postnatally, as the left side of the heart becomes dominant, blood flow via the abnormal ventricular opening(s) permits persistent left-to-right shunting and pulmonary overcirculation, which may increase the risk for CHF.

VSDs are classified into four major types with the embryological basis varying depending on the septal defect location. The four classifications are (a) perimembranous, (b) juxta-arterial (subarterial), (c) muscular, and (d) inlet VSD (Figure 5.17). Perimembranous VSDs are the most common type of VSD, reported in approximately 75% to 80% of all cases (Backer et al., 2016; McRae, 2015a; Puri et al., 2017). This type of VSD occurs in the upper, thinner, membrane-like portion of the ventricular septum as a result of fibrous deficiencies (McRae, 2015a; Puri et al., 2017). Juxta-arterial VSDs arise between the pulmonic and aortic valves, at the infundibular septum. Muscular VSDs are located in the lower, thicker trabecular portion of the ventricular septum (McRae, 2015a). These are understood to occur secondarily due to excessive excavation of myocardial tissue during ventricular growth (Moore et al.,

2016). Inlet VSDs arise inferior to the perimembranous region and slightly below the tricuspid and mitral valves.

Clinical manifestations are contingent on the size and severity of the defect. Small to moderate defects that do not encourage significant pulmonary overcirculation are associated with a harsh pan-systolic murmur best heard over the left lower sternal border. Large VSDs are often hemodynamically significant and present with signs of pulmonary overcirculation with or without CHF.

Life-span implications depend on the type and severity of the VSD. Perimembranous and muscular VSDs may close over time; muscular VSDs close as the septum grows. Closure of a perimembranous VSD may be the result of aortic valve prolapse and therefore must be carefully followed. Hemodynamically significant VSDs often require diuretic therapy to treat pulmonary overcirculation. As such, these infants incur increased risk for nutritional deficits and poor linear growth (Puri et al., 2017).

Atrial Septal Defect. An ASD is an opening or series of openings anywhere within the atrial septum. In the United States, approximately 1,966 babies are born each year with an ASD, either as an isolated defect or part of a more complex CHD. A female-to-male prevalence (2:1) is reported (CDC, 2018b).

ASDs are classified into four major types: (a) ostium secundum defects, (b) ostium primum defects, (c) sinus venosus defects, and (d) coronary sinus defects (Figure 5.18). The ostium secundum is the most common form, constituting about 75% of ASDs; in this type of defect the atrial opening is located in the center of the atrial septum in the area of the foramen ovale (McRae, 2015a). This defect arises secondary to defective development of

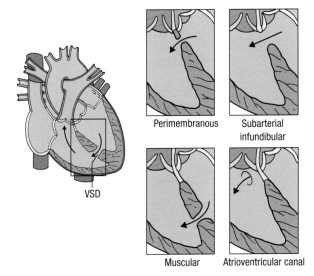

Figure 5.17 Ventricular septal defects.

VSD, ventricular septal defect.

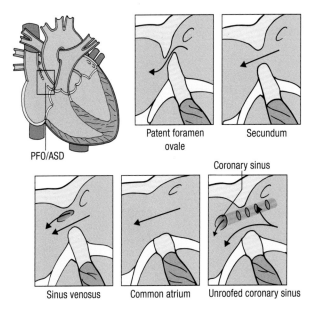

Figure 5.18 Atrial septal defects.

ASD, atrial septal defect; PFO, patent foramen ovale.

the septum primum. Ostium primum defects arise secondary to failed proliferation of the endocardial cushion. Sinus venosus defects are seen at the level of the superior vena or pulmonary veins, and rare coronary defects occur near the coronary sinus (Puri et al., 2017).

After delivery, the amount of shunting is determined by the size of the defect and compliance of both ventricles (Backer et al., 2016). Initially, left-to-right shunting is minimal as the right ventricle is not very compliant. As the right ventricle becomes more compliant with age, left-to-right shunting increases, sending increased blood flow across the pulmonic valve. This increases the risk for right atrial and right ventricular dilatation (Backer et al., 2016).

Clinical manifestations, commonly identified during infancy, include tachypnea, decreased activity levels, and poor linear growth with failure to thrive. A focused cardiovascular examination will typically yield a split murmur heard over the pulmonic region secondary to the aforementioned increased blood flow across the pulmonic valve, as well as potential for a diastolic murmur heard over the left lower sternal border (Puri et al., 2017). Patients who require surgical repair during childhood usually endure uncomplicated postoperative courses and are generally free of latent complications and activity restrictions.

Atrioventricular Septal Defect. An AVSD results from failed fusion of the endocardial cushion (Figure 5.19).

This acyanotic heart lesion leaves a hole in the center of the heart between the atrioventricular septums and is associated with a myriad of valvular anomalies. In the United States, approximately 2,000 infants are born each year with an AVSD. Complete AVSD is present in up to 75% of fetuses with trisomy 21 (Backer et al., 2016; Puri et al., 2017). AVSDs may be associated with a heterotaxy syndrome confirmed by the presence of asplenia or polysplenia. Maternal diabetes mellitus has been associated with increased risk for AVSDs among offspring.

Recall from the review of cardiovascular embryology that the left ventricle connects to the atria by way of the primitive atrioventricular canal. Ridges of mesenchymal tissue comprise the circumference of the canal and naturally divide during development into four distinct endocardial cushions: the (a) inferior (upper part of the ventricular septum), (b) superior (lower part of the atrial septum), (c) left (anterior leaflet of the mitral valve), and (d) right (septal leaflet of the tricuspid valve) endocardial cushions. Abnormal development of the endocardial cushions gives rise to AVSD malformations.

AV canal defects are commonly categorized as either *complete* or *partial*. A complete AVSD is characterized by an AVSD that is contiguous with an inlet VSD and a common AV valve with five leaflets. A partial AVSD is limited to an ASD with cleft anterior mitral leaflet; no inlet VSD is observed (R. J. Martin et al., 2015). Both variations of the defect cause mixing of blood in the centralized areas

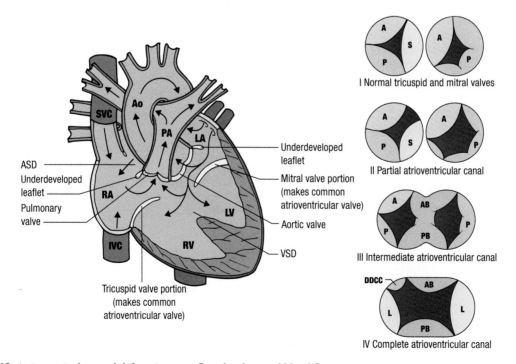

Figure 5.19 Atrioventricular canal defect. Arrows reflect the abnormal blood flow pattern.

A, anterior leaflet; AB, anterior bridging leaflet; Ao, aorta; ASD, atrial septal defect; DDCC, dextrodorsal conus cushion; IVC, inferior vena cava; L, lateral leaflet; LA, left atrium; LV, left ventricle; P, posterior leaflet; PA, pulmonary artery; PB, posterior bridging leaflet; RA, right atrium; RV, right ventricle; S, septal leaflet; SVC, superior vena cava; VSD, ventricular septal defect.

of the heart, but the flow is usually left to right due to the left heart dominance and low pulmonary pressures. Two additional subtypes, *intermediate* and *transitional* AVSDs, are also reported. The intermediate AVSD is a variant of the complete AVSD and involves an ASD, inlet VSD, and common AV valve annulus bifurcated into anterior and posterior segments by a thin flap of septal tissue. The transitional AVSD is considered a variant of the partial AVSD and involves an ASD, inlet VSD, and two annular cavities separated by a cleft anterior mitral leaflet (Puri et al., 2017).

Postnatal clinical manifestations include left-to-right shunting at both the atrial and ventricular levels, as well as mitral valve regurgitation, resulting in pulmonary overcirculation and CHF. Latent consequences of AVSD commonly include arrhythmias, subaortic stenosis, and pulmonary vascular disease. Continuing care involves monitoring for unbalanced pulmonary and systemic circulations with worsening mitral valve regurgitation; 10% to 20% of affected individuals will require additional corrective surgeries. Ten-year survival postsurgical correction exceeds 90% (Minich et al., 2010).

Patent Ductus Arteriosus. The PDA is a normal fetal intracardiac shunt that connects the main pulmonary artery to the descending aorta. This cannula permits shunting of right-sided venous blood to the systemic circulation; elevated fetal PVR facilitates this purposeful pulmonary bypass and functional movement of blood flow (R. J. Martin et al., 2015; Moore et al., 2016).

The pathogenesis of postnatal PDA closure is well understood. Ductal constriction appears to be stimulated by increasing arterial oxygen tension, increasing blood pH, and the increased availability of vasoactive substances. Removal of the low resistance placental circuit, onset of crying and spontaneous respirations, and uptake of oxygen initiate the progressive constriction and functional closure of the PDA. During this time, SVR increases and exceeds PVR, reversing the direction of flow through the intracardiac shunt (PDA). Blood flow entering the PDA is redirected to the pulmonary system through the left-to-right shunt, which temporarily increases demand on the pulmonary circulation. In the full-term infant, ductal closure typically begins within the first 24 hours of life and the ligament is functionally closed by day 4 of postnatal life (R. J. Martin et al., 2015). Of note, infants of more than 28 weeks gestation and weighing more than 1 kg at birth, who do not manifest with respiratory distress, are also likely to experience normal and unassisted postnatal functional closure of the PDA (R. J. Martin et al., 2015).

Failed closure of the PDA results in persistent and increasing left-to-right blood flow to the pulmonary circuit and, likewise, risks atrial and ventricular distension and pulmonary overcirculation. A consistent diversion of systemic blood flow away from the descending aorta and back across the PDA in a left-to-right direction is commonly referred to as the *diastolic steal phenomenon*. This type of flow pattern can lead to inadequate oxygen delivery to the cerebral arteries, mesentery, and renal system and risks associated ischemic damage (R. J. Martin et al., 2015). Factors that favor the postnatal persistence of the PDA include hypoxemia, acidosis, prostaglandin administration, and postnatal glucocorticoid exposure, in addition to other factors associated with prematurity and critical illness.

Common clinical manifestations of PDA include bounding pulses, widened pulse pressures, and increased left ventricular stroke volume with hyperdynamic precordial activity. A holosystolic or "machinery-like" murmur is typically heard over the right upper sternal border; large and even hemodynamically significant defects may offer such low resistance to flow that no murmur may be heard. As excessive blood flow continues, enlargement occurs and additional left-to-right shunting across the foramen ovale occurs leading, to further volume overload and the development of CHF (Backer et al., 2016). In these circumstances, worsening hypercapnia as well as an elevated alveolar-arterial (A-a) gradient, often in combination with increased work of breathing or demand for respiratory support, may be observed.

Life-span implications relate to the direct consequences of pulmonary recirculation and cardiac dysfunction, as well as the consequences of ischemia. Intraventricular hemorrhage, bronchopulmonary dysplasia, necrotizing enterocolitis, renal parenchymal damage, retinopathy of prematurity, and later neurodevelopmental impairment are all associated with cases of treated and untreated PDA. Due to substantial advances in neonatal care, death is rarely reported. Although a discussion of pharmacologic and surgical treatment mechanisms is beyond the scope of this textbook, clinicians should be aware that the management of pathological PDA continues to be a contentious topic and wide variations in clinical practices are observed.

Obstructive Congenital Heart Defects

Obstructive lesions are CHD that result in obstructed blood flow involving either the left or right side of the heart. The majority of clinical manifestations are a result of ventricular hypertrophy and diminished blood flow to the area distal to the obstruction.

Hypoplastic Left Heart Syndrome. Hypoplastic left heart syndrome (HLHS) is a spectrum resulting from underdevelopment of the left heart–aorta complex that involves the atresia, stenosis, or hypoplasia of the mitral and aortic valves, and hypoplasia of the left ventricle, preductal aorta, and aortic arch (**Figure 5.20**; R. J. Martin et al., 2015; Mettler & Pigula, 2016; Tchervenkov, Jacobs, & Tahta, 2000). In the United States, approximately 960 infants are born each year with HLHS; this is equivalent to an incidence of one in every 4,344 live births (CDC,

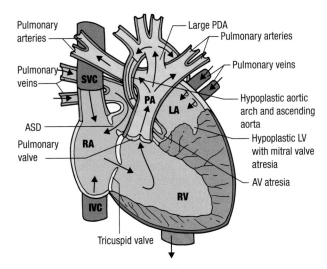

Figure 5.20 Hypoplastic left heart syndrome. Arrows reflect the abnormal blood flow pattern.

ASD, atrial septal defect; AV, atrioventricular valve; IVC, inferior vena cava; LA, left atrium; LV, left ventricle; PA, pulmonary artery; PDA, patent ductus arteriosus; RA, right atrium; RV, right ventricle; SVC, superior vena cava.

2016e). A male prevalence (1.5:1) is reported and sibling recurrence risk is 0.5% (R. J. Martin et al., 2015).

The pathophysiology of HLHS relates to the severity of obstruction caused by the constellation of anatomic defects and associated hypoplasia. HLHS involves parallel pulmonary and systemic circulations, both modulated by the right ventricle. Several factors may implicate left ventricular hypoplasia and predispose the right ventricle to its dueling role. One such factor is incompetence of the aortic valve. An atretic, stenosed, or hypoplastic aortic valve inhibits evacuation of blood from the left ventricle and into the ascending aorta. This leads to increased afterload (pressure) within the left ventricle, which over time leads to left ventricular hypertrophy. The constant distending pressure created by increased afterload inhibits normal flow into the left ventricle, which over time inhibits growth and leads to ventricular hypoplasia.

A second root cause for left ventricular hypoplasia relates to aberrant development of the mitral valve. This leads to reduced preload into the left ventricle. Blood aggregates within the left atrium, which increases afterload within this locale and encourages blood flow to divert across the PFO (if present). Over time, this permits ongoing reductions in blood flow into the left ventricle, thereby encouraging hypoplasia.

Third, right-sided compensation leads to enlargement and inhibits normal development of the left side of the heart. In cases of mitral valve stenosis or atresia, increased left atrial afterload encourages left-to-right movement of blood flow across the foramen ovale and back into the right side of the heart. This results in compensatory

expansion of the right heart. Over time, right-sided enlargement competes spatially with the left side of the heart and contributes to left-sided hypoplasia.

It is important that clinicians understand the need for ductal patency during the postnatal period; early identification and diagnosis is absolutely critical to maintaining function of the PDA after birth. In the immediate postnatal period, PVR exceeds SVR and blood is redirected across the foramen ovale and, most significantly, the PDA. As PVR begins to decrease, blood flow is preferentially directed across the PDA and toward the pulmonary circulation. The PDA is the only mechanism by which gas exchange may occur. This directional flow across the PDA leads to "diastolic stealing," pulmonary overcirculation, edema, and systemic hypoperfusion. As a result, systemic blood flow decreases. Stroke volume and heart rate increase in an attempt to preserve systemic cardiac output, but in doing so limit right ventricular output. This predisposes the infant to CHF, given that the right ventricle modulates both pulmonary and systemic circulation. Should the PDA begin to close, pressure will accumulate within the right ventricle, and perfusion to the systemic circulation, most notable in the coronary arteries, will be further compromised. The right ventricle will dilate and hypertrophy, tricuspid regurgitation may develop, and vital organs, including the kidneys, risk ischemic damage from poor systemic perfusion (Mettler & Pigula, 2016).

Term infants with HLHS who maintain a PFO and do not develop severely restricted disease during fetal development usually present as well-appearing infants after birth. However, the pathogenesis of the disease process quickly leads to pulmonary edema, restricted pulmonary blood flow, and increased work of breathing, tachypnea, cyanosis, and acidosis (R. J. Martin et al., 2015; Mettler & Pigula, 2016). The increased pulmonary blood flow and obstructed outflow from the left atrium leads to increased pulmonary venous pressure, which often causes the neonate to manifest with a "gasping" respiratory effort. This may precede or present alongside cardiogenic shock. Auscultation typically yields a single or third heart sound and any regurgitation across the valves will yield a murmur. Uneven upper and lower extremity pulses are common among infants affected by significant aortic narrowing or coarctation; peripheral pulses become increasingly difficult to palpate after functional closure of the PDA (R. J. Martin et al., 2015).

HLHS is responsible for 25% to 40% of all cardiac-related deaths among neonates (Simeone et al., 2016). Advances in surgical palliation, involving the Norwood, Glenn, and Fontan procedures, have optimized survivability; a 5-year survival rate of 65% to 70% for patients who successfully undergo the stage I Norwood procedure is reported (Gobergs, Salputra, & Labaua, 2016; Tennant, Pearce, Bythell, & Rankin, 2010). Cardiac transplantation is required in certain cases; organ rejection remains a potential contributor to mortality. Commonly reported (postsurgical) life-span implications for infants and children include an increased risk for intracranial hemorrhage, protein-losing enteropathy, arrhythmia, thrombotic stroke, neurodevelopmental impairment, and reduced exercise capacity (Gobergs et al., 2016).

Coarctation of the Aorta. Coarctation of the aorta is a narrowing or constriction of varying lengths of the aortic arch, distal to the aortic root. In the United States, four of every 10,000 infants are diagnosed with coarctation of the aorta (CDC, 2018c). A male-to-female prevalence is reported. Risk factors include chromosomal abnormalities such as Turner syndrome and DiGeorge syndrome. Maternal health influences include preexisting diabetes mellitus (R. J. Martin et al., 2015).

The most common type of coarctation is the juxtaductal coarctation, which arises where the ductus arteriosus invaginates with the aorta (Emani, 2016). The ductus arteriosus is composed of smooth muscle in addition to elastic tissue. Some of this tissue extends into the wall of the aorta, comingling the ductal tissue with a section of the wall of the aorta. After birth, when the ductal smooth muscle begins its normal process of constriction, the tissue that innervated within the wall of the aorta also constricts. This gives rise to the juxtaductal coarctation.

Alternatively, coarctations may arise at a more proximal (preductal) or distal (postductal) segment of the aorta (Figure 5.21). The embryologic basis for this is poorly understood; however, postductal coarctations typically manifest in partnership with other complex heart lesions, including HLHS. Regardless of the etiology, the aortic constriction causes a mechanical outflow tract obstruction.

The pathogenesis of coarctation involves an increase in left ventricular afterload. This results in left ventricular failure, left atrial hypertension, and left-to-right shunting across the foramen ovale. Increasing pulmonary flow encourages a right-to-left shunt across the ductus arteriosus, as pulmonary vascular pressure exceeds systemic vascular pressure. Once the ductus arteriosus closes, cardiac output to the descending aorta and distal organs is interrupted.

Clinical manifestations depend on the location and severity of the coarctation. Approximately 50% of patients will manifest symptoms during the neonatal period (first 28 days of life) and the majority of these cases involve a coarctation at a location on the aortic arch that occurs before innervation with the ductus arteriosus (preductal coarctation; Emani, 2016). Affected infants may exhibit normal perfusion to the upper extremities and decreased perfusion to the lower extremities, as well as feeding difficulties, lethargy, and decreased urine output (Puri et al., 2017). Coarctations that arise proximal to both subclavian arteries will manifest with diminished blood pressures and pulses to all four extremities. Severe narrowing typically manifests as discordant upper versus lower extremity blood pressures, pulses and oxygen saturations, hypoperfusion, metabolic acidosis, and heart failure. Mild cases may remain subclinical through childhood or even into adulthood and manifest as chest pain or involve recurrent headaches. Older children and adults seem to develop collateral circulations over time, which circumvent the coarctation and distribute blood to the distal organs (Emani, 2016; Puri et al., 2017).

Life-span implications relate to operative mortality risk, survivability, and recurrence risk. Operative mortality is estimated at 1% to 5% (Emani, 2016). Survivability

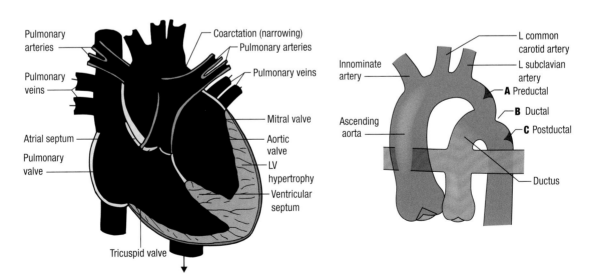

Figure 5.21 Coarctation of the aorta (postductal type). Arrows reflect the abnormal blood flow pattern.

Ao, aorta; IVC, inferior vena cava; LA, left atrium; LV, left ventricle; PA, pulmonary artery; RA, right atrium; RV, right ventricle; SVC, superior vena cava.

at 10 years post-correction is 90%, whereas 70% of individuals survive for an additional three decades after surgical repair (Emani, 2016). Recurrence risk is higher among younger children, who may require additional corrective surgeries if the narrowing reappears. Hypertension is common among affected children.

Pulmonary Atresia (With Stenosis and an Intact Ventricular Septum). PA is a right-sided obstructive lesion. The pulmonary valve is completely fused, which obstructs the egress of blood from the right ventricle and into the lungs. PA affects one in every 10,000 live-born infants within the United States (CDC, 2018e). The atresia may accompany an intact ventricular septum, or present with a VSD and a degree of pulmonary artery stenosis (Figure 5.22).

The pathogenesis of PA with an intact ventricular septum is well understood. Blood enters the right atrium, traverses the tricuspid valve, and travels into the right ventricle. Blood is thereby unable to enter the pulmonary artery, due to the atretic pulmonary valve, and is redirected toward the right atrium. Regurgitation across the tricuspid valve occurs, right atrial preload increases, and blood is preferentially shunted in a right-to-left direction across the foramen ovale. Once within the left atrium, the blood mixes with oxygenated blood exiting the pulmonary system and is routed to the left ventricle and through the aorta. A portion of this blood is redirected across the PDA, which is the only mechanism by which blood reaches the pulmonary system. Once the PDA closes, the conduit to the pulmonary system is removed and

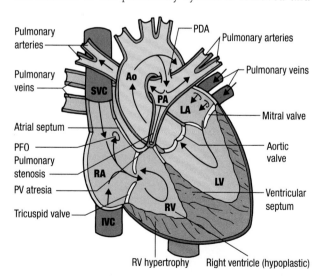

Figure 5.22 Pulmonary valve atresia with stenosis and intact ventricular septum. Arrows reflect the abnormal blood flow pattern.

Ao, aorta; IVC, inferior vena cava; LA, left atrium; LV, left ventricle; PA, pulmonary artery; PDA, patent ductus arteriosus; PFO, patent foramen ovale; PV, pulmonary valve; RA, right atrium; RV, right ventricle; SVC, superior vena cava.

infants quickly manifest cyanosis and respiratory distress. Auscultation of the heart yields a single (not split) second heart sound with or without a murmur. Once surgically corrected, the prognosis is promising. Aerobic and exercise capacity are typically decreased among older adults (Karamlou et al., 2013). In rare circumstances, affected infants require cardiac transplantation.

Aortic Stenosis. Aortic stenosis is the most common valvular disease. It is a left-sided obstructive cardiac defect that results in decreased systemic perfusion to the body. The global incidence of all forms of congenital aortic stenosis is estimated at 1% to 2%, with a male-to-female (3:1) prevalence (Bonow & Greenland, 2015; Mordi & Tzemos, 2012). Narrowing of the valve orifice leads to the left-sided outflow obstruction. We focus this discussion upon bicuspid aortic valve disease, the most common congenital form of aortic stenosis. A male-to-female prevalence of bicuspid (dual-leaflet) aortic stenosis, as well as recurrence risk within families, is reported. Genetic influences, specifically related to mutations in the *NOTCH1* gene, may predispose the fetus to developing a bicuspid aortic valve (Irtyuga et al., 2017).

Normally, heart valves have three fleshy flaps, or cusps, which open with each beat of the heart. Stenotic valves, however, have less leaflet mobility due to thickening or fusion of one or both of the leaflets. This prevents the valve from opening up widely, resulting in obstruction to left ventricular outflow (Figure 5.23).

As previously reviewed, aortic stenosis creates an obstruction to flow out of the left ventricle. As the stenosis progresses, increased afterload is noted within the left ventricle. This leads to endocardial ischemia and hypertrophy, scarring (endocardial fibroelastosis), ventricular failure, and decreased systemic cardiac output. As left ventricular incompetence progresses, blood is diverted in a left-to-right direction across the foramen ovale, which increases pulmonary recirculation and magnifies the ensuing CHF. Once the PDA closes (the only significant conduit to the pulmonary system and systemic circulation), systemic cardiac output significantly decreases (Scholz & Reinking, 2018).

The pathogenesis described here may escalate to a severe level, referred to as *critical aortic stenosis*. In these cases, the aortic pressure gradient increases from 30 mmHg (mild stenosis) to 60 mmHg (severe stenosis), further compromising systemic cardiac output (Scholz & Reinking, 2018). Although manifestations of milder forms of aortic stenosis may be delayed, critical aortic stenosis typically manifests in the immediate postnatal period. Indices of cardiogenic shock, including diminished peripheral pulses with prolonged capillary refill time, are typically observed. Auscultation yields a harsh ejection murmur over the aortic region. Early identification is critical to reestablish ductal patency. Life-span implications extend across the life span. Valvular replacement therapy is not considered curative, and patients often require exercise restrictions.

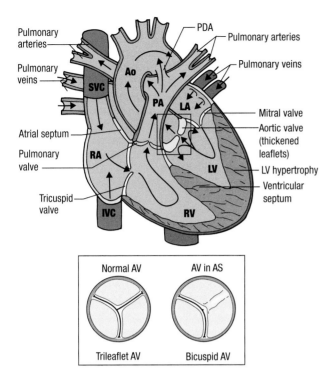

Figure 5.23 Aortic stenosis. Arrows reflect the abnormal blood flow pattern.

Ao, aorta; AS, aortic stenosis; AV, atrioventricular; IVC, inferior vena cava; LA, left atrium; LV, left ventricle; PA, pulmonary artery; PDA, patent ductus arteriosus; RA, right atrium; RV, right ventricle; SVC, superior vena cava.

Other Cardiovascular Disease Processes

Cardiomyopathies. Cardiomyopathies are defined as abnormalities of the ventricular myocardium resulting in mechanical or electrical cardiac dysfunction. Five types of cardiomyopathies are recognized: (a) dilated cardiomyopathy (DCM), (b) hypertrophic cardiomyopathy (HCM), (c) restrictive cardiomyopathy (RCM), (d) arrhythmogenic ventricular cardiomyopathy (AVC), and (e) left ventricular noncompaction cardiomyopathy (LVNC). These diseases are classified as inherited or acquired. Cardiomyopathies affect one in every 100,000 children; children less than 1 year of age are considered at highest risk (Lipshultz et al., 2013). With the exception of AVC, most cardiomyopathies present at birth or during early infancy. If not previously recognized, infants may present with life-threatening decompensation associated with an unrelated minor illness such as viral infection. Cardiomyopathy is the primary reason for heart transplantation in infants and children. This discussion will focus on the two most common cardiomyopathies that implicate infants: DCM and HCM (see Table 5.8). An understanding of these types of cardiomyopathy will allow the practitioner to determine the most appropriate diagnostic work-up. A final diagnosis may lead to optimal

therapy but more importantly may facilitate the genetic evaluation of other family members if indicated.

Dilated Cardiomyopathy. DCM is the most prevalent type of cardiomyopathy in children. DCM affects 0.57 per 100,000 children and accounts for approximately 50% or more of all cases of pediatric cardiomyopathy (Lipshultz et al., 2003). Various etiologies for DCM are reported across the literature. Acquired causes include placental insufficiency, nonimmune hydrops, renal or hepatic failure, acute stress (i.e., hypoxia), myocarditis, and chemotherapy-induced DCM. Alternatively, DCM can develop secondary to genetic mutations, within all of the known genes that code the actin (thin) filament and, to a lesser extent, thick (myosin) filament. In addition, gene mutations in the Z-line, cytoskeleton, and desmosome are reported. Inherited and metabolic forms of the disease include carnitine deficiency and glycogen storage disease (Lee et al., 2017; Polin et al., 2017).

Acquired or genetic causes give rise to abnormal shortening of the sarcomere during contraction and depressed ventricular function. Thinning of the wall of the left ventricle occurs. This leads to progressive myocardial incompetence and enlargement of the left ventricle, with resultant systolic and diastolic dysfunction.

After delivery in the infant with significant DCM, there is impairment of the ventricles to contract, leading to decreased cardiac output. The infant attempts to respond initially by increasing the heart rate to improve cardiac output. Left atrial filling pressure is elevated due to diastolic dysfunction of the dilated left ventricle, especially if there is mitral insufficiency (Everett & Lim, 2007). The clinical presentation ranges from asymptomatic to acute heart failure and shock. Findings reported among neonates include irritability, feeding difficulties, poor distal perfusion, and poor growth velocity. Atrial or ventricular arrhythmias, sinus tachycardia, mitral valve regurgitation, and gallop rhythms are common. Radiographic evidence includes cardiomegaly, pulmonary edema, and pleural effusions as a result of left ventricular dysfunction, increased left atrial pressures, and pulmonary venous congestion. An elevated B-type natriuretic peptide is present as a result of worsening cardiac output. Progressive worsening of myocardial function may manifest with hepatomegaly. Flattening of the T waves and ST segment depression can be seen on EKG; with carnitine deficiency, a giant T wave is seen. Survivability among patients who do not receive cardiac transplantation is between 60% and 75%, and of those patients, merely 20% to 45% recapture normal cardiovascular function (Lee et al., 2017; Polin et al., 2017).

Hypertrophic Cardiomyopathy. HCM is the second most prevalent type of cardiomyopathy in children. The incidence is 0.47 per 100,000 children, and this disease implicates approximately 42% of the pediatric population (Lipshultz et al., 2003). HCM can occur in isolation but it is most commonly a consequence of autosomal dominant genetic

TABLE 5.8 Cardiomyopathies and Associated Co-Morbidities

Diseases Associated with Dilated Cardiomyopathy	Diseases Associated with Hypertrophic Cardiomyopathy
Idiopathic in approximately 75% of cases	Idiopathic in >60% of cases
Myocarditis • Viral – parvovirus B19, coxsackievirus, adenovirus, echovirus, cytomegalovirus	Malformation syndromes • Noonan syndrome (autosomal dominant mutation on the *PTPN11* gene) • Beckwith-Wiedemann syndrome • Costello syndrome • Eagle Barrett (prune belly) syndrome
Neuromuscular disorders • Duchenne or Becker muscular dystrophy (X-linked)	Metabolic disorders • Pompe disease (autosomal recessive glycogen storage type II) Fatty acid oxidation disorders • Carnitine deficiency • Medium-chain acyl-coenzyme A (CoA) dehydrogenase deficiency
Familial dilated cardiomyopathy (majority are autosomal dominant)	Mitochondrial defects • Disorders of oxidative phosphorylation including Complex I, III, and IV deficiency • MELAS syndrome (**m**itochondrial myopathy, **e**ncephalopathy, **l**actic **a**cidosis, and **s**troke-like episodes)
Mitochondrial defects • Barth syndrome • Kearns-Sayre syndrome (tRNAleu(UUR)-3242 mutation most common)	Hyperinsulinism • Infants of diabetic mothers (IDMs) • Congenital hyperinsulinism
	Neuromuscular disorders

Sources: Wallis, G. & Fricker, F. J. (2012). Neonatal cardiomyopathy. *NeoReviews, 13*(12), e711–e723. doi:10.1542/neo.13-12-e711; Wilkinson, J. D., Westphal, J. A., Bansal, N., Czachor, J. D., Razoky, H., & Lipshultz, S. E. (2015). Lessons learned from the Pediatric Cardiomyopathy Registry (PCMR) Study Group. *Cardiology in the Young, 25*(Suppl. 2), 140–153. doi:10.1017/S1047951115000943

inheritance. Genetic etiologies include gene mutations that code the thin (actin) and thick (myosin) filaments in the sarcomere, RASopathies, and neurodegenerative and mitochondrial disorders (Lee et al., 2017). In addition, HCM is a commonly recognized complication in infants of diabetic mothers (IDM), as well as infants with congenital hyperinsulinism. It has been suggested that the hypertrophy in IDMs is a result of fetal hyperinsulinism, leading to proliferation and hypertrophy of cardiac myocytes triggered by increased proteins and fat synthesis (Veille, Hanson, Sivakoff, Hoen, & Ben-Ami, 1993). Few cases have been reported that link transient HCM with perinatal stress.

The pathogenesis of HCM involves symmetrical or asymmetrical hypertrophy, or thickening, of the walls and interventricular septum of the left ventricle, resulting in left ventricular outflow tract obstruction. Some affected infants develop hypertrophy of both the left and right ventricles. Hypertrophy of cardiomyocytes occurs. This leads to aberrant cardiac depolarization and contraction, which gives rise to myofibrillar disarray and interstitial fibrosis (Polin et al., 2017). With significant left ventricular hypertrophy, there is diastolic dysfunction with an increase in the end-diastolic

pressure. Coronary insufficiency and ischemia can occur as a result of decreased coronary perfusion pressure from the increased end-diastolic pressure and the increased myocardial oxygen demand (Everett & Lim, 2007).

Specific to the IDM, fetal hyperinsulinism in response to maternal hyperglycemia results in this pathological, yet reversible, hypertrophy of the ventricular wall and septum. The immediate neonatal course may be complicated by diastolic dysfunction and LVOT obstruction resulting in significant CHF (Yeh & Berger, 2015). In cases of congenital hyperinsulinism, gene mutations to ion channels, including the highly sensitive β-cell ATP-sensitive potassium (K_{ATP}) channel, lead to hypersecretion of insulin by β-cells in either a focal or diffuse manner. Unlike HCM associated with the IDM, that which is associated with congenital hyperinsulinism is not reversible and often refractory to K_{ATP} channel agonists and diazoxide (Huang, Kelly, Becker, Cohen, & Stanley, 2013).

The clinical presentation ranges from asymptomatic to heart failure. Left ventricular outflow tract obstruction and dysfunction, and ventricular arrhythmias, are common. Outflow tract obstructions resulting in an increased afterload on the heart may give rise to mitral valve regurgitation and manifest with an audible murmur. Diastolic dysfunction resulting in elevated pulmonary venous pressure is associated with a pathologic gallop rhythm. Radiographic evidence includes cardiomegaly. Twenty-five percent will have normal EKGs; if there is not left ventricular outflow tract obstruction, the remaining will have ST- and T-wave changes. Mortality risk is 30% among infants diagnosed with HCM as a result of progressive CHF. Five-year survivability is estimated at 97% and 10-year survivability is at 94% (Lee et al., 2017; Polin et al., 2017). Of infants who develop HCM secondary to congenital hyperinsulinism, pancreatectomy is often required.

CONCLUSION

Heart defects are the single most common congenital defects reported in the literature. As such, it is critical that APNs establish core understanding of normal and abnormal fetal and postnatal cardiovascular physiology. APNs are encouraged to adopt active and multisensory learning methods; connecting core content with a clinical vignette adds meaning to the mundane. Rehearsing the creation of simple sketches of heart lesions during the learning process conditions clinicians to provide parents with a concrete look at their child's anatomy during difficult conversations. Parents are often overwhelmed and anxious to blame themselves for their infant's diagnosis. Long-term risks vary; however, cognitive and social impairment are common among children affected by CHDs (Figure 5.24). Therefore, the ability to clearly communicate complex information and evidence-based prognostics, balanced with sentiments of

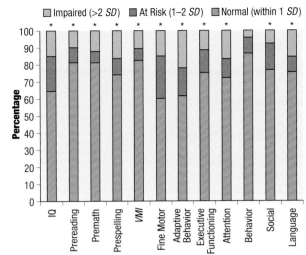

Figure 5.24 Percentage of children with congenital heart disease tested at 4 to 5 years in the normal, at risk, and impaired ranges on neurodevelopmental measures.

VMI, visual motor integration.

Source: Adapted from Brosig, C. L., Bear, L., Allen, S., Hoffmann, R. G., Pan, A., Frommelt, M., & Mussatto, K. A. (2017). Preschool neurodevelopmental outcomes in children with congenital heart disease. *The Journal of Pediatrics, 183*, 80–86. doi:10.1016/j.jpeds.2016.12.044

support and hope for the future, is essential. This allows parents to understand the relationship between current medical management plans and health promotion (Brosig et al., 2017).

This Chapter Is Dedicated to the Memory of Dhillon Shah

A message from Dhillon's family:

Dhillon Jordan Shah was diagnosed with complex single ventricle, a variant of HLHS, in the first few days of life, but despite numerous surgeries and setbacks lived a life of joy, hope, and courage. Sadly, he passed away at the age of 12½ during a long-awaited heart transplant. His family and friends provided him unconditional support during those years, and the skill of his healthcare providers was critical.

What are the attributes of those caregivers, mostly nurses, that we remember most, that prompted us to take photos of them, that produced big hugs and smiles when they were at the bedside? They conveyed caring in so many small things they did: a smile, the appreciation of a joke, a shared board game, the attempt to do treatments just the way he wanted, the tolerance of favorite foods, the offering of respite time for Mom so she could get a shower, their support of his family. They conveyed hope and positive energy along with the technical expertise that we trusted. They communicated effectively, listening carefully and letting us know they were with us every step of the way. They provided information we could hang on to and later read. They listened to our family, respected our needs and rules, and took the time to understand Dhillon's unique

journey, anticipating next steps so we were prepared. They were hypervigilant, always advocating for Dhillon's care. They were our lifeline to other valued members of the health team, our allies, our partners, and some of Dhillon's best friends. When we sadly celebrated his short life in a memorial gathering, they supported us there as well and even beyond as we grieved. Many thanks to those who traveled with Dhillon on his journey, and to all who will have the privilege to do so with other children. You are very special!

LEARNING TOOLS AND RESOURCES

Podcast

 Case-Based Learning: Patent Ductus Arteriosus

Jacqui Hoffman and Nicole Bowie

Discussion Prompts

1. Explain expected cardiovascular embryologic development and defects that may occur as a result of abnormal development.

2. Compare and contrast fetal circulation, transitional circulation after delivery, and neonatal circulation.

3. Sinus bradycardia may be a normal finding in hospitalized infants. Discuss the physiology of sinus bradycardia and how it typically manifests in the newborn.

4. The cardiovascular physical examination aids in the development of a differential diagnosis list with a suspected congenital heart infant. Correlate the pearls of the cardiovascular exam with your understanding of cardiac anatomy and physiology.

Advice From the Authors

"I think one of the easiest ways to wrap your arms around CHDs is to put them into 'buckets' or categories, to help with understanding how you would typically expect them to present. For example, acyanotic heart defects as a group are not seen on day one; they present up to several weeks later with pulmonary overcirculation. The other helpful information, especially as you have more complex defects, is to remember normal blood flow patterns and then map out the abnormal defect and how this changes the circulatory pattern."

–Jacqui Hoffman, DNP, APRN, NNP-BC

"To understand cardiac defects is to first master the laws of 'cardiac plumbing.' Know the normal cardiac blood flow, the heart structures, and understand how the blood normally circulates. If presented with a cardiac defect, figure out how the defect causes an alteration to the normal flow pattern. Envision the flow through the heart, or better yet, draw a picture and follow the flow."

–Nicole Thompson-Bowie, MSN, APRN, NNP-BC, PNP-BC

"The cardiovascular system, at first glance, may seem like a daunting body system to learn. However, I suggest approaching this content in a multisensory manner. If you thrive by listening to content, rely on podcasts and create your own mini-lectures. If you are a visual learner, take the time to draw out the normal heart and common defects, mapping out the blood flow and any mixing that may occur. And last, test yourself by explaining these concepts to others in your workplace. The more senses you incorporate into your learning process, and the more iterations you weave into the learning process, the more likely you are to retain the information and be able to apply it in practice."

–Amy J. Jnah, DNP, APRN, NNP-BC

Mind Map

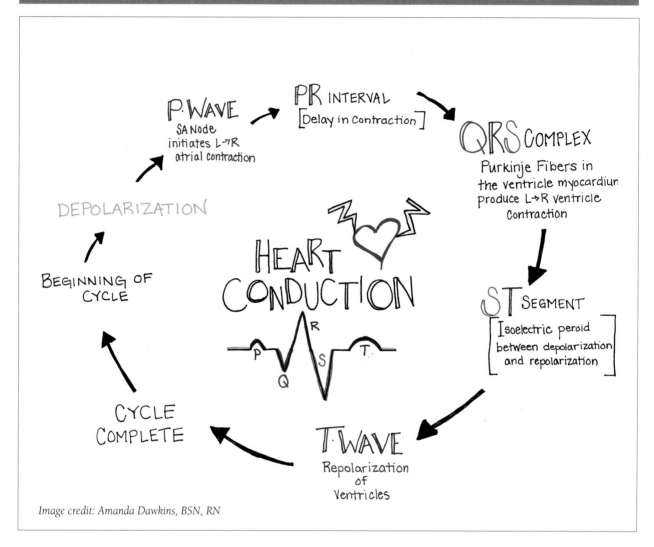

P. WAVE
SA Node
initiates L→R
atrial contraction

PR INTERVAL
[Delay in Contraction]

QRS COMPLEX
Purkinje Fibers in
the ventricle myocardiun
produce L→R ventricle
contraction

DEPOLARIZATION

HEART CONDUCTION

BEGINNING OF CYCLE

ST SEGMENT
[Isoelectric peroid
between depolarization
and repolarization]

CYCLE COMPLETE

T. WAVE
Repolarization
of
Ventricles

Image credit: Amanda Dawkins, BSN, RN

Note: This mind map reflects one student's interpretation of a portion of one or more concepts addressed in this chapter. Readers should regard the mind maps woven throughout this textbook as examples of multi-sensory study tools that can be developed to encourage conceptual understanding. Readers are encouraged to develop their own unique mind maps in consultation with academic faculty or clinical preceptors.

TIMELINE OF ORGAN DEVELOPMENT

NOTE:
Placement of common problems is meant to offer visual/conceptual perspective on the timing of onset of these commonly reported malformations. Variation exists across the literature.

LEGEND
<22 – 27 6/7 weeks = extremely preterm
28 – 31 6/7 weeks = very preterm
32 – 36 6/7 weeks = late/moderate preterm
37 – 40 weeks = term

References

Abqari, S., Gupta, A., Shahab, T., Rabbani, M., Manazir Ali, S., & Firdaus, U. (2016). Profile and risk factors for congenital heart defects: A study in a tertiary care hospital. *Annals of Pediatric Cardiology, 9*(3), 216–221. doi:10.4103/0974-2069.189119

Acharya, G., Gui, Y., Cnota, W., Huhta, J., & Wloch, A. (2016). Human embryonic cardiovascular function. *Acta Obstetricia et Gynecologica Scandinavica, 95*(6), 621–628. doi:10.1111/aogs.12860

Anderson, R., Webb, S., Brown, N., Lamers, W., & Moorman, A. (2003). Development of the heart: (2) Septation of the atriums and ventricles. *Heart, 89*(7), 949–958 doi:10.1136/heart.89.8.949

Artman, M., Mahoney, L., & Teitel, D. (2011). *Neonatal cardiology* (2nd ed.). New York, NY: McGraw-Hill.

Ashworth, M. T. (2013). Embryology of the heart. In S. Suvarna (Ed.), *Cardiac pathology: A guide to current practice* (pp. 109–115). London, UK: Springer-Verlag. doi:10.1007/978-1-4471-2407-8_6

Backer, C., Eltayeb, O., Mongé, M., Mazwi, M., & Costello, J. (2016). Shunt lesions part I: Patent ductus arteriosus, atrial septal defect, ventricular septal defect, and atrioventricular septal defect. *Pediatric Critical Care Medicine, 17*(8 Suppl.), S302–309. doi:10.1097/PCC.0000000000000786

Bakker, M., Christoffels, V., & Moorman, A. (2010). The cardiac pacemaker and conduction system develops from embryonic myocardium that retains its primitive phenotype. *Journal of Cardiovascular Pharmacology, 56*(1), 6–15. doi:10.1097/FJC.0b013e3181e775d3

Baldwin, H. S., & Dees, E. (2012). Embryology and physiology of the cardiovascular system. In C. A. Gleason & S. U. Devaskar (Eds.), *Avery's disease of the newborn* (9th ed., pp. 699–713). New York, NY: Elsevier.

Bensley, J., De Matteo, R., Harding, R., & Black, M. (2016). The effects of preterm birth and its antecedents on the cardiovascular system. *Acta Obstetricia et Gynecologica Scandinavica, 95*(6), 652–663. doi:10.1111/aogs.12880

Bonow, R. O., & Greenland, P. (2015). Population-wide trends in aortic stenosis incidence and outcomes. *Circulation, 131*(11), 969–971. doi:10.1161/CIRCULATIONAHA.115.014846

Bouma, B., & Mulder, B. (2017). Changing landscape of congenital heart disease. *Circulation Research, 120,* 908–922. doi:10.1161/CIRCRESAHA.116.309302

Boyett, M. (2009). "And the beat goes on." The cardiac conduction system: The wiring system of the heart. *Experimental Physiology, 94*(10), 1035–1049. doi:10.1113/expphysiol.2009.046920

Brennan, P., & Young, I. (2001). Congenital heart malformations: Aetiology and associations. *Seminars in Neonatology, 6*(1), 17–25. doi:10.1053/siny.2000.0032

Brosens, E., Eussen, H., van Bever, Y., van der Helm, R. M., Ijsselstijn, H., Zaveri, H. P., ... de Klein, A. (2013). VACTERL association etiology: The impact of de novo and rare copy number variations. *Molecular Syndromology, 4,* 20–26. doi:10.1159/000345577

Brosig, C., Bear, L., Allen, S., Hoffmann, R., Pan, A., Frommelt, M., & Mussatto, K. (2017). Preschool neurodevelopmental outcomes in children with congenital heart disease. *Journal of Pediatrics, 183,* 80–86.e1. doi:10.1016/j.jpeds.2016.12.044

Centers for Disease Control and Prevention. (2018d). Facts about hypoplastic left heart syndrome. Retrieved from https://www.cdc.gov/ncbddd/heartdefects/hlhs.html

Centers for Disease Control and Prevention. (2018a). Congenital heart defects (CHDs). Retrieved from https://www.cdc.gov/ncbddd/heartdefects/index.html

Centers for Disease Control and Prevention. (2018b). Facts about atrial septal defect. Retrieved from https://www.cdc.gov/ncbddd/heartdefects/atrialseptaldefect.html

Centers for Disease Control and Prevention. (2018c). Facts about coarctation of the aorta. Retrieved from https://www.cdc.gov/ncbddd/heartdefects/coarctationofaorta.html

Centers for Disease Control and Prevention. (2018d). Facts about dextro-transposition of the great arteries (d-TGA). Retrieved from https://www.cdc.gov/ncbddd/heartdefects/d-tga.html

Centers for Disease Control and Prevention. (2018e). Facts about pulmonary atresia. Retrieved from https://www.cdc.gov/ncbddd/heartdefects/pulmonaryatresia.html

Centers for Disease Control and Prevention. (2018f). Facts about tetralogy of Fallot. Retrieved from https://www.cdc.gov/ncbddd/heartdefects/tetralogyoffallot.html

Centers for Disease Control and Prevention. (2018g). Facts about total anomalous pulmonary venous return or TAPVR. Retrieved from https://www.cdc.gov/ncbddd/heartdefects/tapvr.html

Chen, H. (2012). *Atlas of genetic diagnosis and counseling* (2nd ed.). New York, NY: Springer Verlag.

Chen, Y., Liu, Z., Chen, J., Zuo, Y., Liu, S., Chen, W., ...Wu, Z. (2016). The genetic landscape and clinical implications of vertebral anomalies in VACTERL association. *Journal of Medical Genetics, 53,* 431–437. doi:10.1136/jmedgenet-2015-103554

Christoffels, V., Smits, G., Kispert, A., & Moorman, A. (2010). Development of the pacemaker tissues of the heart. *Circulation Research, 106,* 240–254. doi:10.1161/CIRCRESAHA.109.205419

Chung, W., Boskovski, M. T., Brueckner, M., Anyane-Yeboa, K., & Gupta, P. (2012). The genetics of fetal and neonatal cardiovascular disease. In C. S. Kleinman & I. Seri (Eds.), *Hemodynamics and cardiology: Neonatology questions and controversies* (2nd ed., pp. 343–376). Philadelphia, PA: Elsevier Saunders.

Clyman, R. I., Couto, J., & Murphy, G. M. (2012). Patent ductus arteriosus: Are current neonatal treatment options better or worse than no treatment at all? *Seminars in Perinatology, 36*(2), 123–129. doi:10.1053/j.semperi.2011.09.022

Congenital Heart Public Health Consortium. (2012). Congenital Heart Public Health Consortium FAQ fact sheet—Long version. Retrieved from https://www.aap.org/en-us/Documents/chphc/chd_fact_sheet_long.pdf

Corrigan, N., Brazil, D., & McAuliffe, F. (2009). Fetal cardiac effects of maternal hyperglycemia during pregnancy. *Birth Defects Research (Part A): Clinical and Molecular Teratology, 85,* 523–530. doi:10.1002/bdra.20567

Crispi, F., & Martinez, J. M. (2018). Anomalies of pulmonary venous return. In J. A. Copel (Ed.), *Obstetric imaging: Fetal diagnosis and care* (2nd ed., pp. 409–411). Philadelphia, PA: Elsevier.

Cunningham, B. K., Hadley, D. W., Hannoush, H., Meltzer, A. C., Niforatos, N., Pineda-Alvarez, D., ... Solomon, B. D. (2013). Analysis of cardiac anomalies in VACTERL association. *Birth Defects Research Part A: Clinical and Molecular Teratology, 97*(12), 792–797. doi:10.1002/bdra.23211

Dobrzynski, H., Anderson, R., Atkinson, A., Borbas, Z., D'Souza, A., Fraser, J., ... Boyett, M. (2013). Structure, function and clinical relevance of the cardiac conduction system, including the atrioventricular ring and outflow tract tissues. *Pharmacology & Therapeutics, 139,* 260–288. doi:10.1016/j.pharmthera.2013.04.010

Dyer, A., & Ikemba, C. (2012). Core concepts. *NeoReviews, 13*(10), e583–e589. doi:10.1542/neo.13-10-e583

Edmondson, A. C., & Kalish, J. M. (2015). Overgrowth syndromes. *Journal of Pediatric Genetics, 4*(3), 136–143. doi:10.1055/s-0035-1564440

Eisner, D. A., Caldwell, J. L., Kistamás, K., & Trafford, A. W. (2017). Calcium and excitation-contraction coupling in the hart. *Circulation Research, 121*(2), 181–195. doi:10.1161/CIRCRESAHA.117.310230

Emani, S. M. (2016). Coarctation of the aorta, and vascular rings. In F. W. Sellke, P. J. del Nido, & S. J. Swanson (Eds.), *Sabiston & Spencer surgery of the chest* (9th ed.). Philadelphia, PA: Elsevier.

England, M. (1996). *Life before birth* (2nd ed.). London, UK: Mosby-Wolfe.

Everett, A. D., & Lim, D. S. (2007). *Illustrated field guide to congenital heart disease and repair* (2nd ed., rev.). Charlottesville, VA: Scientific Software Solutions.

Fahed, A., Gelb, B., Seidman, J., & Seidman, C. (2013). Genetics of congenital heart disease: The glass half empty. *Circulation Research, 112*, 707–720. doi: 10.1161/CIRCRESAHA.112.300853

Fineman, J., & Clyman, R. (2004). Fetal cardiovascular physiology. In R. Creasy, R. Resnik, & J. Iams (Eds.), *Maternal–fetal medicine: Principles and practice* (5th ed., pp. 160–163). New York, NY: Elsevier.

Flanagan, M., Yeager, S., & Weindling, S. (2016). Cardiac disease. In M. G. MacDonald & M. M. Seshia (Eds.), *Avery's neonatology: Pathophysiology and management of the newborn* (7th ed., pp. 487–547). Philadelphia, PA: Wolters Kluwer.

Gittenberger-de Groot, A. C., Bartelings, M. M., Poelmann, R. E., Haak, M. C., & Jongbloed, M. R. M. (2013). Embryology of the heart and its impact on understanding fetal and neonatal heart disease. *Seminars in Fetal and Neonatal Medicine, 18*(5), 237–244. doi:10.1016/j.siny.2013.04.008

Gleason, C. A., & Juul, S. E. (2018). *Avery's diseases of the newborn* (10th ed.). Philadelphia, PA: Elsevier Saunders.

Gobergs, R., Salputra, E., & Lubaua, I. (2016). Hypoplastic left heart syndrome: A review. *Acta Medica Lituanica, 23*(2), 86–98. doi:10.6001/actamedica.v23i2.3325

Goble, M. M., Yeh, J.,von Alvensleben, J., & Panchangam, C. (2016). Cardiology and the newborn. *International Journal of Child Health and Human Development, 9*(1), 39.

Hagen-Ansert, S. L. (2018). *Textbook of diagnostic sonography* (8th ed.). St. Louis, MO: Elsevier.

Hines, M. (2013). Neonatal cardiovascular physiology. *Seminars in Pediatric Surgery, 22*, 174–178. doi:10.1053/j.sempedsurg.2013.10.004

Hoffman, J. I. (2017). At what age should tetralogy of Fallot be corrected? *Cardiology in the Young, 27*(4), 625. doi:10.1017/S104795111600264X

Huang, T., Kelly, A., Becker, S. A., Cohen, M. S., & Stanley, C. A. (2013). Hypertrophic cardiomyopathy in neonates with congenital hyperinsulinism. *Archives of Disease in Childhood: Fetal and Neonatal Edition, 98*(4), F351–F354. doi:10.1136/archdischild-2012-302546

Hund, T. J., Smith, S. A., Makara, M. A., & Mohler, P. J. (2014). Cellular and molecular pathobiology of the cardiac conduction system.. In M. S. Willis, J. W. Homeister, & J. R. Stone (Eds.), *Cellular and molecular pathobiology of cardiovascular disease* (pp. 121–134). London, UK: Elsevier.

Irtyuga, O., Malashicheva, A., Zhiduleva, E., Freylikhman, O., Rotar, O., Bäck, M.,...Moiseeva, O. (2017). NOTCH1 mutations

in aortic stenosis: Association with Osteoprotegerin/RANK/RANKL. *BioMed Research International, 2017*, 6917907–10. doi:10.1155/2017/6917907

Jaramillo, F., Hernandez, C., Garzón, J. P., Sánchez Herrera, A. P., & Velasco Morales, M. L. (2017). Infracardiac type total anomalous pulmonary venous return with obstruction and dilatation of portal vein. *Radiology Case Reports, 12*(2), 229–232. doi:10.1016/j.radcr.2017.01.010

Jones, E. (2011). The initiation of blood flow and flow induced events in early vascular development. *Seminars in Cell & Developmental Biology, 22*, 1028–1035. doi:10.1016/j.semcdb.2011.09.020

Jongbloed, M. R. M., Steijn, R.V., Hahurij, N. D., Kelder, T. P., Schalij, M. J., Gittenberger-de Groot, A. C., & Blom, N. A. (2012). Normal and abnormal development of the cardiac conduction system; implications for conduction and rhythm disorders in the child and adult. *Differentiation, 84*(1), 131–148. doi:10.1016/j.diff.2012.04.006

Karamlou, T., Poynter, J. A., Walters, H. L., Rhodes, J., Bondarenko, I., Pasquali, S. K., ... McCrindle, B. W. (2013). Long-term functional health status and exercise test variables for patients with pulmonary atresia with intact ventricular septum: A Congenital Heart Surgeons Society study. *Journal of Thoracic and Cardiovascular Surgery, 145*(4),. 1018–1027.e3 doi:10.1016/j.jtcvs.2012.11.092

Khairy, P., Clair, M., Fernandes, S. M., Blume, E. D., Powell, A. J., Newburger, J. W., ... Mayer, J. E. (2013). Cardiovascular outcomes after the arterial switch operation for D-transposition of the great arteries. *Circulation, 127*(3), 331–339. doi:10.1161/circulationaha.112.135046

Kirby, M. L. (2002). Embryogenesis of transposition of the great arteries: A lesson from the heart. *Circulation Research, 91*(2), 87–89. doi:10.1161/01.RES.0000028301.40791.4F

Kiserud, T. (2005). Physiology of the fetal circulation. *Seminars in Fetal & Neonatal Medicine, 10*, 493–503. doi:10.1016/j.siny.2005.08.007

Lee, T. M., Hsu, D. T., Kantor, P., Towbin, J. A., Ware, S. M., Colan, S. D., ... Lipshultz, S. E. (2017). Pediatric cardiomyopathies. *Circulation Research, 121*(7), 855–873. doi:10.1161/CIRCRESAHA.116.309386

Lipshultz, S. E., Cochran, T. R., Briston, D. A., Brown, S. R., Sambatakos, P. J., Miller, T. L., ... Wilkinson, J. D. (2013). Pediatric cardiomyopathies: Causes, epidemiology, clinical course, preventive strategies and therapies. *Future Cardiology, 9*(6), 817–848. doi:10.2217/fca.13.66

Lipshultz, S. E., Sleeper, L. A., Towbin, J. A., Lowe, A. M., Orav, E. J., Cox, G. F., ... Colan, S. D. (2003). The incidence of pediatric cardiomyopathy in two regions of the United States. *New England Journal of Medicine, 348*, 1647–1655. doi:10.1056/NEJMoa021715

Mäkikallio, K., Jouppila, P., & Räsänen, J. (2003). Retrograde aortic isthmus net blood flow and human fetal cardiac function in placental insufficiency. *Ultrasound in Obstetrics & Gynecology, 22*(4), 351–357. doi:10.1002/uog.232

Mäkikallio, K., Jouppila, P., & Räsänen, J. (2005). Human fetal cardiac function during the first trimester of pregnancy. *Heart, 91*(3), 334–338. doi:10.1136/hrt.2003.029736

Mari, G., Deter, R., & Uerpairojkit, B. (1996). Flow velocity waveforms of the ductus arteriosus in appropriate and small-for-gestational-age fetuses. *Journal of Clinical Ultrasound, 24*(4), 185–196. doi:10.1002/(SICI)1097-0096(199605)24:4<185::AID-JCU5>3.0.CO;2-B

Martin, B. J., Karamlou, T., & Tabbutt, S. (2016). Shunt lesions part II: Anomalous pulmonary venous connections and truncus arteriosus. *Pediatric Critical Care Medicine, 18*(8 Suppl.), S310–S314. doi:10.1097/PCC.0000000000000822

Martin, R. J., Fanaroff, A. A., & Walsh, M. C. (2015). *Fanaroff and Martin's neonatal–perinatal medicine: Diseases of the fetus and infant* (10th ed.). Philadelphia, PA: Elsevier/Saunders.

McRae, M. (2015a). Long-term outcomes after repair of congenital heart defects: Part 1. *American Journal of Nursing, 115*(1), 24–35. doi: 10.1097/01.NAJ.0000459628.07668.db.

McRae, M. (2015b). Long-term outcomes after repair of congenital heart defects: Part 2. *American Journal of Nursing, 115*(2), 34–45. doi: 10.1097/01.NAJ.0000460674.59200.1f.

Meier, B., Frank, B., Wahl, A., & Diener, H. C. (2012). Secondary stroke prevention: Patent foramen ovale, aortic plaque, and carotid stenosis. *European Heart Journal, 33*(6), 705–713. doi:10.1093/eurheartj/ehr443

Mettler, B. A., & Pigula, F. A. (2016). Hypoplastic left heart syndrome. In F. W. Sellke, P. J. del Nido, & S. J. Swanson (Eds.), *Sabiston & Spencer surgery of the chest* (9th ed., pp. 2295–2312). Philadelphia, PA: Elsevier.

Miller, A., Riehle-Colarusso, T., Siffel, C., Frías, J. L., & Correa, A. (2011). Maternal age and prevalence of isolated congenital heart defects in an urban area of the United States. *American Journal of Medical Genetics Part A, 155A*(9), 2137-2145. doi: 10.1002/ajmg.a.34130

Minich, L. L., Atz, A. M., Colan, S. D., Sleeper, L. A., Mital, S., Jaggers, J., ... Hawkins, J. A. (2010). Partial and transitional atrioventricular septal defect outcomes. *Annals of Thoracic Surgery, 89*(2), 530–536. doi:10.1016/j.athoracsur.2009.10.047

Mone, S., Gillman, M., Miller, T., Herman, E., & Lipshultz, S. (2004). Effects of environmental exposures on the cardiovascular system: Prenatal period through adolescence. *Pediatrics, 113*(Suppl. 3), 1058–1069. Retrieved from http://pediatrics.aappublications.org/content/113/Supplement_3/1058..info

Moore, K. L., Persaud, T. V. N., & Torchia, M. G. (2016). *The developing human: Clinically oriented embryology* (10th ed., pp. 283–335). Philadelphia, PA: Elsevier.

Mordi, I., & Tzemos, N. (2012). Bicuspid aortic valve disease: A comprehensive review. *Cardiology Research and Practice, 2012,* 196037. doi:10.1155/2012/196037

Muntean, I., Togănel, R., & Benedek, T. (2017). Genetics of congenital heart disease: Past and present. *Biochemical Genetics, 55,* 105–123. doi:10.1007/s10528-016-9780-7

Muralidharan, P., Sarmah, S., Zhou, F., & Marrs, J. (2013). Fetal alcohol spectrum disorder (FASD) associated neural defects: Complex mechanisms and potential therapeutic targets. *Brain Science, 3,* 964–991. doi:10.3390/brainsci3020964

Mussa, A., Di Candia, S., Russo, S., Catania, S., De Pellegin, M., Di Luzio, L., ... Ferrero, G. (2016). Genetic forum: Recommendations of the Scientific Committee of the Italian Beckwith-Wiedemann Syndrome Association on the diagnosis, management, and follow-up of the syndrome. *European Journal of Medical Genetics, 59,* 52–64. doi:10.1016/j.ejmg.2015.11.008

National Institutes of Health. (2018a). Genetics home reference: Beckwith-Weidemann syndrome. Retrieved from https://ghr.nlm.nih.gov/condition/beckwith-wiedemann-syndrome#statistics

National Institutes of Health. (2018b). Genetics home reference: Down syndrome. Retrieved from https://ghr.nlm.nih.gov/condition/down-syndrome#statistics

National Institutes of Health. (2018c). Genetics home reference: Jacobsen syndrome. Retrieved from https://ghr.nlm.nih.gov/condition/jacobsen-syndrome#statistics

National Institutes of Health. (2018d). Genetics home reference: Trisomy 18. Retrieved from https://ghr.nlm.nih.gov/condition/trisomy-18#statistics

National Institutes of Health. (2018e). Genetics home reference: Turner syndrome. Retrieved from https://ghr.nlm.nih.gov/condition/turner-syndrome

National Institutes of Health. (2018f). Genetics home reference: VACTERL association. Retrieved from https://ghr.nlm.nih.gov/condition/vacterl-association#statistics

National Institutes of Health. (2018g). Genetics home reference: Williams syndrome. Retrieved from https://ghr.nlm.nih.gov/condition/williams-syndrome#statistics

National Organization for Rare Disorders. (2007). Trisomy 13 syndrome. Retrieved from https://rarediseases.org/rare-diseases/trisomy-13-syndrome

Nies, M., & Brenner, J. I. (2013). Tetralogy of Fallot: Epidemiology meets real-world management: Lessons from the Baltimore–Washington infant study. *Cardiology in the Young, 23*(6), 867–869. doi:10.1017/S1047951113001698

Noori, S., Stavroudis, T., & Seri, I. (2012). Principles of developmental cardiovascular physiology and pathophysiology. In C. S. Kleinman & I. S. Seri (Eds.), *Hemodynamics and cardiology: Neonatology questions and controversies* (2nd ed., pp. 3–28). Philadelphia, PA: Elsevier Saunders.

Oostra, R., & Moorman, A. (2009). Development of the heart. In C. Rodeck & M. Whittle (Eds.), *Fetal medicine: Basic science and clinical practice* (2nd ed., pp. 47–60). London, UK: Elsevier.

Ornoy, A., Reece, E., Pavlinkova, G., Kappen, C., & Miller, R. (2015). Effect of maternal diabetes on the embryo, fetus, and children: Congenital anomalies, genetic and epigenetic changes and developmental outcomes. *Birth Defects Research. Part C, Embryo Today, 105*(1), 53–72. doi:10.1002/bdrc.21090

Ottolia, M., Torres, N., Bridge, J. H. B., Philipson, K. D., & Goldhaber, J. I. (2013). Na/Ca exchange and contraction of the heart. *Journal of Molecular and Cellular Cardiology, 61,* 28–33. doi:10.1016/j.yjmcc.2013.06.001

Park, C. S., Lee, J. R., Lim, H. G., Kim W. H., & Kim, Y. J. (2010). The long-term result of total repair for tetralogy of Fallot. *European Journal of Cardio-Thoracic Surgery, 38*(3), 311–317. doi: 10.1016/j.ejcts.2010.02.030.

Patorno, E., Huybrechts, K. F., Bateman, B. T., Cohen, J. M., Desai, R. J., Mogun, H., ... Hernandez-Diaz, S. (2017). Lithium use in pregnancy and the risk of cardiac malformations. *New England Journal of Medicine, 376*(23), 2245–2254. doi:10.1056/NEJMoa1612222

Peter, A. K., Cheng, H., Ross, R. S., Knowlton, K. U., & Chen, J. (2011). The costamere bridges sarcomeres to the sarcolemma in striated muscle. *Progress in Pediatric Cardiology, 31*(2), 83–88. doi:10.1016/j.ppedcard.2011.02.003

Polin, R. A., Abman, S. H., Rowitch, D. H., Benitz, W. E., & Fox, W. W. (Eds.). (2017). *Fetal and neonatal physiology* (5th ed.). Philadelphia, PA: Elsevier.

Puri, K., Allen, H. D., & Qureshi, A. M. (2017). Congenital heart disease. *Pediatrics in Review, 38*(1), 471–486. doi:10.1542/pir.2017-0032

Ransom, J., & Srivastava, D. (2007). The genetics of cardiac birth defects. *Seminars in Cell & Developmental Biology, 18*(1), 132–139. doi:10.1016/j.semcdb.2006.12.005

Reller, M., Strickland, M., Riehle-Colarusso, T., Mahle, W., & Correa, A. (2008). Prevalence of congenital heart defects in metropolitan Atlanta, 1998–2005. *The Journal of Pediatrics, 153*(6), 807–813. doi: 10.1016/j.jpeds.2008.05.059.

Rosa, R. C., Rosa, R. F., Zen P. R., & Paskulin, G. A. (2013). Congenital heart defects and extracardiac malformations. *Revista Paulista de Pediatria, 31*(2), 243–251. doi:10.1590/S0103-05822013000200017

Rudolph, A. M. (2010). Congenital cardiovascular malformations and the fetal circulation. *Archives of Disease in Childhood: Fetal and Neonatal Edition, 95*(2), F132–F136. doi:10.1136/adc.2007.128777

Rutledge, J. M., Nihill, M. R., Fraser, C. D., Smith, O. E., McMahon, C. J., & Bezold, L. I. (2002). Outcome of 121 patients with congenitally corrected transposition of the great arteries. *Pediatric Cardiology, 23*(2), 137–145. doi:10.1007/s00246-001-0037-8

Scholz, T., & Reinking, B. E. (2018). Congenital heart disease. In C. A. Gleason & S. E. Juul (Eds.), *Avery's diseases of the newborn* (10th ed., pp. 801–827). Philadelphia, PA: Elsevier.

Sedmera, D., & McQuinn, T. (2008). Embryogenesis of heart muscle. *Heart Failure Clinics, 4*(3), 235–245. doi:10.1016/j.hfc.2008.02.007

Shuman, C., Beckwith, J. B., & Weksberg, R. (2016). Beckwith-Wiedemann syndrome. In M. Adams, H. Ardlinger, R. Pagon, M. Adam, H. Ardinger, R. Pagon, & S. Wallace (Eds.), *GeneReviews*. Seattle: University of Washington. Retrieved from https://www.ncbi.nlm.nih.gov/books/NBK1394/

Simeone, R., Tinker, S., Gilboa, S., Agopian, A., Oster, M., Devine, O., … Honein, M. (2016). Proportion of selected congenital heart defects attributable to recognized risk factors. *Annals of Epidemiology, 26*, 838–845. doi:10.1016/j.annepidem.2016.10.003

Solomon, B. D., Baker, L. A., Bear, K. A., Cunningham, B. K., Giampietro, P. F., Hadigan, C., … Warren-Mora, N. (2014). An approach to the identification of anomalies and etiologies in neonates with identified or suspected VACTERL (vertebral defects, anal atresia, tracheaesophageal fistula with esophageal atresia, cardiac defects, renal and limb anomalies) association. *Journal of Pediatrics, 163*(3), 451–457. doi:10.1016/j.jpeds.2013.10.086

St. Louis, J. D., Harvey, B. A., Menk, J. S., Raghuveer, G., O'Brien, J. E., Bryant, R., & Kochilas, L. (2012). Repair of "simple" total anomalous pulmonary venous connection: A review from the pediatric cardiac care consortium. *Annals of Thoracic Surgery, 94*(1), 133–138. doi:10.1016/j.athoracsur.2012.03.006

Swamy, P., Bharadwaj, A., Varadarajan, P., & Pai, R. G. (2015). Echocardiographic evaluation of tetralogy of Fallot. *Echocardiography, 32*, 40–48. doi:10.1111/echo.12437

Taber, L. (2006). Biophysical mechanisms of cardiac looping. *International Journal of Developmental Biology, 50*(2–3), 323–332. doi:10.1387/ijdb.052045lt

Tchervenkov, C. I., Jacobs, M. L., & Tahta, S. A. (2000). Congenital heart surgery nomenclature and database project: Hypoplastic left heart syndrome. *Annals of Thoracic Surgery, 69*(4 Suppl.), S170–S190. doi:10.1016/S0140-6736(09)61922-X

Tennant, P. W., Pearce, M. S., Bythell, M., & Rankin, J. (2010). 20-year survival of children born with congenital anomalies: A population-based study. *Lancet, 375*(9715), 649–656 doi:10.1016/S0140-6736(09)61922-X

Veille, J., Hanson, R., Sivakoff, M., Hoen, H., & Ben-Ami, M. (1993). Fetal cardiac size in normal, intrauterine growth retarded, and diabetic pregnancies. *American Journal of Perinatology, 10*, 275–279.

Verklan, M. T., & Walden, M., (Eds.). (2015). *Core curriculum for neonatal intensive care nursing* (5th ed.). St. Louis, MO: Elsevier Saunders.

Villafañe, J., Feinstein, J. A., Jenkins, K. J., Vincent, R. N., Walsh, E. P., Dubin, A. M., … Adult Congenital and Pediatric Cardiology Section, American College of Cardiology. (2013). Hot topics in tetralogy of Fallot. *Journal of the American College of Cardiology, 62*(23), 2155–2166. doi:10.1016/j.jacc.2013.07.100

Wallis, G., & Fricker, F. J. (2012). Neonatal cardiomyopathy. *NeoReviews, 13*(12), e711–e723. doi:10.1542/neo.13-12-e711

Wilkinson, J. D., Westphal, J. A., Bansal, N., Czachor, J. D., Razoky, H., & Lipshultz, S. E. (2015). Lessons learned from the Pediatric Cardiomyopathy Registry (PCMR) Study Group. *Cardiology in the Young, 25*(Suppl. 2), 140–153. doi:10.1017/S1047951115000943.

Yang, J., Qiu, H., Qu, P., Zhang, R., Zeng, L., & Yan, H. (2015). Prenatal alcohol exposure and congenital heart defects: A meta-analysis. *PLOS One, 10*(6), e0130681. doi:10.1371/journal.pone.0130681

Yazigi, A., De Pecoulas, A., Vauloup-Fellous, C., Grangeot-Keros, L., Ayoubi, J-M., & Picone, O. (2017). Fetal and neonatal abnormalities due to congenital rubella syndrome: A review of literature. *Journal of Maternal-Fetal & Neonatal Medicine, 30*(3), 274–278. doi:10.3109/14767058.2016.1169526

Yeh, J., & Berger, S. (2015). Cardiac findings in infants of diabetic mothers. *NeoReviews, 16*(11), e624-e630. doi:10.1542/neo.16-11-e624

Zahka, K. (2011). Genetic and environmental contributions to congenital heart disease. In R. J. Martin, A. A. Fanaroff, & M. C. Walsh (Eds.), *Fanaroff and Martin's neonatal–perinatal medicine: Diseases of the fetus and infant* (9th ed., pp. 1222–1225). Philadelphia, PA: Mosby Elsevier.

6

THE GASTROINTESTINAL SYSTEM

Aksana Waskosky, Lisa Schepper, Rebecca Rose, and Linda Strickland

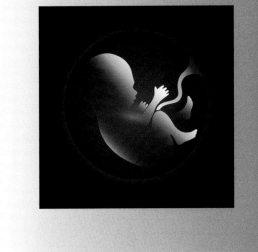

LEARNING OBJECTIVES

After completing this chapter, the reader should be able to:

- Understand normal gastrointestinal (GI) system development.
- Analyze the physiologic function of the fetal and neonatal GI system.
- Discuss common inherited disorders and their effect on fetal and neonatal GI system development and function.
- Identify maternal health issues that have a potential impact on fetal and postnatal GI system development and function.
- Evaluate common disorders that affect the GI system and their implications across the life span.

INTRODUCTION

This chapter is designed to provide knowledge of the embryologic, genetic, and physiologic development of the gastrointestinal (GI) tract. The environmental, maternal, and paternal risk factors that commonly influence GI development are discussed. Included in the chapter are the common abnormalities of GI development and the implications of these abnormalities in the newborn and across the life span. This knowledge provides the foundation for management of feeding and GI disorders in the newborn.

Vital functions of the GI system are the intake, digestion, and absorption of nutrients; the elimination of waste in stool and bile; participation in the maintenance of water balance; and the development of beneficial intestinal microbiota. Normal anatomic development and the functional maturity of the GI tract are crucial in establishing and maintaining these vital functions (Neu, 2012). The alimentary tract is the key component in providing nutrients to the body and plays an essential role in regulating energy homeostasis. It is a primary component of the GI system and consists of the mouth, pharynx, esophagus, stomach, small and large intestine, rectum, and anus (Figure 6.1).

TIMELINE FOR ORGAN DEVELOPMENT

Primitive Gut Development

Similar to the heart (see Chapter 5), GI development begins during week 4 of gestation. The three germ layers (endoderm, mesoderm, ectoderm) differentiate to form various GI structures. The endoderm gives rise to the gut, epithelium, and glands. The mesoderm gives rise to the parietal and visceral peritoneum. These mesenteries will cover and suspend the gut within the abdominal cavity. The ectoderm gives rise to the epithelium of the upper

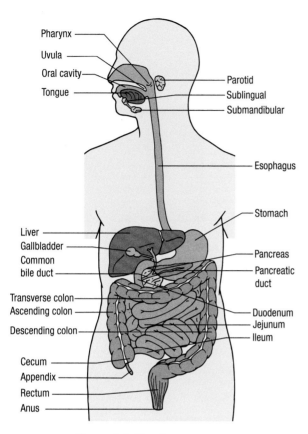

Figure 6.1 The alimentary tract.

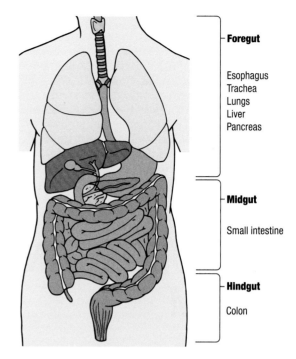

Figure 6.2 Adult structures that arise from foregut, midgut, and hindgut.

and lower GI tract; the distal portion of the anal canal also arises from the ectoderm. In addition, the neural crest gives rise to the nerves and neurons that innervate the walls of the GI tract (Moore, Persaud, & Torchia, 2016; Sadler, 2015).

Early cranial and caudal folding, during week 4 of gestation, causes the ends of the primitive tube to come together like purse strings, incorporating the dorsal side of the umbilicus (yolk sac) within the tube. Initially, this creates a physical barrier at both the cranial and caudal ends of the tube (Moore et al., 2016).

An oropharyngeal membrane covers the cranial end, which regresses during later development and gives rise to the anterior intestinal portal, or foregut, as well as the pharyngeal area (Faure & de Santa Barbara, 2011). Subsequent rupture of the oropharyngeal membrane creates an opening between the pharynx and foregut with the amniotic cavity, making way for the oral cavity (Moore et al., 2016). For the purposes of GI development, the pharyngeal area gives rise to the upper portion of the esophagus.

A cloacal membrane covers the caudal end, which regresses over time to permit formation of the posterior intestinal portal, or hindgut (Faure & de Santa Barbara, 2011). The middle of the primitive gut, or midgut, remains connected to the yolk sac through the vitelline duct (yolk stalk). During lateral-edge fusion, the vitelline duct regresses.

Failed regression is associated with the formation of Meckel's diverticulum, a remnant of the yolk stalk (Moore et al., 2016; Schoenwolf, Bleyl, Brauer, & Francis-West, 2015).

The early events just described permit primitive gut development, or the formation of the foregut, midgut, and hindgut (Figure 6.2; Mahe, Helmraph, & Shroyer, 2017; Moore et al., 2016). While the structures that comprise each region will be described categorically in the text that follows, it is important to understand that the development of the adult structures that arise from each primitive structure often overlap (Table 6.1). The greater majority of GI development occurs during the embryonic phase of development; maturation of the muscular layer and mesenteric attachments, and the formation of meconium occur during the fetal phase of development.

Foregut Development

The foregut is located between the upper part of the duodenum and the tracheobronchial diverticulum. It gives rise to the esophagus and stomach, upper portion of the duodenum, liver and biliary system, gallbladder, pancreas, and spleen (Moore et al., 2016; Sadler, 2015; Schoenwolf et al., 2015). Embryologic development of the spleen will be discussed in Chapter 7, and pancreatic development will be covered in Chapter 10.

Esophagus. The esophagus arises during week 4 of gestation from bifurcation of the trachea, by way of the tracheoesophageal septum (Figure 6.3). The esophagus thereby begins

TABLE 6.1 Embryologic-to-Adult Gastrointestinal Differentiation

Primitive Structure	Vascular Innervation	Adult Structures
Foregut	Celiac artery	• Esophagus • Stomach • Upper duodenum • Liver and biliary system • Gallbladder • Pancreas
Midgut	Superior mesenteric artery	• Lower duodenum • Small intestine • Cecum • Appendix • Ascending colon • Proximal two-thirds of colon
Hindgut	Inferior mesenteric artery	• Distal one-third of colon • Sigmoid colon • Rectum • Upper anal canal

NOTE: The foregut also gives rise to the lower respiratory system and the hindgut also gives rise to the urinary bladder, urethra, and male and female reproductive systems.

Sources: From Gleason, C. A., & Juul, S. E. (2018). *Avery's diseases of the newborn* (10th ed.). Philadelphia, PA: Elsevier; Moore, K. L., Persaud, T.V.N., & Torchia, M. G. (2016). *The developing human: Clinically oriented embryology* (10th ed.). Philadelphia, PA: Elsevier.

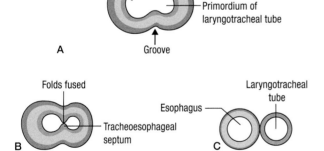

Figure 6.3 The tracheoesophageal septum. The drawing illustrates successful stages in development of the tracheoesophageal septum during the fourth and fifth weeks of gestation in the transverse view. (A) Beginning of partitioning of primordial laryngotracheal tube from primordial pharynx. (B) Developing the tracheoesophageal septum by fusion of tracheoesophageal folds. (C) Formation of the tracheoesophageal septum and complete separation of the foregut into the laryngotracheal tube and esophagus.

a process of growth and stretching. By week 6 of gestation, ciliated epithelia cluster and transform into esophageal glands. During week 7 of gestation, the esophagus reaches its final length; however, due to rapid cellular proliferation, it is functionally obstructed. Therefore, a process of

recanalization ensues. Finally, by week 8 to 9 of gestation, the esophagus achieves patency. By this time, vascular innervations matriculate to the submucosa. The muscular wall of the upper two thirds of the esophagus becomes striated and innervated by the vagus nerve, while the splanchnic plexus innervates the lower third of the esophagus (Moore et al., 2016; Neu, 2012; Schoenwolf et al., 2015).

Several esophageal anomalies may arise during this period of complex and overlapping development. Errors in partition of the foregut into respiratory and digestive parts, resulting from either spontaneous posterior deviation of the tracheoesophageal septum or from mechanical forces pushing the dorsal wall of the foregut anteriorly, lead to isolated esophageal atresia (EA) or EA combined with a tracheoesophageal fistula (TEF). Atresia or stenosis of the esophagus results from incomplete recanalization or narrowing of the lumen. Failure of esophageal elongation pulls the stomach through the diaphragm into the esophageal hiatus and leads to a congenital hiatal hernia (Moore et al., 2016; Neu, 2012; Sadler, 2015; Schoenwolf et al., 2015).

Stomach. The stomach arises during week 4 of gestation. The endoderm of the foregut dilates and migrates 90 degrees on its long axis, and in a counterclockwise direction around the dorso-ventral axis. This is followed by a counterclockwise rotation on the dorsoventral axis (Figure 6.4; Moore et al., 2016; Sadler, 2015). This phenomenon

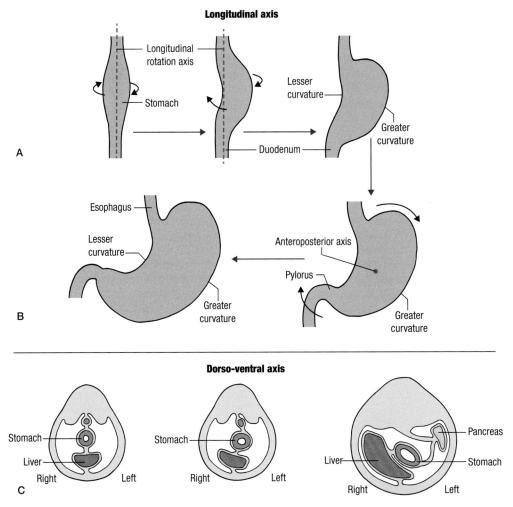

Figure 6.4 Rotation of stomach (longitudinal axis). (A) Original position of primitive stomach, before rotation. (B) Ventral border begins moving in rightward direction while dorsal border moves leftward. (C) Continued migration. Once relocated, the stomach resides on the left side of midline and the liver resides primarily on the right side of midline. Invagination shows early development of the pancreas.

creates the greater and lesser curvatures of the stomach. During this rotation, the cephalic and caudal ends, initially located on the midline, relocate. The caudal (pyloric) end moves upward and to the right, and the cephalic (cardiac) end moves downward and to the left. Once movement is complete, the stomach resides at the C3 to C5 level. Over time, the stomach slowly descends and ultimately occupies a final location between T5 and L3 (Mahe, Helmraph, & Shroyer, 2017).

Next, the greater and lesser omenta (sheets of fat covered by the peritoneum that connect the stomach to the abdominal viscera) arise from the dorsal and ventral mesenteries, respectively (Sadler, 2015). Finally, the pyloric sphincter forms at the caudal end of the stomach, through the proliferation of mesoderm-derived smooth muscles. The pylorus is a muscle located between the stomach and duodenum. This muscle modulates the movement of intestinal contents by way of preventing retrograde reentry from the small intestine back into the stomach. By 6 weeks of gestation, the stomach structure is well established (Mahe et al., 2017).

Compared to other organ systems, the morphologic development of the stomach is rather simple. As such, congenital anomalies are comparatively rare. Incomplete rotation and a developmental arrest in the caudal region may result in microgastria. Hypertrophy, mainly in circular muscles in the pylorus area, leads to pyloric stenosis, *the most common stomach abnormality in neonates* (Moore et al., 2016).

Duodenum. Similar to the esophagus and stomach, the duodenum arises during week 4 of gestation. The duodenum arises from the caudal end of the foregut, the cranial aspect of the midgut, and a segment of the splanchnic mesenchyme (Moore et al., 2016). During its evolution, the duodenum develops into a C-shaped loop (Figure 6.5). Following the normal rotation of the stomach, the duodenal loop rotates to the right and moves to the right upper abdominal quadrant, where it presses against the posterior

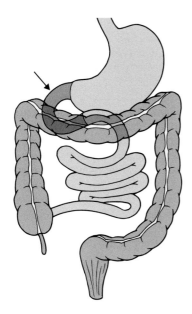

Figure 6.5 The C-shaped duodenum.

Source: The duodenum by Olek Remesz, CC-BY-2.5.

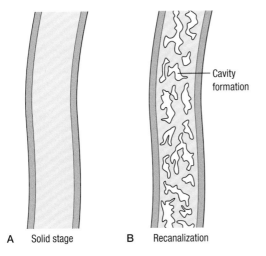

Figure 6.6 Recanalization of the duodenal lumen.

abdominal wall (along with the pancreas) and assumes a retroperitoneal position (Moore et al., 2016; Sadler, 2015).

Similar to the esophagus, rapid proliferation of the endothelial lining of the duodenum temporarily obliterates its lumen. This occlusion typically occurs between weeks 5 and 6 of gestation, with subsequent recanalization between weeks 6 and 7 of gestation (Figure 6.6). Therefore, failed or partial recanalization has the potential to cause duodenal stenosis and/or atresia. Duodenal atresia (DA) is quite rare and suggests genetic involvement (Moore et al., 2016).

Liver, Gallbladder, and Biliary System. The liver, gallbladder, and biliary duct appear during week 4 of gestation. The liver arises as a small bud off the hepatic diverticulum.

At this stage in embryonic development, the hepatic diverticulum is adjacent to the heart (Moore et al., 2016; Sadler, 2015). From weeks 5 to 10 of gestation, the liver undergoes rapid growth, occupying a significant portion of the upper abdominal cavity. The cranial portion of the diverticulum differentiates into the liver and biliary system, whereas the caudal segment differentiates into the gallbladder. The stalk of the diverticulum differentiates into the bile duct. Functional segmentation is determined by oxygen intake from the fetal umbilical veins, one of two major blood supplies to the liver (the other being the portal vein). Over time, the right lobe typically exceeds the size of the left. By week 10 of gestation, the liver accounts for about 10% of total body weight (Moore et al., 2016).

Similar to the esophagus and duodenum, epithelial cells initially clog the extrahepatic biliary apparatus. Recanalization occurs shortly thereafter, and by week 13 of gestation, bile enters the duodenum through the common bile duct. The movement of bile initiates the production of meconium, also during week 13 of gestation. Failed recanalization leads to extrahepatic biliary atresia (BA), the most serious anomaly of the extrahepatic biliary system. Alternatively, intrahepatic BA and hypoplasia may arise during embryonic development, affecting duct formation. Benign variations in liver lobulation are common, yet of little clinical relevance (Moore et al., 2016; Sadler, 2015).

Midgut Development

Derivatives of the midgut include the lower segment of the duodenum, jejunum, ileum, cecum, appendix, ascending colon, and two thirds of the proximal colon. The midgut originates from the dorsal abdominal wall during week 5 of gestation, nourished by the superior mesenteric artery (Moore et al., 2016).

Before week 5 of gestation, the early midgut is a linear tube. During this stage of development, the primitive ileum elongates and quickly exceeds the capacity of the abdominal cavity of the embryo. As a result, U-shaped looping occurs, creating the primary intestinal loop. The primary intestinal loop connects to the yolk sac, at the apex, by the vitelline duct. The cephalic portion of the loop transforms into the distal part of the duodenum, the jejunum, and ileum. The caudal portion rises to the ascending colon and proximal two thirds of the transverse colon (Moore et al., 2016; Parry, 2015). Midgut development then proceeds as four stages: *herniation, rotation, retraction*, and *fixation*.

Because of the rapid growth described previously, the U-shaped midgut loop challenges the strength and capacity of the abdominal cavity. During week 6 of gestation, likely due to excess pressure, *herniation* of the midgut into the umbilicus occurs (Moore et al., 2016; Sadler, 2015). During this time, the midgut *rotates 90 degrees in a counterclockwise direction,* around the axis of the superior mesenteric artery (within the umbilical cord). Rotation is complete by week 8 of gestation, yet the abdominal contents remain in the herniated location, continuously elongating and folding. This proliferation gives rise to the cecum and, shortly after, the appendix, which arises as a small pouch off the dorsal end of the cecum and elongates over time. *Retraction* begins during week 10 of gestation. During this time, the midgut undergoes an *additional 180 degrees of counterclockwise rotation, totaling 270 degrees of rotational movement* (Moore et al., 2016; Sadler, 2015). By week 11 of gestation, and under normal circumstances, all abdominal contents are contained back within the abdomen (**Figure 6.7**). *Fixation* thereby occurs during week 12 of gestation. The cecum and appendix descend into the subhepatic abdominal region and further into the right lower quadrant, the proximal colon transforms into the ascending colon, and the mesenteries fuse with the abdominal wall (Sadler, 2015; Schoenwolf et al., 2015). Postnatally, the cecum continues

to grow, which eventually positions the appendix on its medial side (Moore et al., 2016).

Clearly, midgut development is complex. As a result, multiple anomalies can arise. Intestinal stenosis or atresia arise either from failed recanalization; as a primary defect; from the twisting, inflammatory changes; or secondary to interrupted blood supply. Malrotation results from compartmentalization of intestine to the dorsal intestinal wall, created by abnormal bands of mesenteric tissue (Ladd's bands). Precarious suspension of malrotated intestine from one point on the dorsal intestinal wall can lead to an occlusion of blood supply and resultant volvulus. Errors during retraction can lead to persistently herniated bowel, namely, omphalocele or gastroschisis. Omphalocele is a persistent herniation covered by a peritoneal sac. Gastroschisis, the *second most common consequence of failed intestinal retraction*, is

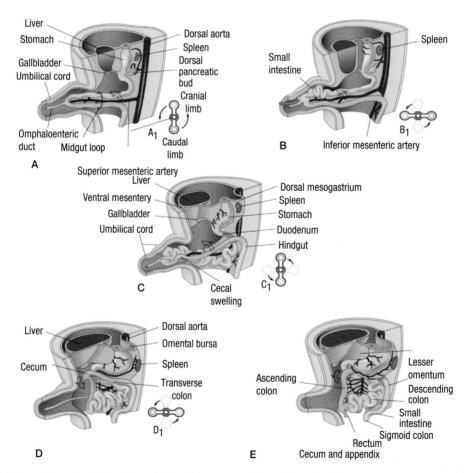

Figure 6.7 Herniation and rotation of the midgut. (A) At the beginning of the sixth week. (A1) Transverse section through the midgut loop, illustrating the initial relationship of the limbs of the loop to the superior mesenteric artery. Note that the midgut loop is in the proximal part of the umbilical cord. (B) Later stage showing the beginning of midgut rotation. (B1) Ilustration of the 90-degree counterclockwise rotation that carries the cranial limb of the midgut to the right. (C) At approximately 10 weeks, showing the intestine returning to the abdomen. (C1) Illustration of a further rotation of 90 degrees. (D) At approximately 11 weeks, showing the location of the viscera after retraction of the intestine. (D1) Illustration of a further 90-degree rotation of the viscera, for a total of 270 degrees. (E) Later in the fetal period, showing the cecum rotating to its normal position in the lower right quadrant of the abdomen.

Source: Moore, K. L., Persaud, T. V. N., & Torchia, M. G. (2016). *The developing human: Clinically oriented embryology* (10th ed.). Philadelphia, PA: Elsevier.

an extravasation of bowel located lateral, and most often to the right, of the umbilical cord (Sadler, 2015; Schoenwolf et al., 2015).

Hindgut Development

Hindgut development is interconnected with genitourinary system development (Chapter 11). The hindgut receives its blood supply from the inferior mesenteric artery. The derivatives of the hindgut are noted in Table 6.1, for visual reference (Moore et al., 2016). This discussion focuses on the development of the anorectal canal, an integral part of the GI system.

The cloaca is regarded as the most developmentally complex portion of the hindgut and arises as early as the end of week 1 of gestation. Between weeks 5 and 7 of gestation, a wall of mesenchyme develops between the allantois and hindgut, serving as a partition for the cloaca. This cloacal membrane divides the cloaca into three separate structures: the (a) urogenital sinus, (b) rectum, and (c) anal canal (Moore et al., 2016; Schoenwolf et al., 2015). The urogenital sinus differentiates into the bladder, which is discussed in more detail in Chapter 8. During week 8 of gestation (approximately), the cloacal membrane ruptures. New evidence suggests that after rupturing, the lumen of the superior portion of the anorectal canal becomes transiently plugged with epithelial cells (Figure 6.8; Moore et al. 2016; Schoenwolf et al., 2015). Clearly, this process of clogging mimics the normal development of other structures, including the

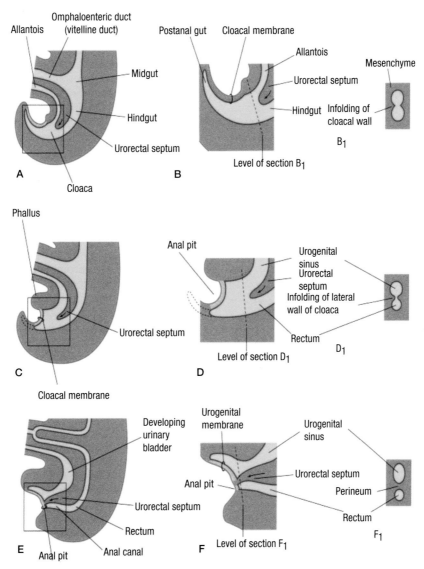

Figure 6.8 Successive stages in the partitioning of the cloaca into the rectum and urogenital sinus by the urorectal septum. (A, C, and E) Views from the left side at 4, 6, and 7 weeks, respectively. (B, D, and F) Enlargements of the cloacal region. (B1 and D1) Transverse sections of the cloaca at the levels shown in B and D. Note that the postanal portion (shown in B) degenerates and disappears as the rectum forms.

esophagus and intestinal tract. Over time, proliferation of the mesenchyme raises the surface ectoderm enough that recanalization occurs. Subsequently, the primitive anal pit forms, and continues, in partnership with the hindgut, to give rise to the inferior portion of the anal canal (proctodeum; Moore et al., 2016). Later formation of the anal sphincter is influenced by multiple genetic factors; a discussion of these factors is beyond the scope of this textbook (Moore et al., 2016; Schoenwolf et al., 2015).

Once anal formation is well underway, the superior rectal artery innervates the superior portion of the anal canal and provides an incoming blood supply, while the superior rectal vein innervates and offers a point of egress. Comparatively, the inferior rectal arteries and inferior rectal vein arise and supply the lower segment of the anal canal. Nervous system innervation differs by location. The superior portion of the anal canal is innervated by the autonomic nervous system (ANS). The inferior portion of the anal canal is innervated by the inferior rectal nerve (Moore et al., 2016)

Disrupted development of the hindgut may yield several developmental abnormalities. Congenital megacolon is the most common cause of lower intestinal obstruction in neonates and results from failed innervation of neural crest cells, typically between weeks 5 and 7 of gestation. Similar to Hirschsprung disease, congenital megacolon involves an absence of ganglion cells. Most anorectal anomalies result from errors of cloacal septation, the most common being an imperforate anus. Cases of imperforate anus may be associated with a urorectal fistula. Other defects include anal stenosis and rectal atresia (Moore et al., 2016; Schoenwolf et al., 2015).

DEVELOPMENTAL PHYSIOLOGY

Molecular Regulation of Gut Tube Development

Molecular signaling patterns are complex and detailed explanations exceed the scope of this textbook, but may be found in several detailed reviews (Batts, Polk, Dubois, & Kulessa, 2006; Chin, Hill, Aurora, & Spence, 2017; G. M. Kelly & Drysdale, 2015; Logan & Nusse, 2004; Zorn, 2008). However, a brief introduction of the major factors that govern development of the digestive organs follows. Development of the GI tract is highlighted by three major developmental points: (a) initial specification of endoderm, (b) formation of the gut tube, and (c) configuration of organs expanding beyond the gut tube (pancreas and liver). During development, endodermal tissues are pluripotent, meaning all tissue can develop into any organ that arises from the endoderm. Signaling from multiple genes is necessary for the correct organ to form in the correct place.

Sonic hedgehog (SHH) signaling protein is expressed throughout the gut tube and stimulates interactions between the endoderm and spatially related mesoderm. These interactions are thought to control the pattern of organ formation. Wingless-type mouse mammary tumor virus (Wnt), retinoic acid (RA), bone morphogenic protein-4 (BMP4), and fibroblast growth factor-4 (FGF4) are secreted by the mesoderm (de Santa Barbara, van den Brink, & Roberts, 2003). Wnt glycoproteins regulate the proliferation of cells and play an important role in early embryologic development and in later tissue growth and maintenance. Wnt and FGF4 promote posterior development and are present in a gradient, highest in the posterior. Wnt and FGF4 must be inhibited for the foregut to form (Chin et al., 2017). RA is not present at the anterior end of the developing embryo, allowing for the formation of the mouth and pharynx. However, RA must be present below the level of the thyroid in order for the formation of the intestinal tract, specifically the region extending from the esophagus to the colon, to occur. BMP4 contributes to hindgut formation, as well as the lengthening of the intestines. The combinations of these signals determine the secondary genes controlling the development of different parts of the gut tube. SOX2 specifies esophagus and stomach, PDX1 the duodenum, CDXC the small intestine, and CDXA the large intestine and rectum (Sadler, 2015).

The liver develops from hepatocyte stem cells that differentiate from the foregut endoderm. The ectoderm and notochord secrete factors that inhibit liver differentiation in most of the foregut. In the area of liver development, these factors are inhibited by FGF2 secreted by the cardiac mesoderm, allowing the liver to form. BMPs facilitate the response of the tissues to the presence of FGF2 and further enhance liver formation. SHH signaling is inhibited in the foregut endoderm, allowing the formation of the dorsal and ventral buds that will become the pancreas (Figure 6.9). PDX1 stimulates formation and enlargement of the pancreatic buds. RA from the adjacent mesoderm is required for full formation of the anterior bud, but not the ventral bud (G. M. Kelly & Drysdale, 2015; Twaroski et al., 2015).

Innervation of the Digestive Tract: Function of the Enteric Nervous System

The enteric nervous system (ENS) is a complex network of both neurons and glia that control bowel motility, secretion, and blood flow without conscious thought. This system arises during early embryogenesis, by way of the neural crest, and is considered the "brain of the gastrointestinal system" (Avetisyan, Schill, & Heuckeroth, 2015, p. 899). The neurons in the myenteric plexus reside between the longitudinal and circular muscle in the bowel wall, and control muscle contraction and relaxation. The neurons in the submucosal plexus reside between the circular muscle and the bowel mucosa, and modulate fluid secretion and absorption, supporting bowel function (Moore et al., 2016; Pathway Medicine, 2017).

Development of the ENS begins with ENS precursors migrating from the vagal neural crest cells to the

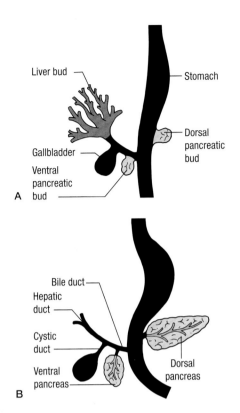

Figure 6.9 Formation of dorsal and ventral pancreatic buds. (A) Early development of pancreatic buds. (B) Progressive development of dorsal and ventral pancreas.

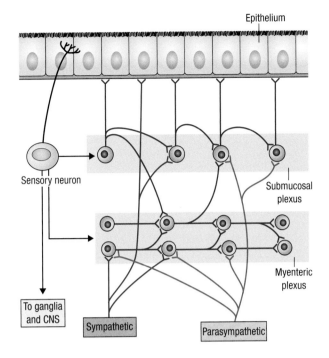

Figure 6.10 Enteric nervous system innervation.

foregut, and subsequently to the rest of the digestive tract in a rostral-to-caudal progression (Figure 6.10: Uesaka, Young, Pachnis, & Emomoto, 2016). These cells first enter the myenteric, or outer region, of the gut, but later they also enter the deeper submucosal layer. ENS precursors differentiate into multiple subtypes to establish the neuronal circuits that control the bowel. RA is extremely important for the survival, proliferation, and migration of these cells. Mice without RA have total intestinal aganglionosis. SHH restricts the ENS precursors to the outer bowel wall. During the migration, cell contact through L1 cell adhesion molecule (L1CAM) is necessary for structured migration throughout the digestive system. Mutations in L1CAM reduce bowel colonization by neurons in mice. Failure of the complete development of the ENS has been implicated in several diseases of the bowel, including Hirschsprung disease, gastroparesis, and irritable bowel syndrome.

Function of the GI Tract

The alimentary canal, or GI tract, is the system where food enters the body, nutrients are digested and absorbed, and waste is eliminated. The four primary functions of the GI tract are (a) digestion and absorption, (b) fluid and electrolyte balance, (c) protection against invaders, and (d) elimination of waste; each function is essential to the

health of the newborn. From the esophagus to the anus, the GI tract contains the same histologic cell layers. The GI mucosa has three layers and modifies these layers in various GI segments regarding the functions of digestion, absorption, and secretion. The GI submucosa is collagenous tissue with nerves and blood vessels. The GI muscularis propria is primarily responsible for moving bulk food. GI adventitia is collagenous tissue with larger vasculature and nerves that regulate the entire tract (Mahe et al., 2017; Pathway Medicine, 2017). The esophagus is a tunnel or "covered bridge" from the mouth to the stomach. It performs its function expertly and no artificial replacement has been developed. Impulses from the swallowing center, where the nuclei of cranial nerves IX and X are located, activate swallowing. Digestion and absorption do not occur in the esophagus (Parry, 2015; Pathway Medicine, 2017).

The GI tract is controlled by the ENS, which is a division of the ANS. More ENS than central nervous system (CNS) activity exists there; the GI tract can completely control function even if the connection to the CNS is severed. The GI tract secretes many hormones, including cholecystokinin, gastrin, secretin, and gastrin inhibitory peptide. It is important to note that the cells producing glucagon are present only in fetal and neonatal glands, indicating a role in growth. Gastric secretions are present by 10 weeks of gestation. Gastrin, hydrochloric acid, pepsin, and intrinsic factor (IF) are present early along with mucus and bicarbonate at about 16 weeks of gestation. Gastric pH of term newborns is neutral but rapidly falls to 3.5 and by 48 hours the pH is 1.0 to 3.0. Premature babies have a prolonged alkaline state secondary to prematurity (Broussard & Altschuler, 2017; Pathway Medicine, 2017).

Carbohydrate digestion and absorption are accomplished primarily in the intestine. The GI system absorbs starch composed of large branched chains of sugars. The intestine is able to absorb sucrose, a disaccharide composed of glucose and fructose, as well as lactose, a disaccharide composed of glucose and galactose. The small intestine mucosa only absorbs monosaccharides. Digestion requires processing of these carbohydrates into their individual component sugars (see Chapter 10; Pathway Medicine, 2017; Vanderhoof & Pauley-Hunter, 2016).

Luminal fluid is responsible for digestion of starches in the small intestine. Starches are broken down into monosaccharide and disaccharide parts. Digestion begins in the mouth with salivary amylase and is completed in the small intestine with pancreatic amylase. Epithelial digestion occurs on the brush border of the small intestine epithelium. Enzymes are present to digest disaccharides into absorbable monosaccharides. The major enzymes include lactase, sucrose, and maltase. Carbohydrate digestion produces glycose, galactose, and fructose and these substances can be transported past the small intestine epithelium. Monosaccharides can be transported through the membrane of the small intestine epithelium using membrane porters. Specialized porters are used for different monosaccharides and both active and passive transport are used (Neu, 2017; Pathway Medicine, 2017; Vanderhoof & Pauley-Hunter, 2016).

Amino acids require digestion into single amino acids or dipeptides and tripeptides. Digestion of proteins is accomplished by a variety of peptidases in the stomach and small intestine. The stomach secretes pepsin, active only in a low pH environment, to begin digestion of proteins. Protein digestion involves the pancreatic enzymes, trypsin, chymotrypsin, elastase, and carboxypeptidase in the small intestine lumen. The final protein digestion occurs on the brush border of the small intestine epithelium. Membrane-bound peptidases complete digestion to single amino acids, dipeptides, or tripeptides. These amino acids are transported into the enterocytes, broken into individual amino acids, and passively transported into the blood (Neu, 2017; Pathway Medicine, 2017; Vanderhoof & Pauley-Hunter, 2016).

Because lipids require the molecule to be broken into small units for absorption, emulsification is the process of breaking large lipid droplets into smaller ones to increase surface area for digestive enzymes. Bile acids and lecithin, both provided by the liver and secreted into the bile, assist with emulsifying lipids. The churning action of gastric motility assists with emulsifying lipids, beginning in the stomach. The small intestine contains the strong liver emulsifiers with strong lipid-digesting enzymes created by the pancreas. The pancreatic enzymes can act on the smaller lipid droplets. The exocrine pancreas provides enzymes to digest lipids into chemical parts. Digested

lipids are hydrophobic and, with the assistance of bile acids, diffuse across the small intestine brush border. The GI tract also absorbs small-molecule vitamins. Fat-soluble vitamins (A, D, E, K) are absorbed with other lipids. Water-soluble vitamins are absorbed in the small intestine (Neu, 2017; Pathway Medicine, 2017; Vanderhoof & Pauley-Hunter, 2016).

The GI system secretes ~8 L of fluid combined with almost 2 L of ingested fluid. Only about 0.1 L to 0.2 L of fluid is excreted in the feces. Water and electrolyte absorption occur in the small and large intestines. Sodium resorption occurs during nutrient absorption in the duodenum and jejunum. In the large intestine, aldosterone enhances sodium resorption. Chloride absorption occurs in the small intestine, especially the duodenum and jejunum, through passive diffusion. Pancreatic secretion results in a large amount of bicarbonate. To maintain acid—base balance, some bicarbonate needs to be resorbed. The respiratory system assists by breathing off the CO_2 produced during bicarbonate resorption. Glucose absorption occurs across the intestine, although it is less efficient in newborns and even more so in premature infants. Water is absorbed through passive osmosis in the GI tract. Water absorption is enhanced by absorption of osmotic electrolytes, such as sodium (Pathway Medicine, 2017; Vanderhoof & Pauley-Hunter, 2016).

Digestion is further facilitated by the motor activity of the GI tract, creating the ability to mix and grind food through contractions. The small intestine muscles appear between 6 to 8 weeks of gestation and some uncoordinated peristalsis is present. Between 32 and 34 weeks of gestation, peristalsis has improved but transit time may be as long as 9 hours, or twice as long as the term infant's transit time. During digestion, food is churned into small particles in the stomach called *chyme*. When the particles are ~1 mm, chyme is emptied into the duodenum. The grinding of digested food improves nutrient accessibility to digestive enzymes and absorption by luminal surfaces. Both the small and large intestines have peristaltic and mixing contractions.

The ileocecal valve and sphincter lie between the small and large intestines. The valve prevents backflow from the colon into the ileum. The sphincter regulates the emptying of the ileum into the cecum. When a large wave of peristalsis is initiated in the transverse colon, feces are pushed into the rectum. The urge to defecate may arise after food consumption and is termed the *gastrocolic reflex*. Defecation begins when the internal anal sphincter relaxes. The external anal sphincter is under voluntary control and must also relax for stool to be expelled (Moore et al, 2016; Pathway Medicine, 2017).

The digestive tract has multiple symbiotic organisms present (see the section "Maternal (and Paternal) Health Influences"). The microbial complex living with the host is referred to as the *microbiota*. Gut microbiota are important in host resistance to invading pathogens. The microbes prevent pathogen colonization by direct interaction with pathogens such as competition for nutrients and microbe enhancement of host defense mechanisms. A protective mechanism against pathogenic invaders from entering the GI tract is gastric acid. Gastric acid protects the upper tract and insulates the bacteria in the intestine against contamination from above (Kamada, Chen, Inohara, & Nunez, 2013; Neu, 2017).

GENETIC INFLUENCES

Many diseases of the GI tract have genetic predispositions. Numerous genes responsible for pathologic GI conditions have been discovered; researchers continue to uncover genes associated with GI diseases whose causes had not previously been fully understood. These discoveries have changed how many GI disorders are diagnosed and treated. Genetic testing is commercially available for many of the GI conditions that have genetic involvement; testing facilitates screening and diagnosing predisposed persons (Roath & Di Palma, 2012). Several such GI conditions with known genetic foundations are discussed in the text that follows. Additional inherited disorders affecting the GI system are provided in Table 6.2.

Autosomal Dominant Disorders

Hereditary Gastrointestinal Cancer Syndromes. Hereditary GI cancer syndromes are inherited as autosomal dominant disorders with penetrance close to 100%; these syndromes account for approximately 3% to 5% of all colon cancers (Online Mendelian Inheritance in Men [OMIM], 2017d). Albeit rare, the risk for colorectal cancer in newborns is increased in the presence of polyposis syndromes or inflammatory

---

TABLE 6.2 Other Inherited Disorders of the Gastrointestinal System

- 22q11.2 deletion syndrome
- Accessory pancreas
- Alpers syndrome
- Alpha-1 antitrypsin deficiency
- Annular pancreas
- Aplasia cutis
- Cholestasis, progressive familial
- Congenital bile duct acid synthesis defects
- Cornelia de Lange syndrome (type 1 and 2)
- Dandy-Walker cyst with renal–hepatic–pancreatic dysplasia
- Hepatoblastoma
- Pentalogy of Cantrell
- Whipple disease
- Zellweger syndrome

NOTE: A more comprehensive list is provided by the National Institutes of Health, Genetic and Rare Diseases Information Center.

---

bowel disease. Both conditions may lead to familial adenomatous polyposis and hereditary nonpolyposis colon cancer. The risk increases dramatically with a positive family history (OMIM, 2017c; Roath & Di Palma, 2012). The incidence of familial adenomatous polyposis ranges from one in 7,000 to 22,000 individuals (Genetic Home Reference [GHR], 2017c). This cancer is caused by a mutation in the *APC* or *MSH3* genes, located on the long arm of chromosome 5. When functional, the *APC* gene modulates cellular proliferation and acts as a tumor suppressor gene (OMIM, 2017d; Roath & Di Palma, 2012).

Hereditary nonpolyposis colon cancer (or Lynch syndrome) is not associated with a high quantity of polyps, but the few that present are large and aggressive (Figure 6.11). Mutations in several genes located on chromosomes 2, 3, and 7 are responsible for hereditary nonpolyposis colon cancer, with mutations of MSH2 on chromosome 2 and MLH1 on chromosome 3 being the most common causes (Jorde, Carey, & Bamshad, 2016; OMIM, 2017d; Roath & Di Palma, 2012). The condition has right-side colon predominance. Affected individuals are at high risk for developing other cancers, including endometrial, ovarian, gastric, brain, urinary tract, and biliary tract cancers.

Permanent Neonatal Diabetes Mellitus. Permanent neonatal diabetes mellitus affects one in every 400,000 infants (GHR, 2017g). Autosomal dominant inheritance is most common. Mutations in the *KCNJ11, INS,* and *ABCC8* genes are reported, which disrupt normal pancreatic function. Essentially, gene dysfunction causes failed closure of K^+–adenosine triposhphate (ATP) channels, which provokes decreased beta cell synthesis of insulin. In about 90% of cases, new gene mutations are identified in the absence of a family history of the disease (GHR, 2017g). Prenatal manifestations include poor fetal growth and intrauterine growth restriction (IUGR). After birth, hyperglycemia with dehydration and failure to thrive results secondary to decreased insulin secretion (GHR, 2017g). Epilepsy and developmental delay, known as *DEND syndrome (developmental delay—epilepsy—neonatal diabetes)*, is associated with this genetic disorder. Patients with an underdeveloped pancreas may manifest with fatty stools and the inability to absorb fat-soluble vitamins (GHR, 2017g). Lifelong insulin therapy is required for adequate weight gain and nutritional balance; there is no chance for remission (Polak & Cave, 2007).

Biliary Hypoplasia (Alagille Syndrome). Biliary hypoplasia, characterized by incomplete development of the biliary system, results in a reduction in intrahepatic bile ducts. This disorder affects approximately one in every 70,000 live births; boys and girls are equally represented (Figure 6.12; GHR, 2017a). The majority of cases involve mutations in the *JAG1* gene (chromosome 20p12); less than 1% of cases are caused by mutations in *NOTCH2*

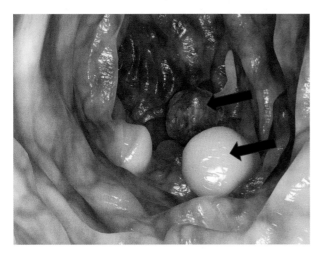

Figure 6.11 Intestinal polyps. Arrows mark two easily identified intestinal polyps.

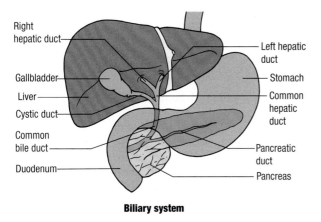

Biliary system

Figure 6.12 Normal anatomy of the biliary system. In cases of abnormal formation of the bile ducts (e.g., Alagille syndrome), failed passage of bile causes buildup of bile within the liver and subsequent hepatic injury.

(Genetic and Rare Diseases Information Center [GARD], 2017b). Gene mutations lead to insufficient bile flow. This provokes liver dysfunction, which manifests as jaundice, pale stools, malabsorption, pruritus, and xanthelasma (soft yellow plaques on eyelids; Kamoth & Piccoli, 2008; Vanderhoof & Pauley-Hunter, 2016). Lifelong continuing care is required.

Autosomal Recessive

Cystic Fibrosis. Recall from Chapter 4 that cystic fibrosis (CF) is an inherited condition characterized by the accumulation of thick, sticky mucus that damages many organs. It is estimated to occur in one in 2,500 to 3,500 Caucasian infants and is less common

in African American (1/17,000) and Asian (1/31,000) races (GHR, 2017b). CF is caused by mutations in the *CFTR* (CF transmembrane regulator) gene. Normally, CFTR protein works as a channel that allows cells to release chloride and other ions. When the *CFTR* gene is defective, it prevents cells from releasing the chloride (Figure 6.13; GHR, 2017b). The outcome is an improper salt balance in the cells and thick, sticky mucus that clogs and damages body organs, especially the GI and respiratory systems. The disease causes alterations in exocrinegland function and pancreatic enzyme deficiency (GHR, 2017b; Larson-Nath, Gurram, & Chelimsky, 2015).

In the newborn, GI symptoms include failure to pass meconium and jaundice, which may be prolonged. The failure to pass meconium is typically the result of the accumulation of multiple meconium plugs within the ileum or distal colon (meconium plug syndrome). The presence of a meconium ileus affects approximately 50% of infants with CF and may lead to further complications, including microcolon, abdominal distension, peritonitis, or even volvulus. Radiographically, APNs may identify small loops of bowel that take on a honeycomb-like ground-glass appearance and low air-fluid levels. The ground glass appearance is due to an accumulation of air bubbles ("soap bubble appearance") trapped around thick meconium (also known as the Nehauser sign). Complimentary low air-fluid levels are a classic manifestation of meconium ileus (due to the presence of tenacious meconium and abnormal mucous-gland secretion) compared to other abdominal obstructions and should raise the index of suspicion for CF. Respiratory symptoms include chronic respiratory failure with wheezing, cough, and recurrent pneumonia.

Life expectancy has improved with earlier diagnosis and treatment; a multidisciplinary approach is critical to optimize outcomes and must be customized according to disease severity and comorbidities. Common lifespan implications include acquired pancreatic insufficiency, which typically requires lifelong supplementation of pancreatic enzyme and fat-soluble-vitamin supplementation, in addition to a high-calorie diet (Larson-Nath et al., 2015). Males may be affected by infertility, secondary to an absence of the vas deferens (GHR, 2017b).

Shwachman–Diamond Syndrome. Shwachman–Diamond syndrome is an autosomal recessive disorder that affects one in 50,000 North American infants (GHR, 2017h; OMIM, 2017f). Alterations in the *RPS19* gene and *SBDS* gene located on chromosome 7 alter normal development of the pancreas, bone marrow, and skeletal system. Pancreatic insufficiency and bone marrow failure result. Clinical manifestations include failure to thrive, malabsorption, and steatorrhea. Similar to CF, pancreatic insufficiency requires lifelong pancreatic enzyme and fat-soluble-vitamin supplementation and high caloric diet (GHR, 2017h; Larson-Nath et al., 2015).

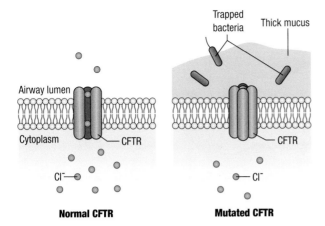

Figure 6.13 Impact of functioning CFTR (left) and nonfunctional CFTR (right). CFTR regulates Chloride (Cl⁻) ion flow in and out of the cells. When CFTR is mutated (nonfunctional), ion flow is impaired, which allows for mucous accumulation. Stagnation of the mucous accumulation may occur in the pancreatic and bile ducts, as well as the respiratory system.

Congenital Chloride Diarrhea. Congenital chloride diarrhea is an autosomal recessive form of severe chronic diarrhea characterized by voluminous, watery stools with high chloride concentration (GARD, 2018). Mutation in the *SLC26A3* gene on chromosome 7 disrupts chloride transport within the distal ileum and colon (OMIM, 2017a). Postnatal clinical manifestations include dehydration, metabolic alkalosis, hyperbilirubinemia, abdominal distention, hyperactive renin–angiotensin system, and hyperaldosteronism. Older infants may present with failure to thrive (GARD, 2018; OMIM, 2017a). The disease affects infants across the life span and no cure is available; treatment is supportive and targets the normalization of electrolyte absorption in the jejunum (GARD, 2018; OMIM, 2017a).

Congenital Sodium Diarrhea. Congenital sodium diarrhea is an autosomal recessive disorder. Mutations in the serine protease inhibitor gene (*SPLINT2*) on chromosome 19q13 disrupt sodium–hydrogen exchange at the jejunal brush border, which manifests with excessive diarrhea shortly after birth (OMIM, 2017b). Infants may develop dehydration, hyponatremia, and metabolic acidosis. Profound volume loss can lead to acute renal failure. Lifelong monitoring is required, and treatment is focused on fluid and electrolyte replacement and managing individual symptoms (Larson-Nath et al., 2015).

Glucose–Galactose Malabsorption. Malabsorption of glucose and galactose is an autosomal recessive disorder (GHR, 2017d). Mutations in the *SLC5A1* gene lead to altered transport of glucose, galactose, and sodium across the intestinal epithelium (GHR, 2017d). As a result, glucose, galactose, and water accumulate within the intestinal tract and are lost in the stool (GHR, 2017d). Hallmark manifestations among infants include severe diarrhea, dehydration, metabolic acidosis, and weight loss (GHR, 2017d). Life-span implications include the risk for development of kidney stones with calcium deposits throughout the kidneys. Lifelong avoidance of glucose and galactose sugars may be required (GHR, 2017d; OMIM, 2017c).

Congenital Lactase Deficiency. Congenital lactase deficiency is an autosomal recessive disorder characterized by an impaired ability to digest lactose. This is considered a rare genetic disorder within the United States; one in 60,000 Finnish-born infants are affected (GHR, 2017f). Congenital lactase deficiency is linked to mutations in the *LCT* gene, which modulates lactase production. Recall that lactase is necessary for the digestion of lactose (see Chapter 10). Clinical manifestations present shortly after the establishment of enteral nutrition (breast or formula feeding) and include the onset of watery diarrhea with resultant poor linear growth; vomiting is reported among some affected infants.

Disorders With Familial Predisposition

Congenital Megacolon (Hirschsprung Disease). Hirschsprung disease is the most common cause for intestinal obstruction in newborns (GHR, 2017e). The incidence of this congenital aganglionosis is one in every 5,000 live births; prevalence among males (4:1) is reported (Bradshaw, 2015; GHR, 2017e). This disorder is commonly associated with trisomy 21 (GHR, 2017e). Mutations in the *RET*, *EDNRB*, or *EDN3* genes alter the normal development and signaling of enteric nerves (ganglia; Figure 6.14; Neu, 2012). The result is a deficiency in normal functioning of the enteric nerves as well as segments of bowel that lack enteric nerves (aganglionic segments), which prevents the normal evacuation of stool. The majority of affected infants (80% to 90%) present with abdominal distention, emesis, and failure to pass meconium within the first 48 hours of life.

Long-term outcomes are reassuring, as 90% of patients achieve normal or near-normal bowel function (Huang, Li, Zhang, & Zhang, 2017; Parry, 2015). Mortality and morbidity risks are associated with the length of bowel involvement and presence or absence of colonic atresia (Sloan & Wagener, 2016). Infants with microcolon or megacolon may incur lifelong bowel dysfunction, including constipation and fecal incontinence, as well as an increased risk for enterocolitis (Sloan & Wagener, 2016).

MATERNAL (AND PATERNAL) HEALTH INFLUENCES

Genetic makeup, the uterine environment, maternal chronic disease, and the external environment all impact the fetus during gestation and may program the baby for lifelong morbidities. The developing GI system may be

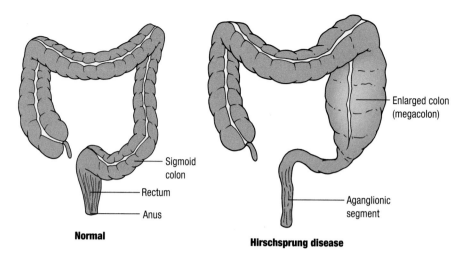

Figure 6.14 Normal intestine and manifestations of Hirschsprung disease. Hirschsprung disease results from failed migration of neural crest cells to the distal colon. As a result, submucosal and myenteric plexuses fail to develop, rendering the distal colon nonfunctional.

impacted directly or indirectly (Friedman & Baker, 2017; Schierding, Vickers, O'Sullivan, & Cutfield, 2017).

External Environmental Factors

Environmental factors with impact on the GI system include drugs, chemicals, radiation, and infections. Common drugs associated with IUGR and/or prematurity in the fetus are alcohol, aminopterin, cocaine, and phenytoin. Alcohol and tobacco smoke containing nicotine, carbon monoxide, and other substances enter the mother's blood and are transported to the placenta. From the placenta, those toxic substances enter the baby's bloodstream. These substances are associated with growth restriction. (Moore et al., 2016). Both women and men are exposed to reproductive toxins such as polychlorinated biphenyls and possible ionizing radiation. Paternal influence, modifications of sperm secondary to environmental exposures via epigenetic processes, is associated with GI defects such as EA and TEF (Day, Savani, Krempley, Nguyen, & Kitlinska, 2016). All of these factors are associated with premature birth, IUGR infants, and birth defects. These exposures increase the risk for prenatal and postnatal GI problems, including poor absorption of nutrients, necrotizing enterocolitis (NEC), faulty glucose regulation, and cholestasis secondary to altered liver metabolism (Friedman & Baker, 2017; Moore et al., 2016). The exact mechanism of environmental factors resulting in fetal disruption, prematurity, and IUGR infants is unknown; however, epigenetic processes are increasingly implicated (Day et al., 2016; Moore et al., 2016).

The Maternal–Fetal Microbiome

Microbes are present in the amniotic fluid, the placenta, and meconium (Neu, 2017). Although microbes in the

placenta are associated with postnatal infection, exposure does not always lead to morbidity. The pregnant mother, embryo, fetus, and neonate live with a number of commensal microbes; interactions between microbes and the host are often beneficial to the developing fetus (Neu, 2017; Tourneur & Chassin, 2013; Wu & Wu, 2012).

The fetal intestine is considered an immunoreactive organ. The interaction of microbes and fetal intestines may be part of early intestinal immune development; however, the mechanism is not understood and research is needed (Gritz & Bhandari, 2015; Wu & Wu, 2012). The microbes in meconium are representative of organisms contained in the amniotic fluid. However, there is limited data to explain how these microbes impact the developing intestine of the fetus and newborn. It is known, however, that a dysbiotic microbial environment may result in an intestine-initiated inflammatory response, which can precipitate premature labor and delivery or increase the risk for NEC (Gritz & Bhandari, 2015; Neu, 2017). Early population of the neonatal gut microbiome indicates exposure to the mother. However, the preterm infant has reduced microbial diversity and an increase in pathogenic organisms; thus, the fragile preterm is at risk for dysbiosis (Gritz & Bhandari, 2015).

Long-term implications focus on the fetal intestine's role in priming the intestinal immune responses that result in tolerance or exacerbation of immune responses. These interactions may be important to autoimmunity and allergic responses later in life. In addition, maternal intestinal microbes may produce metabolic products that are transferred to the fetus via the hematogenous route. Very-low-birth-weight infants have increased risk for obesity later in life, perhaps due to metabolic programing toward energy storage or altered nutrient utilization; more research is needed (Gritz & Bhandari, 2015; Neu, 2017; Wu & Wu, 2012). The oligosaccharides in human milk may enhance the intestinal microbiome of the newborn. Early studies indicate the oligosaccharides promote growth of certain taxa of bacteria and positively impact the infant's GI tract (Neu, 2017).

Maternal Bacterial and Viral Infections

The gut microbiota is a complex, unique, multifunction system that shapes the immune system of the baby. The development of this system begins during antenatal life and continues throughout the neonatal period. External factors, including breastfeeding, environment, delivery mode, and genetic factors, influence this process. Microbiota and microbes plus intestinal epithelial cells are responsible for the development of homeostasis in the neonate. This foundation may allow homeostasis maintenance during adult life. When the immune tolerance balance is upset, inflammatory disease and susceptibility to infections and sepsis may occur (Tourneur & Chassin, 2013; Wu & Wu, 2012).

Despite a protected environment, amniotic infection, chorioamnionitis, can occur with or without rupture of membranes. Microorganisms may enter the amniotic space by (a) ascending through the vagina; (b) accidental introduction during invasive procedures such as amniocentesis, chorionic villus sampling, fetal blood sampling, or transfusion; (c) maternal blood infection circulating through the placenta; or (d) maternal peritoneal cavity infection through the fallopian tubes (Romero, Chaemsaithong, Yeo, Docheva, & Chalyasit, 2017). The infection may be bacterial or viral, with *Ureaplasma urealyticum* and *Mycoplasma hominis* the most commonly cultured bacteria. Amniotic compartment infection, bacterial or viral, sets up an inflammatory response that may be acute or chronic. This inflammatory process is known as systemic fetal inflammatory response syndrome (FIRS), which can progress to multiple-organ failure and death. Preterm delivery is associated with FIRS with risks to the GI system including NEC, poor nutrient absorption, and late-onset sepsis (Romero et al., 2017).

Gut flora contributes to changes in the immune system and energy balance. Human microbe colonization accelerates at birth and is important in resistance to pathogen invasion, immune stimulation, and other developmental cues. Babies experiencing vaginal birth receive inoculation with vaginal and other urogenital microbes, including *Lactobacillus* and *Prevotella* types. Cesarean-section babies have intestinal colonization with epidermal species, including *Clostridium, Staphylococcus, Propinionbacterium*, and *Corynebacterium*. C-section babies also have fewer anaerobes such as *Baceroides* and *Bifidobacterium*. The exact impact on the newborn GI tract is unknown (Gritz & Bhandari, 2015; Neu, 2017). Meconium also has bacteria and Ardissone et al. (2014) found the species were the same as bacteria in the amniotic fluid. The influence of gut colonization may be the programming for adult disease, including autoimmune disorders, obesity, diabetes, cardiovascular disease, and hypertension (Aaguard et al., 2014; Romero et al., 2017; Wu & Wu, 2012). Shifts or dysbiosis in microbe composition can occur secondary to diet, antibiotics, or infection. The growth of pathogens may disrupt the inflammatory balance and lead to the development of NEC, a multifactorial condition (Gritz & Bhandari, 2015; Wu & Wu, 2012).

Gestational Diabetes Mellitus. Gestational diabetes mellitus (GDM) presents during pregnancy and usually disappears after birth; however, the mother remains at risk for type 2 diabetes. Placental overgrowth increases glucose transfer to the fetus with increased levels of GLUT1 protein. GDM increases the risk of premature delivery, hyperinsulinemia, and hypoglycemia in the newborn. Lifelong implications for the fetus include developing type 2 diabetes and obesity (Blickstein, Perlman, Hazan, Topf-Olivestone, & Shinwell, 2015; Simmons et al., 2017).

Maternal Diabetes Mellitus. Diabetes mellitus (DM) is a constellation of metabolic disorders with high blood glucose levels, either due to inadequate insulin sensitivity or insulin resistance. As in GDM, with DM there is increased glucose transfer with an increase in basal plasma membrane GUT1 levels (Simmons et al., 2017). The effect on maternal blood vessels may cause fetal growth restriction or macrosomia depending on the maternal DM disease (Blickstein et al., 2015). Maternal DM increases the risk of preterm birth and macrosomia with mild to severe hypoglycemia from elevated glucose levels in utero. GI disturbances include hypoglycemia, altered absorption, poor insulin regulation, and increased risk for NEC (Navathe, Gerli, Pacella, & Berghella, 2016). DM may also result in IUGR babies with altered cell proliferation in pancreatic beta-islet cells resulting in glucose intolerance. This metabolic change results in dyslipidemia, hepatic cholestasis, and hepatic dysfunction in the fetus and newborn. The consequences of the DM fetal environment include coronary disease, obesity, and diabetes type 2 as adults (Friedman & Baker, 2017).

Maternal Obesity. The Centers for Disease Control and Prevention (CDC) defines *overweight* as a body mass index (BMI) between 25 to 29.9 and obese as a BMI greater than 30 (CDC, 2017a). The impact of maternal obesity begins before conception as a chronic health condition with comorbidities (Arias & Viner-Brown, 2010; Navathe et al., 2016). The impact on the fetus is the increased risk for maternal preeclampsia. Owens et al. (2010) found that preeclampsia is nearly five times greater in obese pregnant women, frequently ending in preterm delivery; delivery at less than 33 weeks gestation occurs twice as often. Preterm delivery increases the risk of altered immunity, feeding intolerance, and NEC.

Gut morbidity increases with decreasing gestational age at birth (Owens et al., 2010; Williams, Mackenzie, & Gahagan, 2014). Initiation and duration of lactation are decreased in obese postpartum women; therefore, fewer infants benefit from the protections/enhancements of breastmilk (Amir & Donath, 2007; Gussler & Arensberg, 2011). Lifelong implications include the risk of obesity, diabetes mellitus, stroke, asthma, and heart disease in the baby. In addition, some evidence implies poorer cognitive function and neurodevelopmental disorders. Preliminary evidence supports a long-term negative impact on the immune and infectious-disease outcomes via epigenetic processes changing the gut microbiome (Friedman & Baker, 2017; Godfrey et al., 2017; Perdu et al., 2016).

Maternal Hypertension. There are currently four types of hypertension used in the care of pregnant women: gestational hypertension, preeclampsia, chronic hypertension, and preeclampsia superimposed on chronic hypertension. Preeclampsia accounts for approximately 12% to 25% of IUGR and small-for-gestational-age (SGA) infants and 15% to 20% of preterm babies. Premature, IUGR, and SGA status increase the risk for altered immune status, NEC, impaired absorption, and feeding intolerance. Lifelong implications include insulin resistance, hypertension, and cardiovascular disease (Jeyabalan, 2015).

In conclusion, any maternal chronic disease processes resulting in preterm birth, IUGR, or macrosomia have a negative impact on the newborn GI system. The impact correlates with gestational age and severity of the maternal disease and may program the fetus for adult disease.

COMMON PROBLEMS WITH IMPLICATIONS ACROSS THE LIFE SPAN

Disorders of the Foregut

Esophageal Atresia and Tracheoesophageal Fistula. EA and TEF occur as a consequence of failed septation of the foregut into separate esophageal and tracheal structures (see Chapter 4, Table 4.9). EA affects one in 4,300 births; approximately 90% of all cases are associated with TEF (CDC, 2017b). According to population studies (CDC, 2017b), increased risk of EA/TEF is associated with advanced paternal age (sperm abnormalities) and assisted reproductive technology (CDC, 2017b; Chia & Shi, 2002; Day et al., 2016). A history of polyhydramnios supports the inability of the fetus to swallow amniotic fluid in utero, and should increase the index of suspicion for EA/TEF (Bradshaw, 2015; Parry, 2015; Vanderhoof & Pauley-Hunter, 2016).

Although a complete understanding of genetic influences remains to be determined, the pathogenesis of some cases of EA and TEF is influenced by gene defects. Research demonstrates that teratogens induce alterations in the expression of genes involved with certain signaling pathways within the dorsal and ventral foregut. This disrupts normal septation of the foregut into the trachea (anteriorly) and the esophagus (posteriorly), between weeks 4 and 7 of gestation (Rayyan, Rommel, Tack, Deprest, & Allegaert, 2017).

An estimated 7% of infants with EA/TEF are affected by a chromosomal abnormality, commonly trisomy 13, 18, or 21 (CDC, 2017b). Other genetic associations include Pierre Robin, DiGeorge, Fanconi, and polysplenia syndrome, as well as VACTERL spectrum (**v**ertebral defects, **a**nal atresia, **c**ardiac defects, **t**racheoesophageal fistula, **r**enal anomalies, and **l**imb abnormalities) and CHARGE syndromes (**c**oloboma, **h**eart defects, cho**a**nal atresia, **r**etardation of growth/development, **g**enital/urinary defects, and **e**ar anomalies). Associated anatomic defects include DA, annular pancreas, jejunoileal atresia, malrotation, diaphragmatic hernia, and abdominal wall defects (Parry, 2015).

Clinical manifestations of EA/TEF are usually evident soon after birth, with the exception of type E (see Chapter 4). The affected infant may exhibit excessive oral secretions that occlude the airway, causing coughing and mild to severe respiratory distress. Radiographic studies display a feeding tube that stops or coils above the stomach. The gut will be gasless if no connection between the trachea and lower esophagus exists, as with types A and B. On the contrary, the stomach may be distended if a distal fistula connects the stomach to the trachea.

Life-span implications include esophageal strictures and gastroesophageal reflux (GER) with chronic esophageal inflammation. Esophageal dysmotility and dysphagia occur secondary to abnormal neural development, or from the EA repair. Approximately 10% to 20% of patients develop clinically significant tracheomalacia. Recurrent bronchitis, pneumonia, wheezing, and daily coughing are also reported (Cartabuke, Lopez, & Thota, 2016).

Infantile Hypertrophic Pyloric Stenosis. Infantile hypertrophic pyloric stenosis (IHPS) is the most common cause of gastric outlet obstruction in infants (Ross & Johnson, 2016). It occurs in about two to 3.5 births per 1,000 live births. The incidence is lowest in urban versus rural areas. IHPS is more common in males (4–5:1) and premature infants. The incidence is reported as 0.1% to 1% in the general population and varies by region (Ranells, Carver, & Kirby, 2011).

There is a convincing familial tendency; the risk for the sibling of a child diagnosed with IHPS increases 20-fold, or almost 200-fold for an identical twin (Feenstra et al., 2012). Although this condition does not fall under the category of Mendelian inheritance, genetic heterogeneity and multiple loci have been implicated in IHPS, including IHPS1 on chromosome 12, IHPS2 on chromosome 16, IHPS3 on chromosome 11, IHPS4 on chromosome X, and IHPS5 on chromosome 16 (OMIM, 2017e). Some reports indicate that 30% to 40% of cases occur among first-born children; additional data is needed to generalize these findings (Parry, 2015; Ranells et al., 2011).

The etiology of IHPS is unclear; however, immaturity of the ENS with aberrant innervation and altered levels of neuropeptides at the pylorus is one possibility (Ranells et al., 2011). Recall that the pylorus muscle is located where the stomach innervates with the intestine. The pathogenesis of IHPS involves overgrowth and tightening of the circumferential muscle around the pyloric channel. This leads to narrowing and elongation of the pylorus, a gastric outlet obstruction, and dilation and hyperperistalsis of the stomach (Moore et al., 2016; Ranells et al., 2011; Ross & Johnson, 2016).

IHPS characteristically manifests in otherwise healthy newborns, usually within the first 2 months of life (Parry, 2015). Classically, these infants present with persistent nonbilious vomiting, dehydration, weight loss, hypoglycemia, hyperbilirubinemia, and hypokalemic, hypochloremic metabolic alkalosis. IHPS may be diagnosed during palpation of the epigastric region; a small, mobile mass or "*palpable olive*," is identified and confers 97% selectivity (Parry, 2015; Vanderhoof & Pauley-Hunter, 2016). Ultrasound and/or upper GI contrast radiographs support the diagnosis. Fluid and electrolyte imbalance require urgent attention. Surgical correction is considered curative (Ross & Johnson, 2016).

Jejunoileal Atresia. Jejunoileal atresia is a rare condition that involves the absence of the fold of the stomach membrane that connects the small intestine to the dorsal abdominal wall. Classified as a rare disorder, only 57 cases have been reported in the literature (National Organization for Rare Disorders [NORD], 2007). The condition occurs equally in males and females. Cases are typically sporadic or follow an autosomal recessive inheritance pattern. Polyhydramnios, fetal distress, and drug exposure are known prenatal risk factors for this type of GI obstruction.

Jejunoileal atresia occurs due to a vascular accident in utero, likely between weeks 8 and 12 of gestation. Because the membrane connecting the small intestine to the abdominal wall is absent, the jejunum twists around the marginal artery of the colon, creating the atresia (NORD, 2007). The resultant loss of blood flow to that particular segment of bowel increases the risk for necrosis, volvulus, or strangulation (Moore et al., 2016). Jejunal and ileal stenosis, on the other hand, are thought to occur

from failed recanalization of the intestinal lumen. Failure of recanalization and vascular insults lead to necrosis and reabsorption of the affected segments (Bradshaw, 2015; Parry, 2015).

Jejunoileal atresia is classified based on primary anatomic derangement (Table 6.3; Parry, 2015). Clinical manifestations include bilious vomiting, varying degrees of dilated bowel proximal to the atretic area, and much smaller bowel loops downstream from the obstruction, as well as failure to pass meconium. On physical exam, the abdomen may be swollen in the epigastric region (NORD, 2007). A contrast enema usually shows microcolon, which occurs due to the lack of intestinal contents passing beyond the obstructed area. On abdominal radiography, jejunoileal atresia presents as a "*triple bubble*" of distended air-filled bowel loops (Parry, 2015).

Life-span implications include bowel leak at postsurgical anastomosis sites and sepsis in the short-term postoperative period. Extensive bowel involvement may lead to significant bowel resection and short gut syndrome, long-term parenteral nutrition, and anastomotic strictures (Nusinovich, Revenis, & Torres, 2013; Parry, 2015).

Duodenal Atresia. DA affects one in every 6,000 births within the United States. Half of affected infants are born prematurely (NORD, 2003). DA most often occurs sporadically; however, in some cases, it is inherited as an autosomal recessive trait. Approximately 30% of affected infants are diagnosed with trisomy 21 (NORD, 2003; Pritchard & Korf, 2016).

DA may be the result of intrinsic or extrinsic derangements. The pathogenesis of intrinsic DA involves failed duodenal recanalization. Extrinsic DA is associated with malrotation with Ladd's bands, annular pancreas, cysts, and duplications near the duodenum (Parry, 2015; Pritchard & Korf, 2016). Annular pancreas occurs when the pancreatic bud fails to rotate behind the duodenum, creating a ring around a segment of the duodenum.

Similar to other proximal GI obstructions, a history of polyhydramnios is suspicious for DA. Affected infants may present with abdominal distention (or nondistention), bilious emesis (or nonbilious emesis), and dilated proximal bowel. APNs should recognize that classic manifestations include abdominal distension paired with non-bilious vomiting. Radiographic findings include the classic "*double bubble*" appearance of the gas-filled stomach and the gas-filled proximal duodenum. The distal intestine is usually gasless. DA and malrotation with midgut volvulus may have similar clinical presentations. However, midgut volvulus is an intestinal emergency requiring prompt intervention. The point of obstruction, in relation to the ampulla of Vater (where the common bile duct innervates with the bowel), is important

TABLE 6.3 Five Classifications of Jejunoileal Atresia

Type	Common Clinical Manifestations	Visual Description
Type I	Mucosal (membranous) web	
Type II	Blind ends connected by a fibrous cord	
Type IIIa	Blind ends separated by a V-shaped mesenteric defect	
Type IIIb	Apple-peel or Christmas-tree deformity (blind ends; distal small bowel segment forms corkscrew around ileocecal artery terminus)	
Type IV	Multiple atresias (string of sausages)	

during repair of DA to protect the duct. Surgical correction is highly successful (GARD, 2009).

Life-span implications include delayed stomach emptying and GER, which occurs postsurgically. Late complications include peptic ulcer, esophagitis, duodenal–gastric reflux, pancreatitis, and cholecystitis. Blind-loop syndrome, an overgrowth of normal bacterial flora that impairs normal function, and megaduodenum, an elongation/dilatation of the duodenum impairing the movement of waste, have been reported (GARD, 2009).

Biliary Atresia. BA is the most common cause of obstructive jaundice in the newborn and the leading cause for liver transplantation among children (Lupo et al., 2017). The incidence is estimated at 0.5 to 0.8 per 10,000 births. African Americans have a twofold higher risk than Caucasians, and females more often than males.

BA is characterized by inflammation and obliteration of the extrahepatic or intrahepatic biliary system, which results in an obstruction of bile excretion from the gallbladder and bile duct into the small intestine (Lupo et al., 2017; Sanchez-Valle et al., 2017). The defect is typically an isolated finding; approximately 15% to 30% of cases occur in patients with situs inversus, polysplenia, asplenia, or other congenital anomalies.

The classification of extrahepatic BA is based on the site of the atresia (Table 6.4; Lupo et al., 2017). The fetal type presents within the first 2 weeks of life, and the postnatal type presents between the first and second month of life. Common clinical manifestations include hyperbilirubinemia, dark urine, and acholic stools. Jaundice may progress to conjugated or direct hyperbilirubinemia; unconjugated hyperbilirubinemia is rarely present after 2 weeks. Hepatosplenomegaly may develop, and an enlarging spleen may be a sign of cirrhosis and portal hypertension. Treatment by 2 months improves the outcome (Sanchez-Valle et al., 2017).

Life-span implications depend on the type of BA, comorbidities, and early treatment. Portal hypertension develops in 60% of patients, whereas cholangitis manifests in 50% of patients post portoenterostomy. Fibrosis and secondary biliary cirrhosis results if the disorder is not surgically corrected (Sanchez-Valle et al., 2017). For patients who develop cirrhosis, hepatocellular cancer is a risk. Liver transplantation is a treatment for long-term survival (Sanchez-Valle et al., 2017).

Disorders of the Midgut

Umbilical Hernia. Umbilical hernia is a central fascial defect underneath the umbilicus that is caused by failed closure of the umbilical ring. It affects 4% of Caucasian infants and 30% of African American infants. Umbilical hernia is more common in premature and low-birth-weight neonates and newborns with congenital thyroid hormone deficiencies and trisomy 21. There is high familial tendency (Gleason & Juul, 2018; K. B. Kelly & Ponsky, 2013).

An umbilical hernia typically forms during week 10 of gestation, when the intestines return to the abdominal cavity and abnormally herniate through the umbilical ring (Moore et al., 2016). The herniated tissue includes the greater omentum, a portion of the small intestine, and is covered by subcutaneous tissue and skin. Umbilical hernias average between 1 and 5 cm in diameter, and can increase in size during crying, straining, or coughing. Typically, they can be easily reduced into the abdomen or preperitoneal fat (Moore et al., 2016).

The risk of incarceration is low, and most umbilical hernias close spontaneously. Surgical correction is only required with large defects, or when a hernia persists in a child over 4 years of age (Gleason & Juul, 2018;

TABLE 6.4 Three Classifications of Biliary Atresia

Type	Incidence	Common Clinical Manifestations	Visual Description
Type I	5%	Obliteration of the common duct; the proximal ducts are patent	liver, CHD, CBD, GB, Bowel
Type II	3%	Atresia of the hepatic duct, with cystic structures found in the porta hepatis	liver, CHD, CBD, GB, Bowel
Type III (>90%)	90%	Atresia of the right and left hepatic ducts to the level of the porta hepatis	liver, CHD, CBD, GB, Bowel

CBD, common bile duct; CHD, common hepatic duct; GB, gallbladder.

NOTE: The dark green shading present within each respective drawing corresponds with the locus of the atresia.

MacDonald & Seshia, 2016). The recurrence risk is low (Bendavid, Abrahamson, Arregui, Flament, & Phillips, 2001; MacDonald & Seshia, 2016).

Omphalocele. Omphalocele is a central herniation of abdominal contents, covered by an amnion membrane, peritoneum, and Wharton's jelly; the umbilical cord connects to the central portion of the membrane (Parry, 2015; Vanderhoof & Pauley-Hunter, 2016). Omphalocele occurs in one in every 5,300 live births in the United States, and is highly associated with other defects, including anomalies of the CNS, cardiovascular, GI, and genitourinary systems. In fact, 50% to 75% of infants with omphalocele have other structural or genetic anomalies, including trisomy 13, trisomy 18, and trisomy 21; VACTERL association; Beckwith-Wiedemann syndrome; ectrodactyly–ectodermal dysplasia–cleft (EEC) syndrome (ectodermal dysplasia, ectrodactyly, cleft palate); and OEIS (omphalocele, exstrophy, imperforate anus, spinal defects). In rare instances, the defect is more cephalic, causing pentalogy of Cantrell: diaphragmatic hernia, sternal cleft, omphalocele, exstrophy of the heart, and intracardiac defects (Jnah, Newberry, & England, 2015). When the defect occurs below the umbilicus, bladder or cloacal exstrophy result (Parry, 2015).

The defect occurs secondary to failed closure of the umbilical ring between weeks 3 to 5 of gestation (Bradshaw, 2015; Watanabe et al., 2017). The underlying cause remains unknown, although genetic and teratogenic influences likely play a role. Population studies indicate that maternal alcohol, tobacco, or selective serotonin-reuptake inhibitor (SSRI) use during pregnancy, as well as obesity, increase the risk for fetal omphalocele development (CDC, 2015). Life-span implications are highly dependent on the presence of comorbidities (Parry, 2015; Watanabe et al., 2017).

Gastroschisis. This defect involves a congenital herniation of abdominal contents through an opening, lateral and to the right of the intact umbilical cord (Parry, 2015). Varying amounts of small and large bowel, which may be edematous and thickened, and rarely the liver, are eviscerated through a small (2–4 cm) abdominal wall defect with no protective covering (Bradshaw, 2015).

The incidence of gastroschisis is increasing, now estimated at 4.9 per 10,000 live births (Jones et al., 2016). Risk factors include low socioeconomic status, young maternal age, and exposure to vasoconstriction as with some decongestants, nonsteroidal anti-inflammatory medications, cocaine, methamphetamine, and marijuana (Souther, Puapong, Woo, & Johnson, 2017). Gastroschisis may arise secondary to failure of the normal attachment between the umbilical cord and the umbilical ring, infarction of the abdominal wall, and failure of mesenchymal migration during early development (Mahe et al., 2017).

Neonates with gastroschisis may present with signs of dehydration and gastric dilatation at birth, as well as varying degrees of edema, matting, and ischemia of the exposed bowel. Between 5% to 20% of affected infants have associated defects, including intestinal atresia or mechanical injury to the eviscerated bowel. These complications may affect long-term morbidity. Dysmotility, adhesions, or strictures at points of resection put the neonate at risk for partial or complete obstruction later in life (Parry, 2015).

Malrotation. Malrotation is an abnormal position of the small bowel within the abdomen. It affects one in every 500 live births, and most cases are subtle and subclinical. Symptomatic malrotation occurs in one in every 6,000 live births; a male prevalence is reported (Appaji, Kulkami, & Kadaba, 2013; Coste & Bhimji, 2017; Martin & Shaw-Smith, 2010). Risk factors include imperforate anus, Marfan syndrome, cardiac anomalies, intestinal atresias, trisomy 13, 18, and 21, as well as Meckel's diverticulum and other congenital anomalies. It is estimated that 75% of all cases occur in newborns and young infants; 90% of symptomatic cases are diagnosed within the first year (Martin & Shaw-Smith, 2010).

Recall that between weeks 4 and 6 of gestation, the midgut portion of the intestine undergoes normal rotation. During this time, the intestine rapidly proliferates and quickly exceeds the constraints of the abdominal cavity. As such, a portion of the intestine herniates into the umbilical cord. A 270-degree counterclockwise intestinal rotation thereby occurs around the superior mesenteric artery. When the bowel rotates correctly, it fixes itself in the abdomen, eliminating the risk for twisting and obstruction. However, if the bowel does not rotate and properly fix itself, a malrotation occurs, which increases the risk for vascular compromise, or volvulus (Figure 6.15; Bradshaw, 2015; Coste & Bhimji, 2017). Genetic mutations likely disrupt the signaling critical for normal intestinal rotation; however, this is poorly understood (Coste & Bhimji, 2017).

Midgut Volvulus. Midgut volvulus is an intestinal emergency. Intestinal twisting causes a blockage of blood flow to a segment of bowel, leading to occlusion and necrosis (Parry, 2015; Vanderhoof & Pauley-Hunter, 2016). A volvulus can occur at any age and may also be identified on prenatal ultrasound; however, the defect is more frequently observed among infants and children (Coste & Bhimji, 2017).

A wide range of clinical manifestations are reported among infants and include hemodynamic instability, shock, acute abdominal pain, and bilious emesis. Bilious emesis should increase the index of suspicion for intestinal malrotation with possible volvulus; prompt evaluation is indicated. A radiograph may be significant for a section of dilated bowel with no distal air beyond the obstruction.

Mortality and morbidity are dependent upon the timing of the diagnosis; a higher mortality risk is associated

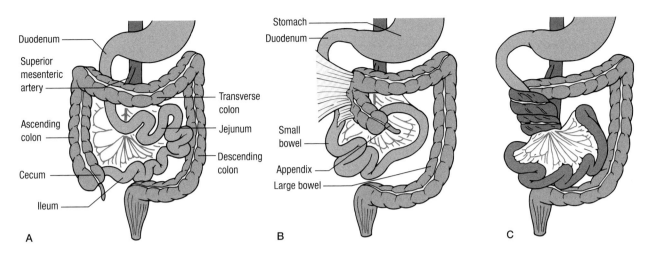

Figure 6.15 Intestinal malrotation and volvulus: (A) Normal positioning of the small and large intestine. (B) Impaired twisting (malrotation) of the midgut around its mesentery, as it returns into the abdominal cavity. Abnormal fixation of the cecum to the right abdominal wall, with obstruction of the duodenum by Ladd bands (bands of peritoneum) occurs. (C) Wrapping of bowel around the superior mesenteric artery causing ischemia (volvulus).

with bowel necrosis. Associated congenital anomalies significantly impact the outcome. If surgery is required, the postoperative course influences the outcome. Intermittent bilious emesis, adhesions, and short gut syndrome are possible lifelong consequences (Coste & Bhimji, 2017).

Gastrointestinal Duplications. GI duplications are rare congenital anomalies characterized by a coating of smooth muscle and epithelial lining that represents some portion of the alimentary tract. The duplication usually requires surgical intervention (Parry, 2015). The etiology is unknown. When present, duplications commonly occur at the ileum, esophagus, or colon, and can be cystic or tubular (Liu & Adler, 2014). Clinical manifestations vary, and presenting symptoms depend on the site of the duplication. Four pathologic criteria are necessary to establish the diagnosis: (a) contiguity with the stomach, (b) an outer smooth muscle layer, (c) a shared blood supply with the stomach, and (d) a gastric epithelial lining (Parry, 2015; Vanderhoof & Pauley-Hunter, 2016).

Surgery is generally curative and likewise carries a good prognosis. However, perforation and peritonitis may occur. Pancreatitis, neoplastic changes, rectal bleeding, and stool incontinence are potential complications of surgery (Rattan, Bansal, & Dhamija, 2017).

Disorders of the Hindgut

Anorectal Malformations. Anorectal malformations (ARMs) comprise a group of conditions that affect the lower intestinal tract and urogenital systems. The incidence is approximately one in every 5,000 births; a slightly higher male predominance is reported (Sloan & Wagener, 2016). Seventy percent of cases are associated with other defects, including abnormal or missing

vertebrae or a tethered cord, as well as cardiac defects and EA, VACTERL, trisomy 21, Currarino syndrome, or cat eye syndrome (Sloan & Wagener, 2016).

The spectrum of ARMs includes a mildly stenotic anus, imperforate anus with genitourinary fistula, and congenital cloaca. Imperforate anus with genitourinary fistula is the most common anorectal defect, known to affect approximately 80% of males (Sloan & Wagener, 2016). Rarely, ARMs are devoid of a fistula and the rectum ends in a blind pouch within the pelvis. Affected females may present with a perineal fistula at the skin level, vestibular or posterior vaginal fistula, or a more complex malformation where the urethra, vagina, and rectum have a common opening onto the perineum, known as a *congenital cloaca* (Pena, 2000).

The pathogenesis of ARMs is poorly understood (Sloan & Wegener, 2016). It is believed that ARMs result from arrested development of the urorectal septum, which normally divides the cloacal cavity into the anterior urogenital sinus and the posterior rectum; this normally occurs between weeks 4 and 8 of gestation. The precise etiology for this developmental arrest is not clear. One theory cites differences in the homeobox and SHH signaling pathways (see the section "Developmental Physiology"; Sloan & Wagener, 2016).

Infants with anorectal defects should be identified during the initial newborn physical examination. Infants who are affected, yet undiagnosed, may present with signs of bowel obstruction if a fistula is absent or too small to allow passage of stool (Sloan & Wagener, 2016). Comorbidities include urosepsis and metabolic acidosis, necessitating monitoring of all involved organs (Pena, 2000). Life-span implications include constipation, incontinence, poor bowel and bladder control, as well as the psychosocial concerns that accompany these issues (Pena, 2000; Sloan & Wagener, 2016).

Other Disorders of the GI System

Necrotizing Enterocolitis. NEC is the most common acquired GI disease and GI surgical emergency in neonates, and carries significant mortality and morbidity risks (Dominguez & Moss, 2012). The foremost risk factor is prematurity. In fact, 85% of all cases of NEC affect infants born at less than 32 weeks or less than 1,500 grams (Markel, Englestad, & Poindexter, 2014). Prenatal risk factors include maternal smoking, placental blood flow abnormalities, intrauterine growth retardation, and neural tube defects. Postnatal risk factors, specific to infants born prematurely, include incomplete gut colonization, formula feeding, congenital heart defects (most notable is patent ductus arteriosus), polycythemia, red blood cell transfusion, and repeated nosocomial infections/antibiotic exposure (Markel et al., 2014). Thirty percent of all affected infants manifest a mild form of NEC that does not require aggressive treatment; however, 40% of infants require treatment, which may include surgical drain placement or bowel resection, and 30% of infants develop NEC totalis. Among surviving infants, postoperative risks include intestinal stricture and infection (Caplan, 2015).

The etiology and pathogenesis of NEC is multifactorial (Markel et al., 2014). Exposure to hypoxic states or infection, two common risk factors associated with prematurity, increase the susceptibility of the gut epithelium to injury. Both ischemia and inflammation, secondary to hypoxia and infection, weaken the bowel. Normally, injury to the intestinal epithelium provokes the synthesis and secretion of enterocytes, cells which seek to heal damaged tissue. However, decreased enterocyte synthesis is observed with NEC, which perpetuates the injured state and increases the risk for bacterial invasion as well as perforation of the intestinal wall.

Dysregulated innate immune responses are thought to exacerbate, rather than mitigate, injury to the intestinal mucosa. Toll-like receptors (TLR) hold a dual role during fetal development and postnatal life. Although there are numerous types of TLR, organized numerically, we will focus on the relationship between TLR4 and NEC. During fetal development, increased concentrations of TLR4 encourage the formation and migration of enterocytes, which forms the intestinal epithelium. TLR4 also maintains the sterility of the intestinal tract during fetal development; high concentrations resist bacterial aggregation. Among term infants, TLR4 levels drop after birth, which permits the establishment of the gut microflora. Thereafter, TLR4 concentrations fluctuate, as needed, to maintain homeostasis between microbial load (lower TLR4 concentrations) and the immune response (higher TLR4 concentrations). In comparison, TLR4 levels remain elevated among preterm infants, which alters postnatal gut maturation and colonization, as well as exacerbates the immune response. Among premature infants affected by NEC, markedly elevated concentrations of TLR4 lead to apoptosis of existing enterocytes and reduce the synthesis of new enterocytes, which would normally be recruited during the healing process (Egan et al., 2016; Sodhi et al., 2012).

In addition, recent research suggests that alterations in intestinal colonization, by way of microbial imbalance, encourage inflammation, increased TLR4 concentrations, and degradation of the intestinal epithelium (Caplan, 2015; Markel et al., 2014). When present, intestinal ischemia and inflammation weaken the bowel and increase its propensity for perforation. Perforation, which may be localized or diffuse, leads to leakage of GI contents into the peritoneal cavity and subsequent peritonitis (Caplan, 2015). Radiographic findings include the presence of air in the bowel wall, which may track across the liver (portal venous gas).

Clinical manifestations include abdominal distention and any combination of the following: hematochezia, emesis, increased gastric residuals, lethargy, apnea, bradycardia, tachycardia, neutropenia, thrombocytopenia, metabolic acidosis, abdominal tenderness/erythema, respiratory failure, and shock (Neu & Walker, 2011). The diagnosis is confirmed in the presence of pneumatosis intestinalis with dissection of bacterial toxins into the bowel wall and/or portal venous gas on radiograph (Caplan, 2015; Vanderhoof & Pauley-Hunter, 2016).

Disease severity is graded by modified Bell staging, which is summarized in Table 6.5. Kliegman and Walsh (1987) modified the original Bell staging to aid clinicians in differentiating between mild and more severe disease states. Laboratory findings are included with staging criteria to alert clinicians of correlations among acidosis, thrombocytopenia, neutropenia, disseminated intravascular coagulation, and disease severity. Life-span implications for surgically treated infants include short gut syndrome, a condition with implications for poor nutrient absorption leading to failure to thrive, and long-term parental nutrition, increased risks of infection, and liver injury. In addition, hearing and visual impairments, as well as recurrent infections, are reported among affected infants (Arnold, Moore, Sidler, & Kirsten, 2010).

Meckel's Diverticulum. Meckel's diverticulum, the most common congenital malformation of the GI tract, is characterized by an outpouching of the small intestine (ileum) caused by persistence of the omphalomesenteric (vitelline) duct. Approximately 2% to 4% of individuals are affected by Meckel's diverticulum (Sagar, Kumar, & Shah, 2006). Failed regression of the omphalomesenteric duct, which normally occurs by week 7 of gestation, leads to the formation of a fibrous band that connects the (ileal) diverticulum to the umbilicus, as well as a cyst or a fistula that opens to the anterior abdomen. Although rare, Meckel's diverticulum may become clinically significant during the neonatal period or infancy. Manifestations include GI bleeding, intestinal obstruction, intussusception, volvulus, bands, internal hernias, or Littre's hernia. Typically, the diverticulum is devoid of clinical significance, and among individuals who require treatment, no long-term complications are reported (Obasi, Ekenze, & Ogbobe, 2015).

Meconium Plug. The meconium plug is a thick tubular accumulation of meconium at the level of the colon. The epidemiology is rather illusive; Keckler et al. (2008) identified 77 newborns with meconium plug; 68% were males and 38% were females. Risk factors include prematurity, infants of diabetic mothers, hypermagnesemia, and hypoglycemia (Parry, 2015). Meconium plug

is not considered a genetic disorder. The pathogenesis involves a functional immaturity of the colon and small intestine (hypomotility). As a result, the large colon may become dilated as meconium accumulates, becomes thick, and forms a plug (Figure 6.16; Parry, 2015).

Clinical manifestations include delayed passage of meconium beyond the first 48 hours of life and abdominal distention. The plug may be difficult to pass and neonates may pass one or more meconium plugs. Life-span implications are related to associated conditions; cystic

TABLE 6.5. Modified Bell Staging

Stage	Classification	Common Clinical Findings	Common Radiographic Findings
I	Suspected NEC	• Abdominal distention • Apnea • Bloody stools • Bradycardia • Emesis/gastric residuals • Lethargy • Temperature instability	 Ileus, gastric dilatation, asymmetric bowel loops
II	Proven NEC	Clinical findings from stage 1 *plus*: • Abdominal tenderness • Peritonitis • Possible metabolic acidosis • Possible cellulitis • Right lower quadrant mass • Thrombocytopenia	 Pneumatosis intestinalis (white arrow) with portal venous gas (black arrow)
III	Advanced NEC	Clinical findings from stages 1 and 2 *plus*: • Acidosis (combined respiratory and metabolic) • Abdominal tenderness and distension (severe) • Apnea (severe) • DIC • Hypotension • Neutropenia • Thrombocytopenia	 Pneumoperitoneum with free intraperitoneal air, ascites

DIC, disseminated intravascular coagulation; NEC, necrotizing enterocolitis.

Sources: Dominguez, K. M., & Moss, R. L. (2012). Necrotizing enterocolitis. *Clinics in Perinatology, 39*(2), 387–401. doi:10.1016/j.clp.2012.04.011; Esposito, F., Mamone, R., Di Serafino, M., Mercogliano, C., Vitale, V., Vallone, G., & Oresta, P. (2017). Diagnostic imaging features of necrotizing enterocolitis: A narrative review. *Quantitative Imaging in Medicine and Surgery, 7*(3), 336–344. doi:10.21037/qims.2017.03.01

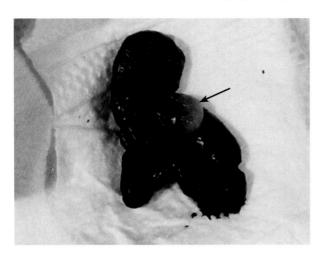

Figure 6.16 Infant with evidence of one meconium plug (arrow).

fibrosis and Hirschsprung disease are both positively associated with meconium plug and warrant further investigation (Parry, 2015).

Meconium Ileus. Meconium ileus is an obstruction of the terminal ileum by tenacious, thick meconium, and accounts for about 33% of all small bowel obstructions in neonates. The obstruction occurs at the terminal ileum and the bowel distal to the obstruction may be empty and small, to the level of microcolon; the reduced size of the colon is secondary to disuse.

Similar to meconium plug, 10% to 20% of cases of meconium ileus are associated with CF. Clinical manifestations include abdominal distention, palpable bowel loops, poor feeding, and bilious emesis. If left untreated, meconium ileus may progress to volvulus, necrosis, peritonitis, and perforation. Life-span implications are dependent on the etiology and associated complications. If CF is present, lifelong treatment is required (Parry, 2015; Vanderhoof & Pauley-Hunter, 2016).

CONCLUSION

The development, physiology, and functioning of the GI system are complex and the transition from fetus to newborn has lifelong implications. The primary GI functions of absorption of nutrients, fluid and electrolyte maintenance, protection from invaders, and waste elimination are essential to health. Careful attention to GI function is vital to the well-being of the newborn.

LEARNING TOOLS AND RESOURCES

Podcasts

 Intestinal Immunity

Rani Delaney, Lauren Fraser, Mary Ellen Lane, and Melissa Bauserman

Discussion Prompts

1. How/why is the fetal gut considered an immunoreactive agent?
2. Discuss major components of the digestive process (mechanical, secretory, absorption) and how this implicates the premature infant.
3. Discuss the role of epigenetics in GI development and function.

Advice From the Authors

"Aristotle said, 'The roots of education are bitter, but the fruit is sweet.' Pursue your desired degree with patience and passion, set up achievable goals, and prize yourself for the hard work and achievements you have made."

–Aksana Waskosky, DNP, APRN, NNP-BC

"Please engage, listen, and commit to being the very best NNP you can be. Maximize your strengths and focus on the strengths in your colleagues. As a novice, choose the very best role model you can find—you will jump start your career."

–Lisa Schepper, MSN, APRN, NNP-BC

"Use of flashcards and practice questions is a great way to learn material. Reading up on the disease processes or clinical questions that come up during your clinical rotations will help you remember the material better. The more extra pieces you have tied to the information, the longer you will remember it."

–Rebecca Rose, MD, MS

"Seek knowledge and couple it with wisdom. Take 10 minutes three times each week to read on a topic of neonatology—you will remain current. Treat everyone with respect and be kind. Use these three rules for communication: Is it true? Is it kind? Is it necessary? Finish each day with the knowledge that you made a difference in a baby's life—be amazed with the wonder of our work."

–Linda Strickland, DNP, APRN, NNP-BC

Mind Maps

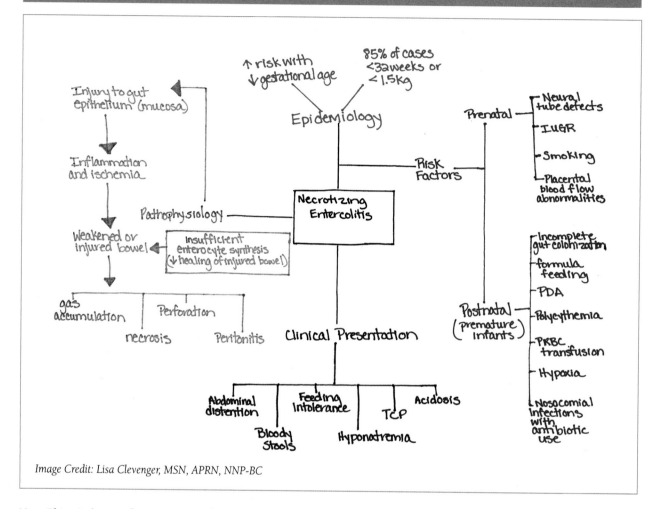

Image Credit: Lisa Clevenger, MSN, APRN, NNP-BC

Note: This mind map reflects one neonatal APN's interpretation of a portion of one or more concepts addressed in this chapter. Readers should regard the mind maps woven throughout this textbook as examples of multi-sensory study tools that can be developed to encourage conceptual understanding. Readers are encouraged to develop their own unique mind maps in consultation with academic faculty or clinical preceptors.

TIMELINE OF ORGAN DEVELOPMENT

NOTE:	LEGEND
Placement of common problems is meant to offer visual/conceptual perspective on the timing of onset of these commonly reported malformations. Variation exists across the literature.	<22 – 27 6/7 weeks = extremely preterm 28 – 31 6/7 weeks = very preterm 32 – 36 6/7 weeks = late/moderate preterm 37 – 40 weeks = term

References

Aaguard, K., Ma, J., Antony, K. M., Ganu, R., Petrosino, J., & Versalovic, J. (2014). The placenta harbors a unique microbiome. *Science Translational Medicine, 6*, 237ra65. doi:10.1126/scitranslmed.3008599

Amir, L. H., & Donath, S. (2007). A systematic review of maternal obesity and breastfeeding intention, initiation, and duration. *BMC Pregnancy and Childbirth 2007, 7*, 9. doi:10.1186/1471-2393-7-9

Appaji, A. C., Kulkami, R., & Kadaba, J. S. (2013). Nonrotation of intestine: A case report. *Journal of Diagnostic Research, 7*(11), 2575–2576. doi:10.7860/JCDR/2013/6177.3616

Ardissone, A. N., de la Cruz, D. M., Davis-Richardson, A. G., Rechcigl, K. T., Li, N., Drew, J. C., … Neu, J. (2014). Meconium microbiome analysis identifies bacteria correlated with premature birth. *PLoS One, 26*, 141–147. doi:10.1371/journal.pone.0090784

Arias, W., & Viner-Brown, S. (2010). Prepregnancy obesity and birth defects in Rhode Island. *Medicine and Health, Rhode Island, 93*(10), 325–326. Retrieved from http://www.rimed.org/medhealthri/2010-10/2010-10-325.pdf

Arnold, M., Moore, S. W., Sidler, D., & Kirsten, G. F. (2010). Long-term outcome of surgically managed necrotizing enterocolitis in a developing country. *Pediatric Surgery International, 26*(4), 355–360. doi:10.1007/s00383-010-2583-8

Avetisyan, M., Schill, E. M., & Heuckeroth, R. O. (2015). Building a second brain in the bowel. *Journal of Clinical Investigation, 125*(3), 899–907. doi:10.1172/JCI76307

Batts, L. E., Polk, D. B., Dubois, R. N., & Kulessa, H. (2006). BMP signaling is required for intestinal growth and morphogenesis. *Developmental Dynamics, 235*(6), 1563–1570. doi:10.1002/dvdy.20741

Bendavid, R., Abrahamson, J., Arregui, M. E., Flament, J. B., & Phillips, E. H. (Eds.). (2001). *Abdominal wall hernias: Principles and management*. New York, NY: Springer Science.

Blickstein, I., Perlman, S., Hazan, Y., Topf-Olivestone, C., & Shinwell, E. S. (2015). Diabetes mellitus during pregnancy. In R. J. Martin, A. A. Fanaroff, & M. C. Walsh, *Fanaroff & Martin's neonatal-perinatal medicine* (10th ed., pp. 265–270). Philadelphia, PA: Elsevier.

Bradshaw, W. T. (2015). Gastrointestinal disorders. In M. Verklan & M. Walden (Eds.), *Core curriculum for neonatal intensive care nursing* (5th ed., pp. 270–275). St. Louis, MO: Saunders.

Broussard, D. L., & Altschuler, S. M. (2017). Development of the enteric nervous system. In R. A. Polin, S. H. Abman, D. H. Rowitch, W. E. Benitz, & W. W. Fox (Eds.), *Fetal and neonatal physiology* (5th ed., Vols. 1 & 2, pp. 870–876). Philadelphia, PA: Elsevier.

Caplan, M. (2015). Neonatal necrotizing enterocolitis. In R. J. Martin, A. A. Fanaroff, & M. C. Walsh (Eds.), *Fanaroff & Martin's neonatal-perinatal medicine* (10th ed. pp. 1423–1432). Philadelphia, PA: Elsevier.

Cartabuke, R. H., Lopez, R., & Thota, P. N. (2016). Long-term esophageal and respiratory outcomes in children with esophageal atresia and tracheoesophageal fistula. *Gastroenterology Report, 4*(4), 310–314. doi:10.1093/gastro/gov055

Centers for Disease Control and Prevention. (2015). Facts about omphalocele. Retrieved from https://www.cdc.gov/ncbddd/birthdefects/omphalocele.html

Centers for Disease Control and Prevention. (2017a). Chronic disease prevention and health promotion: Maternal health. Retrieved from https://www.cdc.gov/chronicdisease/resources/publications/aag/maternal.htm

Centers for Disease Control and Prevention. (2017b). Facts about esophageal atresia. Retrieved from https://www.cdc.gov/ncbddd/birthdefects/esophagealatresia.html

Chia, S. E., & Shi, L. M. (2002). Review of recent epidemiological studies on paternal occupations and birth defects. *Occupational Environmental Medicine, 59*(3), 149–155. doi:10.1136/oem.59.3.149

Chin, A. M., Hill, D. R., Aurora, M., & Spence, J. (2017). Morphogenesis and maturation of the embryonic and postnatal intestine. *Seminars in Cell & Developmental Biology, 66*, 81–93. doi:10.1016/j.semcdb.2017.01.011

Coste, A. H., & Bhimji, S. S. (2017). *Midgut volvulus*. Treasure Island, FL: StatPearls Publishing. Retrieved from https://www.ncbi.nlm.nih.gov/books/NBK441962/

Day, J., Savani, S., Krempley, B. D., Nguyen, M., & Kitlinska, J. B. (2016). Influence of paternal preconception exposures on their offspring: Through epigenetics to phenotype. *American Journal of Stem Cells, 5*(1), 11–18. Retrieved from http://ajsc.us/files/ajsc0030217.pdf

de Santa Barbara, P., van den Brink, G. R., & Roberts, D. J. (2003). Development and differentiation of the intestinal epithelium. *Cellular and Molecular Life Sciences, 60*(7), 1322–1332. doi:10.1007/s00018-003-2289-3

Dominguez, K. M., & Moss, R. L. (2012). Necrotizing enterocolitis. *Clinics in Perinatology, 39*(2), 387–401. doi:10.1016/j.clp.2012.04.011

Egan, C. E., Sodhi, C. P., Good, M., Lin, J., Jia, H., Yamaguchi, Y., … Hackam, D. J. (2016). Toll-like receptor 4-mediated lymphocyte influx induces neonatal necrotizing enterocolitis. *Journal of Clinical Investigation, 126*(2), 495. doi:10.1172/JCI83356

Esposito, F., Mamone, R., Di Serafino, M., Mercogliano, C., Vitale, V., Vallone, G., & Oresta, P. (2017). Diagnostic imaging features of necrotizing enterocolitis: A narrative review. *Quantitative Imaging in Medicine and Surgery, 7*(3), 336–344. doi:10.21037/qims.2017.03.01

Faure, S., & de Santa Barbara, P. (2011). Molecular embryology of the foregut. *Journal of Pediatric Gastroenterology and Nutrition, 52*(Suppl. 1), S2–S3. doi:10.1097/MPG.0b013e3182105a1a

Feenstra, B., Geller, F., Krogh, C., Hollegaard, M. V., Gortz, S., Boyd, H. A., … Melbye, M. (2012). Common variants near MBNL1 and NKX2-5 are associated with infantile hypertrophic pyloric stenosis. *Nature Genetics, 44*, 224–337. doi:10.1038/ng.1067

Friedman, J., & Baker, P. R. (2017). Fetal origins of adult disease: A classic hypothesis with new relevance. In R. A. Polin, S. H. Abman, D. H. Rowitch, W. E. Benitz, & W. W. Fox (Eds.), *Fetal and neonatal physiology* (5th ed., Vols. 1 & 2, pp. 160–166). Philadelphia, PA: Elsevier.

Genetic and Rare Diseases Information Center. (2009). Duodenal atresia. Retrieved from https://rarediseases.info.nih.gov/diseases/54/duodenal-atresia

Genetic and Rare Diseases Information Center. (2018). Congenital chloride diarrhea. Retrieved from https://rarediseases.info.nih.gov/diseases/10001/congenital-chloride-diarrhea

Genetic and Rare Diseases Information Center. (2017). Hirschsprung's disease. Retrieved from https://rarediseases.info.nih.gov/diseases/6660/hirschsprungs-disease

Genetic Home Reference. (2017a). Alagille syndrome. Retrieved from https://ghr.nlm.nih.gov/condition/alagille-syndrome#inheritance

Genetic Home Reference. (2017b). Cystic fibrosis. Retrieved from https://ghr.nlm.nih.gov/condition/cystic-fibrosis

Genetic Home Reference. (2017c). Familial adenomatous polyposis. Retrieved from https://ghr.nlm.nih.gov/condition/familial-adenomatous-polyposis#genes

Genetic Home Reference. (2017d). Glucose–galactose malabsorption. Retrieved from https://ghr.nlm.nih.gov/condition/glucose-galactose-malabsorption

Genetic Home Reference (2017e). Hirschsprung disease. Retrieved from https://ghr.nlm.nih.gov/condition/hirschsprung-disease

Genetic Home Reference. (2017f). Lactose intolerance. Retrieved from https://ghr.nlm.nih.gov/condition/lactose-intolerance#genes

Genetic Home Reference. (2017g). Permanent neonatal diabetes. Retrieved from https://ghr.nlm.nih.gov/condition/permanent-neonatal-diabetes-mellitus

Genetic Home Reference. (2017h). Shwachman–Diamond syndrome. Retrieved from https://ghr.nlm.nih.gov/condition/shwachman-diamond-syndrome#diagnosis

Gleason, C. A., & Juul, S. E. (2018). *Avery's diseases of the newborn* (10th ed.). Philadelphia, PA: Elsevier.

Godfrey, K. M., Reynolds, R. M., Prescott, S. L., Nyirenda, M., Jaddoe, V. W., Eriksson, J. G., & Broekman, B. F. (2017). Influence of maternal obesity on the long-term health of offspring. *Lancet Diabetes Endocrinology*, 5(1), 53-64. doi:10.1016/S2213-8587(16)3017-3

Gritz, E. C., & Bhandari, V. (2015). The human neonatal gut microbiome: A brief review. *Frontiers in Pediatrics*, 3, 1-12. doi:10.3389/fped.2015.00017

Gussler, J., & Arensberg, M. B. (2011). Impact of maternal obesity on pregnancy and lactation: The health care challenge. *Nutrition Today*, 46(1), 6-11. doi:10.1097/NT.0b013e3181c988ea

Huang, W., Li, X., Zhang, J., & Zhang, S. (2017). Prevalence, risk factors, and prognosis of postoperative complications after surgery for Hirschsprung disease. *Journal of Gastrointestinal Surgery*, 22(2), 335–343. doi:10.1007/s11605-017-3596-6

Jeyabalan, A. (2015). Hypertensive disorders of pregnancy. In R. J. Martin, A. A. Fanaroff, & M. C. Walsh (2015), *Fanaroff & Martin's neonatal–perinatal medicine* (10th ed, pp. 251–264). Philadelphia, PA: Elsevier.

Jnah, A. J., Newberry, D. M., & England, A. (2015). Pentalogy of Cantrell: Case report with review of the literature. *Advances in Neonatal Care*, 15(4), 261–268. doi:10.1097/ANC.0000000000000209

Jones, A. M., Isenburg, J., Salemi, J. L., Arnold, K. E., Mai, C. T., Aggarwal, D. … Honein, M. A. (2016). Increasing prevalence of gastroschisis—14 States 1995-2012. *Morbidity and Mortality Weekly Report*, 65(2), 23–26. doi:10.15585/mmwr.mm6502a2

Jorde, L. B., Carey, J. C., & Bamshad, M. J. (2016). *Medical genetics* (5th ed.). Philadelphia, PA: Elsevier.

Kamada, N., Chen, G., Inohara, N., & Nunez, G. (2013). Control of pathogens and pathobionts by the gut microbiota. *Nature Immunology*, 14(7), 685–690. doi:10.1038/ni.2608

Kamoth, B. M., & Piccoli, D. A. (2008). Alagille syndrome. In C. A. Liacouras & D. A. Piccoli (Eds.), *Pediatric gastroenterology: Requisites* (pp. 227–232). Philadelphia, PA: Mosby Elsevier.

Keckler, S. J., St. Peter, S. D., Spilde, T. L., Tsao, K-J., Ostlie, D. J., & Snyder, C. L. (2008). Current significance of meconium plug syndrome. *Journal of Pediatric Surgery*, 43(5), 896–898. doi:10.1016/j.jpedsurg.2007.12.035

Kelly, G. M., & Drysdale, T. A. (2015). Retinoic acid and the development of the endoderm. *Journal of Developmental Biology*, 3(2), 25–56. doi:10.3390/jdb3020025

Kelly, K. B., & Ponsky, T. A. (2013). Pediatric abdominal wall defects. *Surgical Clinics of North America*, 93(5), 1255–1267. doi:10.1016/j.suc.2013.06.016

Kliegman, R. M., & Walsh, M. C. (1987). Neonatal necrotizing enterocolitis: Pathogenesis, classification, and spectrum of illness. *Current Problems in Pediatrics*, 17(4), 213. doi:10.1016/0045-9380(87)90031-4

Larson-Nath, C., Gurram, B., & Chelimsky, G. (2015). Disorders of digestion in the neonate. In R. J. Martin, A. A. Fanaroff, & M. C. Walsh (Eds.), *Fanaroff & Martin's neonatal–perinatal medicine* (10th ed., pp. 1379–1394). Philadelphia, PA: Elsevier.

Liu, R., & Adler, D. G. (2014). Duplication cysts: Diagnosis, management, and the role of endoscopic ultrasound. *Endoscopic Ultrasound*, 3(3), 152–160. doi:10.4103/2303-9027.138783

Logan, C. Y., & Nusse, R. (2004). The Wnt signaling pathway in development and disease. *Annual Review Cell Developmental Biology*, 20, 781–810. doi:10.1146/annurev.cellbio.20.010403.113126

Lupo, P. J., Isenburd, J. L., Salemi, J. L., Mai, C. T., Liberman, R. F., Canfield, M. A., … The National Birth Defects Prevention Network. (2017). Population-based birth defects data in the United States, 2010-2014: A focus on gastrointestinal defects [Special issue]. *Birth Defects Research*, 109(18), 1504–1515. doi:10.1002/bdr2.1145

MacDonald, M. G., & Seshia, M. M. K. (2016). *Avery's neonatology* (7th ed.). Philadelphia, PA: Wolters Kluwer.

Mahe, M. M., Helmraph, M. A., & Shroyer, N. F. (2017). Organogenesis of the gastrointestinal tract. In R. A. Polin, S. H. Abman, D. H. Rowitch, W. E. Benitz, & W. W. Fox (Eds.), *Fetal and neonatal physiology* (5th ed., Vols. 1 & 2, pp. 861–869). Philadelphia, PA: Elsevier.

Markel, T. A., Engelstad, H., & Poindexter, B. B. (2014). Predicting disease severity of necrotizing enterocolitis: How to identify infants for future novel therapies. *Journal of Clinical Neonatology*, 3(1), 1–9. doi:10.4103/2249-4847.128717

Martin, V., & Shaw-Smith, C. (2010). Review of genetic factors in intestinal malrotation. *Pediatric Surgery International*, 26(8), 769–781. doi:10.1007/s00383-010-2622-5

Moore, K. L., Persaud, T. V. N., & Torchia, M. G. (2016). *The developing human: Clinically oriented embryology* (10th ed.). Philadelphia, PA: Elsevier.

National Organization for Rare Disorders. (2003). Duodenal atresia or stenosis. Retrieved from https://rarediseases.org/rare-diseases/duodenal-atresia-or-stenosis

National Organization for Rare Disorders. (2007). Jejunal atresia. Retrieved from https://rarediseases.org/rare-diseases/jejunal-atresia

Navathe, R., Gerli, S., Pacella, E., & Berghella, V. (2016). Diabetes in pregnancy. In A. Malvasi, A. Tinelli, & G. C. Di Renzo (Eds.), *Management and therapy of early pregnancy complications: First and second trimesters* (pp. 315–331). Basel, Switzerland: Springer International.

Neu, J. (2012). *Gastroenterology and nutrition: Neonatology questions and controversies*. Philadelphia, PA: Saunders.

Neu, J. (2017). The developing microbe of the fetus and newborn. In R. A. Polin, S. H. Abman, D. H. Rowitch, W. E. Benitz, & W. W. Fox (Eds.), *Fetal and neonatal physiology* (5th ed., Vols. 1 & 2, pp. 905–908). Philadelphia, PA: Elsevier.

Neu, J., & Walker, W. A. (2011). Necrotizing enterocolitis. *New England Journal of Medicine, 364*(3), 255–264. doi:10.1056/NEJMra1005408

Nusinovich, Y., Revenis, M., & Torres, C. (2013). Long-term outcomes for infants with intestinal atresia followed at Children's National Medical Center, Washington, DC. *Journal of Pediatric Gastroenterology and Nutrition, 57*(3), 324–329. doi:10.1097/MPG.0b013e318299fd9f

Obasi, A. A., Ekenze, S. O., & Ogbobe, U. (2015). Ileal obstruction from Meckel's diverticulum in a neonate: A case report and review of literature. *Journal of Pediatric Surgery Case Reports, 3*(10), 423–425. doi:10.1016/j.epsc.2015.08.013

Online Mendelian Inheritance in Men. (2017a). Diarrhea 1, secretory chloride, congenital, with or without other congenital anomalies, DIAR3. Retrieved from https://www.omim.org/entry/270420

Online Mendelian Inheritance in Men. (2017b). Diarrhea 3, secretory sodium, congenital, DIAR1. Retrieved from https://www.omim.org/entry/214700

Online Mendelian Inheritance in Men. (2017c). Glucose/galactose malabsorption; GGM. Retrieved from https://www.omim.org/entry/606824

Online Mendelian Inheritance in Men. (2017d). Inherited GI cancer. Retrieved from www.omim.org/entry/120437

Online Mendelian Inheritance in Men. (2017e). Pyloric stenosis, infantile hypertrophic. Retrieved from https://www.omim.org/entry/179010

Online Mendelian Inheritance in Men. (2017f). Shwachman–Diamond syndrome; SDS. Retrieved from www.omim.org/entry/260400

Owens, L. A., O'Sullivan, E. P., Kirwan, B., Avalos, G., Gaffney, G., & Dunne, F. (2010). For the ATLANTIC DIP collaborators: The impact of obesity on pregnancy outcome in glucose-tolerant women. *Diabetes Care, 33*, 577–579. https://doi:10.2337/dc09-0911

Parry, R. L. (2015). Selected gastrointestinal anomalies in the neonate. In R. J. Martin, A. A. Fanaroff, & M. C. Walsh (Eds.), *Fanaroff & Martin's neonatal–perinatal medicine* (10th ed., pp. 1395–1422). Philadelphia, PA: Elsevier.

Pathway Medicine. (2017). Gastrointestinal medicine. Retrieved from http://www.pathwaymedicine.org/gastrointestinal-medicine

Pena, A. (2000). Imperforate anus and cloacal malformations. In K. W. Ashcraft (Ed.), *Pediatric surgery* (3rd ed., p. 473). Philadelphia, PA: Saunders.

Perdu, S., Castellana, B., Kim, Y., Chan, K., DeLuca, L., & Beristain, A. G. (2016). Maternal obesity drives functional alterations in uterine NK cells. *Journal of Clinical Investigation: Insight, 1*(11), e 85560. doi:10.1172/jci.insight.85560

Polak, M., & Cave, H. (2007). Neonatal diabetes mellitus: A disease linked to multiple mechanisms. *Orphanet Journal of Rare Diseases, 2*, 12. doi:10.1186/1750-1172-2-12

Pritchard, D. J., & Korf, B. R. (2016). *Medical genetics at a glance* (3rd ed., pp. 229–233). Chichester, UK: Wiley-Blackwell.

Ranells, J. D., Carver, J. D., & Kirby, R. S. (2011). Infantile hypertrophic pyloric stenosis: Epidemiology, genetics, and clinical update. *Advances in Pediatrics, 58*(1), 195–206. doi:10.1016/j.yapd.2011.03.005

Rattan, K. N., Bansal, S., & Dhamija, A. (2017). Gastrointestinal duplication presenting as neonatal intestinal obstruction: An experience of 15 years at a tertiary care center. *Journal of Neonatal Surgery, 6*(1), 5. doi:10.21699/jns.v5i4432

Rayyan, M., Rommel, N., Tack, J., Deprest, J., & Allegaert, K. (2017). Esophageal atresia: Future directions for research on the digestive tract. *European Journal Pediatric Surgery 2017, 27*(04), 306–312. doi:10.1055/s-0036-1587330

Roath, M. C., & Di Palma, J. A. (2012). Genetics in gastroenterology: What you need to know. *Consultant, 52*(2). doi:10.1038/ng.1067

Romero, R., Chaemsaithong, P., Yeo, L., Docheva, N., & Chalyasit, N. (2017). Fetal and maternal responses to intraamniotic infection. In R. A. Polin, S. H. Abman, D. H. Rowitch, W. E. Benitz, & W. W. Fox (Eds.), *Fetal and neonatal physiology* (5th ed., Vols. 1 & 2, pp. 144–159). Philadelphia, PA: Saunders.

Ross, A., & Johnson, R. V. R. (2016). Infantile hypertrophic pyloric stenosis. *Surgery, 34*(12), 609–611. doi:10.1016/j.mpsur.2016.09.003

Sadler, T. W. (2015). *Langman's medical embryology* (13th ed.). Philadelphia, PA: Lippincott Williams & Wilkins.

Sagar, J., Kumar, V., & Shah, D. K. (2006). Meckel's diverticulum: A systematic review. *Journal of the Royal Society of Medicine, 99*(10), 501–505. doi:10.1258/jrsm.99.10.501

Sanchez-Valle, A., Kassira, N., Vardla, V. C., Radu, S. C., Paidas, C., & Kirby, R. S. (2017). Biliary atresia: Epidemiology, genetics, clinical update, and public health perspective. *Advances in Pediatrics 64*(1), 285–305. doi:10.1016/j.yapd.2017.03.012

Schierding, W., Vickers, M. H., O' Sullivan, J. M., & Cutfield, W. S. (2017). Epigenetics. In R. A. Polin, S. H. Abman, D. H. Rowitch, W. E. Benitz, & W. W. Fox (Eds.), *Fetal and neonatal physiology* (5th ed., Vols. 1 & 2, pp. 89–100). Philadelphia, PA: Elsevier.

Schoenwolf, G. C., Bleyl, S. B., Brauer, P. R., & Francis-West, P. H. (2015). *Larsen's human embryology* (5th ed.). Philadelphia, PA: Churchill Livingstone.

Simmons, R. K., Griffin, S. J., Witte, D. R., Borch-Johnsen, K., Lauritzen, T., & Sandbæk, A. (2017). Effect of population screening for type 2 diabetes and cardiovasular risk factors on mortality rate and cardiovascular events: A controlled trial among 1,912,392 Danish adults. *Diabetologia, 60*(11), 2183–2191. doi:10.1007/s00125-017-4323-2

Sloan, K., & Wagener, S. (2016). Updates in Hirschsprung's disease and anorectal malformations. *Journal of Pediatric Surgical Specialties, 10* (3), 43–51. Retrieved from http://www.jpss.eu/index.php/future-meetings/item/889-updates-in-hirschsprung's-disease-and-anorectal-malformations

Sodhi, C. P., Neal, M. D., Siggers, R., Sho, S., Ma, C., Branca, M. F., . . . Hackam, D. J. (2012). Intestinal epithelial toll-like receptor 4 regulates goblet cell development and is required for necrotizing enterocolitis in mice. *Gastroenterology, 143*(3), 708. doi:10.1053/j.gastro.2012.05.053

Souther, C., Puapong, D. P., Woo, R., & Johnson, S. M. (2017). Possible etiologies of increased incidence of gastroschisis. *Pediatric Surgery International, 33*(11), 1209–1213. doi:10.1007/s00383-017-4166-4

Tourneur, E., & Chassin, C. (2013). Neonatal immune adaptation of the gut and its role during infections. *Clinical and Developmental Immunology, 2013*. doi:10.1155/2013/270301

Twaroski, K., Mallana, S. K., Jing, R., DiFurio, F., Urick, A., & Duncan, S. A. (2015). FGF2 mediates hepatic progenitor cell formation during human pluripotent stem cell differentiation by inducing the WNT antagonist NKD1. *Genes & Development, 29*(23), 2463-2474. doi:10.1101/gad.268961.115

Uesaka, T., Young, H. M., Pachnis, V., & Emomoto, H. (2016). Development of the intrinsic and extrinsic innervation of the gut. *Developmental Biology, 417*(2), 158–167. doi:10.1016/j.ydbio.2016.04.016

Vanderhoof, J. A., & Pauley-Hunter, R. J. (2016). Gastrointestinal disease. In M. G. McDonald & M. K. Seshia (Eds.), *Avery's neonatology: Pathophysiology and management of the newborn* (7th ed., pp. 719–739). Philadelphia, PA: Wolters Kluwer.

Watanabe, S., Suzuki, T., Hara, F., Yasui, T., Uga, N., & Naoe, A. (2017). Omphalocele and gastroschisis in newborns: Over 16 years of experience from a single clinic. *Journal of Neonatal Surgery, 6*(2), 27. doi:10.21699/jns.v6i2.530

Williams, C. B., Mackenzie, K. C., & Gahagan, S. (2014). The effect of maternal obesity on the offspring. *Clinical Obstetric Gynecology, 57*(3), 508–515. doi:10.1097/GRF.0000000000000043

Wu, H., & Wu, E. (2012). The role of gut microbiota in immune homeostasis and autoimmunity. *Gut Microbes, 3*(1), 4–14. doi:10.4161/gmic.19320

Zorn, A. M. (Ed.). (2008). Liver development. In *StemBook.* Cambridge, MA. Retrieved from https://www.ncbi.nlm.nih.gov/books/NBK27068/

7

THE HEMATOPOIETIC SYSTEM

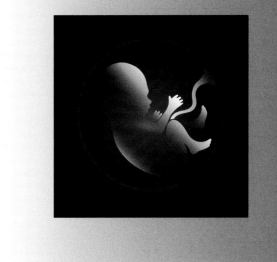

Uduak Akpan, Erin Orth, Ryan Moore, Paula M. Timoney, Terri A. Cavaliere, Rebecca Chuffo Davila, and Darlene A. Calhoun

LEARNING OBJECTIVES

After completing this chapter, the reader should be able to:

- Understand normal hematopoietic system development.
- Analyze the physiologic function of the fetal and neonatal hematopoietic system.
- Discuss common inherited disorders and their effect on fetal and neonatal hematopoietic system development and function.
- Identify maternal health issues that have a potential impact on fetal and postnatal hematopoietic system development and function.
- Evaluate common disorders that affect the hematopoietic system and their implications across the life span.

INTRODUCTION

The hematologic system is one of the first to achieve operational activity in utero, available to support life, growth, and well-being. Hematopoiesis, or the formation of blood cells, begins during early embryonic development and continues across the life span. Epigenetic, genetic, or environmental shocks may impact hematologic development or function and impose pathophysiologic dysfunction. A developmentally and functionally competent hematologic system is critical to survival of life in utero and after birth.

TIMELINE OF ORGAN DEVELOPMENT

The study of hematopoiesis allows clinicians to understand normal development across the life span, which aids in understanding the pathogenesis of blood disorders and certain cancers. All cellular components of the hematologic system originate from hematopoietic stem cells (HSCs), or pluripotent cells, of the embryonic mesoderm. The initial site for hematopoiesis is the extraembryonic yolk sac, with blood cells noted as early as week 3 of gestation. However, the production site changes throughout gestation, from the yolk sac, to the liver, and then to the bone marrow (Jagannathan-Bogdan, & Zon, 2013).

Embryonic HSCs are ultimately capable of self-renewal and differentiation into either myeloid or lymphoid lineages. When these HSCs proliferate, some persist as stem cells for autonomous regeneration. The remaining cells form the various blood cell lineages: erythroid (red blood cell [RBC]), lymphoid (T-cells and B-cells), and myeloid (granulocytes and platelets; Figure 7.1; Pouzolles, Oburoglu, Taylor, & Zimmermann, 2016). In fact, the greatest percentage of hematopoiesis involves granulopoiesis (production of neutrophils). This is crucial for later innate and adaptive immune responses (see Chapter 9).

Given the complexity involved with the proliferation and maturation of the hematologic system, we offer an

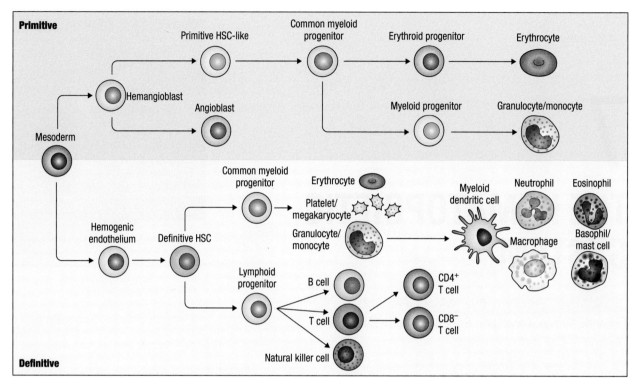

Figure 7.1 Primitive/definitive erythropoiesis.

HSC, hematopoietic stem cells.

Source: Adapted from Jagannathan-Bogdan, M., & Zon, L. I. (2013). Hematopoiesis. *Development, 140*(12), 2463–2467. doi:10.1242/dev.083147

integrated approach to the study of this system. Major embryologic milestones are woven into the following discussion of functional maturation.

DEVELOPMENTAL PHYSIOLOGY

There are two phases of hematopoiesis: primitive and definitive. The yolk sac is the first hematopoietic site in the developing human, with definitive hematopoietic progenitors of the erythroid and myeloid lines arising there before migrating to the liver (Palis, Robertson, Kennedy, Wall, & Keller, 1999; Wang, Menendez, Cerdan, & Bhatia, 2005). These phases facilitate functional maturation of the hematologic system, which is summarized in Table 7.1.

Physiology of Hematopoiesis

Red Blood Cells. The RBC is an anucleated biconcave cell that is responsible for oxygen delivery to tissues, as well as carbon dioxide removal. The earliest RBCs are detectable during week 2 of gestation, and continue to be produced for an entire lifetime (Moore, Persaud, & Torchia, 2016). As one of the earliest differentiated cell lines, RBCs play a vital role in embryonic and fetal

development. Without the development of early RBCs, life could not be sustained (Baron, Isern, & Fraser, 2012). In fact, to maintain normal RBC numbers in the adult human, HSCs produce 2.4 million new cells each second (Dzierzak & Philipsen, 2013).

Erythropoiesis defines the process of RBC development, which occurs in two distinct waves. In the first trimester, hematopoietic precursors undergo primitive erythropoiesis primarily within the yolk sac, and to a lesser degree within the liver and bone marrow. Mesodermal cells migrate to the yolk sac, enter, and interact with cells within the endoderm (cells with vascular endothelial and hematopoietic potential), forming blood islands. It is here, within the blood islands of the yolk sac, that erythroid progenitor cells emerge and give rise to primitive erythrocytes, termed erythroblasts. The erythroblasts are large, nucleated cells distinctly different than mature red cells, which lack a nucleus. These red cells are necessary to promote embryonic tissue oxygenation and development, yet are subject to a short life span (Dzierzak & Philipen, 2013). Because these cells are transient, this period of hematopoiesis is considered primitive. Generally, primitive erythrocytes are noted within the yolk sac between weeks 2 and 10 of gestation, within the liver between weeks 4 and 5 of gestation, and within the bone

TABLE 7.1 Major Physiologic Functions of the Hematologic System

Major Function	Examples
Transport	• Antibodies
	• Carbon dioxide
	• Electrolytes
	• Heat
	• Hormones
	• Oxygen
	• Waste products
Modulation	• Acid–base homeostasis
	• Body temperature
	• Coagulation
	• Fluid homeostasis
Protection	• Infectious response (white blood cells)

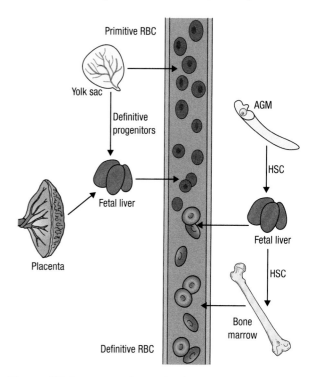

Figure 7.2 Transition of RBC development during development. Initially, larger, nucleated primitive erythrocytes are produced in the yolk sac. HSCs located in the AGM region lead to production of definitive RBC. The location of HSCs shifts during development from the AGM to the liver and they ultimately reside in the bone marrow throughout adult life.

AGM, aorta–gonad–mesonephros region; HSC, hematopoietic stem cells; RBC, red blood cell.

marrow between weeks 8 and 9 of gestation (Figure 7.2). A continuous transition toward the production of mature erythroblasts continues within the liver and bone marrow, while production within the yolk sac terminates around week 10 of gestation.

The second wave of erythropoiesis is termed the definitive wave. This wave involves the production of lineage-committed, multipotent, and ultimately pluripotent definitive stem cells (HSCs) and progenitors that can give rise to all cell types in the body (Figure 7.3). Lineage-committed progenitors are erythroid-myeloid progenitors (EMPs), which first arise within the yolk sac (Gomez Perdiguero et al., 2015). During week 5 of gestation (concurrent with the onset of the heart-beat and primitive circulation), EMPs appear within the aorta-gonad-mesonephros region (AGM), vitelline veins, umbilical arteries, and vasculature in the head. It is within the primitive heart (aortic region) that multipotent definitive HSCs arise and mature erythropoiesis begins (Dzierzak & Philipsen, 2013). By week 6, EMPs colonize the liver and likewise, erythropoiesis shifts to the liver. During this time, HSCs differentiate from lineage-committed into multipotent cells, capable of replenishing into multiple cell types, yet in a limited capacity. Meanwhile, the bone marrow increases its proficiency and assumes the role of primary site for erythropoiesis, as HSCs become pluripotent cells capable of indefinite replenishing of all blood cell types (including erythrocytes), during week 24 of gestation; the bone marrow remains the primary locus for hematopoiesis across the lifespan (Ohls, 2017; Woolthius & Park, 2016).

Erythropoietin. Erythropoietin (EPO) is a hormone that regulates RBC production; however, its precise role in RBC synthesis and secretion remains a subject of ongoing research. During fetal development, EPO is largely produced within the fetal liver. The timing of EPO production within the liver, and its involvement in the regulation of erythrocyte production, has been a topic of dispute. Originally thought not to occur during primitive erythropoiesis, more recent studies have demonstrated its presence and potential role in erythrocyte development within the yolk sac, during primitive hematopoiesis (Suzuki, Hirano, Pan, Minegishi, & Yamamoto, 2013).

EPO holds a significant role in definitive erythropoiesis, which occurs across the life span. An inverse correlation exists with EPO synthesis and secretion, and tissue oxygenation (Figure 7.4; Koury & Bondurant, 1992; Polin, Abman, Rowitch, Benitz, & Fox, 2017). When oxygen levels are high, EPO activity is low. Conversely, when oxygen levels are low, transcription factors including hypoxia-inducible factor (HIF) and hepatic nuclear factor4, simulate an increase in EPO production (Bunn & Aster, 2017). These principles will be discussed later in this chapter, relative to the pathophysiology of anemia.

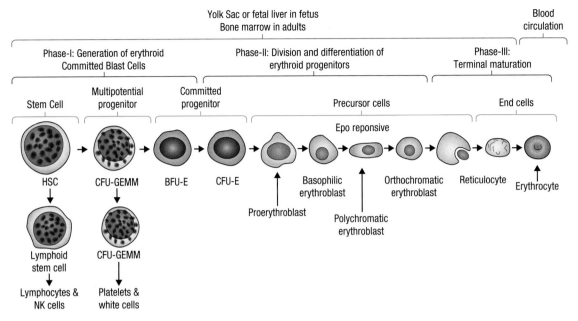

Figure 7.3 Process of erythropoiesis from HSC to fully differentiated anucleated RBC.

BFU-E, burst-forming unit–erythrocyte; CFU-E, colony-forming unit–erythrocyte; CFU-GEMM, colony-forming unit–granulocyte, erythrocyte, monocyte, megakaryocyte; EPO, erythropoietin; HSC, hematopoietic stem cell; NK, natural killer cells.

Source: Adapted from Singh, V. K., Saini, A., Kalson, M., Kumar, N., & Chandra, R. (2016). Stage-specific regulation of erythropoiesis and its implications in ex-vivo RBCs generation. *Journal of Stem Cells, 11*(3), 149–169.

Hemoglobin

Hemoglobin provides the RBC with the capability to carry and release oxygen to the tissues. This protein is composed of two pairs of globin chains that are connected to the heme molecule and required for oxygen binding. The α-like globin peptides and β-like globin peptides work in conjunction to regulate oxygen delivery. Different forms of these globin peptides are expressed through fetal development and into adult life, and determine the type of hemoglobin produced. During the embryonic phase, primitive erythrocytes produce the β-like globin known as *ε-globin*. Hemoglobins produced during this embryonic phase are Hb Gower 1, Hb Gower 2, and Hb Portland (Diab & Luchtman-Jones, 2015). With the transition to definitive erythropoiesis, the major β-like globin produced is γ-globin. The combination of γ-globin and α-globin produces fetal hemoglobin (Hb F). Hb F is the primary hemoglobin produced during the remainder of fetal life and has higher oxygen-binding capabilities than adult hemoglobin. After birth, the γ-globin production decreases and is replaced by production of β-globin heterodimers (Figure 7.5). The resulting tetramer is known as *Hb A*. Hb A will remain the primary form of hemoglobin through adult life (Sankaran & Orkin, 2013). After about 6 months of postnatal life, Hb F comprises less than 1% of total hemoglobin (Diab & Luchtman-Jones, 2015).

As stated previously, hemoglobin allows red cells to carry oxygen to the tissues. The affinity for oxygen binding determines how well the hemoglobin picks up oxygen and releases it to the tissues. If affinity is high, the hemoglobin can hold onto oxygen more easily. But, high oxygen affinity also means the hemoglobin will not release oxygen at the tissue level as readily. If oxygen affinity is lowered, the hemoglobin does not bind oxygen as well, but will readily release the oxygen to the tissues.

Oxygen affinity is lessened in the presence of increased intracellular 2,3 diphosphoglycerate (2,3 DPG) levels, elevated temperature, decreased pH, or increased CO_2 levels. Therefore, the oxygen will not bind as tightly to the hemoglobin and will be released to the tissues as they are experiencing higher metabolic demand. Alternatively, oxygen affinity is increased when the temperature is lowered, intracellular levels of 2,3 DPG decrease, pH is elevated, or CO_2 levels decrease. In these circumstances, hemoglobin will bind oxygen more easily, but the metabolic demands of the tissues are lessened; therefore, oxygen delivery is decreased as well.

The structure of Hb F provides higher oxygen affinity to the developing fetus. In utero, maternal blood and fetal blood do not mix. The placenta acts as the site for oxygen exchange; however, the blood coming to the placenta contains a lower oxygen content. Therefore, the fetal RBCs need to have a stronger ability to capture as much of the

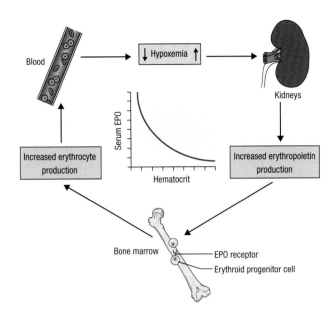

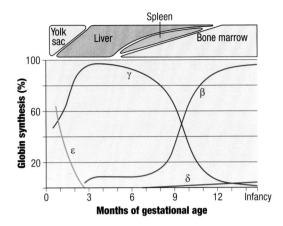

Figure 7.5 Globulin peptide synthesis and hemoglobin. Timing of β-like gene expression from embryonic period to infancy. The β-like subunits, when paired with the α-like subunits, form different types of hemoglobin produced during gestation

Source: Adapted from Sankaran, V. G., & Orkin, S. H. (2013). Genome-wide association studies of hematologic phenotypes: A window into human hematopoiesis. *Current Opinion in Genetics & Development, 23*(3), 339–344. doi:10.1016/j.gde.2013.02.006

Hemoglobin	Predominates	Globin composition
Hb Gower 1	Embryonic (yolk sac)	$\zeta_2\epsilon_2$
Hb Gower 2	Embryonic (yolk sac)	$\alpha_2\epsilon_2$
Hb Portland	Embryonic (yolk sac)	$\zeta_2\gamma_2$
Hb F	Fetal (liver)	$\alpha_2\gamma_2$
Hb A	Adult (bone marrow)	$\alpha_2\beta_2$
Hb A2	Minor adult (bone marrow)	$\alpha_2\delta_2$
Hb Barts	Fetal-alpha thalassemia	γ_4
Hb H	Adult-alpha thalassemia	β_4

Figure 7.4 Response of EPO production in the presence of low oxygen levels. HIF located in the kidney responds to the hypoxia and increases EPO production. The EPO then stimulates bone marrow to produce more RBCs released to the system to deliver oxygen. The inset graph shows the relationship between hematocrit and EPO production. At lower hematocrits, more EPO is produced. At higher hematocrits, less EPO is produced.

EPO, erytropoietin; Hb, hemoglobin; HIF, hypoxia-inducible factor; RBC, red blood cell.

Source: Adapted from Son-Hing, J. P. & Thompson, G. H., (2015). Congenital abnormalities of the upper and lower extremities and spine. In R. J. Martin, A. A. Fanaroff, & M. C. Walsh (Eds.), *Fanaroff & Martin's neonatal–perinatal medicine: Diseases of the fetus and infant* (10th ed., pp. 1789–1808). Philadelphia, PA: Elsevier-Mosby; Spivak, J. L. (2005). The anaemia of cancer: Death by a thousand cuts. *Nature Reviews Cancer, 5,* 543–555. doi:10.1038/nrc1648

available oxygen as possible. The fetal circulation has a higher number of RBCs to assist in oxygen delivery to tissues (Figure 7.6).

Red Cell Indices. RBC indices include the *mean cell volume* (MCV), *mean cell hemoglobin* (MCH), and *mean corpuscular hemoglobin concentration* (MCHC). The MCV

defines the size of the RBC. The MCH and MCHC define the hemoglobin concentration within the RBC. More specifically, MCH quantifies the concentration of hemoglobin content per individual RBC. The MCHC is slightly different, in that it quantifies the concentration of hemoglobin per unit volume. In that regard, the MCHC offers a correlation between the volume of the cell (MCV) and hemoglobin content. Each of these indices can be calculated if the RBC count, hemoglobin, and hematocrit are known.

MCV and MCHC values are classified as low, normal, or elevated. Therefore, red cells are termed microcytic, normocytic, or macrocytic, based upon the calculated MCV. RBCs affixed with a low concentration of hemoglobin (MCHC) are termed hypochromic, whereas RBCs with a normal MCHC are termed normochromic. An elevated MCHC is considered to be hyperchromic.

To calculate the MCV, the following formula is used:

$$MCV = \frac{\text{hematocrit}\,(\%) \times 10}{\text{RBC count (millions/mm}^3)}$$

To calculate the MCH, the following formula is used:

$$MCH = \frac{\text{hemoglobin}\,(\text{g}/100\,\text{mL}) \times 10}{\text{RBC count (millions/mm}^3)}$$

To calculate the MCHC, the following formula is used:

$$MCHC = \frac{\text{hemoglobin}\,(\text{g}/100\,\text{mL}) \times 100}{\text{hematocrit}\,(\%)}$$

Advanced practice nurses may be asked to analyze red cell indices. Recall from prior discussions that red cell

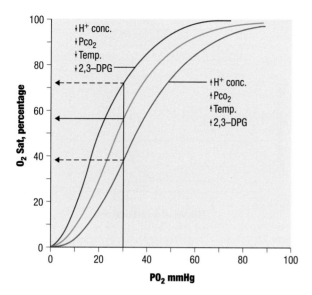

Figure 7.6 Oxyhemoglobin dissociation curve. At the same PO2 delivered, the percentage of oxygen saturation changes by shift of the curve. A shift to the left shows higher oxygen affinity with a higher amount of oxygen bound at PO2 30 mmHg. On the standard dissociation curve, the oxygen saturation is about 67%. A shift to the right leads to lower oxygen affinity and the oxygen saturation of the hemoglobin is about 39%. The factors affecting the shifts in the curve are hydrogen ion concentration (pH), carbon dioxide content (CO2), temperature, and intracellular levels of 2,3 DPG.

Source: Adapted from Goldsmith, J. P., Karotkin, E., Suresh, G., & Keszler, M. (2016). *Assisted ventilation of the neonate (6th ed.).* Philadelphia, PA: Elsevier.

indices of a term newborn immediately after birth often reflect a nonpathologic and transient state of macrocytosis, which may be paired with polycythemia and polychromasia. This slowly transitions to a state of anemia as erythropoiesis is suppressed, secondary to increased extrauterine tissue oxygenation and other factors (see physiologic anemia of infancy, physiology anemia of prematurity). Less common etiologies associated with macrocytosis include congenital hypothyroidism (macrocytic, normochromic RBCs) and megaloblastic anemia.

Conditions associated with microcytosis include hereditary spherocytosis (HS), iron deficiency, and the thalassemias. While these conditions will be addressed later in this chapter, it is timely to associate red cell indices with each disease process. Red cells among neonates with HS are commonly microcytic and hyperchromic (MCHC >36.5–37 g/dL; Christensen, Yaish & Gallagher, 2015). In fact, dividing the MCHC by the MCV aids in the identification and diagnosis of this condition. Among infants with iron deficiency anemia, RBCs are commonly microcytic and hypochromic. Finally, infants

who present with alpha thalassemia (α thal) commonly manifest with microcytosis and hypochromia.

Physiology of Clotting

Clotting factors are vital to the formation of clots when hemostasis (*heme* = blood; *stasi* = stopping) is required. The human fetus begins expressing most clotting factors by week 10 of gestation. Coagulation proteins cannot cross from mother to fetus through the placenta. Therefore, they are produced by the fetus as part of its normal development. Concentration differences exist between neonatal clotting factors and adult clotting factors. For example, vitamin K-dependent factors (II, VII, IX, and X) are all about 50% of normal adult values at birth. The contact factors (XI and XII) are similarly reduced. Factors V, VIII, and XIII are equivalent to adult normal values. Fibrinogen (factor I) is present by 3 to 5 weeks of gestation and is present in concentrations equivalent to adult normal values (Bunn & Aster, 2017). However, the fetal fibrinogen is distinct in its makeup and has decreased capability of clot formation due to decreased fibrin polymerization (Ignjatovic, Ilhan, & Monagle, 2011).

Two pathways lead to clot formation: *intrinsic* and *extrinsic* coagulation. The intrinsic coagulation pathway is activated with trauma to the cells. The pathway begins with the activation of factor XII to its active form, XIIa. Activated factor XIIa, in the presence of high-molecular-weight kininogen (HMWK), converts factor XI to its active form, XIa. Next, factor XIa, in the presence of calcium, elicits the activation of factor IX. Active factor IXa, in the presence of activated factor VIIIa and calcium, prompts the conversion of factor X into its active form, Xa. Finally, activated factor Xa, in the presence of calcium and factor V, forms the prothrombin activator (Bunn & Aster, 2017; Mackman, 2009).

The extrinsic pathway is activated by way of trauma to the vascular endothelium or tissue. The pathway begins with the activation of tissue factor (TF), a membrane-bound protein located in the endothelium. TF modulates the conversion of factor VII to activated factor VIIa. Next, TF and activated factor VIIa combine with calcium and convert factor X to activated factor Xa. Activated factor Xa, in the presence of calcium and factor V, forms the prothrombin activator (Bunn & Aster, 2017; Mackman, 2009).

Both intrinsic and extrinsic pathways converge when prothrombin activator is formed. Prothrombin activator, in the presence of calcium, converts prothrombin into thrombin, the active enzyme. When sufficient thrombin concentrations are present in the plasma, it leads to the conversion of fibrinogen into fibrin monomers. Through an interaction with calcium and fibrinogen stabilizing factor (factor XIII), fibrin polymers are created. These fibrin polymers aggregate with platelets and phospholipids, which forms a clot and achieves hemostasis. The maturation process of the coagulation system continues until birth (Table 7.2; Bleyer, Hakami, & Shepard, 1971).

Platelet Production

Megakaryocytopoiesis is the process by which bone marrow progenitor cells develop into mature megakaryocytes. Megakaryocytes are the precursors of platelets. They are large cells that exist in small numbers in the bone marrow, comprising less than 0.1% of the nucleated marrow cells (Sims & Gewirtz, 1989). Fragmentation of the cytoplasm of mature megakaryocytes leads to the release of platelets. Platelets are small anucleated cells that are the first cells to respond to injury to the vascular endothelium. Following an event, there is platelet activation and migration to the site of injury. Subsequently, various mediators are generated that contribute to clotting. The process of platelet production is as follows: production of thrombopoietic factors → proliferation of megakaryocyte

TABLE 7.2 Functional Maturation of Major Hemostatic Factors

Major Hemostatic Factors	Maturation (Postnatal Age)
Tissue plasminogen activator	5 days
Platelet	2–4 weeks
Coagulation factor VIII	1 month
Protein S	1 month
Coagulation factor VIII	1 month
Antithrombin	3 months
Von Willebrand factor	3 months
Plasminogen	6 months
Coagulation factor XI	1 year
Fibrinogen	5 years
Coagulation factor II, VII, IX, X	16 years
Coagulation factor V	16 years
Coagulation factor XII	16 years
Protein C	16 years

Source: Diaz-Miron, J., Miller, J., & Vogel, A. M. (2013). Neonatal hematology. *Seminars in Pediatric Surgery*, 22(4), 199–204. doi:10.1053/j.sempedsurg.2013.10.009.

progenitors → differentiation and maturation of megakaryocytes → production and release of platelets into the circulation (Machlus & Italiano, 2013). Platelet number is thus dependent on the size and number of megakaryocytes (Mazzi, Lordier, Debili, Raslova, & Vainchenker, 2018). The period between maturation of megakaryocyte to release of platelets is about 5 days long in humans (Machlus & Italiano, 2013).

In the classic model of differentiation, it is believed that megakaryocytes are developed from a committed myeloid progenitor cell (CMP), the CFU-GEMM cell. This committed CMP gives rise to a common megakaryocyte–erythroid progenitor (Debili et al., 1996). The megakaryocyte–erythroid progenitor subsequently separates into different cell lineages that result in the production of RBCs and platelets. Recently, there is some developing evidence that other pathways may exist that end in the formation of megakaryocytes directly from the stem cell, but these theories need to be fully developed (Figure 7.7; Adolfsson et al., 2005).

Megakaryocytopoiesis is first noted in the yolk sac during the primitive phase of hematopoiesis (Pang, Weiss, & Poncz, 2005; Xu et al., 2001). Megakaryocytes are present by week 5 of gestation and can be seen in the liver and spleen by week 10. The first platelets appear by weeks 8 to 9 of gestation. There are two types of megakaryocyte progenitors: the burst-forming unit-megakaryocyte (BFU-MK), which is the most primitive cell committed to the megakaryocyte line, and the more differentiated colony-forming-unit megakaryocyte (CFU-MK; Briddell, Brandt, Straneva, Srour, & Hoffman, 1989). Another cell, thought to be an even more primitive megakaryocyte progenitor than the BFU-MK, the high proliferative potential cell megakaryocyte (HPPC-MK), can produce colonies with more than 300 cells (Bruno & Hoffman, 1998; Nishihira, Toyoda, Miyazaki, Kigasawa, & Ohsaki, 1996; Sola, Du, Hutson, & Christensen, 2000). This cell is lacking in adults, but is present in fetal marrow. Large quantities of megakaryocyte progenitors are present in cord blood with only small quantities seen in the fetal bone marrow. BFU-MK predominates in the fetal blood with a ratio of about 2.5:1 BFU-MK:CFU-MK (Zauli, Valvassori, & Capitani, 1993). Fetal BFU-MK colonies are larger than those in adults, but show fewer foci of development (Zauli et al., 1993). CFU-MK predominates in the bone marrow of both children and adults but also in preterm and term cord blood (Murray, Watts, & Roberts, 1998; T. A. Olson, Levine, Mazur, Wright, & Salvado, 1992). In fetal blood and adult marrow, CFU-MKs are similar in size. Megakaryocyte progenitor concentrations are inversely proportional to gestational age and this persists in neonatal life in babies born prematurely, with the concentration decreasing with increasing postnatal age (Deutsch et al., 1995; Murray & Roberts, 1995;

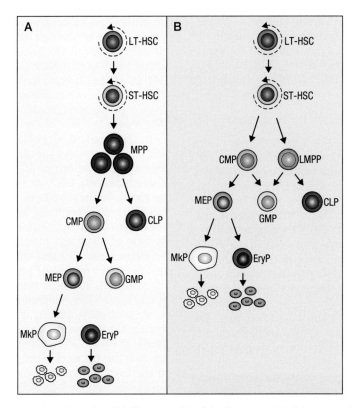

Figure 7.7 Models of the hematopoietic hierarchy. (A) Classic model of the hematopoietic hierarchy with a strict separation between the myeloid and lymphoid branches as the first step in lineage commitment downstream of the HSC. (B) Alternative model as proposed by Adolfsson et al. (2005), incorporating the identification of LMPPs. The relationship between the LMPP and the CMP has not yet been resolved, but they are placed at similar positions in the hierarchy based on their lineage potential.

NOTE: Nearly all of the studies described were performed in mice, and therefore the model shown should be considered to apply only to the murine hematopoietic system at this time.

CLP, common lymphoid progenitor; CMP, myeloid progenitor cell; EryP, erythroid progenitor; GMP, granulocyte macrophage progenitors; LMPP, lymphoidprimed multipotent progenitors; LT-HSC, long-term human stem cell; MEP, megakaryocyte/erythrocyte progenitors; MkP, megakaryocyte progenitor; MPP, multipotential progenitors; ST-HSC, short-term human stem cell.

Source: Adapted from Woolthuis, C. M., & Park, C.Y. (2016). Hematopoietic stem/progenitor cell commitment to the megakaryocyte lineage. *Blood, 127*(10), 1242–1248. doi:10.1182/blood-2015-07-607945

Nishihira et al., 1996). As a result, megakaryocyte progenitors and even the multipotential CFU-GEMM are more numerous in fetal/neonatal blood than in adults (T. A. Olson et al., 1992; Zauli et al., 1993). These progenitor cells exist in a high proliferative state. Proliferation occurs at the expense of further differentiation; as such, fetal megakaryocytes are more immature and produce significantly fewer platelets than adult megakaryocytes (Mattia et al., 2002). Megakaryocyte progenitors in adults mainly reside in the bone marrow and exist in a quiescent state, which allows for greater differentiation.

Unlike megakaryocyte progenitors, megakaryocyte precursors (megakaryoblasts) have lost their ability to proliferate and instead undergo a process known as endomitosis or endoreduplication, by which they evolve from small mononuclear cells to large polyploidal cells. This process involves cycles of DNA replication (doubling of chromosomes within cells) without cell division and is called polyploidization. This process is necessary to establish effective hemostasis. Polyploidization leads to an increase in cell mass, cell size, and metabolic output (Ravid, Lu, Zimmet, & Jones, 2002). Ploidy levels range from 2N to 64N with the mode being about 16N in adults but less than 8N in cord blood (Chang, Bluteau, Debili, & Vainchenker, 2007; de Alarcón & Graeve, 1996; Mattia et al., 2002; Miyazaki et al., 2000; Schipper et al., 1998).

Polyploidization is not necessary in megakaryocytes because these cells are able to shed platelets at any ploidy level. In fetuses and neonates, the low ploidy megakaryocytes are mature, while adult megakaryocytes at the same ploidy levels are not (Liu & Sola-Visner, 2011; Mattia et al., 2002). These low ploidy fetal cells are called micromegakaryocytes (Levine, Olson, Shoff, Miller, & Weisman, 1996). However, higher ploidy cells shed a larger number of platelets, resulting in a more efficient process. For example, a 32N megakaryocyte is capable of shedding ~3000 platelets and a 16N megakaryocyte ~2000 platelets, compared to a 2N cell that yields only a few platelets (Mazzi et al., 2018; Winkelmann, Pfitzer, & Schneider, 1987). As differentiation proceeds, the cells go from small, diploid cells with a basophilic cytoplasm to larger, granular, multilobed nuclear cells with an eosinophilic cytoplasm. Megakaryocyte differentiation occurs in four stages. These stages are as follows: megakaryoblast (Stage I) → promegakaryocyte (Stage II) → granular megakaryocyte (Stage III) → mature megakaryocyte (Stage IV).

Functional maturation of megakaryocytes occurs across fetal development, with low ploidy megakaryocyte cells common in the embryo, and increased ploidy observed in cells in the fetus and highest among adults (Figure 7.8; Bluteau et al., 2009). This unique pattern of megakaryocyte maturation in the fetus enables rapid proliferation to meet the demands of an expanding blood volume and maintenance of normal platelet counts (Liu et al., 2011). Platelet counts reach normal values by the second trimester (Forestier, Daffos, Catherine, Renard, & Andreux, 1991).

Several cytokines affect the development of megakaryocytes. Those that stimulate the development of megakaryocytes include thrombopoietin (TPO), interleukin -3 (IL-3), and interleukin-6 (IL-6), which affects maturation. Others appear to inhibit megakaryocyte development and include platelet factor 4 and transforming growth factor-β (TGF-β; Gewirtz, Calabretta, Rucinski, Niewiarowski, & Xu, 1989; Ishibashi, Miller, & Burstein, 1987; Liu et al., 2011). Low expression of inhibitory factors may explain the existence of cord blood megakaryocyte progenitors in the high proliferative state (Mattia et al., 2002).

TPO stimulates all stages of megakaryocyte formation and development (Debili et al., 1995; Murray et al., 1998). TPO is primarily produced in the liver throughout fetal and adult life (Wolber et al., 1999). TPO levels are similar in preterm and term cord blood, and these are greater than the concentrations in the blood of healthy adults (Murray et al., 1998; Sola et al., 1999; Walka, Sonntag, Dudenhausen, & Obladen, 1999).

TPO levels peak on day 2 of postnatal life, remain elevated for about a month, and then gradually decline to adult levels (Ishiguro, Nakahata, & Matsurbara, 1999). Preterm neonates, both healthy and thrombocytopenic, show increased sensitivity to TPO compared to term neonates (Murray et al., 1998). This may explain the higher numbers and proliferative capabilities of megakaryocyte precursors in cord blood (Mwamtemi, Higuchi, Sawai,

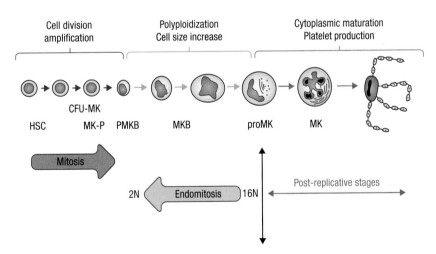

Figure 7.8 Overview of megakaryopoiesis. Megakaryopoiesis is characterized by four steps: (a) proliferation in early stages; (b) endomitosis, which leads to polyploid MKs; (c) post-replicative stage with MK cytoplasmic maturation; and (d) proplatelet formation and MK fragmentation.

CFU-MK, colony-forming-unit megakaryocyte; HSC, hematopoietic stem cells; MK, megakaryocyte; MKB, megakaryoblast; MK-P, megakaryocyte progenitor; PMKB, promegakaryoblast.

Source: Adapted from Mazzi, S., Lordier, L., Debili, N., Raslova, H., & Vainchenker, W. (2018). Megakaryocyte and polyploidization. *Experimental Hematology, 57,* 1–13. doi:10.1016/j.exphem.2017.10.001

Hidaka, & Koike, 2000). However, there is no correlation between TPO levels and platelet count (Ishiguro et al., 1999; Walka et al., 1999). From murine studies, some very important transcription factors have been identified that are essential in the development of megakaryocytes and, subsequently, platelets. Among these factors are GATA-1 and NF-E2. Mutated or absent GATA-1 leads to significant thrombocytopenia and dysmorphic megakaryocytes, which may be observed among infants with transient myeloproliferative disorder (associated with trisomy 21). The absence of NF-E2 leads to undetectable circulating platelets because of a late block in megakaryocyte maturation (Table 7.3; Figure 7.9; Shivdasani, McDevitt, Orkin, & Fujiwara, 1997).

Neonatal thrombocytopenia is common, especially in preterm infants. Fetal megakaryocytes are significantly

TABLE 7.3 Major Differences in Megakaryopoiesis Between Neonates and Adults

	Neonates	Adults
TPO concentrations	Slightly higher in healthy neonates than in healthy adults	Lower in healthy adults than in healthy neonates
Megakaryocytes progenitors	Abundant in the blood	Sparse in the blood
	Give rise to large colonies	Give rise to small colonies
	More sensitive to TPO	Less sensitive to TPO
Megakaryocytes	Small	Large
	Low ploidy levels	High ploidy levels
Effects of rTPO	Inhibits megakaryocyte polyploidization	Stimulates megakaryocyte polyploidization
	Stimulates cytoplasmic maturation	Stimulates cytoplasmic maturation

Source: From Liu, Z., & Sola-Visner, M. (2011). Neonatal and adult megakaryopoiesis. *Current Opinion in Hematology, 18*(5), 330–337. doi:10.1097/MOH.0b013e3283497ed5

rTPO, recombinant thrombopoietin; TPO, thrombopoietin.

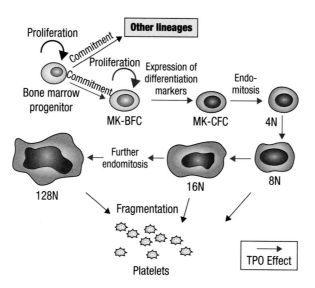

Figure 7.9 TPO and megakaryocyte development.

MK-BFC, megakaryocyte burst-forming cell; MK-CFC, megakaryocyte colony-forming cell; TPO, thrombopoietin.

Source: Adapted from Ravid, K., Lu, J., Zimmet, J. M., & Jones, M. R. (2002). Roads to polyploidy: The megakaryocyte example. *Journal of Cellular Physiology, 190*(1), 7–20. doi:10.1002/jcp.10035

smaller in size than in adults and demonstrate a predominance of less mature forms (T. A. Olson et al., 1992). The megakaryocyte size increases as the fetus matures (Ma, Sun, Chang, & Zuo, 1996). Fetal megakaryocytes are ultimately smaller than those in infants, which are in turn smaller than those seen in children and adults. The point at which megakaryocytes attain normal adult sizes is unknown, as there is insufficient data in children from birth to 1 year of age. However, adult-size megakaryocytes have been identified in the bone marrow of children around 2 years of age (Fuchs et al., 2012). The fetal cells also exist in lower ploidy states than the adults (Ma et al., 1996). Together, these factors may lead to the production of fewer platelets, explaining the tendency for thrombocytopenia in newborns.

In neonates who develop early thrombocytopenia, there is a decrease in circulating megakaryocyte progenitors and precursors at birth that may imply impaired megakaryopoiesis at birth. In addition, these neonates do not exhibit an increase in size or ploidy of their megakaryocytes in response to thrombocytopenia (Fuchs et al., 2012; Murray & Roberts, 1995) due to a combination of intrinsic cell properties and factors in the fetal/neonatal environment (Slayton et al., 2005). However, there is an increase in the number of circulating megakaryocyte progenitors leading to an increase in megakaryocyte numbers and, thus, a compensatory increase in platelet count. Preterm infants exhibit platelet counts that, although within normal range, are, on the average, lower than those for term infants (Sola-Visner, Christensen, Hutson, & Rimsza, 2007; Wiedmeier, Henry, Sola-Visner, & Christensen, 2009).

Physiology of Phagocytes

Around week 4 to 5 of gestation, macrophage production predominates in the liver (Slayton et al., 1998). Making up about 70% of the cells, neutrophils first appear in the fetal marrow between weeks 11 and 12 of gestation (Slayton et al., 1998), with mature neutrophils being seen after week 14 (Ohls et al., 1995; Thomas & Yoffey, 1962). By the end of the first trimester, neutrophil precursors can be detected in the peripheral blood.

Early fetal bone marrow activity shows increased granulocytopoiesis (Charbord, Tavian, Humeau, & Péault, 1996) causing a decrease in the relative concentration of erythroid cells and a decrease in macrophage predominance (Slayton et al., 1998). Still, myelopoiesis is limited in fetal life, and the number of neutrophils only increases late in gestation (Forestier et al., 1986; Thomas & Yoffey, 1962). White blood cells (WBCs) make up less than 5% of the fetal nucleated marrow cells (Ohls et al., 1995). The neutrophil count doubles by 18 weeks with a further doubling by 32 weeks (Figure 7.10; Thomas & Yoffey, 1962). Very high levels of granulocyte progenitors are seen in fetal blood from about 15 weeks of gestation.

Mature blood cells are of two separate lineages—lymphoid and myeloid. The lymphoid lineage consists of T

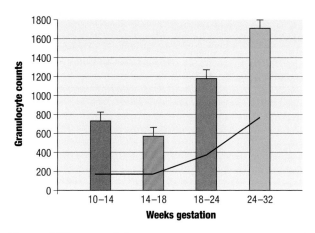

Figure 7.10 Neutrophil counts across gestation. Mean and range of neutrophil counts at 10 to 14, 14 to 18, 18 to 24, and 24 to 32 weeks' gestational age.

cells, B cells, and natural killer (NK) cells. The myeloid line includes the WBCs—granulocytes (neutrophils, eosinophils, basophils), monocytes, and macrophages, as well as erythrocytes, megakaryocytes, and mast cells. The function of the granular and agranular leukocytes is summarized in Table 7.4. In the classic model of stem cell differentiation, multipotent progenitor cells differentiate into either the lymphoid progenitor cell (CLP) or the CMP. This is the earliest process exhibited by a developing multipotent progenitor cell; this decision cannot be reversed.

The myeloid lineage appears to be the default line and, if lymphoid gene expression is not achieved, the multipotent cell then differentiates into a CMP and further down the myeloid line (Iwasaki & Akashi, 2007). The commitment of a stem cell to the lymphoid line is an active process, dependent on lymphoid gene expression and other processes such as shutting down the expression of GM-CSFR (granulocyte–macrophage colony-stimulating factor receptor; Kondo, Scherer, King, Manz, & Weissman, 2011; Martins, Han, & Kim, 2010). As CLPs never express GM-CSFR, although CMPs frequently express this receptor, downgrading GM-CSFR leads the multipotent cell to differentiate into a CLP. Recently, this theory has been challenged.

A common myelo-lymphoid progenitor is now believed to exist, which then develops through myeloid/T or myeloid/B stages before committing to T cells, B cells, or myeloid cells (Katsura, 2002). A common progenitor with only T and B cell capabilities has not been identified (Kawamoto, Ohmura, Fujimoto, & Katsura, 1999). T cells are produced by the thymus from hematopoietic precursors in the fetal liver, migrating to the thymus at 8 to 9 weeks of gestation. It is unclear whether early progenitor cells are T cell committed before coming to the thymus, where further development of T cells, NK cells, or dendritic cells occurs (Masuda et al., 2005), or whether T cell commitment occurs after these cells arrive in the thymus. Although the earliest T cell progenitors are specified to the lymphoid lineage, they retain

TABLE 7.4 Function of Granular and Agranular Leukocytes

Category of Leukocyte	Site of Production	Type of Cell	Mature Life Span	Function
Granulocyte	Bone marrow	Basophil	• 24–48 hours	• Allergic histamine inflammatory response
		Eosinophil	• 12–72 hours	• Allergic detoxifying response
		Neutrophil	• 10 hours	• Phagocytosis
Agranulocyte	Spleen	Lymphocyte	• 4–12 months	• Immune response
		Monocyte	• 4–12 months	• Phagocytosis

NOTE: Basophils contain histamine, which is released during a hypersensitivity reaction. Eosinophils are released during an allergic (hypersensitivity) reaction to detoxify the body. Neutrophils are also regarded as polymorphonuclear cells or segmented neutrophils. Because neutrophils phagocytize bacteria, yet are the shortest-living leukocyte, increased bone marrow production of immature neutrophils ("bands") may be observed. Monocytes are converted into macrophages, the phagocytic form of that cell line; elevated counts suggest an acute viral, fungal, or chronic disease state.

the potential to differentiate into macrophages, NK cells, or dendritic cells (Kawamoto et al., 2009; Masuda et al., 2005). Early progenitor cells within the thymus are incapable of self-renewal and thus the thymus must continuously be seeded from the bone marrow (Bhandoola, Sambandam, Allman, Merz, & Schwarz, 2003; Foss, Donskoy, & Goldschneider, 2001).

The fetal liver and omentum are the first sites of B cell development. The first recognizable cell in the B cell lineage is the pre-B cell. This is first identified in the fetal liver around week 8 of gestation. From week 12, the bone marrow gradually takes over the function of B cell production and this is sustained until adulthood (Asma, Langlois van den Bergh, & Vossen, 1984).

The pluripotent CFU-GEMM (colony-forming unit granulocyte–erythrocyte–megakaryocyte–monocyte) and the myeloid committed CFU-GM (CFU granulocyte–macrophage) are present in the fetal liver between weeks 12 and 14; they appear later in the fetal marrow, around weeks 15–16 (Hann, Bodger, & Hoffbrand, 1983). CFU-GEMMs are mainly found in the fetal liver, not the bone marrow, as is the case in adults. Even though progenitor cells are plentiful in the liver, no mature neutrophils are seen (Ohls et al., 1995). These are only present in the fetal bone marrow. The concentration of both progenitors is also greatly increased in the blood of neonates, preterm more than term (Haneline, Marshall, & Clapp, 1996; Hann et al., 1983; Luzo et al., 2007). These levels are higher than in adult peripheral blood. Cord blood CFU-GM colonies proliferate at a maximal or near maximal rate compared to colonies in adult peripheral blood (Christensen & Rothstein, 1984).

Highly specific protein factors called *colony-stimulating factors (CSFs)* regulate and control the white cell lineage

by stimulating the proliferation and differentiation of CMP (Cairo, 1989; Carr & Modi, 1997). At least two classes of CSFs exist. Class 1 CSFs such as *granulocyte-macrophage colony-stimulating factor (GM-CSF)* stimulate the proliferation of pluripotent and immature progenitor cells with the capability of producing cells of different lineages (Sieff, 1987). Class 2 factors, such as granulocyte (G-CSF) and macrophage colony-stimulating factor (M-CSF), act late in the developmental cycle, leading to proliferation and differentiation of late progenitor cells. They affect the function and survival of mature peripheral cells such as neutrophils and macrophages (Begley, Nicola, & Metcalf, 1988; Clark & Kamen, 1987). The growth factors G-CSF and GM-CSF were also found to be higher in neonatal cord blood than adult peripheral blood (Laver et al., 1990).

Granulocytopoiesis is the process of production and maturation of granulocytes (neutrophils, eosinophils, and basophils). G-CSF is the major cytokine involved in the regulation of granulocytopoiesis. It controls the proliferation, differentiation, and survival of granulocytes (Akbarzadeh & Layton, 2001). This happens in steady state as well as emergency situations, such as in cases of infection (Demetri & Griffin, 1991). G-CSF is produced in many cells, mainly mature macrophages and monocytes, and production is stimulated by cytokines such as tumor necrosis factor α (TNFα), interferon γ (IFN-γ), and lipopolysaccharides (present on the cell membrane of Gram-negative bacteria). In emergency situations, the concentration of G-CSF increases to allow production of an increased number of neutrophils (Gessler et al., 1993). The effects of G-CSF are mediated via the G-CSF receptor (G-CSFR), which regulates the production of committed myeloid progenitors (Richards, Liu, Iwasaki,

Akashi, & Link, 2003) and enhances bactericidal and phagocytic activity. In healthy neonates, both preterm and term, serial G-CSF concentrations show a peak between the first 4 to 7 hours of life, with subsequent decrease to normal adult range by days 4 to 7 (Gessler et al., 1993). The concentrations in term infants are higher than for preterm infants.

Neutrophils make up many of the total circulating leukocytes in the human body and exist in the proliferative pool, the circulating pool, and the storage pool within the bone marrow. They are the first immune cells to respond to pathogens. They have a short half-life of about 7 hours, requiring constant replenishing from the storage pool. The proliferative pool consists of myeloblasts, promyelocytes, and myelocytes that have the capacity to divide, whereas metamyelocytes and segmented neutrophils and bands, which have lost the ability to divide, make up the storage pool (Lawrence, Corriden, & Nizet, 2017). The proliferative pool of neutrophils is responsible for replenishing neutrophil numbers. This process is dependent on G-CSF. Information derived from rat studies show that the percentage of cells in the proliferative pool in neonates is about 10% the adult values (Christensen & Rothstein, 1984). Absolute neutrophil cell mass per gram body weight is approximately 25% of adult values among term neonates. In premature neonates, that number is lower still, consisting of about 20%. Neutrophil counts eventually attain adult levels at about 4 weeks postnatal age (Erdman, Christensen, Bradley, & Rothstein, 1982).

It is important that learners understand that unlike adults, granulocytic progenitors do not increase during an infection in neonates (Christensen, Hill, & Rothstein, 1983). In addition, the storage pool is significantly smaller in premature infants compared to term neonates and adults (Erdman et al., 1982). Similar to G-CSF concentrations, there is a surge in circulating neutrophils during the peripartum period that will never happen again in the life span of an individual (Schmutz, Henry, Jopling, & Christensen, 2008). This surge occurs at 6 to 12 hours of life in neonates born at greater than 28 weeks of gestation and by 24 hours in those born at younger gestational ages. From the storage pool, available mature neutrophils are released into the circulation. Therefore, the combination of the small percentage of cells in the proliferative pool, inability to increase proliferation rates due to the already high rates, and low numbers of granulocytes in the storage pool leads to an increased risk for neutropenia in the face of infections. The neonate is simply not able to churn out mature neutrophils into the circulation quickly enough (Christensen et al., 1983). This contributes to the increased sepsis-associated morbidity and mortality seen in neonates.

The high rate of proliferation of cells may also negatively affect their normal protective function, namely, their bacterial killing effect. Myeloperoxidase and other contents of the granules present in the neutrophil and responsible for bacterial killing are only produced in the promyelocyte, which then divides. Human neonatal neutrophils, particularly in those born before 32 weeks of gestation, undergo several divisions, perhaps in an attempt to increase the number of cells in the storage pool. However, each division leads to a halving of the myeloperoxidase content. The mature neutrophil as a result has a decreased quantity of myeloperoxidase, making the fetal/neonatal neutrophil less lethal to bacteria (Christensen, 1989). A summary of blood cell types and their differentiation is offered in Figure 7.11.

GENETIC INFLUENCES

Numerous genetic conditions impact the neonate's hematologic system; therefore, clinicians should always consider the hematologic system at risk until proven otherwise. Three common genetic defects that affect normal hematopoietic cell development, synthesis, and function are presented in the text that follows. Additional inherited disorders affecting the hematopoietic system are provided in Table 7.5.

Thalassemias

The thalassemias are a heterogeneous grouping of inherited hemolytic anemias that occur secondary to defective synthesis of globin chains and are regarded as the single most common inherited (single-gene) disorder in the world. More than 300,000 children actively manifest the disorder and more than 270 million individuals are unaffected carriers (Cappellini, 2016). Risk factors for both alpha (α) and beta (β) thalassemia are summarized in Table 7.6.

The pathogenesis of the thalassemias involves deficient, defective, or completely deleted (absent) globin genes. This destabilizes the normal 1:1 (ratio of α:β) globin chain and causes a variable degree of dysfunction with globin formation with red cell membrane damage, insufficient erythropoiesis in the face of increased hemolysis, and hypochromic, microcytic anemia (Figure 7.12; Diab & Luchtman-Jones, 2015). We present an overview of the two most common thalassemias: alpha thalassemia and beta thalassemia.

Alpha Thalassemia. Alpha thalassemia is defined as a deficiency or absence of alpha globin chains, which is usually the result of one or more α gene deletions. This leads to the formation of excess beta globin chains. Recall that alpha chains are synthesized during fetal development and shared by fetal and adult hemoglobin (Hb); therefore, α thalassemia can manifest during fetal development and present as early as the immediate postnatal period.

In some cases, affected infants possess no defective α globin genes (found on chromosome 16), and display a normal phenotype, normal hematologic findings, and require no medical intervention. However, most infants

A

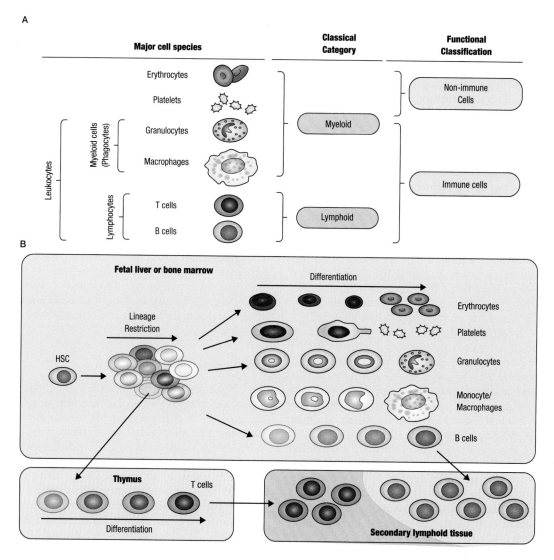

Figure 7.11 Blood cell types and their differentiation. (A) Major types of hematopoietic cells. Historically, erythroid and myeloid cells have been grouped into the "myeloid" lineage, and T and B lymphocytes into the "lymphoid'" lineage. Functionally, blood cells can be classified into "non-immune" cells and "immune" cells. For the sake of simplicity, we group hematopoietic cells here into four major classes: (a) erythroid, including erythrocytes and platelets; (b) myeloid, including granulocytes and macrophages; (c) T lymphoid; and (d) B lymphoid. (B) Sites of hematopoiesis. Note that T cells are produced in the thymus, but all other cell types are produced in fetal liver or bone marrow, where HSCs reside. Extensive proliferation occurs during both lineage restriction and differentiation phases. T cells and B cells undergo further maturation in secondary lymphoid organs such as the spleen or lymph nodes upon encountering specific antigens.

HSC, hematopoietic stem cell.

Source: Adapted from Kawamoto, H., & Yoshimoto K. (2009). A new paradigm for hematopoietic cell lineages: Revision of the classical concept of the myeloid–lymphoid dichotomy. *Trends in Immunology, 30*(5), 193–200. doi:10.1016/j.it.2009.03.001

inherit one to four alpha gene deletions, which leads to an inability to cleave an appropriate number of alpha globin chains. α thalassemia can be classified genetically or clinically. The three clinical classifications are: (a) minor disease (silent carrier status), (b) α thalassemia trait (HbH disease), or (c) major disease (Hb Bart syndrome; Table 7.7; Cappellini, 2016). Hemoglobin H (HbH) disease typically manifests with hemolytic anemia, microcytosis, and splenomegaly. Hb Bart syndrome typically leads to fetal demise secondary to fatal hydrops fetalis.

TABLE 7.5 Other Inherited Disorders of the Hematologic System

- Aplasia cutis
- Diamond–Blackfan anemia
- Ehlers–Danlos syndrome
- Factor V, VII, X, XI, XII, XIII deficiencies
- Fanconi anemia
- Hemochromatosis
- Klippel–Trenaunay syndrome
- Noonan syndrome
- Shwachman–Diamond syndrome
- Sturge–Weber syndrome
- Twin–twin transfusion syndrome

NOTE: A more comprehensive list is provided by the National Institute of Health, Genetic and Rare Diseases Information Center.

TABLE 7.6 Risk Factors for α and β Thalassemia

Type of Thalassemia	Ethnic Risk Factors
Alpha (α)	Ethnicity (country of origin) • Africa • China • Malaysia • Vietnam
Beta (β)	Ethnicity (country of origin) • Africa • China • Middle Eastern countries • Pakistan • India

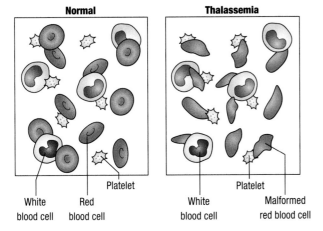

Figure 7.12 Cell morphology: normal versus thalassemias.

Beta Thalassemia. Beta thalassemia results from deficient or, in rare circumstances, absent synthesis of beta globin chains, which is usually the result of β gene deletions at chromosome 11. This leads to the formation of excess alpha and, in some circumstances, excess beta globin chains. Similar to α thalassemia, β thalassemia can be classified genetically or clinically. The three clinical classifications are: (a) minor disease, (b) β thalassemia intermedia, or (c) major disease (Table 7.8; Cappellini, 2016).

Neonatal APNs should recognize that unlike α thalassemia, most cases of β thalassemia do not manifest during the birth hospitalization or the neonatal period. The exception to this principle involves situations where infants require extensive postnatal blood transfusions. In these circumstances, HbF is rapidly replaced with HbA. This provokes early stimulation and expression of this inherited genetic disorder that would otherwise manifest during childhood or adulthood.

For older children, beta thalassemia minor (one gene defect) is associated with asymptomatic microcytic, hypochromic anemia, and erythrocytosis. The manifestations of beta thalassemia intermedia (two gene defects) and beta thalassemia major (two gene defects) are similar, albeit less severe among children with the intermediate disease state. Manifestations include microcytic and hypochromic anemia, abdominal swelling, life-long blood transfusions, jaundice, and growth retardation (Diab & Luchtman-Jones, 2015). Chelation therapy is indicated to prevent iron overload.

Hereditary Spherocytosis

HS is the third most common inherited defect in RBC membrane structure, superseded only by glucose-6-phosphate dehydrogenase deficiency (G6PD) and ABO isoimmunization (Mahajan & Jain, 2016; Will, Henderson, Jnah, & Newberry, 2017). The incidence of spherocytosis is one in every 2,000 infants and is most common among individuals of Northern European descent (Guizzetti, 2016; Rencic, Zhou, Hsu, & Dhaliwal, 2017; Will et al., 2017). The majority of cases are inherited in an autosomal dominant (AD) manner (75%), though spontaneous mutations and autosomal recessive (AR) inheritance have been described in about 25% of cases (Christensen, 2018; Christensen, Yaish, & Gallagher, 2015). This defect may occur in one of several membrane proteins, including Ankryn-1 (most common AD protein defect), Spectrin, Band 3 (SCL4A1), and protein 4.2 (Table 7.9). Defective Ankryn-1 protein is reported in 40% to 50% of all HS cases (Will et al., 2017). These proteins provide the RBC with its biconcave shape and membrane integrity, and when deficient, lead to RBC membrane instability, decreased deformability, and the characteristic spherical shape identified with this disorder (Figure 7.13).

The abnormally formed RBCs are sequestered in the spleen, where they are prematurely broken down by macrophages, resulting in hemolytic anemia, neonatal jaundice, and splenomegaly (Kaplan, Wong, Sibley, & Stevenson, 2015; Will et al., 2017). Jaundice is reported in more than 80% of affected infants, whereas 28% to 43% of infants are anemic at birth (Will et al., 2017). Commonly, MCH concentrations (MCHC) are elevated among affected infants, reflecting membrane loss and red cell dehydration. An elevated reticulocyte count (3% to 7%) is common within the first 72 hours of life, indicating early hemolysis with compensatory cleavage of immature cells. These red cell indices make powerful screening tools (Christensen, Juul, & Del Vecchio, 2015; Will et al., 2017). Table 7.10 describes other common clinical laboratory findings indicative of HS.

There are several life-span implications for children with moderate to severe spherocytosis. Affected individuals have ongoing anemia, sometimes requiring blood transfusions. Up to 50% of patients develop gallstones (Will et al., 2017). Aplastic crises may occur as a result of viral infections such as parvovirus B19 (Christensen, Juul et al., 2015). Splenic sequestration of abnormal RBCs results in splenomegaly and hypersplenism and may eventually require splenectomy once the child reaches school age or adolescence.

TABLE 7.7 Effect of Gene Dysfunction With Alpha Thalassemia

Type of Alpha Thalassemia	Number of Defective α Genes	Common Clinical Manifestations
Minor	1	• Asymptomatic
α *trait*	2	• Mild hemolytic anemia • Childhood iron deficiency anemia
Hb H disease	3	• Bone marrow expansion • Moderate hemolytic anemia • Iron hyperabsorption • Splenomegaly
Major disease (Hb Bart syndrome)	4	• Congestive heart failure • Genitourinary abnormalities • Hepatomegaly • Hydrops fetalis • Severe hemolytic anemia • Splenomegaly

α, alpha; Hb, hemoglobin.

TABLE 7.8 Effect of Gene Dysfunction With Beta Thalassemia

Type of Beta Thalassemia	Number of Defective β Genes	Common Clinical Manifestations
Minor	1	• Asymptomatic to mild hemolytic anemia • Increased HbF
Intermediate	2	• Increased HbF • Iron hyperabsorption • Hepatosplenomegaly • Iron hyperabsorption • Moderate to severe hemolytic anemia that may require lifelong blood transfusions
Major	2	• Iron hyperabsorption • Hepatosplenomegaly • Severe decrease in β globulin synthesis • Severe hemolytic anemia that will require lifelong blood transfusions

β, beta; HbF, fetal hemoglobin.

TABLE 7.9 Proteins and Genetic Influences With Heredity Spherocytosis

Molecular Defect	Prevalence in HS Population	Inheritance	Prevalent	Protein Low Expressed	Disease Severity	Cytologic Feature (MGG) Coloration of the Blood Smears
Ankyrin-1 (*ANK1*)	40%–60% in Europe and USA	AD, AR, *de novo*	AD or *de novo:* null mutation AR: missense or promoter mutation	Spectrin and Ankyrin: 11% and 50%	Minor to moderate form	Spherocytes
Band 3 (*SLC4A1*)	20%–35%	AD	Functionally null mutation	Band 3: 31%–35%	Minor to moderate form	Spherocytes, rare mushroom red cells
α spectrin (*SPTA1*)	<5%	AR	α-LEPRA and null mutation	α spectrin: 50%–75%	Severe	Spherocytes, poikilocytosis, contracted red cells
β spectrin (*SPTB*)	15%–30%	AD, *de novo*	Null mutation	β spectrin: 15%–40%	Minor to moderate form	Spherocytes, 5%–10% acanthocytes
4.2 Protein (*EPB42*)	<5% in Europe and USA (45–50% in Japan)	AR	Missense mutation	4.2 Protein: 95%–100%	Minor to moderate form	Spherocytes, ovalostomatocytes

AD, autosomal dominant; AR, autosomal recessive; HS, hemolytic spherocytosis; LEPRA, low-expression allele Prague; MGG, May-Grunwald-Giemsa.

Source: Reprinted from Da Costa, L., Galimand, J., Fenneteau, O., & Mohandas, N. (2013). Hereditary spherocytosis, elliptocytosis, and other red cell membrane disorders. *Blood Reviews.* 27(4), 167–178. doi:10.1016/j.blre.2013.04.003. With permission from Elsevier.

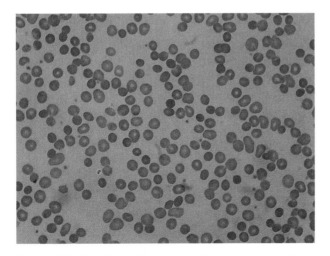

Figure 7.13 Peripheral blood smear of patient with heriditary spherocytosis.

Asplenic or functionally asplenic individuals are at an increased lifelong risk of sepsis with encapsulated organisms, such as *Streptococcus pneumoniae* and *Haemophilus influenza*, necessitating vaccination and anticipatory guidance for children and families (Guizzetti, 2016). Growth failure, folate deficiency, and bony abnormalities may occur in children with severe disease due to increased hematopoiesis in the bone marrow in the setting of severe, chronic anemia (Christensen, Juul et al., 2015). Life expectancy is typically unaffected.

Sickle Cell Disease

Sickle cell disease (SCD) is one of the most common autosomal recessive, single-gene blood disorders reported within in the United States and across the globe. Within the United States, approximately 70,000 to 80,000 infants,

TABLE 7.10 Red Cell Indices and HS

Lab Value	Definition	Associated Laboratory Finding	Rationale
MCHC	Represents the average gram per deciliter (g/dL) of hemoglobin within the RBC	MCHC >36 g/dL	Mild cellular dehydration causes increased cellular hyperdensity.
MCV	Represents the average volume or size in femtoliters (fL) of the RBC	MCV<100 fL in case of HS	Caused by decreased spectrin content on the RBC membrane
MCHC/MCV ratio	MCHC ÷ MCV = MCHC/MCV ratio which is represented as a percentage	MCHC/MCV ratio >36% (0.36)	
RDW percentile	Reflects the average width of the RBC based on fL	RDW >14 fL	Caused by a greater variation in the size of RBC, known as anistocytes

HS, hereditary spherocytosis; MCHC, mean corpuscular hemoglobin concentration; MCV, mean corpuscular volume; RBC, red blood cells; RDW, red cell distribution width.

Source: From Will, A., Henderson, C. A., Jnah, A. J., & Newberry, D. (2017). Hereditary spherocytosis in the neonatal period: A case report. *Neonatal Network, 36*(5), 280–288. doi:10.1891/0730-0832.36.5.280

particularly African American (1 in 500) and Hispanic American (1 in 1,000 to 4,000) infants, are affected by SCD each year (National Institutes of Health [NIH], 2018a). On a global scale, SCD affects approximately 300,000 infants each year; experts posit that the incidence may continue to rise, to upward of 400,000 infants, by the year 2050 (Figure 7.14; (Piel, Hay, Gupta, Weatherall, & Williams, 2013). Global risk factors include African, Mediterranean, Arabian, Indian, South and Central American, and Caribbean descent (Diab & Luchtman-Jones, 2015; NIH, 2018a).

Hemoglobin S (HbS) was first discovered by Linus Pauling in 1949, and its presence is the root cause for sickling of RBCs. The pathogenesis involves the deoxygenation and polymerization of HbS, which deforms the RBC, turning it from a normal biconcave cell into an oblong, stiff, and fragile, "sickle" shaped cell (Figure 7.15; Odièvre, Verger, Silva-Pinto, & Elion, 2011; Piel, Steinberg, & Rees, 2017). The sickle cell has difficulty traversing the vasculature, which leads to clogging of the vascular lumen. The occlusion provokes a vascular occlusive event, the hallmark manifestation of SCD. Although a discussion of the complex cellular responses that are elicited with a vascular occlusive event are beyond the scope of this textbook, it is important to understand that sickle cells readily adhere to the vascular endothelium and this propensity, along with several cellular processes, encourages a painful, proinflammatory state within the blood vessels (Odièvre et al., 2011).

Associated clinical manifestations are summarized in Figure 7.16. Symptoms usually manifest in early childhood and vary from mild to severe. Factors that affect disease severity include climate, outside air quality, smoking, and viral infections; most notable are pneumococcus, *Haemophilus influenzae*, and malaria. Life-span implications include delayed growth and development in children and increased risk for activity-induced fatigue. Affected individuals typically fare better in warmer climates, as cold weather seems to provoke acute complications of SCD (NIH, 2018a; Piel, et al., 2017).

Thrombocytopenia-Absent Radii Syndrome

Thrombocytopenia-absent radius (TAR) syndrome is characterized by limb anomalies, including bilateral absence of radii (with normally developed thumbs) and thrombocytopenia. The platelet count is typically less than 50 x 10⁹/L (normal 150–400 x 10⁹/L). The incidence of TAR is less than one per 100,000 infants (NIH, 2018b). Inheritance is autosomal recessive, though de novo cases have been described (Son-Hing & Thompson, 2015).

Affected infants may have other limb anomalies affecting upper and/or lower extremities as well as involvement of other organ systems, including cardiac and renal anomalies. Thrombocytopenia may be congenital or may develop in the months after birth and is usually transient and self-limited (Toriello, 2011). However, severe thrombocytopenia may result in

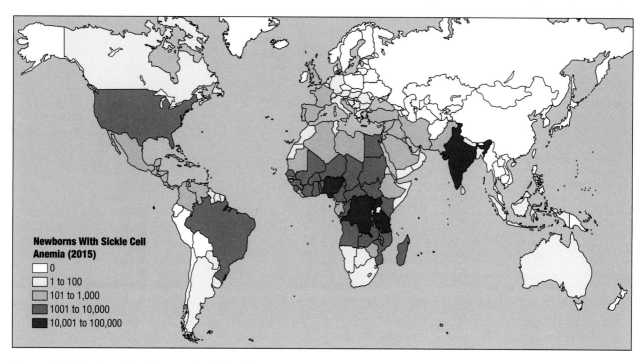

Figure 7.14 Number of newborns with sickle cell anemia in each country in 2015.

Source: Adapted from Kato, G. J., Piel, F. B., Reid, C. D., Gaston, M. H., Ohene-Frempong, K., Krishnamurti, L., . . . Vichinsky, E. P. (2018). Sickle cell disease. *Nature Reviews: Disease Primers, 4,* 18010. doi:10.1038/nrdp.2018.10

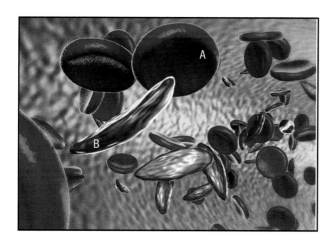

Figure 7.15 (A) Normal, biconcave RBC versus (B) an abnormally oblong and stiff, sickled RBC.

RBC, red blood cell.

life-threatening bleeding such as intracranial hemorrhage. The pathogenesis of thrombocytopenia in TAR is not well understood, but thought to be related to a poor response to thrombopoietin (Toriello, 2011).

There are several life-span implications related to TAR. First, it is possible for thrombocytopenia to recur intermittently during childhood. In addition, 67% of

individuals with TAR syndrome exhibit an allergy to cow's milk; exposure is associated with thrombocytic episodes (Bertoni et al., 2016; Toriello, 2011). Individuals with TAR may also develop transient leukemoid reactions, with WBC counts greater than 35×10^9/L. There have also been case reports of individuals with TAR developing acute lymphocytic leukemia and acute myeloid leukemia, but it remains unclear if this is directly related to the underlying TAR syndrome (Toriello, 2011).

Von Willebrand Disease

Von Willebrand disease is the most common inherited bleeding disorder with a prevalence of one in every 100 individuals, though only 1% of those individuals experience symptomatic disease (1/1000; Proud & Ritchey, 2017). Males and females are equally affected. The mutation results in a decrease in quantity or function of Von Willebrand factor (vWF).

vWF facilitates adherence of platelets to areas of endothelial injury within blood vessels, initiating platelet aggregation and allowing formation of a platelet plug at the site of injury (Figure 7.17; Castaman & Linari, 2017; Sola-Visner & Ramsey, 2017). This process is known as *primary hemostasis*. vWF is also involved in the stabilization and binding of factor VIII, which is essential in formation of fibrin clots (secondary hemostasis; Sola-Visner & Ramsey, 2017).

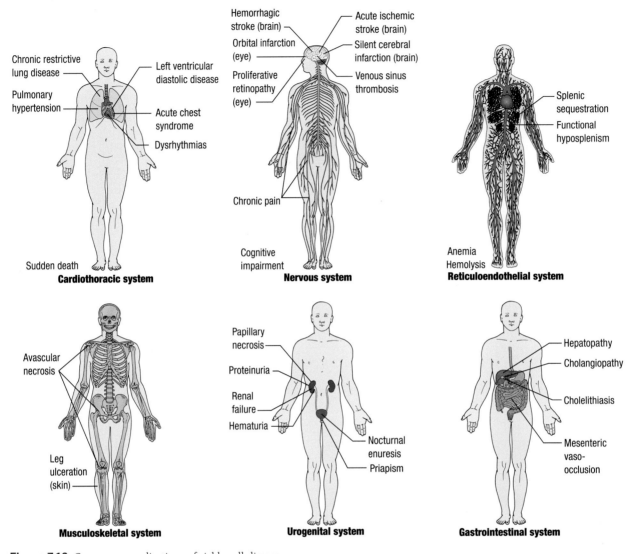

Figure 7.16 Common complications of sickle cell disease.

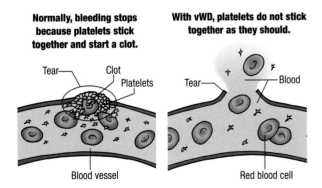

Figure 7.17 Von Willebrand disease.

vWD, von Willebrand disease.

There are three major types of von Willebrand disease. Type I involves decreased concentrations of vWF, and is responsible for 75% of cases; type II results from abnormal function of vWF, and may present with thrombocytopenia. Type III, the most severe form, is characterized by the absence or near-complete deficiency of vWB, and may present similarly to hemophilia A due to its effects on factor VIII. Types I and II are inherited in an autosomal dominant manner and type III is typically autosomal recessive (Diab & Luchtman-Jones, 2015).

Symptoms include mucosal bleeding and easy bruising, which can range from mild to severe and life-threatening (Diab & Luchtman-Jones, 2015). Less common, hematomas and hemarthrosis (bleeding into the joints) may occur (Castaman & Linari, 2017). Von Willebrand disease commonly presents after the neonatal period, though types II and III may present soon after birth due to their severity (Diab & Luchtman-Jones, 2015). Unexplained or excessive bleeding after procedures, such as circumcision, should prompt concern. Usually, the disease will become clinically apparent later in childhood or early in adulthood with chronic mucosal bleeding such as recurrent epistaxis, gastrointestinal bleeding, or increased bleeding after trauma or procedures, including dental surgery, or may present as menorrhagia in young women (Castaman & Linari, 2017). Von Willebrand disease is a lifelong disease that requires ongoing medical management and prophylactic treatment prior to invasive procedures (Schinco et al., 2017).

MATERNAL HEALTH INFLUENCES

The influence of maternal health on the developing fetal and neonatal hematologic system is a well-recognized and expanding area. More than 45 years ago, Dr. Frank Oski declared that investigation of maternal status is necessary to interpret neonatal disease (Oski & Naiman, 1982). This portion of the chapter reviews infectious etiologies, immune-mediated processes, maternal diseases, and the effect of maternally administered drugs on fetal/neonatal hematopoiesis. Future directions include understanding the mechanisms for neutropenia and thrombocytopenia in non–antibody-mediated maternal conditions, including pregnancy-induced hypertension (PIH), systemic lupus erythematosus (SLE), maternal diabetes mellitus, and hyperthyroidism.

Maternal Antibodies and the Fetus and Neonate

Maternal antibodies, commonly referred to as *immunoglobulins (IG)*, transfer to the fetus by receptor-mediated endocytosis. Only maternal IgG is transported across the placenta (Martin et al., 2015). The antibodies are glycoproteins that are naturally produced in response to a foreign antigen. Intact antibodies are transferred after internalization within vesicles. The vesicles are then delivered from the cytoplasm of the syncytiotrophoblast within the placenta through the capillary endothelial cell and given entry into the fetal circulation (Figure 7.18). Several diseases will be described within the "Common Problems With Implications Across the Life-Span" section of this chapter that highlight the hematologic effects of maternal antibodies targeting RBCs, neutrophils, lymphocytes, and platelets. These diseases include hemolytic disease of the fetus and newborn, ABO incompatibility, Rh (D) hemolytic disease, neonatal neutropenia, and thrombocytopenia.

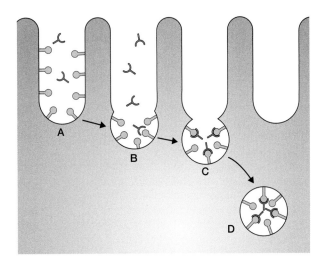

Figure 7.18 Receptor-mediated endocytosis.

Maternal Viral Infections

TORCH and Other Related Infections. As a group, neonatal TORCH infections traditionally include *Toxoplasma gondii*, "other" (*Treponema pallidum*), rubella virus, cytomegalovirus (CMV–human herpes virus 5), and herpes simplex virus (HSV) because of their similar presentations. CMV is the most common congenital viral infection. These infections can alter the hematologic profile of infected neonates resulting in anemia, neutropenia, thrombocytopenia, and disseminated intravascular coagulation (DIC). Other viral infections, including parvovirus, HIV, and enteroviruses (coxsackie B and echovirus), also have the potential to affect the hematopoietic system. As a result, the concept of an expanded TORCH has been proposed (Johnson, 2017; Kinney & Kumar, 1988). In some cases, particularly among neonates with congenital HSV, coxsackie B virus, and echovirus infections, disseminated intravascular coagulation can be profound. An overview of the major clinical manifestations of TORCH infections and related infections is provided in the text that follows.

Anemia is a well-recognized manifestation among neonates and infants with parvovirus B19 and congenital syphilis, and sometimes occurs in congenital CMV infection. The anemia is due to hemolysis of the RBCs as evidenced by increased reticulocytes and hyperbilirubinemia with elevations in both the direct and indirect components (de Alarcón, Werner, & Christensen, 2013; Lanzkowsky, Lipton, & Fish, 2016). With parvovirus and congenital syphilis, severe fetal and neonatal anemia may result in fetal hydrops. In infants with congenital syphilis, the presence of anemia is variable, occurring in up to 64% of patients less than 4 weeks of age and 89% of those over 4 weeks of age (Barron & Pass, 1995). Although hemolytic anemia is commonly reported in those infants with symptomatic congenital CMV, the presence of anemia is variable. In CMV, infection of hematopoietic precursor cells may result in a more pronounced anemia secondary to diminished RBC production. (de Alarcón et al., 2013). In neonates with HIV infection, a transient anemia may be the result of the maternal antiretroviral therapy altering neonatal hematopoiesis (de Alarcón et al., 2013; Lanzkowsky et al., 2016). In addition, postnatal treatment with zidovudine is well recognized for its effect on the development of anemia and neutropenia in the infant (de Alarcón et al., 2013).

Both neutrophilia and neutropenia have been described in neonates and infants with congenital toxoplasmosis and congenital rubella (de Alarcón et al., 2013). Eosinophilia has been reported in as many as 18% to 25% of neonates with congenital toxoplasmosis (Calhoun, 2016; de Alarcón et al., 2013). Similarly, extreme variability in WBC count has been described in newborn infants with congenital syphilis. Several leukocyte abnormalities have been associated with congenital CMV, including lymphocytosis and neutropenia (de Alarcón et al., 2013). A prolonged neutropenia has also been reported in infants with congenital CMV infection (de Alarcón et al., 2013; Ivarsson & Ljung, 1988). However, unlike CMV infection, enteroviral infection has been associated with leukocytosis, neutrophilia, and an increase in band forms (de Alarcón et al., 2013).

Thrombocytopenia is the most common manifestation of many of the viral infections described previously (Johnson, 2017). Of those neonates with congenital CMV, thrombocytopenia affects about 80% and is the result of nearly absent megakaryocytes. In neonates infected with the protozoan parasite *Toxoplasma gondii*, thrombocytopenia affects approximately 10%. The mechanism for the resultant thrombocytopenia in toxoplasmosis is thought to be the result of increased peripheral destruction.

Multi-organ involvement is a common feature of both neonatal enterovirus and neonatal HSV infections (de Alarcón et al., 2013). In neonatal HSV, up to 30% of infections are disseminated and involve multiple organs (Cherpes, Matthews, & Maryak, 2012). DIC, neutropenia, and thrombocytopenia are frequently reported in conjunction with congenital HSV infection. DIC, neutrophilia, and thrombocytopenia are commonly observed with enteroviral infection (de Alarcón et al., 2013). The presence of DIC increases the infant's risk of death, which may be as high as 80% in untreated patients with neonatal HSV (Aswad & Suryadevara, 2014; de Alarcón et al., 2013).

Maternal Autoimmune Disorders

Maternal Autoimmune Hemolytic Anemia. Maternal autoimmune hemolytic anemia may occur during pregnancy and is recognized by Coombs's positivity in the mother and the infant in the absence of a setup for Rh or ABO incompatibility. The anemia in the fetus results from the passive transfer of IVIG antibodies. In this manner, maternal autoimmune hemolytic disease is similar to maternal immune diseases, such as SLE and rheumatoid arthritis, which may also transfer IVIG antibodies to the fetus. In addition to the production of anemia, the IVIG antibodies may not be specific to antigens on the fetal RBC and may affect neutrophils and platelets.

Systemic Lupus Erythematosus. Maternal SLE is commonly defined as a multi-system autoimmune disorder. This condition can be passively acquired by way of maternal antibody acquisition and genetic/environmental factors and lead to neonatal lupus (Ohls & Maheshwari, 2012). The antibodies which impose pathogenic function upon the developing fetus are usually anti-Ro (SS-A) or anti-La (SS-B), which begin crossing the placenta around week 12 of gestation and matriculate into fetal tissues. This gives rise to a spectrum of disorders which may include hemolytic anemia, thrombocytopenia, and neutropenia; each have been reported in 10% to 20% of all affected neonates (Brucato, Cimaz, Caporali, Ramoni, & Buyon, 2011; de Alarcón et al., 2013). In addition, congestive heart failure may develop secondary to anemia and immune-mediated myocarditis. Fetal heart block may develop secondary to antibody complement deposition within the myocardium, which leads to fibrosis and a blockage of the cardiac conduction system (Diab & Luchtman-Jones, 2015). For those infants with thrombocytopenia, the degree of the condition may be severe with platelet counts as low as 30,000/mm³. The specific cause of the thrombocytopenia is not known in all cases, but in at least some, anti-SS-A/Ro antibodies are involved. The occurrence of disseminated intravascular coagulation has been reported as well as hepatosplenomegaly and pericarditis. Hematologic manifestations of neonatal lupus are self-limited; the timing of resolution mirrors the disappearance of circulating maternal antibodies.

Maternal Leukemia and Malignancies

Maternal cancer during pregnancy is more frequent than the occurrence of appendicitis, thyrotoxicosis, nephrolithiasis, and deep vein thrombosis, complicating one in every 1,000 to 1,500 pregnancies (Azim, Pavlidis, & Peccatori, 2010). More than 400 cases of maternal leukemia, including monocytic, myelocytic, lymphocytic, and lymphoblastic leukemia, have all been reported during pregnancy. In each of these cases, offspring developed leukemia during infancy (Cramblett, Friedman, & Najjar, 1958; Hoffman et al., 2018).

Maternal Cardiac Disease

Compared to unaffected infants, infants of mothers with chronic hypoxia are noted to possess higher HgF concentrations as a result of maternal congenital cardiac disease (de Alarcón et al., 2013). In addition to higher hemoglobin concentrates, these infants also present with lower

WBC counts when compared with neonates whose mothers did not have heart disease. When the bone marrow of these infants was examined, increased erythropoiesis was noted (de Alarcón et al., 2013).

Maternal Metabolic Disorders

Hyperthyroidism. Maternal thyroid disease can result in neonatal hyperviscosity syndrome and thrombocytopenia (van der Kaay, Wasserman, & Palmert, 2016). The precise mechanisms are not clearly understood.

Diabetes Mellitus. Infants born to women with diabetes mellitus can present with a variety of hematologic abnormalities, including increased RBC mass (resulting in hyperviscosity syndrome), hyperaggregable platelets (resulting in thrombosis), and neutropenia (Hay, 2012). The etiology of the increased incidence of thrombosis is felt to be multifactorial (de Alarcón et al., 2013).

Widness and colleagues (1981) noted that infants with increased RBC mass and those with hyperviscosity syndrome had increased plasma concentrations of EPO associated with fetal hypoxia (Rennie, 2012). Insulin may also contribute to the increased red cell mass as it may further promote erythropoiesis (de Alarcón et al., 2013). *In vitro* studies using tissue culture have demonstrated that insulin concentrations similar to those found in infants of diabetic mothers (IDM) stimulate the growth of late erythroid progenitors (Perrine, Greene, Lee, Cohen, & Faller, 1986). This may explain the correlation of fetal EPO concentrations and fetal insulin levels reported by Widness and colleagues (1981) and the lack of an increase in EPO concentrations in IDMs whose mothers exhibited glycemic control during the pregnancy.

The etiology for increased thrombosis is multifactorial (de Alarcón et al., 2013). Unlike the relationship between EPO concentrations and hyperviscosity, evaluation of IDM with thrombosis did not demonstrate any abnormalities in plasma coagulation factors. To be specific, no difference in the prothrombin time, activated partial thromboplastin time, or fibrinogen; von Willebrand antigen; or factors V, X, or XII were found (de Alacórn et al., 2013; Easa & Coen, 1979). Prothrombotic risk factors were evaluated by Sarkar and colleagues (2005), who reported that although there was no difference in the frequency of factor V Leiden, prothrombin gene mutation P20210A, methylene-tetrahydrofolate reductase C677T, or other common genetic risk factors, protein C levels were lower in IDMs regardless of whether the mother was gestational-diet controlled or insulin dependent. Homocysteine levels, a well-recognized risk factor for thrombosis, are known to be elevated in IDMs (Fonseca, Reynolds, & Fink, 1998).

Increased insulin concentrations found in women with gestational diabetes and maternal hyperglycemia may contribute to impaired platelet function, as has been demonstrated in animal studies. The proposed mechanisms may include inhibition of platelet-activating factor biosynthesis, reduction of the levels of platelet-activating factor, and impairment of thromboxane synthesis.

Neonatal thrombocytopenia that is self-limiting (resolving within 10 days) has been described in infants born to women with diabetes during pregnancy. The mechanism is thought to involve fetal hypoxia, similar to that occurring in PIH, preeclampsia, and intrauterine growth restriction. Although common in these infants, the platelet count is usually greater than 50,000/μL. Platelet hyperactivity was reported by Knobler and coworkers (1998), whereas increased reactivity and platelet endoperoxide formation was noted in the mothers and transiently in IDMs (Christensen, Juul, & DelVecchio, 2015; Knobler, Savion, Shenkman, Kotev-Emeth, & Varon, 1998; Orkin, 2015).

For infants with neutropenia related to maternal diabetes, the duration is generally brief (2–3 days) and self-resolving. The precise cause of the neutropenia remains unknown, but is believed to relate to fetal-tissue hypoxia (Watts & Roberts, 1999). Mehta and Petrova (2005) noted that neutrophil chemotaxis, chemiluminescence, and random motility were decreased in IDMs when compared to control patients.

Pregnancy-Related Maternal Conditions and Common Hematologic Problems

Pregnancy-Induced Hypertension. PIH can affect fetal and neonatal hematologic function. Neutropenia, thrombocytopenia, and DIC are commonly reported, and are the focus of this discussion.

Neutropenia is reported in as many as 40% to 50% of offspring (de Alarcón et al., 2013). It increases with the severity of maternal hypertension and is most evident in those neonates delivered of women with severe or prolonged maternal hypertension associated with fetal intrauterine growth restriction. The kinetic mechanism for the neutropenia is decreased neutrophil production, but the specific etiology of the decreased production is unclear (Christensen, 2000). Possible etiologies include a placentally derived inhibitor of neutrophil production, a decreased responsiveness of precursor cells to G-CSF, the erythrocyte steal phenomena seen with intrauterine hypoxia, and/or downregulation of white cell production due to placental dysfunction and FAS–FAS ligand interaction abnormalities (de Alarcón et al., 2013; Ohls & Maheshwari, 2012). Although some have reported that these infants have an increased incidence of nosocomial infection that may be as high as 6% compared to non-neutropenic infants, the published literature is conflicting (Paul, Leef, Sciscione, Tuttle, & Stefano, 1999; Procianoy & Brazillian Network on Neonatal Research, 2010). Stoll and colleagues noted that the presence of maternal hypertension/preeclampsia actually decreased the risk of neonatal infection (Stoll & Hansen, 2003).

Thrombocytopenia, or impaired platelet function, is also reported among offspring of women with PIH. Thrombocytopenia is felt to be the direct result of chronic fetal hypoxia, similar to that reported in infants of diabetic mothers and those with preeclampsia (Rennie, 2012). Thrombocytopenia may occur in 15% to 36% of infants born to women with PIH (De Alarcon et al., 2013). Although the precise mechanism for reduced platelet function is not known, proposed mechanisms include altered metabolism of calcium, alteration of platelet membrane glycoproteins, increased release of plasma β-thromboglobulin, and altered nitric oxide bioavailability (Christensen, Juul et al., 2015). The platelet surface expression of P-selectin and CD63, GPIIb/IIIa, and CD9 are diminished in neonates born to women with PIH (Christensen, Juul et al., 2015). Thrombopoietin levels did not differ between those infants born to mothers with and without PIH (Tsao, Teng, Chou, & Tsou, 2002).

In addition, DIC has been identified among offspring of women with PIH, preeclampsia, and platelet counts less than 50,000/μL (Ramesh Bhat & Cherian, 2008). The pathogenesis of DIC in the neonate is not fully understood, is complex, and is secondary to a variety of underlying diseases and conditions including congenital viral infections and adverse events that affect the feto–placental unit. The diagnosis is confirmed by prolongation of the prothrombin time, activated partial thromboplastin time, thrombocytopenia, and decreased fibrinogen with increased concentrations of fibrinogen degradation products (de Alarcón et al., 2013).

Placental Insufficiency. Placental insufficiency is felt to be an underlying cause for fetal and neonatal thrombocytopenia. Megakaryocytopoiesis is severely impaired as shown by a marked reduction in circulating megakaryocytes and their precursor/progenitor cells. The reduced megakaryocytopoiesis results in reduced fetal platelet production and the resultant thrombocytopenia (Rennie, 2012).

Intra-Amniotic Infection. In addition to the viral infections previously discussed, maternal intra-amniotic infection affects the neonate's hematopoietic system. Numerous cytokine concentrations, including interleukins (IL)-1, IL-6, IL-8, TNF, and G-CSF, are significantly increased with maternal intra-amniotic infection. Recall that G-CSF is recognized as a lineage-specific growth factor and the primary regulator of neutrophil production, differentiation, and function. Concentrations of G-CSF may be 10- to 100-fold higher in the amniotic fluid obtained from preterm pregnancies with culture-proven infection (de Alarcón et al., 2013). In a study by Calhoun and coworkers (1996), 71% of infants who had leukemoid reactions within the first 4 days of birth were born to women with intra-amniotic infection (Calhoun, Kirk, & Christensen, 1996). None of the infants demonstrated culture-proven infection.

Betamethasone Administration. Antenatal betamethasone exposure has been reported to have a variable effect on neutrophil counts in neonates. The first report of the effect of antenatal steroids (dexamethasone) was reported by Anday and Harris (1982). Similarly, in a study involving 45 preterm infants whose mothers were treated with betamethasone within 36 hours of delivery, Barak and coworkers (1992) noted higher WBC and neutrophil counts when compared to controls (Barak, Cohen, & Herschkowitz, 1992). In addition, the effect of the drug lasted 3 days and, in some infants, for as long as 7 days. However, others have reported inconsistent effects of antenatal betamethasone on the neonatal neutrophil population (Juul, Haynes, & McPherson, 2004). In a study of infants less than 32 weeks of gestation at birth, neutrophilia was observed in 28%, whereas neutropenia was reported in 26% of infants whose mothers had received antenatal betamethasone (Juul et al., 2004). In those infants experiencing a leukemoid reaction (absolute neutrophil count [ANC] > 50,000/μL), some of the mothers were noted to have received betamethasone. In a study examining the incidence of leukemoid reactions in the NICU, we previously reported that of the six infants less than 34 weeks who experienced a leukemoid reaction within the first 4 days after birth, 67% had a history of antenatal betamethasone exposure within 48 hours of their birth (Calhoun et al., 1996). Larger studies are necessary in order to determine whether the effect of antenatal betamethasone consistently results in an increase in WBC counts in infants who are exposed prior to delivery. At this time, monitoring of the WBC count and neutrophil count after birth should be considered.

Indomethacin Administration. Limited information exists related to maternal indomethacin exposure and the effect on the fetal hematologic system; however, some experts contend that maternal ingestion can increase the risk for fetal and neonatal neutropenia. Although Juul and coworkers (2004) did not report any increase in white cell count with the administration of this drug, Bengtsson and colleagues (2006) reported an infant who developed neutropenia after being treated with indomethacin and then developed Gram-negative sepsis. Upon further inquiry, the infant's mother also reported the development of neutropenia after treatment with indomethacin (Bengtsson, Milstein, & Sherman, 2006). The authors noted that indomethacin-induced neutropenia has been reported in adults, and monitoring of the WBC count as well as platelet count is warranted when neonates are treated with indomethacin.

Intravenous Immunoglobulin (IVIG) Administration. Neonatal thrombocytopenia may occur as the direct result of maternal IVIG alloantibodies that have been produced by platelet-specific fetal antigens of paternal origin. The use of IVIG has remained the primary antenatal treatment of neonatal alloimmune thrombocytopenia (NAIT) since 1988. Weekly infusions of IVIG (with or without concomitant steroid therapy) continue to be the most commonly used therapeutic regimen (Christensen, Juul et al., 2015). IVIG may act by several proposed mechanisms, which include suppressing platelet antibody synthesis, blocking antiplatelet antibody transfer across the placenta, and interfering with phagocyte-mediated immune clearance by the reticulo-endothelial system. Recommendations for using IVIG and prednisolone together are supported for those fetuses where fetal blood sampling demonstrates a platelet count less than 20K. When the platelet count is greater than 20K, either treatment may be used. When the fetal platelet count is not known (e.g., cordocentesis is not performed), treatment with IVIG (2 gm/kg) was comparable to standard dosing of IVIG 1 gm/kg and prednisone 0.5 mg/kg (Berkowitz et al., 2007; de Alarcón et al., 2013).

Folic Acid and Vitamin B$_{12}$ Deficiency. Both folate and vitamin B$_{12}$ are effectively transported across the placenta (de Alarcón et al., 2013). Folate deficiency results in a megaloblastic anemia and is associated with impaired nuclear maturation of the hematopoietic cells in the marrow. The characteristic marrow finding is a delay of nuclear maturation compared with cytoplasmic maturation, resulting in a macrocytic anemia, thrombocytopenia, and hypersegmentation of neutrophils and a reduction in the number of granulocytes.

Prolonged breastfeeding by mothers with vitamin B$_{12}$ deficiency (pernicious anemia) or dietary restrictions (e.g., strict vegetarians and vegans) limiting B$_{12}$ intake may also cause megaloblastic anemia, which is observed later during infancy (Guez et al., 2012; Obeid, Munz, Jäger, Schmidt, & Herrmann, 2005; Van Sande, Jacquemyn, & Karepouan, 2013).

Thiazide Drug Administration. Neonatal thrombocytopenia has been reported in newborn infants whose mothers had neither a platelet deficiency nor detectable antiplatelet antibodies in their serum (Prescott, 1964). In one series of mothers receiving chlorothiazide, hydrochlorothiazide, or methylclothiazide during pregnancy, infants demonstrated spontaneous recovery of platelet counts between 2 and 12 weeks of age. Two different mechanisms have been proposed for the thrombocytopenia: One is reduced platelet production in the fetus associated with decreased megakaryocytes in the fetal marrow *without* affecting the maternal platelet count and the second involves a hapten–antibody-mediated process that results in the destruction of platelets (Christensen, 2000). The former mechanism is thought to be the more common of the two. Although the firm establishment of the drug as the cause of the fetal–neonatal thrombocytopenia is difficult with this association, it remains a consideration for unexplained thrombocytopenia when maternal use of these medications is documented. (de Alarcón et al., 2013).

Zidovudine Administration. Zidovudine treatment for maternal HIV infection has been associated with fetal and neonatal anemia. However, treatment of pregnant women with zidovudine is the standard of care in those women who are HIV positive in order to prevent vertical transmission of the virus to the fetus. Zidovudine crosses the placenta to the fetus by active transport that is energy-dependent (Schleiss & Marsh, 2018). The reduction in transmission of infection to the fetus was found to be from 25.5% to 8.3% in those seropositive women who were treated with oral zidovudine during the pregnancy and then intravenous zidovudine during labor (Schleiss & Marsh, 2018). Zidovudine provokes anemia by inhibiting fetal erythropoiesis; neonates whose mothers received treatment have lower hemoglobin concentrations and hematocrits (Christensen, 2000).

COMMON PROBLEMS WITH IMPLICATIONS ACROSS THE LIFE SPAN

Hematological diseases have the potential to involve RBCs, granulocytes, lymphocytes, and monocytes, as well as platelets and clotting proteins. Here we present common disorders of the hematologic system with implications across the life span.

Disorders of RBCs

Polycythemia. *Polycythemia* is defined as hematocrit and hemoglobin levels more than 2 *SD*s above the norm, or more simple, a hemoglobin greater than 20 g/dL and a hematocrit greater than 65% (Brown & Chang, 2018; Diab & Luchtman-Jones, 2015). Polycythemia is thought to occur in about 2% to 5% of all term infants, and is associated with hyperviscosity syndrome, which leads to impairment of the circulatory system.

Infants at highest risk for developing polycythemia include postterm infants; infants who are small for gestational age (SGA) and large for gestational age (LGA); those born at high altitude; IDM; and infants with genetic syndromes, including trisomy 21 and Beckwith–Weidemann syndrome. Placental transfusion, such as maternal–fetal transfusion or twin-to-twin transfusion, contributes, as does prolonged intrauterine tobacco exposure (Diab & Luchtman-Jones, 2015). Neonatal thyrotoxicosis, perinatal asphyxia, delayed cord clamping, and postnatal dehydration may increase the risk for polycythemia (de Alarcón et al., 2013; Diab & Luchtman-Jones, 2015).

The pathogenesis of polycythemia involves one of two pathways: (a) increased fetal erythropoiesis or

(b) erythrocyte transfusion. Conditions that increase fetal erythropoiesis include preeclampsia, placental abruption, maternal heart disease, smoking or alcohol abuse, and maternal diabetes. Inherited conditions that lead to increased fetal erythropoiesis include trisomy 13, 18, 21, and Beckwith-Wiedemann syndrome, yet the pathogenesis is poorly understood (Remon, Raghavan, & Maheshwari, 2011). Many of the aforementioned conditions give rise to placental insufficiency, decreased fetal tissue oxygenation, and a resultant increase in fetal erythropoiesis. Polycythemia caused by erythrocyte transfusion is associated with maternal oxytocin administration, delayed cord clamping (>3 minute delay), placenta-to-fetus-transfusion (lowering infant >15 cm above or below level of placenta after birth), and among fetuses affected by twin-twin transfusion syndrome (TTTS).

After birth, an infant's hematocrit level will increase. Levels peak at about 2 hours of age, and then demonstrate a steady decrease to normal levels by about 12 hours of age (Ohls, 2017). Symptomatic infants may display plethora, tachypnea, lethargy, hypoglycemia,

thrombocytopenia, hyperbilirubinemia, and, rarely, thrombosis. Possible complications include acute kidney injury and cerebral infarction as a result of venous thrombosis, sludging, or thromboembolic events (Diab & Luchtman-Jones, 2015).

The long-term outcomes for infants with polycythemia are controversial. Some studies suggest that infants with polycythemia have worse neurodevelopmental outcomes compared to infants without polycythemia. This may be reflective of the underlying cause rather than the presence of polycythemia given the currently available evidence (Diab & Luchtman-Jones, 2015).

Anemia. *Anemia* is defined as decreased RBC mass with hemoglobin or hematocrit measurement 2 *SD*s below the mean for age (Diab & Luchtman-Jones, 2015; Zitelli, McIntire, & Nowalk, 2018). Risk factors range from the aforementioned maternal health influences, to blood loss or sequestration, underproduction, or increased destruction of RBCs (Table 7.11). The mean corpuscular volume (MCV) of RBCs and degree of reticulocytosis are important in differentiating among the various etiologies of anemia (Diab &

TABLE 7.11 Causes of Neonatal Anemia

Blood Loss	Underproduction of RBCs	Increased Destruction of RBCs
1. Coagulation defect	1. Anemia of prematurity	1. Immune mediated
2. Fetal-maternal hemorrhage	2. Congenital underproduction related to chronic disease	• ABO/Rh incompatibility
3. Twin-to-twin transfusion		2. Nonimmune mediated Structural erythrocyte defects
4. Abnormal placentation	• Hypothyroidism	
5. Placental abruption	• Adrenal insufficiency	• Hereditary spherocytosis
6. Cord accidents	• Hypopituitarism	• Hereditary eliptocytosis
7. Traumatic birth	3. Congenital bone marrow failure syndromes	3. Erythrocyte enzyme defects
8. Iatrogenic blood draws		• G6PD deficiency
9. Sequestration	• Diamond–Blackfan	• Pyruvate kinase deficiency
	• Fanconi anemia	4. Hemoglobinopathies
• Subdural hematoma	• Aplastic anemia	
• Cephalohematoma	4. Infection-related	• Microangiopathic hemolytic anemia
• Hemangioma		5. Infection (bacterial, viral, fungal)
• Vascular malformations	• Parvovirus B19	
• Extensive ecchymosis	• Hepatitis	
• Subgaleal hemorrhage	• HIV	
	• Syphilis	
	5. Nutritional deficiency	
	• Iron	
	• Folate	
	• Vitamin B_{12}	

RBC, red blood cell

Sources: MacDonald, M. G., & Seshia, M. M. K. (Eds.). (2015). *Avery's neonatology: Pathophysiology and management of the newborn* (7th ed.). Philadelphia, PA: Wolters Kluwer; Martin, R. J., Fanaroff, A. A., & Walsh, M. C. (Eds.). (2015). *Fanaroff & Martin's neonatal–perinatal medicine: Diseases of the fetus and infant* (10th ed.). Philadelphia, PA: Elsevier Saunders.

Luchtman-Jones, 2015). The following sections will review the most common causes of anemia resulting from diminished production, accelerated destruction, or blood loss.

Anemia due to diminished production. Typical causes for decreased RBC production include aplastic or hypoplastic anemia, bone marrow suppression, and iron deficiency. Aplastic or hypoplastic anemias may be the result of a wide array of rare congenital and acquired conditions. Examples include Diamond–Blackfan and Fanconi anemias. Diamond–Blackfan is a rare autosomal dominant condition that causes bone marrow failure and a pure red cell aplasia. This leads to anemia and deficient erythropoiesis; laboratory findings include a low hematocrit and low reticulocyte count. Diamond-Blackfan is known to present in the neonatal period or during infancy. Fanconi anemia is a rare autosomal recessive disorder resulting in severe anemia that typically presents around school age rather than in the neonatal period. Both of these conditions may be associated with other physical findings, such as growth failure; microcephaly; and skeletal, cardiac, ophthalmologic, and genitourinary anomalies (Zitelli et al., 2018). In addition, a transient deficiency of EPO synthesis observed during the early postnatal period may occur. Among term infants, this is named physiologic anemia of infancy. Among premature infants, this is named physiologic anemia of prematurity.

Anemia of infancy is a normocytic, normochromic anemia that afflicts term infants. Recall that hypoxia and anemia stimulate erythropoiesis, and the fetus resides in a relatively hypoxic intrauterine environment. Birth exposes the newborn to a new environment, rich in oxygen. Tissue oxygenation quickly increases, which transiently suppresses EPO production and the synthesis of new RBCs. In addition, the birth process typically causes an increased rate of turnover among existing RBCs. Remaining RBCs are subject to a shortened life span (60-80 days among term infants), as compared to adults (100–120 days). Therefore, the reduced ability to establish normal hematopoiesis after birth, and compensate for any RBC losses imposed during the birth process, gives rise to a transient state of physiologic anemia while the body adjusts to life outside the womb. Physiologic anemia of infancy typically persists through the first 2 months of postnatal life (6–9 weeks); a hemoglobin nadir of 10–12 mg/dL paired with low reticulocyte counts, is observed (MacDonald & Seshia, 2015). Postnatal iron ingestion aids in establishing normal iron stores, as EPO production shifts from the liver to the kidneys and normalizes.

Physiologic anemia of prematurity is a normocytic, normochromic anemia that afflicts premature infants (<32 weeks' gestation). Birth exposes the premature newborn to a new environment, rich in oxygen. Tissue oxygenation quickly increases, which transiently suppresses EPO production and the synthesis of new RBCs. In addition, the birth process typically causes an increased rate of turnover among existing RBCs. Remaining RBCs are subject to a shortened life span (<60 days among premature infants; likely shorter in proportion to gestational age), as compared to 60 to 80 days among

term infants (Christensen & Yaish, 2016). Therefore, the reduced ability to establish normal hematopoiesis after birth, and compensate for any RBC losses imposed during the birth process, gives rise to a transient state of physiologic anemia of prematurity, while the body adjusts to life outside the womb.

Additional factors often exacerbate the pathogenesis of anemia of prematurity. First, consider the short life span of the RBC among premature infants (when compared to term counterparts). Second, consider that premature infants are, in part or in full, deprived of third trimester maternal iron transfer; 80% of iron is transferred to the fetus during this third trimester (MacDonald & Seshia, 2015). Next, recall that erythropoiesis is modulated by transcription factors, which may be poorly developed among premature infants. These factors, in combination with other comorbid states (e.g., illness) place premature infants at-risk for a more severe and prolonged physiologic anemia of prematurity. A hemoglobin nadir of less than 10 mg/dL, with a low reticulocyte count, is often observed at 6 weeks postnatal age (Diab & Luchtman-Jones, 2015; MacDonald & Seshia, 2015). Factors such as blood loss and blood transfusions may further prolong the recovery to baseline and necessitate intervention (Martin et al., 2015).

Anemia due to blood loss. Anemia from blood loss may occur in utero, intrapartum, or postnatally. Several etiologies are known and described here. Prenatally, blood loss may occur due to transfusion from the fetus to the mother (*fetal–maternal hemorrhage*), reported in one in every 300 births. Alternatively, anemia from blood loss may occur due to monochorionic–diamniotic placentation (*twin–twin transfusion syndrome*), reported in one in every 2,000 births (Martin et al., 2015). Traumatic births may result in *intracranial bleeding or bleeding within solid organs*, such as the liver or spleen. Iatrogenic losses secondary to *frequent blood draws* may predispose the infant to anemia; this is particularly problematic among premature infants with reduced circulating blood volume (A. Olson & Aher, 2017). Blood loss in these cases may be profound. There is also the potential for significant blood loss within *sequestrations*, such as cephalohematomas or subgaleal hemorrhages. Acute blood loss typically results in normocytic anemia without reticulocytosis, whereas chronic blood loss leads to reticulocytosis to compensate for ongoing losses (Diab & Luchtman-Jones, 2015).

Anemia due to accelerated destruction. The pathogenesis of hemolytic anemia involves the destruction of RBCs by a variety of mechanisms. Most hemolytic anemias will present within the first week of life. Generally, hemolytic anemias are normocytic with increased reticulocyte counts. Nonimmune hemolytic anemias include structural defects, such as HS, enzyme defects such as G6PD deficiency and pyruvate kinase deficiency, and hemoglobinopathies such as SCD and the thalassemias (Diab & Luchtman-Jones, 2015). Some hemoglobinopathies, particularly those affecting the beta globin chains, do not present until after the neonatal period.

Hemolysis in nonimmune cases may be intravascular, with RBC rupture within small blood vessels due to decreased deformability, or extravascular, with breakdown in the reticuloendothelial system occurring earlier than normal due to the inherent red cell abnormalities (Diab & Luchtman-Jones, 2015). In contrast, immune-mediated hemolysis is caused by maternal antibodies (IVIG and less commonly IgM) recognizing fetal blood cells as foreign due to antigens expressed on their surface. Examples include hemolytic disease of the newborn (HDFN) and ABO incompatibility, with Rh disease being more severe. Hemolysis is extravascular, with phagocytosis of immunoglobulin-bound RBCs in the spleen and liver (Martin et al., 2015). These immune-mediated hemolytic anemias typically improve over time as maternal antibodies are gradually cleared from the neonate's bloodstream, typically within 3 to 4 months (Diab & Luchtman-Jones, 2015; Nassin, Lapping-Carr, & de Jong, 2015).

Hemolytic disease of the fetus and newborn. HDFN relates to pathology associated with the maternal–fetal or neonatal destruction of RBCs that subsequently result in anemia. HDFN involves the major blood groups of Rhesus (Rh), A, B, AB, and O. However, minor blood group incompatibilities, including Kell, Duffy, MNS, P, and Diego systems, can also result in significant disease. For this review, because of the low frequency of HDFN related to the minor blood groups, they will not be discussed.

ABO incompatibility. Four major blood groups make up the ABO system in humans—A, B, AB, and O. The natural development of antibodies to A and/or B antigens begins to occur at approximately 3 to 6 months and can occur in the first pregnancy. The most common maternal–infant relationship is if the mother is blood type O and the baby is A, B, or AB. If the firstborn infant is severely affected, subsequent pregnancies can be expected to be affected to a similar degree (de Alarcón et al., 2013).

> A simple method to use to remember the relationship that sets up a mother and baby for ABO incompatibility involves spelling Mom ("O" in mOm) and the baby (B-A-By or B-ABy).

Although ABO incompatibility may occur in up to 15% of all pregnancies, it results in neonatal hemolytic anemia in only 4% of affected pregnancies (Calhoun, 2016; de Alarcón et al., 2013). ABO incompatibility likely results in less severe anemia than Rh incompatibility, as A and B antigens are present on other tissues in addition to fewer sites on the RBC (Calhoun, 2016). Infants with ABO incompatibility are generally asymptomatic at birth, but may develop hyperbilirubinemia in the first 24 hours due to cell deformation and destruction. Hydrops fetalis is rare, and most infants will have either no anemia or mild anemia. Use of phototherapy, intravenous immune globulin (IVIg), or exchange transfusion may be necessary for those neonates with the most severe hemolysis who develop hyperbilirubinemia. Recommendations for management of affected infants is based on the guidelines from the American Academy of Pediatrics (AAP Subcommittee on Hyperbilirubinemia, 2004).

Rh (D) hemolytic disease. The best recognized HDFN is secondary to Rh (D) incompatibility as it results in the most severe (and rare) form of the disease hydrops fetalis. Individuals are classified as rhesus (Rh) negative or positive based on the expression of the major D antigen on their RBCs. Rh negative results from either the absence of the Rh (D) gene or alterations in the gene that result in its inactivation (Calhoun, 2016).

Mothers who are Rh negative become sensitized due to a prior exposure to the Rh antigen. This can occur through blood transfusion or a previous pregnancy with an Rh-positive fetus. As such, the occurrence of HDFN does not usually occur during the first pregnancy (Figure 7.19). The obstetrical practice of providing Rh (D) immune globulin prophylaxis to pregnant women who are Rh negative during pregnancy has significantly reduced the rate of alloimmune sensitization.

Although Rh (D) incompatibility remains the most frequent cause of HDFN, there are more than 44 Rh antigens. Careful review of the maternal blood type and antibody panel is essential in order to identify at-risk pregnancies and those neonates who may be at risk for hyperbilirubinemia in the neonatal period.

Affected neonates may exhibit the full spectrum from mild self-limited hemolytic disease to severe life-threatening anemia as is seen in hydrops fetalis. Fetal anemia develops secondary to placental clearing of bilirubin; cord blood bilirubin levels greater than 4 mg/dL are highly suspicious for severe isoimmunization. Extramedullary hematopoiesis results in hepatosplenomegaly. Therefore, affected fetuses incur a higher risk for rupture of the spleen as well as asphyxia due to decreased circulating RBCs. The severity of the HDFN increases with subsequent pregnancies. Common postnatal clinical manifestations are summarized in Table 7.12.

Neonates affected by HDFN should be monitored closely for the development of hyperbilirubinemia and late anemia (anemia at 4–6 weeks of age). Attention to adequate hydration, use of phototherapy, and administration of supplemental iron may be important interventions for neonates affected by hemolysis as a result of maternal Rh alloimmunization.

Hyperbilirubinemia

We begin with a review of bilirubin metabolism. Bilirubin is a protein derived from heme-containing proteins (hemoglobin) during RBC turnover. Bilirubin production begins when the enzyme heme oxygenase converts heme into biliverdin. The enzyme biliverdin reductase

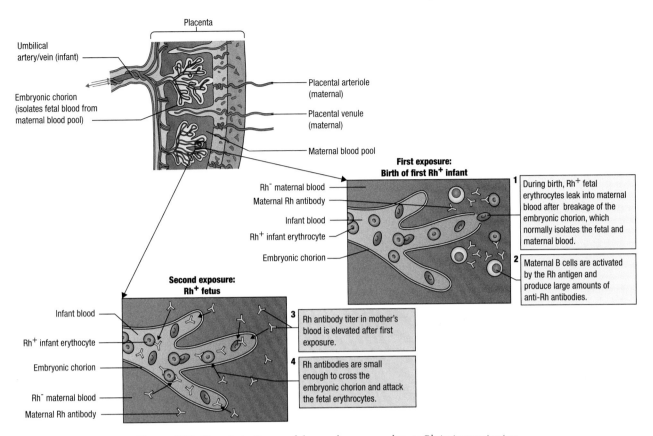

Figure 7.19 Hemolytic disease of the newborn secondary to Rh isoimmunization.

TABLE 7.12 Common Postnatal Manifestations of Rh (d) Hemolytic Disease

Clinical Manifestation	Etiology
Coagulopathies	• Thrombocytopenia • Decreased clotting factors
Edema	• Hydrops • Thrombocytopenia
Hyperbilirubinemia	• Increased RBC destruction
Hypoglycemia	• Hyperinsulinemia
Kernicterus	• Severe hyperbilirubinemia

then converts the biliverdin into bilirubin. In its current, fat-soluble, and unconjugated state, bilirubin readily binds with albumin and is transported to the liver. Once within the hepatic microcirculation, albumin dissociates from the bilirubin. This permits bilirubin uptake into the hepatocyte, a process facilitated by ligandin (a receptor protein). Ligandin transports the bilirubin to the smooth endoplasmic reticulum (SER). It is here that

bilirubin binds with glucuronate, a process modulated by the enzyme uridine diphosphoglucuronate (UDP) glucuronyltransferase, and is conjugated. Conjugation changes bilirubin from a fat-soluble to a water-soluble molecule. The bilirubin is thereby excreted into the bile and travels down the common bile duct and into the intestine, where it is converted (by bacterial action) into urobilinogen. The majority continues to the colon, is oxidized into stercobilin (brown pigment), and is eliminated from the body via the stool. A small portion of urobilinogen is excreted from the urine (MacDonald & Seshia, 2015).

During fetal development, bilirubin that reaches the intestinal tract is reversed to its unconjugated state by the enzyme beta-glucourinidase. This is necessary in order for the bilirubin to travel to the placenta for excretion. Postnatally, conjugated bilirubin is primarily excreted by the stool (98%), with a small amount of bilirubin eliminated in the urine (2%). Risk factors for severe hyperbilirubinemia are summarized in Table 7.13. Table 7.14 summarizes the major causes for unconjugated hyperbilirubinemia.

Neonatal advanced practice nurses employed within primary care facilities, community hospitals, and larger centers must recognize hyperbilirubinemia as one of the most common, yet preventable, causes for hospital readmission within the first week of life (Christensen, 2000; Lain, Roberts, Bowen, & Nassar, 2015). Noteworthy risk

TABLE 7.13 Risk Factors for Severe Hyperbilirubinemia Among Infants Greater Than 35 Weeks Gestation

	Major Risk Factors	Minor Risk Factors	Protective Factors
Clinical jaundice and discharge timing	Clinical jaundice apparent in first 24 hours	Clinical jaundice apparent before discharge	Discharge after 72 hours
Infant medical conditions	DAT positive blood group incompatibility or other hemolytic anemia Cephalohematoma, significant bruising, or other blood sequestration	Macrosomic infant of diabetic mother	
Gestational age	Late prematurity (35–36 weeks' gestation)	Gestational age between 37–38 weeks	Post-term gestational age (41 weeks)
Family history	History of sibling requiring phototherapy	History of sibling with jaundice	
Feeding	Exclusive breastfeeding (particularly poor feeding, excessive weight loss)		Exclusive bottle feeding
Race	East Asian race		Black race

DAT, direct antibody test.

Source: Adapted from Kaplan, M., Wong, R. J., Sibley, E., & Stevenson, D. K. (2015). Neonatal jaundice and liver diseases. In R. J. Martin, A. A. Fanaroff, & M. C. Walsh (Eds.), *Fanaroff and Martin's neonatal–perinatal medicine: Diseases of the fetus and infant* (10th ed., pp. 1618–1673). Philadelphia, PA: Elsevier Mosby.

TABLE 7.14 Causes for Neonatal Hyperbilirubinemia

Increased Production or Destruction of Bilirubin	Decreased Excretion of Bilirubin
• ABO/Rh incompatibility	• Dehydration-induced jaundice
• Structural abnormalities of erythrocytes (e.g., spherocytosis, elliptocytosis)	• Disorders of hepatic uptake (e.g., Gilbert syndrome)
• Erythrocyte enzyme defects (e.g., G6PD deficiency, pyruvate kinase deficiency)	• Disorders of conjugation (e.g., Crigler–Najjar)
• Sequestered blood (e.g., cephalohematoma, ecchymoses, hemangiomas)	• GI obstructive processes (e.g., pyloric stenosis, duodenal, or jejunal obstruction)
• Polycythemia	• Hypothyroidism
• Sepsis/infection	• Breast-milk jaundice

GI, gastrointestinal.

factors for readmission secondary to hyperbilirubinemia include exclusive breastfeeding, discharge to home within the first 2 days of life, primigravida status, maternal age <20 years, and Asian ethnicity (Lain et al., 2015).

Physiologic Hyperbilirubinemia. Approximately 80% of premature and term infants develop clinically apparent unconjugated (indirect) hyperbilirubinemia within the first week of life (MacDonald & Sheshia, 2015; Wu et al., 2015). The pathogenesis involves increased bilirubin production, impaired conjugation, or delayed clearance during the peripartum period. Of these etiologies, the majority of cases are attributed to increased bilirubin production (twofold higher than adults) and physiologic immaturity of hepatic bilirubin metabolic pathways. Low hepatic UDP-glucuronyl transferase (or glucuronyltransferase) levels limit the liver's ability to conjugate bilirubin into a water-soluble entity, which limits movement through the common bile duct and into the intestinal tract for excretion. Of the bilirubin that is conjugated and reaches the gut, transiently increased beta-glucouronidase levels and decreased intestinal flora, secondary to reduced enteral intake during the peripartum period, encourage deconjugation and enterohepatic recirculation of bilirubin. Delayed passage of meconium stalls its excretion.

For term infants, serum bilirubin levels peak between days 3 and 5 of postnatal life, with an average concentration of 8 mg/dL to 10 mg/dL. For most infants, subsequent regression occurs; this regression can be delayed among infants who develop breast-milk jaundice. Premature infants tend to garner higher peak bilirubin levels, between days 4 and 7 of postnatal life. A slower return to normalcy among premature neonates, when compared to term neonates, is common (MacDonald & Seshia, 2015).

Pathologic Hyperbilirubinemia. Pathologic hyperbilirubinemia may result from hemolytic diseases of the newborn, altered bilirubin conjugation and recirculation, or structural or other problems that impede normal excretion of conjugated bilirubin (cholestatic jaundice). *Hemolytic* causes for increased bilirubin levels include Rh incompatibility; ABO incompatibility; and enzyme defects, including G6PD deficiency. Recall that with Rh incompatibility, maternal anti-Rh antibodies cross the placenta and destroy fetal RBCs. The increased destruction of cells causes an increase in circulating bilirubin, which extends into the peripartum period. ABO incompatibility involves maternal recognition of foreign antigens on fetal erythrocytes. In these circumstances, maternal antibodies are generated in response to the foreign antigens, which cross the placenta and provoke hemolysis of fetal RBCs. Similar to Rh incompatibility, this causes an increase in circulating bilirubin, which extends into the peripartum period. The most common enzyme defect is G6PD deficiency. A deficient amount of this enzyme weakens RBCs, resulting in an increased (premature) rate of destruction. Of note, male infants of Middle Eastern and African American descent are 12.2% more likely to inherit G6PD deficiency (Bhutani, 2012).

Nonhemolytic causes for indirect hyperbilirubinemia include bruising secondary to the birth process; blood sequestrations, including cephalohematoma and subgaleal bleeding; and polycythemia. Infections, including sepsis and urinary tract infections, inherited disorders, congenital hypothyroidism, breastfeeding, and breast-milk jaundice are also causative factors (Diab & Luchtman-Jones, 2015). Inherited disorders, such as Gilbert's syndrome and Crigler–Najiir syndrome, involve a reduction in available UDP-glucoruronyltransferase and resultant hyperbilirubinemia. Congenital hypothyroidism typically manifests with reduced tone, including gastrointestinal tone. This provokes reduced enteral intake among some affected infants as well as decreased gastrointestinal motility.

Exclusively breastfed infants are considered at higher risk for pathologic hyperbilirubinemia secondary to dehydration from delayed onset of lactogenesis II (*dehydration-induced jaundice*). Delayed lactogenesis II stalls the establishment of adequate enteral intake and stooling and voiding patterns and encourages enterohepatic recirculation of bilirubin. Some breastfed infants may develop a more prolonged unconjugated hyperbilirubinemia, even after the onset of lactogenesis II (*breast-milk jaundice*). Particular substances found in the breast milk, glucouronidases and nonesterified fatty acids, are understood to modulate the unconjugation of bilirubin and perpetuate enterohepatic recirculation of bilirubin. Breast-milk jaundice may persist for several weeks before resolution is observed. Other pathologic causes for increased enterohepatic circulation include gastrointestinal obstructions, intestinal atresia, meconium ileus, and Hirschsprung disease.

Clinical Manifestations. Jaundice typically progresses in a cranial to caudal direction, yet visual severity and progression cannot be relied on for diagnostic or management purposes. Most infants with mild to moderate jaundice are well appearing during the physical examination. However, severe hyperbilirubinemia has the potential to manifest with signs of bilirubin-induced neurologic dysfunction (BIND), a spectrum of findings that includes lethargy, poor feeding, high-pitched crying, and hypotonia followed by the development of hypertonicity and opisthotonos (back arching) as the condition progresses (Kaplan et al., 2015). Although a discussion of management is beyond the scope of this book, it is essential that clinicians recognize bilirubin-induced encephalopathy as abnormal and time-sensitive in order to prevent the development of kernicterus. Criteria for exchange transfusion have been established by the AAP (2004).

Fortunately, the AAP offers a phototherapy and hour-specific nomogram for hyperbilirubinemia. This promotes the early identification, treatment, and timely postdischarge follow-up for at-risk or affected infants (Figure 7.20; Wickremasinghe et al., 2015; Wu et al., 2015). Advanced practice nurses must align post-discharge follow-up plans for interval repeat serum bilirubin testing among infants ≥35 weeks' gestation with the guidance provided by the American Academy of Pediatrics (2004) and Maisels et al. (2009). The hour-specific risk zone and other clinical risk factors (exclusive breastfeeding, >8%–10% [excessive] weight loss, isoimmune or other hemolytic disease, previous sibling with jaundice, cephalohematoma or significant bruising, East Asian race) must be jointly considered when formulating a plan for discharge.

Life-Span Implications. The aim of treatment is to prevent kernicterus, or irreversible damage to the basal ganglia, brainstem, and cerebellum by neurotoxic bilirubin that has crossed the blood–brain barrier (AAP, 2004; MacDonald & Seshia, 2015; Martin et al., 2015). The majority of cases of mild to moderate unconjugated hyperbilirubinemia are

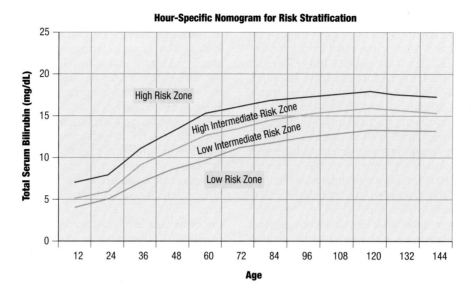

Figure 7.20 Hour-specific nomogram for risk stratification. Total serum bilirubin (TSB) nomogram for designation of risk in 2,840 well newborns delivered at 36 or more weeks' gestation with birth weight of at least 2,000 g (4 lb, 7 oz), or those delivered at 35 or more weeks' gestation with birth weight of at least 2,500 g (5 lb, 8 oz), based on hour-specific TSB values. The TSB level was obtained before discharge, and the zone in which it fell predicted the likelihood of a subsequent bilirubin level exceeding the 95th percentile (high-risk zone). This nomogram should not be used to represent the natural history of neonatal hyperbilirubinemia.

Source: Adapted from American Academy of Pediatrics Subcommittee on Hyperbilirubinemia. (2004). Management of hyperbilirubinemia in the newborn infant 35 or more weeks of gestation. *Pediatrics, 114*(1), 297–316. doi:10.1542/peds.114.1.297

benign and associated with no long-term effects. Severe neurotoxicity may result in kernicterus, which is fatal in about 10% of infants; the majority of surviving infants develop cerebral palsy, sensorineural hearing loss, and other neurodevelopmental disabilities (Martin et al., 2015). There is evidence to suggest that those infants with bilirubin encephalopathy in the setting of hemolysis have worse neurologic outcomes than those without hemolysis (MacDonald & Seshia, 2015).Chronic bilirubin encephalopathy is rare, with an estimated incidence of 0.4 to two per every 100,000 infants (Kaplan et al., 2015).

Cholestasis. Cholestasis, or impaired bile flow, affects one in every 1,500 to 2,500 infants. Premature infants are particularly susceptible to cholestasis due to immaturity of the hepatobiliary system and the need for prolonged parenteral nutrition (Satrom & Gourley, 2016).

The presence of conjugated hyperbilirubinemia should raise suspicion for underlying hepatobiliary disease. Etiologies include structural anomalies such as biliary atresia, neonatal hepatitis, viral or bacterial infections, endocrinopathies, and metabolic diseases (Feldman & Sokol, 2013; Kaplan et al., 2015). Clinical manifestations of conjugated hyperbilirubinemia are summarized in Table 7.15. Laboratory findings point to the elevation of the conjugated form of bilirubin greater than 5 mg/dL, or greater than 20% of the total bilirubin level.

Life-long medical surveillance and management is indicated, as symptoms may recur. Certain cholestatic

TABLE 7.15 Common Manifestations of Cholestasis

Clinical Manifestation	Etiology
Acholic stools	• Decreased stercobilin
Jaundice	• Aggregation of conjugated bilirubin
Hepatomegaly	• Hepatic obstruction

processes resulting in conjugated hyperbilirubinemia resolve spontaneously or with treatment of the underlying cause without further sequelae. Other etiologies are chronic with some cases requiring prompt operative management, as in the case of biliary atresia (Feldman & Sokol, 2013).

Disorders Associated With Hemostatic Elements

Neonatal Thrombocytopenia. Neonatal thrombocytopenia is defined as a platelet count less than 150,000/µL. Mild thrombocytopenia is a platelet count between 100,000 to 150,000/µL, moderate thrombocytopenia is

50,000 to 100,000/µL, and severe neonatal thrombocytopenia presents with a platelet count less than 50,000/µL (Kamphuis, Paridaans, Porcelijn, Lopriore, & Oepkes, 2014). However, despite the definitions, the evaluation of neonates and the specific platelet concentration for treatment varies on whether the patient is actively bleeding, his or her gestational age (term versus preterm), whether he or she is sick/ill, or whether he or she is being prepared for an invasive procedure.

Alloimmune thrombocytopenia. Rh hemolytic disease of the newborn, maternal sensitization to fetal platelet antigens results in IVIG antibodies that cross the placenta and subsequently destroy the fetal platelets. However, unlike the maternal antibody-related hemolytic anemia, cases of alloimmune thrombocytopenia occur in the first pregnancy in nearly 50% of cases (Rennie, 2012). The incidence of NAIT has been estimated to be one in 1,000 to 2,000 live births (Bussel et al., 2005; Crighton et al., 2017; MacDonald & Seshia, 2015). The most serious complication of NAIT is intracranial hemorrhage, which occurs in 10% to 20% of affected newborns, with one quarter of these occurring in utero (Baer, Lambert, Henry, & Christensen, 2009; Fernandes, 2017; Sola-Visner, Saxonhouse, & Brown, 2008).

The pathophysiology of alloimmune thrombocytopenia involves the expression of a paternally inherited antigen on the fetus's platelets, against which the mother produces antibodies. During the pregnancy, there is placental transfer of these IVIG antibodies to the fetus's bloodstream. The antibodies recognize the paternal antigen on fetal platelets as foreign, resulting in platelet destruction within the fetus's reticuloendothelial system (MacDonald & Seshia, 2015). In contrast to Rh disease, it is not unusual for maternal sensitization, and therefore fetal platelet destruction, to occur during the first pregnancy (Blickstein & Friedman, 2015). Human platelet antigen (HPA)-1a is the most common antigen to result in this process, accounting for 85% of cases among Caucasians (Blickstein & Friedman, 2015). Of note, maternal platelets are unaffected, and the maternal platelet count is normal, helping to distinguish alloimmune thrombocytopenia from autoimmune thrombocytopenia (ITP; MacDonald & Seshia, 2015).

The diagnosis should be considered in any well-appearing term infant who presents with severe unexplained thrombocytopenia during the first 48 hours of life. However, a high index of suspicion should also be considered in ill-appearing infants. A study by Bussel and coworkers noted that in a series of 220 neonates with thrombocytopenia, one third of 110 cases of NAIT occurred in infants who were clinically ill (Bussel et al., 2005).

Clinical manifestations of alloimmune thrombocytopenia range from asymptomatic to catastrophic. Thrombocytopenia is often severe ($<50 \times 10^9$/L; normal $150–400 \times 10^9$/L) and signs may include petechiae, bruising, hematomas, melena, or intracranial hemorrhage (ICH; Kamphuis et al., 2014). Many infants will not display overt signs at birth, and the diagnosis may go unrecognized even though the infant is at risk for significant bleeding. In severe cases, the effects occur in utero and the fetus may experience ICH or even intrauterine demise. The estimated incidence of ICH related to NAIT is 10 per every 100,000 newborns, the majority of which occur in utero (Kamphuis et al., 2014). The mortality rate for NAIT-related ICH is estimated at 33%; a male prevalence is reported (Brojer et al., 2016).

NAIT itself typically does not have long-term implications for affected individuals; platelet counts continue to fall for several days after birth, followed by platelet count recovery over days to weeks. Following recovery, the infant should not experience further thrombocytopenia or complications related to NAIT (Brojer et al., 2016). If ICH has occurred, the infant's long-term neurodevelopmental outcome can be negatively impacted depending on the degree of neurological injury sustained (Brojer et al., 2016, Kamphuis et al., 2014). Parents should be counseled about the high risk of recurrence in subsequent pregnancies. A 50% (heterozygous father) to 100% (homozygous father) recurrence risk is understood to implicate future family planning (Blickstein & Friedman, 2015; MacDonald & Seshia, 2015).

Autoimmune thrombocytopenia. When the mother has thrombocytopenia that is the direct result of antibodies directed against her own platelets, those antibodies may also cross the placenta and bind to fetal platelets, resulting in their destruction. This condition occurs in maternal autoimmune disorders (e.g., immune thrombocytopenic purpura [ITP] and SLE). Affected infants are otherwise well appearing. Those with moderate to severe thrombocytopenia may present with petechiae, bruising, and bleeding. While most infants will have platelet counts greater than 50,000/µL, in a series of cases of mothers with ITP, there is a risk of 4% to 10% that the infant will have a platelet count that is less than this (Burrows & Kelton, 1993).

Disseminated Intravascular Coagulopathy. The pathophysiology of DIC is not fully understood, and the actual incidence of DIC is unknown as it is thought to be widely underdiagnosed. No one laboratory test can be used to diagnose DIC early. However, it is known that the neonatal population is at higher risk of developing DIC when compared to older patients (Veldman, Fischer, Nold, & Wong, 2010). Risk factors for DIC include sepsis, perinatal hypoxic ischemia, respiratory disorders, necrotizing enterocolitis, metabolic disorders, and vascular anomalies. The process seems to be triggered by damaged tissue factor and cytokines that are released, causing widespread activation of the coagulation cascade and fibrinolysis. Clinical manifestations include generalized bleeding, persistent oozing from puncture sites, and pulmonary hemorrhage (Roberts & Murray, 2012). DIC represents a continuum of severity of symptoms.

DIC is a common feature of both neonatal enterovirus and HSV infections. In both infections, multiorgan involvement is common (Werner, Chescheir, & Fisher, 2012). In neonatal HSV, approximately one fourth of infections are the disseminated form involving multiple organs (Demmler-Harrison, 2018). DIC along with neutropenia and thrombocytopenia are frequently reported with congenital HSV infection, whereas DIC, neutrophilia, and thrombocytopenia are noted with enteroviral infection (Werner et al., 2012). The presence of DIC increases the infant's risk of death in both viral infections and may be as high as 80% in untreated patients with neonatal HSV (Demmler-Harrison, 2018; Werner et al., 2012).

Vitamin K Deficiency Bleeding (Formerly Hemorrhagic Disease of the Newborn). Vitamin K deficiency in the neonate leads to an unexpected bleeding diathesis known as vitamin K deficiency bleeding (VKDB). Risk factors include lack of placental transfer, poor neonatal hepatic reserves, and parental refusal of intramuscular (IM) vitamin K prophylaxis immediately after birth (MacDonald & Seshia, 2015). The incidence of late VKDB among infants receiving prophylaxis is estimated to be 0.25 to 2.8 per 100,000 infants, in contrast to 5.8 to 80 per 100,000 infants among those who do not receive prophylaxis (Sankar et al., 2016).

Vitamin K is a fat-soluble vitamin that has two forms: (a) K1, which is available in green vegetables, and (b) K2, which is synthesized by gut bacteria and contributes to the daily requirement in humans (Shearer, 2017). Vitamin K is an essential cofactor for several coagulation factors, including factors II, VII, IX, and X as well as proteins C and S, and its absence, therefore, leads to defective coagulation with increased bleeding risk (Diab & Luchtman-Jones, 2015; MacDonald & Seshia, 2015).

Early-onset disease typically presents within the first 24 hours of age and results from parental refusal of postnatal prophylaxis or intrauterine exposure to medications that affect vitamin K utilization or production, such as anticonvulsants, warfarin, and antibiotics. Classic hemorrhagic disease presents between 2 to 7 days postnatal age, and is commonly a result of parental refusal of postnatal prophylaxis or inadequate exogenous intake of vitamin K. Breastfed infants are at risk due to poor passage of vitamin K into breast milk. Late-onset disease presents between 2 and 12 weeks of age, as a result of inadequate postnatal prophylaxis or exogenous vitamin K intake, malabsorption, or hepatobiliary disease affecting coagulation factor synthesis and absorption of fat-soluble vitamins (MacDonald & Seshia, 2015; Sankar et al., 2016; Shearer, 2017). Symptoms may include gastrointestinal bleeding, umbilical cord bleeding, intracranial hemorrhage, or prolonged bleeding after blood draws or procedures, such as circumcision (Diab & Luchtman-Jones, 2015).

Given the decreased endogenous levels of vitamin K at birth, the risk for VKDB is increased. This underpins the need for intramuscular (IM) postnatal vitamin K prophylaxis. Oral vitamin K is available, but less efficacious for preventing late-onset disease based on observational studies; thus, the IM formulation remains the standard of care (Diab & Luchtman-Jones, 2015; Shearer, 2017). Life-span implications depend on the severity of bleeding. Irreversible cerebral injury or death is associated with the development of ICH.

Hemophilia. Hemophilia is an inherited bleeding disorder that results from a deficiency of factor VIII (hemophilia A) or factor IX (hemophilia B). Hemophilia type A is reported in one in every 5,000 males, whereas hemophilia B is reported in one out of every 30,000 males (Diab & Luchtman-Jones, 2015; Roberts & Murray, 2012). The deficiency of factor VIII or IX causes reduced thrombin formation, which leads to excessive bleeding.

Clinical manifestations primarily present in the neonatal period and may be the result of injections, punctures, or birth trauma; most affected infants are diagnosed within the first month of life (Figure 7.21). Intracranial and extracranial hemorrhage occur in up to one third of severe cases of hemophilia (Diab & Luchtman-Jones, 2015). Bleeding can be minimized by tailoring care to avoid exposure to any type of trauma, for example, injections, punctures, and unnecessary procedures. Hemophilia is a lifelong condition and care should be coordinated through a hemophilia center.

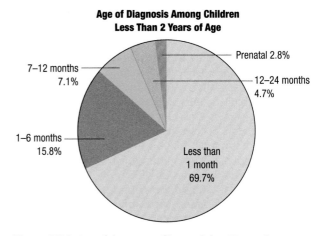

Age of Diagnosis Among Children Less Than 2 Years of Age

- Prenatal 2.8%
- 12–24 months 4.7%
- Less than 1 month 69.7%
- 1–6 months 15.8%
- 7–12 months 7.1%

Figure 7.21 Age of diagnosis of hemophilia. The median age at diagnosis is 36 months (mild hemophilia), 8 months (moderate hemophilia), and 1 month (severe hemophilia). Approximately 1/3 of affected infants have no family history of hemophilia; unusual bleeding patterns lead to the diagnostic evaluation.

Source: Centers for Disease Control and Prevention. (2016). Hemophilia: Data & statistics. Retrieved from https://www.cdc.gov/ncbddd/hemophilia/data.html

Thrombotic Disorders

Due to a decreased concentration of the inhibitory factors of coagulation, ill neonates, particularly those born preterm, are at an increased risk of thrombotic events. Coupled with a significant need for vascular access devices, it is estimated that 2.4/1,000 infants admitted to the neonatal intensive care unit (NICU) will have a thrombotic complication (Monagle et al., 2012). Predisposing factors to thrombosis include mechanical devices, such as intravascular catheters, hypotension, hyperviscosity, severe genetic and acquired deficiencies and/or mutations of specific anticoagulation factors, and maternal diabetes mellitus. Monagle and associates (2012) reported that up to 94% of thrombotic events in the NICU are catheter related. Both venous and arterial catheters may lead to thromboses. Infants may be asymptomatic; however, swelling, decreased pulses, and discoloration may be present.

Renal Vein Thrombosis. The most common non–catheter-related thrombotic event is renal vein thrombosis (RVT), which accounts for up to 20% of all thrombosis in the NICU. Males are most likely to be affected. Risk factors include perinatal asphyxia, prematurity, dehydration, sepsis, congenital heart disease, and gestational diabetes (Diab & Luchtman-Jones, 2015). Depending on the severity of the occlusion, the infant may present with hematuria, thrombocytopenia, and palpable flank mass (Brandão, Simpson, & Lau, 2011). Long-term complications of RVT include renal impairment; nephrology follow-up is imperative.

Disorders of White Blood Cells

Neutropenia. Neutropenia is common among infants and children. It is generally defined as an absolute neutrophil count (ANC) less than the fifth percentile for postnatal age (1,500/µL; Marins, Anizelli, Romanowski, & Sarquis, 2017). Calculation of the ANC is determined by the following formula: ANC = total WBC (cells/µL) x percentage (neutrophils + bands) ÷ 100. Mild neutropenia is considered to be 1,000 to 15,000/µL, moderate is 500 to 1,000/µL, and severe is less than 500/µL. Neutrophil count norms are dynamic in early life. After birth, infants' neutrophil counts rise for the first 48 to 72 hours, followed by a gradual decrease until reaching adult norms by about 2 months of age (Diab & Luchtman-Jones, 2015; Koening, Bliss, & Mariscalco, 2017).

There is a wide array of etiologies of neutropenia, ranging from congenital to acquired and transient to chronic. Neutropenia is a more common finding among premature infants compared to term infants, particularly those of low birth weight, though otherwise healthy term infants may also be affected. At around 22 weeks of gestation, the fetal bone marrow assumes hematopoiesis; however, neutrophil production does not become well established until the third trimester, therefore putting premature infants at higher risk for neutropenia. In addition, these early neutrophils may not function as effectively as neutrophils of term infants or older children and may increase the risk of sepsis (Dale, 2017).

Risk factors for other acquired neutropenias include intrauterine factors, such as growth restriction, preeclampsia, and acute or chronic intrauterine hypoxia, each of which relates to decreased placental blood flow leading to decreased neutrophil production in favor of increased erythrocyte precursor production in the bone marrow (Dale, 2017; Koening et al., 2017). Sepsis itself may cause neutropenia due to consumption of the neutrophil supply and the neonate's inability to appropriately upregulate neutrophil production in the bone marrow in times of stress (Koenig et al., 2017). Drug-induced neutropenia may be caused by a wide variety of medications that lead to bone marrow suppression or direct neutrophil destruction (Diab & Luchtman-Jones, 2015). Neutropenia in neonates may also be immune mediated, including alloimmune and autoimmune neutropenias. Each of the immune-mediated neutropenias is the result of accelerated neutrophil destruction that begins before birth or shortly after birth of the infant.

Although the common immune-mediated neutropenias will be described individually, infection is a common manifestation of forms of neutropenia. In fact, neutropenia confers an increased risk for infection, particularly bacterial and fungal infections, which may be severe or life-threatening. Common organisms include staphylococci, streptococci, pneumococci, enterococci, Gram-negative organisms, and Candida species (Diab & Luchtman-Jones, 2015). Infants with neutropenia most commonly acquire infections in cutaneous, mucosal, and pulmonary sites (Diab & Luchtman-Jones, 2015). Immune-mediated neutropenias may present with fever in the first few days of life and may develop pneumonia, cutaneous infections, omphalitis, or sepsis. Congenital neutropenia tends to have more of a chronic course with signs that include recurrent oral ulcers, gingivostomatitis, cellulitis, pharyngitis, respiratory infections, and perianal disease (Dale, 2017; Diab & Luchtman-Jones, 2015).

Alloimmune neonatal neutropenia. Alloimmune neonatal neutropenia has an incidence of 0.5 to two cases per 1,000 births. This form of neutropenia is also known as *neonatal isoimmune neutropenia.* The disorder is the result of maternally produced antibodies of the IVIG type directed against antigens on fetal neutrophils (Calhoun et al., 2001). The antigens are paternally derived. Like Rh hemolytic disease of the newborn, maternal sensitization to fetal neutrophil antigens results in antibodies that cross the placenta and subsequently destroy the fetal neutrophils. However, unlike the maternal antibody-related hemolytic anemia, cases of alloimmune neutropenia can occur in the first pregnancy. Human neutrophil antigens (HNA) of the groups HNA1, HNA2, HNB1, and HNC1 are most frequently involved (de Alarcón et al., 2013).

This form of neutropenia should be suspected in neonates with unexplained neutropenia that persists for several days. Often the infants are well appearing. Although the condition is self-limited, and the duration of the neutropenia can range from a few weeks to months, the neutropenia may not be benign. Infants with severe neutropenia are at risk for serious bacterial infections, including cellulitis, omphalitis, pneumonia, and meningitis, and mortality can be as high as 5%.

Autoimmune neutropenia of infancy. Autoimmune neutropenia of infancy (AINI) occurs when infants produce antibodies that attack their own neutrophils; no maternal antibodies are to blame for this form of neutropenia (Calhoun et al., 2001). The development of autoimmune antibodies can occur as an isolated phenomenon resulting in AINI. Some cases have been associated with parvovirus B19 infection, whereas others have been linked to the use of beta-lactam antibiotics, molecular mimicry, changes in endogenous antigens, enhanced human leucocyte antigen (HLA) expression, or loss of suppression of clones of self-reacting lymphocytes (de Alarcón et al., 2013). AINI has been described in one of monozygotic twins, indicating that the mechanism is not solely genetic. This condition is self-limiting, with a median duration of 30 months. Common clinical manifestations include isolated neutropenia, lack of dysmorphic features, no hepatosplenomegaly, absence of bone pain, no diarrhea, no severe or unusual infections, and no other signs suggestive of a significant underlying disorder (Black & Maheshwari, 2009; Coates, 2016). At least 95% of affected infants recover by 4 years of age. Like infants with alloimmune neutropenia, infections, including cellulitis, gastroenteritis, otitis media, and respiratory infections, may be present at the time of diagnosis.

Neonatal neutropenia resulting from maternal autoimmune neutropenia. This form of immune neutropenia is found in neonates who are born to women with autoimmune neutropenia. The condition in the neonate tends to be transient and generally is mild. However, in some cases infection may occur.

CONCLUSION

The hematologic system performs some of the most critical functions of the body—oxygen transport, protection against infections, and coagulation. Development of this system begins very early in fetal life. In the fetus, hematopoiesis takes place in several locations. The process begins in the yolk sac, eventually ending in the bone marrow, which then carries out hematopoiesis through adulthood. Fetal and neonatal hematologic cells are less mature compared to adult cells, leading to decreased function of these cells. This knowledge is important in understanding the difference in response to certain conditions, such as infections, anemia, or clotting problems in the neonate, as compared to the adult human. Maternal influences—genetic, metabolic, autoimmune, among others—could lead to dysfunction of the hematologic system and thus illness. Therefore, complete evaluation of any hematologic disorder in the neonate involves careful history and possibly laboratory testing of the mother. Although some diseases of the hematologic system are transient or curable, they may have long-term sequelae; for example, renal vein thrombosis leads to chronic renal disease or intraventricular hemorrhage results in neurodevelopmental impairment. Some other diseases, such as hemophilia, are chronic and persist for the lifetime of the individual. Understanding the development, physiology, and function of the hematologic system is instrumental in the long-term management of these disorders.

LEARNING TOOLS AND RESOURCES

Podcast

 Physiologic Hyperbilirubinemia

Christie del Castillo-Hegyi

Discussion Prompts

1. Discuss the role of genetics in the pathogenesis of neonatal hemophilia.
2. Review the pathogenesis of neonatal thrombocytopenia.
3. Compare and contrast the various methods by which maternal antibodies may lead to immune-mediated hemolysis of fetal blood cells.

Advice From the Authors

"Be sure to review charts/pictures/tables after studying every section. It should help imprint the information in your mind."

–Uduak Akpan, MD

"Hematologic problems are quite common among newborns of all gestational ages and sizes. It is important to understand the physiology of the hematologic system in order to construct a thorough differential diagnosis and decide which next steps are needed in the diagnosis and management of your patient. As you see patients with hematologic problems, review the physiology behind those problems—you'll be pleasantly surprised to see how much you learned when you next come across a similar newborn!"

–Erin Orth, MD

"Remember that medicine is a team activity. We can't be successful if we try to act alone. Reach out and ask questions when needed, and be generous when someone asks you for help."

–Ryan Moore, MD, FAAP

"The most effective teaching strategy is peer teaching. Through peer teaching, 90% of knowledge is retained. Therefore, working in teams and learning from each other is instrumental in developing a strong foundation of knowledge in any subject. Develop study groups, share worksheets and notes, and challenge each other! Grasp of pathophysiology is one of the key elements in developing a strong knowledge base in neonatal care. Through effective teamwork, you will be successful and develop a zest for lifelong learning."

–Paula M. Timoney, DNP, ARNP, NNP-BC

"Research has shown that learners remember information presented in lectures or gained by reading for only a short period of time, perhaps to the end of a semester or long enough to pass their certification or licensing exams. Active learning techniques are the most productive methods of pedagogy. The most productive learner is the one who actively seeks whatever resources are needed to acquire new knowledge. A few suggestions are: (1) Form groups of other learners. Divide the work, read the material, take notes, and meet with group members to discuss what you have learned. Take a risk; volunteer to explain things to your teammates. If you are knowledgeable in an area, take the initiative and share your expertise. (2) Find a mentor who is an expert in the area. Your mentor is a guide to answer questions, provide further references, and help you to understand the material. Keep an open mind. As a student, your role is to LEARN by as many means as possible. Adopt the attitude that you do not already know all there is to know. Learning is a journey. Enjoy the trip!"

−Terri A. Cavaliere, DNP, APRN, NNP-BC

"Learning is a lifelong process and as educators we understand that. This book will help you understand neonatal concepts in a unique and interesting way. By doing so, I believe this will be an exciting learning journey for you as the student."

−Rebecca Chuffo Davila, DNP, ARNP, NNP-BC, FAANP

"A thorough understanding of maternal influences on the hematologic system of the neonate is often critical to the interpretation of hematologic testing in the immediate neonatal period."

−Darlene A. Calhoun, DO

Mind Maps

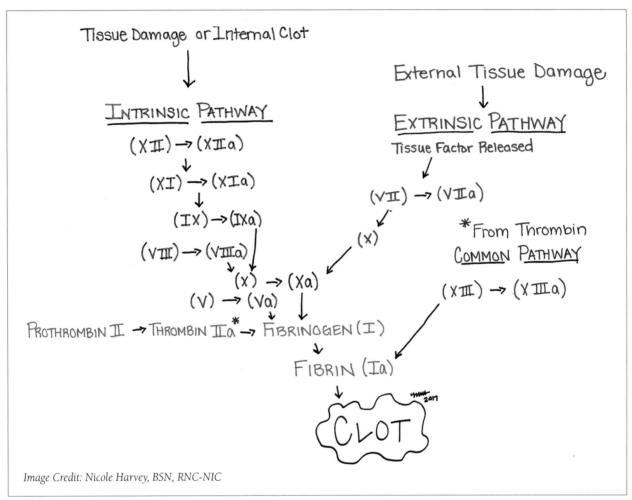

Image Credit: Nicole Harvey, BSN, RNC-NIC

(*continued*)

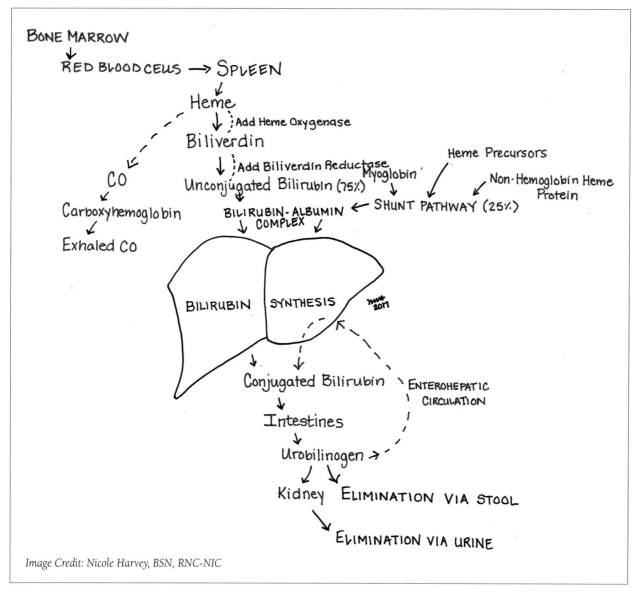

Image Credit: Nicole Harvey, BSN, RNC-NIC

Note: This mind map reflects one student's interpretation of a portion of one or more concepts addressed in this chapter. Readers should regard the mind maps woven throughout this textbook as examples of multi-sensory study tools that can be developed to encourage conceptual understanding. Readers are encouraged to develop their own unique mind maps in consultation with academic faculty or clinical preceptors.

TIMELINE OF ORGAN DEVELOPMENT

NOTE:	LEGEND
Placement of common problems is meant to offer visual/conceptual perspective on the timing of onset of these commonly reported malformations. Variation exists across the literature.	<22 – 27 6/7 weeks = extremely preterm 28 – 31 6/7 weeks = very preterm 32 – 36 6/7 weeks = late/moderate preterm 37 – 40 weeks = term

References

Adolfsson, J., Månsson, R., Buza-Vidas, N., Hultquist, A., Liuba, K., Jensen, C. T., … Jacobsen, S. E. W. (2005). Identification of Flt3⁺ lympho-myeloid stem cells lacking erythro-megakaryocytic potential: A revised road map for adult blood lineage commitment. *Cell*, *121*(2), 295. doi:10.1016/j.cell.2005.02.013

Akbarzadeh, S., & Layton, J. E. (2001). Granulocyte colony-stimulating factor receptor: Structure and function. *Vitamins & Hormones, 63, 159–194.* doi:10.1016/S0083-6729(01)63006-1

American Academy of Pediatrics Subcommittee on Hyperbilirubinemia. (2004). Management of hyperbilirubinemia in the newborn infant 35 or more weeks of gestation. *Pediatrics*, *114*(1), 297–316. doi:10.1542/peds.114.1.297

Anday, E. K., & Harris, M. C. (1982). Leukemoid reaction associated with antenatal dexamethasone administration. *Journal of Pediatrics*, *101*(4), 614–616. doi:10.1016/S0022-3476(82)80723-3

Asma, G. E., Langlois van den Bergh, R., & Vossen, J. M. (1984). Development of pre-B and B lymphocytes in the human fetus. *Clinical and Experimental Immunology*, *56*(2), 407–414.

Aswad, M. A., & Suryadevara, M. (2014). Neonatal herpes simplex virus presenting with isolated liver failure. *IDCases*, *1*(2), 14–16. doi:10.1016/j.idcr.2014.03.001

Azim, H. A., Pavlidis, N., & Peccatori, F. A. (2010). Treatment of the pregnant mother with cancer: A systematic review on the use of cytotoxic, endocrine, targeted agents and immunotherapy during pregnancy. Part II: Hematological tumors. *Cancer Treatment Reviews*, *36*(2), 110–121. doi:10.1016/j.ctrv.2009.11.004

Baer, V. L., Lambert, D. K., Henry, E., & Christensen, R. D. (2009). Severe thrombocytopenia in the NICU. *Pediatrics*, *124*(6), e1095–e1100. doi:10.1542/peds.2009-0582

Barak, M., Cohen, A., & Herschkowitz, S. (1992). Total leukocyte and neutrophil count changes associated with antenatal betamethasone administration in premature infants. *Acta Pediatrica*, *81*(10), 760–763. doi:10.1111/j.1651-2227.1992.tb12098.x

Baron, M. H., Isern, J., & Fraser, S. T. (2012). The embryonic origins of erythropoiesis in mammals. *Blood*, *119*(21), 4828–4837. doi:10.1182/blood-2012-01-153486

Barron, S., & Pass, R. (1995). Infectious causes of hydrops fetalis. *Seminars in Perinatology*, *19*, 493–501. doi:10.1016/S0146-0005(05)80056-4

Begley, C. G., Nicola, N. A., & Metcalf, D. (1988). Proliferation of normal human promyelocytes and myelocytes after a single pulse stimulation by purified GM-CSF or G-CSF. *Blood*, *71*(3), 640–645. Retrieved from http://www.bloodjournal.org/content/bloodjournal/71/3/640.full.pdf

Bengtsson, B. S., Milstein, J. M., & Sherman, M. P. (2006). Indomethacin-associated neutropenia with subsequent gram-negative sepsis in a preterm infant: Cause or coincidence? *Journal of Perinatology*, *26*(6), 381–383. doi:10.1038/sj.jp.7211515

Berkowitz, R. L., Lesser, M. L., McFarland, J. G., Wissert, M., Primiani, A., Hung, C., & Bussel, J. B. (2007). Antepartum treatment without early cordocentesis for standard-risk alloimmune thrombocytopenia: A randomized controlled trial. *Obstetrics and Gynecology*, *110*(2 Pt. 1), 249–255. doi:10.1097/01.AOG.0000270302.80336.dd

Bertoni, N. C., Pereira, D. C., Araujo Júnior, E., Bussamra, L. C., & Aldrighi, J. M. (2016). Thrombocytopenia-absent radius syndrome: Prenatal diagnosis of a rare syndrome. *Radiologia Brasileira*, *49*(2), 128–129. doi:10.1590/0100-3984.2015.0117

Bhandoola, A., Sambandam, A., Allman, D., Meraz, A., & Schwarz, B. (2003). Early T lineage progenitors: New insights, but old questions remain. *Journal of Immunology*, *171*(11), 5653–5658. doi:10.4049/jimmunol.171.11.5653

Bhutani, V. K. (2012). Jaundice due to glucose-6-phosphate dehydrogenase deficiency. *NeoReviews*, *13*(3), e166–e177. doi:10.1542/neo.13-3-e166

Black, L. V., & Maheshwari, A. (2009). Immune-mediated neutropenia in the neonate. *NeoReviews*, *10*(9), e446–e453. doi:10.1542/neo.10-9-e446

Bleyer, W. A., Hakami, N., & Shepard, T. H. (1971). The development of hemostasis in the human fetus and newborn infant. *Journal of Pediatrics*, *79*(5), 838–853. doi:10.1016/S0022-3476(71)80405-5

Blickstein, I., & Friedman, S. (2015). Fetal effects of autoimmune disease. In R. J. Martin, A. A. Fanaroff, & M. C. Walsh (Eds.), *Fanaroff and Martin's neonatal–perinatal medicine: Diseases of the fetus and infant* (10th ed., pp. 304–311). Philadelphia, PA: Elsevier Mosby.

Bluteau, D., Lordier, L., Di Stefano, A., Chang, Y., Raslova, H., Debili, N., & Vainchenker, W. (2009). Regulation of megakaryocyte maturation and platelet formation. *Journal of Thrombosis and Haemostasis*, *7* (Suppl. 1), 227–234. doi:10.1111/j.1538-7836.2009.03398.x

Brandão, L. R., Simpson, E. A., & Lau, K. K. (2011). Neonatal renal vein thrombosis. *Seminars in Fetal and Neonatal Medicine*, *16*(6), 323–328. doi:10.1016/j.siny.2011.08.004

Briddell, R. A., Brandt, J. E., Straneva, J. E., Srour, E. F., & Hoffman, R. (1989). Characterization of the human burst-forming unit-megakaryocyte. *Blood*, *74*(1), 145–151. Retrieved from http://www.bloodjournal.org/content/bloodjournal/74/1/145.full.pdf

Brojer, E., Husebekk, A., Dębska, M., Uhrynowska, M., Guz, K., Orzińska, A., … Maślanka, K. (2016). Fetal/neonatal alloimmune thrombocytopenia: Pathogenesis, diagnostics and prevention. *Archivum Immunologiae et Therapiae Experimentalis*, *64*(4), 279–290. doi:10.1007/s00005-015-0371-9

Brown, Z., & Chang, J. (2018). Maternal diabetes. In C. A. Gleason & S. E. Juul (Eds.), *Avery's diseases of the newborn* (10th ed., pp. 90–103). Philadelphia, PA: Elsevier.

Brucato, A., Cimaz, R., Caporali, R., Ramoni, V., & Buyon, J. (2011). Pregnancy outcomes in patients with autoimmune diseases and anti-Ro/SSA antibodies. *Clinical Reviews in Allergy & Immunology, 40*(1), 27–41. doi:10.1007/s12016-009-8190-6

Bruno, E., & Hoffman, R. (1998). Human megakaryocyte progenitor cells. *Seminars in Hematology*, *35*(3), 183–191.

Bunn, H., & Aster, J. C. (2017). *Pathophysiology of blood disorders* (2nd ed.). New York, NY: McGraw-Hill Medical.

Burrows, R. F., & Kelton, J. G. (1993). Pregnancy in patients with idiopathic thrombocytopenic purpura: Assessing the risks for the infant at delivery. *Obstetrical & Gynecological Survey*, *48*(12), 781–788. doi:10.1097/00006254-199312000-00003

Bussel, J. B., Zacharoulis, S., Kramer, K., McFarland, J. G., Pauliny, J., Kaplan, C., & Neonatal Alloimmune Thrombocytopenia Registry Group. (2005). Clinical and diagnostic comparison of neonatal alloimmune thrombocytopenia to non-immune cases of thrombocytopenia. *Pediatric Blood & Cancer*, *45*(2), 176–183. doi:10.1002/pbc.20282

Cairo, M. S. (1989). Review of G-CSF and GM-CSF: Effects on neonatal neutrophil kinetics. *American Journal of Pediatric*

Hematology/Oncology, *11*(2), 238–244. Retrieved from https://journals.lww.com/jpho-online/Fulltext/1989/11020/Review_of_G_CSF_and_GM_CSF_Effects_on_Neonatal.21.aspx

Calhoun, D. A. (2016). Postnatal diagnosis and management of hemolytic disease of the fetus and newborn.In M. S. Kim (Ed.), UpToDate. Retrieved from https://www.uptodate.com/contents/postnatal-diagnosis-and-management-of-hemolytic-disease-of-the-fetus-and-newborn

Calhoun, D. A., Kirk, J. F., & Christensen, R. D. (1996). Incidence, significance, and kinetic mechanism responsible for leukemoid reactions in patients in the neonatal intensive care unit: A prospective evaluation. *Journal of Pediatrics*, *129*(3), 403–409. doi:10.1016/S0022-3476(96)70073-2

Calhoun, D. A., Rimsza, L. M., Burchfield, D. J., Millsaps, M., Christensen, R. D., Budania, J., & McCullough, J. (2001). Congenital autoimmune neutropenia in two premature neonates. *Pediatrics*, *108*(1), 181–184. doi:10.1542/peds.108.1.181

Cappellini, M. D. (2016). The thalassemias. In L. Goldman & A. I. Schafer (Eds.), *Goldman-Cecil medicine* (25th ed, pp. 1089–1095.e2). New York, NY: Elsevier.

Carr, R., & Modi, N. (1997). Haemopoietic colony stimulating factors for preterm neonates. *Archives of Disease in Childhood: Fetal and Neonatal Edition*, *76*(2), F128–F133. doi:10.1136/fn.76.2.F128

Castaman, G., & Linari, S. (2017). Diagnosis and treatment of von Willebrand disease and rare bleeding disorders. *Journal of Clinical Medicine*, *6*(4), 45. doi:10.3390/jcm6040045

Centers for Disease Control and Prevention. (2016). Hemophilia: Data & statistics. Retrieved from https://www.cdc.gov/ncbddd/hemophilia/data.html

Chang, Y., Bluteau, D., Debili, N., & Vainchenker, W. (2007). From hematopoietic stem cells to platelets. *Journal of Thrombosis and Haemostasis*, *5*(Suppl. 1), 318–327. doi:10.1111/j.1538-7836.2007.02472.x

Charbord, P., Tavian, M., Humeau, L., & Péault, B. (1996). Early ontogeny of the human marrow from long bones: An immunohistochemical study of hematopoiesis and its microenvironment. *Blood*, *87*(10), 4109–4119. Retrieved from http://www.bloodjournal.org/content/bloodjournal/87/10/4109.full.pdf

Cherpes, T. L., Matthews, D. B., & Maryak, S. A. (2012). Neonatal herpes simplex virus infection. *Clinical Obstetrics and Gynecology*, *55*(4), 938–944. doi:10.1097/GRF.0b013e31827146a7

Christensen, R. D. (1989). Neutrophil kinetics in the fetus and neonate. *American Journal of Pediatric Hematology/Oncology*, *11*(2), 215–223. Retrieved from https://journals.lww.com/jpho-online/Fulltext/1989/11020/Neutrophil_Kinetics_in_the_Fetus_and_Neonate.17.aspx

Christensen, R. D. (2000). *Hematologic problems of the neonate*. Philadelphia, PA: W. B. Saunders.

Christensen, R. D. (2018). *Neonatal erythrocyte disorders*. In C. A. Gleason & S. E. Juul (Eds.), *Avery's diseases of the newborn* (10th ed., pp. 1152–1179). Philadelphia, PA: Elsevier.

Christensen, R. D., Hill, H. R., & Rothstein, G. (1983). Granulocytic stem cell (CFUc) proliferation in experimental group B streptococcal sepsis. *Pediatric Research*, *17*(4), 278–280. doi:10.1203/00006450-198304000-00010

Christensen, R. D., Juul, S. E., & Del Vecchio, A. (2015). Neonatal hematology and transfusion medicine. *Clinics in Perinatology*, *42*(3), i. doi:10.1016/S0095-5108(15)00068-8

Christensen, R. D., & Rothstein, G. (1984). Pre- and postnatal development of granulocytic stem cells in the rat. *Pediatric Research*, *18*(7), 599–602. doi:10.1203/00006450-198407000-00006

Christensen, R. D., & Yaish, H. M. (2016). Hemolysis in preterm neonates. *Clinics in Perinatology*, *43*(2), 233–240. doi:10.1016/j.clp.2016.01.002

Christensen, R. D., Yaish, H. M., & Gallagher, P. G. (2015). A pediatrician's practical guide to diagnosing and treating hereditary spherocytosis in neonates. *Pediatrics*, *135*(6), 1107–1114. doi:10.1542/peds.2014-3516

Clark, S., & Kamen, R. (1987). The human hematopoietic colony-stimulating factors. *Science*, *236*(4806), 1229–1237. doi:10.1126/science.3296190

Coates, T. D. (2016). Immune neutropenia. In A. G. Rosmarin (Ed.), *UpToDate*. Retrieved from https://www.uptodate.com/contents/immune-neutropenia

Cramblett, H. G., Friedman, J. L., & Najjar, S. (1958). Leukemia in an infant born of a mother with leukemia. *New England Journal of Medicine*, *259*(15), 727–729. doi:10.1056/NEJM195810092591507

Crighton, G. L., Scarborough, R., McQuilten, Z. K., Phillips, L. E., Savoia, H. F., Williams, B., . . . Cole, S. A. (2017). Contemporary management of neonatal alloimmune thrombocytopenia: Good outcomes in the intravenous immunoglobulin era: Results from the Australian neonatal alloimmune thrombocytopenia registry. *Journal of Maternal Fetal & Neonatal Medicine*, *30*(20), 2488–2494. doi:10.1080/14767058.2016.1253064

Da Costa, L., Galimand, J., Fenneteau, O., & Mohandas, N. (2013). Hereditary spherocytosis, elliptocytosis, and other red cell membrane disorders. *Blood Reviews*, *27*(4), 167–178. doi:10.1016/j.blre.2013.04.003

Dale, D. C. (2017). How I manage children with neutropenia. *British Journal of Haematology*, *178*, 51–363. doi:10.1111/bjh.14677

de Alarcón, P. A., & Graeve, J. L. (1996). Analysis of megakaryocyte ploidy in fetal bone marrow biopsies using a new adaptation of the feulgen technique to measure DNA content and estimate megakaryocyte ploidy from biopsy specimens. *Pediatric Research*, *39*(1), 166–170. doi:10.1203/00006450-199601000-00026

de Alarcón, P. A., Werner, E. J., & Christensen, R. D. (Eds.). (2013). *Neonatal hematology: Pathogenesis, diagnosis, and management of hematologic problems* (2nd ed.). Cambridge, UK: Cambridge University Press.

Debili, N., Coulombel, L., Croisille, L., Katz, A., Guichard, J., Breton-Gorius, J., & Vainchenker, W. (1996). Characterization of a bipotent erythro-megakaryocytic progenitor in human bone marrow. *Blood*, *88*(4), 1284–1296. Retrieved from http://www.bloodjournal.org/content/bloodjournal/88/4/1284.full.pdf

Debili, N., Wendling, F., Katz, A., Guichard, J., Breton-Gorius, J., Hunt, P., & Vainchenker, W. (1995). The mpl-ligand or thrombopoietin or megakaryocyte growth and differentiative factor has both direct proliferative and differentiative activities on human megakaryocyte progenitors. *Blood*, *86*(7), 2516–2525. Retrieved from http://www.bloodjournal.org/content/bloodjournal/86/7/2516.full.pdf

Demetri, G. D., & Griffin, J. D. (1991). Granulocyte colony-stimulating factor and its receptor. *Blood*, *78*(11), 2791–2808. Retrieved from http://www.bloodjournal.org/content/bloodjournal/78/11/2791.full.pdf

Demmler-Harrison, G. J. (2018). Overview of cytomegalovirus infections in children. In C. Armsby (Ed.), *UpToDate.* Retrieved from https://www.uptodate.com/contents/acquired -cytomegalovirus-infection-in-children

Deutsch, V. R., Olson, T. A., Nagler, A., Slavin, S., Levine, R. F., & Eldor, A. (1995). The response of cord blood megakaryocyte progenitors to IL-3, IL-6 and aplastic canine serum varies with gestational age. *British Journal of Haematology, 89*(1), 8–16. doi:10.1111/j.1365-2141.1995.tb08917.x

Diab, Y., & Luchtman-Jones, L. (2015). Hematologic and onco- logic problems in the fetus and neonate. In R. J. Martin, A. A. Fanaroff, & M. C. Walsh (Eds.), *Fanaroff and Martin's neonatal–perinatal medicine: Diseases of the fetus and infant* (10th ed., pp. 1294–1343). Philadelphia, PA: Elsevier Mosby.

Diaz-Miron, J., Miller, J., & Vogel, A. M. (2013). Neonatal hematology. *Seminars in Pediatric Surgery, 22*(4), 199–204. doi:10.1053/j.sempedsurg.2013.10.009

Dror, Y., Chan, A. K. C., Baker, J. M., & Avila, M. L. (2016). Hematology. In M. MacDonald & M. M. Seshia (Eds.), *Avery's neonatology: Pathophysiology & management of the newborn* (7th ed., pp 872–929). Philadelphia, PA: Wolters Kluwer.

Dzierzak, E., & Philipsen, S. (2013). Erythropoiesis: Development and differentiation. *Cold Spring Harbor Perspectives in Medicine, 3*(4), a011601. doi:10.1101/cshperspect .a011601

Easa, D., & Coen, R. W. (1979). Coagulation stud- ies in infants of diabetic mothers. *American Journal of Diseases of Children, 133*(8), 851–852. doi:10.1001/ archpedi.1979.02130080091019

Erdman, S. H., Christensen, R. D., Bradley, P. P., & Rothstein, G. (1982). Supply and release of storage neutrophils: A devel- opmental study. *Biology of the Neonate, 41*(3-4), 132–137. doi:10.1159/000241541

Feldman, A. G., & Sokol, R. J. (2013). Neonatal cholestasis. *Neoreviews, 14*(2), e63–e73. doi:10.1542/neo.14-2-e63

Fernandes, C. J. (2017). Clinical manifestations, evalua- tion, and management of neonatal thrombocytopenia. In M. S. Kim (Ed.), *UpToDate.* Retrieved from https://www .uptodate.com/contents/clinical-manifestations-evaluation- and-management-of-neonatal-thrombocytopenia

Fonseca, V. A., Reynolds, T., & Fink, L. M. (1998). Hyperhomocysteinemia and microalbuminuria in dia- betes. *Diabetes Care, 21*(6), 1028–1028. doi:10.2337/ diacare.21.6.1028

Forestier, F., Daffos, F., Catherine, N., Renard, M., & Andreux, J. P. (1991). Developmental hematopoiesis in normal human fetal blood. *Blood, 77*(11), 2360–2363. Retrieved from http:// www.bloodjournal.org/content/bloodjournal/77/11/2360 .full.pdf

Forestier, F., Daffos, F., Galactéros, F., Bardakjian, J., Rainaut, M., & Beuzard, Y. (1986). Hematological val- ues of 163 normal fetuses between 18 and 30 weeks of gestation. *Pediatric Research, 20*(4), 342–346. doi:10.1203/00006450-198604000-00017

Foss, D. L., Donskoy, E., & Goldschneider, I. (2001). The impor- tation of hematogenous precursors by the thymus is a gated phenomenon in normal adult mice. *Journal of Experimental Medicine, 193*(3), 365–374. doi:10.1084/jem.193.3.365

Fuchs, D. A., McGinn, S. G., Cantu, C. L., Klein, R. R., Sola- Visner, M. C., & Rimsza, L. M. (2012). Developmental differ- ences in megakaryocyte size in infants and children. *American

Journal of Clinical Pathology, 138*(1), 140–145. doi:10.1309/ AJCP4EMTJYA0VGYE

Gessler, P., Kirchmann, N., Kientsch-Engel, R., Haas, N., Lasch, P., & Kachel, W. (1993). Serum concentrations of granulocyte colony-stimulating factor in healthy term and preterm neonates and in those with various diseases includ- ing bacterial infections. *Blood, 82*(10), 3177–3182. Retrieved from http://www.bloodjournal.org/content/bloodjour- nal/82/10/3177.full.pdf

Gewirtz, A. M., Calabretta, B., Rucinski, B., Niewiarowski, S., & Xu, W. Y. (1989). Inhibition of human megakaryocytopoiesis in vitro by platelet factor 4 (PF4) and a synthetic COOH- terminal PF4 peptide. *Journal of Clinical Investigation, 83*(5), 1477–1486. doi:10.1172/JCI114041

Goldsmith, J. P., Karotkin, E., Suresh, G., & Keszler, M. (2016). *Assisted ventilation of the neonate* (6th ed.). Philadelphia, PA: Elsevier.

Gomez Perdiguero, E., Klapproth, K., Schulz, C., Busch, K., Azzoni, E., Crozet, L., ... Rodewald, H. (2015). Tissue- resident macrophages originate from yolk-sac-derived erythro-myeloid progenitors. *Nature, 518*(7540), 547–551. doi:10.1038/nature13989

Guez, S., Chiarelli, G., Menni, F., Salera, S., Principi, N., & Esposito, S. (2012). Severe vitamin B12 deficiency in an exclusively breastfed 5-month-old Italian infant born to a mother receiving multivitamin supplementation during preg- nancy. *BMC Pediatrics, 12*(1), s85. doi:10.1186/1471-2431- 12-85

Guizzetti, L. (2016). Total versus partial splenectomy in pedi- atric hereditary spherocytosis: A systematic review and meta-analysis. *Pediatric Blood & Cancer, 63*(10), 1713–1722. doi:10.1002/pbc.26106

Haneline, L. S., Marshall, K. P., & Clapp, D. W. (1996). The highest concentration of primitive hematopoietic pro- genitor cells in cord blood is found in extremely pre- mature infants. *Pediatric Research, 39*(5), 820–825. doi:10.1203/00006450-199605000-00013

Hann, I. M., Bodger, M. P., & Hoffbrand, A. V. (1983). Development of pluripotent hematopoietic progenitor cells in the human fetus. *Blood, 62*(1), 118–123. Retrieved from http://www.bloodjournal.org/content/bloodjournal/ 62/1/118.full.pdf

Hay, W. W., Jr. (2012). Care of the infant of the diabetic mother. *Current Diabetes Reports, 12*(1), 4–15. doi:10.1007/ s11892-011-0243-6

Hoffman, R., Benz, E. J., Jr., Silberstein, L. E., Heslop, H., Weitz, J. I., Anastasi, J., & Salama, M. E. (Eds.). (2018). *Hematology: Basic principles and practice* (7th ed.). Philadelphia, PA: Elsevier.

Ignjatovic, V., Ilhan, A., & Monagle, P. (2011). Evidence for age-related differences in human fibrinogen. *Blood Coagulation & Fibrinolysis, 22*(2), 110–117. doi:10.1097/ MBC.0b013e328343312f

Ishibashi, T., Miller, S. L., & Burstein, S. A. (1987). Type beta transforming growth factor is a potent inhibitor of murine megakaryocytopoiesis in vitro. *Blood, 69*(6), 1737–1741. Retrieved from http://www.bloodjournal.org/content/ bloodjournal/69/6/1737.full.pdf

Ishiguro, A., Nakahata, T., Matsubara, K., Hayashi, Y., Kato, T., Suzuki, Y., & Shimbo, T. (1999). Age-related changes in thrombopoietin in children: Reference interval for serum thrombopoietin levels. *British Journal of Haematology, 106*(4), 884–888. doi:10.1046/j.1365-2141.1999.01641.x

Ivarsson, S. A., & Ljung, R. (1988). Neutropenia and congenital cytomegalovirus infection. *Pediatric Infectious Disease Journal*, 7(6), 436–437. doi:10.1097/00006454-198806000-00019

Iwasaki, H., & Akashi, K. (2007). Myeloid lineage commitment from the hematopoietic stem cell. *Immunity*, 26(6), 726–740. doi:10.1016/j.immuni.2007.06.004

Jagannathan-Bogdan, M., & Zon, L. I. (2013). Hematopoiesis. *Development*, 140(12), 2463–2467. doi:10.1242/dev.083147

Johnson, K. E. (2017). Overview of TORCH infections. In C. Armsby (Ed.), *UpToDate*. Retrieved from https://www.uptodate.com/contents/overview-of-torch-infections#references

Juul, S. E., Haynes, J. W., & McPherson, R. J. (2004). Evaluation of neutropenia and neutrophilia in hospitalized preterm infants. *Journal of Perinatology*, 24(3), 150–157. doi:10.1038/sj.jp.7211057

Kamphuis, M. M., Paridaans, N. P., Porcelijn, L., Lopriore, E., & Oepkes, D. (2014). Incidence and consequences of neonatal alloimmune thrombocytopenia: A systematic review. *Pediatrics*, 133(4), 715–721. doi:10.1542/peds.2013-3320

Kaplan, M., Wong, R. J., Sibley, E., & Stevenson, D. K. (2015). Neonatal jaundice and liver diseases. In R. J. Martin, A. A. Fanaroff, & M. C. Walsh (Eds.), *Fanaroff and Martin's neonatal–perinatal medicine: Diseases of the fetus and infant* (10th ed., pp. 1618–1673). Philadelphia, PA: Elsevier Mosby.

Kato, G. J., Piel, F. B., Reid, C. D., Gaston, M. H., Ohene-Frempong, K., Krishnamurti, L., . . . Vichinsky, E. P. (2018). Sickle cell disease. *Nature Reviews: Disease Primers, 4*, 18010. doi:10.1038/nrdp.2018.10

Katsura, Y. (2002). Redefinition of lymphoid progenitors. *Nature Reviews Immunology*, 2(2), 127–132. doi:10.1038/nri721

Kawamoto, H., Ohmura, K., Fujimoto, S., & Katsura, Y. (1999). Emergence of T cell progenitors without B cell or myeloid differentiation potential at the earliest stage of hematopoiesis in the murine fetal liver. *Journal of Immunology*, 162(5), 2725–2731. Retrieved from http://www.jimmunol.org/content/jimmunol/162/5/2725.full.pdf

Kawamoto, H., & Yoshimoto, K. (2009). A new paradigm for hematopoietic cell lineages: Revision of the classical concept of the myeloid–lymphoid dichotomy. *Trends in Immunology, 30*(5), 193–200. doi:10.1016/j.it.2009.03.001

Kinney, J. S., & Kumar, M. L. (1988). Should we expand the TORCH complex? A description of clinical and diagnostic aspects of selected old and new agents. *Clinics in Perinatology*, 15(4), 727–744. doi:10.1016/S0095-5108(18)30670-5

Knobler, H., Savion, N., Shenkman, B., Kotev-Emeth, S., & Varon, D. (1998). Shear-induced platelet adhesion and aggregation on subendothelium are increased in diabetic patients. *Thrombosis Research*, 90(4), 181–190. doi:10.1016/S0049-3848(98)00050-4

Koenig, J. M., Bliss, J. M., & Mariscalco, M. M. (2017). Normal and abnormal neutrophil physiology in the newborn. In R. A. Polin, S. H. Abman, D. H. Rowitch, W. E. Benitz, & W. W. Fox (Eds.), *Fetal and neonatal physiology* (5th ed., pp. 1216–1229). Philadelphia, PA: Elsevier.

Kondo, M., Scherer, D. C., King, A. G., Manz, M. G., & Weissman, I. L. (2001). Lymphocyte development from hematopoietic stem cells. *Current Opinion in Genetics & Development, 11*(5), 520–526. doi:10.1016/S0959-437X(00)00227-6

Koury, M. J., & Bondurant, M. C. (1992). The molecular mechanism of erythropoietin action. *European Journal of Biochemistry*, 210(3), 649–663. doi:10.1111/j.1432-1033.1992.tb17466.x

Lain, S. J., Roberts, C. L., Bowen, J. R., & Nassar, N. (2015). Early discharge of infants and risk of readmission for jaundice. *Pediatrics*, 135(2), 314–321. doi:10.1542/peds.2014-2388

Lanzkowsky, P., Lipton, J. M., & Fish, J. D. (Eds.). (2016). *Lanzkowsky's manual of pediatric hematology and oncology* (6th ed.). Amsterdam, The Netherlands: Elsevier.

Laver, J., Duncan, E., Abboud, M., Gasparetto, C., Sahdev, I., Warren, D., … Moore, M. A. (1990). High levels of granulocyte and granulocyte-macrophage colony-stimulating factors in cord blood of normal full-term neonates. *Journal of Pediatrics*, 116(4), 627–632. doi:10.1016/S0022-3476(05)81617-8

Lawrence, S. M., Corriden, R., & Nizet, V. (2017). Age-appropriate functions and dysfunctions of the neonatal neutrophil. *Frontiers in Pediatrics, 5,* 2296-2360. doi:10.3389/fped.2017.00023

Levine, R. F., Olson, T. A., Shoff, P. K., Miller, M. K., & Weisman, L. E. (1996). Mature micromegakaryocytes: An unusual developmental pattern in term infants. *British Journal of Haematology*, 94(2), 1–9. doi:10.1046/j.1365-2141.1996.00666.x

Liu, Z., Italiano, J., Ferrer-Marin, F., Gutti, R., Bailey, M., Poterjoy, B., … Sola-Visner, M. (2011). Developmental differences in megakaryocytopoiesis are associated with up-regulated TPO signaling through mTOR and elevated GATA-1 levels in neonatal megakaryocytes. *Blood*, 117(15), 4106–4117. doi:10.1182/blood-2010-07-293092

Liu, Z., & Sola-Visner, M. (2011). Neonatal and adult megakaryopoiesis. *Current Opinion in Hematology*, 18(5), 330–337. doi:10.1097/MOH.0b013e3283497ed5

Luzo, A. C. M., Duarte, T. S. I., Salles, M. L. S., Lorand-Metze, I., Costa, F. F., & Saad, S. T. O. (2007). Early proliferation of umbilical cord blood cells from premature neonates. *Vox Sanguinis*, 93(2), 145–153. doi:10.1111/j.1423-0410.2007.00936.x

Ma, D. C., Sun, Y. H., Chang, K. Z., & Zuo, W. (1996). Developmental change of megakaryocyte maturation and DNA ploidy in human fetus. *European Journal of Haematology*, 57(2), 121–127. doi:10.1111/j.1600-0609.1996.tb01349.x

MacDonald, M. G., & Seshia, M. M. K. (2015). *Avery's neonatology: Pathophysiology and management of the newborn* (7th ed.). Philadelphia, PA: Wolters Kluwer.

Machlus, K. R., & Italiano, J. E. (2013). The incredible journey: From megakaryocyte development to platelet formation. *Journal of Cell Biology*, 201(6), 785. doi:10.1083/jcb.201304054

Mackman, N. (2009). The many faces of tissue factor. *Journal of Thrombosis and Haemostasis, 7 (Suppl. 1)*, 136–139. doi:10.1111/j.1538-7836.2009.03368.x

Mahajan, V., & Jain, S. K. (2016). Hereditary spherocytosis. *NeoReviews*, 17(12), e697–e704. doi:10.1542/neo.17-12-e697

Marins, L. R., Anizelli, L. B., Romanowski, M. D., & Sarquis, A. L. (2017). How does preeclampsia affect neonates? Highlights in the disease's immunity. *Journal of Maternal Fetal & Neonatal Medicine*, 20, 1–8. doi:10.1080/14767058.2017.1401996

Martins, A., Han, J., & Kim, S. O. (2010). The multifaceted effects of granulocyte colony-stimulating factor in immunomodulation and potential roles in intestinal immune homeostasis. *IUBMB Life*, 62(8), 611–617. doi:10.1002/iub.361

Masuda, K., Itoi, M., Amagai, T., Minato, N., Katsura, Y., & Kawamoto, H. (2005). Thymic anlage is colonized by progenitors restricted to T, NK, and dendritic cell lineages.

Journal of Immunology, 174(5), 2525–2532. doi:10.4049/jimmunol.174.5.2525

Mattia, G., Vulcano, F., Milazzo, L., Barca, A., Macioce, G., Giampaolo, A., & Hassan, H. J. (2002). Different ploidy levels of megakaryocytes generated from peripheral or cord blood CD34+ cells are correlated with different levels of platelet release. *Blood, 99*(3), 888–897. doi:10.1182/blood.V99.3.888

Mazzi, S., Lordier, L., Debili, N., Raslova, H., & Vainchenker, W. (2018). Megakaryocyte and polyploidization. *Experimental Hematology, 57*, 1–13. doi:10.1016/j.exphem.2017.10.001

Medvinsky, A., Rybtsov, S., & Taudi, S. (2011). Embryonic origin of the adult hematopoietic system: Advances and questions. *Development, 138*, 1017–1031. doi:10.1242/dev.040998

Mehta, R., & Petrova, A. (2005). Neutrophil function in neonates born to gestational diabetic mothers. *Journal of Perinatology, 25*(3), 178–181. doi:10.1038/sj.jp.7211241

Miyazaki, R., Ogata, H., Iguchi, T., Sogo, S., Kushida, T., Ito, T., … Kobayashi, Y. (2000). Comparative analyses of megakaryocytes derived from cord blood and bone marrow. *British Journal of Haematology, 108*(3), 602–609. doi:10.1046/j.1365-2141.2000.01854.x

Monagle, P., Chan, A. K. C., Goldenberg, N. A., Ichord, R. N., Journeycake, J. M., Nowak-Göttl, U., & Vesely, S. K.. (2012). Antithrombotic therapy in neonates and children: Antithrombotic therapy and prevention of thrombosis, 9th ed: American College of Chest Physicians evidence-based clinical practice guidelines. *Chest, 141* (2 Suppl.), e737S–e801S. doi:10.1378/chest.11-2308

Moore, K. L., Persaud, T. V. N., & Torchia, M. G. (2016). The *developing human: Clinically oriented embryology* (10th ed.). Philadelphia, PA: Elsevier.

Murray, N. A., & Roberts, I. A. (1995). Circulating megakaryocytes and their progenitors (BFU-MK and CFU-MK) in term and pre-term neonates. *British Journal of Haematology, 89*(1), 41–46. doi:10.1111/j.1365-2141.1995.tb08913.x

Murray, N. A., Watts, T. L., & Roberts, I. A. (1998). Endogenous thrombopoietin levels and effect of recombinant human thrombopoietin on megakaryocyte precursors in term and preterm babies. *Pediatric Research, 43*(1), 148–151. doi:10.1203/00006450-199801000-00023

Mwamtemi, H. H., Higuchi, T., Sawai, N., Hidaka, E., & Koike, K. (2000). Quantitative and qualitative differences in thrombopoietin-dependent hematopoietic progenitor development between cord blood and bone marrow. *Transplantation, 69*(8), 1645–1654. Retrieved from https://journals.lww.com/transplantjournal/Fulltext/2000/04270/QUANTITATIVE_AND_QUALITATIVE_DIFFERENCES_IN.21.aspx.

Nassin, M. L., Lapping-Carr, G., & de Jong, J. L. O. (2015). Anemia in the neonate: The differential diagnosis and treatment. *Pediatric Annals, 44*(7), e159–e163. doi:10.3928/00904481-20150710-08

National Institutes of Health. (2018a). Genetics home reference: Sickle cell disease. Retrieved from https://ghr.nlm.nih.gov/condition/sickle-cell-disease

National Institutes of Health. (2018b). Genetics home reference: Thrombocytopenia absent radius syndrome. Retrieved from https://ghr.nlm.nih.gov/condition/thrombocytopenia-absent-radius-syndrome#statistics

Nishihira, H., Toyoda, Y., Miyazaki, H., Kigasawa, H., & Ohsaki. (1996). Growth of macroscopic human megakaryocyte

colonies from cord blood in culture with recombinant human thrombopoietin (c-mpl ligand) and the effects of gestational age on frequency of colonies. *British Journal of Haematology, 92*(1), 23–28. doi:10.1046/j.1365-2141.1996.00287.x

Obeid, R., Munz, W., Jäger, M., Schmidt, W., & Herrmann, W. (2005). Biochemical indexes of the B vitamins in cord serum are predicted by maternal B vitamin status. *American Journal of Clinical Nutrition, 82*(1), 133–139. doi:10.1093/ajcn.82.1.133.

Odièvre, M. H., Verger, E., Silva-Pinto, A. C., & Elion, J. (2011). Pathophysiological insights in sickle cell disease. *Indian Journal of Medical Research, 134*(4), 532–537. Retrieved from https://www.ncbi.nlm.nih.gov/pmc/articles/PMC3237253

Ohls, R. (2017). Developmental erythropoiesis. In R. A. Polin, S. H. Abman, D. H. Rowitch, W. E. Benitz, & W. W. Fox (Eds.), *Fetal and neonatal physiology* (5th ed., pp. 1112–1134). Philadelphia, PA: Elsevier.

Ohls, R. K., Li, Y., Abdel-Mageed, A., Buchanan, J. G., Mandell, L., & Christensen, R. D. (1995). Neutrophil pool sizes and granulocyte colony-stimulating factor production in human mid-trimester fetuses. *Pediatric Research, 37*(6), 806–811. doi:10.1203/00006450-199506000-00022

Ohls, R. K., & Maheshwari, A. (2012). *Hematology, immunology and infectious disease: Neonatology questions and controversies* (2nd ed.). Philadelphia, PA: Elsevier/Saunders.

Olson, A., & Aher, S. (2017). Early erythropoiesis-stimulating agents in preterm or low birth weight infants. *Cochrane Database of Systematic Reviews, 2017*(11). doi:10.1002/14651858.CD004863.pub5

Olson, T. A., Levine, R. F., Mazur, E. M., Wright, D. G., & Salvado, A. J. (1992). Megakaryocytes and megakaryocyte progenitors in human cord blood. *American Journal of Pediatric Hematology/Oncology, 14*(3), 241–247.

Orkin, S. H. (2015). *Nathan and Oski's hematology and oncology of infancy and childhood* (8th ed.). Philadelphia, PA: Elsevier Saunders.

Oski, F. A., & Naiman, J. L. (1982). *Hematologic problems in the newborn* (3rd ed.). Philadelphia, PA: Saunders.

Palis, J., Robertson, S., Kennedy, M., Wall, C., & Keller, G. (1999). Development of erythroid and myeloid progenitors in the yolk sac and embryo proper of the mouse. *Development, 126*(22), 5073–5084. Retrieved from http://dev.biologists.org/content/develop/126/22/5073.full.pdf

Pang, L., Weiss, M. J., & Poncz, M. (2005). Megakaryocyte biology and related disorders. *Journal of Clinical Investigation, 115*(12), 3332–3338. doi:10.1172/JCI26720

Paul, D., Leef, K., Sciscione, A., Tuttle, D., & Stefano, J. (1999). Preeclampsia does not increase the risk for culture proven sepsis in very low birth weight infants. *American Journal of Perinatology, 16*(7), 365–372. doi:10.1055/s-2007-993886

Perrine, S. P., Greene, M. F., Lee, P. D., Cohen, R. A., & Faller, D. V. (1986). Insulin stimulates cord blood erythroid progenitor growth: Evidence for an aetiological role in neonatal polycythaemia. *British Journal of Haematology, 64*(3), 503–511. doi:10.1111/j.1365-2141.1986.tb02206.x

Piel, F. B., Hay, S. I., Gupta, S., Weatherall, D. J., & Williams, T. N. (2013). Global burden of sickle cell anaemia in children under five, 2010-2050: Modelling based on demographics, excess mortality, and interventions. *PLoS Medicine, 10*(7), e1001484. doi:10.1371/journal.pmed.1001484

Piel, F. B., Steinberg, M. H., & Rees, D. C. (2017). Sickle cell disease. *New England Journal of Medicine, 376*(16), 1561–1573. doi:10.1056/NEJMra1510865

Polin, R. A., Abman, S. H., Rowitch, D. H., Benitz, W. E., & Fox, W. W. (2017). *Fetal and neonatal physiology* (5th ed.). Philadelphia, PA: Elsevier.

Pouzolles, M., Oburoglu, L., Taylor, N., & Zimmermann, V. S. (2016). Hematopoietic stem cell lineage specification. *Current Opinion in Hematology, 23*(4), 311–317. doi:10.1097/MOH.0000000000000260

Prescott, L. F. (1964). Neonatal thrombocytopenia and thiazide drugs. *British Medical Journal, 1*(5395), 1438. doi:10.1136/bmj.1.5395.1438

Procianoy, R., & Brazilian Network on Neonatal Research. (2010). Sepsis and neutropenia in very low birth weight infants delivered of mothers with preeclampsia. *Journal of Pediatrics, 157*(3), 434–438.e1. doi:10.1016/j.jpeds.2010.02.066

Proud, L., & Ritchey, A. K. (2017). Management of type 2b Von Willebrand disease in the neonatal period: Proud and Ritchey. *Pediatric Blood & Cancer, 64*(1), 103–105. doi:10.1002/pbc.26168

Ramesh Bhat, Y., & Cherian, C. S. (2008). Neonatal thrombocytopenia associated with maternal pregnancy induced hypertension. *Indian Journal of Pediatrics, 75*(6), 571–573. doi:10.1007/s12098-008-0110-x

Ravid, K., Lu, J., Zimmet, J. M., & Jones, M. R. (2002). Roads to polyploidy: The megakaryocyte example. *Journal of Cellular Physiology, 190*(1), 7–20. doi:10.1002/jcp.10035

Remon, J. I., Raghavan, A., & Maheshwari, A. (2011). Polycythemia in the newborn. *NeoReviews, 12*(1), e20-e28. doi:10.1542/neo.12-1-e20

Rencic, J., Zhou, M., Hsu, G., & Dhaliwal, G. (2017). Circling back for the diagnosis. *New England Journal of Medicine, 377*(18), 1778–1784. doi:10.1056/NEJMcps1701742

Rennie, J. M. (2012). *Rennie and Roberton's textbook of neonatology* (5th ed.). New York, NY: Churchill Livingstone Elsevier.

Richards, M. K., Liu, F., Iwasaki, H., Akashi, K., & Link, D. C. (2003). Pivotal role of granulocyte colony-stimulating factor in the development of progenitors in the common myeloid pathway. *Blood, 102*(10), 3562–3568. doi:10.1182/blood-2003-02-0593

Roberts, I. A. G., & Murray, N. A. (2012). Haematology. In J. M. Rennie (Ed.), *Rennie and Roberton's textbook of neonatology* (5th ed., pp. 755-790). London, UK: Churchill Livingstone.

Sankaran, V. G., & Orkin, S. H. (2013). Genome-wide association studies of hematologic phenotypes: A window into human hematopoiesis. *Current Opinion in Genetics & Development, 23*(3), 339–344. doi:10.1016/j.gde.2013.02.006

Sankar, M. J., Chandrasekaran, A., Kumar, P., Thukral, A., Agarwal, R., & Paul, V. K. (2016). Vitamin K prophylaxis for prevention of vitamin K deficiency bleeding: A systematic review. *Journal of Perinatology: Official Journal of the California Perinatal Association, 36*(Suppl 1), S29–S35. doi: 10.1038/jp.2016.30

Sarkar, S., Hagstrom, N. J., Ingardia, C. J., Lerer, T., & Herson, V. C. (2005). Prothrombotic risk factors in infants of diabetic mothers. *Journal of Perinatology, 25*(2), 134–138. doi:10.1038/sj.jp.7211222

Satrom, K., & Gourley, G. (2016). Cholestasis in preterm infants. *Clinics in Perinatology, 43*(2), 355–373. doi:10.1016/j.clp.2016.01.012

Schinco, P., Castaman, G., Coppola, A., Cultrera, D., Ettorre, C., Giuffrida, A. C., … Federici, A. B. (2017). Current challenges in the diagnosis and management of patients with inherited von Willebrand's disease in Italy: An expert meeting report on the diagnosis and surgical and secondary long-term prophylaxis. *Blood Transfusion, 16*(4),371–381. doi: 10.2450/2017.0354-16

Schipper, L. F., Brand, A., Reniers, N. C., Melief, C. J., Willemze, R., & Fibbe, W. E. (1998). Effects of thrombopoietin on the proliferation and differentiation of primitive and mature haemopoietic progenitor cells in cord blood. *British Journal of Haematology, 101*(3), 425–435. doi:10.1046/j.1365-2141.1998.00737.x

Schleiss, M. R., & Marsh, K. J. (2018). Viral infections of the fetus and newborn. In C. A. Gleason & S. E. Juul (Eds.), *Avery's diseases of the newborn* (10th ed., pp. 1152–1179). Philadelphia, PA: Elsevier.

Schmutz, N., Henry, E., Jopling, J., & Christensen, R. D. (2008). Expected ranges for blood neutrophil concentrations of neonates: The Manroe and Mouzinho charts revisited. *Journal of Perinatology, 28*(4), 275–281. doi:10.1038/sj.jp.7211916

Shearer, M. J. (2017). Vitamin K metabolism in the fetus and neonate. In R. A. Polin, S. H. Abman, D. H. Rowitch, W. E. Benitz, & W. W. Fox (Eds.), *Fetal and neonatal physiology* (5th ed., pp. 336–341). Philadelphia, PA: Elsevier.

Shivdasani, R. A., McDevitt, M. A., Orkin, S. H., & Fujiwara, Y. (1997). A lineage-selective knockout establishes the critical role of transcription factor GATA-1 in megakaryocyte growth and platelet development. *EMBO Journal, 16*(13), 3965–3973. doi:10.1093/emboj/16.13.3965

Sieff, C. A. (1987). Hematopoietic growth factors. *Journal of Clinical Investigation, 79*(6), 1549–1557. doi:10.1172/JCI112988

Sims, R. B., & Gewirtz, A. M. (1989). Human megakaryocytopoiesis. *Annual Review of Medicine, 40*(1), 213–224. doi:10.1146/annurev.me.40.020189.001241

Singh, V. K., Saini, A., Kalson, M., Kumar, N., & Chandra, R. (2016). Stage-specific regulation of erythropoiesis and its implications in ex-vivo RBCs generation. *Journal of Stem Cells, 11*(3), 149–169.

Slayton, W. B., Li, Y., Calhoun, D. A., Juul, S. E., Iturraspe, J., Braylan, R. C., & Christensen, R. D. (1998). The first-appearance of neutrophils in the human fetal bone marrow cavity. *Early Human Development, 53*(2), 129–144. doi:10.1016/S0378-3782(98)00049-8

Slayton, W. B., Wainman, D. A., Li, X. M., Hu, Z., Jotwani, A., Cogle, C. R., . . . Sola, M. C. (2005). Developmental differences in megakaryocyte maturation are determined by the microenvironment. *Stem Cells, 23*(9), 1400–1408. doi:10.1634/stemcells.2004-0373

Sola, M. C., Du, Y., Hutson, A. D., & Christensen, R. D. (2000). Dose-response relationship of megakaryocyte progenitors from the bone marrow of thrombocytopenic and non-thrombocytopenic neonates to recombinant thrombopoietin. *British Journal of Haematology, 110*, 449–453. doi:10.1046/j.1365-2141.2000.02163.x

Sola, M. C., Juul, S. E., Meng, Y. G., Garg, S., Sims, P., Calhoun, D. A., … Christensen, R. D. (1999). Thrombopoietin (tpo) in the fetus and neonate: Tpo concentrations in preterm and term neonates, and organ distribution of tpo and its receptor (c-mpl) during human fetal development. *Early Human Development, 53*(3), 239–250. doi:10.1016/S0378-3782(98)00077-2

Sola-Visner, M., & Ramsey, H. (2017). Developmental megakaryocytopoiesis. In cc Polin, S. H. Abman, D. H. Rowitch, W. E. Benitz, & W. W. Fox (Eds.), *Fetal and neonatal physiology* (5th ed., pp. 1135–1150). Philadelphia, PA: Elsevier.

Sola-Visner, M. C., Christensen, R. D., Hutson, A. D., & Rimsza, L. M. (2007). Megakaryocyte size and concentration in the bone marrow of thrombocytopenic and nonthrombocytopenic neonates. *Pediatric Research, 61*(4), 479–484. doi:10.1203/pdr.0b013e3180332c18

Sola-Visner, M. C., Saxonhouse, M. A., & Brown, R. E. (2008). Neonatal thrombocytopenia: What we do and don't know. *Early Human Development*, 84(8), 499–506. doi:10.1016/j.earlhumdev.2008.06.004

Son-Hing, J. P., & Thompson, G. H. (2015). Congenital abnormalities of the upper and lower extremities and spine. In R. J. Martin, A. A. Fanaroff, & M. C. Walsh (Eds.), *Fanaroff and Martin's neonatal-perinatal medicine: Diseases of the fetus and infant* (10th ed., pp. 1789–1808). Philadelphia, PA: Elsevier Mosby.

Spivak, J. L. (2005). The anaemia of cancer: Death by a thousand cuts. *Nature Reviews Cancer*, 5, 543–555. doi:10.1038/nrc1648

Stoll, B. J., & Hansen, N. (2003). Infections in VLBW infants: Studies from the NICHD neonatal research network. *Seminars in Perinatology*, 27(4), 293–301. doi:10.1016/S0146-0005(03)00046-6

Suzuki, N., Hirano, I., Pan, X., Minegishi, N., & Yamamoto, M. (2013). Erythropoietin production in neuroepithelial and neural crest cells during primitive erythropoiesis. *Nature Communications*, 4, 2902. doi:10.1038/ncomms3902

Thomas, D. B., & Yoffey, J. M. (1962). Human foetal haemopoiesis. I. The cellular composition of foetal blood. *British Journal of Haematology*, 8(3), 290–295. doi:10.1111/j.1365-2141.1962.tb06523.x

Toriello, H. (2011). Thrombocytopenia-absent radius syndrome. *Seminars in Thrombosis and Hemostasis*, 37(6), 707–712. doi:10.1055/s-0031-1291381

Tsao, P., Teng, R., Chou, H., & Tsou, K. (2002). The thrombopoietin level in the cord blood in premature infants born to mothers with pregnancy-induced hypertension. *Biology of the Neonate*, 82(4), 217–221. doi:10.1159/000065888

van der Kaay, D. C. M., Wasserman, J. D., & Palmert, M. R. (2016). Management of neonates born to mothers with Graves' disease. *Pediatrics*, 137(4), 1–10. doi:10.1542/peds.2015-1878

Van Sande, H., Jacquemyn, Y., & Karepouan, M. A. (2013). Vitamin B12 in pregnancy: Maternal and fetal/neonatal effects—A review. *Open Journal of Obstetrics and Gynecology*, 3, 599–602. doi:10.4236/ojog.2013.37107.

Veldman, A., Fischer, D., Nold, M., & Wong, F. (2010). Disseminated intravascular coagulation in term and preterm neonates. *Seminars in Thrombosis and Hemostasis*, 36(4), 419–428. doi:10.1055/s-0030-1254050

Walka, M. M., Sonntag, J., Dudenhausen, J. W., & Obladen, M. (1999). Thrombopoietin concentration in umbilical cord blood of healthy term newborns is higher than in adult controls. *Biology of the Neonate*, 75(1), 54–58. doi:10.1159/000014077

Wang, L., Menendez, P., Cerdan, C., & Bhatia, M. (2005). Hematopoietic development from human embryonic stem cell lines. *Experimental Hematology*, 33(9), 987–996. doi:10.1016/j.exphem.2005.06.002

Watts, T., & Roberts, I. (1999). Haematological abnormalities in the growth-restricted infant. *Seminars in Neonatology*, 4(1), 41–54. doi:10.1016/S1084-2756(99)80006-2

Werner, E. J., Chescheir, N. C.,s & Fisher, R. G. (2012). Disorders of the feto-maternal unit. In P. A. de Alarcón, E. Werner, & R. D. Christensen (Eds.), *Neonatal hematology* (pp. 269–384). Cambridge, UK: Cambridge University Press.

Wickremasinghe, A. C., Risley, R. J., Kuzniewicz, M. W., Wu, Y. W., Walsh, E. M., Wi, S., … Newman, T. B. (2015). Risk of sensorineural hearing loss and bilirubin exchange transfusion thresholds. *Pediatrics*, 136(3), 505–512. doi:10.1542/peds.2014-3357

Widness, J. A., Susa, J. B., Garcia, J. F., Singer, D. B., Sehgal, P., Oh, W., … Schwartz, H. C. (1981). Increased erythropoiesis and elevated erythropoietin in infants born to diabetic mothers and in hyperinsulinemic rhesus fetuses. *Journal of Clinical Investigation*, 67(3), 637–642. doi:10.1172/JCI110078

Wiedmeier, S. E., Henry, E., Sola-Visner, M. C., & Christensen, R. D. (2009). Platelet reference ranges for neonates, defined using data from over 47000 patients in a multihospital healthcare system. *Journal of Perinatology*, 29(2), 130–136. doi:10.1038/jp.2008.141

Will, A., Henderson, C. A., Jnah, A. J., & Newberry, D. (2017). Hereditary spherocytosis in the neonatal period: A case report. *Neonatal Network*, 36(5), 280–288. doi:10.1891/0730-0832.36.5.280

Winkelmann, M., Pfitzer, P., & Schneider, W. (1987). Significance of polyploidy in megakaryocytes and other cells in health and tumor disease. *Klinische Wochenschrift*, 65(23), 1115–1131. doi:10.1007/BF01734832

Wolber, E. M., Dame, C., Fahnenstich, H., Hofmann, D., Bartmann, P., Jelkmann, W., & Fandrey, J. (1999). Expression of the thrombopoietin gene in human fetal and neonatal tissues. *Blood*, 94(1), 97–105.

Woolthuis, C. M., & Park, C. Y. (2016). Hematopoietic stem/progenitor cell commitment to the megakaryocyte lineage. *Blood*, 127(10), 1242–1248. doi:10.1182/blood-2015-07-607945

Wu, Y. W., Kuzniewicz, M. W., Wickremasinghe, A. C., Walsh, E. M., Wi, S., McCulloch, C. E., & Newman, T. B. (2015). Risk for cerebral palsy in infants with total serum bilirubin levels at or above the exchange transfusion threshold: A population-based study. *JAMA Pediatrics*, 169(3), 239–246. doi:10.1001/jamapediatrics.2014.3036

Xu, M., Matsuoka, S. Y, F. C., Ebihara, Y., Manabe, A., Tanaka, R., Eguchi, M., … Tsuji, K. (2001). Evidence for the presence of murine primitive megakarycytopoiesis in the early yolk sac. *Blood*, 97(7), 2016–2022. doi:10.1182/blood.V97.7.2016

Zauli, G., Valvassori, L., & Capitani, S. (1993). Presence and characteristics of circulating megakaryocyte progenitor cells in human fetal blood. *Blood*, 81(2), 385–390. doi:http://www.bloodjournal.org/content/bloodjournal/81/2/385.full.pdf

Zitelli, B. J., McIntire, S. C., & Nowalk, A. J. (2018). *Zitelli and Davis' atlas of pediatric physical diagnosis* (7th ed.). Philadelphia, PA: Elsevier.

8

THE RENAL SYSTEM

Bobby Bellflower, Curry Bordelon, Elizabeth Sharpe, and Amy J. Jnah

LEARNING OBJECTIVES

After completing this chapter, the reader should be able to:

- Understand normal renal organ development.
- Analyze the physiologic function of the fetal and neonatal kidney and bladder.
- Discuss common inherited disorders and their effect on fetal and neonatal renal system development and function.
- Identify maternal health conditions that have a potential impact on fetal and postnatal renal system development and function.
- Evaluate common disorders that affect the renal system and their implications across the life span.

INTRODUCTION

Morphologic and physiologic development of the renal system involves complex, genetically influenced adaptations that span from early gestation to postnatal life. Once functional, the kidneys modulate ion concentrations, hormone levels, and the excretion of metabolic waste products as well as blood pressure, the composition of blood, and blood volume. Therefore, appropriate renal function is critical to maintaining physiologic homeostasis. A lack of architectural precision during fetal development, or that which occurs secondary to premature birth, as well as epigenetic errors may give rise to renal dysfunction. Problems including acute kidney injury (AKI) and electrolyte imbalances are commonly observed among premature and critically ill newborns and require astute identification, diagnosis, and timely treatment by advanced practice clinicians. This is essential to prevent long-term renal damage. Understanding normal morphologic development and physiologic function of the fetal and neonatal kidney helps clinicians associate normal function with renal maladaptation.

TIMELINE OF ORGAN DEVELOPMENT

The renal system consists of the kidneys, bladder, ureters, and urethra. Each structure arises from either the pronephros, mesonephros, or metanephros and is explained in linear progression from early embryonic development through maturation.

Embryonic Period

Kidneys. The renal system arises from the intermediate mesenchyme, located at the dorsal wall of the embryo (Moore, Persaud, & Torchia, 2016). This period is marked by the genesis of not two, but three primitive kidneys. These early structures are known as the *pronephros, mesonephros*, and *metanephros*.

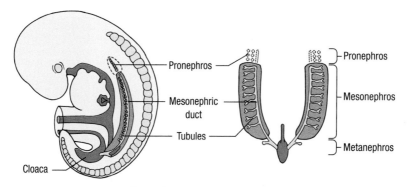

Ureteric bud and metanephric diverticulum

Figure 8.1 Regression of the pronephros.

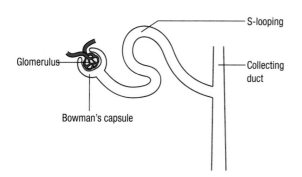

Figure 8.2 S-looping of primitive kidney.

The pronephros arises early in week 4 of gestation and regresses by the end of that same week (Moore et al., 2016). It gives rise to balls of epithelial tubular cells, or nephrotomes, which drain into the primary nephric duct ("Wolffian duct"). The nephrotomes make contact with the cloaca by the end of week 4 of gestation and form into primitive canals (ducts) in the caudo-cephalad direction. By the end of the pronephric period, when the nephrotomes regress, the mesonephric ducts are present (Figure 8.1; Moore et al., 2016).

The mesonephros appears toward the end of week 4 of gestation, concurrent with regression of the pronephros (Moore et al., 2016). The mesonephric ducts stretch (elongate), and during this process undergo a process of S-looping (Figure 8.2). This ultimately gives rise to four critical structures: the (a) glomeruli, (b) mesonephric tubules, (c) mesonephric ducts, and (d) cloaca (Moore et al., 2016). The primitive glomeruli and Bowman's capsule sit at the proximal end of the S-loop, whereas the Wolffian duct resides at its distal end (Vogt & Dell, 2015). This early and programmed shaping of the nephron permits primitive renal function, which typically commences after day 23 of gestation, just after early cardiac contractions (heart beats) begin.

During week 5 of gestation, hypertrophy of the caudal end of the mesonephric duct permits the genesis of the ureteric bud (Figure 8.3). The ureteric bud grows laterally, toward the mesenchyme, and ultimately invades and imbeds itself within the mesenchyme (the primitive renal parenchyma, or kidney). Once imbedded, the ureteric bud undergoes a process of branching, which forms the collecting system and major and minor calices (Figure 8.4). Proximal ends of the metanephric tubules approximate with the existing glomeruli and the tube differentiates into its adult structures: the (a) proximal tubule, (b) loop of Henle (LOH), (c) distal convoluted tubule (DCT), and (d) collecting duct (Moore et al., 2016). In addition, some metanephric mesenchyme cells undergo mesenchymal-to-epithelial conversion and form the epithelial lining of the nephron (Moore et al., 2016; Scott, Maezawa, Kreidberg, & Quaggin, 2016). It is within week 8 of gestation that nephrons form and a process of structural elongation and functional maturation begins.

Ureters and Bladder. Weeks 5 through 7 of gestation mark a period of cloacal division. The cloaca divides into the urogenital sinus and anorectal canal. The urogenital sinus further differentiates into the primitive bladder and membranous urethra. The urethra proliferates toward the developing kidney and also toward the urogenital sinus, while forming a functional lumen; failed formation of the lumen results in obstruction of the mesonephros, causing the nephrons to fill with fluid, become cystic, and lead to multicystic (polycystic) kidney disease. In addition, narrowing or obstruction at the juncture of the ureter and renal pelvis may lead to pooling of urine within the pelvis, or hydronephrosis. In males, the prostatic urethra drains into the penile urethra as the ejaculatory duct. In females, the mesonephric duct regresses and forms a vestibule (Vogt & Dell, 2015). Urine formation and excretion begin between weeks 6 and 10 of gestation, likely a result of earlier urine formation during mesonephric tubular development (Moore et al., 2016; Schoenwolf, Bleyl, Brauer, & Francis-West, 2015).

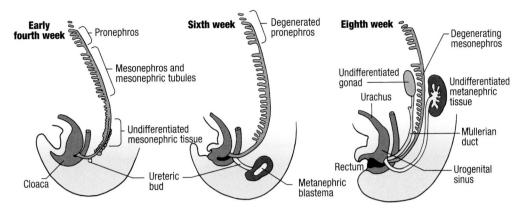

Figure 8.3 Early kidney development.

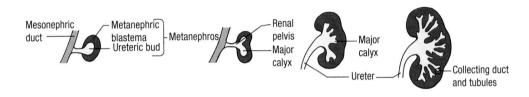

Figure 8.4 Ureteric bud branching. The ureteric bud gives rise to the ureter, major calyx, minor calyx, and collecting system.

Fetal Period

Kidneys. The fetal period of development marks a period of vertical ascent and shift in blood supply for each kidney; failed ascent leads to pelvic (ectopic) kidney formation. These two structures, once nestled within the pelvis and receiving nourishment from the common iliac arteries, migrate upward and outward from one another as a result of normal embryonic growth toward the thoracolumbar region. Once the migration is finished, each kidney resides on either side of the spine and receives its blood supply from a dedicated renal artery. Each renal artery is a branch off the abdominal aorta (Moore et al., 2016).

Concurrent with migration, glomerular proliferation occurs. The nephrons' glomerular filtration barrier (GFB), glomeruli, and glomerular vasculature develop centrifugally, beginning with the juxtamedullary glomeruli and with progressive maturation of the cortical glomeruli. In other words, the superficial cortical nephrons are the newest nephrons and the deeper juxtamedullary nephrons are more mature. Glomerular filtration commences during week 9 of gestation, and between weeks 10 through 18 of gestation, significant and steady proliferation occurs. Weeks 19 through 36 of gestation involve an exponential increase in the number of glomeruli, as the fetus begins to prepare for the demands of extrauterine life (Moore et al., 2016). Nephrogenesis is considered complete in the term infant.

Ureters and Bladder. The end of the fetal period of development (week 8 of gestation) through week 12 of gestation involves continued development and differentiation of the cloaca. In addition, the anatomic development of other portions of the urogenital system occur. The caudal end of the mesonephric duct melds into the nearby wall of the bladder and becomes a portion of connective tissue within the trigone, or triangular region, of the bladder (Moore et al., 2016). The caudal portions of the left and right ureters begin to migrate down and into the developing urinary bladder, giving rise to two of three trigone regions. Shortly thereafter, an opening appears, one at each vertex of the inverted triangle. The right and left upper vertices (openings) permit the innervation of the corresponding ureter, while the third opening communicates with the ureter. Once the ureter innervates with the trigone, a muscular band, or internal urethral sphincter, encircles this opening.

During weeks 13 to 17 of gestation, the urinary bladder epithelium undergoes thickening and transforms from two layers of cuboidal epithelial cells into a trilayered urothelium. The urothelium expresses the growth factor Sonic hedgehog (SHH), which is likely the signal that stimulates mesenchymal proliferation and smooth muscle differentiation in the urinary bladder (Tasian, Cunha, & Baskin, 2010). Throughout the rest of fetal development, the bladder differentiates into a structure comprising three linings. The innermost mucosal layer of the bladder is affixed with the identical epithelium as each ureter. When empty, this mucosa folds in a rugated, or accordion-like, fashion, which allows for later expansion secondary to the accumulation of urine. The middle layer of the bladder is affixed with connective and elastic tissue. The outermost layer becomes the muscular layer of the bladder, responsible for expelling urine from the bladder.

Neonatal Period

Nephrogenesis is considered complete by week 36 of gestation, as greater than 80% of nephrons have formed (Faa et al., 2010). Once mature, each healthy kidney contains between 800,000 and 2 million nephrons, although variability is reported and may occur as a result of altered epigenetic programming, the number of nephron progenitors present during nephrogenesis, and prematurity (Moore et al., 2016; Vogt & Dell, 2015). In fact, premature infants born prior to week 36 of gestation undergo active extrauterine nephrogenesis. This continued development, which occurs due to glomerular hypertrophy and renal tubular elongation (not by postnatal nephrogenesis), is influenced by the fetal and/or maternal factors that initiated the premature birth, maintenance of adequate renal blood flow and oxygenation, and toxic exposure to medications (Pan & Avner, 2016).

DEVELOPMENTAL PHYSIOLOGY

The kidneys are one of the most astute organ systems, intricately equipped to modulate fluid, electrolyte, and acid–base homeostasis in the face of minimal to severe pathologic threats. In addition, the renal vascular system participates in the modulation of arterial blood pressure through the secretion of various vasoregulators. In order to understand the core concepts related to fetal and neonatal renal physiology discussed in this section of the chapter, several core terms are presented in Table 8.1.

Glomerular Filtration

The placenta serves as the major source of filtration and fluid and electrolyte homeostasis for the developing fetus, offering the renal system a margin for anatomic and functional maturation throughout the first 16 weeks of gestation. Early glomerular filtration commences at approximately 8 weeks of gestation and continues to advance throughout fetal and postnatal development (Matsell & Hiatt, 2017; Rosenblum, Pal, & Reidy, 2017). Several factors influence the maturation of the glomerular filtration rate (GFR), including ongoing anatomic kidney maturation and expansion of the glomerular bed, increasing fetal body mass index, increasing hydrostatic pressure at the glomerulus, increasing renal blood flow, and functional integration of vasoregulators (Pan & Avner, 2016). Risk factors for alterations in normal maturation of GFR include placental insufficiency; fetal intrauterine exposure to environmental toxins; maternal dietary protein restriction; and structural anomalies, including urinary tract obstruction (Guignard, 2017).

Expansion of glomerular surface area offers a wider capillary bed for filtration and future urine formation. GFR is measured by creatinine clearance, *the most consistent marker of GFR in the fetus and neonate* (Kastl, 2017). Around 20 weeks of gestation, creatinine clearance is estimated to be less than 1 mL/min, but with rapid nephrogenesis increases to 4 to 5 mL/min at term and doubles to 8 to 10 mL/min by 2 weeks of postnatal age (Guignard, 2017).

During gestation, fetal maturation and growth result in an increase in fetal mean arterial pressure, which increases glomerular capillary hydrostatic pressure. This process, in synergy with increasing renal blood flow, increases the pressure gradient at the glomerulus and facilitates increasing filtration. In fact, studies using fetal pigs suggest that the steady increase of hydrostatic pressure and renal blood flow facilitate a 20-fold increase in GFR in the postnatal period (Matsell & Hiatt, 2017).

In the newborn, glomerular filtration is essential for body fluid homeostasis, electrolyte homeostasis, and elimination of drugs (Guignard, 2017). The GFR is dependent on arterial pressure within the glomerular capillaries, renal blood flow, and the glomerular plasma flow rate; therefore, GFR is the most consistent measure for renal

---

TABLE 8.1 Core Terminology

Term	Definition
Glomerular filtration	Filtration of plasma from the glomerulus into Bowman's capsule.
Tubular reabsorption	Reabsorption of solute from the tubular lumen back into the peritubular capillaries. This occurs by simple, facilitated, or active transport.
Tubular secretion	Movement of solute from the peritubular capillaries into the tubular lumen.

function. Postnatal GFR is estimated at 15 mL/min/1.73 m^2 to 25 mL/min/1.73 m^2 among term infants (Abitbol, DeFreitas, & Strauss, 2016). This rate doubles to 45 mL/min/1.73 m^2 to 55 mL/min/1.73 m^2 by 2 months postnatally (Abitbol et al., 2016). Adult renal function of GFR of 110 mL/min/1.73 m^2 to 120 mL/min/1.73 m^2 is achieved by approximately 2 years of age in the healthy infant and directly determined by the maturation and growth of the kidney based on the increasing surface area of the glomeruli present at birth (Abitbol et al., 2016; Alpern, Caplan, & Moe, 2013; Matsell & Hiatt, 2017).

Several vasoactive agents produced in the body help regulate GFR by affecting afferent and efferent capillary resistance. It is interesting to note that agents that cause efferent vasoconstriction may decrease renal blood flow, yet increase GFR, by increasing the amount of fluid available for filtration at the glomerulus. Agents that cause afferent vasoconstriction and efferent dilation decrease both renal blood flow and GFR, whereas agents that lead to afferent vasodilation increase renal blood flow and GFR.

Factors that may contribute to an increase in postnatal GFR include (a) an increase in renal blood flow and increase in glomerular plasma flow rate, (b) an increase in systemic blood pressure within the first weeks of life, and (c) maturational changes in the surface and permeability of the filtration barrier (Guignard, 2017). New evidence suggests that delayed cord clamping may increase the GFR over the first week of life (Guignard, 2017).

Factors that may impair or delay postnatal functional maturation of the GFR include perinatal hypoxemia and asphyxia, ventilation, angiotensin-converting enzyme (ACE) inhibitors, prostaglandin inhibitors, and other drugs. Perinatal hypoxemia causes a decrease in GFR because of renal vascular vasoconstriction as a result of increased renin–angiotensin aldosterone system activation and other vaso-restrictive substances (Alpern et al., 2013). Ventilation of newborns may cause decreased venous return and low cardiac output, thus decreasing renal blood flow (Guignard, 2017). Mothers with hypertensive disorders may receive ACE inhibitors and mothers in preterm labor may receive prostaglandin synthesis inhibitors; thus, a potent vasodilator of the afferent arteriole may be blocked (Guignard, 2017).

Renal Blood Flow

Blood flow to the kidneys occurs by way of the afferent arteriole (Figure 8.5). Fetal blood flow to the kidney is low and is the result of high renal vascular resistance, low perfusion pressure, and the diversion of 65% of fetal cardiac output to the placenta (Solhaug & Jose, 2017). This preferential blood-flow pattern explains why most developing organ systems acclimate to a persistent state of increased vascular resistance in utero. With maturation

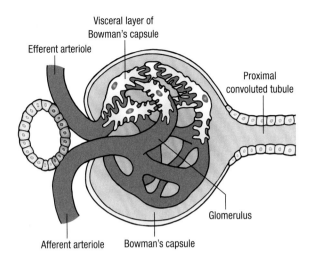

Figure 8.5 Renal blood flow (afferent and efferent arterioles).

during gestation, fetal blood flow increases as renal vascular resistance decreases, most likely due to an increase in the number of glomeruli and increased renin–angiotensin–aldosterone system (RAAS) activity. Renal blood flow in the fetus is about 3% to 5% of cardiac output (Solhaug & Jose, 2017; Vogt & Dell, 2015).

Postnatally, renal blood flow steadily increases through the second year of life (Vogt & Dell, 2015). Renal blood flow is approximately 4% to 6% of total cardiac output within the first 12 hours and increases to 8% to 10% of cardiac output by the first week of life (Nada, Bonachea, & Askenazi, 2017; Vogt & Dell, 2015). This phenomenon is the result of decreased perfusion pressure due to increased renal vascular resistance, which is initially low in the newborn period and increases steadily over the first 2 years of life. In fact, high renal vascular resistance accounts for the decreased GFR after birth and may affect the newborn's ability to respond to any untoward events, such as hypoxic–ischemic insults, that may precede acute renal failure. By 2 years of age, renal blood flow reaches the adult status of about 20% to 25% of cardiac output (Nada et al., 2017).

Renal Vasoregulators

Vaso-regulatory factors play an important role in *regulating* GFR both during fetal development and postnatally. Major vasoactive factors include nitric oxide (NO), prostaglandins, atrial natriuretic peptide (ANP), the sympathetic nervous system, catecholamines, and the RAAS (Solhaug & Jose, 2017). These factors either increase or decrease GFR, and often work to modulate the effects of one another to preserve homeostatic renal function.

Nitric Oxide. NO is a potent vasodilator and is derived from endothelium in the early embryonic kidney, especially in the glomeruli and intrarenal capillaries (Vogt & Dell, 2015). NO inhibits the strong vasoconstrictive effects of angiotensin II in the fetal kidney and promotes blood flow through smooth muscle relaxation (Solhaug & Jose, 2017).

Prostaglandins. Prostaglandins affect both renal development and function. Recent studies indicate that prostaglandins are important in normal development of the kidneys by maintaining cyclooxygenase activity to prevent severe renal anomalies (Matsell & Hiatt, 2017). Similar to NO, prostaglandins are potent vasodilators. They serve to inhibit the strong vasoconstrictive effects of angiotensin II and decrease afferent (incoming) arteriolar tone through vasodilation, thus improving blood flow into the glomerulus (Matsell & Hiatt, 2017).

Atrial Natriuretic Peptide. ANP is a vasoactive hormone produced in the atria and ventricles of the heart in response to stretching associated with fluid overload. ANP may help regulate GFR by dilating the afferent arterioles and constricting the efferent arterioles simultaneously (Wein, Kavoussi, Partin, & Peters, 2016). ANP levels are highest during fetal development and decrease to adult levels within the first few weeks after birth. Although ANP has important vascular and renal effects in mature kidneys, it does not increase renal blood flow in the newborn period (Solhaug & Jose, 2017).

Endothelin. Endothelin is a peptide produced by the vascular epithelium. Peptide levels increase throughout fetal development. Endothelin functions to increase efferent (outgoing) arteriolar tone through vasoconstriction, thus improving blood flow to the glomerulus (Solhaug & Jose, 2017).

Renin–Angiotensin–Aldosterone System. The RAAS is a negative feedback hormonal system in the human body that regulates many biologic processes, including cell growth and remodeling, blood pressure, and fluid and electrolyte homeostasis. The vasculature, kidneys, liver, heart, lungs, brain, and adrenal glands orchestrate the actions of the RAAS. The RAAS serves a key role in maintaining systemic blood pressure during fetal and postnatal development by regulating systemic and renal vascular tone (resistance within the vessels); mechanisms that regulate on-and-off switching of this system are poorly understood (Figure 8.6; Sparks, Crowley, Gurley, Mirotsou, & Coffman, 2014).

Juxtaglomerular (JG) cells, located within the afferent arteriole in the glomerulus, are the main source for the storage and release of renin (Klabunde, 2012).

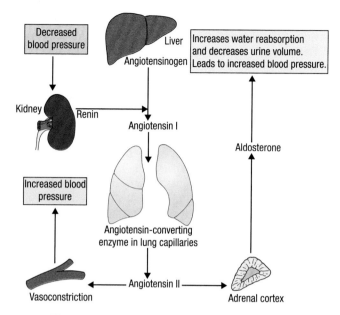

Figure 8.6 Renin-angiotensin-aldosterone system.

Any decrease in pressure to the afferent arteriole may decrease glomerular filtration and sodium chloride concentrations in the distal tubules, triggering the release of renin by the JG cells (Klabunde, 2012). Renin is the highly sensitive baroreceptor secreted by the JG cells in response to alterations in blood pressure or sodium chloride levels. It is considered the rate-limiting step of the RAAS and is secreted as early as week 2 of gestation (Sparks et al., 2014). Initially, renin is found scattered along the intralobular artery and afferent arterioles. Throughout gestational development and into the postnatal period, renin release is narrowed to only the terminal lip of the afferent arteriole.

Events that comprise the RAAS response to hypotension include the following: Renin is secreted at the afferent arteriole and acts on circulating angiotensinogen to cleave angiotensin I (Klabunde, 2012). Next, angiotensin I traverses the portal and cardiovascular systems in order to reach the pulmonary circuit. Here, ACE, found mainly within the pulmonary vascular epithelium, cleaves two amino acids from angiotensin I, converting it into angiotensin II (Klabunde, 2012). Angiotensin II is the biologically active hormone produced by the RAAS and initiates three key processes: (a) an increase in vascular resistance; (b) water and solute reabsorption in the nephron; and (c) the release of vasopressin, which promotes vascular retention of fluid (Brown & Fenton, 2016).

Increased vascular resistance (vasopressive effects) occurs by way of specialized receptors (AGTR1 and

AGTR2) that transmit a vaso-stimulating agent at the efferent arteriole. The efferent arteriole thereby constricts and renal blood flow increases. Water and solute reabsorption occur through two pathways: (a) aldosterone release and (b) vasopressin release. Aldosterone release occur secondary to stimulation of the adrenal cortex. Aldosterone facilitates reabsorption of sodium and water at the distal convoluting tubules and the cortical collecting ducts, thereby increasing circulating blood volume and blood pressure (Klabunde, 2012). Vasopressin (an antidiuretic hormone [ADH]) release occurs secondary to stimulation of the posterior pituitary gland. Circulating ADH increases solute-free water reabsorption through the DCTs and collecting ducts and increases systemic blood pressure (Brown & Fenton, 2016; Klabunde, 2012). Additional effects of ADH include increased sodium reabsorption and potassium excretion, increased prostaglandin synthesis, and increased adrenocorticotropic hormone secretion; this serves to increase fluid volume and renal blood flow (Wein et al., 2016).

Prenatal factors that affect RAAS function include maternal malnutrition and placental insufficiency; both conditions are regarded as perinatal shocks (see Chapter 1) and may negatively impact fetal programming and thereby contribute to the development of latent chronic disease (Alexander, Dasinger, & Intapad, 2015). Postnatally, any issue that decreases blood flow to the glomeruli, such as a decrease in systemic blood pressure, renal artery stenosis, or decrease in filtrate sodium chloride concentration, may implicate orderly RAAS function (Klabunde, 2012).

Acid–Base Homeostasis

The fetal kidney is capable of reabsorbing filtered bicarbonate, delivered by way of the placenta. However, the fetal kidney is less capable of generating bicarbonate. As such, acid–base regulation is immature during early fetal development (and handled by way of the placenta) and increases throughout gestation. The synthesis of bicarbonate requires the reciprocal excretion of acid and ammonia and a mature, elongated proximal tubule (Azhibekov, Friedlich, & Seri, 2017).

Postnatally, bicarbonate is a critical component of acid-based homeostasis. Acute changes to the pH call on the carbonic–anhydrase buffering system to exchange hydrogen ions (H^+) and potassium (K^+). Acidemia provokes H^+ influx into the cell, buffered primarily by bone apatite. Alkalemia prompts an efflux of H^+ from the cell in exchange for K^+. Long-term acid–base compensation relies on balanced intake and excretion of acid, or a balance of carbon dioxide (CO_2) and bicarbonate. Acid intake occurs through the production of CO_2 (volatile acid) and metabolic acids, as well as the ingestion of acids

through enteral feedings (nonvolatile acids) (Dell, 2015). Acid–base homeostasis (long-term) occurs through chemical buffering, which facilitates the "blowing off" of CO_2 through respiration and renal reabsorption, excretion, and supplemental generation of bicarbonate.

Buffer System Modulation. Buffers are substances that can minimize changes in pH when acid or base is added to the system. Intracellular buffers facilitate entry of H^+ into the cell and include hemoglobin, organic phosphates, and bone apatite. Bone apatite is responsible for nearly 50% of all intracellular buffering among premature infants, and in some cases may explain poor linear growth among infants with frequent acid–base imbalance. Extracellular buffers include phosphates, plasma proteins, and the bicarbonate–carbonic acid system, the most important extracellular buffer system (Azhibekov et al., 2017; Dell, 2015).

Carbonic acid buffering primarily implicates the respiratory system. An increase in H^+ levels prompt its binding with bicarbonate, facilitated by the enzyme carbonic anhydrase, and the formation of carbonic acid. The molecules thereby cross the blood–brain barrier, where the hydrogen ions disassociate and stimulate chemoreceptors. Because the majority of the daily acid load consists of volatile acids, this buffering system is critically important to acid–base homeostasis and is utilized to normalize acute acid–base imbalances.

Bicarbonate buffering in the kidneys facilitates modulation of bicarbonate reabsorption, excretion, and new production. The two primary regions that acidify the urine are the proximal tubule and thick ascending LOH. This buffering system is slower compared to the bicarbonate–carbonic acid system and participates in long-term acid–base compensation (Dell, 2015).

Respiratory Modulation. Respiratory modulation of acid–base balance involves the elimination of CO_2 (volatile acid). This is modulated by alveolar ventilation, which adjusts to ensure appropriate elimination of CO_2. This process is regulated by the effect of H^+ and CO_2 on central and peripheral chemoreceptors, located within the medulla oblongata of the brain. Central chemoreceptors regulate respiration at the level of the brain-stem. Increased partial pressure of carbon dioxide, or hypercarbia, causes an increase in CO_2 influx into the cerebrospinal fluid (CSF). Once immersed within the CSF, CO_2 combines with water and forms carbonic acid (Figure 8.7). The H^+ at the ends of the carbonic acid molecule disassociate. This increase in H^+ upregulates the central chemoreceptors. Simultaneously, the hypercarbic state lowers the pH, which alerts peripheral chemoreceptors, located within the aortic arch. The net result is an increase in the respiratory rate, which redirects the pH toward homeostasis (Figure 8.8).

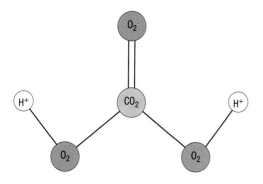

Figure 8.7 Carbonic acid molecule.

CO_2, carbon dioxide; H^+, hydrogen; O_2, oxygen.

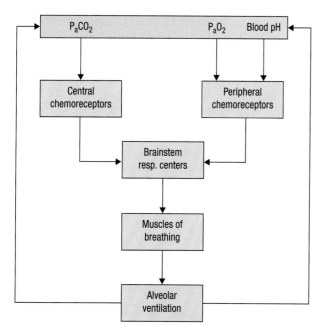

Figure 8.8 The role of central and peripheral chemoreceptors on acid-base balance.

Renal Modulation. Renal modulation of acid–base balance involves permissive excretion of normal daily acid load, with the prevention of excessive bicarbonate losses into the urine. The majority of bicarbonate (80%) is reabsorbed within the proximal tubule and the remainder is primarily reabsorbed within the thick ascending LOH (10%) and more distal segments (10%; Azhibekov et al., 2017). Bicarbonate reabsorption increases during acidic states and under the influence of adrenergic agonists and angiotensin II as well as parathyroid hormone. Reabsorption decreases during alkaline states (Dell, 2015).

In addition, the kidneys are responsible for the production of new bicarbonate. The production of new bicarbonate occurs through the exchange of acid (H^+ ions) for bicarbonate; the amount of acid excreted into the urine typically equals the amount of new bicarbonate generated by the kidneys. However, during illness or other pathological states, the kidneys may be tasked with generating additional bicarbonate to compensate for acid load. In these circumstances, net acid and ammonium excretion increases to permit more rapid cleavage of bicarbonate.

Tubular Regulation of Solutes Within the Nephron

The basic functions of the tubular system include reabsorption (transport of substances from the lumen to the blood), secretion (transport of substances from blood to the lumen), and transport of solute through the nephron and into the ureters for excretion as urine (Figure 8.9). Substances can follow one of two pathways: (a) transcellular (across the lumen and cell membrane) or (b) paracellular (between cells). The proximal duct, LOH, distal tubules, and collecting ducts primarily serve to reabsorb solutes from glomerular filtration, secrete other ions, concentrate and dilute urine, and maintain fluid and electrolyte homeostasis. Multiple pathways, genes, pumps, and transcriptors facilitate this process; a discussion of each is beyond the scope of this textbook. Factors that influence the movement of water and major substrates are described in the following section of this chapter.

Tubular Transport of Solutes Within the Nephron

Proximal Convoluting Tubule. The proximal convoluting tubule (PCT) consists of two parts, the pars convoluta and the pars recta, spread over three segments (Baum, 2017). The PCT has low transepithelial cell resistance and tight cell junctions that result in high paracellular transport and has often been called a *leaky epithelium* (Baum, 2017). The majority of filtered solutes are reabsorbed in this portion of the nephron. Approximately 60% of water, sodium (67%), potassium (70%), bicarbonate (80%), chloride (65%), calcium (>90%), phosphate (85%), and 100% of filtered glucose and amino acids are reabsorbed as the filtrate passes through the proximal tubule (Gattineni & Baum, 2015; Johnson, Lynch, Newberry, & Jnah, 2017; Wright, Posencheg, Seri, & Evans, 2018). The active transport of sodium occurs through the sodium-potassium-adenosine triphosphatase (Na^+-K^+-ATPase) pump at the proximal convoluted tubule and NKCC2 (NA^+, K^+, $2Cl^-$) pathways at the thick ascending LOH (Baum, 2017). Passive reabsorption of sodium in the proximal tubule occurs by way of Cl^--Na^+ transport within the distal and collecting tubules, and occurs by way of the epithelial sodium channels (ENaC).

Loop of Henle. The proximal tubule leads directly to the LOH, which consists of four segments: the (a) thin descending limb (TDL), (b) thin ascending limb (TAL), (c) medullary

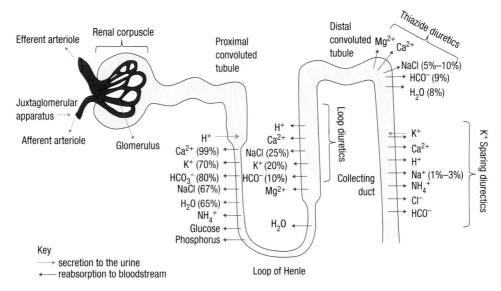

Figure 8.9 Movement of solute within the nephron. Learners are encouraged to use this diagram to gather a conceptual understanding of the movement of solute. Further study of neonatal and pediatric pharmacology offers an opportunity to understand the implications of diuretic use in the neonatal population. Percentage of reabsorption of solute is estimated and reflects a synthesis of the best evidence to date; variation exists across the literature.

Design Credit: Mya Jnah

thick ascending limb (mTAL), and (d) cortical thick ascending limb (cTAL; Wein et al., 2016). The TDL descends and forms a boundary between the inner and outer strips of the medulla. This descending limb is known for its high water permeability; no active transport of solutes occurs in this portion of the nephron (Baum, 2017). As filtered solute curves toward the TAL, the water permeability of the nephron disappears. Here, at the TAL, a high permeability to sodium is observed. As fluid moves from the TAL into the mTAL, significant solute reabsorption occurs. Cellular transport mechanisms aid in the reabsorption of water (15%), sodium (25%), potassium (20%), and bicarbonate (10%), as well as in the reabsorption of chloride and calcium (Gattineni & Baum, 2015; Johnson et al., 2017; Wein et al., 2016; Wright et al., 2018). Loop diuretics act on this portion of the nephron, inhibiting the reabsorption of sodium, potassium, and chloride through off-switching of the Na+-K+-2Cl−-cotransporter; in these circumstances, a portion of the filtered sodium may be captured and reabsorbed once it reaches the distal tubule (Holmes, 2016: Johnson et al., 2017; Taketomo, Hodding, & Kraus, 2017; Yaffe & Aranda, 2011).

Distal Tubule. From the mTAL, tubular fluid flows through the distal DCT, a relatively water-impermeable environment (Baum, 2017). The distal tubule is anatomically subdivided into the DCT and the connecting tubule (CNT); the DCT is of primary significance as this is the major location for solute reabsorption (Wein et al., 2016). Sodium (5%–10%), calcium (10%–15%), bicarbonate (8%–9%), magnesium (5%–10%), and water reabsorption occurs within the DCT. Thiazide

diuretics act on this portion of the nephron, inhibiting the reabsorption of sodium and chloride through off-switching of the Na+Cl− co-transporter (Holmes, 2016; Taketomo et al., 2017; Yaffe & Aranda, 2011).

Collecting Ducts. From the CNT, filtrate approaches the collecting ducts. This segment of the nephron is subdivided into three regions: (a) the cortex connecting duct (CCD), (b) the outer medulla collecting duct (OMCD), and (c) the inner medulla collecting duct (IMCD; Baum, 2017). Sodium reabsorption (1%–3%), acid secretion, and K+ regulation occurs in the CCD. Acidification of the urine occurs between the OMCD and IMCD by way of H+ secretion and reciprocal reabsorption of bicarbonate (Baum, 2017).

Aldosterone and vasopressin exert effects on water and solute traversing the collecting ducts. Increased aldosterone secretion increases the excretion of K+. Increased levels of circulating vasopressin open water channels, thereby facilitating water reabsorption. Potassium-sparing diuretics act on this portion of the nephron, inhibiting the reabsorption of Na+ and therefore decreasing the secretion of K+ into soon-to-be excreted filtrate (urine; Holmes, 2016; Taketomo et al., 2017; Wein et al., 2016; Yaffe & Aranda, 2011).

Urine Formation and Composition

The fetal kidney is particularly inept at concentrating and dilating the urine. Factors that contribute to this immature state, discussed throughout this chapter, include a blunted response to ADH and anatomically immature nephrons, most notably during early fetal development. The primitive nephron is devoid of a deeply extending LOH and, as a result, is devoid of its thick ascending limb. Their superficial location renders the nephrons functionally immature at water and solute reabsorption. For example, fetal urinary excretion of sodium, expressed as fractional excretion of sodium (FE_{Na}), is much higher in the fetus than in the newborn (Segar, 2016). Around 30 weeks of gestation, FE_{Na} is about 14% to 15%, near term it is approximately 5%, and a term newborn has a FE_{Na} of 1% or less. Maturational changes, including an increase in tubular transporters, increased functional (intracellular and extracellular) transport of sodium, and increased sensitivity to angiotensin II, glucocorticoids, and catecholamines, explain the progressive maturational process.

Fortunately, the placenta is the principal source of fluid and electrolyte homeostasis during early fetal development (Segar, 2016). Urine formation occurs early in fetal development, between 9 and 12 weeks of gestation, and is essentially composed of free water with small amounts of solutes (Scott et al., 2016). Filtration, reabsorption, and secretion of solutes begins at week 14 of gestation (Chestnut et al., 2014). After 16 to 20 weeks of gestation, GFR contributes to adequate fetal urine production (up to 300 mL/kg fetal weight/day; Rosenblum et al., 2017). By 20 weeks of gestation, renal function is demonstratively improved, as the volume of amniotic fluid measures approximately 320 mL (90% of total amniotic fluid at term) and thereby increases to around 800 mL from 28 weeks until term (Lindower, 2017). Urine formation guarantees appropriate circulating amniotic fluid levels, essential for normal development of many body systems, including the pulmonary and gastrointestinal systems (Dell, 2015).

GENETIC INFLUENCES

Congenital abnormalities of the kidney and urinary tract (CAKUT) comprise 20% to 50% of all cases of pediatric end-stage renal disease and account for 20% of all birth defects (Capone, Morello, Taroni, & Montini, 2017; dos Santos, de Miranda, & Simoese Silva, 2014). There are more than 500 CAKUT; a positive family history of renal or urinary anomalies occurs in about 10% of all renal anomalies (dos Santos et al., 2014). Common CAKUT disorders will be presented in this section of the chapter. Additional inherited disorders affecting the renal system are provided in Table 8.2.

Autosomal Dominant Polycystic Kidney Disease

Autosomal dominant polycystic kidney disease (ADPKD) is a severe malformation of one or both kidneys involving the formation of multiple, nonfunctioning cysts that dominate normal functioning renal tissue (Figure 8.10).

It is a multisystem disorder. Cysts may present in other locations, including the liver, seminal vesicles, pancreas, and arachnoid membrane. Vascular abnormalities, including intracranial aneurysms, dilatation of the aortic root, and dissection of the thoracic aorta, have been reported (Harris & Torres, 2015).

ADPKD is the most common Mendelian kidney disease; offspring of parental carriers incur a 50% inheritance risk (dos Santos et al., 2014). ADPKD is reported in one of every 500 to 1,000 live births; males and females are equally affected (Chebib & Torres, 2016; NIH, 2018b; Ring & Huether, 2014). In 95% of patients with ADPKD, there is an affected parent; 10% of cases involve de novo mutations. Two genes, *PKD1* and *PKD2*, are associated with ADPKD. Approximately 85% of cases are associated with *PKD1* and the remaining 15% of cases involve *PKD2* (Chebib & Torres, 2016; National Human Genome Research Institute, 2013). *PKD2* gene mutations are associated with milder disease, whereas *PKD1* mutations correlate with more severe disease states.

TABLE 8.2 Other Inherited Disorders of the Renal System

- Alagille syndrome
- Fanconi syndrome
- Meckel syndrome
- Systemic lupus erythematosus
- Nephrotic syndrome
- Renal agenesis
- Trisomy 13, 18, 21
- Zellweger syndrome

NOTE: A more comprehensive list is provided by the National Institute of Health, Genetic and Rare Diseases Information Center (GARD).

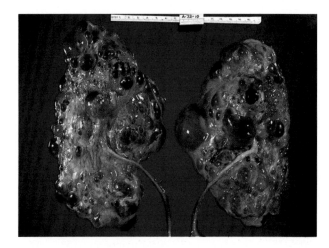

Figure 8.10 Polycystic kidneys.

The etiology for ADPKD involves mutations in the aforementioned genes, which disrupt normal coding for proteins (in this case, polycystins) that reside on the primary cilia within the collecting duct and modulate intracellular calcium levels. Disrupted coding decreases intracellular calcium levels, increases cyclic adenosine monophosphate levels, and increases vasopressin sensitivity at the collecting duct (Chebib & Torres, 2016). These factors alter tubular formation and differentiation of the primary cilia as well as increase fluid secretion within the distal tubule of the nephron (Chebib & Torres, 2016; Harris & Torres, 2015; NIH, 2014). As the cysts matriculate, they increase in size with some detaching into the tubules. This causes a secondary release of cytokines and chemokines and subsequent inflammation. Persistent inflammation can alter the renal vascular network and increase the risk for fibrosis.

ADPKD rarely presents in the neonatal period; manifestations during this period include vesicoureteral reflux (VUR) and renal failure. More commonly, fluid accumulation within the distal tubule and collecting ducts progress throughout infancy and even into childhood, leading to the formation of more and more cysts, localized to the epithelia. Latent manifestations include hypertension, hematuria, and renal pain (Harris & Torres, 2015). Approximately 50% of affected individuals with ADPKD will develop end-stage renal disease before 60 years of age (Harris & Torres, 2015; Reule et al., 2014).

Autosomal Recessive Polycystic Kidney Disease

Autosomal recessive polycystic kidney disease (ARPKD) is a rare congenital malformation that causes the formation of nonfunctional, fluid-filled cysts within the collecting tubules of the nephron. ARPKD is the rarest type of polycystic kidney disease, with an estimated incidence of 1 in 20,000 live births (Kenner & Lott, 2014). This statistic is likely underrepresented due to cases of unaffected carriers who do not manifest the disease process.

ARPKD is unique in that the disease manifests *after* normal in utero renal tubular development occurs. Mutations in the *PKHD1* are responsible for the pathogenesis, as the mutations disrupt normal coding for proteins (in this case, fibrocystin proteins; NIH, 2014). This causes dilation of the collecting tubules (nephromegaly) with cyst formation. The fluid-filled cysts matriculate into the collecting tubules and supersede previously formed, normal renal parenchyma.

Unlike the dominant form, ARPKD disease is more likely to manifest earlier in life. Phenotypic findings noted during fetal development may include echogenic kidneys and oligohydramnios; however, oligohydramnios is regarded as a poorly sensitive indicator of disease severity (Mallett, O'Hagan, & McKeever, 2015). Phenotypic findings during infancy include respiratory failure, hypertension, liver and gastrointestinal dysfunction, and, of course, renal failure. Latent clinical manifestations include hypertension, urinary tract infections, and proteinuria. Progressive fibrosis of the parenchyma is common (Dell, Matheson, Hartung, Warady, & Furth, 2016).

Advances in neonatal care have improved the survivability for affected infants. Now, more than 70% of affected patients survive the newborn period and more than 80% live past 10 years of age (Dell et al., 2016). Mortality risk of infantile ARPKD is commonly linked to pulmonary hypoplasia. Portal and systemic hypertension is quite common across the life span. Nearly half (40% to 50%) of affected patients develop end-stage renal disease by midadolescence (age 15; Dell et al., 2016; Mallett et al., 2015).

Multicystic Dysplastic Kidney Disease

Multicystic dysplastic kidney (MCDK) disease is the most common cause of cystic disease in children. The incidence of unilateral disease is estimated at one in every 1,000 to 4,300 live births; bilateral disease is rare (Cooper, Said, Khalillullah, Salameh, & Hernandez, 2013; Engen & Hingorani, 2018).

The pathogenesis of MCDK is poorly understood. Recall that under normal circumstances the ureteric bud grows laterally during early development and invades the nearby renal parenchyma. One widely published explanation for MCDK suggests that failed invasion of the metanephric blastema (parenchyma) predisposes the kidney to MCDK (Holcomb, Murphy, & Ostlie, 2014). An alternative explanation suggests an atresia or obstruction of the ureters causes MCDK. Environmental shocks, including viral infections, have been reported as other potential triggers for MCDK (Cardona-Grau & Kogan, 2015).

MCDK manifests as severe hydronephrosis secondary to ureteropelvic junction (UPJ) obstruction. Hydronephrosis, secondary to UPJ obstruction, may implicate the contralateral, otherwise structurally normal, kidney. Radiographic scans may yield a renal parenchyma notably "saturated" with fluid (echogenic). Cysts may be irregularly placed on one or both kidneys. It is also not uncommon for MCDK to occur in association with other renal anomalies, including fetal aplastic kidney (cystic remnants on a ureter), horseshoe, or ectopic kidney disease.

Life-span implications vary depending on the degree of cystic matriculation as well as degree of involution. Most cysts involute during fetal development or over the first 2 years of life (Holcomb et al., 2014). Malignancy risk, or the risk for acquired Wilms' tumor or renal cell carcinoma, is very low among children affected by MCDK (Eickmeyer et al., 2014).

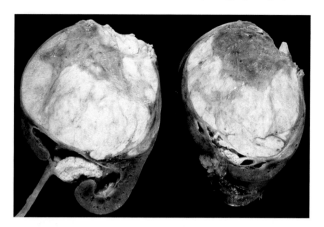

Figure 8.11 Wilms' tumor.

Source: The Armed Forces Institute of Pathology

Wilms' Tumor (Nephroblastoma)

Nephroblastoma, also known as Wilms' tumor, is a solid and malignant tumor of the kidney (Figure 8.11). Nephroblastoma is caused by a mutation of the *WT1* gene, located on chromosome 11p15. The incidence of Wilms' tumor in neonates is rare, at 0.2%, due to its subclinical presentation during early infancy (Kenner & Lott, 2014). However, Wilms' tumor accounts for 92% of all pediatric renal tumors diagnosed among children less than 5 years of age; an increased prevalence among females is reported (Ward, DeSantis, Robbins, Kohler, & Jemal, 2014). Clinical manifestations include a large abdominal mass, vomiting, and hematuria. Life-span implications include intellectual disability, genitourinary abnormalities, kyphosis and scoliosis, end-stage renal failure, and recurrence risk; survival is estimated at 90% (Ward et al., 2014).

Bartter Syndrome

Bartter syndrome is a rare constellation of renal disorders that derange ion channels and renal tubular cotransporters within the distal segments of the nephron. The incidence is estimated at one per every 1 million individuals worldwide (NIH, 2018a). This leads to failed Na$^+$ and Cl$^-$ reabsorption within the thick ascending LOH and DCT and resultant wasting into the urine. This salt-wasting is also associated with hypokalemia and metabolic alkalosis. Bartter syndrome, specifically types 1, 2, 4a, and 4b, manifests during fetal development or infancy, whereas the other subtypes commonly manifest during adulthood (Phadke, Goodyer, & Bitzan, 2014).

During fetal development, this syndrome manifests as polyhydramnios; affected fetuses are often subject to premature birth. Postnatally, Bartter syndrome may manifest with physical abnormalities, including a triangular face, prominent occiput, proptosis, and pointed ears. Affected infants often fail to thrive and develop nephrocalcinosis and renal calcifications and are at risk for osteopenia. Life-span implications associated with chronic electrolyte imbalance include sensorineural hearing loss and deafness as well as cognitive deficits. There is currently no cure for Bartter syndrome (Phadke et al., 2014).

MATERNAL HEALTH INFLUENCES

Maternal health has a great impact on the renal health of the newborn. Research indicates that the intrauterine environment has a significant impact on determining the number of nephrons a baby has at birth. A low nephron count or endowment is associated with chronic renal disease (CRD) in childhood and adult life (McAleer, 2018; Rosenblum et al., 2017). Several maternal health factors implicate the developing renal system and will be discussed here.

Recall from Chapter 1 that fetal exposure to various intrauterine shocks can provoke intrauterine growth retardation, premature delivery, and low birth weight (LBW; Calkins & Devaskar, 2011; Currie, 2013). Specific to the renal system, prematurity and LBW have been positively correlated with reduced nephrogenesis, childhood hypertension, and reduced insulin reactivity. In fact, a direct linear association exists between birth weight and nephron number; infants are affixed with approximately 250,000 additional nephrons for each 1 kg increase in birth weight (Smyth, Cullen-McEwen, Caruana, Black, & Bertram, 2017). *Infants born prior to 36 weeks of gestation or those weighing less than 2.5 kg are deficient of nephrons and incur a 70% higher risk for latent kidney disease* (Brophy, 2017). Given the integral role that the renal system holds in cardiovascular and endocrine homeostasis, and 31 to 36 weeks of gestation as the critical renal programming period, the reduction in total number of nephrons either due to altered perinatal programming or prematurity offers a reasonable explanation for later pancreatic insufficiency and latent chronic disease (McAleer, 2018). Essentially, fewer nephrons offer a reduced landscape for glomerular filtration and sodium excretion, despite any compensatory glomerular hypertrophy, which favors hypertension (Luyckx et al., 2013).

Other maternal health factors that may influence perinatal programming and low fetal nephron endowment include prior LBW status as an infant, hypertensive disorders during pregnancy, gestational diabetes, smoking, vitamin A deficiency, low socioeconomic status, and minority status (Brophy, 2017; Collins, Rankin, & David, 2011; McAleer, 2018). Mothers born weighing less than 2.5 kg are more likely to deliver offspring of similar LBW (Odds Ratio (OR) 1.8, 95% CI, 1.3–2.5; Collins et al., 2011). Transgenerational passage of genetic determinants of chronic kidney disease, defined as low nephron number, has been reported among Cuban women

(Collins et al., 2011). Gestational diabetes incurs a three-fold increase in risk for altered fetal renal development (renal agenesis or renal dysgenesis) and increased fetal growth with resultant increased birth weight greater than 4 kg (large for gestational age). Increased birth weight is associated with an increased risk for latent cardiovascular disease and diabetes. Maternal smoking and alcohol consumption have also been positively correlated with reduced nephrogenesis (Davis, Peck, Thompson, Wild, & Langlois, 2010).

Maternal malnutrition, specific to caloric, protein, and vitamin A deficiency, has been linked to reduced nephrogenesis. This is particularly significant in resource-poor countries where maternal micronutrient and protein deficiencies are common (Collins et al., 2011). Recall the effects of famine on pregnant women and their offspring (see Chapter 1). Specific to the developing renal system, a dose-dependent relationship between micronutrients, such as vitamin A, and nephrogenesis has been reported. Retinoic acid, the active metabolite in vitamin A, is responsible for modulating nephrogenesis. Therefore, insufficient vitamin A intake during pregnancy has been linked to a LBW and a reduction in fetal nephrogenesis, thereby increasing the risk for latent chronic cardiovascular and renal disease. Recent studies using animal models also suggest a dose-dependent relationship between vitamin D intake and nephrogenesis (Nascimento, Ceciliano, Aguila, & Mandarim-de-Lacerda, 2012).

Several maternal medications, as well as ingestion of licit and illicit drugs, have been associated with renal anomalies. ACE inhibitors or angiotensin receptor blockers have been associated with renal agenesis or anomalies, and cocaine, tobacco, and alcohol use are risk factors for diminished nephron endowment and renal anomalies (Charlton & Chevalier, 2017). Maternal ingestion of nonsteroidal anti-inflammatory drugs, such as indomethacin for preterm labor, interferes with the production of prostaglandins necessary for vasodilation in renal blood flow, thereby reducing nephrogenesis and predisposing the fetus to kidney dysfunction (Charlton & Chevalier, 2017).

Clinicians must consider the increase in survivability among extremely premature infants during modern times as well as those born to mothers with risk factors, as noted previously. A thorough investigation into the past medical and prenatal medical history is essential for neonatal clinicians to appraise the relative risk for altered kidney function among newborns. As noted, premature, LBW, and large for gestational age infants are at increased risk for low nephron counts, childhood hypertension, and progressive chronic kidney disease in addition to diabetes and coronary artery disease. Therefore, risks must be communicated to pediatric primary care providers and kidney function must be followed closely throughout childhood.

COMMON PROBLEMS WITH IMPLICATIONS ACROSS THE LIFE SPAN

The kidney is vulnerable to a host of insults during fetal development, which may give rise to a number of defects that affect renal development and function. Common problems that may affect the renal system are discussed here.

Acute Kidney Injury

AKI, also known as *acute renal failure*, is characterized as the abrupt deterioration in renal function resulting in the inability to maintain fluid and electrolyte homeostasis. Approximately 26% of extremely LBW infants (<1,500 grams) and 56% of infants with perinatal asphyxia develop AKI (Nada et al., 2017). A 25% to 50% mortality risk is conferred (Kenner & Lott, 2014).

Risk factors for the development of AKI are multifactorial and include very LBW status and prematurity; both are associated with incomplete nephrogenesis. Other risks include maternal and neonatal medications (anti-inflammatory agents and certain antibiotics), patent ductus arteriosus, phototherapy, neonatal diuretics, and respiratory distress syndrome (Nada et al., 2017; Vogt & Dell, 2015).

AKI is classified as prenal (hemodynamic), renal (intrinsic), or postrenal (obstructive) and the pathogenesis of each subtype is unique (Table 8.3). Prerenal failure (prerenal azotemia) is reported in up to 70% of all cases of renal failure; prerenal azotemia marks the earliest phase of kidney failure. Decreased blood flow to the kidney causes a reduction in glomerular filtration and an induced state of oliguria. Given that the renal tubules are intact at this stage, enhanced reabsorption of sodium and water is observed with increased urine osmolarity. FE_{Na} is often less than 2.5% among premature infants and less than 1% among term infants with prerenal azotemia (Holcomb et al., 2014). If recognized in a timely manner, prerenal failure is considered curable.

Intrinsic renal failure affects 6% to 8% of all hospitalized neonates requiring inpatient intensive care. Intrinsic failure occurs secondary to cellular damage to the glomerulus or renal parenchyma. Sloughing of epithelial cells precedes loss of renal function, as sodium and water reabsorption are impaired and urine osmolarity is observed. Intrinsic failure manifests as one of four possible subtypes, which are summarized in Table 8.4.

Postrenal failure involves an obstruction to the flow of urine. This prevents the evacuation of urine from the body and may affect one or both kidneys. Three common causes for obstructive failure are (a) UPJ obstruction, (b) posterior urethral valves (PUVs), and (c) ureterovesical obstruction (Holcomb et al., 2014). Although typically reversible, long-standing obstructions may progress

TABLE 8.3 Categories of Acute Kidney Injury

Category of AKI	Etiology	Incidence	Common Predisposing Factors
Prerenal	Decreased renal blood flow to kidney	85%	• Asphyxia • Cardiac tamponade • Central nephrogenic diabetes insipidus • Congestive heart failure • Dehydration • Hemorrhagic conditions • Pericarditis • Respiratory distress • Salt-wasting diseases • Septic shock (third space losses)
Intrinsic	Structural damage and loss of renal function	11%	• Acute tubular necrosis[a] • Congenital renal anomalies • Direct nephrotoxic injury • Hypoxemia • Infection • Inflammatory conditions • Perinatal asphyxia • Prolonged renal hypoperfusion • Vascular conditions
Postrenal	Obstruction altering normal renal outflow	3%	• Meningomyelocele • Neurogenic bladder • Posterior urethral valves • Prolonged administration of paralytic agents or sedatives • Spina bifida • Ureteropelvic juncture obstruction

[a]Acute tubular necrosis, which commonly manifests secondary to perinatal asphyxia, is the most common cause for intrinsic acute renal failure.

Source: Vogt, B. A., & Dell, K. R. (2015). The kidney and urinary tract of the neonate. In R. Martin, A. A. Fanaroff, & M. Walsh (Eds.), *Fanaroff and Martin's neonatal–perinatal medicine: Diseases of the fetus and infant* (10th ed., pp. 1676–1699). Philadelphia, PA: Elsevier.

TABLE 8.4 Intrinsic Renal Failure

Subtype	Common Predisposing Factors
Ischemic	• Acute tubular necrosis
Nephrotoxic	• Aminoglycoside administration • Indomethacin administration
Congenital	• Autosomal recessive polycystic disease
Vascular	• Renal artery thrombosis • Renal vein thrombosis

Source: Askenazi, D., Selewski, D., Willig, L., & Warady, B. A. (2018). Acute kidney injury and chronic renal disease. In C. A. Gleason & S. E. Juul (Eds.), *Avery's diseases of the newborn* (10th ed., pp. 1280–1300). Philadelphia, PA: Elsevier.

to intrinsic renal failure and permanent kidney damage (Nada et al., 2017; Vogt & Dell, 2015).

Clinical manifestations of AKI include elevated serum BUN and creatinine (greater than 1.5 mg/dL), hyperkalemia (peaked T waves or ventricular fibrillation on electrocardiogram), and metabolic acidosis. In particular, metabolic acidosis accumulates due to insufficient renal H^+ production and resultant reduction of serum bicarbonate. These children may hyperventilate to attempt respiratory compensation; however, that is not sustainable in most situations (Holcomb et al., 2014; Vogt & Dell, 2015).

Life-span implications include cystic kidney disease, altered glomerular filtration, hyperfiltration, proteinuria, and hypertension (Nada et al., 2017). In the aging post AKI patient, latent chronic hypertension and other cardiovascular problems may arise.

Renal Tubular Acidosis

Renal tubular acidosis (RTA) is a state of normal anion gap metabolic acidosis resulting from renal incompetence with bicarbonate reabsorption within the proximal tubule, or renal secretion of hydrogen (H^+) ions into the distal tubule (Dell, 2015; Eichenwald, Hansen, Martin, & Stark, 2017; Gil-Peña, Mejía, & Santos, 2014). Normal glomerular function is present. Risk factors for RTA include maternal exposure to toxins, such as toluene (found in glue and paint), inheritance risks, aberrant fetal development, prematurity, and birth-related injuries (Sherman, 2015).

The three most common types of RTA are type I (distal), type II (proximal), and type IV (hyperkalemic; Table 8.5). Type I RTA may present secondary to autosomal recessive inheritance (primary) or tubular injury (secondary). Typically, faulty genes alter solute cotransport mechanisms in the distal tubule and disrupt bicarbonate reabsorption or H^+ secretion. The end result is impaired distal tubular acidification and acidosis. Type II RTA disrupts bicarbonate reabsorption within the proximal tubule, a site for significant solute reabsorption. Reduced bicarbonate reabsorption encourages a persistent acidotic state. Type IV RTA involves hyperkalemia-induced reductions in ammonia secretion into the distal tubule and collecting ducts. This may be a consequence of aldosterone deficiency (hypoaldosteronism), renal parenchymal damage secondary to obstructive kidney disease, or nephrotoxic medication administration (Holcomb et al., 2014; Dell, 2015; Gil-Peña et al., 2014; Sherman, 2015).

RTA commonly manifests as metabolic acidosis with a normal serum anion gap (Gil-Peña et al., 2014). Prognostics vary and are strongly dependent on the underlying cause of RTA. Chronic RTA may result in a state of sustained serum acidosis, potentially resulting in poor growth, renal calculi, bone disease, or renal failure (Gil-Peña et al., 2014).

Congenital Hydronephrosis

Congenital hydronephrosis (CH), the *most common cause of nephron loss among neonates*, is characterized by abnormal accumulation of urine within the collecting system (renal pelvis) resulting in renal cavity distention. CH is identified in approximately one of every 500 to 700 pregnancies. Approximately 30% to 40% of all cases persist into the postnatal period and of that statistic, 40% spontaneously resolve (Charlton & Chevalier, 2017; Ferri, 2018; Vogt & Dell, 2015). Risk factors for CH in the fetal and neonatal period include the aforementioned obstructive disorders, renal calculi, renal thrombosis, and renal tumors; however, CH may also be the result of obstructive or nonobstructive abnormalities and affect one or both kidneys (Vogt & Dell, 2015; Yang, Hou, Niu, & Wang, 2010). It is essential that clinicians recognize that CH is not a primary disorder; the underlying pathogenesis is attributed to the primary disease process.

TABLE 8.5 Renal Tubular Acidosis

Category of RTA	Etiology	Common Predisposing Factors
Type I (Primary distal)	• Alterations in hydrogen secretion in distal renal tubule	• Low serum bicarbonate • Hyperchloremia • Alkaline urine • Hypotonia
Type II (Proximal)	• Reduced reabsorption of bicarbonate in the proximal tubule	• Acidosis
Type IV (Hyperkalemic)	• Altered ability to excrete hydrogen and potassium ions • Aldosterone deficiency	• Aldosterone deficiency • Angiotensin-converting enzyme administration • Decreased urine potassium • Elevated urine sodium • Hyperkalemia • Metabolic acidosis (non-anion gap) • Thiazide diuretic administration

NOTE: Type III renal tubular acidosis is more common among Middle Eastern and North African infants and usually presents as a combination of types I and II.

Sources: Richardson, K., & Yonekawa, K. (2018). Glomerulonephropathies and disorders of tubular function. In C. A. Gleason & S. E. Juul (Eds.), *Avery's diseases of the newborn* (10th ed., pp. 1301-1307). Philadelphia, PA: Elsevier; Sherman, J. (2015). Renal and genitourinary disorders. In M. T. Verklan & M. Walden (Eds.), *Core curriculum for neonatal intensive care nursing* (5th ed., pp. 719-733). St. Louis, MO: Saunders.

TABLE 8.6 Grading and Severity of Hydronephrosis

Grade	Severity	Clinical Finding	Visual Description
I	Mild	Slight splitting of the central renal echo complex with normal calyces	
II	Mild	Dilated renal pelvis with marginal fluid in calyces	
III	Moderate	Dilated renal pelvis beyond sinus with equally dilated calyces	
IV	Severe	Thinning of renal parenchyma with dilated pelvis and calyces	
V	Severe	Severe dilation with atrophic cortex	

The Society of Fetal Urology offers a severity scale for CH (Table 8.6). In most cases, CH is detected on prenatal ultrasound as a consequence of oligohydramnios (Kenner & Lott, 2014). Although most radiologists use terminology commensurate with the severity scale (mild, moderate, and severe) when rendering radiographic reports, poor interrater reliability and subjectivity confound a standardized approach to interpretation and reporting; this can make classification challenging (Hagen-Ansert, 2018; Rickard et al., 2017).

Postnatal manifestations include a large, firm, palpable abdominal mass in the kidney region. Renal function is dependent on disease severity and unilateral or bilateral presentation. Infants with unilateral involvement, or mild to moderate hydronephrosis, may demonstrate normal renal function.

Most cases of hydronephrosis self-resolve and are considered a benign finding. Life-span implications of clinically significant moderate to severe hydronephrosis include recurrent urinary tract infection, hypertension, and urinary reflux. VUR, if severe, may cause glomerulosclerosis and progressive renal insufficiency (Charlton & Chevalier, 2017; Kenner & Lott, 2014). Severe bilateral hydronephrosis may manifest with renal failure, pulmonary hyperplasia, or recurrent urinary tract infections and progress to end-stage renal disease (Kenner & Lott, 2014).

Developmental and Positional Anomalies

Developmental and positional disorders of the renal system may include complete absence of renal tissue, alterations in the functional number of nephrons, or renal parenchymal malformations. Associated diagnoses include renal agenesis, supernumerary kidneys, renal ectopia, fusion defects, renal tumors, and cystic renal diseases. We will focus our attention on renal agenesis, renal dysplasia and hypoplasia, and horseshoe kidney, the more common developmental and positional anomalies that affect the renal system.

Renal Agenesis. Renal agenesis is the congenital absence of one or both kidneys (Figure 8.12). Unilateral renal agenesis occurs in one in 500 to 3,200 live births with bilateral renal agenesis occurring in one in 4,000 to 10,000 births; a higher incidence of left-sided agenesis is reported (Moore et al., 2016). A male prevalence is reported, with a ratio of 1.7 to every one affected female (McCance & Huether, 2014; Moore et al., 2016).

Risk factors include genetic and environmental agents. Mutations in many genes, such as *RET, BMP4, FRAS1, FREM1,* or *UPK3A,* correlate with unilateral renal agenesis, whereas mutations in *RET, FGF20,* or *ITGA8* genes are reported with bilateral renal agenesis (NIH, 2014). Renal agenesis may be associated with other structural defects, such as vertebral and anal abnormalities, tracheoesophageal atresia, renal agenesis or dysplasia, and limb defects (VACTERL), CAKUT, and extrarenal anomalies (Vogt & Dell, 2015, Westland, Schreuder, Ket, & van Wijk, 2013). Maternal consumption of teratogens, including alcohol, cocaine, thalidomide, and warfarin, has been associated with fetal renal agenesis.

Renal agenesis results when the ureteric bud fails to differentiate into the ureters, renal pelvis, and collecting ducts, and the mesenchyme fails to differentiate into the nephrons (Moore et al., 2016). This results in failed renal differentiation and nephrogenesis. As such, reduced or absent urine formation causes a significantly decreased (oligohydramnios) or absent (anhydramnios) amniotic fluid level. Oligohydramnios is a common finding in prenatal ultrasound.

Renal agenesis may be associated with other CAKUT disorders or extrarenal complications. Common associated CAKUT disorders include VUR (24%), 22q11 syndrome, and extrarenal malformations (Westland et al., 2013).

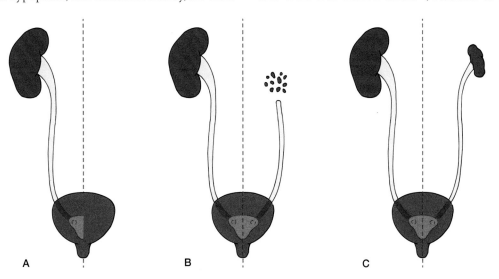

Figure 8.12 (A) Renal agenesis, (B) dysplasia, and (C) hypoplasia.

Associated extrarenal anomalies may include malformations of the skeletal, auditory, respiratory, and cardiovascular systems, as well as the genitalia.

Unilateral renal agenesis is often asymptomatic during the infancy period; the unaffected kidney hypertrophies as a compensatory mechanism (Moore et al., 2016). Manifestations of bilateral agenesis are more severe and include visible yet grossly dysmorphic (cystic) kidneys with or without a bladder outlet obstruction and absence of urine formation.

Life-span implications include hypertension, persistent hypertrophy of the unaffected kidney (considered normal compensation), hydronephrosis, altered GFR, and evidence of CRD (Moore et al., 2016; Vogt & Dell, 2015; Westland et al., 2013).

Renal Dysplasia. Renal dysplasia is characterized by errors in renal induction. Approximately 4% of fetuses and infants are affected by renal dysplasia, with unilateral disease reported in one of every 1,000 live births and bilateral dysplasia in one of every 5,000 live births (Winyard & Chitty, 2008). Renal dysplasia may be confounded by other associated congenital diseases including VATER sequence, Meckel syndrome, renal–coloboma syndrome, and prune belly syndrome. Furthermore, renal dysplasia is regarded as the most common cause for chronic kidney disease and end-stage renal failure among children, with a prevalence of 34% and 2:1 male to female preference (Chen & Chang, 2015; Phua & Ho, 2016). Epigenetic, genetic, and environmental factors are postulated to implicate this disease process.

Renal dysplasia involves aberrant metanephric development (Chen & Chang, 2015). The pathogenesis of renal dysplasia involves defective differentiation of the renal parenchyma. Less common, renal dysplasia occurs secondary to other obstructive pathologies, including PUV or UPJ obstruction. Regardless of the pathogenesis, the end result is the persistence of immature, primitive tubules and parenchymal damage secondary to cyst formation or interstitial fibrosis (Phua & Ho, 2016).

Fetal manifestations of renal dysplasia include oligohydramnios and hydronephrosis. Neonatal manifestations may include a palpable mass associated with the affected kidney and reflux to the affected (and possibly the normal) kidney. Later manifestations include persistent urinary incontinence and dysfunction, urinary infections, and renal failure. Adult females are more likely to report urinary incontinence, which should increase the index of suspicion for a congenital anomaly of the kidneys or urinary tract (Chen & Chang, 2015).

Prognosis of infants with renal dysplasia is related to unilateral or bilateral disease presentation (Vogt & Dell, 2015). Long-term outcomes for unilateral dysplasia are positive. Infants with bilateral dysplasia disease exhibit more complicated comorbidities and symptoms. Infants

with renal dysplasia may present with oligohydramnios prenatally, CH, and impaired renal function.

Renal Hypoplasia. Primary renal hypoplasia is characterized by a kidney that is normally developed, yet abnormally small, affixed with a decreased number of intact nephrons. Secondary hypoplasia manifests as a consequence of infection or a mechanical obstruction. Most cases are sporadic; however, genetic and environmental influences are reported. For example, mutations in the *PAX2* gene have been linked to reductions in kidney size. Environmental influences include uteroplacental insufficiency, vitamin A deficiency, low dietary protein intake during pregnancy, alcohol and cocaine ingestion, and fetal exposure to glucocorticoids and thalidomides (Cain, Di Giovanni, Smeeton, & Rosenblum, 2010).

Associated inherited disorders include branchio-oto-renal syndrome, renal–coloboma syndrome, trisomy syndromes, Cenani–Lenz syndrome, and CHARGE syndrome (Chen & Chang, 2015; Gribouval et al., 2012). Histological studies offer insight into the pathogenesis of renal hypoplasia. A reduction in ureteral bud branches is observed, secondary to an increased apoptosis. Although nephrogenesis is possible, fewer nephrons develop, yielding the anatomically small kidney. The clinical presentation mimics renal dysplasia. Life-span implications include adult-onset hypertension and chronic renal failure (Cain et al., 2010).

Horseshoe Kidney. A horseshoe-shaped kidney is characterized by fusion of the lower poles, causing the formation of a U-shaped kidney (**Figure 8.13**; Moore et al., 2016). The incidence of horseshoe kidney is approximately one in 400 live births, with a 2:1 male

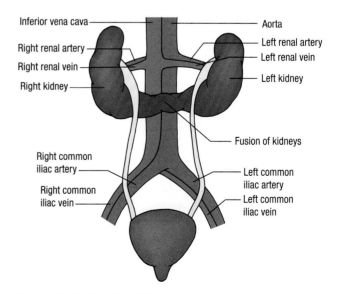

Figure 8.13 Horseshoe kidney.

to female preference reported among the literature (Holcomb et al., 2014). Associated renal defects include VUR, UPJ obstruction, and renal duplication. The most common genetic association is Turner's syndrome (Zitelli, McIntire, & Nowalk, 2018).

Recall that the early fetal period of development involves the vertical ascent of each kidney. Both kidneys migrate upward and outward from one another toward the thoracocolumnar region, ultimately situating on either side of the spine. Horseshoe shaping of the kidney occurs as a result of fusion of the metanephric blastemal prior to vertical ascent (Rumack & Levine, 2018). The process of fusion creates a structural barrier to normal ascent as the inferior mesenteric artery lies within the pathway of the abnormally merged kidneys (Moore et al., 2016). This causes abnormal rotation and axial position changes with anterior positioning of each kidney. Each kidney typically remains affixed with a normal collection system and ureter; however, the abnormal rotation of the renal pelves increases the risk for UPJ obstruction. As a result, affected individuals incur a higher risk for kidney stones and infection.

Hydronephrosis should increase the index of suspicion for horseshoe kidney (Rumack & Levine, 2018). Up to 33% of affected infants who are not diagnosed during fetal development are clinically asymptomatic (Moore et al., 2016). Children or adults may present with idiopathic back or abdominal pain. Kidney stones and hypocitraturia are commonly reported among affected individuals and may recur across the life span.

Ureteropelvic Junction Obstruction. UPJ obstruction is the most common cause of lower urinary tract obstruction and hydronephrosis in infants. The incidence of UPJ obstruction is approximately one in every 1,500 live births; a male prevalence is reported (Merguerian & Rowe, 2018; Vogt & Dell, 2015). UPJ may be associated with genetic syndromes, congenital anomalies, or genitourinary malformations (Vogt & Dell, 2015).

Congenital UPJ obstruction is caused by anatomic or functional disturbances restricting urinary flow through the UPJ (Figure 8.14; Kenner & Lott, 2014). This obstruction is typically a result of intrinsic proximal ureter stenosis or extrinsic compression (less common; Greenbaum, 2016). Intrinsic stenosis occurs if the upper segment is narrow or kinked as the ureter enters the pelvis (McCance & Huether, 2014). Extrinsic compression occurs from the compression of the UPJ by an aberrant or accessory artery crossing the lower pole of the kidney. Glomerular function may be reduced due to the effects of mechanical compression; however, normal glomerular function is reported in up to 50% of all cases (Greenbaum, 2016; Vogt & Dell, 2015).

Fetal hydronephrosis with or without a dilated ureter should raise the index of suspicion for UPJ obstruction. Manifestations during the newborn period or infancy

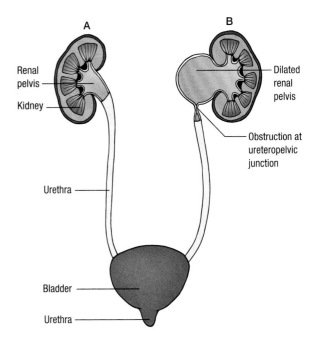

Figure 8.14 Ureteropelvic junction (UPJ) obstruction. (A) Normal kidney; (B) kidney affected by UPJ obstruction.

include a palpable mass, hematuria, or, in older children, flank pain (60% of cases affect the left kidney; Greenbaum, 2016). As pyeloplasty is associated with a 91% to 98% success rate, long-term sequelae are uncommon.

Posterior Urethral Valve Disease. PUV disorder is the most common obstructive anomaly of the urethra and urinary system (Greenbaum, 2016; Vogt & Dell, 2015). PUV occurs in one in 5,000 to 8,000 live births and only affects male infants (Greenbaum, 2016; Sherman, 2015).

Recall that the male urethra develops during the early fetal period of development. A portion of that process includes the generation of urethral valves. Normally, during the downward evacuation of urine from bladder to the penis, pressure from the solute pushes the valves open and allows outflow of urine. With PUV, the anterior fusion of the valves obstructs outflow of urine from the bladder. As a result, persistent urinary pressure induces thickening, trabeculations, sacculations, diverticula, and hypertrophy of the bladder wall with urethral dilatation (Figure 8.15; Dogra, MacLennan, Turgut, Canacci, & Onur, 2014).

Fetal manifestations of PUV include hydronephrosis and oligohydramnios; more severe manifestations include urinoma, urine ascites, and urothorax (Kenner & Lott, 2014). Male newborns frequently present with a visible or palpable distended bladder and weak urinary stream; as onset of urinary output may extend into the second postnatal day, diagnosis may be delayed accordingly (Sherman, 2015). Life-span implications include urinary

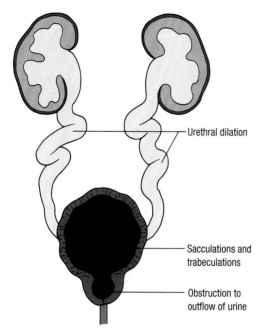

Figure 8.15 Posterior urethral valves (PUV).

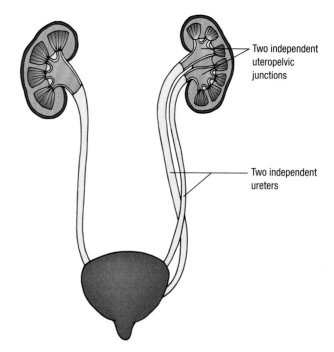

Figure 8.16 Complete ureteral duplication.

incontinence, urosepsis, and VUR (Talabi, Sowande, Etonyeaku, Salako, & Adejuyigbe, 2015). Between 25% to 40% of affected males exhibit renal insufficiency, which progresses to end stage renal disease within 10 years of diagnosis (Bhadoo, Bajpai, & Panda, 2014; Flynn, 2018; Kenner & Lott, 2014; Roth, Carter, & Chan, 2001).

Ureteral Anomalies

Errors in ureteral bud development and differentiation may give rise to several ureteral anomalies. These include ureteral duplication, ureteral triplication, megaureter, and ectopic ureters. The focus for this section will be on ureteral duplication, the most common ureteral anomaly.

Renal Duplication. Renal duplication (also known as *renal duplex*) is a partial or complete duplication of the renal collecting system. Ureteral anomaly is the most common urinary tract anomaly, with an incidence of 1% to 10%; a female prevalence is reported (Wein et al., 2016). Females are twice as likely to be affected by this defect in renal development.

Recall from our review of embryologic kidney development that the ureteric bud arises from the mesonephric duct. The bud grows laterally, toward the metanephric blastema (or future kidney) and innervates it. Once imbedded within the mesenchyme, the ureteric bud undergoes a series of divisions (branching), which gives rise to the collecting ducts and tubules and major and minor calices (Moore et al., 2016). If the ureteric bud begins its process

of division before innervating with the mesenchyme, a ureteral duplication occurs.

Ureteral duplications may be complete or partial. A complete duplication involves the genesis of two separate and independent ureters, both of which drain urine from the kidney and innervate the bladder (Figure 8.16). A partial duplication, or "bifid collecting system," may present in two forms. A bifid pelvis involves the genesis of two separate ureters that fuse together at the UPJ and then innervate the bladder as one conjoined unit (Figure 8.17). A bifid ureter involves the genesis of two separate ureters that fuse together below the UPJ, yet above the bladder, and thereby innervate the bladder as one conjoined unit (Figure 8.18; Doery, Ang, & Ditchfield, 2015; Rodriguez, 2014).

Infants with uncomplicated or partial renal duplication may be asymptomatic. More complex or complete duplication may result in obstructive disorders or VUR. Based on ectopic insertion location in complete duplication, sexual dysfunction and urinary incontinence may occur. Additional evaluation is warranted for patients with a history of urinary tract infection, renal system dilation, or alterations in urine flow.

Urachal Anomalies

Recall that the allantois, a fingerlike projection of the yolk sac, develops during early embryologic development and connects the umbilicus to the ventral cloaca (bladder). Between weeks 5 and 7 of gestation, the allantois canalizes into the urachus, a primitive conduit for the evacuation

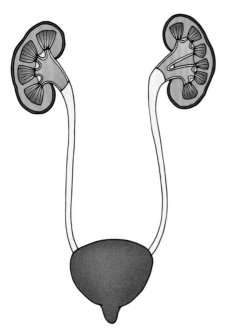

Figure 8.17 Partial ureteral duplication (bifid pelvis). A bifid pelvis involves the fusion of two separate ureters at the UPJ. The fused ureter innervates the bladder as one conjoined unit.

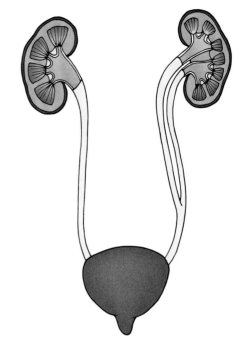

Figure 8.18 Partial ureteral duplication (bifid ureter). A bifid ureter involves the creation of two separate ureters that fuse together below the UPJ, yet above the bladder, and thereby innervate the bladder as one conjoined unit.

of liquid waste and exchange of gases in the time frame preceding the genesis of the umbilical cord and bladder. Once these structures develop and renal function begins, the urachus shifts from a functionally significant duct to a remnant of early embryologic development. As the bladder descends toward the pelvic region, between weeks 16 and 20 of gestation, the urachus is stretched between both poles and into a closed, fibrous ligament. This ligament typically ranges between 8 cm and 10 cm in length and 8 mm to 10 mm in diameter and after birth rests on top of the obliterated umbilical arteries (de Queiroz Garcia, de Queiroz Garcia, & Barral, 2015; Wein et al., 2016).

Four types of congenital urachal anomalies are known: patent urachus (50%), urachal cysts (30%), umbilical–urachal sinus (15%), and vesicourethral diverticula (3%–5%) (Wein et al., 2016).

Patent Urachus. A host of urachal anomalies may present during embryologic development or in later adulthood. Patent urachus, first identified by Bartholomaeus Cabrolius in 1550, involves persistent canalization of the urachus and backflow of urine from the bladder out the umbilicus. Associated defects include Meckel's diverticulum, umbilical hernia, PUV, and urethral atresia (Wein et al., 2016). Manifestations of patent urachus include drainage or edema from the umbilicus and delayed detachment of the umbilical stump during the first weeks of life. Fever should raise the index of suspicion for infection; common pathogens include *Staphylococcus aureus, Escherichia coli,* and *Enterococcus* (Wein et al., 2016). Surgical correction is considered curative.

CONCLUSION

The renal system is a complex, yet exquisitely organized system designed to regulate fluid and electrolytes, assist in acid–base regulation, filter waste products, and respond to hemodynamic instability. Glomerular precursors arise during the early embryonic period and glomerulogenesis is complete by 34 to 36 weeks. As the urinary system develops, the ureters, bladder, and urethra develop, providing a route of excretion for water and waste products. Renal blood flow, hormonal development, and increasing gestational age contribute to renal and urinary maturation. Genetic disorders, environmental and developmental disorders, low nephron endowment, infection, and prematurity may contribute to prenatal or postnatal renal or urinary injury. Unlike other body systems, birth halts renal (glomerular) proliferation, placing premature infants at a particularly high risk for renal dysfunction and later injury. Most newborns, especially premature newborns who require neonatal intensive care, will require regular outpatient monitoring. Clinicians must be vigilant, yet mindful of therapies that risk nephrotoxicity or intrinsic injury, when managing critically ill infants.

LEARNING TOOLS AND RESOURCES

Podcast

 The Renin-Angiotensin-Aldosterone System

Amy Jnah

Discussion Prompts

1. Interruption of nephrogenesis by preterm birth may interfere with renal function. Discuss the short- and long-term effects of preterm birth on renal function. Choose a common problem that premature infants face during the postnatal period; how might renal hypertrophy affect the infant's ability to maintain homeostasis?

2. Acute renal failure may manifest as a consequence of premature birth, or as a result of a pathological condition. Apply your knowledge of acute renal failure by reflecting upon your years as a neonatal nurse or clinician. Describe a clinical scenario in which an infant manifested with each type of failure and associate the clinical or laboratory findings with a physiologic explanation.

3. Maternal history may have a profound impact on fetal and neonatal development and function. Maternal nutrition, disease processes, and medications may disrupt normal embryological development and nephrogenesis. Discuss some of the more common maternal influences on fetal and neonatal renal development. What should you look for in the maternal history?

Advice From the Authors

"Although the renal system is a complicated system to learn and understand, it is elegant in nature and plays an integral part in establishing and maintaining homeostasis in the human body. From the early stages of development, the renal system helps to establish and maintain fluid, electrolyte, and metabolic balance. You will need to read the chapter more than once, review the tables and figures closely, and listen to the podcasts in order to integrate your newfound knowledge. In term and preterm newborns, interruption of development and pathological interference in the renal system has lifelong consequences and it is well worth your time to master a complete understanding of the renal system."

—Bobby Bellflower, DNSc, APRN, NNP-BC

"Invest the time to understand the renal system based on the embryological beginnings and genetic influences. This will enhance your understanding of how renal development progresses to achieve full function and the impact of pathophysiologic interceptors in that process."

—Elizabeth Sharpe, DNP, APRN, NNP-BC, VA-BC, FAANP

"Learn at a pace. Do not feel as though you need to consume all content at once. For a topic as complex as fetal/neonatal renal disorders, I recommend starting with the 'how.' How do the kidneys develop? How important is the sequential development? Once you are able to 'visualize' the development, you can explore the 'what.' What (epigenetic, maternal, environmental) influences affect the renal system? What complications may occur? What are common complications? What organs are impacted by defective kidneys? Then explore the 'why.' For example, why do infants develop acidosis from kidney disorders? Why are electrolyte imbalances common? This approach is helpful with other body systems as well."

—Curry Bordelon, DNP, MBA, APRN, NNP-BC, CPNP-AC

"The study of renal development and function is one of the most critical investigations for a budding advanced practice nurse. The renal system is, by all accounts, the smartest organ system—resilient and masterful at modulating homoeostasis. While studying this content may seem daunting, understanding the concepts will guide a successful clinical learning experience. Get on the floor, markers, pens, pencils in hand, and draw out feedback loops, processes, and defects. This will help you establish a concrete understanding that you can apply in practice!"

–Amy J. Jnah, DNP, APRN, NNP-BC

Mind Map

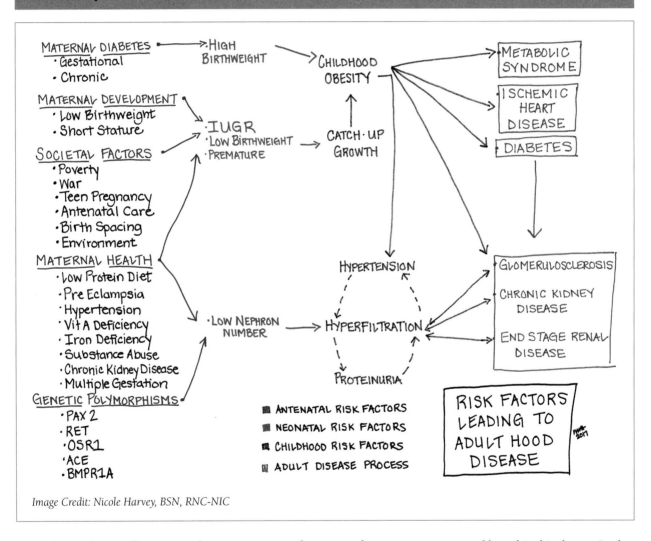

Image Credit: Nicole Harvey, BSN, RNC-NIC

Note: This mind map reflects one student's interpretation of a portion of one or more concepts addressed in this chapter. Readers should regard the mind maps woven throughout this textbook as examples of multi-sensory study tools that can be developed to encourage conceptual understanding. Readers are encouraged to develop their own unique mind maps in consultation with academic faculty or clinical preceptors.

TIMELINE OF ORGAN DEVELOPMENT

NOTE:
Placement of common problems is meant to offer visual/conceptual perspective on the timing of onset of these commonly reported malformations. Variation exists across the literature.

LEGEND
<22 – 27 6/7 weeks = extremely preterm
28 – 31 6/7 weeks = very preterm
32 – 36 6/7 weeks = late/moderate preterm
37 – 40 weeks = term

References

Abitbol, C. L., DeFreitas, M. J., & Strauss, J. (2016). Assessment of kidney function in preterm infants: Lifelong implications. *Journal of Pediatric Nephrology, 31*(12), 2213–2222. doi:10.1007/s00467-016-3320-x

Alexander, B. T., Dasinger, J. H., & Intapad, S. (2015). Fetal programming and cardiovascular pathology. *Comprehensive Physiology, 5*(2), 997–1025. doi:10.1002/cphy.c140036

Alpern, R. J., Caplan, M. J., & Moe, O. W. (Eds.). (2013). *Seldin and Giebisch's the kidney: Physiology & pathophysiology* (5th ed.). Burlington, MA: Elsevier Science.

Askenazi, D., Selewski, D., Willig, L., & Warady, B. A. (2018). Acute kidney injury and chronic renal disease. In C. A. Gleason & S. E. Juul (Eds.), *Avery's diseases of the newborn* (10th ed., pp. 1280–1300). Philadelphia, PA: Elsevier.

Azhibekov, T., Friedlich, P. S., & Seri, I. (2017). Regulation of acid-base balance in the fetus and neonate. In R. A. Polin, S. H. Abman, D. H. Rowitch, W. E. Benitz, & W. W. Fox (Eds.), *Fetal and neonatal physiology* (5th ed., pp. 1089–1093). Philadelphia, PA: Elsevier.

Baum, M. (2017). Renal transport of sodium during development. In R. A. Polin, S. H. Abman, D. H. Rowitch, W. E. Benitz, & W. W. Fox (Eds.), *Fetal and neonatal physiology* (5th ed., pp. 1002–1010). Philadelphia, PA: Elsevier.

Bhadoo, D., Bajpai, M., & Panda, S. S. (2014). Posterior urethral valve: Prognostic factors and renal outcome. *Journal of Indian Association of Pediatric Surgeons, 19*(3), 133–137. doi:10.4103/0971-9261.136459

Brophy, P. (2017). Maternal determinants of renal mass and function in the fetus and neonate. *Seminars in Fetal & Neonatal Medicine, 22*(2), 67–70. doi:10.1016/j.siny.2017.01.004

Brown, D., & Fenton, R. A. (2016). The cell biology of vasopressin action. In K. Skorecki, G. M. Chertow, P. A. Marsden, M. W. Taal, & A. S. L. Yu (Eds.), *Brenner and Rector's the kidney* (10th ed., pp. 281–302). Philadelphia, PA: Elsevier.

Cain, J. E., Di Giovanni, V., Smeeton, J., & Rosenblum, N. D. (2010). Genetics of renal hypoplasia: Insights into the mechanisms controlling nephron endowment. *Pediatric Research, 68*(2), 91–98. doi:10.1203/PDR.0b013e3181e35a88

Calkins, K., & Devaskar, S. U. (2011). Fetal origins of adult disease. *Current Problems in Pediatric and Adolescent Health Care, 41*(6), 158–176. doi:10.1016/j.cppeds.2011.01.001

Capone, V. P., Morello, W., Taroni, F., & Montini, G. (2017). Genetics of congenital anomalies of the kidney and urinary tract: The current state of play. *International Journal Molecular Science, 18*(4), 796. doi:10.3390/ijms18040796

Cardona-Grau, D., & Kogan, B. A. (2015). Update on multicystic dysplastic kidney. *Current Urology Reports, 16*(10), 1–5. doi:10.1007/s11934-015-0541-7

Charlton, J. R., & Chevalier, R. L. (2017). Response to nephron loss in early development. In R. A. Polin, S. H. Abman, D. H. Rowitch, W. E. Benitz, & W. W. Fox (Eds.), *Fetal and neonatal physiology* (5th ed., pp. 1074–1080). Philadelphia, PA: Elsevier.

Chebib, F. T., & Torres, V. E. (2016). Autosomal dominant polycystic kidney disease: Core curriculum 2016. *American Journal of Kidney Diseases, 67*(5), 792–810. doi:10.1053/j.ajkd.2015.07.037

Chen, R., & Chang, C. (2015). Renal dysplasia. *Archives of Pathology & Laboratory Medicine, 139*(4), 547–551. doi:10.5858/arpa.2013-0660-RS

Chestnut, D. H., Wong, C. A., Tsen, L. C., Kee, W. D., Beilin, Y., & Mhyre, J. (Eds.). (2014). *Chestnut's obstetric anesthesia: Principles and practice E-book* (5th ed.). New York, NY: Saunders.

Collins, J. W., Rankin, K. M., & David, R. J. (2011). Low birth weight across generations: The effect of economic environment. *Maternal and Child Health Journal, 15*(4), 438–445. doi:10.1007/s10995-010-0603-x

Cooper, C. J., Said, S., Khalillullah, S., Salameh, H. J., & Hernandez, G. T. (2013). Multicystic dysplastic kidney complicated by pyelonephritis. *American Journal of Case Reports, 14*, 412–415. doi:10.12659/AJCR.889557

Currie, J. (2013). Weathering the storm: Hurricanes and birth outcomes. *Journal of Health Economics, 32*(3), 487–503. doi:10.1016/j.jhealeco.2013.01.004

Davis, E. M., Peck, J. D., Thompson, D., Wild, R. A., & Langlois, P. (2010). Maternal diabetes and renal agenesis/dysgenesis. *Birth Defects Research: Part A. Clinical and Molecular Teratology, 88*(9), 722–727. doi:10.1002/bdra.20702

Dell, K. M. (2015). Fluid, electrolytes, and acid-base homeostasis. In R. Martin, A. A. Fanaroff, & M. Walsh (Eds.), *Fanaroff and Martin's neonatal–perinatal medicine: Diseases of the fetus and infant* (10th ed., pp. 613–629). Philadelphia, PA: Elsevier.

Dell, K. M., Matheson, M., Hartung, E. A., Warady, B. A., & Furth, S. L. (2016). Kidney disease progression in autosomal recessive polycystic kidney disease. *Journal of Pediatrics, 171*, 196–201.e1. doi:10.1016/j.jpeds.2015.12.079

de Queiroz Garcia, M., de Queiroz Garcia, M., & Barral, C. M. (2015). Patent urachus presenting as acute abdomen. *Journal of Medical Ultrasound, 23*(4), 189–192. doi:10.1016/j.jmu.2015.08.003

Doery, A. J., Ang, E., & Ditchfield, M. R. (2015). Duplex kidney: Not just a drooping lily. *Journal of Medical Imaging and Radiation Oncology, 59*(2), 149–153. doi:10.1111/1754-9485.12285

Dogra, V., MacLennan, G. T., Turgut, A. T., Canacci, A., & Onur, M. R. (2014). *Genitourinary radiology: Kidney, bladder and urethra: The pathologic basis.* New York, NY: Springer.

dos Santos, J. A. C. S., de Miranda, D. M., & Simoes e Silva, A. C. (2014). Congenital anomalies of the kidney and urinary tract: An embryogenetic review. *Birth Defects Research: Part C 102*, 374–381. doi:10.1002/bdrc.21084

Duong, H. P., Piepsz, A., Collier, F., Khelif, K., Christophe, C., Cassart, M., … & Ismaili, K. (2013). Predicting the clinical outcome of antenatally detected unilateral pelviureteric junction stenosis. *Urology, 82*(3), 691–696. doi:10.1016/j.urology.2013.03.041

Eichenwald, E. C., Hansen, A. R., Martin, C. R., & Stark, A. R. (Eds.). (2017). *Cloherty and Stark's manual of neonatal care* (8th ed.). Philadelphia, PA: Lippincott Williams & Wilkins.

Eickmeyer, A. B., Casanova, N. F., He, C., Smith, E. A., Wan, J., Bloom, D. A., & Dillman, J. R. (2014). The natural history of the multicystic dysplastic kidney–Is limited follow-up warranted? *Journal of Pediatric Urology, 10*(4), 655–661. doi:10.1016/j.jpurol.2014.06.001

Engen, R., & Hingorani, S. (2018). Developmental abnormalities of the kidneys. In C. A. Gleason & S. E. Juul (Eds.), *Avery's diseases of the newborn* (10th ed., pp. 1250–1259). Philadelphia, PA: Elsevier Saunders.

Faa, G., Gerosa, C., Fanni, D., Nemolato, S., Locci, A., Cabras, T., … Fanos, V. (2010). Marked interindividual variability in renal maturation of preterm infants: Lessons from autopsy.

Journal of Maternal-Fetal & Neonatal Medicine, 23(Suppl. 3), 120–133. doi:10.3109/14767058.2010.510646

Ferri, F. F. (2018). *Ferri's clinical advisor 2018: 5 books in 1.* Philadelphia, PA: Elsevier.

Gattineni, J., & Baum, M. (2015). Developmental changes in renal tubular transport—An overview. *Pediatric Nephrology, 30,* 2085–2098. doi:10.1007/s00467-013-2666-6

Gil-Peña, H., Mejía, N., & Santos, F. (2014). Renal tubular acidosis. *Journal of Pediatrics, 164*(4), 691–698.e1. doi:10.1016/j.jpeds.2013.10.085

Greenbaum, L. A. (2016). Electrolyte and acid-base disorders. In R. M. Kliegman, B. F. Stanton, J. W. St Geme, III, & N. F. Schor (Eds.), *Nelson textbook of pediatrics* (20th ed., pp. 346–384). Philadelphia, PA: Elsevier.

Gribouval, O., Morinière, V., Pawtowski, A., Arrondel, C., Sallinen, S.-L., Saloranta, C.,...& Gubler, M. C. (2012). Spectrum of mutations in the renin–angiotensin system genes in autosomal recessive renal tubular dysgenesis. *Human. Mutation: Variation, Informatics, and Disease, 33,* 316–326. doi:10.1002/humu.21661

Guignard, J.-P. (2017). Postnatal development of glomerular filtration rate in neonates. In R. A. Polin, S. H. Abman, D. H. Rowitch, W. E. Benitz, & W. W. Fox. (Eds.), *Fetal and neonatal physiology* (5th ed., pp. 993–1002). Philadelphia, PA: Elsevier.

Hagen-Ansert, S. L. (2018). *Textbook of diagnostic sonography* (8th ed.). St. Louis, MO: Elsevier.

Harris, P. C., & Torres, P. C. (2015). Polycystic kidney disease, autosomal dominant. In M. Adams, H. Ardlinger, R. Pagon, M. Adam, H. Ardinger, R. Pagon, & S. Wallace (Eds.), *GeneReviews*. Retrieved from https://www.ncbi.nlm.nih.gov/books/NBK1246

Holcomb, G. W., Murphy, J. P., & Ostlie, D. J. (Eds.). (2014). *Ashcraft's pediatric surgery* (6th ed.). New York, NY: Saunders/Elsevier.

Holmes, A. P. (Ed.). (2016). *NICU primer for pharmacists.* Bethesda, MD: American Society of Health-System Pharmacists.

Johnson, A. K., Lynch, N., Newberry, D., & Jnah, A. J. (2017). Impact of diuretic therapy in the treatment of bronchopulmonary dysplasia and acute kidney injury in the neonatal population. *Advances in Neonatal Care, 17*(5), 337–346. doi:10.1097/ANC.0000000000000427

Kastl, J. T. (2017). Renal function in the fetus and neonate – The creatinine enigma. *Seminars in Fetal & Neonatal Medicine, 22*(2), 82–89. doi:10.1016/j.siny.2016.12.002

Kenner, C., & Lott, J. W. (Eds.). (2014). *Comprehensive neonatal nursing care* (5th ed.). New York, NY: Springer Publishing.

Klabunde, R. E. (2012). *Cardiovascular physiology concepts* (2nd ed., pp. 137–140). Baltimore, MD: Lippincot, Williams & Wilkins.

Lindower, J. B. (2017). Water balance in the fetus and neonate. *Seminars in Fetal & Neonatal Medicine, 22*(2), 71–75. doi:10.1016/j.siny.2017.01.002

Luyckx, V. A., Bertram, J. F., Brenner, B. M., Fall, C., Hoy, W. E., Ozanne, S. E., & Vikse, B. E. (2013). Effect of fetal and child health on kidney development and long-term risk of hypertension and kidney disease. *Lancet, 382*(9888), 273. doi:10.1016/S0140-6736(13)60311-6

Madan-Khetarpal, S., & Arnold, G. (2018). Genetic disorders and dysmorphic conditions. In B. J. Zitelli, S. C. McIntire, & A. J. Nowalk (Eds.), *Zitelli and Davis' atlas of pediatric physical diagnosis* (7th ed., pp. 1–43). Philadelphia, PA: Elsevier.

Mallett, T. M., O'Hagan, E., & McKeever, K. G. (2015). Early bilateral nephrectomy in infantile autosomal recessive polycystic kidney disease. *BMJ Case Reports.* doi:10.1136/bcr-2015-211106

Matsell, D. G., & Hiatt, M. J. (2017). Functional development of the kidney in utero. In R. A. Polin, S. H. Abman, D. H. Rowitch, W. E. Benitz, & W. W. Fox (Eds.)., *Fetal and neonatal physiology* (5th ed., pp. 965–976). Philadelphia, PA: Elsevier.

McAleer, I. (2018). Renal development. In C. A. Gleason & S. E. Juul (Eds.), *Avery's diseases of the newborn* (10th ed., pp. 1238–1249). Philadelphia, PA: Elsevier Saunders.

McCance, K. L., & Huether, S. E. (Eds.). (2014). *Pathophysiology: The biologic basis for disease in adults and children* (7th ed.). St. Louis, MO: Elsevier.

Moore, K. L., Persaud, T. B. N., & Torchia, M. G. (2016). *The developing human: Clinically oriented embryology* (10th ed.). Philadelphia, PA: Elsevier Saunders.

Nada, A., Bonachea, E. M., & Askenazi, D. J. (2017). Acute kidney injury in the fetus and neonate. *Seminars in Fetal & Neonatal Medicine, 22*(2), 90–97. doi:10.1016/j.siny.2016.12.001

Nascimento, F. A. M., Ceciliano, T. C., Aguila, M. B., & Mandarim-de-Lacerda, C. A. (2012). Maternal vitamin D deficiency delays glomerular maturity in F1 and F2 offspring. *PloS One, 7*(8), e41740. doi:10.1371/journal.pone.0041740

National Human Genome Research Institute. (2013). Learning about autosomal dominant polycystic kidney disease. Retrieved from https://www.genome.gov/20019622/learning-about-autosomal-polycystic-kidney-disease

National Institutes of Health. (2014). Genetic and Rare Diseases Information Center: Renal agenesis. Retrieved from https://rarediseases.info.nih.gov/diseases/9228/renal-agenesis

National Institutes of Health. (2018a). Genetics home reference: Bartter syndrome. Retrieved from https://ghr.nlm.nih.gov/condition/bartter-syndrome#statistics

National Institutes of Health. (2018b). Genetics home reference: Polycystic kidney disease. Retrieved from https://ghr.nlm.nih.gov/condition/polycystic-kidney-disease#statistics

Pan, C. G., & Avner, E. D. (2016). Introduction to glomerular diseases. In R. M. Kliegman, B. F. Stanton, J. W. St Geme, & N. F. Schor (Eds.), *Nelson textbook of pediatrics* (20th ed., pp. 2490–2493). Philadelphia, PA: Elsevier.

Phadke, K., Goodyer, P., & Bitzan, M. (Eds.). (2014). *Manual of pediatric nephrology* (1st ed.). Berlin, Germany: Springer Verlag. doi:10.1007/978-3-642-12483-9

Phua, Y. L., & Ho, J. (2016). Renal dysplasia in the neonate. *Current Opinion in Pediatrics, 28*(2), 209–215. doi:10.1097/MOP.0000000000000324

Reule, S., Sexton, D. J., Solid, C. A., Chen, S., Collins, A. J., & Foley, R. N. (2014). ESRD from autosomal dominant polycystic kidney disease in the United States, 2001-2010. *American Journal of Kidney Diseases, 64*(4), 592–599. doi:10.1053/j.ajkd.2014.05.020

Richardson, K., & Yonekawa, K. (2018). Glomerulonephropathies and disorders of tubular function. In C. A. Gleason & S. E. Juul (Eds.), *Avery's diseases of the newborn* (10th ed., pp. 1301-1307). Philadelphia, PA: Elsevier.

Rickard, M., Easterbrook, B., Kim, S., Farrokhyar, F., Stein, N., Arora, S., . . . Braga, L. H. (2017). Six of one, half a dozen of the other: A measure of multidisciplinary inter/intra-rater reliability of the society for fetal urology and urinary tract dilation grading systems for hydronephrosis. *Journal of Pediatric Urology, 13*(1), 80–80.e5. doi:10.1016/j.jpurol.2016.09.005

Ring, P., & Huether, S. E. (2014). Alterations of renal and urinary tract function in children. In K. L. McCance & S. E. Huether (Eds.), *Pathophysiology: The biologic basis for disease in adults and children* (7th ed., pp. 1376–1391). St. Louis, MO: Elsevier.

Rodriguez, M. M. (2014). Congenital anomalies of the kidney and the urinary tract (CAKUT). *Fetal & Pediatric Pathology, 33*(5-6), 293–320. doi:10.3109/15513815.2014.959678

Rosenblum, S., Pal, A., & Reidy, K. (2017). Renal development in the fetus and premature infant. *Seminars in Fetal & Neonatal Medicine, 22*(2), 58–66. doi:10.1016/j.siny.2017.01.001

Roth, K. S., Carter Jr., W. H., & Chan, J. C. M. (2001). Obstructive nephropathy in children: Long-term progression after relief of posterior urethral valve. *Pediatrics, 107*(5), 1004–1010. doi:10.1542/peds.107.5.1004

Rumack, C. M., & Levine, D. (Eds.). (2018). *Diagnostic ultrasound* (5th ed.). Philadelphia, PA: Elsevier.

Schoenwolf, G. C., Bleyl, S. B., Brauer, P. R., & Francis-West, P. H. (2015). *Larsen's human embryology* (5th ed.). Philadelphia, PA: Churchill Livingstone.

Scott, R. P., Maezawa, Y., Kreidberg, J., & Quaggin, S. E. (2016). Embryology of the kidney. In K. Skorecki, G. M Chertow, P. A. Marsden, M. W. Taal, & A. S. L. Yu (Eds.), *Brenner and Rector's the kidney* (10th ed., pp. 2–41). Philadelphia, PA: Elsevier.

Segar, J. L. (2016). Renal adaptive changes and sodium handling in the fetal-to-newborn transition. *Seminars in Fetal and Neonatal Medicine, 22*(2), 76–82. doi:10.1016/j.siny.2016.11.002

Sherman, J. (2015). Renal and genitourinary disorders. In T. W. Verklan & M. Walden (Eds.), *Core curriculum for neonatal intensive care nursing* (5th ed., pp. 719–733). St. Louis, MO: Elsevier.

Smyth, I. M., Cullen-McEwen, L. A., Caruana, G., Black, M. J., & Bertram, J. F. (2017). Development of the kidney: Morphology and mechanisms. In R. A. Polin, S. H. Abman, D. H. Rowitch, W. E. Benitz, & W. W. Fox (Eds.), *Fetal and neonatal physiology* (5th ed., 953–964). Philadelphia, PA: Elsevier.

Solhaug, M. J., & Jose, P. A. (2017). Development and regulation of renal blood flow in the neonate. In R. A. Polin, S. H. Abman, D. H. Rowitch, W. E. Benitz, & W. W. Fox (Eds.), *Fetal and neonatal physiology* (5th ed., pp. 977–982). Philadelphia, PA: Elsevier.

Sparks, M., Crowley, S. D., Gurley, S. B., Mirotsou, M., & Coffman, T. M. (2014). Classical renin-angiotensin system in kidney physiology. *Comprehensive Physiology, 4*(3), 1201–1228. doi:10.1002/cphy.c130040

Taketomo, C. K., Hodding, J. H., & Kraus, D. M. (2017). *Lexicomp pediatric & neonatal dosage handbook with international trade names index: A global resource for clinicians treating pediatric and neonatal patients* (24th ed.). Hudson, OH: Wolters Kluwer.

Talabi, A. O., Sowande, O. A., Etonyeaku, A. C., Salako, A. A., & Adejuyigbe, O. (2015). Posterior urethral valves in children: Pattern of presentation and outcome of initial treatment in Ile-Ife, Nigeria. *Nigerian Journal of Surgery 21*(2), 151–156. doi:10.4103/1117-6806.162591

Tasian, G., Cunha, G., & Baskin, L. (2010). Smooth muscle differentiation and patterning in the urinary bladder. *Differentiation, 80*(2–3), 106–117. doi:10.1016/j.diff.2010.05.004

Vogt, B. A., & Dell, K. R. (2015). The kidney and urinary tract of the neonate. In R. Martin, A. A. Fanaroff, & M. Walsh (Eds.), *Fanaroff and Martin's neonatal–perinatal medicine: Diseases of the fetus and infant* (10th ed., pp. 1676–1699). Philadelphia, PA: Elsevier.

Ward, E., DeSantis, C., Robbins, A., Kohler, B., & Jemal, A. (2014). Childhood and adolescent cancer statistics, 2014. *CA: A Cancer Journal for Clinicians, 64*(2), 83–103. doi:10.3322/caac.21219

Wein, A. J., Kavoussi, L. R., Partin, A. W., & Peters, C. A. (Eds.). (2016). *Campbell–Walsh urology* (11th ed.). Philadelphia, PA: Elsevier.

Westland, R., Schreuder, M. F., Ket, J. C., & van Wijk, J. A. (2013). Unilateral renal agenesis: A systematic review on associated anomalies and renal injury. *Nephrology, Dialysis, and Transplantation, 28*(7), 1844–1855. doi:10.1093/ndt/gft012

Winyard, P., & Chitty, L. S. (2008). Dysplastic kidneys. *Seminars in Fetal and Neonatal Medicine, 13*, 142–151. doi:10.1016/j.siny.2007.10.009

Wright, C. J., Posencheg, M. A., Seri, I., & Evans, J. R. (2018). Fluid, electrolyte, and acid–base balance. In C. A. Gleason & S. E. Juul (Eds.), *Avery's diseases of the newborn* (10th ed., pp. 368–389). Philadelphia, PA: Elsevier Saunders.

Yaffe, S. J., & Aranda, J. V. (Eds.). (2011). *Neonatal and pediatric pharmacology: Therapeutic principles in practice* (4th ed.). Philadelphia, PA: Lippincott Williams & Wilkins.

Yang, Y., Hou, Y., Niu, Z. B., & Wang, C. L. (2010). Long-term follow-up and management of prenatal detected, isolated hydronephrosis. *Journal of Pediatric Surgery, 45*(8), 1701–1706. doi:10.1016/j.jpedsurg.2010.03.030

Zitelli, B. J., McIntire, S. C., & Nowalk, A. J. (Eds.). (2018). *Zitelli and Davis' atlas of pediatric physical diagnosis* (7th ed.). Philadelphia, PA: Elsevier.

9

THE IMMUNE SYSTEM

Rani M. Delaney, Lauren C. Frazer, Maryellen Lane, and Melissa S. Bauserman

LEARNING OBJECTIVES

After completing this chapter, the reader should be able to:

- Understand normal immune system development.
- Analyze the physiologic function of the fetal and neonatal immune system.
- Discuss common inherited disorders and their effect on fetal and neonatal immune system development and function.
- Identify maternal health issues that have a potential impact on fetal and postnatal immune system development and function.
- Evaluate common disorders that affect the immune system and their implications across the life span.

INTRODUCTION

The human immune system is composed of a heterogenous network of cells, tissues, and organs that work together to defend the body against a wide variety of foreign pathogens—from bacteria to parasites—that have the potential to cause disease or even death. During pregnancy, the fetus develops within the sterile intrauterine environment; however, after birth (and in some cases even before) the neonate is immediately exposed to a number of potentially pathogenic organisms, against which it has a limited defense. Although maternal antibodies acquired through the placenta and through breast milk provide some limited protection to the newborn, many of the components of the innate and adaptive immune system are functionally immature, rendering the neonate vulnerable to infectious diseases. As it encounters antigens, the neonatal immune system develops rapidly during the first 3 to 6 months of life, but it does not fully mature until early childhood. Consequently, sepsis in the newborn represents a major cause of mortality and morbidity worldwide. In this chapter, we review the developmental physiology of the innate and adaptive arms of the immune system; maternal and genetic influences on neonatal immune function; and common bacterial, viral, fungal, and protozoal pathogens implicated in neonatal infections, including their potential implications across the life span.

TIMELINE OF IMMUNE SYSTEM DEVELOPMENT

Recall from Chapter 7 that white blood cells develop from pluripotent stem cells, which serve as a renewable source of mature erythrocytes, platelets, and white blood cells throughout life (Figure 9.1). The site of fetal hematopoiesis changes several times during gestation as stem cells migrate from one site to another. From weeks 3 through 6 of gestation, the first stem cell progenitors

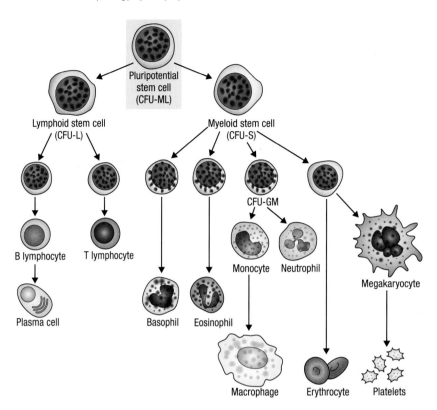

Figure 9.1 The first progenitor stem cells appear in the fetal yolk sac as early as 3 weeks gestation. All blood cell lines originate from pluripotent stem cells. Lymphoid stem cells go on to differentiate into B lymphocytes and T lymphocytes. Myeloid stem cells are the precursors to neutrophils, macrophages, and dendritic cells.

CFU, colony-forming unit; GM granulocyte and monocyte; L, lymphocyte; ML, myeloid and lymphoid; S spleen.

Source: Adapted from Carlson, B. M. (2014). *Human embryology and developmental biology* (5th ed.). Philadelphia, PA: Elsevier/Saunders.

appear in the blood islands of the yolk sac. From weeks 4 to 24 of gestation, the liver is the primary site of hematopoiesis, with increasing contribution from the bone marrow. The bone marrow ultimately assumes the primary role near 24 weeks of gestation (Fernandez & de Alarcon, 2013; Hong & Lewis, 2016). Lymphoid stem cells form two lines of lymphocytes: B lymphocytes or B cells, which produce antibodies; and T lymphocytes or T cells, which are responsible for cell-mediated immune responses. Myeloid stem cells are precursors to other cell lines, including neutrophils, macrophages, and dendritic cells (Carlson, 2014). Growth factors and cellular interactions that occur in the bone marrow influence the differentiation of immune progenitors into their final cell lineage.

The thymus begins to develop from the third pharyngeal pouch during week 4 of gestation (Figure 9.2) and descends to its final position in the mediastinum near week 7 (Haddad et al., 2006; Schoenwolf, Bleyl, Brauer, & Francis-West, 2015). Colonization of the thymus begins at week 8, after it is seeded by circulating progenitor cells suspected to come from the bone

marrow (Erdos, Toth, & Marodi, 2017; Haddad et al., 2006). The mature structure of the thymus, which is crucial for the complex processes that result in diverse T cell receptors that are necessary for self-tolerance, prevention of infection, and prevention of autoimmune disease, appear by week 14 (Haddad et al., 2006). Naïve T cells originating from the thymus differentiate into specific subtypes based on interactions with antigens presented by myeloid cells and the cytokine milieu in which this takes place.

B cells develop from progenitor cells in the fetal liver at 8 weeks of gestation and the bone marrow by week 13 (LeBien, 2017). B cell numbers continue to increase in the bone marrow, circulation, and peripheral lymphoid tissues with levels similar to adults reached by 22 weeks of gestation (LeBien, 2017). B cell receptors (BCRs) undergo a complex process of gene rearrangement similar to that of T cells with the goal of promoting the formation of a diverse array of BCRs with strong affinity for foreign antigens. Naïve B cells subsequently differentiate into plasma cells, which serve as the source of antibody production throughout life.

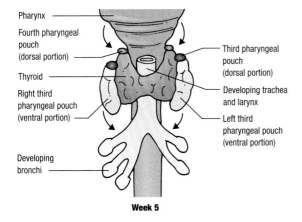

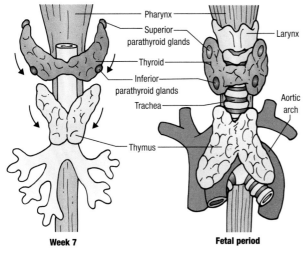

Figure 9.2 Beginning in week 4 of gestation, the fetal thymus begins to form from the third pharyngeal pouch. By week 5, the ventral portions of the left and right pharyngeal pouches begin to migrate inferiorly. By week 7 of gestation, the left and right third pharyngeal pouches fuse to form the bilobed thymus, which descends into its final position in the mediastinum.

DEVELOPMENTAL PHYSIOLOGY OF THE IMMUNE SYSTEM

The neonatal immune system has two major lines of protection: innate and adaptive immunity. The innate immune system is the first line of defense against potentially infectious organisms. The adaptive immune system confers specificity and immunological memory, but can take days to mount an appropriate antigenic response (Figure 9.3). Together, innate and adaptive immune responses function interdependently to provide host protection against invasive infection.

Innate Immunity

The body's first line of defense from infection is referred to as *innate immunity*. Anatomical barriers, such as skin; mucous membranes; and urogenital, gastrointestinal (GI), and respiratory tract epithelium, provide the primary defense in preventing microbes from entering the body. These anatomical barriers are equipped with defense mechanisms that prevent the invasion of microbes (Figure 9.4).

A practical example of an innate defense is the skin. The surface of the skin is dry, which offers limited nutrients for microbes. The skin can shed or slough its cells to remove microbes, and it can produce toxic lipid and acid secretions. In addition, the skin is colonized with nonpathogenic, commensal flora with whom incoming microbes must compete, and it is replete with infection-fighting cells (e.g., Langerhans cells) as well as antimicrobial peptides that kill bacteria, viruses, and fungi (Buckland, 2016). When microbes breech the mechanical barriers of the skin and mucous membranes, other elements of the innate immune system are responsible for recognizing them and rapidly (within minutes to hours) mounting a defense.

The cells of the innate immune system recognize any material (protein, protein fragment, polysaccharide, or lipid) that is foreign as a potential threat. These antigens are known as *pathogen associated molecular patterns (PAMPs)*. PAMPs are recognized by *pattern recognition receptors (PRRs)*, which are highly effective in initiating inflammatory responses (Medzhitov, 2013). The inflammatory cascade that results consists of both cellular and soluble components, which will be discussed in the text that follows.

Cellular Components of Innate Immunity. The cellular components of the innate immune system include *phagocytic* cells, of which there are multiple examples in various body compartments (Table 9.1). Neutrophils, mononuclear phagocytes, dendritic cells, natural killer (NK) cells, and mast cells are the most common cells that participate in the innate immune response.

Neutrophils. Neutrophils, also known as *polymorphonuclear leukocytes (PMN)*, are the first cells to respond to infection; therefore, PMN play a key role in the acute response. In the presence of infection, multiple cell types produce cytokines, also known as *colony-stimulating factors (CSF)*, which stimulate the bone marrow to increase neutrophil production. Once signaled, neutrophils rapidly leave the bone marrow and enter the bloodstream. They travel to the site of infection and phagocytize (destroy) the offending organism. Although they are the early cellular responders to infection, neutrophils have a short life span (2 to 3 hours). Neutrophils that are not recruited to the site of infection go through apoptosis and are cleared by the reticuloendothelial system (Abbas, Lichtman, & Pillai, 2016; Rich et al., 2013).

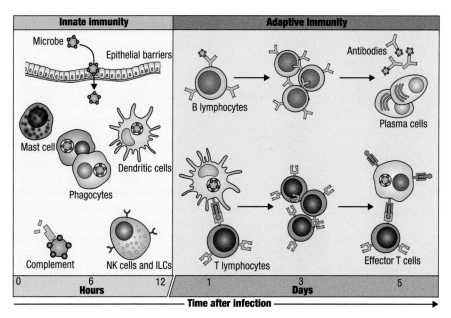

Figure 9.3 The innate immune response and the adaptive immune response comprise the two major arms of the immune system. The innate immune system responds to infection within hours and requires no previous exposure to mount a response. The adaptive immune system can take days to mount an immune response; however, once activated it confers specificity and immunologic memory to ensure a more robust and efficient response in the event of a future exposure.

ILC, innate lymphoid cells; NK, natural killer.

Source: Adapted from Abbas, A. K., Lichtman, A. H., & Pillai, S. (2016). *Basic immunology: Functions and disorders of the immune system* (5th ed.). St. Louis, MO: Elsevier.

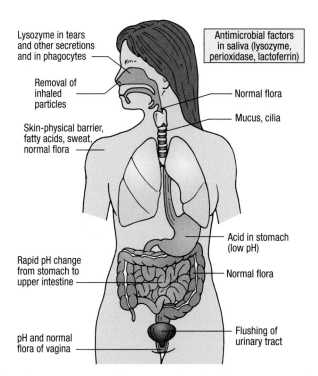

Figure 9.4 Through a variety of mechanisms, anatomical barriers, such as the skin, mucous membranes, and respiratory epithelium, provide the first line of defense against invading organisms.

TABLE 9.1 Cells of the Innate Immune System

Cell Type	Characteristics	Location
Neutrophil	First responder to the site of infection or trauma. Neutrophils are the most abundant white blood cell in humans. They participate in the innate immune response through phagocytosis as well as the expression and release of cytokines that amplify the immune reaction in other cells.	Migrates from the bone marrow and the blood vessels to the site of infection.
Macrophage	Phagocytic cell that also produces cytokines, participates in tissue repair, and serves as an APC.	Migrates from blood vessels into the tissues.
Dendritic Cell	Phagocytic cell that also interacts with the adaptive immune system by serving as an APC.	Present on epithelial tissue including the skin, lungs, and tissues of the digestive tract. Migrates to lymph nodes upon activation.
Natural Killer Cell	Recognizes and kills viral-infected cells. Releases cytokines that increase the microbicidal activity of macrophages.	Circulates in the blood and migrates into the tissues.
Mast Cell	Dilates blood vessels and induces inflammation through the release of histamine. Recruits macrophages and neutrophils. Can participate in phagocytosis and plays a role in allergic reactions.	Present on the skin, GI tract, and respiratory tract.
Basophil	Responsible for defense against parasites. Releases histamine that induces inflammation.	Circulates in the blood and migrates to the tissues.
Eosinophil	Releases toxins that kill bacteria and parasites but can also cause tissue damage.	Circulates in the blood and migrates to the tissues.

APC, antigen-presenting cell; GI, gastrointestinal.

Mononuclear phagocytes. Mononuclear phagocytes include monocytes and macrophages. Like neutrophils, monocytes originate from the bone marrow and then migrate into the circulation and tissues to the site of infection. Once in the tissue, monocytes mature into macrophages. Therefore, blood monocytes and tissue macrophages represent two stages of the same cell lineage (Abbas et al., 2016; Rich et al., 2013). Macrophages play several important roles in innate immunity, including the production of cytokines, phagocytosis, and the destruction of microbes. They also work to clear dead tissue and initiate tissue repair (Abbas et al., 2016). Macrophages have a longer life span than neutrophils, and they persist as the predominant innate immune cells days after an infection (Rich et al., 2013).

Dendritic cells. Dendritic cells are widely distributed throughout the body and are found in higher concentrations in tissues that interface with the environment, like the skin (Heath & Carbone, 2009). Like macrophages, dendritic cells are important phagocytic cells whose primary roles are to ingest and kill microbes. Dendritic cells also provide a link to the adaptive immune system by processing antigens and presenting them (attached to their surface) to naïve T cells. For this reason, both macrophages and dendritic cells are also referred to as *professional antigen-presenting cells* (APCs; Table 9.2).

Natural killer cells. NK cells are derived from lymphoid progenitor cells and are named because of their ability to kill various target cells. NK cells recognize infected cells and respond by releasing cytoplasmic granules that then enter the infected cell and induce apoptosis. Activated NK cells also synthesize the cytokine interferon-γ (IFN-γ), which enhances the microbicidal activity of macrophages (Abbas et al., 2016).

TABLE 9.2 Professional Antigen-Presenting Cells

	Dendritic Cell	**Macrophage**	**B Cell**
Cell type			
Location in lymph node			
Antigen presented	Peptides Viral antigens Allergens	Particulate antigens Intracellular and extracellular pathogens	Soluble antigens Toxins Viruses

NOTE: Dendritic cells, macrophages, and B cells are all professional antigen-presenting cells found in secondary lymphoid tissues, but are distributed in different locations, reflecting the variation in their functions. In lymph nodes, dendritic cells are confined to the cortical T cell areas and play an important role in viral antigen presentation. Macrophages are found throughout the cortex of lymph nodes and respond to particulate antigens, while B cells only reside in the lymphoid follicles of lymph nodes, and acquire soluble antigens. The three cells also vary in their relative effectiveness in presenting antigens to naïve T cells. Dendritic cells are most effective, followed by macrophages and then B cells.

Source: Adapted from Parham, P. (2009). *The immune system* (3rd ed.). New York, NY: Garland Science.

Mast cells. Mast cells, which are present in the skin, GI tract, and respiratory tract, are another type of phagocytic cell. Mast cells are activated when microbial products, such as PAMP, bind to cellular receptors. This induces the synthesis and secretion of proinflammatory cytokines and chemokines.

Phagocytosis. Phagocytosis, the manner by which phagocytic cells of the innate immune system ingest and kill microbes, is a multistep process (Figure 9.5; Flannagan, Jaumouille, & Grinstein, 2012). The first step of phagocytosis is activation. This involves the release of inflammatory mediators, such as bacterial products, cytokines, or complement proteins. The second step, *chemotaxis*, involves movement of phagocytic cells toward target bacteria or cytokines. Next, phagocytes attach to microbes using the PRR. Each phagocyte thereby forms arm-like structures, called *pseudopodia*, which engulf each microbe and bring it into a vesicle called a *phagosome*. The phagosome then fuses with a lysosome, becoming a *phagolysosome*. Once contained inside of the phagolysosome, the microbe is exposed to noxious substances that degrade and ultimately destroy it. The phagolysosome then forms

a residual body that contains cellular waste products that are eventually expelled from the cell (J. A. Swanson, 2013).

Soluble Components of Innate Immunity

Cytokines. Cytokines play a key role in the systemic inflammatory response seen in neonatal sepsis (Table 9.3). Triggered by pathogenic stimuli such as bacteria, mononuclear phagocytes secrete proinflammatory cytokines, which in turn promote the production of secondary inflammatory mediators by neutrophils and T cells (Sugitharini, Prema, & Berla Thangam, 2013). In addition to phagocytosis, neutrophils also release preformed mediators, such as elastase and myeloperoxidase, that are stored in their granules. Among other things, these enzymes participate in the formation of extracellular networks that trap and kill bacteria (Papayannopoulos, Metzler, Hakkim, & Zychlinsky, 2010). The net result is a robust inflammatory response that occurs during the onset of sepsis. While this inflammatory response can be protective, excessive inflammation is detrimental and can lead to tissue and organ damage (Sugitharini et al., 2013).

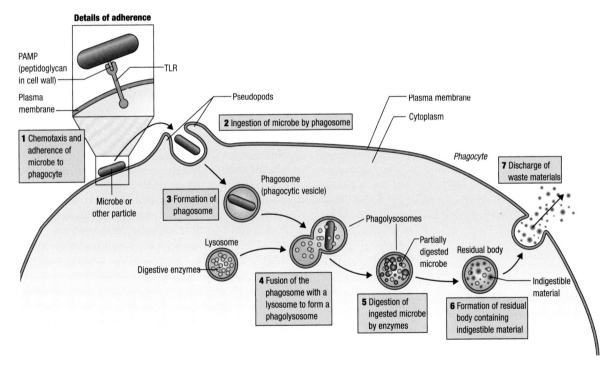

Figure 9.5 Phagocytosis is the process by which phagocytes ingest and kill pathogens. Once activated, the phagocyte moves toward the microbe and attaches itself to it. Once attached, the phagocyte forms pseudopods that envelop the organism to create a phagosome. The phagosome then fuses with a lysosome to form a phagolysosome. The microbe is subsequently destroyed by the release of lytic enzymes. A residual body is formed and the waste materials are discharged from the cell.

PAMP, pathogen-associated molecular pattern; TLR, toll-like receptor.

TABLE 9.3 Cytokines and Their Major Activities		
Cytokine	**Cellular Source(s)**	**Major Activities**
IL-1	Macrophages	Activation of T cells and macrophages; promotion of inflammation
IL-2	Helper T cells	Activation of lymphocytes, NK cells, and macrophages
IL-4	Helper T cells, mast cells, basophils, and eosinophils	Activation of lymphocytes, monocytes, and IgE class switching
IL-5	Helper T cells, mast cells, and eosinophils	Differentiation of eosinophils
IL-6	Helper T cells and macrophages	Activation of lymphocytes; differentiation of B cells; stimulation of the production of acute-phase proteins
IL-8	T cells and macrophages	Chemotaxis of neutrophils, basophils, and T cells
IL-11	Bone marrow and stromal cells	Stimulation of the production of acute-phase proteins
IL-12	Macrophages, B cells, and dendritic cells	Stimulation of the production of IFN-γ by helper T cells and by NK cells; induction of helper T cells
TNF-α	Macrophages, NK cells, T cells, B cells, and mast cells	Promotion of inflammation
IFN-α	Virally infected cells	Induction of resistance of cells to viral infection
IFN-β	Virally infected cells	Induction of resistance of cells to viral infection
IFN-γ	Helper T cells and NK cells	Activation of macrophages

IFN; interferon; IgE, immunoglobulin E; NK, natural killer.

Source: Adapted from Dhama, K., Saminathan, M., Jacob, S.S., Singh, M., Karthik, K., Amarpal, R. T., . . . Singh, R. S. (2015). Effect of immunomodulation and immunomodulatory agents on health with some bioactive principles, modes of action and potent biomedical applications. *International Journal of Pharmacology, 11*, 253–290. doi:10.3923/ijp.2015.253.290

The increased production of inflammatory cytokines during the early stages of infection is also associated with increased hepatic production of innate immune proteins known as acute phase reactants (APR; Wynn & Levy, 2010). Inducible by IL-1, IL-6, and TNF-α, APRs such as C-reactive protein (CRP) function to reduce host bacterial load through improved cellular recruitment, opsonin function, and direct antimicrobial activity (Fattah et al., 2017; Wynn & Levy, 2010). CRP levels typically begin to rise within 6 to 8 hours of exposure to an infection, and peak at 24 to 48 hours, before gradually returning to normal as the initial inflammatory response resolves. Several studies indicate that a CRP level >1 mg/dL has a sensitivity between 70% to 93%, and specificity between 41% to 98% in identifying true neonatal sepsis (Fattah et al., 2017). Trending of CRP levels over time can aid the advanced practice nurse in determining length of antibiotic treatment. Among infants who respond to therapy, CRP levels are known to return to normalcy within 5 to 6 days of treatment (Martin et al., 2015).

Complement. The complement system is an essential component of the innate immune system that works in conjunction with the antibody response of the acquired immune system (Walport, 2001a, 2001b). The proteins that make up the complement system are named with a capital C and a number indicating the order in which they were discovered (e.g., C1, C2, C3, C4; Kemper, Pangburn, & Fishelson, 2014). The goal of the complement system is to identify foreign particles for elimination and identify damaged parts of the host, or to identify debris that can promote inflammatory or immune responses. The complement system can be activated through three major pathways: the (a) classical pathway, (b) lectin pathway, or (c) alternative pathway (Figure 9.6). The *classical pathway* is triggered by antibodies and becomes engaged when immunoglobulin M (IgM) or immunoglobulin G (IgG) antibodies bind antigens. It can also be triggered by plasma proteins, such as CRP. The *lectin pathway* is specifically designed to recognize carbohydrates on microbial pathogens. The lectins bind to repetitive sugar patterns on the surface of the bacteria. The *alternative pathway* is the most

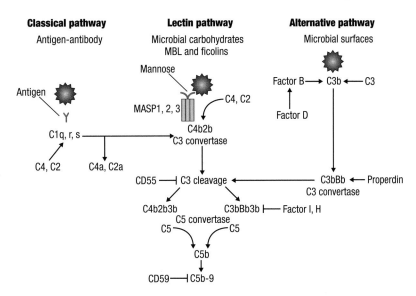

Figure 9.6 The complement system can be activated by one of three pathways. The classical pathway is activated by an antibody bound to microbial surfaces. The lectin pathway is activated by the binding of mannose-binding lectin (MBL) to carbohydrate residues on the microbial surface. The alternative pathway is activated by the binding of the C3 protein to the microbial surface.

Source: Adapted from Rich, R., Fleisher, T. A., Shearer, W. T., Schroeder, H. W., Jr., Frew, A. J., & Weyand, C. M. (2013). *Clinical immunology: Principles and practice* (4th ed.). St. Louis, MO: Elsevier Saunders.

primitive portion of the immune system and represents a set of proteins (C3) that continuously survey the blood and tissue. If they do not identify a target for activation, they are removed from circulation. As such, C3 proteins are in a consistent state of turnover (Rich et al., 2013).

All three of the aforementioned pathways lead to the activation of a set of proteins (C5, C6, C7, C8, C9) called the *membrane attack complex (MAC)*. The MAC disrupts cell walls of bacteria leading to their destruction. The three pathways also create an inflammatory response. Because the complement pathway can lead to destruction of organisms and clearance of debris, it must be tightly regulated. Therefore, much of the role of the complement system is to self-regulate and prevent self-destruction or autoimmune conditions (Abbas et al., 2016).

One example of the mechanism by which complement helps to mediate the innate immune response would be the interaction of the alternative pathway with gram-positive organisms. The cell walls of gram-positive bacteria, such as Group B *Streptococcus*, activate complement via the alternative pathway. Fragments of C3 are deposited on the surface of the bacteria priming them for subsequent phagocytosis through opsonization (Zilow, Zilow, Burger, & Linderkamp, 1993). Through chemotaxis, small peptides (C3a and C5a) attract neutrophils to the site of inflammation, stimulating them to release active mediators such as reactive oxygen species and enzymes. Meanwhile, the C5b-9 complex

provides the lytic activity of complement (Zilow et al., 1993). Together, these actions facilitate the destruction and clearance of potentially pathogenic organisms and contribute to an important and efficient means of host defense (Zilow et al., 1993).

Acquired or Adaptive Immunity

The acquired immune system has important features that distinguish it from the innate immune system. It must be *induced*, or activated, to mount an immune response. Once activated, it produces a *specific* response to antigens, and *immunologic memory* develops. Simply stated, once a pathogen has been encountered and a response mounted, the adaptive immune system will be ready to act again in the event of a future exposure. The first time a pathogen is encountered, a *primary response* occurs. After the pathogen is cleared, the acquired immune system "remembers" it, allowing subsequent encounters with the same pathogen to occur faster, stronger, and with greater specificity. The subsequent responses are termed *memory responses*.

The primary cells that constitute the acquired immune system are lymphocytes, specifically (a) B cells that are produced in the bone marrow, mature in the secondary lymphoid tissues, and subsequently differentiate into antibody secreting cells; and (b) T cells that differentiate into CD4+ and CD8+ cells in the thymus, and go on to inhabit peripheral tissues including the spleen and lymph nodes

(Martin, Fanaroff, & Walsh, 2015). B cells also participate in the *humoral immune* response, because antibodies are found in the blood and body fluids, the body's so-called *humors*. T cells, on the other hand, interact directly with other cells to mediate an adaptive immune response, and are therefore part of the cell-mediated immune response (Helbert, 2017).

Humoral Immunity. The primary functions of B cells are to make antibodies against antigens, act as APCs, and eventually develop into memory B cells. B cells develop and mature in the bone marrow and must go through an "education process" prior to becoming mature lymphocytes. Once they are mature, they patrol the secondary lymphoid organs for target cells presenting with foreign antigens (LeBien & Tedder, 2008).

B cell education occurs in two stages in the bone marrow and assures that B cells produce antibodies that can recognize foreign antigens but not self-antigen. The first stage is called *positive selection*. In this stage, BCRs must recognize the protein that will present foreign antigens in the future. It is known as a *major histocompatibility molecule (MHC)*. MHC can bind to the body's own peptides (self-antigens) as well as pathogenic peptides from invading microorganisms. The second stage in the B cell education process is *negative selection*. If B cells recognize self-antigens presented by the MHC too strongly, they will be deleted or

their BCRs will be restructured. This process ensures that dangerous autoreactive B cells are deleted (Helbert, 2017). Once B cells are educated, they are said to be *mature*.

Mature B cells migrate out of the bone marrow to secondary lymphoid organs, such as the lymph nodes and spleen, to be activated. Each B cell must be activated by a series of two signals that induces the B cell to multiply. The first signal involves antigen binding to the BCR (Gauld, Dal Porto, & Cambier, 2002). The second signal relies on communication from the cell-mediated immune system and is provided by activated T cells (Figure 9.7). Once fully activated, the B cell undergoes clonal expansion, creating antibody producing plasma cells or memory cells.

B cells produce five classes of immunoglobulins or antibodies (IgG, IgM, IgA, IgE, and IgD) that have varying immune functions (Table 9.4; Gleason & Juul, 2018). Antibodies work in a variety of ways to rid the body of pathogens. Some antibodies bind bacteria directly, which promotes their recognition and phagocytosis by macrophages. This process is called *opsonization* (binding to bacteria). Antibodies can also function by binding to and neutralizing microbes, or by activating other aspects of the immune system to destroy pathogens, through NK cells, complement activation, or cellular activation of eosinophils or mast cells.

Naïve B cells display IgM and IgD on their surface that function as BCRs to recognize antigens. Once a B cell is activated by antigen, the *primary humoral response* is IgM

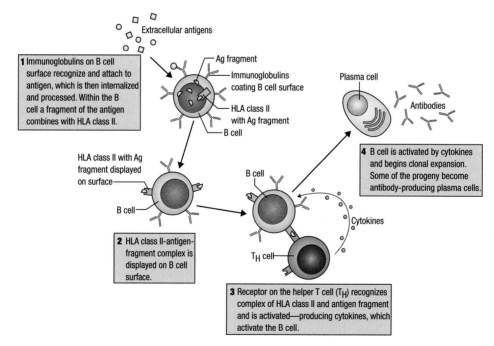

Figure 9.7 It takes two signals for a B cell to be activated and become a plasma cell. The first signal involves the binding of the B cell receptor to an antigen. The second signal comes from cytokines released by a helper T cell that has been activated by the same antigen. Once activated, the B cell undergoes clonal expansion, producing plasma cells and memory cells.

Ag, antigen; HLA, human leucocyte antigen.

TABLE 9.4 Antibody Isotypes

Name	Properties	Structure
IgA	Found in mucus, saliva, tears, and breast milk. Protects against pathogens.	
IgD	Part of the B cell receptor. Activates basophils and mast cells.	
IgE	Protects against parasitic worms. Responsible for allergic reactions.	
IgG	Secreted by plasma cells in the blood. Able to cross the placenta into the fetus.	
IgM	May be attached to the surface of a B cell or secreted into the blood. Responsible for early stages of immunity.	

Ig, immunoglobulin.

production, which begins within 5 to 10 days (Peakman & Vergani, 2009). B cells produce IgM as the default antibody until cytokines from the T cells instruct them to produce a different antibody for the specific immune response, a process called *class switching*. As activated B cells begin multiplying into plasma cells and memory cells, the portion of their DNA that encodes for antibody production is rearranged and only retains the gene that produces the antibody specific to the antigen (Stavnezer, Guikema, & Schrader, 2008). After this transition occurs, the plasma cell, or memory cell, will only produce the specific antibody that is required to fight that specific antigen invader. The plasma cells will continue to fight until they are turned off or destroyed after elimination of the pathogen. Memory cells will remain in circulation, primed for a repeat exposure to the same infectious organism.

The *secondary immune response* is a rapid response to a previously recognized pathogen. Because class switching of antibodies does not need to occur, this process is much faster than the primary response, taking only 3 to 5 days.

In the secondary response, a memory cell does not require a second signal for activation; the B cell receptor binding an antigen and cross-linking alone (first signal) are sufficient to induce the B cell to start producing a specific antibody. The activated memory cell will clonally expand to make plasma cells with specific antibodies and more memory cells (Peakman & Vergani, 2009; Tangye, Avery, Deenick, & Hodgkin, 2003).

Cell-Mediated Immunity. T cells are produced in the bone marrow but migrate to the thymus for training. T cells are educated through positive and negative selection in a manner similar to B cells. During negative selection, if a T cell binds too strongly to an antigen it is deleted or changed into a cell capable of shutting down autoreactive immune responses (Haks, Oosterwegel, Blom, Spits, & Kruisbeek, 1999). Once educated, T cells can inhabit secondary lymphoid organs, such as the spleen and lymph nodes.

Like B cells, mature T cells are naïve until they are activated by a series of two signals. The first signal involves the T cell receptor recognizing and binding to the MHC that is displaying an antigen. The second costimulatory signal is provided when the CD28 receptor on T cells bind to B7 ligand on APC (Figure 9.8). The expression of B7 proteins on APC is induced by pathogens during the innate immune response to an infection (Martin et al., 2015). Both signals must come from an APC to prompt the naïve T cell to differentiate into an effector T cell. If a T cell is only activated by one signal, it will lead to *anergy*, or become unresponsive until a second signal is received. If, on the other hand, the T cell receives both signals it will proliferate and differentiate into an effector T cell that migrates to the site of the infection. Effector T cells can either be T helper cells (also known as *CD4+ cells*) or cytotoxic T cells (also known as *CD8+ cells*; Abbas et al., 2016). CD4+ T cells recognize antigens displayed by MHC class II molecules, which are found on APCs. CD8+ T cells recognize antigens presented by MHC class I molecules, which are present on all nucleated cells in the body.

T helper cells are effector T cells whose primary role is to regulate both cellular and humoral immunity. Among other things, T helper cells secrete cytokines that propagate and enhance the response of the innate immune system to the invading organism. They are also essential in the activation of cytotoxic T cells and B cell antibody class switching. The primary role of cytotoxic T cells is to find infected cells and kill them. Upon antigen recognition on the surface of a target cell, cytotoxic T cells release lytic enzymes, or *granzymes*, that induce apoptosis of the infected cell.

A subset of antigen-activated T lymphocytes differentiates into memory cells that survive even after the infection has been eradicated and the antigen cleared. Following activation both memory CD4+ cells and CD8+ cells only require the first signal to become activated. Therefore, subsequent encounters with the same antigen lead to a

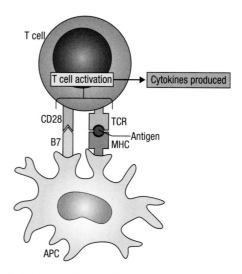

Figure 9.8 Like B cells, T cells require two signals to become activated. The first signal comes from the T cell receptor binding to the MHC on the APC. The second, costimulatory signal is produced when the CD28 receptor on the T cell binds with B7 ligand on the APC.

APC, antigen-presenting cell; MHC, major histocompatibility complex; TCR, T-cell receptor.

secondary response that is quicker and more robust than the primary response (Abbas et al., 2016).

Passive Immunity. *Passive immunity* refers to the process by which a person with no previous antigenic exposure acquires humoral immunity, including specific antibodies or sensitized lymphocytes from another individual (Martin et al., 2015). In the fetus and newborn, maternally derived antibodies help to mediate host defense mechanisms and eliminate invading organisms. Although transient, passive immunity provides important immunologic protection to newborns who are otherwise immunocompromised. Among newborns, the primary means by which passive immunity is conferred is through transplacental acquisition of maternal IgG, and transfer of maternal secretory IgA through colostrum and mature breast milk.

Although B cells are present in the fetus by the end of the first trimester, there is little to no fetal antibody production because the process relies on antigenic exposure (Martin et al., 2015). Transplacental transfer of maternal IgG begins as early as 13 weeks of gestation; however, the majority of IgG is acquired by the fetus during the final 4 weeks of gestation. Therefore, preterm infants have significantly lower levels of IgG than their term counterparts (Palmeira, Quinello, Silveira-Lessa, Zago, & Carneiro-Sampaio, 2012). Maternal IgG is the only immunoglobulin transported across the placenta; therefore, elevated levels of IgM or IgA in cord or neonatal blood are typically suspicious for congenital infection (Martin et al., 2015). Over time, passively acquired maternal IgG degrades and the infant will begin making his

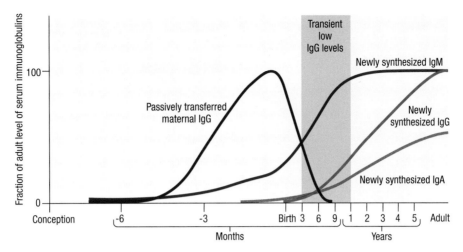

Figure 9.9 Placental transfer of maternal IgG begins early in the second trimester and peaks during the final 4 weeks of pregnancy. After birth, passively acquired IgG degrades over the first few months of life as the infant gains antigenic exposure and begins to produce his or her own IgG.

IgG, immunoglobulin G; IgM, immunoglobulin M.

own antibodies (Figure 9.9). All antibody classes can be detected in colostrum; however, secretory IgA is the most prominent of the isotypes present in breast milk. There is no evidence that the immunoglobulins present in breast milk enter the systemic circulation; rather, they direct their activity against enteric bacterial and viral pathogens.

Communication Within the Adaptive Immune System

The humoral and cell-mediated arms of the immune system interact to coordinate the immune response after an exposure to antigens. APCs from the innate immune system activate both B and T cells during the recognition phase, and induce clonal expansion and differentiation. During this activation phase, the cells become antibody-producing plasma cells and effector T cells. These cells eliminate pathogens using antibodies or through cell-mediated immunity. After the antigen is eliminated, the body returns to homeostasis as the numbers of effector cells decline. Memory B and T cells survive for subsequent interaction with the same pathogen and a quicker secondary response (Figure 9.10).

NEONATAL HOST FACTORS THAT INFLUENCE THE IMMUNE RESPONSE

Both the innate and adaptive immune responses are functionally immature at birth, placing the neonate at increased risk for infection (Table 9.5). In general, neonatal immune function improves with increasing gestational age. Therefore, preterm infants are most limited in their

ability to protect themselves from infection. However, all newborns, regardless of gestational age, exhibit limitations in their ability to mount an effective immune response.

As stated earlier in this chapter, the skin and mucous membranes are important elements of the innate immune system and provide a first line of defense against invading organisms. However, the skin of preterm infants exhibits inadequate barrier function and increased permeability to potential pathogens (see Chapter 12). In addition, vernix caseosa, which has been shown to contain antimicrobial peptides and spectrum of activity against common bacterial pathogens, is sparse in very preterm infants (Akinbi, Narendran, Pass, Markart, & Hoath, 2004; Simonsen, Anderson-Berry, Delair, & Davies, 2014).

The cellular and soluble components of the innate immune system also demonstrate quantitative and qualitative deficiencies in the neonate. Neonatal neutrophils, dendritic cells, and macrophages have been shown to be deficient in number and function when compared to older children or adults. For example, in neonates, neutrophils demonstrate diminished response to chemotactic factors and impairment in phagocytosis (Basha, Surendran, & Pichichero, 2014; Camacho-Gonzalez, Spearman, & Stoll, 2013). Although the capacity for neonatal dendritic cells to process and present antigens is similar to that of adults, neonatal cells have impaired cytokine production, which may result in blunted activation of T cells and NK cells (Gold et al., 2007). NK cells can be detected in fetal circulation as early as 6 weeks of gestation and are essentially equivalent in number to adults during the neonatal period. However, NK cell cytolytic activity against target cells is diminished during the neonatal period, potentially contributing to an increased vulnerability to viral infections (Martin et al., 2015). Although complement levels

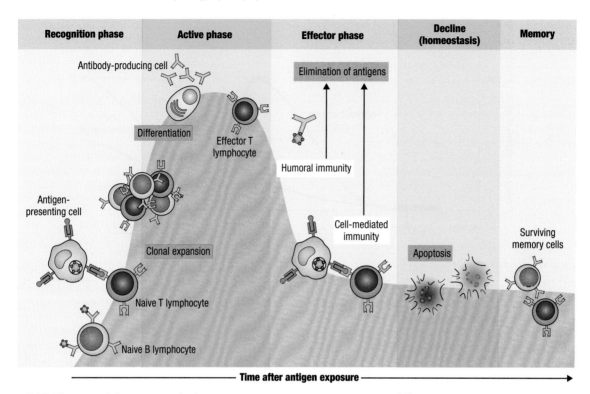

Figure 9.10 Elements of the innate and adaptive immune system interact to successfully mount an immune response. Antigen-presenting cells from the innate immune system activate B cells and T cells to undergo clonal expansion and eliminate the antigen. Once the antigen has been eliminated, the body returns to homeostasis as the effector cells decline in number. A few B and T cells remain as memory cells to mount a stronger and more efficient immune response in the event of a subsequent exposure.

Source: Adapted from Abbas, A. K., Lichtman, A. H., & Pillai, S. (2010). *Cellular and molecular immunology* (updated 6th ed.). Philadelphia, PA: Saunders Elsevier.

increase with increasing gestational age, term newborns possess 50% of adult levels. In particular, neonates have extremely low levels of C9, which is critical for the formation of the MAC and is associated with increased susceptibility to *Escherichia coli* (Wynn & Levy, 2010; Zilow et al., 1993). These deficiencies in the cellular and non-cellular components of the innate immune system lead to reduced phagocytosis and impaired pathogen clearance (Camacho-Gonzalez et al., 2013; Melville & Moss, 2013).

Maturation of the adaptive immune system is dependent on antigenic exposure; therefore, all newborns have deficiencies in T cell activation and B cell antibody production (Melville & Moss, 2013). The combination of low levels of circulating lymphocytes, increased proportion of naïve T and B cells to memory cells, and impairment in antibody isotype switching limit the neonate's ability to respond effectively to infection (Camacho-Gonzalez et al., 2013). Passive immunity acquired through the transplacental transfer of maternal IgG provides important humoral protection against a variety of organisms during the vulnerable period in which the neonatal immune system is developmentally immature. However, because the majority of maternal IgG is transferred to the fetus late in gestation (after 32 weeks), preterm infants lack the benefit of this protective mechanism

conferred to their term counterparts, further increasing their susceptibility to infection (Camacho-Gonzalez et al., 2013; Melville & Moss, 2013).

GENETIC INFLUENCES

Genetic mutations cause an array of immunodeficiencies that range in severity from clinically irrelevant to fatal. One in 2,000 children is diagnosed with an immunodeficiency by the age of 18 (Boyle & Buckley, 2007). The timing of presentation, between birth and adulthood, depends on which immune cells are involved and the severity of the defect (Cooper, Pommering, & Koranyi, 2003). For example, antibody deficiencies generally do not present until after 6 months of age, when the passive immunity provided by maternal antibodies wanes. In contrast, deficits in T cells can be detected in infancy when patients present with infection or poor growth. DiGeorge syndrome, Wiskott–Aldrich syndrome (WAS), and X-linked severe combined immunodeficiency (XSCID) are examples of genetic syndromes that can present in the neonatal period. Additional inherited disorders affecting the immune system are provided in Table 9.6.

TABLE 9.5 Impairments in Neonatal Immune Function

Immune System Component	Functional Impairment	Clinical Implications
Innate Immunity		
Skin and mucous membranes	Impaired barrier function	Decreased ability to prevent invasion from pathogenic organisms
Neutrophils	Limited pool of neutrophils; impaired chemotaxis and phagocytosis	Decreased ability to respond to and kill pathogens
Macrophages	Decreased antigen presentation and cytokine production	Limited ability to activate T cells
Dendritic cells	Decreased production of inflammatory cytokines	Reduced induction of T cells; decreased activation of NK cells
Complement	Deficient complement proteins	Reduced phagocytosis and impaired pathogen clearance by phagocytes; increased risk of invasive bacterial infection
Adaptive Immunity		
T lymphocytes	Relatively low circulating levels of T cells; greater proportion of naïve T cells to memory T cells	Reduced cell-mediated immunity which increases the risk of infection from intracellular pathogens such as *Listeria*, Herpes simplex virus, and cytomegalovirus
B lymphocytes	Decreased B cell antibody production; decreased ability to class-switch	Reduced pathogen opsonization
Passive Immunity		
Maternally acquired IgG	Low circulating levels of IgG in preterm infants	Lack of opsonization and deficient phagocytosis

Ig, immunoglobulin; NK, natural killer.

TABLE 9.6 Other Inherited Disorders of the Immune System

- Ataxia telangiectasia
- Bloom's syndrome
- Common variable immunodeficiency
- MHC class I deficiency
- MHC class II deficiency
- Selective IgA deficiency
- X-linked agammaglobulinemia
- X-linked lymphoproliferative syndrome
- X-linked hyper-IgM syndrome

NOTE: A more comprehensive list is provided by the National Institute of Health, Genetic and Rare Diseases Information Center (GARD).

Ig, immunoglobulin; MHC, major histocompatibility molecule.

DiGeorge Syndrome (22q11.2 Deletion Syndrome)

Deletions in 22q11.2 are the most common genetic cause of cleft palate and the second most common genetic cause of developmental delays and congenital heart disease (McDonald-McGinn et al., 2015). Deletions in this region can be found in one in 100 fetuses with serious anomalies on prenatal ultrasound (Grati et al., 2015; Wapner et al., 2012). More than 90% of cases of DiGeorge syndrome occur as the result of a *de novo* mutation on the long arm of chromosome 22, meaning that it is not inherited from either parent (McDonald-McGinn et al., 2001). Embryologically, it is characterized by abnormal development of the third and fourth pharyngeal arches, which are the origin of the palate, thymus, parathyroid glands, and heart (McDonald-McGinn et al., 2015). DiGeorge syndrome should be suspected in any infant presenting with a combination of cleft palate, immunodeficiency, hypocalcemia, and congenital heart disease.

DiGeorge syndrome causes a wide spectrum of immunologic compromise. Lymphopenia (low numbers of T cells) is present in 75% of affected infants, but the severity of the lymphopenia ranges from a complete absence of T cells to a T cell count that is near normal (Gennery, 2012). A small fraction (1/1000) of infants display a complete absence of T cells due to thymic agenesis and may come to attention after a positive newborn screen, which detects decreased T cell production of any etiology (Kwan et al., 2014; Ryan et al., 1997). Infants with less severe lymphopenia may develop recurrent or severe infections despite seemingly normal adaptive immune function in vitro (Morsheimer, Brown Whitehorn, Heimall, & Sullivan, 2017). Recurrent infections represent a major cause of morbidity in children with DiGeorge syndrome. Cardiac disease and hypocalcemia are responsible for the majority of cases of premature death (McDonald-McGinn et al., 2015; Repetto et al., 2014).

Wiskott–Aldrich Syndrome

WAS is a rare X-linked recessive disorder that occurs in one to four cases per 1 million male births, and is characterized by immunodeficiency, thrombocytopenia, and eczema (Sullivan, Mullen, Blaese, & Winkelstein, 1994). This inheritance pattern means that it only affects males born to mothers who are carriers. It is caused by a mutation in the WAS protein (WASp) on the X-chromosome (Derry, Ochs, & Francke, 1994; de Saint Basile et al., 1989). WASp is a cytosolic protein important for proper function of T cells and platelets. In T cells, WASp is crucial for stabilizing the site where the T cell receptor and the APCs interface, known as the *immunological synapse* (Dupré et al., 2002). Mutations in WASp lead to inappropriately weak T cell activation upon antigen sensing, which can then negatively influence the magnitude and character of the subsequent immune response (Dupré et al., 2002). The severity of the clinical phenotype in patients with WAS can be correlated with the size of the genetic mutation and the degree of protein expression (Ochs, 2009).

Classically, these patients present with excessive bleeding and bruising due to thrombocytopenia and platelet dysfunction (Albert, Notarangelo, & Ochs, 2011; Buckley, 2002). WAS may first be detected in an infant with bleeding after circumcision or with unexplained bruising, petechiae, or mucosal or intracranial bleeding (Albert et al., 2011). In addition, infants have immune dysfunction, characterized by susceptibility to severe infections resulting from defective T cell and B cell responses to pathogens. Patients with WAS are generally not severely lymphopenic; however, T cell function and B cell responses to vaccines are impaired (Sullivan et al., 1994). Infants diagnosed with WAS are at risk for death before age 10 due to infection, bleeding, and malignancy, with bone marrow transplant sometimes necessary for survival (Sullivan et al., 1994).

X-Linked Severe Combined Immunodeficiency

Severe combined immunodeficiency (SCID) is a combined group of genetic disorders characterized by impaired development and function of T cells and B cells, which is caused by a variety of gene mutations. XSCID is the most common type of SCID and affects approximately one in 100,000 live births (Kalman et al., 2004). XSCID has an X-linked recessive mode of inheritance, meaning that it is either inherited from an asymptomatic maternal carrier or the result of a de novo gene mutation (Puck et al., 1997). It is the result of a mutation of a gene located on the X chromosome called *IL-2 receptor gamma*, which is necessary for cytokine signaling (Buckley, 2002; Noguchi et al., 1993). Infants with XSCID develop severe, recurrent, and life-threatening infections within the first few months of life (Buckley, 2002). All newborns with XSCID are lymphopenic and have absent or dramatically reduced T cell function (Buckley, 2002). They may also have absent immunoglobulins and no significant immunologic response to vaccination (Buckley, 2002). Forty-four states now have newborn screens that can detect SCID (Immune Deficiency Foundation, 2017). Early diagnosis of these infants is crucial because the infants who receive a bone marrow transplant in the first 3.5 months of life have significantly better outcomes than those transplanted later (Buckley, 2011). Without bone marrow transplantation, XSCID is fatal.

MATERNAL HEALTH INFLUENCES

The prenatal period is a delicate time during which maternal health conditions can influence the growth and development of fetal organ systems, including the immune system. Maternal HIV infection, autoimmune disease, and immunosuppressive therapy have been shown to have short- and long-term impacts on neonatal immune function.

Maternal HIV Infection

Maternal HIV infection can be passed to the fetus or infant transplacentally, during childbirth, or through breast milk. The availability of antiretroviral agents, access to comprehensive HIV and pregnancy services, and avoidance of breastfeeding in resource-rich countries, such as the United States, have been shown to decrease the risk of mother-to-child HIV transmission to as low as 1% to 2% (Nesheim et al., 2012). However, in those parts of the world where access to preventative interventions are limited, the risk of vertical HIV transmission ranges between 15% to 45% (John & Kreiss, 1996).

Infants born with HIV may present with poor growth, recurrent and/or persistent infections, multiorgan dysfunction, or death (Wilson, Nizet, Maldonado, Remington, & Klein, 2016). These children experience immune defects due to depletion of CD4+ T cells in the periphery and thymus as well as abnormal B cell responses due to the absence of CD4+ T cell help (Wilson et al., 2016). Although early treatment with antiretroviral therapy dramatically improves survival, children with HIV face a long-term battle to maintain viral control and immune system function. Even children born to HIV-infected mothers who are not themselves infected are at risk for immunological deficits, increased mortality, and increased susceptibility to infection (Tobin & Aldrovandi, 2013). For example, these infants have been shown to have a reduced CD4+ T cell count relative to infants born to HIV-uninfected mothers, which is thought to be related to decreased generation of T cells in the thymus during fetal development (Nielsen et al., 2001).

Maternal Autoimmune Disease

Autoimmune diseases are characterized by an immune attack on the body's own tissues in the absence of an infection. Autoimmune disorders are the result of autoantibodies produced by the immune system that are directed at one's own proteins. Maternal autoantibodies that are present in patients with lupus, Sjogren's disease, and unspecified connective tissue diseases can cross the placenta and affect the fetus (Zuppa et al., 2017). The most serious complication of these maternal antibodies is third-degree heart block in the fetus or neonate, which can result in bradycardia, pacemaker implantation, or death.

Children born to mothers with autoimmune diseases can also develop hematologic abnormalities, including thrombocytopenia, anemia, and neutropenia. In a small study of 50 infants born to mothers with anti-SSA/Ro antibodies, it was determined that the percentage of infants with neutropenia (<1000 neutrophils/mm³) peaked at 3 months of age, and only a small percentage of children were still neutropenic by 9 months. Despite the presence of neutropenia, and in utero exposure to maternal immunosuppressive therapy, these children did not exhibit an increased susceptibility to infection or require further treatment, suggesting a normal ability to combat infection (Zuppa et al., 2017).

Maternal Biologic Therapy

Treatment of maternal autoimmune diseases with antibodies directed against cytokines or inflammatory mediators continues to increase as research identifies more immunologic targets for treatment. Many of these antibodies are of the IgG subclass and can cross the placenta. Thus, the influence of these antibodies on the developing fetus and newborn is a growing area of study. Maternal use of anti-TNF-α antibodies has been correlated with an increased incidence of infection and neutropenia in infants in a small number of case reports; however, other studies have demonstrated normal immune development and no major complications in these children (Ling & Koren, 2016). The Pregnancy in Inflammatory Bowel Disease and Neonatal Outcomes (PIANO) study, a large registry of 1,000 patients with Crohn's disease and ulcerative colitis being treated with anti-TNF-α agents, has shown no difference in infant development or susceptibility to infection in the first year of life (Mahadevan, 2012).

Another type of antibody commonly used to treat autoimmune disease and malignancies is anti-CD20, which targets B cells. Infants exposed to these antibodies in the second or third trimester may have reduced circulating B cell numbers and decreased levels of immunoglobulins in the peripheral blood. Despite these reductions, studies have generally shown no increase in rates of infections in exposed infants (Ling & Koren, 2016). As new biologic agents are developed, and an increasing number of patients are being treated with these therapies, the influence on the fetus and infant will need to be monitored for both short- and long-term effects. The potentially adverse effects of immunosuppression will have to be weighed against the risks of uncontrolled maternal autoimmune disease, which in and of itself can have adverse effects.

COMMON PROBLEMS AND IMPLICATIONS ACROSS THE LIFE SPAN

Sepsis is a major cause of neonatal mortality and morbidity. Despite the lack of a universally agreed upon definition, neonatal sepsis typically refers to the isolation of a bacterial, viral, or fungal pathogen from normally sterile body fluids, such as blood or cerebrospinal fluid (CSF), on or before 28 days of life (Shane, Sánchez, & Stoll, 2017; Simonsen et al., 2014; Wynn et al., 2014). Neonatal sepsis can be further classified as either early-onset or late-onset sepsis based on the postnatal days when it is discovered. *Early-onset sepsis (EOS)* usually refers to an infection that occurs at less than or equal to 72 hours in the hospitalized very-low-birth-weight (VLBW; weight less than 1,500 g) infant or less than 7 days in the term infant. EOS is most often the result of vertical transmission of an infectious organism from mother to infant during the intrapartum period (Mukhopadhyay & Puopolo, 2015; Simonsen et al., 2014). *Late-onset sepsis (LOS)*, defined as an infection that occurs after 72 hours in the VLBW infant or 7 days of life in the term infant, can be attributed to horizontal transmission of pathogens acquired postnatally (Simonsen et al., 2014).

Common Bacterial Pathogens

The overall incidence of bacterial neonatal sepsis in high-resource countries is estimated at one to 12 infants per 1,000 live births (Bakhuizen et al., 2014); however, rates of both EOS and LOS have been shown to be inversely related to birth weight and gestational age (Dong & Speer, 2014; Simonsen et al., 2014). Population-based studies estimate the risk of EOS to be less than one case per 1,000 live births (Stoll et al., 2011; Weston et al., 2011). LOS is estimated to affect between 0.6% to 14.2% of hospitalized preterm and term neonates (Dong & Speer, 2014). Several maternal and infant factors have been identified that increase the risk of early- and late-onset sepsis (Table 9.7). Risk factors for EOS include maternal

Table 9.7 Risk Factors for Bacterial Sepsis in the Newborn	
Early-Onset Sepsis	**Late-Onset Sepsis**
Prematurity	Prematurity
Low birth weight	Low birth weight
Maternal GBS colonization	Poor hand hygiene
Maternal history of GBS bacteriuria	Prolonged indwelling catheter use
Chorioamnionitis	Invasive procedures
Maternal fever	Prolonged exposure to antibiotics
Premature rupture of membranes	Delayed enteral feedings
Prolonged rupture of membranes (>18 hours)	

GBS, group B *Streptococcus.*

group B *Streptococcus* (GBS) colonization, maternal history of GBS bacteriuria (with or without a positive screen), prolonged rupture of membranes (greater than 18 hours), maternal fever, and preterm birth (Simonsen et al., 2014). Risk factors for LOS include prematurity, prolonged use of indwelling catheters, delayed enteral feedings with maternal breast milk, and prolonged exposure to empiric antibiotics (Dong & Speer, 2014; Kuppala, Meinzen-Derr, Morrow, & Schibler, 2011).

Early-Onset Sepsis. Organisms that colonize the maternal genitourinary tract predominate the bacterial causes of EOS. Group B *Streptococcus* (GBS or *Streptococcus agalactiae*) and *Escherichia coli* (*E. coli*) represent the most common organisms responsible for EOS in both term and preterm infants, and combined account for approximately 70% of all EOS cases (Stoll et al., 2011). *Listeria monocytogenes* accounts for approximately 5% of EOS cases in preterm infants (Simonsen et al., 2014).

Group B Streptococcus. GBS is a Gram-positive, facultative diplococcus that has been known to colonize the genitourinary tract and pharyngeal mucosa of pregnant women. GBS is responsible for 38% to 43% of all cases of EOS and is the most common cause of EOS in term infants (Shane et al., 2017; Stoll et al., 2011). GBS was first discovered as a distinct organism in the 1930s; however, it was not until the early 1960s that it was recognized as an important pathogen responsible for neonatal sepsis (Koenig & Keenan, 2009; Randis, Baker, & Ratner, 2017). In 1996, the Centers for Disease Control and Prevention (CDC) released a consensus statement that called for identification of maternal GBS carriers based on prenatal and intrapartum risk factors by obtaining cultures between 35 and 37 weeks gestation. They further recommended treatment with intrapartum antibiotic prophylaxis (IAP) for women found to be at high risk for GBS carriage or with culture-proven GBS colonization (CDC, 1996). In 2002, the CDC revised and re-released their policy

statement, specifically to promote the use of universal screening at 35 to 37 weeks gestation over the risk-based approach, which had been shown to be less efficacious (Schrag, Gorwitz, Fultz-Butts, & Schuchat, 2002). The most recent treatment guidelines for the prevention of perinatal GBS disease were released in 2010 and are summarized in Table 9.8 (Verani, McGee, & Schrag, 2010). Since the widespread adoption of universal screening and IAP, rates of EOS due to GBS have declined, but GBS continues to be a common pathogen implicated in EOS (Simonsen et al., 2014).

Rates of maternal GBS colonization vary geographically. In the United States approximately 20% to 30% of women are believed to be colonized at any given time (Mukhopadhyay & Puopolo, 2015). Risk factors for maternal GBS colonization include African American race, obesity, diabetes, and GBS colonization during a previous pregnancy (Randis et al., 2017). Fetal and neonatal exposure to GBS typically occurs during the antepartum or intrapartum period during which time the organism can ascend from the vaginal mucosa into the uterus. This most commonly occurs after rupture of the amniotic membranes; however, there is some evidence to suggest that GBS is capable of breaching the intact amnion. Once in the amniotic fluid, the organism replicates and can be aspirated into the fetal lungs (Randis et al., 2017). Vertical transmission can also occur during labor, through direct contact as the infant passes through the vaginal canal (Simonsen et al., 2014).

Although the exact mechanisms by which GBS progresses from asymptomatic colonization to invasive disease are not completely understood, the organism is known to possess several characteristics that contribute to its virulence. GBS possesses the ability to adhere to vascular endothelium and epithelium, including rectovaginal tissue, chorionic membranes, and neonatal lungs—a characteristic that is essential in establishing colonization and ultimately invasive disease (Koenig & Keenan, 2009; Rajagopal, 2009). In addition, GBS works to evade and blunt the host's immune response through a variety

TABLE 9.8 CDC Recommendations for Intrapartum Antibiotic Prophylaxis to Prevent Early-Onset GBS Sepsis

Intrapartum GBS Prophylaxis Indicated	Intrapartum GBS Prophylaxis Not Indicated
Previous infant with invasive GBS disease GBS bacteriuria during any trimester of the current pregnancy Positive GBS screening culture during current pregnancy[a] (unless a cesarean delivery is performed before onset of labor on a woman with intact amniotic membranes) Unknown GBS status at the onset of labor (culture not done, incomplete, or results unknown) and any of the following: • Delivery at less than 37 weeks of gestation[b] • Amniotic membrane rupture greater than or equal to 18 hours • Intrapartum temperature greater than or equal to 100.4°F (greater than or equal to 38.0°C)[c] • Intrapartum NAAT[d] positive for GBS	Colonization with GBS during a previous pregnancy (unless an indication for GBS prophylaxis is present for current pregnancy) GBS bacteriuria during previous pregnancy (unless another indication for GBS prophylaxis is present for current pregnancy) Cesarean delivery performed before onset of labor on a woman with intact amniotic membranes, regardless of GBS colonization status or gestational age Negative vaginal and rectal GBS screening culture result in late gestation[a] during the current pregnancy, regardless of intrapartum risk factors

CDC, Centers for Disease Control and Prevention; GBS, group B *Streptococcus*; NAAT, nucleic acid amplification test.

[a]Optimal timing for prenatal GBS screening is at 35 to 37 weeks of gestation.
[b]Recommendations for the use of intrapartum antibiotics for prevention of early-onset GBS disease in the setting of preterm delivery are presented in Figure 3.
[c]If amnionitis is suspected, broad-spectrum antibiotic therapy that includes an agent known to be active against GBS should replace GBS prophylaxis.
[d]NAAT testing for GBS is optional and may not be available in all settings. If intrapartum NAAT result is negative for GBS but any other intrapartum risk factor (delivery at less than 37 weeks of gestation, amniotic membrane rupture at 18 hours or more, or temperature greater than or equal to 100°4F [greater than or equal to38.0°C]) is present, then intrapartum antibiotic prophylaxis is indicated.

Source: Adapted from American College of Obstetricians and Gynecologists. (2011). Committee Opinion, No 485. Prevention of early-onset group B streptococcal disease in newborns. *Obstetrics & Gynecology, 117*(4), 1019–1027. doi:10.1097/AOG.0b013e318219229b

of processes. It produces a polysaccharide capsule that inhibits the innate immune functions of opsonization and phagocytosis. It also plays a role in the inactivation of complement components and upregulation of inhibitory immune receptors (Rajagopal, 2009; Randis et al., 2017).

Escherichia coli. *E. coli* are facultative, anaerobic, Gram-negative rods that are ubiquitous in the human GI tract (Mukhopadhyay & Puopolo, 2015). Overall, *E. coli* is the second leading cause of early-onset bacterial sepsis, accounting for approximately 29% of all cases, and it is the most common cause of EOS in VLBW infants (Stoll et al., 2011). As is the case with other coliform bacteria, *E. coli* has also been found to colonize the maternal vaginal canal where the infant is exposed during birth. Multiple serotypes of *E. coli* exist and are categorized based on their antigenic structure. Strains with the K1 capsular antigen, in particular, have been identified as being important in neonatal sepsis and meningitis (Simonsen et al., 2014; Stenutz, Weintraub, & Widmalm, 2006). Virulence factors associated with the K1 antigenic strain include the synthesis of polysialic acid, which impairs opsonization and phagocytosis and facilitates complement resistance,

as well as surface proteins that facilitate invasion and binding of the brain endothelium (Simonsen et al., 2014).

Listeria monocytogenes. *Listeria monocytogenes* is a facultative, intracellular, Gram-positive bacillus that is found primarily in soil, fecal flora, and unprocessed food (Camacho-Gonzalez et al., 2013). *L. monocytogenes* has the unique capability to enter, survive, and multiply in phagocytic and nonphagocytic cells. This property is believed to be essential for *L. monocytogenes* to cause disease in humans (Lecuit, 2005). Although the overall incidence (5%) of neonatal sepsis with *Listeria* is low, up to 70% of all neonatal infections from *L. monocytogenes* involve infants of less than 35 weeks gestation (Simonsen et al., 2014).

Human listeriosis is typically seen in individuals who are immunocompromised, including diabetics, the elderly, and individuals who are HIV positive or taking immunosuppressive drugs. Because of depression of cell-mediated immunity that occurs during pregnancy, there is a 17-fold increase in the incidence of listeriosis during this period. The unborn fetus, who also has weakened cell-mediated immunity, is at increased risk of vertical transmission of the organism (Mylonakis, Paliou, Hohmann, Calderwood, & Wing, 2002). Maternal listeriosis usually occurs after ingestion of contaminated food. *Listeria* can then be transmitted to the fetus transplacentally, or less common, after the organism has ascended from the colonized vaginal canal (Mylonakis et al., 2002; Simonsen et al., 2014). In addition to fulminant EOS, consequences of feto–maternal listeriosis include chorioamnionitis with placental abscesses, spontaneous abortion, stillbirth, and preterm delivery (Simonsen et al., 2014).

Late-Onset Sepsis. As survival rates of extremely premature infants have improved over the years, LOS has emerged as an important contributor to neonatal mortality and morbidity, particularly in VLBW infants. Gram-positive organisms, most notable coagulase-negative staphylococci, or CoNS, (which include the species *S. epidermis, S. haemolyticus, S. capitis,* and *S. hominis*) and *Staphylococcus aureus* are the predominant pathogens responsible for LOS. Combined, they account for approximately 45% to 78% of all cases (Dong & Speer, 2014; Downey, Smith, & Benjamin, 2010). A variety of Gram-negative bacilli (GNB) also contribute to the burden of LOS.

CoNS and Staphylococcus aureus. In most humans, CoNS represent commensal organisms that are part of the normal skin flora with relatively low capacity to cause invasive disease. However, neonates requiring intensive care, such as preterm or low-birth-weight infants, are vulnerable to CoNS infections secondary to impaired defense barriers, immature immune response, the presence of indwelling devices, and repeated invasive procedures (Becker, Heilmann, & Peters, 2014).

Although CoNS tend to be less virulent and have a more indolent clinical course than other pathogens, *S. epidermis* species have been shown to have the unique capability to form biofilms that permit invasive disease

(Becker et al., 2014; Dong & Speer, 2014). Biofilm formation is the process by which bacteria adhere to a foreign body, such as a central venous catheter or indwelling urinary catheter, and form an extracellular matrix (Figure 9.11). Once formed, the biofilm allows the organism to evade host defense mechanisms and may even contribute to antimicrobial resistance. As the biofilm matures, intact sections can slough off and seed to other organ systems, leading to systemic infection (Becker et al., 2014; Dong & Speer, 2014; Fey & Olson, 2010).

Staphylococcus aureus represents both a commensal and infectious pathogen. Approximately 30% of the population are asymptomatic carriers of *S. aureus,* yet it is a common cause of invasive neonatal disease and is associated with myriad complications, including skin and soft tissue infection, brain abscesses, meningitis, osteomyelitis, septic arthritis, infective endocarditis, pneumatoceles, lung abscesses, and death (Dolapo, Dhanireddy, & Talati, 2014; Tong, Davis, Eichenberger, Holland, & Fowler, 2015). *S. aureus* is typically classified as either methicillin susceptible (MSSA) or methicillin resistant (MRSA) based on its sensitivity to beta-lactam antibiotics. Over the past two decades there have been increasing reports of both hospital-acquired MRSA (HA-MRSA) and community-acquired MRSA (CA-MRSA) outbreaks in neonatal intensive care units (NICUs) across the country (Dolapo et al., 2014). This underscores the importance of practicing good hand hygiene and strict compliance with infection-control practices in this population.

S. aureus has several characteristics that contribute to its virulence and potential to lead to invasive disease. As with CoNS, *S. aureus* can produce biofilms that adhere to host tissues or foreign materials, enabling it to evade host defense responses and antimicrobials. In addition, *S. aureus* produces a microcapsule that prevents phagocytosis and opsonization. It also produces proteins that

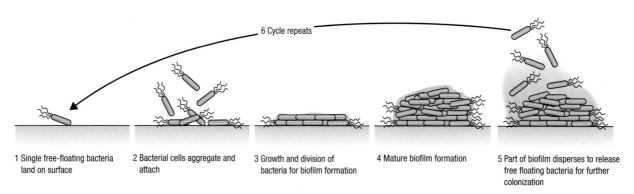

Figure 9.11 The six stages of biofilm formation. Stage 1: Single free-floating bacteria adhere to an endothelial or prosthetic surface. Stage 2: The bacterial cells aggregate, form microcolonies, and excrete extracellular polymers, creating an irreversible attachment. Stage 3: The bacterial cells grow and divide, creating a biofilm. Stage 4: The biofilm matures, providing protection to the bacterial colonies against host defense mechanisms and antimicrobials. Stage 5: As the biofilm reaches a critical mass, intact portions break off. Stage 6: Free-floating bacteria that have detached from the biofilm seed to other parts of the body and repeat the cycle.

interfere with chemotaxis and limit the extravasation of neutrophils to the site of infection, and cytotoxins that cause leukocyte destruction (Gordon & Lowy, 2008; Tong et al., 2015).

There remains some debate as to whether MRSA is more virulent than MSSA. Evidence suggests that there is no significant difference in morbidity and mortality among VLBW infants with MRSA bacteremia when compared to those with MSSA bacteremia (Shane et al., 2012). However, the increase in CA-MRSA outbreaks in NICUs that have been recently observed have been associated with more severe clinical presentation and worse outcomes (Dolapo et al., 2014). Regardless of the strain isolated, MRSA is universally associated with increased healthcare costs and limited treatment options (Gordon & Lowy, 2008).

Gram-negative bacilli. As a group, GNB represent the second most common cause of LOS, accounting for 20% to 30% of all cases (Camacho-Gonzalez et al., 2013; Downey et al., 2010). Although less prevalent, Gram-negative LOS carries a significantly higher risk of mortality, with 19% to 36% of those affected ultimately dying (Downey et al., 2010). Gram-negative pathogens responsible for LOS primarily include *E. coli, Klebsiella, Enterobacter, Serratia,* and *Pseudomonas* (Camacho-Gonzalez et al., 2013; Dong & Speer, 2014). Considered alone, *Pseudomonas aeruginosa,* a Gram-negative organism that tends to thrive in moist environments, has been found to have the highest mortality rate among preterm infants (Downey et al., 2010). Horizontal transmission of these pathogens typically occurs via the hands of healthcare workers, contamination of parenteral nutrition, or through bacterial translocation of intestinal flora (Camacho-Gonzalez et al., 2013; Sherman, 2010).

Once introduced, GNB exhibit several virulence factors that enhance their ability to cause systemic disease and evade a host's defenses. One of the most important virulence factors of GNB is endotoxins. Endotoxins are large molecules consisting of a lipid and polysaccharide found on the outer membrane of GNB. Endotoxin expression plays a significant role in the exaggerated release of proinflammatory cytokines (IL-8, IL-6, IL-1β, and TNF-α) that can lead to tissue damage, septic shock, and death (Ramachandran, 2014).

Group B Streptococcus. Although the implementation of universal screening and routine IAP significantly decreased the incidence of EOS secondary to GBS, it has had no meaningful impact on rates of LOS from GBS, which are estimated to be between 0.28 to 0.35 per 1,000 live births (Berardi et al., 2013; Randis et al., 2017). Although IAP has not been shown to decrease the risk of LOS from GBS, there is some evidence to suggest that IAP is associated with delayed onset and milder presentation of late-onset GBS neonatal infection (Berardi et al., 2013). The routes of transmission and pathogenesis of late-onset GBS infection are not completely understood. Approximately 50% of infants who develop late-onset GBS disease are colonized at the time of delivery by GBS that is of the same serotype as that carried by their mothers (Randis et al., 2017). Some reports suggest that contaminated human milk from mothers with either clinical or subclinical mastitis may also represent a source of late-onset or recurrent neonatal GBS infections, suggesting bacterial translocation from intestinal sources to the bloodstream as a potential mechanism by which GBS can access sterile sites (Berardi et al., 2013; Randis et al., 2017). Horizontal transmission from healthcare workers or community sources is another possible source of neonatal exposure. Virulence factors associated with late-onset GBS disease are similar to those associated with EOS GBS infection and include the presence of surface structures that facilitate its adherence to vascular endothelium and production of a polysaccharide capsule that help it to evade host immune defenses.

Clinical manifestations. The clinical manifestation of early- and late-onset sepsis on the neonate is broad and nonspecific. The signs and symptoms of bacterial sepsis include apnea, respiratory distress, temperature instability, tachycardia, lethargy, and hypotension. Left untreated, the symptoms of sepsis in preterm and term infants can quickly progress from subtle, vital-sign abnormalities to profound septic shock.

Implications across the life span. Regardless of the organism isolated or the timing of onset, bacterial sepsis is associated with several serious short- and long-term complications. The mortality rate associated with bacterial sepsis ranges between 5% to 20% (Bakhuizen et al., 2014). Those who survive are more likely to develop bronchopulmonary dysplasia, visual impairment, and auditory impairment. Children evaluated at 2 and 5 years of age, with a history of either EOS or LOS, are more likely to have cerebral palsy and cognitive impairment (Bakhuizen et al., 2014; Mitha et al., 2013; Schlapbach et al., 2011). It is important to point out that many of the risk factors for developing sepsis, such as prematurity and low birth weight, are also associated with subsequent poor outcomes. Therefore, although the evidence suggests a strong correlation between sepsis and poor neurodevelopmental outcomes, it is difficult to establish a causal link between the two. There is a relative paucity of data on the outcomes of patients with a history of bacterial sepsis beyond early childhood. The impact of bacterial sepsis on long-term quality of life and future burden of disease is largely unknown.

Other Bacterial Pathogens

Treponema pallidum. *T. pallidum* is a thin, tightly coiled, motile spirochete that causes syphilis (Martin et al., 2015). Humans are the only natural host for *T. pallidum* (Woods, 2005). In adult women, syphilis is usually acquired through sexual contact and progresses through several well-described stages if left untreated: a primary stage, which presents with a chancre at the site of inoculation;

a secondary stage characterized by fever, malaise, and a mucocutaneous rash; an asymptomatic, latent stage; and a late tertiary stage involving damage to multiple organ systems (Janier et al., 2014). The incidence of congenital syphilis generally mirrors that of primary and secondary disease in women. Since 2012, the rate of congenital syphilis has been steadily increasing and is estimated to be between eight and 12 cases per 100,000 live births (Bowen, Su, Torrone, Kidd, & Weinstock, 2015). Limited or no prenatal care are risk factors for congenital syphilis.

Transmission of *T. pallidum* most often occurs transplacentally, but can also occur through direct contact with an infectious lesion during delivery. Although transplacental transfer of *T. pallidum* can occur at any point during gestation, risk of transmission increases with advancing gestational age. Infants born to women with primary or secondary disease are more likely to acquire congenital syphilis than infants born to women with latent disease (Martin et al., 2015). Once introduced in the fetal bloodstream, *T. pallidum* multiplies, resulting in spirochetemia and widespread dissemination of the organism to nearly every organ system in the body. Intrauterine syphilis infection can result in spontaneous abortion, stillbirth, or preterm delivery (Martin et al., 2015).

Clinical manifestations. Congenital syphilis is classified as either early or late disease based on the age at the onset of symptoms. Symptoms of early congenital syphilis are present before 2 years of age; however, 60% to 90% of infants with congenital syphilis are asymptomatic at birth (Bowen et al., 2015; Ortiz-Lopez, Diez, Diaz, Simon, & Diaz, 2012). When present, clinical manifestations in infected infants include hepatosplenomegaly, maculopapular eruptions, anemia, bone abnormalities, persistent rhinitis (snuffles), chorioretinitis, nonimmune hydrops, and generalized lymphadenopathy (Martin et al., 2015; Ortiz-Lopez et al., 2012). Advanced practice nurses should recognize that "Hutchinson's triad" is a common aggregate of three key clinical manifestations associated with congenital syphilis. This triad manifests with (a) interstitial keratitis, (b) nerve deafness, and (c) peg-shaped upper incisor teeth ("Hutchinson's teeth").

Implications across the life span. Left untreated, congenital syphilis leads to late-stage disease findings, which typically occur after 2 years of age, most often presenting during puberty (Chakraborty & Luck, 2008). Children with a history of congenital syphilis may experience neurologic sequelae, including cognitive impairment, hydrocephalus, cranial nerve palsies, and seizure disorders (Martin et al., 2015). Eighth-cranial-nerve deafness is common and typically occurs suddenly at 8 to 10 years of age (Chakraborty & Luck, 2008). Interstitial keratitis is a classic finding in children with a history of congenital syphilis. They may also demonstrate abnormalities in permanent dentition characterized by centrally notched, peg-shaped upper central incisors, known as *Hutchinson's teeth* (Martin et al., 2015).

Common Fungal and Protozoal Pathogens

Candida spp. Candida organisms are ubiquitous, saprophytic (feeds on dead or decaying matter) yeasts that comprise the normal commensal flora of humans and rarely cause disease in the immunocompetent host (Martin et al., 2015). Under certain conditions, however, *Candida* can cause infections ranging in severity from superficial cutaneous infection to disseminated candidiasis. *Candida* species are the most common cause of fungal infections in the neonate. Approximately 60% of invasive fungal infections in NICU patients are caused by *Candida albicans* (Fridkin, Kaufman, Edwards, Shetty, & Horan, 2006). *Candida parapsilosis* has emerged as an important etiologic species and is implicated in up to 25% of invasive fungal infections in the VLBW infant (Chow, Linden, & Bliss, 2012; Martin et al., 2015; Pammi, Holland, Butler, Gacser, & Bliss, 2013). Other less common species that have been isolated include *Candida glabrata, Candida tropicalis,* and *Candida lusitaniae.*

Like infections caused by bacterial pathogens, *Candida* infections can be the result of vertical transmission from mother to infant during the intrapartum period resulting in early onset of disease. However, the vast majority of invasive *Candida* infections are late onset and the result of horizontal transmission. Risk factors for *Candida* infection include presence of a central catheter, exposure to broad-spectrum antibiotics (particularly third-generation cephalosporins), fungal colonization, exposure to corticosteroids, prematurity, and low birth weight (Benjamin et al., 2010). The incidence of candidiasis varies widely by center and has been reported to affect anywhere between 2% to 28% of infants weighing less than 1,000 grams (Manzoni, Mostert, & Castagnola, 2015).

Candida species possess several attributes that support its virulence and ability to cause invasive disease. They have a specialized set of proteins, called *adhesins* and *invasins*, that mediate adherence to and invasion of host cells (Mayer, Wilson, & Hube, 2013). Another important virulence factor of *Candida* organisms is the ability to form biofilms on prosthetic or endothelial surfaces that act as a reservoir for systemic seeding. Similar in nature to bacterial biofilms, yeast biofilms consist of fungal colonies that are protected from host defense mechanisms and antifungal medications (Manzoni et al., 2015; Mayer et al., 2013). Once mature, sections of the biofilm can detach and disseminate to other organ systems, including the heart, kidneys, central nervous system, eyes, lungs, liver, spleen, bones, and joints (Manzoni et al., 2015; Martin et al., 2015).

Clinical manifestations. The clinical manifestations of neonatal fungal infections are similar in nature to the signs and symptoms of bacterial infections and include apnea, respiratory distress, temperature instability, and lethargy. The combination of persistent hyperglycemia and thrombocytopenia are strongly associated with systemic candidiasis in the extremely low-birth-weight infant (Dyke & Ott, 1993).

Implications across the life span. Implications of invasive candidiasis in the neonate are similar to those for bacterial infections. Among extremely premature infants with invasive candidiasis, the risk of death is 45% compared to 7% in unaffected infants (Barton et al., 2014). Survivors are more likely to have visual impairment, deafness, and cerebral palsy at 18 to 22 months corrected gestational age and the risk of poor outcomes increases when there is CNS involvement (Barton et al., 2014; Benjamin et al., 2006).

Toxoplasma gondii. *Toxoplasma gondii* (*T. gondii*) is an obligate intracellular protozoan parasite that causes the human disease toxoplasmosis. Cats are the only known definitive hosts for the organism and therefore serve as the main reservoirs for infection (McAuley, 2014). *T. gondii* exist in three forms: oocysts, which are excreted in cat feces; tachyzoites or trophozoites, which proliferate and destroy infected cells during acute infection; and bradyzoites, which multiply in tissue cysts (Martin et al., 2015; McAuley, 2014). Humans can acquire the infection through ingestion of poorly cooked contaminated meat containing *T. gondii* cysts, ingestion of oocysts through food or water contaminated by cat feces, organ transplantation, blood transfusion, or via the placenta (McAuley, 2014).

Congenital toxoplasma infections most commonly occur after a primary maternal infection, although transmission in immunocompromised women experiencing reactivation of infection has been described (Lindsay & Dubey, 2011). The incidence of primary maternal infection during pregnancy is estimated to be about 1.1 per 1,000 women (Martin et al., 2015). In infected women, the risk of vertical transmission is 25% in the first trimester of pregnancy and increases to 65% by the third trimester. In the United States, congenital toxoplasmosis is estimated to occur between one in 3,000 to one in 10,000 live births (McAuley, 2014).

In humans, ingesting tissue cysts or oocytes results in the release of sporozoites that disseminate in the body and multiply intracellularly. As the host cell dies, it releases tachyzoites that invade adjacent cells and continue the process. Pressure from the host's immune response ultimately causes the tachyzoites to transform into bradyzoites that form tissue cysts in the skeletal muscle, myocardium, and brain (Figure 9.12; McAuley, 2014).

Clinical manifestations. Most infants with congenital toxoplasmosis are asymptomatic at birth; however, symptoms of disease can manifest within the first few months to years of life. A subset of newborns with congenital toxoplasmosis will have signs of generalized disease at birth that can include chorioretinitis, intracranial calcifications, hydrocephalus, microcephaly, jaundice, thrombocytopenia, anemia, and hepatosplenomegaly (Maldonado & Read, 2017; Martin et al., 2015).

Implications across the life span. The long-term implications of congenital toxoplasmosis depend heavily on whether the infant receives prompt treatment for the infection. Without treatment, nearly all infants with symptomatic congenital toxoplasmosis develop long-term sequelae, including intellectual impairment, severe visual impairment, deafness, and seizures (Wilson, Remington, Stagno, & Reynolds, 1980). Likewise, most infants with subclinical toxoplasmosis who do not receive treatment go on to develop chorioretinitis during childhood that can lead to blindness. They are also at high risk for sensorineural hearing loss and cognitive impairment (Wilson et al., 1980). If, on the other hand, congenital toxoplasmosis is treated immediately, the risks of chorioretinitis and neurologic impairment are substantially decreased, and the prognosis is generally favorable (Berrebi et al., 2010). Most adults with a history of congenital toxoplasmosis who received early treatment report normal to near normal quality of life and minimal visual impairment (Peyron et al., 2011).

Common Viral Pathogens

Herpes Simplex Virus. Herpes simplex virus types 1 (HSV-1) and 2 (HSV-2) are members of the herpesvirus family that consist of several closely related viruses. Structurally, the herpesviruses are characterized by a double-stranded DNA core that is enveloped by an icosahedral (20 sided) nucleocapsid consisting of 162 capsomeres (Figure 9.13; Kimberlin, 2004; Martin et al., 2015). Transmission of HSV most commonly occurs through contact with mucosal surfaces or open areas of skin. Between 20% to 25% of adults in the United States have genital herpes due to HSV-2; however, in recent years HSV-1 has emerged as a frequent cause of genital herpes cases (Kimberlin & Baley, 2013). Approximately 30% of pregnant women have serologic evidence of HSV-2 infection, the majority of whom lack a history or symptoms of infection (Martin et al., 2015). This is consistent with the finding that up to 80% of women who deliver HSV-infected newborns have no past history of HSV infection and no evidence of infection at the time of delivery (Kimberlin, 2004)

The mother must be experiencing either symptomatic or asymptomatic viral shedding of HSV for mother-to-infant transmission to occur. Studies of nonpregnant HSV-seropositive women have demonstrated that HSV is shed asymptomatically in the genital tract as frequently as 1 out of every 3 days, which has important implications as it relates to the spread of HSV through sexual contact and maternal-to-infant transmission (Wald et al., 1997). Infants born to mothers who have a first-episode primary infection (infections in which the mother is experiencing a new infection with HSV-1 or HSV-2 and has not previously been infected with the virus of the other serotype) near the time of delivery are at the greatest risk for contracting the virus (Kimberlin & Baley, 2013). The risk of acquiring HSV is close to 60% in infants born to mothers

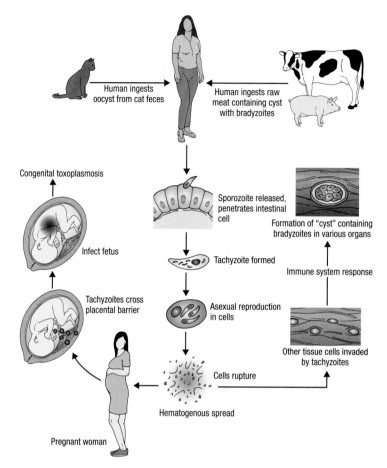

Figure 9.12 The life cycle of *T. gondii*. Humans either ingest tissue cysts from contaminated meat or oocysts from hands, food, or water contaminated by cat feces. Once ingested, the tissue cyst or oocyst ruptures, releasing sporozoites that penetrate the intestinal epithelium, disseminate through the body, and multiply intracellularly. As the host's cells die they release tachyzoites that invade adjacent cells and continue the process. Pressure from the host's immune response prompts the tachyzoites to transform into bradyzoites that form tissues cysts in various organs. In pregnant women with primary infections, tachyzoites cross the placenta infecting the fetus.

with first-episode primary infections, whereas infants born to mothers with recurrent infection have a less than 5% chance of contracting the virus. The decreased risk in recurrent infection is believed to be secondary to transplacentally acquired antibodies against HSV (Wilson et al., 2016). Other factors that increase the risk of transmission are prolonged rupture of membranes and vaginal mode of delivery.

HSV infection in the newborn can be acquired in utero, during the intrapartum period, or postnatally. In utero HSV infection from transplacental transfer of the virus is rare, accounting for approximately 5% of all cases of neonatal disease. Approximately 85% of cases are transmitted during the intrapartum period, during which time the infant comes in direct contact with the maternal genital tract. The remaining 10% of cases are acquired postnatally and are almost always attributed to HSV-1 because

the source is not genital (Wilson et al., 2016). HSV infections acquired during the intrapartum period can be further classified as either disseminated infection affecting multiple organ systems, including the lungs, liver, adrenal glands, skin, eyes, and CNS; CNS disease with or without skin lesions; or disease localized to the skin, eye, and/ or mouth (SEM disease). Approximately 25% of neonatal HSV cases are disseminated, CNS disease accounts for 30% of cases, and SEM disease makes up 45% of all cases (Kimberlin, 2004).

Clinical manifestations. Infants who acquire HSV in utero typically have a triad of clinical findings at birth that include cutaneous manifestations (scarring, active lesions, cutis aplasia, erythematous macular exanthem), ophthalmologic findings (chorioretinitis, microphthalmia, optic atrophy), and neurologic findings

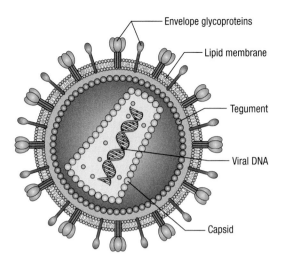

Envelope glycoproteins

Lipid membrane

Tegument

Viral DNA

Capsid

Figure 9.13 All herpes viruses have the same basic structure: an inner core containing large double-stranded viral DNA enclosed within an icosahedral capsid. The capsid is surrounded by a protein coat called the *tegument*, which is encased in a glycoprotein bearing lipid membrane.

Source: Adapted from Wilson, C. B., Nizet, V., Maldonado, Y. A., Remington, J. S., & Klein, J. O. (Eds.). (2016). *Remington and Klein's infectious diseases of the fetus and newborn infant* (8th ed.). Philadelphia, PA: Saunders Elsevier.

(microcephaly, encephalomalacia, hydranencephaly; Kimberlin, 2004). Infants who acquire the virus during the intrapartum period usually present with symptoms between 10 days and 4 weeks of life. Among infants with disseminated disease, encephalitis is a common finding. Additional clinical findings in disseminated HSV include liver dysfunction, coagulopathy, and pneumonitis. Cutaneous lesions may or may not be present (Kimberlin, 2004). Clinical manifestations of CNS disease include seizures, temperature instability, lethargy, irritability, poor feeding, and bulging fontanelle. Approximately 60% to 70% of infants with CNS will also present with skin vesicles at some point in their clinical course (Kimberlin, 2004). SEM infection is characterized by vesicular lesions of the skin, eyes, and/or mouth without evidence of visceral organ or CNS involvement.

Implications across the life span. Despite the availability of effective antiviral therapy, neonatal HSV infection is a lifelong condition that may be characterized by viral reactivation and recurrence of SEM lesions and CNS disease. The short- and long-term sequelae associated with neonatal HSV infection depend on the degree of organ system involvement. Even with appropriate therapy, 31% of patients with disseminated disease die by 2 years of life (Kimberlin et al., 2001). Approximately 80% of patients with disseminated HSV infection who survive have normal neurologic development (Kimberlin, 2007). The remainder have neurodevelopmental impairment that

includes seizures, blindness, hemiparesis, and developmental delay. Fulminant liver failure requiring liver transplantation in patients with disseminated HSV infection has also been reported in the literature (Egawa et al., 1998; Twagira et al., 2004).

Prior to the availability of antiviral therapy, 50% of infants with CNS disease died by 1 year of life, but with appropriate therapy that mortality rate has decreased significantly to 4% (Kimberlin, 2007; Kimberlin et al., 2001). Seventy percent of patients with CNS disease who survive go on to develop some degree of neurodevelopmental impairment (Kimberlin, 2007). Seizures that present before the initiation of antiviral therapy are a poor prognostic indicator and increase the likelihood of neurodevelopmental impairment in patients with CNS disease as well as disseminated disease (Kimberlin, 2007). Although mortality in patients with SEM disease is low, recurrence of lesions on the skin, eyes, and mouth are common and can be a problem for them for their entire lives (Kimberlin, 2007). Overall, the risk of neurodevelopmental impairment is patients with SEM disease is low; however, patients who have three or more recurrences in the first 6 months of life have a greater risk of neurologic impairment (Whitley et al., 1991).

Cytomegalovirus. Cytomegalovirus (CMV) is a ubiquitous herpesvirus spread by close personal contact through blood, saliva, genital secretions, urine, and breast milk. Up to 90% of individuals contract CMV infection at some point during their lifetime, and once introduced, the virus establishes lifelong latency in monocytes and granulocytes (E. C. Swanson & Schleiss, 2013). In the immunocompetent host, CMV infection is usually clinically silent, but individuals with impaired cell-mediated immunity may have difficulty controlling CMV infection (Pass & Anderson, 2014). Maternal transmission of a new or reactivated infection can occur at any point during gestation leading to congenital CMV infection.

In the United States, approximately 20,000 to 40,000 infants per year are born with CMV, making it the most common congenital viral infection (Martin et al., 2015). Transplacental transmission of CMV occurs in approximately 35% of pregnancies in which there is primary maternal infection (Pass & Anderson, 2014). Maternal-to-child transmission can also occur during the intrapartum period through direct contact with cervical and vaginal secretions or through breast milk. Postnatal transmission can also occur from blood-product exposure.

Clinical manifestations. Only 5% to 10% of congenital CMV infections are symptomatic, and symptomatic infections are more likely to occur after a primary maternal infection (van Zuylen et al., 2014). Among infants with clinical symptoms at birth, common findings include small size for gestational age, microcephaly, petechiae, jaundice, hepatosplenomegaly, thrombocytopenia, chorioretinitis, and sensorineural hearing loss (SNHL; Kylat,

Kelly, & Ford-Jones, 2006). Term infants who acquire CMV during the intrapartum period or through maternal breast milk often remain asymptomatic, whereas preterm VLBW infants who do not have congenital CMV but contract the virus during birth or through breast milk have been reported to have signs of acute illness characterized by respiratory distress, hematological changes, and abnormal liver function (Martin et al., 2015; Pass & Anderson, 2014).

Implications across the life span. SNHL is the most common sequelae associated with congenital CMV infection (Dreher et al., 2014). Over half of infants with symptomatic infection and 10% to 35% of infants with asymptomatic infection will develop SNHL (Boppana, Ross, & Fowler, 2013; Dreher et al., 2014). Other sequelae associated with congenital CMV infection include motor defects, cognitive impairment, and seizures. Many children with chorioretinitis go on to develop strabismus or visual impairment (Martin et al., 2015). In general, patients with asymptomatic infection have fewer sequelae and more favorable outcomes than patients with symptomatic CMV infection (Boppana et al., 2013; Dreher et al., 2014).

Rubella Virus. Rubella virus is a ribonucleic acid (RNA) virus in the *Togaviridae* family that, in adults, produces a relatively mild but extremely contagious disease, characterized by a maculopapular rash, lymphadenopathy, conjunctivitis, and malaise (Martin et al., 2015). Maternal-to-fetal rubella transmission occurs when a mother with no previous antigenic exposure to the virus develops a primary infection causing viremia. The timing of maternal infection is the most important determinant of fetal infection. Maternal infections that occur before 11 weeks gestation or during the last month of pregnancy have the greatest risk of congenital infection (Martin et al., 2015). The rubella virus is teratogenic, resulting in a spectrum of findings known as *congenital rubella syndrome (CRS)* when fetal infection occurs during the first trimester. The exact mechanism by which rubella infection leads to teratogenesis is not completely understood, but it is believed to be the result of necrosis or apoptosis, and inhibition of cell division of precursor cells involved in organogenesis (Lee & Bowden, 2000).

Clinical manifestations. Most patients with congenital rubella infection are asymptomatic at birth; however, clinical manifestations may develop over time (Forrest et al., 2002). When present, clinical manifestations of congenital rubella infection in the neonate may include hearing loss, cataracts, cardiac defects, jaundice, hepatosplenomegaly, thrombocytopenia, and "blueberry muffin" lesions. Congenital heart disease, deafness, and cataracts are the classic findings associated with CRS (Lambert, 2007).

Implication across the life span. The long-term sequelae associated with congenital rubella syndrome include hearing impairment, ophthalmologic problems, cardiac disease, and endocrine disease. Hearing impairment is the single most common defect seen in patients with CRS, which, if left undetected, can go on to affect speech and language development as well as school performance (Reef et al., 2000). Ophthalmologic problems associated with CRS include cataracts, chorioretinopathy, and glaucoma. Adults with a history of congenital rubella have been reported to have a high prevalence of visual problems, including blindness (Forrest et al., 2002; McIntosh & Menser, 1992). Approximately 50% of patients with CRS have congenital heart defects; most common are patent ductus arteriosus and pulmonary stenosis, and adults with a history of CRS are at increased risk for hypertension later in life (Forrest et al., 2002; Menser, Dods, & Harley, 1967; Reef et al., 2000). Children and adults with a history of CRS are also at higher risk for developing chronic conditions such as diabetes and thyroid disorders (McIntosh & Menser, 1992; Menser, Forrest, & Bransby, 1978).

Respiratory Syncytial Virus. Respiratory syncytial virus (RSV), a single-stranded RNA virus of the *Paramyxoviridae* family, is the most common respiratory pathogen in infants and young children, and the most frequent cause of bronchiolitis and pneumonia (Martin et al., 2015). Nearly all children have been infected with RSV by 2 years of age, with the peak incidence occurring between 2 to 3 months of age as passively acquired maternal IgG wanes (Piedimonte & Perez, 2014). Infants most vulnerable to severe RSV infection include premature infants, infants with chronic lung disease, and infants with hemodynamically significant congenital heart disease. Transmission of RSV occurs through direct inoculation of the nasopharyngeal or conjunctival mucosa with infected secretions or through contact with aerosolized droplets. Once introduced to the nasopharyngeal epithelium, RSV spreads to the lower airways where it replicates, leading to sloughing of epithelial cells and influx of inflammatory mediators that cause submucosal edema and swelling (Piedimonte & Perez, 2014).

Clinical manifestations. Infants with RSV commonly present with poor feeding, irritability, rhinorrhea, cough, sneezing, fever, wheezing, and respiratory distress. Apnea, which is associated with up to 20% of hospitalizations in RSV-positive infants, is most commonly observed in preterm infants (Eiland, 2009). Most of the symptoms generally peak around day 5 of the illness, and improve by a week to 10 days. The cough, however, may take up to 4 weeks to resolve (Eiland, 2009).

Implications across the life span. The overall mortality rate associated with RSV infection is low, but mortality increases in infants who are premature or have complex congenital heart disease or neuromuscular disorders (Byington, Wilkes, Korgenski, & Sheng, 2015). The main long-term complication of RSV infection is episodic and recurrent wheezing that may persist into early childhood (Carbonell-Estrany et al., 2015; Kneyber, Steyerberg, de Groot, & Moll, 2000). Some evidence also suggests the children and adolescents with a history of RSV that required hospitalization are at increased risk for childhood asthma (Szabo et al., 2013).

Human Immunodeficiency Virus. HIV is an RNA-containing retrovirus that causes AIDS. As of 2015, 36.7 million individuals across the globe were living with HIV (World Health Organization, n.d.). In the United States, approximately 1.2 million people are living with HIV/AIDS, 280,000 of whom are women (Fauci & Folkers, 2012). Women of color, including African American and Latina women, are disproportionately affected and the majority of newly diagnosed cases are contracted through heterosexual contact (Wilson et al., 2016). According to the 2011 CDC estimates, over 75% of women diagnosed with AIDS are in their reproductive years at the time of diagnosis (CDC, 2013). It is estimated that in the United States, nearly 11,000 children are infected with HIV, 88% of whom contracted the disease through mother-to-child transmission (MTCT; Wilson et al., 2016).

MTCT of the HIV virus can occur in utero, during the intrapartum period, or postnatally. In utero transmission can occur through infection of the placenta or through fetal exposure to the virus in the amniotic fluid (Wilson et al., 2016). Approximately 20% to 25% of MTCT occurs in utero, and the fetus is most vulnerable during the final few weeks to days of pregnancy, when the vascular integrity of the placenta is disturbed (Wilson et al., 2016; Kourtis, Lee, Abrams, Jamieson, & Bulterys, 2006). Intrapartum transmission occurs at or near the time of delivery, when the infant's mucous membranes come in direct contact with the cervical and vaginal secretion of the mother (Martin et al., 2015). Postnatal transmission typically occurs through breast milk. Infants are at greatest risk for contracting the virus through breast milk during the first 4 to 6 weeks of life (Wilson et al., 2016). In high-income countries, maternal use of antiretroviral therapy during pregnancy and avoidance of breastfeeding have been shown to decrease the risk of MTCT to as low as 1%, whereas without treatment the risk of transmission is as high as 45% (John & Kreiss, 1996; Nesheim et al., 2012).

The HIV virus works by using the enzyme *reverse transcriptase* to produce viral DNA that is then integrated into the DNA of host cells containing the surface molecule CD4+ (mostly T helper cells and macrophages; Figure 9.14; Weber, 2001). The early, latent phase of HIV infection is characterized by a relative absence of clinical symptoms as CD4+ T cells targeted by the infection are replenished in near equal numbers. Although the latent phase of the disease is clinically quiet, the virus is highly dynamic during this time, actively replicating in the lymph nodes and circulating CD4+ cells. As the concentration of virus in the plasma increases, the pool of CD4+ cells is depleted to a critical threshold at which point cell-mediated immunity becomes impaired (Martin et al., 2015; Weber, 2001). The host subsequently becomes vulnerable to pathogens that normally have a low capacity for causing disease.

Left untreated, infants with HIV experience a more rapid progression of disease than adults. HIV infection in the fetus—when T cells and NK are functionally immature—likely facilitates rapid disease progression. Fetal and neonatal immune cells may also provide a better substrate for HIV infection and replication than mature cells. As a result, HIV-infected infants often demonstrate high plasma viral loads, which is a strong predictor of disease manifestation (Martin et al., 2015).

Clinical manifestations. Newborns with congenital HIV infection are rarely symptomatic at birth, but may present with symptoms within the first 1 to 2 months of life as their CD4+ cells are increasingly depleted. One of the earliest indications of HIV infection in the infant is *Pneumocystis carinii* (also known as pneumocystis jiroveci) pneumonia. Other signs and symptoms of HIV infection include lymphadenopathy, recurrent bacterial infections, failure to thrive, and mucocutaneous candidiasis refractory to treatment (Burchett & Pizzo, 2003).

Implications across the life span. With the advancements in the efficacy of antiretroviral therapy over the past two decades, HIV has progressed to a chronic manageable disease, rather than an acute life-threatening one. As the first generation of patients with perinatal HIV infection are beginning to enter adolescence and adulthood, we are learning more about the long-term effects of HIV infection and life-long exposure to antiretroviral therapy. Overall, survival rates of patients with perinatal HIV infection are good if highly active antiretroviral therapy (HAART) is initiated early. However, even with HAART, a subset of patients with perinatal HIV infection progress to AIDS and/or die by adolescence (Dollfus et al., 2010). Those who survive are at an increased risk for dyslipidemia, premature atherosclerotic cardiovascular disease, and renal injury secondary to exposure to drug therapy (Patel et al., 2014; Purswani et al., 2013). An increased risk of hearing loss has also been associated with perinatal HIV infection, especially in advanced disease (Torre et al., 2012). As the first cohort of patients with a history of perinatal HIV infection and access to HAART age further into adulthood, we will continue to learn more about the implications of HIV across the life span.

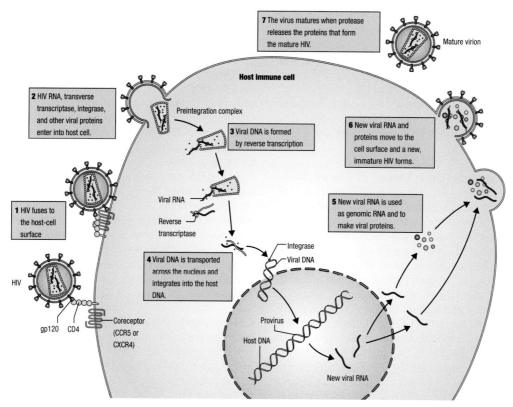

Figure 9.14 The life cycle of HIV. HIV binds to the CD4 receptor of the T cell and fuses to the cell membrane. Inside the cell, HIV uses reverse transcriptase to convert HIV RNA into HIV DNA. HIV DNA is transported into the nucleus of the CD4 cell where it uses the enzyme integrase to integrate the viral DNA into the host DNA. Once integrated into the CD4 DNA, HIV uses the machinery of the CD4 to produce viral proteins. New HIV proteins and viral proteins move to the cell surface and assemble into immature (noninfectious) HIV. The newly formed immature HIV pushes itself out of the CD4 cell and releases the enzyme protease, which breaks up the long protein chains that form the immature (noninfectious) HIV virion. The smaller HIV proteins combine to form the mature (infectious) HIV virion.

RNA, ribonucleic acid.

Common Sites of Infection in the Newborn

Pathogens that cause infection in the newborn may be isolated from the blood (bloodstream infection) or they may be localized in specific tissues or organ systems. Table 9.9 lists the common sites of infection in the newborn and the organisms typically responsible.

CONCLUSION

The immune system has two major arms: the innate immune system and the adaptive immune system. When confronted with a potentially infectious organism, the innate immune system—which is mediated by various phagocytic cells, cytokines, and the complement system—works quickly to neutralize and remove the threat.

The adaptive immune system, on the other hand, can take days to weeks to mount an immune response, but has the added benefit of immunologic memory. Together, the innate and adaptive arms of the immune system protect the host from a range of infectious organisms, including bacteria, viruses, fungi, protozoa, and parasites.

In the fetus, immune system development begins as early as 3 weeks gestation; however, it is not fully mature until early childhood. The neonate, therefore, is relatively immunocompromised and vulnerable to infection. Consequently, bacterial, fungal, viral, and protozoal infections are a major cause of neonatal mortality and morbidity that have significant implications across the life span. It is important that clinicians who care for neonatal patients are familiar with those organisms commonly implicated in infectious diseases of the newborn, and recognize the signs and symptoms associated with infection.

TABLE 9.9 Common Sites of Infection in the Newborn

Site of Infection	Common Pathogens	Potential Sources	Common Clinical Manifestations	Complications
Bloodstream Infection	*Early-Onset: GBS, E. coli, L. monocytogenes, H. influenzae, S. aureus Enterococci *Late-Onset: CoNS, S. aureus, E. coli, Enterobacter, Serratia, Klebsiella, Enterococci, GBS, Candida spp.	*Early-Onset: Vertical transmission from exposure to maternal genital tract *Late-Onset: Horizontal transmission through exposure to contaminated objects or hands of healthcare workers/ family members	*Respiratory distress *Apnea *Hypotension *Temperature instability *Lethargy	*Meningitis *Pneumonia *Osteomyelitis *Death
Meningitis	*GBS, E. coli, L. monocytogenes, Klebsiella, HSV, Candida spp.	*Hematogenous spread from bloodstream infection *Open neural tube defect *Contamination during lumbar puncture	*Respiratory distress *Apnea *Temperature instability *Lethargy *Seizures	*Hearing impairment *Persistent seizures *Neurological impairment *Death
Pneumonia	*GBS, E. coli, Klebsiella, Serratia, Pseudomonas, S. aureus, C. trachomatis *RSV, HSV, CMV, adenovirus, rhinovirus, enterovirus *Candida spp.	*Aspiration of infected amniotic fluid *Aspiration of vaginal organisms *Prolonged endotracheal intubation *Inhalation of aerosolized infectious particles *Hematogenous spread from bloodstream infection	*Respiratory distress *Apnea	*Respiratory failure *Death
Urinary Tract	*E. coli, Klebsiella, Enterobacter, Enterococcus, S. aureus *Candida spp.	*Ascension of skin or intestinal flora into the urinary tract *Indwelling urinary catheter *Hematogenous spread of bloodstream infection	*Temperature instability *Poor feeding/weight gain *Hyperbilirubinemia	*Pyelonephritis *Renal scarring
Cellulitis	*S. aureus, E. coli, CoNS, Group A Streptococcus	*Invasion of skin flora to the soft tissues through a break in the skin	*Erythema *Tenderness	*Sepsis *Tissue necrosis

(continued)

TABLE 9.9 Common Sites of Infection in the Newborn (*continued*)

Site of Infection	Common Pathogens	Potential Sources	Common Clinical Manifestations	Complications
Omphalitis	*S. aureus, E. coli, Klebsiella*, Group A *Streptococcus*	*Invasion of umbilical stump by skin or vaginal flora	*Periumbilical erythema and tenderness *Purulent drainage	*Necrotizing fasciitis *Myonecrosis *Sepsis
Osteomyelitis	*S. aureus, E. coli, Klebsiella*, GBS	*Hematogenous spread from bloodstream infection *Invasive procedures *Vascular access devices *Surgical wounds	*Localized edema and tenderness *Irritability with handling	*Bony deformities *Growth plate damage
Endocarditis	*S. aureus, CoNS, Streptococcus viridans*, GBS	*Bacteremia *Central venous catheters	*New murmur *Congestive heart failure	*Persistent bacteremia *Structural heart damage *Septic emboli *Death
Conjunctivitis (Ophthalmia neonatorum)	* C. trachomatis, N. gonorrhea, S. aureus, E. coli, Klebsiella* *HSV,	*Exposure to infectious organisms in the maternal genital tract	*Purulent eye drainage *Eyelid edema *Erythema of the palpebral conjunctiva	*Visual impairment *Blindness

CMV, cytomegalovirus; CoNS, coagulase-negative staphylococci; GBS, group B *Streptococcus*; HSV, herpes simplex virus; RSV, respiratory syncytial virus.

LEARNING TOOLS AND RESOURCES

Podcast

 Antibiotic Use in the NICU and the Role of the Neonatal Early-Onset Sepsis Calculator in Decreasing Antibiotic Consumption

Rani Delaney, Lauren Fraser, Maryellen Lane, and Melissa Bauserman

Discussion Prompts

1. Discuss the differences between the function and response of the innate immune system and the adaptive immune system.
2. Discuss the host factors specific to the neonatal population that make them more vulnerable to infection.
3. List some of the risk factors for early-onset and late-onset sepsis and the organisms commonly responsible.

Advice From the Authors

"Invest the time early in your academic career to establish a firm understanding of the normal physiology of each of the body's systems. It will be the foundation upon which everything else you learn will be based. Once you feel like you've mastered a concept, try explaining it aloud to someone else. It can help to reinforce what you've learned or identify areas where you need to revisit your textbook and brush up."

–Rani M. Delaney, DNP, APRN, NNP-BC

"Studying for an advanced degree entails learning a large amount of material in a short period of time, which can feel overwhelming. I would recommend making a study plan to ensure that you cover the required amount of material in the time that you have. Then, you can focus only on the small piece of information you need to cover each day. I also find that I retain information more efficiently when I make chapter outlines, flashcards, or drawings. Eventually, you will start seeing patients with the conditions you are studying and what you have learned will be solidified. Just remember to go back to the literature and refresh your memory on the physiology."

–Lauren C. Frazer, MD, PhD

"There is nothing more insightful than a thorough exam."

–Maryellen Lane, BSN, APRN, NNP-BC

"It is important to understand the natural course of common neonatal diseases. By understanding the natural disease progression, you will be able to recognize when a patient's signs and symptoms deviate from the expected course and you will be prepared to expand your differential diagnosis accordingly."

–Melissa S. Bauserman, MD, MPH

Mind Map

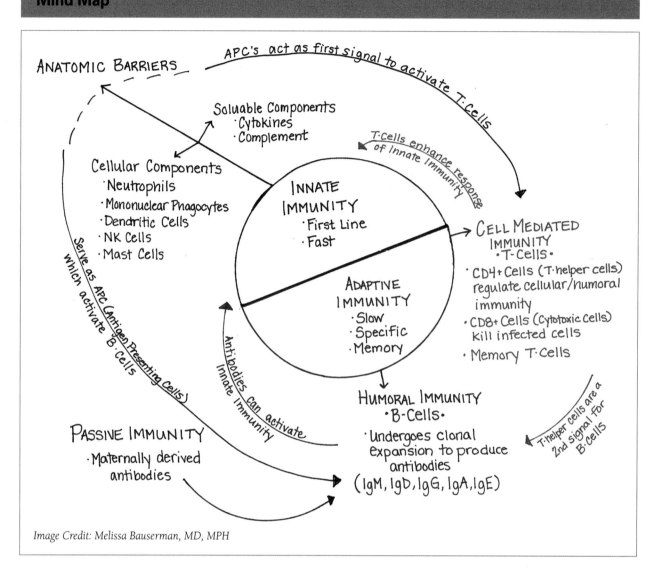

Image Credit: Melissa Bauserman, MD, MPH

Note: This mind map reflects one physician's interpretation of a portion of one or more concepts addressed in this chapter. Readers should regard the mind maps woven throughout this textbook as examples of multi-sensory study tools that can be developed to encourage conceptual understanding. Readers are encouraged to develop their own unique mind maps in consultation with academic faculty or clinical preceptors.

TIMELINE OF ORGAN DEVELOPMENT

NOTE:	LEGEND
Placement of common problems is meant to offer visual/conceptual perspective on the timing of onset of these commonly reported malformations. Variation exists across the literature.	<22 – 27 6/7 weeks = extremely preterm 28 – 31 6/7 weeks = very preterm 32 – 36 6/7 weeks = late/moderate preterm 37 – 40 weeks = term

References

Abbas, A. K., Lichtman, A. H., & Pillai, S. (2010). *Cellular and molecular immunology* (updated 6th ed.). Philadelphia, PA: Saunders Elsevier.

Abbas, A. K., Lichtman, A. H., & Pillai, S. (2016). *Basic immunology: Functions and disorders of the immune system* (5th ed.). St. Louis, MO: Elsevier.

Akinbi, H. T., Narendran, V., Pass, A. K., Markart, P., & Hoath, S. B. (2004). Host defense proteins in vernix caseosa and amniotic fluid. *American Journal of Obstetrics and Gynecology*, 191(6), 2090–2096. doi:10.1016/j.ajog.2004.05.002

Albert, M. H., Notarangelo, L. D., & Ochs, H. D. (2011). Clinical spectrum, pathophysiology and treatment of the Wiskott-Aldrich syndrome. *Current Opinion in Hematology*, 18(1), 42–48. doi:10.1097/MOH.0b013e32834114bc

American College of Obstetricians and Gynecologists. (2011). Committee Opinion, No 485. Prevention of early-onset group B streptococcal disease in newborns. *Obstetrics & Gynecology*, 117(4), 1019–1027. doi:10.1097/AOG.0b013e318219229b

Bakhuizen, S. E., de Haan, T. R., Teune, M. J., van Wassenaer-Leemhuis, A. G., van der Heyden, J. L., van der Ham, D. P., & Mol, B. W. (2014). Meta-analysis shows that infants who have suffered neonatal sepsis face an increased risk of mortality and severe complications. *Acta Paediatrica*, 103(12), 1211–1218. doi:10.1111/apa.12764

Barton, M., O'Brien, K., Robinson, J. L., Davies, D. H., Simpson, K., Asztalos, E., ... Richardson, S. E. (2014). Invasive candidiasis in low birth weight preterm infants: Risk factors, clinical course and outcome in a prospective multicenter study of cases and their matched controls. *BMC Infectious Diseases*, 14, 327. doi:10.1186/1471-2334-14-327

Basha, S., Surendran, N., & Pichichero, M. (2014). Immune responses in neonates. *Expert Review of Clinical Immunology*, 10(9), 1171–1184. doi:10.1586/1744666X.2014.942288

Becker, K., Heilmann, C., & Peters, G. (2014). Coagulase-negative staphylococci. *Clinical Microbiology Reviews*, 27(4), 870–926. doi:10.1128/CMR.00109-13

Benjamin, D. K., Stoll, B. J., Fanaroff, A. A., McDonald, S. A., Oh, W., Higgins, R. D., ... Goldberg, R. (2006). Neonatal candidiasis among extremely low birth weight infants: Risk factors, mortality rates, and neurodevelopmental outcomes at 18 to 22 months. *Pediatrics*, 117(1), 84–92. doi:10.1542/peds.2004-2292

Benjamin, D. K., Stoll, B. J., Gantz, M. G., Walsh, M. C., Sánchez, P. J., Das, A., ... Goldberg, R. N. (2010). Neonatal candidiasis: Epidemiology, risk factors, and clinical judgment. *Pediatrics*, 126(4), e865–e873. doi:10.1542/peds.2009-3412

Berardi, A., Rossi, C., Lugli, L., Creti, R., Bacchi Reggiani, M. L., Lanari, M., ... Ferrari, F. (2013). Group B *Streptococcus* late-onset disease: 2003-2010. *Pediatrics*, 131(2), e361–e368. doi:10.1542/peds.2012-1231

Berrebi, A., Assouline, C., Bessieres, M. H., Lathiere, M., Cassaing, S., Minville, V., & Ayoubi, J. M. (2010). Long-term outcome of children with congenital toxoplasmosis. *American Journal of Obstetrics and Gynecology*, 203(6), 552 e551–556. doi:10.1016/j.ajog.2010.06.002

Boppana, S. B., Ross, S. A., & Fowler, K. B. (2013). Congenital cytomegalovirus infection: Clinical outcome. *Clinical Infectious Diseases*, 57 (Suppl. 4), S178–S181. doi:10.1093/cid/cit629

Bowen, V., Su, J., Torrone, E., Kidd, S., & Weinstock, H. (2015). Increase in incidence of congenital syphilis—United States, 2012–2014. *Morbidity and Mortality Weekly Report*, 64(44), 1241–1245. doi:10.15585/mmwr.mm6444a3

Boyle, J. M., & Buckley, R. H. (2007). Population prevalence of diagnosed primary immunodeficiency diseases in the United States. *Journal of Clinical Immunology*, 27(5), 497–502. doi:10.1007/s10875-007-9103-1

Buckland, M. (2016). *Clinical immunology*. Oxford, UK: Oxford University Press.

Buckley, R. H. (2002). Primary cellular immunodeficiencies. *Journal of Allergy and Clinical Immunology*, 109(5), 747–757. doi:10.1067/mai.2002.123617

Buckley, R. H. (2011). Transplantation of hematopoietic stem cells in human severe combined immunodeficiency: Longterm outcomes. *Immunologic Research*, 49(1-3), 25–43. doi:10.1007/s12026-010-8191-9

Burchett, S. K., & Pizzo, P. A. (2003). HIV infection in infants, children, and adolescents. *Pediatrics in Review*, 24(6), 186–194. doi:10.1542/pir.24-6-186

Byington, C. L., Wilkes, J., Korgenski, K., & Sheng, X. (2015). Respiratory syncytial virus-associated mortality in hospitalized infants and young children. *Pediatrics*, 135(1), e24–e31. doi:10.1542/peds.2014-2151

Camacho-Gonzalez, A., Spearman, P. W., & Stoll, B. J. (2013). Neonatal infectious diseases: Evaluation of neonatal sepsis. *Pediatric Clinics of North America*, 60(2), 367–389. doi:10.1016/j.pcl.2012.12.003

Carbonell-Estrany, X., Perez-Yarza, E. G., Garcia, L. S., Guzman Cabanas, J. M., Boria, E. V., Atienza, B. B., & Group, I. S. (2015). Long-term burden and respiratory effects of respiratory syncytial virus hospitalization in preterm infants—The SPRING study. *PloS One*, 10(5), e0125422. doi:10.1371/journal.pone.0125422

Carlson, B. M. (2014). *Human embryology and developmental biology* (5th ed.). Philadelphia, PA: Elsevier/Saunders.

Centers for Disease Control and Prevention. (1996). Prevention of perinatal GBS disease: A public health perspective. *Morbidity and Mortality Weekly Report*, 45(RR-7), 1–24. Retrieved from https://www.cdc.gov/mmwr/preview/mmwrhtml/00043277.htm

Centers for Disease Control and Prevention. (2013). HIV surveillance report, 2011. Retrieved from https://www.cdc.gov/hiv/pdf/statistics_2011_hiv_surveillance_report_vol_23.pdf

Chakraborty, R., & Luck, S. (2008). Syphilis is on the increase: The implications for child health. *Archives of Disease in Childhood*, 93(2), 105–109. doi:10.1136/adc.2006.103515

Chow, B. D., Linden, J. R., & Bliss, J. M. (2012). Candida parapsilosis and the neonate: Epidemiology, virulence and host defense in a unique patient setting. *Expert Review of Anti-Infective Therapy*, 10(8), 935–946. doi:10.1586/eri.12.74

Cooper, M. A., Pommering, T. L., & Koranyi, K. (2003). Primary immunodeficiencies. *American Family Physician*, 68(10), 2001–2008. Retrieved from https://www.aafp.org/afp/2003/1115/p2001.html

Cotten, C. M. (2015). Antibiotic stewardship: Reassessment of guidelines for management of neonatal sepsis. *Clinics in Perinatology*, 42(1), 195–206. doi:10.1016/j.clp.2014.10.007

Cotten, C. M., Taylor, S., Stoll, B., Goldberg, R. N., Hansen, N. I., Sanchez, P. J., ... Benjamin, D. K., Jr. (2009). Prolonged duration of initial empirical antibiotic treatment is associated with increased rates of necrotizing enterocolitis and death for extremely low birth weight infants. *Pediatrics*, 123(1), 58–66. doi:10.1542/peds.2007-3423

Dardas, M., Gill, S. R., Grier, A., Pryhuber, G. S., Gill, A. L., Lee, Y. H., & Guillet, R. (2014). The impact of postnatal antibiotics on the preterm intestinal microbiome. *Pediatric Research, 76*(2), 150–158. doi:10.1038/pr.2014.69

Derry, J. M., Ochs, H. D., & Francke, U. (1994). Isolation of a novel gene mutated in Wiskott–Aldrich syndrome. *Cell, 78*(4), 635–644. doi:10.1016/0092-8674(94)90528-2

de Saint Basile, G., Fraser, N. J., Craig, I. W., Arveiler, B., Boyd, Y., Griscelli, G., & Fischer, A. (1989). Close linkage of hypervariable marker DXS255 to disease locus of Wiskott–Aldrich syndrome. *Lancet, 334*(8675), 1319–1321. doi:10.1016/S0140-6736(89)91920-X

Dhama, K., Saminathan, M., Jacob, S. S., Singh, M., Karthik, K., Amarpal, R. T., … Singh, R. S. (2015). Effect of immunomodulation and immunomodulatory agents on health with some bioactive principles, modes of action and potent biomedical applications. *International Journal of Pharmacology, 11*, 253–290. doi:10.3923/ijp.2015.253.290

Dolapo, O., Dhanireddy, R., & Talati, A. J. (2014). Trends of *Staphylococcus aureus* bloodstream infections in a neonatal intensive care unit from 2000–2009. *BMC Pediatrics, 14*, 121. doi:10.1186/1471-2431-14-121

Dollfus, C., Le Chenadec, J., Faye, A., Blanche, S., Briand, N., Rouzioux, C., & Warszawski, J. (2010). Long-term outcomes in adolescents perinatally infected with HIV-1 and followed up since birth in the French perinatal cohort (EPF/ANRS CO10). *Clinical Infectious Diseases, 51*(2), 214–224. doi:10.1086/653674

Dominguez-Bello, M. G., Costello, E. K., Contreras, M., Magris, M., Hidalgo, G., Fierer, N., & Knight, R. (2010). Delivery mode shapes the acquisition and structure of the initial microbiota across multiple body habitats in newborns. *Proceedings of the National Academy of Sciences, 107*(26), 11971–11975. doi:10.1073/pnas.1002601107

Dong, Y., & Speer, C. P. (2014). Late-onset neonatal sepsis: Recent developments. *Archives of Disease in Childhood—Fetal and Neonatal Edition, 100*, F257–F263. doi:10.1136/archdischild-2014-306213

Downey, L. C., Benjamin, D. K., Jr., Clark, R. H., Watt, K. M., Hornik, C. P., Laughon, M. M., … Smith, P. B. (2013). Urinary tract infection concordance with positive blood and cerebrospinal fluid cultures in the neonatal intensive care unit. *Journal of Perinatology, 33*(4), 302–306. doi:10.1038/jp.2012.111

Downey, L. C., Smith, P. B., & Benjamin, D. K., Jr. (2010). Risk factors and prevention of late-onset sepsis in premature infants. *Early Human Development, 86* (Suppl. 1), 7–12. doi:10.1016/j.earlhumdev.2010.01.012

Dreher, A. M., Arora, N., Fowler, K. B., Novak, Z., Britt, W. J., Boppana, S. B., & Ross, S. A. (2014). Spectrum of disease and outcome in children with symptomatic congenital cytomegalovirus infection. *Journal of Pediatrics, 164*(4), 855–859. doi:10.1016/j.jpeds.2013.12.007

Dupré, L., Aiuti, A., Trifari, S., Martino, S., Saracco, P., Bordignon, C., & Roncarolo, M. G. (2002). Wiskott–Aldrich syndrome protein regulates lipid raft dynamics during immunological synapse formation. *Immunity, 17*(2), 157–166. doi:10.1016/S1074-7613(02)00360-6

Dyke, M. P., & Ott, K. (1993). Severe thrombocytopenia in extremely low birthweight infants with systemic candidiasis. *Journal of Paediatrics and Child Health, 29*(4), 298–301. doi:10.1111/j.1440-1754.1993.tb00516.x

Egawa, H., Inomata, Y., Nakayama, S., Matsui, A., Yamabe, H., Uemoto, S., … Tanaka, K. (1998). Fulminant hepatic failure secondary to herpes simplex virus infection in a neonate: A case report of successful treatment with liver transplantation and perioperative acyclovir. *Liver Transplantation and Surgery, 4*(6), 513–515. doi:10.1002/lt.500040601

Eiland, L. S. (2009). Respiratory syncytial virus: Diagnosis, treatment and prevention. *Journal of Pediatric Pharmacology and Therapeutics, 14*(2), 75–85. doi:10.5863/1551-6776-14.2.75

Erdos, M., Toth, B., & Marodi, L. (2017). T cell development. In R. A. Polin, S. H. Abman, D. H. Rowitch, W. E. Benitz, & W. W. Fox (Eds.), *Fetal and neonatal physiology* (5th ed., pp. 1198–1201). Philadelphia, PA: Elsevier/Saunders.

Escobar, G. J., Puopolo, K. M., Wi, S., Turk, B. J., Kuzniewicz, M. W., Walsh, E. M., … Draper, D. (2014). Stratification of risk of early-onset sepsis in newborns ≥ 34 weeks' gestation. *Pediatrics, 133*(1), 30–36. doi:10.1542/peds.2013-1689

Fattah, M. A., Omer, A. F. A., Asaif, S., Manlulu, R., Karar, T., Ahmed, A., … Nasr, A. (2017). Utility of cytokine, adhesion molecule and acute phase proteins in early diagnosis of neonatal sepsis. *Journal of Natural Science, Biology, and Medicine, 8*(1), 32–39. doi:10.4103/0976-9668.198362

Fauci, A. S., & Folkers, G. K. (2012). Toward an AIDS-free generation. *Journal of the American Medical Association, 308*(4), 343–344. doi:10.1001/jama.2012.8142

Fernandez, K. S., & de Alarcon, P. A. (2013). Development of the hematopoietic system and disorders of hematopoiesis that present during infancy and early childhood. *Pediatric Clinics of North America, 60*(6), 1273–1289. doi:10.1016/j.pcl.2013.08.002

Fey, P. D., & Olson, M. E. (2010). Current concepts in biofilm formation of *Staphylococcus epidermidis*. *Future Microbiology, 5*(6), 917–933. doi:10.2217/fmb.10.56

Flannagan, R. S., Jaumouille, V., & Grinstein, S. (2012). The cell biology of phagocytosis. *Annual Review of Pathology, 7*, 61–98. doi:10.1146/annurev-pathol-011811-132445

Fluhr, J. W., Darlenski, R., Taieb, A., Hachem, J. P., Baudouin, C., Msika, P., … Berardesca, E. (2010). Functional skin adaptation in infancy—Almost complete but not fully competent. *Experimental Dermatology, 19*(6), 483–492. doi:10.1111/j.1600-0625.2009.01023.x

Forrest, J. M., Turnbull, F. M., Sholler, G. F., Hawker, R. E., Martin, F. J., Doran, T. T., & Burgess, M. A. (2002). Gregg's congenital rubella patients 60 years later. *Medical Journal of Australia, 177*(11–12), 664–667. Retrieved from https://www.mja.com.au/journal/2002/177/11/greggs-congenital-rubella-patients-60-years-later

Fridkin, S. K., Kaufman, D., Edwards, J. R., Shetty, S., & Horan, T. (2006). Changing incidence of Candida bloodstream infections among NICU patients in the United States: 1995–2004. *Pediatrics, 117*(5), 1680–1687. doi:10.1542/peds.2005-1996

Gauld, S. B., Dal Porto, J. M., & Cambier, J. C. (2002). B cell antigen receptor signaling: Roles in cell development and disease. *Science, 296*(5573), 1641–1642. doi:10.1126/science.1071546

Gennery, A. R. (2012). Immunological aspects of 22q11.2 deletion syndrome. *Cellular and Molecular Life Sciences, 69*(1), 17–27. doi:10.1007/s00018-011-0842-z

Giuffre, M., Geraci, D. M., Bonura, C., Saporito, L., Graziano, G., Insinga, V., … Mammina, C. (2016). The increasing challenge of multidrug-resistant Gram-negative bacilli: Results of a 5-year active surveillance program in a neonatal intensive care unit. *Medicine, 95*(10), e3016. doi:10.1097/md.0000000000003016

Gleason, C. A., & Juul, S. E. (Eds.). (2018). *Avery's diseases of the newborn* (10th ed.). Philadelphia, PA: Elsevier.

Gold, M. C., Robinson, T. L., Cook, M. S., Byrd, L. K., Ehlinger, H. D., Lewinsohn, D. M., & Lewinsohn, D. A. (2007). Human neonatal dendritic cells are competent in MHC Class I antigen processing and presentation. *PloS One*, *2*(9), e957. doi:10.1371/journal.pone.0000957

Gordon, R. J., & Lowy, F. D. (2008). Pathogenesis of methicillin-resistant *Staphylococcus aureus* infection. *Clinical Infectious Diseases: An Official Publication of the Infectious Diseases Society of America*, *46*(Suppl. 5), S350–S359. doi:10.1086/533591

Grati, F. R., Molina Gomes, D., Ferreira, J. C., Dupont, C., Alesi, V., Gouas, L., … Vialard, F. (2015). Prevalence of recurrent pathogenic microdeletions and microduplications in over 9500 pregnancies. *Prenatal Diagnosis*, *35*(8), 801–809. doi:10.1002/pd.4613

Greenberg, R. G., Kandefer, S., Do, B. T., Smith, P. B., Stoll, B. J., Bell, E. F., … Cotten, C. M. (2017). Late-onset sepsis in extremely premature infants: 2000–2011. *Pediatric Infectious Diease Journal*, *36*(8), 774–779. doi:10.1097/INF.0000000000001570

Gritz, E. C., & Bhandari, V. (2015). The human neonatal gut microbiome: A brief review. *Frontiers in Pediatrics*, *3*, 17. doi:10.3389/fped.2015.00017

Haddad, R., Guimiot, F., Six, E., Jourquin, F., Setterblad, N., Kahn, E., … Canque, B. (2006). Dynamics of thymus-colonizing cells during human development. *Immunity*, *24*(2), 217–230. doi:10.1016/j.immuni.2006.01.008

Haks, M. C., Oosterwegel, M. A., Blom, B., Spits, H. M., & Kruisbeek, A. M. (1999). Cell-fate decisions in early T cell development: Regulation by cytokine receptors and the pre-TCR. *Seminars in Immunology*, *11*(1), 23–37. doi:10.1006/smim.1998.0153

Heath, W. R., & Carbone, F. R. (2009). Dendritic cell subsets in primary and secondary T cell responses at body surfaces. *Nature Immunology*, *10*(12), 1237–1244. doi:10.1038/ni.1822

Helbert, M. (2017). *Immunology for medical students* (3rd ed.). Philadelphia, PA: Elsevier.

Hong, D. K., & Lewis, D. B. (2016). Developmental immunology and role of host defences in fetal and neonatal susceptibility to infection. In C. B. Wilson, V. Nizet, Y. A. Maldonado, J. S. Remington, & J. O. Klein (Eds.), *Remington and Klein's infectious diseases of the fetus and newborn infant* (8th ed., pp. 81–188). Philadelphia, PA: Saunders/Elsevier.

Immune Deficiency Foundation. (2017). IDF SCID newborn screening campaign. Retrieved from http://primaryimmune.org/idf-advocacy-center/idf-scid-newborn-screening-campaign

Janier, M., Hegyi, V., Dupin, N., Unemo, M., Tiplica, G. S., Potocnik, M., … Patel, R. (2014). 2014 European guideline on the management of syphilis. *Journal of the European Academy of Dermatology and Venereology*, *28*(12), 1581–1593. doi:10.1111/jdv.12734

Johansson, M. E., Larsson, J. M., & Hansson, G. C. (2011). The two mucus layers of colon are organized by the MUC2 mucin, whereas the outer layer is a legislator of host-microbial interactions. *Proceedings of the National Academy of Sciences*, *108*(Suppl. 1), 4659–4665. doi:10.1073/pnas.1006451107

Johansson, M. E., Phillipson, M., Petersson, J., Velcich, A., Holm, L., & Hansson, G. C. (2008). The inner of the two Muc2 mucin-dependent mucus layers in colon is devoid of bacteria. *Proceedings of the National Academy of Sciences*, *105*(39), 15064–15069. doi:10.1073/pnas.0803124105

John, G. C., & Kreiss, J. (1996). Mother-to-child transmission of human immunodeficiency virus type 1. *Epidemiologic Reviews*, *18*(2), 149–157. doi:10.1093/oxfordjournals.epirev.a017922

Kalman, L., Lindegren, M. L., Kobrynski, L., Vogt, R., Hannon, H., Howard, J. T., & Buckley, R. (2004). Mutations in genes required for T-cell development: *IL7R, CD45, IL2RG, JAK3, RAG1, RAG2, ARTEMIS*, and *ADA* and severe combined immunodeficiency: HuGE review. *Genetics in Medicine*, *6*(1), 16–26. doi:10.1097/01.GIM.0000105752.80592.A3

Kemper, C., Pangburn, M. K., & Fishelson, Z. (2014). Complement nomenclature 2014. *Molecular Immunology*, *61*(2), 56–58. doi:10.1016/j.molimm.2014.07.004

Kerste, M., Corver, J., Sonnevelt, M. C., van Brakel, M., van der Linden, P. D., Braams-Lisman, B. A., & Plotz, F. B. (2016). Application of sepsis calculator in newborns with suspected infection. *Journal of Maternal–Fetal & Neonatal Medicine*, *29*(23), 3860–3865. doi:10.3109/14767058.2016.1149563

Kimberlin, D. W. (2004). Neonatal herpes simplex infection. *Clinical Microbiology Reviews*, *17*(1), 1–13. doi:10.1128/cmr.17.1.1-13.2004

Kimberlin, D. W. (2007). Herpes simplex virus infections of the newborn. *Seminars in Perinatology*, *31*(1), 19–25. doi:10.1053/j.semperi.2007.01.003

Kimberlin, D. W., & Baley, J. (2013). Guidance on management of asymptomatic neonates born to women with active genital herpes lesions. *Pediatrics*, *131*(2), e635–e646. doi:10.1542/peds.2012-3216

Kimberlin, D. W., Lin, C. Y., Jacobs, R. F., Powell, D. A., Corey, L., Gruber, W. C., … Whitley, R. J. (2001). Safety and efficacy of high-dose intravenous acyclovir in the management of neonatal herpes simplex virus infections. *Pediatrics*, *108*(2), 230–238. doi:10.1542/peds.108.2.230

Kneyber, M. C. J., Steyerberg, E. W., de Groot, R., & Moll, H. A. (2000). Long-term effects of respiratory syncytial virus (RSV) bronchiolitis in infants and young children: A quantitative review. *Acta Paediatrica*, *89*(6), 654–660. doi:10.1111/j.1651-2227.2000.tb00359.x

Koenig, J. M., & Keenan, W. J. (2009). Group B *Streptococcus* and early-onset sepsis in the era of maternal prophylaxis. *Pediatric Clinics of North America*, *56*(3), 689–708. doi:10.1016/j.pcl.2009.04.003

Kourtis, A. P., Lee, F. K., Abrams, E. J., Jamieson, D. J., & Bulterys, M. (2006). Mother-to-child transmission of HIV-1: Timing and implications for prevention. *Lancet Infectious Diseases*, *6*(11), 726–732. doi:10.1016/S1473-3099(06)70629-6

Kuppala, V. S., Meinzen-Derr, J., Morrow, A. L., & Schibler, K. R. (2011). Prolonged initial empirical antibiotic treatment is associated with adverse outcomes in premature infants. *Journal of Pediatrics*, *159*(5), 720–725. doi:10.1016/j.jpeds.2011.05.033

Kwan, A., Abraham, R. S., Currier, R., Brower, A., Andruszewski, K., Abbott, J. K., … Bonagura, V. R. (2014). Newborn screening for severe combined immunodeficiency in 11 screening programs in the United States. *Journal of the American Medical Association*, *312*(7), 729–738. doi:10.1001/jama.2014.9132

Kylat, R. I., Kelly, E. N., & Ford-Jones, E. L. (2006). Clinical findings and adverse outcome in neonates with symptomatic congenital cytomegalovirus (SCCMV) infection. *European Journal of Pediatrics*, *165*(11), 773-778. doi:10.1007/s00431-006-0172-6

Lambert, S. R. (2007). Congenital rubella syndrome: The end is in sight. *British Journal of Ophthalmology, 91*(11), 1418–1419. doi:10.1136/bjo.2007.117960

LeBien, T. W. (2017). B cell development. In R. A. Polin, S. H. Abman, D. H. Rowitch, W. E. Benitz, & W. W. Fox (Eds.), *Fetal and neonatal physiology* (5th ed., pp. 1202–1207). Philadelphia, PA: Elsevier/Saunders.

LeBien, T. W., & Tedder, T. F. (2008). B lymphocytes: How they develop and function. *Blood, 112*(5), 1570–1580. doi:10.1182/blood-2008-02-078071

Lecuit, M. (2005). Understanding how *Listeria monocytogenes* targets and crosses host barriers. *Clinical Microbiology and Infection, 11*(6), 430–436. doi:10.1111/j.1469-0691.2005.01146.x

Lee, J. Y., & Bowden, D. S. (2000). Rubella virus replication and links to teratogenicity. *Clinical Microbiology Reviews, 13*(4), 571–587. doi:10.1128/CMR.13.4.571

Lindsay, D. S., & Dubey, J. P. (2011). Toxoplasma gondii: The changing paradigm of congenital toxoplasmosis. *Parasitology, 138*(14), 1829–1831. doi:10.1017/s0031182011001478

Ling, J., & Koren, G. (2016). Challenges in vaccinating infants born to mothers taking immunoglobulin biologicals during pregnancy. *Expert Review of Vaccines, 15*(2), 239–256. doi:10.1586/14760584.2016.1115351

Macpherson, A. J., & Uhr, T. (2004). Induction of protective IgA by intestinal dendritic cells carrying commensal bacteria. *Science, 303*(5664), 1662–1665. doi:10.1126/science.1091334

Mahadevan, U., Martin, C. F., Sandler, R. S., Kane, S. V., Dubinsky, M., Lewis, J. D., ... Sands, B. E. (2012). 865 PIANO: A 1000 patient prospective registry of pregnancy outcomes in women with IBD exposed to immunomodulators and biologic therapy. *Gastroenterology, 142*(5 Suppl. 1), S-149. doi:10.1016/S0016-5085(12)60561-7

Maldonado, Y. A., & Read, J. S. (2017). Diagnosis, treatment, and prevention of congenital toxoplasmosis in the United States. *Pediatrics, 139*(2). doi:10.1542/peds.2016-3860

Manzoni, P., Mostert, M., & Castagnola, E. (2015). Update on the management of Candida infections in preterm neonates. *Archives of Disease in Childhood: Fetal and Neonatal Edition, 100*(5), F454–F459. doi:10.1136/archdischild-2012-303350

Martin, R. J., Fanaroff, A. A., & Walsh, M. C. (Eds.). (2015). *Fanaroff and Martin's neonatal-perinatal medicine: Diseases of the fetus and infant* (10th ed.). Philadelphia, PA: Elsevier/Saunders.

Mayer, F. L., Wilson, D., & Hube, B. (2013). Candida albicans pathogenicity mechanisms. *Virulence, 4*(2), 119–128. doi:10.4161/viru.22913

McAuley, J. B. (2014). Congenital toxoplasmosis. *Journal of the Pediatric Infectious Disease Society, 3* (Suppl. 1), S30–S35. doi:10.1093/jpids/piu077

McDonald-McGinn, D. M., Sullivan, K. E., Marino, B., Philip, N., Swillen, A., Vorstman, J. A., ... Bassett, A. S. (2015). 22q11.2 deletion syndrome. *Nature Review Disease Primers, 1*, 15071. doi:10.1038/nrdp.2015.71

McDonald-McGinn, D. M., Tonnesen, M. K., Laufer-Cahana, A., Finucane, B., Driscoll, D. A., Emanuel, B. S., & Zackai, E. H. (2001). Phenotype of the 22q11.2 deletion in individuals identified through an affected relative: Cast a wide FISHing net! *Genetics in Medicine, 3*(1), 23–29. doi:10.109700125817-200101000-00006

McIntosh, E. D., & Menser, M. A. (1992). A fifty-year follow-up of congenital rubella. *Lancet, 340*(8816), 414–415. doi:10.1016/0140-6736(92)91483-O

Medzhitov, R. (2013). Pattern recognition theory and the launch of modern innate immunity. *Journal of Immunology, 191*(9), 4473–4474. doi:10.4049/jimmunol.1302427

Melville, J. M., & Moss, T. J. (2013). The immune consequences of preterm birth. *Frontiers in Neuroscience, 7*, 79. doi:10.3389/fnins.2013.00079

Menser, M., Dods, L., & Harley, J. D. (1967). A twenty-five year follow-up of congenital rubella. *Lancet, 290*(7530), 1347–1350. doi:10.1016/S0140-6736(67)90932-4

Menser, M., Forrest, J. M., & Bransby, R. (1978). Rubella infection and diabetes mellitus. *Lancet, 311*(8055), 57–60. doi:10.1016/S0140-6736(78)90001-6

Mitha, A., Foix-L'Hélias, L., Arnaud, C., Marret, S., Vieux, R., Aujard, Y., ... Ancel, P.-Y. (2013). Neonatal infection and 5-year neurodevelopmental outcome of very preterm infants. *Pediatrics, 132*(2), e372–e380. doi:10.1542/peds.2012-3979

Moore, K. L., Persaud, T. V. N., & Torchia, M. G. (2016). *The developing human: Clinically oriented embryology* (10th ed.). Philadelphia, PA: Elsevier.

Morsheimer, M., Brown Whitehorn, T. F., Heimall, J., & Sullivan, K. E. (2017). The immune deficiency of chromosome 22q11.2 deletion syndrome. *American Journal of Medical Genetics Part A, 173*(9), 2366–2372. doi:10.1002/ajmg.a.38319

Mukhopadhyay, S., Eichenwald, E. C., & Puopolo, K. M. (2013). Neonatal early-onset sepsis evaluations among well-appearing infants: Projected impact of changes in CDC GBS guidelines. *Journal of Perinatology, 33*(3), 198–205. doi:10.1038/jp.2012.96

Mukhopadhyay, S., & Puopolo, K. M. (2015). Neonatal early-onset sepsis: Epidemiology and risk assessment. *NeoReviews, 16*(4), e221–e230. doi:10.1542/neo.16-4-e221

Mylonakis, E., Paliou, M., Hohmann, E. L., Calderwood, S. B., & Wing, E. J. (2002). Listeriosis during pregnancy: A case series and review of 222 cases. *Medicine (Baltimore), 81*(4), 260–269.

Nesheim, S., Taylor, A., Lampe, M. A., Kilmarx, P. H., Fitz Harris, L., Whitmore, S., ... Mermin, J. (2012). A framework for elimination of perinatal transmission of HIV in the United States. *Pediatrics, 130*(4), 738–744. doi:10.1542/peds.2012-0194

Nielsen, S. D., Jeppesen, D. L., Kolte, L., Clark, D. R., Sørensen, T. U., Dreves, A. M., ... Nielsen, J. O. (2001). Impaired progenitor cell function in HIV-negative infants of HIV-positive mothers results in decreased thymic output and low CD4 counts. *Blood, 98*(2), 398–404. doi:10.1182/blood.V98.2.398

Niess, J. H., Brand, S., Gu, X., Landsman, L., Jung, S., McCormick, B. A., ... Reinecker, H. C. (2005). CX3CR1-mediated dendritic cell access to the intestinal lumen and bacterial clearance. *Science, 307*(5707), 254–258. doi:10.1126/science.1102901

Noguchi, M., Yi, H., Rosenblatt, H. M., Filipovich, A. H., Adelstein, S., Modi, W. S., ... Leonard, W. J. (1993). Interleukin-2 receptor γ chain mutation results in X-linked severe combined immunodeficiency in humans. *Cell, 73*(1), 147–157. doi:10.1016/0092-8674(93)90167-O

Ochs, H. D. (2009). Mutations of the Wiskott-Aldrich syndrome protein affect protein expression and dictate the clinical phenotypes. *Immunology Research, 44*(1–3), 84–88. doi:10.1007/s12026-008-8084-3

Ortiz-Lopez, N., Diez, M., Diaz, O., Simon, F., & Diaz, A. (2012). Epidemiological surveillance of congenital syphilis in

Spain, 2000–2010. *Pediatric Infectious Disease Journal, 31*(9), 988–990. doi:10.1097/INF.0b013e31825d3152

Palmeira, P., Quinello, C., Silveira-Lessa, A. L., Zago, C. A., & Carneiro-Sampaio, M. (2012). IgG placental transfer in healthy and pathological pregnancies. *Clinical & Developmental Immunology, 2012*, 985646. doi:10.1155/2012/985646

Pammi, M., Holland, L., Butler, G., Gacser, A., & Bliss, J. M. (2013). Candida parapsilosis is a significant neonatal pathogen: A systematic review and meta-analysis. *Pediatric Infectious Disease Journal, 32*(5), e206–e216. doi:10.1097/INF.0b013e3182863a1c

Pammi, M., O'Brien, J. L., Ajami, N. J., Wong, M. C., Versalovic, J., & Petrosino, J. F. (2017). Development of the cutaneous microbiome in the preterm infant: A prospective longitudinal study. *PLoS One, 12*(4), e0176669. doi:10.1371/journal.pone.0176669

Papayannopoulos, V., Metzler, K. D., Hakkim, A., & Zychlinsky, A. (2010). Neutrophil elastase and myeloperoxidase regulate the formation of neutrophil extracellular traps. *Journal of Cell Biology, 191*(3), 677–691. doi:10.1083/jcb.201006052

Parham, P. (2009). *The immune system* (3rd ed.). New York, NY: Garland Science.

Pass, R. F., & Anderson, B. (2014). Mother-to-child transmission of cytomegalovirus and prevention of congenital infection. *Journal of the Pediatric Infectious Disease Society, 3* (Suppl. 1), S2–S6. doi:10.1093/jpids/piu069

Patel, K., Wang, J., Jacobson, D. L., Lipshultz, S. E., Landy, D. C., Geffner, M. E., … Miller, T. L. (2014). Aggregate risk of cardiovascular disease among adolescents perinatally infected with the human immunodeficiency virus. *Circulation, 129*(11), 1204–1212. doi:10.1161/CIRCULATIONAHA.113.001978

Peakman, M., & Vergani, D. (2009). *Basic and clinical immunology* (2nd ed.). Edinburgh, Scotland: Churchill Livingstone.

Penders, J., Thijs, C., Vink, C., Stelma, F. F., Snijders, B., Kummeling, I., … Stobberingh, E. E. (2006). Factors influencing the composition of the intestinal microbiota in early infancy. *Pediatrics, 118*(2), 511–521. doi:10.1542/peds.2005-2824

Peyron, F., Garweg, J. G., Wallon, M., Descloux, E., Rolland, M., & Barth, J. (2011). Long-term impact of treated congenital toxoplasmosis on quality of life and visual performance. *Pediatric Infectious Disease Journal, 30*(7), 597–600. doi:10.1097/INF.0b013e31820bb5f3

Piedimonte, G., & Perez, M. K. (2014). Respiratory syncytial virus infection and bronchiolitis. *Pediatrics in Review, 35*(12), 519–530. doi:10.1542/pir.35-12-519

Pitter, G., Ludvigsson, J. F., Romor, P., Zanier, L., Zanotti, R., Simonato, L., & Canova, C. (2016). Antibiotic exposure in the first year of life and later treated asthma: A population based birth cohort study of 143,000 children. *European Journal of Epidemiology, 31*(1), 85–94. doi:10.1007/s10654-015-0038-1

Puck, J. M., Pepper, A. E., Henthorn, P. S., Candotti, F., Isakov, J., Whitwam, T., … Buckley, R. H. (1997). Mutation analysis of IL2RG in human X-linked severe combined immunodeficiency. *Blood, 89*(6), 1968–1977. Retrieved from http://www.bloodjournal.org/content/bloodjournal/89/6/1968.full.pdf

Puopolo, K. M., Draper, D., Wi, S., Newman, T. B., Zupancic, J., Lieberman, E., … Escobar, G. J. (2011). Estimating the probability of neonatal early-onset infection on the basis of maternal risk factors. *Pediatrics, 128*(5), e1155–e1163. doi:10.1542/peds.2010-3464

Purswani, M., Patel, K., Kopp, J. B., Seage, G. R. I., Chernoff, M. C., Hazra, R., … Van Dyke, R. B. (2013). Tenofovir treatment duration predicts proteinuria in a multiethnic United States cohort of children and adolescents with perinatal HIV-1 infection. *Pediatric Infectious Disease Journal, 32*(5), 495–500. doi:10.1097/INF.0b013e31827f4eff

Rajagopal, L. (2009). Understanding the regulation of Group B streptococcal virulence factors. *Future Microbiology, 4*(2), 201–221. doi:10.2217/17460913.4.2.201

Ramachandran, G. (2014). Gram-positive and gram-negative bacterial toxins in sepsis: A brief review. *Virulence, 5*(1), 213–218. doi:10.4161/viru.27024

Randis, T. M., Baker, J. A., & Ratner, A. J. (2017). Group B streptococcal infections. *Pediatrics in Review, 38*(6), 254–262. doi:10.1542/pir.2016-0127

Reef, S. E., Plotkin, S., Cordero, J. F., Katz, M., Cooper, L., Schwartz, B., … Wharton, M. (2000). Preparing for elimination of congenital rubella syndrome (CRS): Summary of a workshop on CRS elimination in the United States. *Clinical Infectious Diseases, 31*(1), 85–95. doi:10.1086/313928

Repetto, G. M., Guzman, M. L., Delgado, I., Loyola, H., Palomares, M., Lay-Son, G., … Alvarez, P. (2014). Case fatality rate and associated factors in patients with 22q11 microdeletion syndrome: A retrospective cohort study. *BMJ Open, 4*(11), e005041. doi:10.1136/bmjopen-2014-005041

Rich, R., Fleisher, T. A., Shearer, W. T., Schroeder, H. W., Jr., Frew, A. J., & Weyand, C. M. (2013). *Clinical immunology: Principles and practice* (4th ed.). St. Louis, MO: Elsevier Saunders.

Ryan, A. K., Goodship, J. A., Wilson, D. I., Philip, N., Levy, A., Seidel, H., … Scambler, P. J. (1997). Spectrum of clinical features associated with interstitial chromosome 22q11 deletions: A European collaborative study. *Journal of Medical Genetics, 34*(10), 798–804. doi:10.1136/jmg.34.10.798

Schlapbach, L. J., Aebischer, M., Adams, M., Natalucci, G., Bonhoeffer, J., Latzin, P., … Latal, B. (2011). Impact of sepsis on neurodevelopmental outcome in a Swiss national cohort of extremely premature infants. *Pediatrics, 128*(2), e348–e357. doi:10.1542/peds.2010-3338

Schoenwolf, G. C., Bleyl, S. B., Brauer, P. R., & Francis-West, P. H. (2015). Development of the pharyngeal apparatus and face. In G. C. Schoenwolf, S. B. Bleyl, P. R. Brauer, & P. H. Francis-West (Eds.), *Larsen's human embryology* (5th ed., pp. 429–472). Philadelphia, PA: Churchill Livingstone.

Schrag, S. J., Farley, M. M., Petit, S., Reingold, A., Weston, E. J., Pondo, T., … Lynfield, R. (2016). Epidemiology of invasive early-onset neonatal sepsis, 2005 to 2014. *Pediatrics, 138*(6), 1–11. doi:10.1542/peds.2016-2013

Schrag, S., Gorwitz, R., Fultz-Butts, K., & Schuchat, A. (2002). Prevention of perinatal group B streptococcal disease. *Morbidity and Mortality Weekly Report, 51*(RR-11), 1–22. Retrieved from https://www.cdc.gov/mmwr/preview/mmwrhtml/rr5111a1.htm

Schulfer, A., & Blaser, M. J. (2015). Risks of antibiotic exposures early in life on the developing microbiome. *PLoS Pathogens, 11*(7), e1004903. doi:10.1371/journal.ppat.1004903

Shah, J., Jefferies, A. L., Yoon, E. W., Lee, S. K., Shah, P. S., & Canadian Neonatal Network. (2015). Risk factors and outcomes of late-onset bacterial sepsis in preterm neonates born at < 32 weeks' gestation. *American Journal of Perinatology, 32*(7), 675–682. doi:10.1055/s-0034-1393936

Shane, A. L., Hansen, N. I., Stoll, B. J., Bell, E. F., Sanchez, P. J., Shankaran, S., … Higgins, R. D. (2012). Methicillin-resistant and susceptible *Staphylococcus aureus* bacteremia and meningitis in preterm infants. *Pediatrics, 129*(4), e914–e922. doi:10.1542/peds.2011-0966

Shane, A. L., Sánchez, P. J., & Stoll, B. J. (2017). Neonatal sepsis. *Lancet, 390*(10104), 1770–1780. doi:10.1016/s0140-6736(17)31002-4

Sherman, M. P. (2010). New concepts of microbial translocation in the neonatal intestine: Mechanisms and prevention. *Clinics in Perinatology, 37*(3), 565–579. doi:10.1016/j.clp.2010.05.006

Simonsen, K. A., Anderson-Berry, A. L., Delair, S. F., & Davies, H. D. (2014). Early-onset neonatal sepsis. *Clinical Microbiology Reviews, 27*(1), 21–47. doi:10.1128/cmr.00031-13

Stavnezer, J., Guikema, J. E. J., & Schrader, C. E. (2008). Mechanism and regulation of class switch recombination. *Annual Review of Immunology, 26*, 261–292. doi:10.1146/annurev.immunol.26.021607.090248

Stenutz, R., Weintraub, A., & Widmalm, G. (2006). The structures of *Escherichia coli* O-polysaccharide antigens. *FEMS Microbiology Reviews, 30*(3), 382–403. doi:10.1111/j.1574-6976.2006.00016.x

Stoll, B. J., Hansen, N. I., Sanchez, P. J., Faix, R. G., Poindexter, B. B., Van Meurs, K. P., ... Higgins, R. D. (2011). Early onset neonatal sepsis: The burden of group B *Streptococcal* and *E. coli* disease continues. *Pediatrics, 127*(5), 817–826. doi:10.1542/peds.2010-2217

Sugitharini, V., Prema, A., & Berla Thangam, E. (2013). Inflammatory mediators of systemic inflammation in neonatal sepsis. *Inflammation Research, 62*(12), 1025–1034. doi:10.1007/s00011-013-0661-9

Sullivan, K. E., Mullen, C. A., Blaese, R. M., & Winkelstein, J. A. (1994). A multiinstitutional survey of the Wiskott-Aldrich syndrome. *Journal of Pediatrics, 125*(6 Pt. 1), 876–885. doi:10.1016/S0022-3476(05)82002-5

Swanson, E. C., & Schleiss, M. R. (2013). Congenital cytomegalovirus infection: New prospects for prevention and therapy. *Pediatric Clinics of North America, 60*(2), 335–349. doi:10.1016/j.pcl.2012.12.008

Swanson, J. A. (2013). *Macrophage phagocytosis* [electronic resource]. London, UK: Henry Stewart Talks.

Szabo, S. M., Levy, A. R., Gooch, K. L., Bradt, P., Wijaya, H., & Mitchell, I. (2013). Elevated risk of asthma after hospitalization for respiratory syncytial virus infection in infancy. *Paediatric Respiratory Reviews, 13*, S9–S15. doi:10.1016/S1526-0542(12)70161-6

Tangye, S. G., Avery, D. T., Deenick, E. K., & Hodgkin, P. D. (2003). Intrinsic differences in the proliferation of naive and memory human B cells as a mechanism for enhanced secondary immune responses. *Journal of Immunology, 170*(2), 686–694. doi:10.4049/jimmunol.170.2.686

Ting, J. Y., Synnes, A., Roberts, A., Deshpandey, A., Dow, K., Yoon, E. W., ... Shah, P. S. (2016). Association between antibiotic use and neonatal mortality and morbidities in very low-birth-weight infants without culture-proven sepsis or necrotizing enterocolitis. *JAMA Pediatrics, 170*(12), 1181–1187. doi:10.1001/jamapediatrics.2016.2132

Tobin, N. H., & Aldrovandi, G. M. (2013). Immunology of pediatric HIV infection. *Immunology Reviews, 254*(1), 143–169. doi:10.1111/imr.12074

Tong, S. Y., Davis, J. S., Eichenberger, E., Holland, T. L., & Fowler, V. G., Jr. (2015). *Staphylococcus aureus* infections: Epidemiology, pathophysiology, clinical manifestations, and management. *Clinical Microbiology Reviews, 28*(3), 603–661. doi:10.1128/CMR.00134-14

Torre, P. I., Zeldow, B., Hoffman, H. J., Buchanan, A., Siberry, G. K., Rice, M., ... Williams, P. L. (2012). Hearing loss in perinatally HIV-infected and HIV-exposed but uninfected children and adolescents. *Pediatric Infectious Disease Journal, 31*(8), 835–841. doi:10.1097/INF.0b013e31825b9524

Twagira, M., Hadzic, N., Smith, M., Ramaswamy, M., Verma, A., Dhawan, A., ... Geretti, A. M. (2004). Disseminated neonatal herpes simplex virus (HSV) type 2 infection diagnosed by HSV DNA detection in blood and successfully managed by liver transplantation. *European Journal of Pediatrics, 163*(3), 166–169. doi:10.1007/s00431-003-1383-8

van Zuylen, W. J., Hamilton, S. T., Naing, Z., Hall, B., Shand, A., & Rawlinson, W. D. (2014). Congenital cytomegalovirus infection: Clinical presentation, epidemiology, diagnosis and prevention. *Obstetric Medicine, 7*(4), 140–146. doi:10.1177/1753495X14552719

Verani, J. R., McGee, L., & Schrag, S. J. (2010). Prevention of perinatal group B streptococcal disease: Revised guidelines from CDC, 2010. *Morbidity and Mortality Weekly Report, 59*(RR-10), 1–32. Retrieved from https://www.cdc.gov/mmwr/preview/mmwrhtml/rr5910a1.htm

Visscher, M. O., Adam, R., Brink, S., & Odio, M. (2015). Newborn infant skin: Physiology, development, and care. *Clinics in Dermatology, 33*(3), 271–280. doi:10.1016/j.clindermatol.2014.12.003

Wald, A., Corey, L., Cone, R., Hobson, A., Davis, G., & Zeh, J. (1997). Frequent genital herpes simplex virus 2 shedding in immunocompetent women. Effect of acyclovir treatment. *Journal of Clinical Investigation, 99*(5), 1092–1097. doi:10.1172/JCI119237

Walker, A. (2014). Intestinal colonization and programming of the intestinal immune response. *Journal of Clinical Gastroenterology, 48* (Suppl. 1), S8–S11. doi:10.1097/MCG.0000000000000230

Walport, M. J. (2001a). Complement. First of two parts. *New England Journal of Medicine, 344*(14), 1058–1066. doi:10.1056/NEJM200104053441406

Walport, M. J. (2001b). Complement. Second of two parts. *New England Journal of Medicine, 344*(15), 1140–1144. doi:10.1056/NEJM200104123441506

Wapner, R. J., Martin, C. L., Levy, B., Ballif, B. C., Eng, C. M., Zachary, J. M., ... Jackson, L. (2012). Chromosomal microarray versus karyotyping for prenatal diagnosis. *New England Journal of Medicine, 367*(23), 2175–2184. doi:10.1056/NEJMoa1203382

Warren, S., Garcia, M., & Hankins, C. (2016). Impact of neonatal early-onset sepsis calculator on antibiotic use within two tertiary healthcare centers. *Journal of Perinatology, 37*(4), 394–397. doi:10.1038/jp.2016.236

Weber, J. (2001). The pathogenesis of HIV-1 infection. *British Medical Bulletin, 58*(1), 61–72. doi:10.1093/bmb/58.1.61

Weston, E. J., Pondo, T., Lewis, M. M., Martell-Cleary, P., Morin, C., Jewell, B., ... Schrag, S. J. (2011). The burden of invasive early-onset neonatal sepsis in the United States, 2005–2008. *Pediatric Infectious Disease Journal, 30*(11), 937–941. doi:10.1097/INF.0b013e318223bad2

Whitley, R., Arvin, A., Prober, C., Corey, L., Burchett, S., Plotkin, S., ... Soong, S. (1991). Predictors of morbidity and mortality in neonates with herpes simplex virus infections. *New England Journal of Medicine, 324*(7), 450–454. doi:10.1056/nejm199102143240704

Wilson, C. B., Nizet, V., Maldonado, Y., Remington, J. S., & Klein, J. O. (2016). *Remington and Klein's infectious diseases of the fetus and newborn infant* (8th ed.). Philadelphia, PA: Saunders/Elsevier.

Wilson, C. B., Remington, J. S., Stagno, S., & Reynolds, D. W. (1980). Development of adverse sequelae in children born with subclinical congenital toxoplasma infection. *Pediatrics*, *66*(5), 767–774. Retrieved from https://journals.lww .com/obgynsurvey/Fulltext/1981/08000/Development_of_ Adverse_Sequelae_in_Children_Born.13.aspx

Woods, C. R. (2005). Syphilis in children: Congenital and acquired. *Seminars in Pediatric Infectious Diseases*, *16*(4), 245–257. doi:10.1053/j.spid.2005.06.005

World Health Organization. (n.d.). Global health observatory (GHO) data. Retrieved from http://www.who.int/gho/hiv/en

Wynn, J. L., & Levy, O. (2010). Role of innate host defenses in susceptibility to early onset neonatal sepsis. *Clinics in Perinatology, 37*(2), 307–337. doi:10.1016/ j.clp.2010.04.001

Wynn, J. L., Wong, H. R., Shanley, T. P., Bizzarro, M. J., Saiman, L., & Polin, R. A. (2014). Time for a neonatal-specific consensus definition for sepsis. *Pediatric Critical Care Medicine*, *15*(6), 523–528. doi:10.1097/pcc.0000000000000157

Zilow, G., Zilow, E. P., Burger, R., & Linderkamp, O. (1993). Complement activation in newborn infants with early onset infection. *Pediatric Research, 34*(2), 199–203. doi:10 .1203/00006450-199308000-00020

Zuppa, A. A., Riccardi, R., Frezza, S., Gallini, F., Luciano, R. M., Alighieri, G., … De Carolis, S. (2017). Neonatal lupus: Follow-up in infants with anti-SSA/Ro antibodies and review of the literature. *Autoimmunity Reviews, 16*(4), 427–432. doi:10.1016/j. autrev.2017.02.010

10

THE METABOLIC AND ENDOCRINE SYSTEM

Stephanie M. Blake, Amy J. Jnah, and Deanna W. Adkins

LEARNING OBJECTIVES

After completing this chapter, the reader should be able to:

- Understand normal endocrine organ development.
- Describe the effects of hormones produced by endocrine organs.
- Discuss common inherited disorders and their effect on fetal and neonatal endocrine system development and function.
- Identify maternal health issues that have a potential impact on fetal and postnatal endocrine system development and function.
- Evaluate common disorders that affect the endocrine system and their implications across the life span.

INTRODUCTION

The human endocrine system is an intricately connected aggregate of glands located throughout the human body. Endocrine glands produce various hormones which regulate human physiology. In fact, the word *hormone* originates from the Greek term *impetus*, or to arouse activity. These hormones, when synthesized and secreted into the bloodstream, bind with target receptors and elicit cellular responses within a target organ. Normal endocrine function is critical for proper physical growth and development, metabolism, fluid and electrolyte homeostasis, stress responses, and reproductive and immune development. This chapter addresses the hypothalamus as well as the pituitary, adrenal, thyroid, pancreas, pineal and parathyroid glands. The embryologic development of each gland will be summarized and followed by a discussion of the function of each gland. Critical processes, including calcium-magnesium homeostasis and carbohydrate metabolism, will be explored. In addition, we present a discussion of glucose metabolism focused to the special populations which align with neonatal intensive care nursing. A discussion of genetic and maternal influences, including inherited inborn errors of metabolism, will be identified and discussed. Finally, we present a discussion of common metabolic disorders, their pathogenesis, key clinical manifestations, and lifespan implications. Our intent is to take this perceivably dense content and present it in a clear, concise and multi-sensory manner for advanced practice nursing students. We strongly suggest that learners actively annotate while reading this chapter and develop unique, visual learning tools when studying the feedback loops, inherited disorders, and disease processes.

TIMELINE OF ORGAN DEVELOPMENT

The metabolic and endocrine system is a complex network of glands. "Classical" endocrine glands include the anterior pituitary, thyroid, parathyroids, adrenals, gonads, and pancreas. These glands are modulated by the "master glands," the hypothalamus and pituitary glands, which serve a neuroendocrine role (Neal, 2016). Here, we begin the chapter with an overview of normal embryologic development of the master and classic endocrine glands.

Hypothalamus

The hypothalamus, once mature, is a collection of neurons that reside in the midbrain. The hypothalamus secretes stimulating hormones (e.g., growth hormone-releasing hormone), which communicate with the anterior pituitary gland and prompt its synthesis and secretion of hormones. The hypothalamus also secretes inhibitory hormones (e.g., dopamine), which inhibit further synthesis and secretion of target hormones (e.g., prolactin) from the anterior pituitary.

Embryonic Period. During week 5 of gestation, the ventral portion of the diencephalon (brain) is formed. This gives rise to both the hypothalamus and thalamus. As early as week 6 of gestation, hypothalamic-releasing hormones, many of which travel through the hypophyseal portal system and to the anterior pituitary, are detected in the systemic circulation (Melmed, Polonsky, Larsen, & Kronenberg, 2016).

Fetal Period. Characterization of the differentiating structures of the hypothalamus continues from weeks 9 through 14 of gestation. By week 18, the portal-vessel system that delivers the hypothalamic-releasing hormones to the anterior pituitary is fully developed, giving rise to the future hypothalamic–pituitary–end organ axis (Fora, 2006; Koutcherov, Mai, Ashwell, & Paxinos, 2002; Melmed et al., 2016).

Pituitary Gland

The pituitary gland, once mature, lies at the base of the skull. The anterior lobe synthesizes hormones including adrenocorticotropic hormone (ACTH), growth hormone (GH), prolactin, thyroid-stimulating hormone (TSH), and luteinizing hormone. The secretion of each hormone is contingent upon stimulating hormones secreted by the hypothalamus, which reach the pituitary by way of the humoral system (hypophyseal portal system). The posterior lobe does not produce hormones. Rather, it is comprised of the terminal ends of neurons which originate from the hypothalamus. As such, the posterior pituitary stores certain hormones (e.g., antidiuretic hormone, oxytocin) produced by the hypothalamus and releases them when stimulated to do so.

Embryonic Period. During week 4 of gestation, a finger-like protrusion ("Rathke's pouch") extends dorsally from the ectoderm and grows in an outward direction, heading toward the roof of the mouth. This is the early adenohypophysis and future anterior pituitary gland. During week 7 of gestation, a similarly shaped finger-like protrusion extends ventrally from the ectoderm and grows in an outward direction, heading toward the diencephalon (brain). The ventral extension proliferates into the posterior pituitary gland.

Evolution of the pituitary gland continues through week 8 of gestation. Shortly thereafter, the anterior walls of both glands merge in tight apposition to one another. Despite this anatomic connection, both glands remain separate, unique structures with differentiated responsibilities.

Fetal Period. Between weeks 9 and 10, GH, ACTH, TSH, follicle-stimulating hormone (FSH), and leutinizing hormone (LH) synthesis and secretion are ongoing in the anterior pituitary. Oxytocin and vasopressin (antidiuretic hormone [ADH]) secretion, via the posterior pituitary, is detectable by week 10. By week 16, the pituitary is considered fully formed and resides at the base of the skull. Thereafter, vesicular connections arise and link the hypothalamus to the anterior pituitary. This connection is essential for the hypothalamic–pituitary–adrenal interface and is functional by week 20 of gestation. GH levels peak between weeks 20 to 24 of gestation, with a steady decline thereafter (Hill, 2017f; Melmed et al., 2016).

Adrenal Glands

The adrenal glands, which reside atop the kidneys, are typically regarded as the "fight or flight" glands. Under the direction of the anterior pituitary, the adrenals secrete hormones (e.g., epinephrine, hydrocortisone) which, during periods of stress, seek to return the body to physiologic homeostasis.

Embryonic Period. The adrenal glands (suprarenal glands) arise from a region of intermediate mesoderm adjacent to the kidneys. The adrenal cortex and medulla arise between weeks 5 and 6 of gestation. Beginning with week 5, the outer portion of the adrenal gland epithelium forms the adrenal cortex. The adrenal medulla then forms from a chain of interconnected ganglia that lie both laterally and parallel to the spinal vertebrae extending from the base of the skull to the sacrum. Cortisol synthesis is evident by the end of week 8 of gestation (Quintos & Boney, 2010).

Fetal Period. Prior to the third month of gestation, the adrenal gland develops into two distinct zones: the (a) permanent or adult zone (outer mass of cells) and the (b) transient fetal zone (inner mass of cells). By midgestation, the adrenal cortex accounts for 80% to 90% of the mass of the gland (Kaludjerovic & Ward, 2012). The hypothalamic–pituitary–adrenal (HPA) axis is considered formed by week 20 of gestation. Mineralocorticoids are synthesized after 22 weeks of gestation, with glucocorticoid synthesis evident between 25 to 30 weeks of gestation. Migration of neural cells into the adrenal medulla continues until birth (Hill, 2017b; Quintos & Boney, 2010).

Thyroid Gland

The thyroid gland is regarded as one of the larger (if not the largest) endocrine glands. Under the influence of the anterior pituitary gland, this gland releases thyroid hormones, which increase the basal metabolic rate.

Embryonic Period. Thyroid development begins with week 3 of gestation. The embryonic thyroid develops from the third and fourth branchial pouch, appearing as an outgrowth at the floor of the primitive buccal cavity (the future site of the mouth and pharynx). Early synthesis of thyroglobulin (thyroid hormone precursor) is evident by the end of week 4 of gestation. Shortly thereafter, the gland descends to a position anterior to the hyoid bone and larynx cartilage (voicebox). An isthmus develops and connects the two lateral lobes, measuring approximately 2 inches in length. Evolution of the thyroid gland continues through week 8. At this time, the thyroid exhibits its definitive external form and begins secreting thyroid hormone (Hill, 2017g). Beginning with week 9, iodine absorption is noted.

Fetal Period. By week 13 of gestation, follicular cells secrete thyroid hormones (TSH, T_3, and T_4). Parafollicular cells (C cells) secrete calcitonin by the 16th week. Beginning with week 34 of gestation, total thyroid receptors mature and autoregulation of iodine begins (Melmed et al., 2016).

Pancreas

The pancreas resides within the upper left quadrant of the abdomen, behind the stomach. Its function, as an exocrine gland, is to secrete digestive enzymes. The pancreatic islets (islets of Langerhans) secrete glucagon, insulin, somatostatin, and pancreatic polypeptide. As such, the pancreas holds an important role in glucose metabolism.

Embryonic Period. Outgrowths of the duodenum form the ventral and dorsal pancreatic buds, which, in turn, eventually join together to form the adult pancreas. Weeks 4 through 6 of development involve the rotation of the ventral pancreas to the right and invagination of the common bile duct. By week 7, pancreatic hormone secretion is evident and increasing (Cowett, 2012; Hill, 2017d).

Fetal Period. Week 10 of gestation involves rotation of the dorsal and ventral pancreatic buds. The buds thereby fuse and form the pancreas, a flat gland measuring 6 inches long, located between the stomach and spine and connected to the duodenum. Islets of Langerhans bud from the pancreatic duct system, forming clusters of endocrine cells: alpha, then beta, then delta. Insulin secretion thereby begins, and glucagon is detectable in the fetal plasma by week 15 of gestation. Pancreatic abnormalities, although rare, include strangulation of duodenum secondary to malrotation of dorsal pancreatic bud (annular pancreas) or missing pancreas during embryonic development (Hill, 2017d; Sargis, 2015b).

Pineal Gland

Posterior to the thalamus is the pineal gland. Devoid of direct photosensitivity, this gland is responsible for the synthesis and secretion of melatonin, which is understood to occur on a circadian cycle.

Embryonic Period. During weeks 5 and 6 of development, the pineal body forms at the roof of the posterior part of the forebrain. Cellular migration, invagination, and midline epithelial thickening occur during week 7, which gives rise to the gland's distinct anterior lobe. The most caudal part of the roof plate develops into the pineal body or epiphysis (Hill, 2017e; Macchi & Bruce, 2004). Once fully formed, the pineal gland nestles between the two hemispheres of the brain, where the thalamai join.

Fetal Period. The pineal gland matures throughout fetal development and into early childhood (age 2). Melatonin synthesis and secretion begins after birth. Among infants born at term, rhythmicity (circadian rhythm) is observed approximately 8 to 12 weeks after birth. Synthesis, secretion, and rhythmicity are often delayed among infants born prematurely (Ferber, Als, McAnulty, Peretz, & Zisape, 2011; Melmed et al, 2016; Neal, 2016; Sargis, 2014a).

Parathyroid Gland

The parathyroid gland is a compilation of four smaller glands which reside posterior to the thyroid gland. Most notably, the parathyroid gland secretes parathyroid hormone (PTH), which facilitates the synthesis and secretion of active vitamin D (1, 25-dihydroxyvitamin D). In addition, the parathyroid gland regulates calcium and phosphorus homeostasis.

Embryonic Period. The parathyroid glands originate from the endoderm of the third and fourth pharyngeal pouches, typically during week 3 of development. The inferior parathyroid glands arise from the third pharyngeal pouch and migrate with the thymus. Separation of the inferior glands occurs just prior to reaching their final anatomic position, at the level of the inferior pole of each thyroid lobe. The superior parathyroid glands arise from the fourth pharyngeal pouch and take their final position along the posterior part of the middle third of each thyroid lobe. Glandular development continues through week 8 of gestation. During this time the inferior parathyroid glands begin producing PTH (Hill, 2017g).

Fetal Period. The parathyroids are mature and physiologicaly active by week 14 of gestation (Melmed et al., 2016; Sargis, 2015c). Parathyroid abnormalities, such as congenital hypoparathyroidism, are commonly associated with inherited diseases or syndromes, such as DiGeorge syndrome.

ENDOCRINE SIGNALING

The endocrine system communicates by way of chemical signaling (Sargis, 2016; Stokowski, 2015). Signaling cells synthesize and secrete ligands (hormones) into the bloodstream. The circulation carries these hormones to target hormone receptors. Hormones bind with select receptors and a cellular response is observed. Endocrine signaling is primarily modulated by negative feedback loops, which are essential to maintain homeostasis. After all, endocrine function modulates fetal and postnatal growth and development, metabolism, reproductive development and function, as well as responses to stress and/or injury (Hill, 2017a). In order to better understand how hormones effect body function, and apply that knowledge in clinical practice, a brief discussion of the key components of endocrine signaling, namely hormone receptors, regulation, and negative feedback, is provided.

Hormone Receptors

The process by which hormones are released into the circulation, travel long distances, reach target cells within the body, and elicit cellular responses is known as endocrine signaling. For this to occur, hormones and hormone receptors must be present. Hormones are either water-soluble or fat-soluble. Water-soluble hormones (peptide hormones) cannot permeate the cell membrane and are therefore limited to binding with receptors at the surface of the target cell. Alternatively, fat-soluble hormones (steroid hormones) can penetrate the cell membrane and bind with receptors inside the cell. Likewise, hormone receptors are proteins that either reside within or on the surface of human cells and exhibit an affinity to one or more circulating hormones. Intracellular hormone receptors have an affinity for the fat-soluble hormones (e.g. testosterone), lie within the cell, and regulate gene transcription. Surface hormone receptors have an affinity for water-soluble peptide hormones (e.g. insulin), lie on the surface of the cell, and regulate enzymatic activity. The binding of a hormone to a receptor yields a hormone-receptor complex. These complexes elicit immediate or delayed biological responses; APNs must recognize that small changes in circulating hormone concentrations can yield a significant (and potentially untoward) effect on the fetus and newborn (Divall & Merjaneh, 2017).

Endocrine signaling can be studied as a stepwise sequence of events. First, a hormone is synthesized and released into the circulation. The circulation "carries" the hormone to a target cell. As the hormone approaches the cell it binds with a target surface or intracellular hormone receptor. This elicits a biological response. Therefore, the relationship between hormones and hormone receptors can be compared to a "lock and key" mechanism. In other words, the affinity of a hormone receptor to a particular hormone draws it near. Once the hormone contacts the receptor, it "locks" with the receptor. When this occurs, the hormone undergoes a conformational change and a cellular response (e.g. metabolic activity) is observed.

Hormone Regulation

Several factors contribute to hormone regulation, by either increasing, decreasing, or normalizing hormone levels. These factors include (a) blood flow patterns/velocity,

(b) rate of metabolism and excretion (of circulating hormones), and (c) feedback loops. Blood flow patterns implicate the rate (or speed) of transport of a hormone to its target organ. The rate at which a hormone is metabolized and excreted from the body affects further synthesis and secretion of additional hormone. Collectively, these factors implicate the negative feedback system.

Negative Feedback

Collectively, the aforementioned components of endocrine signaling implicate the negative feedback system, the primary mechanism by which hormone levels are regulated (Figure 10.1; Roberts & Kruchten, 2016). Negative feedback describes a process in which the output of a pathway inhibits the input of a pathway. In other words, as the serum circulating concentration of a target hormone or output of a feedback loop approaches the upper acceptable limit, a negative message is transmitted to inhibit further release of precursors that encourage the synthesis and secretion of that hormone.

For example, consider the synthesis and secretion of GH. Low circulating GH alerts the hypothalamus to release growth hormone-releasing hormone (GHRH). GHRH travels to the anterior pituitary gland and stimulates the synthesis and secretion of GH. GH, the desirable "end hormone" in this pathway, is released into the circulation. It stimulates adipose cells to breakdown stored fat and release free fatty acids to fuel growth. GH also stimulates an increase in amino acid uptake from the circulation, glycogenolysis, and hepatic release of insulin-like growth factor (IGF-1) into the circulation. In aggregate, this encourages the proliferation of bone cells, muscle cells, nervous system and immune cells. However, once IGF-1 levels reach the upper acceptable limit, GHRH secretion stops. In exchange, the hypothalamus secretes growth hormone inhibiting hormone (GHIH). GHIH (also known as somatostatin) inhibits the release of GH and stops the feedback loop. Thyroid hormone and cortisol are also regulated by negative feedback, and are discussed later in this chapter.

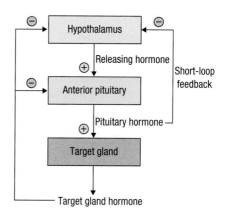

Figure 10.1 The negative feedback loop.

ENDOCRINE HORMONE CLASSES

Several classes of hormones are produced within the human body and can be systematically investigated based on their chemical structure. These classes of hormones include the amino acid derivatives, polypeptides and proteins, and steroids. These hormone classes differ based on their cell-specific distribution, the type of receptors they bind to, their cellular permeability, and the resultant cellular response (Table 10.1).

Peptide, Polypeptide, and Protein Hormones

The majority of hormones found within the human body are made from peptides and proteins—linked chains of amino acids. These chains range from short (e.g., vasopressin) to long, 200-link chains (Neal, 2016). More specific, the short chain amino acids are the peptide hormones, whereas the polypeptide or protein hormones exemplify the longer chains. Both are synthesized like other body

TABLE 10.1 Major Endocrine Glands, Hormones, and Hormone Functions

Primary Endocrine Glands/Tissues	Hormone(s)	Hormone Class	Specific Hormone Function(s)
Hypothalamus	Corticotropin-releasing hormone	Protein	Stimulates the release of ACTH from the anterior pituitary gland (stress response)
	Gonadotropin-releasing hormone	Amine	Stimulates the release of LH and FSH (sexual and reproductive functions; pregnancy and lactation)
	Thyrotropin-releasing hormone	Peptide	Assists with hormonal control of lactation; stimulates TSH secretion
	Growth hormone-releasing hormone	Peptide	Most abundant pituitary hormone; controls the body's growth and development; stimulates GH secretion
	Somatostatin	Peptide	Inhibits GH and TSH release
	Dopamine	Neurotransmitter	Inhibits prolactin release
Anterior Pituitary	ACTH	Peptide	Stimulates hormone release from adrenal cortex (stress response)
	LH	Protein	Excites the gonads to stimulate androgen production (ovulation or testosterone production)
	FSH	Protein	Is crucial in the promotion of normal gonad function (follicle development or sperm production)
	TSH	Protein	Stimulates the synthesis and release of thyroid hormone
	GH	Protein	Stress hormone; produces somatostatin for body growth and development; promotes glucose release with hypoglycemia and inhibits glucose release with hyperglycemia
	Prolactin	Peptide	Controls lactation (human milk production)
Posterior Pituitary	Antidiuretic hormone	Peptide	Stimulates the reabsorption of water by the kidneys
	Oxytocin	Peptide	Is responsible for uterine contraction stimulation

(continued)

TABLE 10.1 Major Endocrine Glands, Hormones, and Hormone Functions (*continued*)

Primary Endocrine Glands/Tissues	Hormone(s)	Hormone Class	Specific Hormone Function(s)
Thyroid	Thyroxine and Triiodothyronine	Amine	Influences metabolism, body temperature, cell growth, and cellular differentiation (all cells)
	Calcitonin	Peptide	Reduces calcium blood levels (calcium metabolism)
Parathyroid	Parathyroid hormone	Peptide	Produces vitamin D (calcitrol), which is an important regulator of blood calcium levels that helps maintain the proper functioning of cells, and builds muscles and bones
Adrenal Cortex	Aldosterone	Steroid	Helps regulate salt, water balance, and blood pressure in the body
	Cortisol	Steroid	Released in response to stress
Adrenal Medulla	Epinephrine, norepinephrine	Amine	Released in response to stress
	Histamine	Amine	Participates in local immune response (allergic reaction) by causing vasodilation and fluid secretion at the site of infection; stimulates gastric acid secretion
Pineal	Melatonin	Amine	Helps to control circadian rhythm and regulate certain reproductive hormones
Pancreas	Insulin	Protein	Facilitates cellular glucose uptake; regulates carbohydrate, lipid and protein metabolism
	Glucagon	Protein	Responds to hypoglycemia by mobilizing glucose into the circulation by inhibiting glycogen synthesis (glycogenesis), promoting the breakdown of glycogen into glucose (glycogenolysis), and promoting glucose synthesis (gluconeogenesis).
Testes	Testosterone	Steroid	Among males, modulates the development of primary sex characteristics (e.g., testes, prostate, sperm production), and secondary sex characteristics (e.g., muscle mass, fat distribution, body hair production)
Ovaries	Estrogen	Steroid	Influences development of female sexual characteristics and reproductive development; essential for normal uterine functioning of the uterus and breasts and also protects bone health
	Progesterone	Steroid	Stimulates the lining of the uterus for fertilization and prepares the breasts for milk production
Secondary Endocrine Glands/Tissues	**Hormone(s)**	**Hormone Class**	**Specific Hormone Function(s)**
Heart	Atrial natriuretic hormone	Peptide	Produced by the right atrium of the heart in response to elevated blood pressure; stimulates the excretion of sodium and water by the kidneys

(continued)

TABLE 10.1 Major Endocrine Glands, Hormones, and Hormone Functions (*Continued*)

Secondary Endocrine Glands/Tissues	Hormone(s)	Hormone Class	Specific Hormone Function(s)
Kidneys	Erythropoietin	Peptide	Produced in the kidneys; promotes the formation of red blood cells by the bone marrow
	Calcitrol	Steroid	Calcium absorption
Adipose Tissue	Leptin	Protein	Released from adipose tissue after meals; facilitates feeling of satiety
Gastrointestinal Tract	Gastrin, secretin, cholecystokinin	Peptide	Digestion of food
Pancreas and GI tract	Glucose-dependent insulinotropic peptide, Glucagon-like peptide	Peptide	Pancreatic β-cell stimulation and insulin release
Skin	Cholecalciferol	Steroid	Vitamin D formation
Bones	Osteocalcin	Protein	Insulin production
Liver	Angiotensinogen	Peptide	Elevation of blood pressure
	Hepcidin	Peptide	Regulates iron homeostasis
	Insulin-like growth factor 1	Protein	Growth and development
	Thrombopoietin	Protein	Platelet synthesis
Thymus	Thymosins	Protein	T-lymphocyte development

ACTH, adrenocorticotropic hormone; FSH, follicle-stimulating hormone; GH, growth hormone; GI, gastrointestinal; LH, luteinizing hormone; TSH, thyroid-stimulating hormone, GI, gastrointestinal.

Source: From Neal, J. M. (2016). *How the endocrine system works* (2nd ed.). Hoboken, NJ: John Wiley & Sons.

proteins: DNA is transcribed into messenger ribonucleic acid (mRNA), which is translated into an amino acid chain of a certain length and thereby labeled as either a peptide or protein hormone (Neal, 2016).

It is worth mentioning one additional type of peptide hormone. Unlike the traditional peptide and polypeptides, the glycoproteins are a blend of peptide and carbohydrate. There are only four known glycoprotein hormones: LH, TSH, human chorionic gonadotropin hormone (HCG), and FSH. Clearly, those hormones affect the developing fetus and neonate and therefore are included in this chapter.

Amine Hormones

Amine hormones are derived from amino acids or lipids. They are synthesized from the amino acids tryptophan or tyrosine. Amine hormones are secreted from both the adrenal medulla and thyroid gland (Neal, 2016).

Steroid Hormones

Some steroids originate from the adrenal cortex (e.g., cortisol, aldosterone) and others (e.g., testosterone, progesterone, estrogen) originate in the gonads (testes and ovaries) and are derived primarily from cholesterol. Steroid hormones are not soluble in water (hydrophobic). Rather, because they are composed of lipids, they easily permeate the cell membrane. The receptors for steroid hormones are found within the cell, either in the cytoplasm or the nucleus. Steroid hormones travel to their target cell bound to a transport protein. Once inside the cell, they effect changes that result in the transcription and translation of new proteins inside the cell. Because of this complex structure, the half-life of steroid hormones is much longer than that of those hormones derived from amino acids (Neal, 2016).

MAJOR ENDOCRINE GLANDS

Endocrine glands play a major role in maintaining physiologic homeostasis. These glands produce, store, and secrete hormones that evoke specific responses in other cells, tissues, and organs found throughout the body. An investigation into the structure and function of the major glands of the endocrine system will be presented next. A summary of organs with secondary endocrine functions is provided in Table 10.1.

Hypothalamus

The hypothalamus is an almond-shaped and sized gland. It is one of the smallest (in adults <4 cm³) yet most powerful control centers within the human body (Figure 10.2). The hypothalamus is composed of four major substructures: the tuber cinereum, median eminence, infundibulum, and mammillary bodies. Situated in the midbrain region, the hypothalamus sits below the thalamus and above the pituitary gland and brainstem. The hypothalamus regulates systemwide physiologic equilibrium (homeostasis). It is the link between the body's endocrine and nervous system and plays a key role in the regulation of the pituitary and peripheral endocrine organ functions (Table 10.2).

The hypothalamus contains neurosecretory neurons that, based on feedback signals from the general circulation and pituitary, synthesize peptides and catecholamines to act as hormones. When indicated, hypothalamic hormones either enter the systemic circulation for systemwide delivery to target cells or the hypophyseal portal circulation for focused delivery to the pituitary gland. In these situations, the pituitary responds to the hypothalamic-mediated hormonal communication by stimulating or inhibiting further hormone synthesis and secretion.

Pituitary Gland

The pituitary gland is a pea-sized structure, measuring approximately 0.3 inches in adults, located below the hypothalamus at the base of the skull (Figure 10.3). Anatomically, the pituitary gland consists of two parts—the *anterior pituitary* lobe (adenohypophysis), which synthesizes and secretes hormones, and the *posterior pituitary* lobe (neurohypophysis), which stores hormones that are synthesized and secreted by the hypothalamus and releases them upon command (Melmed, 2017; Sargis, 2014b).

TABLE 10.2 Major Functions of the Hypothalamus
• Autonomic control
• Hormonal control
• Biological rhythms
• Emotion and behavior
• Short-term memory
• Thermoregulation
• Appetite, body weight, insulin regulation
• Parturition and human milk let-down

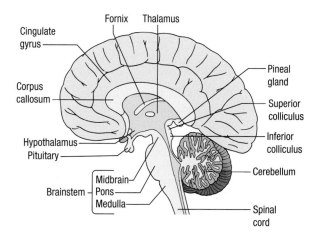

Figure 10.2 Hypothalamus, pituitary, and pineal glands.

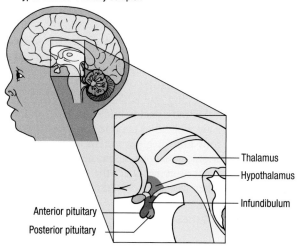

Figure 10.3 The hypothalamic-pituitary interface.

Hypothalamic–Pituitary Interface. The hypothalamic–pituitary (HP) axis is regarded as the "master command center" of the endocrine system. Anatomically connected by the infundibulum, the HP axis is a neuroendocrine communication pathway that mediates signals between the brain and the peripheral hormone-secreting target glands. Stimuli (circadian, pulsatile, or acute brain stimuli) prompt hypothalamic neurons to secrete hypothalamic-releasing or hypothalamic-inhibiting hormones. This regulates hormone synthesis and release by way of positive and negative feedback signals. Hypothalamic-secreted hormones travel to the pituitary by way of the humoral system, or hypophyseal portal system. Hormones secreted by the pituitary in response to the hypothalamic stimulus reach the systemic circulation through an intricate capillary plexus situated between both glands (Neal, 2016).

Adrenal Gland

The adrenal glands, or suprarenal glands, are two wedge-shaped glands that measure approximately 1.5 inches by 3 inches in adults. The adrenal glands, also known as the *fight or flight glands*, sit within the retroperitoneal cavity atop the kidneys, and comprise a larger outer cortex and smaller inner medulla (Neal, 2016; Sargis, 2015a).

The adrenal cortex is composed of three layers, each with its own functional responsibilities. Their importance to establishing and maintaining physiologic homeostasis among neonates, older infants, children, and adults cannot be understated. The outer layer (cortical layer) synthesizes sodium-retaining hormone (aldosterone) and the middle layer synthesizes glucocorticoids (cortisol). The inner layer synthesizes androgen hormones (testosterone, estrogen). The medulla is responsible for the synthesis and secretion of catecholamines, namely, epinephrine and norepinephrine. These hormones enter the systemic circulation by way of the left and right suprarenal veins (Figure 10.4).

Hypothalamic–Pituitary–Adrenal Axis. Collectively, the paraventricular nucleus of the hypothalamus, anterior pituitary, and adrenal cortex comprise the HPA axis. The HPA axis is activated in response to a stressor. A systematic, complex cascade of hormonal communications follows,

which regulates the synthesis and secretion of adrenal hormones in an attempt to restore physiologic equilibrium.

The stress response can be described as a series of carefully executed stimuli. First, neurons within the paraventricular nucleus of the hypothalamus are alerted to an environmental, physical, or physiological stressor. The hypothalamus releases corticotropin-releasing hormone (CRH) and arginine vasopressin (AVP). These hormones traverse the median eminence and portal capillary network and reach the anterior pituitary gland. The anterior portion of the pituitary releases ACTH into the circulation. ACTH travels to the adrenal cortex, where it binds to its receptors in the adrenals and triggers the release of glucocorticoids (cortisol and corticosterone). The glucocorticoids travel to and act on target cardiovascular tissues (muscle, adipose tissue, and vasculature). Thereafter, the kidney signals the release of mineralocorticoids, primarily aldosterone, from the adrenal cortex to preserve blood volume. Finally, once homeostasis is restored, feedback is sent to the hypothalamus to inhibit the axis (Figure 10.5; Melmed et al., 2016; Neal, 2016).This normal feedback loop may be impaired among premature infants with transient adrenal insufficiency, commonly caused by developmental immaturity or critical illness, especially septic shock. These infants may require treatment with corticosteroids to stimulate the HPA axis, in particular during periods of illness or prior to invasive surgical procedures.

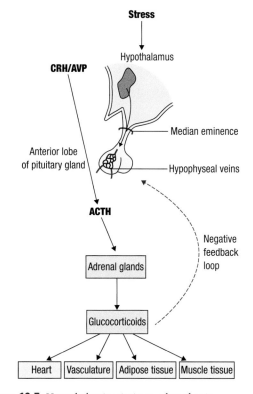

Figure 10.5 Hypothalamic-pituitary-adrenal axis.

ACTH, adrenocorticotropic hormone; AVP, arginine vasopressin; CRH, corticotropin-releasing hormone.

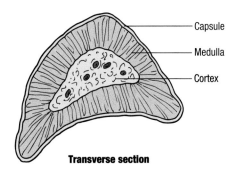

Transverse section

Figure 10.4 The adrenal gland (transverse section).

Thyroid Gland

The thyroid gland, one of the largest endocrine glands, is a butterfly- shaped gland that measures approximately 2 inches in length in adults with normal function (thyroid disease causes the gland to swell). The gland is situated inferior to the larynx and just below the thyroid and cricoid cartilage, attached to the ventral floor of the pharynx by way of the thyroglossal duct. It is divided into two lobes, which reside on either side of the trachea. This gives them the appearance of two distinct (yet interconnected) wings (American Association of Endocrine Surgeons, 2017b). The thyroid gland is composed primarily of small globular sacs called follicles that house colloid. Colloid is integral to thyroid function, as it influences the processing of iodine and thyroid hormone synthesis. Thyroid tissue may be found anywhere in the body between the tongue and anterior mediastinum. The thyroid begins processing iodine and secreting thyroid hormones by week 10 of gestation (G. Kim, Nandi-Munshi, & DiBlasi, 2018).

Hypothalamic–Pituitary–Thyroid Axis. The thyroid gland contains the only in vivo cells that absorb iodine, which is then processed in the presence of the amino acid tyrosine to produce the hormones thyroxine (T_4) and triiodothyronine (T_3). Approximately 80% of thyroid hormone production is in the form of T_4, but it is T_3 that is the more active agent. T_4 consists of four iodine molecules and one tyrosine molecule. These hormones are an integral part of the hypothalamic–pituitary–thyroid (HPT) axis, which controls somatic growth, thermogenesis, and brain development in the fetus and infant.

The HPT axis is activated when the feedback loop notifies the hypothalamus and pituitary of low circulating T_4 and T_3 levels. Hypothalamic thyrotropin-releasing hormone (TRH) is then transported through the hypothalamic-hypophyseal portal system to the anterior pituitary gland. This process stimulates the pituitary gland to synthesize and release TSH. TSH secretion stimulates an increase in organification of iodine, which triggers organification within the colloid and synthesis of T_3 and T_4 from the follicle. Through a process of proteolysis, regulated by TSH, T_4 is synthesized and secreted into the blood and peripheral tissues. In addition, one of the four iodine molecules bound to T_4 disengages, reducing T_4 to T_3. The unbound iodine atom is returned to the follicle and oxidized by thyroid peroxidase (TPO). Adequate circulating thyroid hormone levels activate the negative feedback loop, and inhibit TRH and TSH release (Figure 10.6; Khetan, 2014; Neal, 2016).

In addition to T_4 and T_3 feedback, the hypothalamus responds to hypothermia with secretion of TRH and

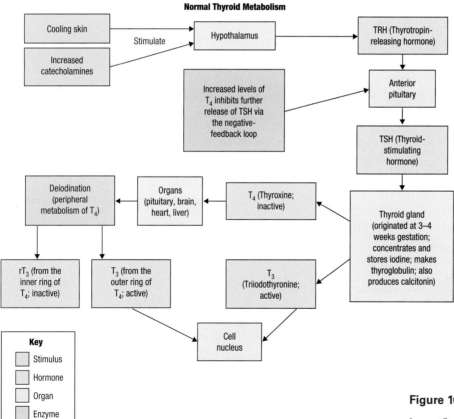

Figure 10.6 Normal thyroid metabolism.

Image Credit: Oksana Kasko, MSN, NNP-BC

activation of the feedback loop. In addition, the hypothalamus is sensitive to dopamine, epinephrine, and cortisol. Elevated levels of these hormones (as often occurs in neonates with hypotension requiring pharmacologic intervention) leads to decreased secretion of TRH and TSH and activation of the loop.

Parathyroid Glands

The four parathyroid glands are small, yellow-brown-colored glands, measuring approximately 2 to 7 mm in length by 2 to 4 mm wide and 0.5 to 2 mm thick in adults. These glands control calcium levels in the body through the secretion of PTH. Similar to the other endocrine glands, a feedback loop controls the secretion of PTH; deviations in calcium levels will either stimulate the release of PTH to normalize calcium levels or halt parathyroid release once homeostasis is achieved (Bilezikian et al., 2015; Polin, Abman, Rowitch, Benitz, & Fox, 2017; Sargis, 2015c).

The Fetal Calcium–Parathyroid–Vitamin D Axis. The calcium–parathyroid–vitamin D axis is responsible for regulating bone resorption, distal renal tubular calcium reabsorption, and 1,25-$(OH)_2$D-mediated intestinal calcium absorption. Under normal circumstances, low circulating serum ionized calcium concentrations stimulate the synthesis and secretion of PTH. PTH, in turn, acts directly on bone by stimulating the release of calcium and phosphorus into the extracellular fluid (ECF) and systemic circulation. Simultaneously, PTH stimulates the kidney to increase phosphorus excretion through the urine, which results in resorption of calcium in the distal tubule. In addition, PTH facilitates gastrointestinal absorption of calcium through its effects on synthesis of 1,25-dihydroxyvitamin D (1,25-$[OH]_2$D; American Association of Endocrine Surgeons, 2017a; Polin et al., 2017; Sargis, 2015c).

Calcitonin (CT) is a hormone primarily secreted by the thyroid gland; CT can also be found in lung and gastrointestinal tissues. It is primarily metabolized in the kidneys and can rapidly decrease serum calcium levels in infants and children by inactivating osteoclast activity. Osteoclast activity is typically high in infants and neonates due to high rates of bone turnover during early development. During periods of hypercalcemia, the calcium-sensing receptor (CaSR) protein is activated. This protein, synthesized within the parathyroid glands, stimulates CT secretion from the thyroid gland, thereby increasing calcium deposition in the bones, decreasing intestinal uptake, and decreasing renal calcium reabsorption in the distal convoluted tubule (Blaine, Chonchol, & Levi, 2015). This negative feedback loop inhibits PTH secretion and increases renal calcium excretion (Figure 10.7). A further discussion of calcium and phosphorus homeostasis follows the discussion of these major endocrine glands (Felsenfeld & Levine, 2015).

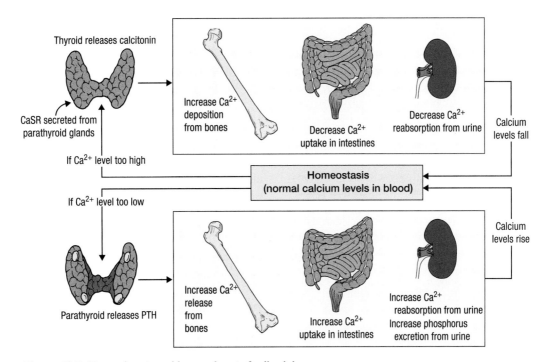

Figure 10.7 Hypocalcemia and hypercalcemia feedback loops.

CaSR, calcium-sensing receptor; PTH, parathyroid hormone.

Pancreas

The pancreas, a flat gland measuring approximately 6 inches in adults, is housed deep in the abdomen between the stomach and spine, near the duodenum. It is composed of clusters of exocrine cells. The green-colored product of these pancreatic exocrine cells is bile, an alkaline fluid comprised of beneficial digestive enzymes. Bile drains into the duodenum by way of the common bile duct and ampulla of Vater. The splenic artery supplies the pancreas, whereas venous blood drains from the pancreas into the hepatic portal vein. Therefore, the liver is the primary recipient of pancreatic hormones and responsible for facilitating first-pass metabolism of those hormones as they approach the heart and systemic circulation (Felsenfeld & Levine, 2015; Neal, 2016).

Pancreatic endocrine cells can be subdivided into two major types, each with its own primary function. Pancreatic α-cells account for approximately 20% of pancreatic cells; their primary function is the secretion of glucagon in cases of hypoglycemia. First, glucagon binds to the G-protein coupled receptor (GPCR) on target cells. This activates adenylate cyclase and raises cyclic adenosine monophosphate (cAMP) levels. An increase in protein kinase A activity results, which facilitates glucagon release, which acts to covert glycogen stores to glucose (glycogenolysis) and release these glucose stores into the circulation. In addition, glucagon stimulates the liver to increase amino acid uptake and converts it into glucose (gluconeogenesis). On a smaller scale, stored triglycerides are mobilized into free fatty acids and glycerol and transported to the liver for conversion into glucose (gluconeogenesis).

Pancreatic β-cells comprise the majority of all pancreatic cells; these cells are glucose sensors and modulate the secretion of insulin. Control of insulin secretion during hyperglycemia involves the activation of glucose (glycolysis) and oxidative glucose metabolism. Glucokinase, found in the pancreas, liver, pituitary gland, and brain, is the rate-limiting enzyme in the glycolytic pathway; it has a low affinity for glucose and therefore controls the rate and affinity for glucose entry into the glycolytic pathway and insulin release. Once glucokinase senses increased extracellular glucose load, it activates tyrosine kinase receptors, triggering uptake of glucose by GLUT2 transporters and the phosphorylation and conversion of glucose to glucose-6-phosphate. This process facilitates the rise in the adenosine triphosphate (ATP) to adenosine diphosphate (ADP) ratio, inactivates potassium channels, and depolarizes the beta cell membrane. Calcium channels open, allowing their influx into the cell with subsequent release of insulin (Figure 10.8; Molina, 2013).

Two additional subtypes of pancreatic cells are delta and pancreatic polypeptide cells. These cells are responsible for secreting somatostatin and pancreatic polypeptides, respectively (Felsenfeld & Levine, 2015; Martin, Fanaroff, & Walsh, 2015; Molina, 2013).

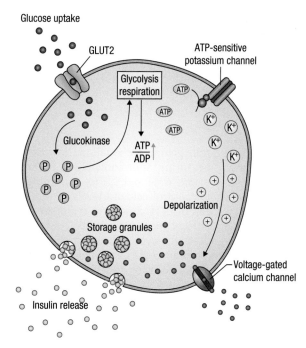

Figure 10.8 Glycolytic pathway.

ADP, adenosine monophosphate; ATP, adenosine triphosphate: GLUT2, glucose transporter, type 2.

Pineal Gland

The pineal gland is a small, red-gray-colored and pinecone-shaped organ that is approximately 1/3 inch in length in adults. It is located distal to the third cerebral ventricle and is composed of pineal and neuroglial cells (Figure 10.2; Molina, 2013). Blood flow to the pineal gland is supplied by the posterior cerebral artery. Despite its seemingly modest role in endocrine function, the pineal gland receives the second-largest blood supply, second only to the kidney. The purpose for this generous circulatory supply is poorly understood, but likely related to the pineal gland's role in synthesizing and secreting melatonin. Melatonin, derived from the amino acid tryptophan, is responsible for the regulation of circadian rhythm and reproductive hormones as well as skin and eye coloration (Pfaff & Joëls, 2017).

DEVELOPMENTAL PHYSIOLOGY

Calcium–Phosphorus–Magnesium Homeostasis

Calcium, phosphorus, and magnesium dysregulation can place the neonate at risk for a host of complications, including neurologic dysfunction, arrhythmias, and respiratory derangements. The regulation and transport of calcium, phosphate, and magnesium is essential to maintain homeostatic biologic and cellular functioning. In the text that follows, we describe regulatory hormonal influences and transport of these ions.

Calcium. Calcium is the most abundant ion in the human body. Nearly all calcium (99%) is found in the bones and teeth. The remaining 1% of calcium is found in the ECF and the soft tissues. Total body calcium levels rapidly rise during the final trimester of fetal development and then drop shortly after birth. After birth, total body calcium can be found in three distinct forms: (a) "free" or ionized (50%); (b) bound to albumin and globulins (40%); or (c) bound to bicarbonate, phosphate, or citrate (10%). Free calcium is the only active form of calcium and can cross the plasma membrane. Calcium ions are essential for maintenance and control of many biologic processes, including cell-to-cell communication, cell aggregation and division, coagulation, neuromuscular excitability, cardiomyocyte depolarization, membrane integrity and permeability, and enzymatic synthesis and secretion (Blaine, Choncol & Levi, 2014; Namgung & Tsang, 2017).

Postnatal calcium concentrations are regulated by PTH secretion, $1,25\text{-}(OH)_2D$ (active vitamin D_3), and calcitonin. Both PTH and vitamin D_3 work to promote calcium absorption, whereas calcitonin works to increase calcium excretion. PTH promotes calcium resorption in the bone and renal system and within the intestine by way of facilitating $1,25\text{-}(OH)_2D$-mediated intestinal aborption of calcium. Similarly, vitamin D stimulates the absorption of calcium (and phosphorus) from the bone, intestine, and kidney. As vitamin D can only be obtained through exposure to sunlight and enterally through the ingestion of infant formulas or vitamin supplements, the influence of vitamin D on calcium homeostasis is considered a "long-loop" (time-consuming) process, which often does not reach an influential status for the first few weeks of life (Namgug & Tsang, 2017). Conversely, calcitonin acts to facilitate calcium homeostasis through *inhibition*. Calcitonin works to prevent hypercalcemic states by inhibiting calcium (and phosphorus) release from bone as well as facilitating renal excretion of calcium (and phosphorus). Both calcitonin and PTH are considered faster-acting "short loops" once PTH maturation is complete.

The neonate must quickly adapt to extrauterine life and the cessation of maternal calcium supplies. Unfortunately for the newborn, the parathyroid response to evolving hypocalcemia is diminished in the first days after birth. As such, ionized calcium concentrations fall over the first 24 to 48 hours of life, reaching a nadir of approximately 4.9 mg/dL (term infants) before rebounding over the next 4 to 6 days of life in a quest to reach childhood levels by the end of postnatal week 1 (Loughead, Mimouni, & Tsang, 1988; Namgug & Tsang, 2017). Of infants born prematurely, very-low-birth-weight infants tend to reach the lowest ionized calcium nadirs.

Parathyroid immaturity, or the transient hypoparathyroid state observed after birth, is not fully understood, yet it contributes significantly to the risk for hypocalcemia in premature and term newborns. Factors understood to contribute to a stunted parathyroid response include method of delivery, decreased enteral calcium intake during the first days of life, as well as the functional immaturity of the gastrointestinal and renal systems. Higher PTH values are reported in the umbilical cords of infants born by elective cesarean section, compared to those delivered by elective cesarean *with* trial of labor, emergent cesarean, and spontaneous vaginal delivery (Namgug & Tsang, 2017). It is understood that both breastfed and bottle-fed newborns slowly increase ingested enteral volumes, which leads to a steady increase in exogenous calcium intake over the first week of life. Similarly, intestinal absorption of essential nutrients steadily increases over the first 2 to 4 weeks of life (Namgug & Tsang, 2017), concurrent with increasing enteral feeding volumes. As the majority of calcium is absorbed in the small intestine, delayed intestinal maturity contributes to the observed decrease and slow restoration of calcium levels to normal values after birth. In addition, the renal system undergoes a process of functional maturation after birth, reaching competency by the second week of life. Once mature, virtually all filtered calcium is reabsorbed within the proximal tubules, with additional reabsorption occurring later in the distal convoluted tubules (Blaine et al., 2015; Namgug & Tsang, 2017).

Premature infants, infants of diabetic mothers, and those who suffer perinatal asphyxia are at a higher risk for calcium dysregulation. These risk factors and their mechanism of action in facilitating a hypocalcemic state are provided in Table 10.3. Life-span implications associated with altered calcium homeostasis include osteopenia.

Phosphorus. Second to calcium, phosphorus is the most abundant mineral in the human body. Like calcium, nearly all phosphorus (85%) is found in the bones and teeth. The remaining 15% of phosphorus is found in ECF and soft tissues. Total body phosphorus exists as (a) "free" or ionized (85%); (b) bound to albumin (11%); and (c) bound to sodium, calcium, or magnesium (5–15%; Molina, 2013; Namgung & Tsang, 2017). Serum phosphorus concentrations vary, altered by factors, including gender, age, acidity, or alkalinity, and as influenced by other circulating hormones (Namgung & Tsang, 2017).

Phosphorus load is regulated by renal, skeletal, and intestinal transport mechanisms. In situations in which phosphorus load is decreased (hypophosphatemia), several mechanisms are activated to restore homeostasis in a manner that does not disrupt calcium concentrations. First, renal tubular reabsorption of phosphorus occurs. During this time frame, calcium and phosphorus are mobilized from the bone. In addition, $1,25\text{-}(OH)_2D$ is synthesized by the kidneys and released into the intestinal tract to promote increased absorption of calcium and phosphorus. The reverse of this cascade of events is elicited in the face of hyperphosphatemia (Namgung & Tsang, 2017).

Similar to calcium, total body phosphorus levels rapidly increase during the final trimester of fetal

TABLE 10.3 Factors Associated with Early-Onset Postnatal Hypocalcemia

Factor	Mechanism
Intrauterine growth restriction	Decreased placental calcium transfer
Maternal diabetes	Maternal renal loss of magnesium with glycosuria results in fetal hypomagnesemia and inability to produce sufficient PTH
	Fetal macrosomia may encourage premature delivery and resultant decreased PTH activity
Prematurity	Early termination of placental calcium transfer
	Inadequate calcium intake enterally or intravenously
	Urinary calcium loss secondary to immature renal function
Birth asphyxia	Inadequate calcium intake enterally or intravenously
	Renal failure, acute tubular necrosis
Immunodeficiency disorder	22q11.2 deletion (DiGeorge syndrome)
Hyperphosphatemia	Increased phosphorus load (e.g., inappropriate enteral intake, high phosphorus, cow's milk)
Vitamin D deficiency	Low production of PTH secondary to hypomagnesemia triggered by insufficient vitamin D
Medications	Diuretics, aminoglycosides (e.g., gentamicin) increase urinary losses of calcium

NOTE: Infants born via elective cesarean *with* trial of labor, emergent cesarean, and by spontaneous vaginal delivery risk postnatal hypocalcemia. Intrauterine-growth-restricted infants who succumb to any of the risk factors listed are considered at-risk for hypocalcemia.

PTH, parathyroid hormone.

Sources: From Molina, P. E. (2013). *Endocrine physiology* (4th ed.). New York, NY: McGraw-Hill Medical; Pfaff, D. W., & Joëls, M. (Eds.). (2017). *Hormones, brain and behavior* (3rd ed.). Amsterdam, The Netherlands: Elsevier/Academic Press.

development and then drop over the first 48 hours after birth. Beginning around the second day of life, and as PTH and Calcium levels begin to increase, an increase in plasma phosphorus is observed. It is likely that transient postnatal renal immaturity, which typically spans the first 1 to 2 postnatal days (see Chapter 8) spares newborns of renal phosphorus losses and facilitates the progressive increase in phosphorus load. Concurrently, as postnatal gluconeogenesis is established, circulating phosphorus levels increase; phosphorus is liberated from amino acids with this metabolic pathway.

Life-span implications associated with phosphorus dysregulation include parathyroid cell hyperplasia and phosphorus depletion syndrome. Both extremes are regarded as preventable, rare diseases of the neonate. Careful management of fluid and electrolyte status, and the provision of enteral and parenteral nutrition, is indicated among critically ill neonates who require a prolonged birth hospitalization.

Magnesium. Magnesium is an abundant intracellular cation whose serum concentrations influence calcium homeostasis. Nearly all magnesium (99%) is stored in the bone, muscle, and soft tissues. A small percentage (1%) of magnesium can be found in the ECF. Similar to both calcium and phosphorus, magnesium exists as three fractions: (a) "free" or ionized (50–90%); (b) bound to albumin (20–30%); and (c) bound to bicarbonate, phosphate, or citrate (5–15%); due to differences in measurement methods, ranges for each fraction of magnesium vary considerably across the literature (Jahnen-Dechent & Ketteler, 2012). Magnesium is essential to bone and teeth development, and influences cardiovascular smooth muscle contractility, neuromuscular excitability and transmission (e.g., twitches, cramps, muscle spasms), and many enzyme reactions (often involving ATP; Blaine et al., 2015; Long & Romani, 2014; Namgug & Tsang, 2017).

Total body magnesium levels are tightly regulated by intestinal, renal, and bone transport mechanisms. Intestinal transport involves the active transport of magnesium across the ileum, with passive absorption occurring throughout the small intestine. Renal transport of magnesium involves filtration and reabsorption. Approximately 70% of total circulating (absorbed) serum magnesium is transported and filtered through the glomerulus. Nearly all (96%) of this filtered magnesium is reabsorbed within the proximal tubule, ascending loop of Henle, and distal convoluted tubule. As such, and under normal circumstances, little magnesium is lost to the urine. Magnesium transport and absorption within the bone are dynamic; however, transport mechanisms are currently poorly understood (Blaine et al., 2015; Long & Romani, 2014; Namgug & Tsang, 2017).

Life-span implications associated with magnesium dysregulation include fetal magnesium toxicity (rickets) secondary to maternal magnesium tocolysis leading to inhibition of PTH secretion and hypocalcemia.

CARBOHYDRATE METABOLIC PATHWAYS

Carbohydrates are an essential source of energy for living cells. All organs use glucose; however, the brain relies almost exclusively on glucose as its source for energy metabolism. Furthermore, cerebral glycogen stores are low, and for that reason, glucose delivery to the brain is an ongoing process that must be tightly regulated to maintain homeostasis. For infants, this is particularly important, as cerebral glucose requirements are increased compared to adults and alternative energy sources (lactate, ketone bodies) are limited. Cerebral glucose consumption accounts for approximately 90% of total glucose consumption among newborns (McGowan, 1999). Increased consumption is reported among premature infants (including late preterm infants) due to the increased brain-to-body ratio (Kalhan & Parimi, 2000).

Four major metabolic pathways control carbohydrate metabolism, either through the synthesis of glucose from precursors for release into the bloodstream, synthesis of glycogen for storage in the liver or muscle cells, or the synthesis of pyruvate (Table 10.4; Figure 10.9). These energy-generating carbohydrate-mediated metabolic pathways are essential "core knowledge" for the advanced practice nurse (APN). Among newborns, functional operation of two particular pathways, glycogenolysis and gluconeogenesis, are necessary within the first hours after birth in order to maintain necessary basal glucose utilization (4 to 6 mg/kg/minute).

Glycogenesis

By definition, glycogenesis describes the biosynthesis of sugar into glycogen for storage and later use, which among newborns occurs immediately after the ingestion of carbohydrate sources. Glycogenesis occurs primarily within the hepatocyte, and to a lesser degree within muscle cells. Three hormones, namely insulin, glucagon, and epinephrine, modulate this process (Nelson & Cox, 2017). We know that glycogen begins accumulating within fetal tissues as early as week 9 of gestation. Thereafter, glycogen stores gradually increase across fetal development and at term, healthy, appropriate-for-gestational age (AGA) infants possess increased glycogen stores than adults. In some (but not all) circumstances, these accumulated glycogen stores are sufficient to maintain euglycemia among AGA infants, as the mother-infant dyad adjusts to oral enteral feeding

TABLE 10.4 The Four Major Carbohydrate Metabolic Pathways

Metabolic Pathway	Major Function
Glycogenesis	Synthesis of glycogen
Glycogenolysis	Breakdown of glycogen → glucose
Glycolysis	Breakdown of glucose → pyruvate
Gluconeogenesis	Synthesis of non-carbohydrate sources (pyruvate, lactate, amino acids) → glucose

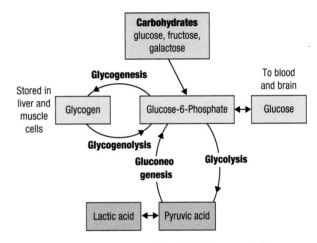

Figure 10.9 Summary of carbohydrate metabolism.

regimens. Comparatively, premature, late preterm, and small for gestational age (SGA) infants typically possess too few glycogen stores at birth. As a result, these infants are likely to develop postnatal hypoglycemia during the birth hospitalization; APNs and clinical nurses are responsible for ensuring the prompt and consistent provision of appropriate exogenous carbohydrates (by way of breast milk, formula, or a combination of both), as this is the primary mechanism by which glucose can be delivered to the brain. The stepwise biochemical process involved with the synthesis of glycogen is presented in Figure 10.10. The process of mobilization of stored glycogen is termed glycogenolysis, which will be described next.

Glycogenolysis

Recall that glycogen is the stored form of glucose, and under normal circumstances, is mobilized from either hepatic or muscle cells when blood glucose levels fall. This process is termed glycogenolysis. By definition, glycogenolysis involves the breakdown of glycogen stores into glucose-1-phosphate (muscle cells) and glucose

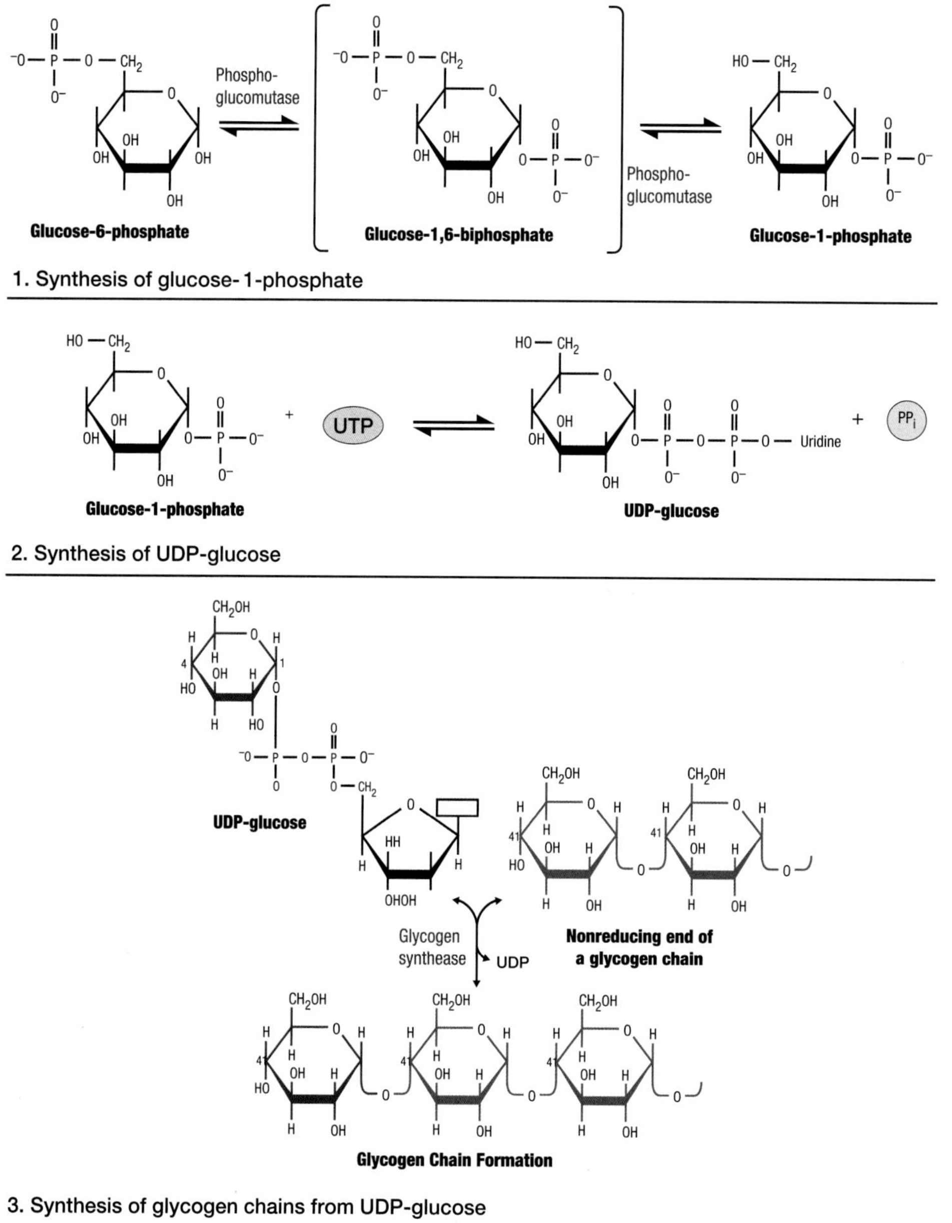

1. Synthesis of glucose-1-phosphate

2. Synthesis of UDP-glucose

3. Synthesis of glycogen chains from UDP-glucose

Figure 10.10 Glycogenesis pathway. The steps are as follows: (1) phosphorylation of glucose into glucose-6-phosphate (modulated by glucokinase, within the liver); (2) glucose-6-phosphate is converted into glucose-1-phosphate (modulated by phosphoglucomutase); (3) glucose-1-phosphate is converted into UDP-glucose (modulated by UDP-glycose pyrophosphatase). This ultimately leads to the attachment of UDP-glucose to a glycogen primer, glycogen synthesis, branching, and elongation. The glycogen is thereby stored in the liver and muscle cells, for later use.

ADP, adenosine monophosphate; ATP, adenosine triphosphate; UDP, uridine 5'-diphosphate; UTP, uridine 5'-triphosphate.

(hepatocytes). Glucose-1-phosphate offers a source of energy for muscle contraction, whereas hepatic conversion of glycogen into glucose increases serum glucose levels. The same hormones (insulin, glucagon, and epinephrine) that regulate glycogenesis also modulate glycogenolysis. In that sense, glycogenolysis is hormonally regulated. It is rare for glycogenolysis to occur in significant amounts during fetal development, despite the presence of the enzymes necessary for this metabolic process. The exception to this principle applies in situations where the fetus is exposed to a prolonged delay in umbilical glucose uptake. Among newborns, this process is initiated secondary to a normal postnatal surge in glucagon concentrations after birth, during periods of hypoglycemia, or periods involving accelerated glucose uptake, which may occur with oxygen deprivation or seizures (Volpe, 2018). Again, appropriate glycogen stores must be present for glucose production to occur via this pathway.

A summary of glycogenolysis will be presented next. Learners should understand that this summary describes a normal physiologic response to postnatal hypoglycemia. However, the precise glucose nadir required to trigger this postnatal metabolic process is unknown. Otherwise healthy newborns may develop clinically unrecognizable hypoglycemia after birth, with glucose levels as low as 20 to 25 mg/dL (Adamkin, 2016). Routine postnatal glucose screening for healthy infants, including infants who are exclusively breast fed prior to the onset of lactogenesis II, is uncommon, which may result in underreporting of severe or prolonged hypoglycemia in the postnatal period. While a decrease in circulating glucose may be necessary to elicit physiologic glycogenolysis (and gluconeogenesis), the threshold at which hypoglycemia surpasses that which is required to initiate this process, and threatens organ health, remains unclear.

When blood glucose levels fall, the pancreas secretes glucagon. Glucagon travels to the liver, where it binds to hepatic receptors and initiates an increase in cAMP levels. The cAMP stimulates a phosphorylation cascade, activating glycogen phosphorylase and other proteins. The glycogen phosphorylase cleaves the α (1,4) ends of glycogen. This yields four glucose-1-phosphate molecules. Three of the four glucose-1-phosphate molecules are transferred to a non-reducing end of glycogen, by way of a debranching enzyme, and diverted to muscle cells for optimized muscle contractility. The fourth molecule is converted to glucose within the hepatocyte and then released into the bloodstream as glucose (Figure 10.11; Nelson & Cox 2017). This provides a rapid source of glucose for newborns; however, glycogen stores are usually limited in the immediate postnatal period. For this reason, glycogenolysis may be limited to the first 10 to 12 hours of postnatal life. Resumption is possible once adequate enteral or parenteral nutrition is offered and glycogen stores are replenished for later mobilization.

Glycolysis

Glycolysis, an anaerobic process, is believed to be the oldest and most widely understood carbohydrate metabolic pathway. By definition, glycolysis involves the extraction of energy from glucose. To accomplish this, circulating glucose molecules are oxidized, split into two equal parts, and converted into pyruvate (a ketoacid). In addition, energy, primarily in the form of ATP, is cleaved and stored for later use. In order to best appreciate the complexity

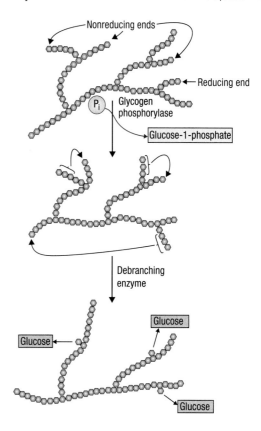

Figure 10.11 Glycogenolysis pathway.

of chemical reactions involved in the production of pyruvate, the glycolytic pathway is summarized as a series of 10 specific chemical reactions in Figure 10.12. The reverse of glycolysis is gluconeogenesis.

Gluconeogenesis

Gluconeogenesis is the metabolic process that results in the synthesis of glucose and glycogen from noncarbohydrate sources, including lactate, glycerol, pyruvate, and amino acids. It is modulated by hormonal changes, including a reduction in the plasma insulin concentration and increased circulating concentrations of glucagon, catecholamines, GH, TSH, and corticosteroids (Nelson & Cox 2017; Thureen & Hay, 2006). Similar to glycogenolysis, gluconeogenesis is initiated secondary to a normal surge in glucagon concentrations after birth.

The first step in gluconeogenesis involves the conversion of pyruvate to phosphoenolpyruvic acid (PEP). The second step is the conversion of fructose-1,6 biphosphate to fructose-6-phosphate with the use of the enzyme fructose-1,6-phosphatase. The conversion of fructose-6-phosphate to glucose-6-phosphate is modulated by the enzyme

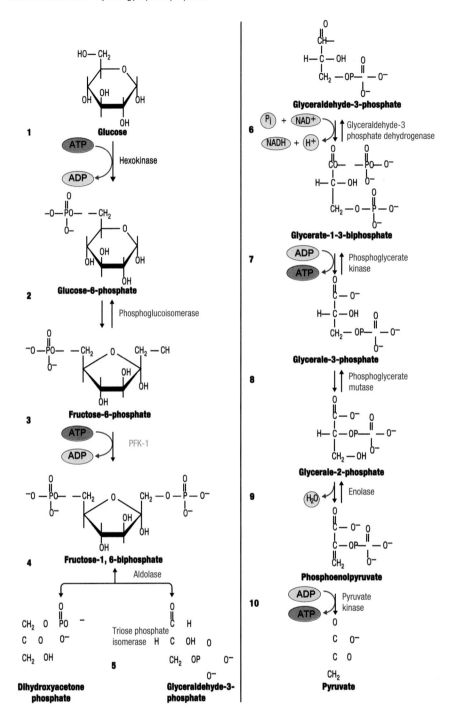

Figure 10.12 The glycolytic pathway. The steps are as follows: (1) synthesis of glucose-6-phosphate; (2) conversion of glucose-6-phosphate to fructose-6-phosphate; (3) phosphorylation of fructose-6-phosphate; (4) cleavage of fructose-1,6-biphosphate; (5) conversion of glyceraldehyde-3-phosphate and dihydroxyacetone phosphate; (6) oxidation of glyceraldehyde-3-phosphate; (7) phosphoryl group transfer; (8) conversion of 3-phosphoglycerate and 2-phosphoglycerate; (9) dehydration of 2-phosphoglycerate; (10) synthesis of pyruvate.

ADP, adenosine diphosphate; ATP, adenosine triphosphate; NAD+, nicotinamide adenine dinucleotide in oxidized form; NADH, nicotinamide adenine dinucleotide in reduced form; PKF-1, Phosphofructokinase-1.

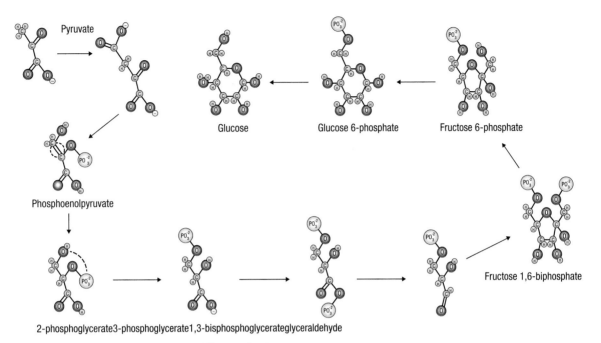

Pyruvate

Glucose

Glucose 6-phosphate

Fructose 6-phosphate

Phosphoenolpyruvate

Fructose 1,6-biphosphate

2-phosphoglycerate 3-phosphoglycerate 1,3-bisphosphoglycerate glyceraldehyde

Figure 10.13 Gluconeogenesis pathway.

phosphoglucoisomerase. The final operational step in gluconeogenesis involves the conversion of glucose-6-phosphate to glucose with the enzyme glucose-6-phosphatase, for use as an energy source throughout the body and, in particular, within the brain (Figure 10.13; Baynes, 2014; Nelson & Cox 2017; Thureen & Hay, 2006). Gluconeogenesis also provides newborns with a source of glucose for cerebral and tissue consumption. However, sufficient production of enzymes necessary for the initiation of this pathway typically takes between 4 to 6 hours after birth. Therefore, this pathway cannot be considered immediately effective in mitigating postnatal hypoglycemia that occurs within the first hours after birth.

FETAL GLUCOSE METABOLISM

Under normal conditions, the fetus does not independently produce glucose. Transplacental glucose, amino acids, free fatty acids, ketones, and glycerol are easily funneled from mother to fetus and glucose is obtained through a process of oxidation. The fetus is never directly exposed to periods of fasting and therefore does not develop associated compensatory mechanisms.

The fetus does demonstrate some competency with insulin secretion and regulation in response to the maternal glucose load; however, the function of insulin in utero differs from its postnatal function. It is important to understand that insulin secretion is responsive to fetal glucose concentrations. However, fetal glucose concentrations are controlled by the mother. Maternal hyperglycemia can elicit fetal hyperglycemia and a compensatory increase in insulin secretion. Conversely, maternal hypoglycemia can elicit fetal hypoglycemia and fetal suppression of insulin synthesis. Despite the fact that insulin does not regulate fetal glucose stores, it does influence fetal growth. Prolonged fetal exposure to uncontrolled maternal hyperglycemia can lead to persistent (excessive) glycogenesis. Manifestations include macrosomia and hypertrophic cardiomyopathy, which will be addressed later in this chapter (Adamkin, 2015).

During the third trimester, fetal glycogen production and storage are increased, with suppression of glycogenolysis. Cortisol and circulating insulin levels rise, which suppresses lipolysis and allows for subcutaneous energy storage. These subcutaneous storage sites, when established in adequate amounts, will become easily accessible sites for glucose mobilization in the hours immediately after birth (Adamkin, 2015).

POSTNATAL GLUCOSE METABOLISM: "TRANSITIONAL HYPOGLYCEMIA"

The neonate's ability to independently produce glucose after the cessation of the transplacental lifeline is one of the most critical events involved in the "transition to extrauterine life." It is well-documented that glucose levels drop after birth; current evidence suggests that the plasma glucose nadir is reached within approximately 60 to 90 minutes after birth. This occurs secondary to the (a) transient surge in catecholamines and glucagon, (b) transient state of hyperinsulinism, and (c) sluggish initiation of glycogenolysis and gluconeogenesis (Adamkin, 2015). Specific to newborns, there is currently no consensus on a precise laboratory threshold associated with neuroglycopenia, or hypoglycemia which causes impaired brain function. Both the American Academy of Pediatrics (2011) and Pediatric Endocrine Society (2015) endorse conflicting plasma glucose levels that warrant clinical intervention; this is one of the most contested topics among clinicians who oversee the care of term and late preterm infants (Adamkin et al, 2011; Thornton et al., 2015).

In the presence of a normally functioning endocrine system, three factors are essential to normalize hepatic glucose production. First, hepatic enzymes must be present for glycogenolysis and gluconeogenesis. Second, the neonate must possess adequate stores of glycogen, free fatty acids, glycerol, amino acids, and lactate. However, three significant risk factors threaten the postnatal establishment of euglycemia after birth: (a) a persistent hypoketotic state, (b) inappropriate conservation of glycogen stores, and (c) incomplete suppression of insulin secretion. A summary of normal postnatal glucose metabolism is provided in Figure 10.14. Risk factors for transient and persistent hypoglycemia are summarized in Table 10.5. Regardless of risk stratification, as hepatic processes normalize in the immediate postnatal period, exogenous glucose must be provided to establish and maintain euglycemia. Even transient periods of hypoglycemia risk long-term neurodevelopmental dysfunction.

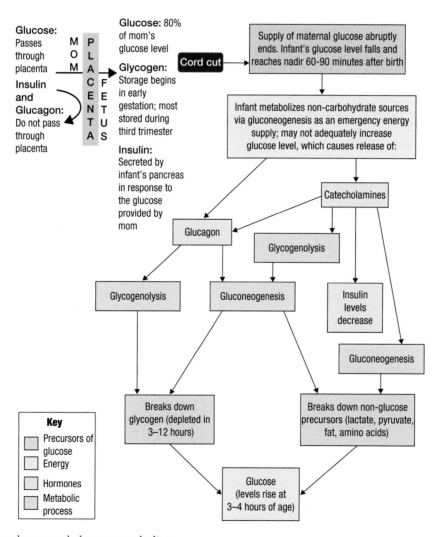

Figure 10.14 Normal postnatal glucose metabolism.

Image Credit: Oksana Kasko, MSN, NNP-BC

TABLE 10.5 Risk Factors for Transient and Persistent Neonatal Hypoglycemia

Transient Neonatal Hypoglycemia	Preterm and IUGR infants
	Transient hyperinsulinism (IDM/GDM)
	Perinatal stressors
Persistent Neonatal Hypoglycemia	Hyperinsulinism
	Hormone regulation deficiency
	Inborn errors of metabolism

GDM, gestational diabetes mellitus; IDM, infants born of diabetic mothers; IUGR, intrauterine growth restriction.

Source: Adapted from Rozance, P. J., & Rosenberg, A. A. (2017). The neonate. In S. G. Gabbe , J. R. Niebyl, J. L. Simpson, M. B. Landon, H. L. Galan, E. R. M. Jauniaux, . . . W. A. Grobman (Ed.), *Obstetrics: Normal and problem pregnancies* (7th ed., pp. 468–498). Philadelphia, PA: Elsevier/Saunders.

EXOGENOUS CARBOHYDRATE SOURCES

Sugar Composition of Carbohydrate Sources

The majority of premature and term infant formulas (excluding those used for lactose intolerance) consist of greater than or equal to 20% carbohydrate sugars (≥93% as lactose; Gidrewicz & Fenton, 2014; Walker & Goran, 2015). Comparatively, human milk contains up to 7% sugar (as lactose; Cooper, Barnett, Gentles, Cairns, & Simpson, 2013; Jenness, 1979). In order to avoid a fasting state, consistent and adequate calories from carbohydrate sources must be provided.

Caloric Density of Carbohydrate Sources

Most newborns that are healthy enough to receive exclusive (oral) enteral nutrition gradually increase intake over the first few days of life, toward an average goal of 150 ml/kg/day and 100 kcal/kg/day. This goal meets basal energy requirements and offers appropriate additional energy for the growth phase; variation may exist based upon individual patient needs. Carbohydrate sources, an infant's primary source for fuel, include breast milk, commercial formulas, or a combination of thereof. Breast milk is the gold standard for infant feedings; however, supplementation with commercial formula (or human milk fortifiers) may be indicated among at-risk newborns to avoid weight loss > 8%, postnatal hypoglycemia and poor growth velocity. Alternatively, some parents choose a blend of breastfeeding and formula feeding, or exclusive formula feeding. This may occur for a variety of reasons that may not be immediately shared with each member of the healthcare team, including personal or cultural preferences, or medical necessity (e.g. history of double mastectomy). A balanced and unbiased approach to counseling families who seek or require information regarding nutritional regimens, grounded in the provision of support and encouragement and which considers parental decision-making capacity and

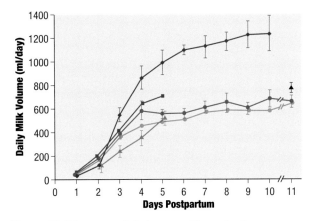

Figure 10.15 Average daily human milk production.

Source: Adapted from Neville, M. C., Keller, R., Seacat, J., Lutes, V., Neifert, M., Casey, C., . . . Archer, P. (1988). Studies in human lactation: Milk volumes in lactating women during the onset of lactation and full lactation. *The American Journal of Clinical Nutrition, 48*(6), 1375–1386. doi:10.1093/ajcn/48.6.1375.

the medical needs of their infant, is essential. Nutritional information specific to commercial formulas is readily available on product packaging; however, data specific to human milk may not be readily available to APNs. Therefore, we offer a summary of the caloric density of human colostrum and mature human milk. In addition, we present the limited body of evidence specific to average daily milk yield among lactating women; additional studies are needed.

The average caloric content of human colostrum is approximately 16.2 kcal/fl. oz, which falls below the average caloric density of term commercial formulas (Hester, Hustead, Mackey, Signhal & Marriage, 2012; Sapsford & Smith, 2016). An average milk yield of 56ml (30.24 calories) of colostrum is reported on postpartum day 1. This output increases to an average of 185ml (99.9 calories) on postpartum day 2 (Neville et al., 1988). By postpartum day three, the average daily human milk yield is 383 mL/day (206.8 total calories), and this increases to 580 mL/day (313.2 total calories) by the fourth postpartum day (Figure 10.15;

Neville et al., 1988). Mature breast milk, which is typically established on or about the third to fourth postpartum day, provides an average caloric density of 19.2 to 20.7 kcal/fl. oz, similar to commercial formulas (Kleinman & Greer, 2014; Sapsford & Smith, 2016). APNs should recognize that enteral intake which falls below basal energy requirements can limit a newborn's capacity for glycogenesis and glycogenolysis, and increase the risk for hypoglycemia.

POSTNATAL FASTING

Glucose is the primary fuel for the brain. The brain uses glucose at a rate 20 times faster than other vital organs. Glucose, amino acids, and lipids, in the form of commercially available infant formulas, expressed maternal breast milk, or parenteral nutrition, must be provided to newborns within the first hour after birth. Nourishing the newborn is critical to maintain the basic architecture and function of the brain and other vital organs. Premature, growth-restricted, critically ill infants, infants of diabetic mothers, or otherwise healthy term infants may struggle to maintain euglycemia due to factors discussed earlier in this chapter. These factors include (a) reduced glycogen stores, (b) increased metabolic needs, (c) insufficient compensatory responses to hypoglycemia, or (d) increased glucose uptake by peripheral tissues.

Other factors that may yield transient, persistent, and/or pathologic postnatal hypoglycemia include dehydration-induced (also regarded as starvation-induced) hypoglycemia, hyperinsulinism, and inborn errors of metabolism. Starvation-induced hypoglycemia, which occurs secondary to a prolonged fasting state, can yield a transient or persistent state of hypoglycemia. Hyperinsulinism, which commonly occurs secondary to maternal diabetes, can further exacerbate a hypoglycemic state during the immediate postnatal period. Pathologic hypoglycemia, which persists despite compensatory efforts, may arise secondary to inborn errors of metabolism (IEMs). Impaired glycogenolysis is associated with glycogen storage diseases, whereas impaired gluconeogenesis is associated with metabolic errors includeing fructose-1-bisphosphatase deficiency and pyruvate carboxylase deficiency (Weinstein, Steurwald, De Souza, Carolina, & Derks, 2018). More rare endocrine disorders, such as congenital hyperinsulinism, also correlate with impaired glycogenolysis.

A stepwise review of the metabolic adaptation to a postabsorptive state, which seeks to provide endogenous compensation for postnatal hypoglycemia, is provided in the text that follows. We define the immediate newborn period as the first 72 to 96 hours of life, or until such time as an infant achieves an approximate caloric intake of 100 calories/kg/day.

The Postabsorptive Stage

The postabsorptive stage marks the postprandial time after the absorption of ingested exogenous nutrition is complete. Unlike older infants, children, and adults, newborns are born into a postabsorptive, fasting state. As previously stated, metabolic pathways are evoked during this period immediately following birth. In aggregate, they modulate a rather immediate release of endogenous glucose through an increase in glycogen breakdown and later gluconeogenesis, as well as breakdown of fat as an alternative fuel source (Hay, Adamkin, Harding, & Hawdon, 2018).

Compensatory Glycogenolysis
Glycogenolysis is initiated as a compensatory mechanism to low circulating glucose levels. Immediately after birth as well as during postabsorptive stages, hepatic glycogen stores are hydrolyzed and released into the systemic circulation (glycogenolysis). Once these glycogen stores are depleted, lipolysis and ketogenesis occur, contingent upon available supplies, as a second-tier attempt to recruit glucose for energy and to support the metabolic demands of CNS. Should adequate circulating glucose levels be achieved, insulin activates a phosphorylation cascade that inhibits glycogenolysis.

Compensatory Gluconeogenesis
During periods of fasting, the CNS extracts ketones (primarily β-hydroxybutyrate and acetoacetate) from the circulation to use as a fuel source during the postabsorptive phase. However, the newborn's response to ketone synthesis is stunted. Circulating β-hydroxybutyrate (BOB) levels, a major circulating ketone body, are estimated at only 0.4 mmol/L in fasting newborns, compared to 2.4 to 3.8 mmol/L in old infants and children (Stanley, Anday, Baker, & Delivoria-Papadopolous, 1979). Clearly, this is not a significant compensatory pathway in the immediate newborn period.

Life-Span Implications. Prevention of fasting and accompanying hypoglycemia is one of the most critical means for preserving human potential. Neurologic resiliency to hypoglycemia remains unclear; however, the inability for transient hypoglycemia (in the immediate neonatal period) to cause neurodevelopmental consequences is no longer an accepted conversation. Dehydration-induced hypoglycemia among otherwise healthy late preterm and term newborns is an increasingly litigious topic.

As previously mentioned, a clear definition of clinically significant and pathologic hypoglycemia is lacking. However, recent research suggests that even infants with transient and moderate hypoglycemia are at-risk for neurologic impairment. A glucose level of less than 46 mg/dL within the first 24 hours of life has been associated with a 3.7-fold increased risk of brain injury on MRI and a 4.8-fold increased odds of lower motor, cognitive, and language scores at 1 year of age (Tam et al., 2012). A study of 1,395 newborns, some of whom were considered high-risk (i.e. premature), indicated that newborns who developed hypoglycemia of less than 40 mg/dL within the first hours of life incur a 50% reduction in passing fourth-grade literacy and math tests (Kaiser et al., 2015). Among a recent study of 1,396 infants, the risk for adverse neurodevelopmental (motor or cognitive) impairment among moderately hypoglycemic (serum glucose <40 mg/dL) infants was approximately 2- to

3-fold higher than normoglycemic counterparts (Wickström, Skiöld, Petersson, Stephansson, & Altman, 2018). Some studies which report neurodevelopmental risks are notably underpowered or include high-risk populations (e.g., premature infants, infants with CNS disorders; Burns, Rutherford, Boardman, & Cowan, 2008; Kaiser et al., 2015; Kinnala et al., 1999). Others report similar neurologic outcomes among normoglycemic and hypoglycemic infants (McKinlay et al., 2015; Tin, Brunskill, Kelly, & Fritz, 2012). Therefore, this issue remains contentious and further investigation is indicated to safely define hypoglycemia and ensure that quality and safety remain at the forefront of clinical medicine.

GLUCOSE METABOLISM AND SPECIAL POPULATIONS

The Late-Preterm and Small-for-Gestational-Age Infant

Late-preterm infants are defined as those born between 34 and 36 6/7 weeks of gestation. *Small-for-gestational-age infants*

(SGA) are defined as infants who weigh less than 2,500 grams and fall below the tenth percentile for their stated gestational age. Both of these special populations incur an increased risk for hypoglycemia within the first few days of life. In particular, approximately 8% of all late-preterm infants develop hypoglycemia during the birth hospitalization.

Both late-preterm infants and SGA infants lack adequate glycogen stores, the primary source of glucose in the first 6 hours of postnatal life. In addition, decreased glucose production in the liver, limited fat stores, ketogenesis, and the inability to oxidize free fatty acids and triglycerides and hyperinsulinism are often present (Figure 10.16). This is due to a deficiency in enzymatic precursors necessary for gluconeogenesis. In addition, transient hyperinsulinism is observed; this is the most common cause of hyperinsulinemic hypoglycemia. Resolution is usually quick, although transient hypoglycemia can persist over the first 7 months of life, or beyond (Sperling, 2016).

Hypoglycemia can be exacerbated with the provision of limited enteral intake, poor suck–swallow coordination, or delayed or ineffective oral feeding with or

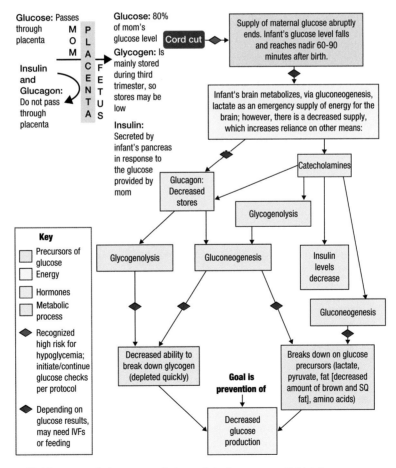

Figure 10.16 Postnatal glucose metabolism of the late preterm/SGA infant.

Image Credit: Oksana Kasko, MSN, NNP-BC

IVF, intravenous fluids; SGA, small for gestational age; SQ, subcutaneous.

without associated pathologies (i.e., sepsis or cold stress, respectively; Gouyon, Iacobelli, Ferdynus, & Bonsante, 2012; Sperling, 2016). As such, exclusively breast-fed late-preterm and SGA infants are at higher risk for hypoglycemia as compared to their bottle-fed counterparts. Establishing early enteral feeding regimens within 1 hour after birth, diligent trending of serum glucose levels, and ensuring the provision of adequate enteral volume, which may include judicious use of supplemental nutrition for exclusively breastfed newborns, are essential to facilitate glucose homeostasis (Gouyon et al., 2012).

The Infant of a Diabetic Mother

Gestational diabetes affects between 1% to 14% of the pregnant women, with approximately one in 1,000 women diagnosed with insulin-dependent diabetes (type 1 or type 2; DeSisto, Kim, & Sharma, 2014; Kansra, 2018). Infants of diabetic mothers (IDM) are at significant risk for hypoglycemia, as the fetal response to maternal

glucose load (hyperglycemia) involves secretion of insulin (hyperinsulinemia). Consequences of maternally-induced fetal hyperglycemia (and hyperinsulinemia) include decreased surfactant production, increased glycogenesis, and increased erythropoiesis (Martin et al., 2015). The increase in glycogenesis risks the development of macrosomia or a hypertrophic cardiomyopathy. A complimentary increase in fetal tissue oxygen uptake in observed, which elicits a state of hypoxemia. Erythropoietin production increases in response to hypoxia, which may lead to a state of polycythemia. In some circumstances, persistent hypoxemia can lead to stillbirth.

Postnatally, insulin secretion remains transiently elevated. In addition, elevated levels of epinephrine and decreased glucagon levels are observed. As a consequence, endogenous glucose production is severely inhibited, predisposing these infants to hypoglycemia (Sperling, 2016). The subsequent downregulation of insulin secretion occurs slowly, over the first few days of life, leaving the IDM infant vulnerable to periods of hypoglycemia (Figure 10.17; Kansra, 2018).

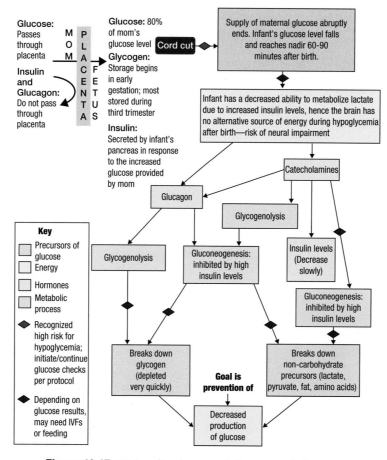

Figure 10.17 IDM-mediated postnatal glucose metabolism.

Image Credit: Oksana Kasko, APRN, MSN, NNP-BC

IDM, infants of diabetic mothers; IVF, intravenous fluids.

Similar to late-preterm and SGA infants, IDM infants who are exclusively breastfed incur a higher risk for hypoglycemia as compared to their bottle-fed counterparts. Establishing early enteral feeding regimens within 1 hour after birth, diligent trending of glucose values, and ensuring compliance with a regular feeding interval and provision of adequate enteral volume are essential to facilitate glucose homeostasis (Gouyon et al., 2012).

IDM-related deaths account for 50% of all perinatal mortalities (Ornoy, Reece, Pavlinkova, Kappen, & Miller, 2015). Among surviving infants, cardiac and neural tube defects are most severe. Additional manifestations include macrosomia, secondary to the growth-stimulating effects of insulin (Figure 10.17; Kansra, 2018). Of interest, some infants born to insulin-dependent diabetic mothers may be SGA. This is secondary to maternal vascular complications, hypertension, renal disease, or congenital infant malformations, which disrupt placental blood flow to the fetus (Ornoy et al., 2015).

GENETIC INFLUENCES: INBORN ERRORS OF METABOLISM

Under normal circumstances, metabolic reactions occur within the body as a means to break down nutrients, such as amino acids, to create energy, such as glucose. IEMs occur secondary to genetic mutations that block normal metabolic pathways and cause disordered cellular functioning. The end result is an accumulation of toxic precursors (metabolites) or a deficiency of end-product production. IEMs are commonly classified by the pattern of inheritance, enzyme involvement, and clinical manifestations. These genetically influenced metabolic disorders commonly affect amino acid, carbohydrate, and lipid metabolisms, as well as other degradation pathways. Three common metabolic disorders are presented here, as is a list of the most commonly screened IEMs (Table 10.6).

Amino Acidopathies

Phenylketonuria. Phenylketonuria (PKU) is an autosomal recessive genetic disorder that affects one out of every 10,000 to 15,000 newborns in the United States (Cleary, 2015; National Institutes of Health [NIH], 2018d). PKU is an enzyme deficiency, caused by mutations in the hepatic enzyme phenylalanine hydroxylase (PAH), normally coded by the *PAH* gene located on chromosome 12 (Figure 10.18). PKU is detected on the newborn metabolic screening test as an abnormal ratio of phenylalanine (abnormally elevated) to tyrosine (abnormally decreased; Cleary, 2015; NIH, 2018d).

Phenylalanine is an essential amino acid normally metabolized by the PAH enzyme within the liver to tyrosine. Tyrosine is an essential amino acid, instrumental in the production of hormones, including thyroid hormones, epinephrine, and norepinephrine. However, with PKU, the lack of PAH enzyme results in abnormally elevated circulating phenylalanine levels and abnormally low circulating tyrosine levels.

Clinical manifestations of PKU are not evident at birth; therefore, diligent history taking and timely follow-up of the newborn screening test is indicated to ensure early identification and treatment. After a few months of life, if left untreated, PKU increases urinary phenyl ketone and phenylacetic acid levels, altering the smell of urine ("mousey odor"). Other manifestations observed among untreated infants include eczema, pale skin and blue eyes (elevated phenylalanine levels reduce tyrosine metabolism and the subsequent formation of melanin, which alters skin and eye pigmentation), and seizures (Merritt & Gallagher, 2017).

Life-span implications are contingent on early identification and treatment. Infants who remain undiagnosed for the first 3 or more weeks of life risk severe and irreversible intellectual impairment. A favorable long-term prognosis is offered to infants identified within the first week of life who are provided a medical diet supplemented with artificial amino acids. Females of childbearing age must undergo strict monitoring, as conception that occurs concurrent with a period of hyperphenylalanemia has been associated with maternal PKU syndrome (Cleary, 2015).

Carbohydrate Disorders

Galactosemia. Galactosemia is an autosomal recessive inherited disorder caused by mutations in the *GALT*, *GALK1*, and *GALE* genes. Three types of galactosemia are reported in the literature. Type I galactosemia occurs in one of every 30,000 to 60,000 newborns, type II is estimated to occur in less than one out of every 100,000 newborns, and type III galactosemia is extremely rare (NIH, 2018b).

Galactosemia, or abnormally elevated levels of galactose, results from a deficiency of enzymes needed to metabolize the simple sugar, galactose. Galactose is found within lactose, a milk carbohydrate. Lactose is normally broken down into galactose and glucose by way of the lactase enzyme. Galactose is primarily metabolized within the liver. Enzymes, including galactokinase and Gal-1-P uridyl transferase (GALT), convert galactose into galactose 1-phosphate and eventually glucose. Type I galactosemia (classic galactosemia), the most severe form, results from mutations in the *GALT* gene that prevent the conversion of galactose into glucose. Type II galactosemia (galactokinase deficiency) results from mutations in the galactokinase 1 (*GALK1*) gene, which stunts, but does not completely eradicate, the production of GALK1 enzymes necessary for processing of galactose (Figure 10.19).

Clinical manifestations vary depending on the affected gene mutation. Most newborns are typically well appearing after birth, and can remain so for the first 10 to 14 days of life. Thereafter, classic clinical manifestations of type I galactosemia include hyperbilirubinemia, hepatomegaly, poor growth, frequent emesis, lethargy, and cataracts (Varela-Lema et al., 2016). Type II and type III galactosemia are associated with less severe symptoms.

Early onset of dietary restrictions and compliance is not significantly correlated with reduced observance of

TABLE 10.6 Newborn Screening Disorders

Metabolic Disorder (Type)	Screening Inborn Error of Metabolism
Organic Acid	Propionic acidemia
	Methylmalonic acidemia (methylmalonyl–CoA mutase)
	Methylmalonic acidemia (cobalamin disorders)
	Isovaleric acidemia
	3-Methylcrotonyl-CoA carboxylase deficiency
	3-Hydroxy-3-methyglutaric aciduria
	Holocarboxylase synthase deficiency
	ß-Ketothiolase deficiency
	Glutaric acidemia type I
Fatty Acid Oxidation	Carnitine uptake defect/carnitine transport defect
	Medium-chain acyl-CoA dehydrogenase deficiency
	Very long-chain acyl-CoA dehydrogenase deficiency
	Long-chain L-3 hydroxyacyl-CoA dehydrogenase deficiency
	Trifunctional protein deficiency
Amino Acid	Argininosuccinic aciduria
	Citrullinemia, type I
	Maple syrup urine disease
	Homocystinuria
	Classic phenylketonuria
	Tyrosinemia, type I
Endocrine	Primary congenital hypothyroidism
	Congenital adrenal hyperplasia
Hemoglobinopathies	S,S disease (Sickle cell anemia)
	S, ß-thalassemia
	S,C disease
Miscellaneous	Biotinidase deficiency
	Cystic fibrosis
	Classic galactosemia
	Glycogen storage disease type II (Pompe)
	Mucopolysaccharidosis type
	X-linked adrenoleukodystrophy
	Severe combined immunodeficiencies

NOTE: This list is nonexhaustive. Disorders provided in this table are commonly included in mandatory newborn screening tests across U.S. states.

Source: Advisory Committee on Heritable Disorders in Newborns and Children. (n.d.). Recommended uniform screening panel. Retrieved from https://www.hrsa.gov/advisory-committees/heritable-disorders/rusp/index.html

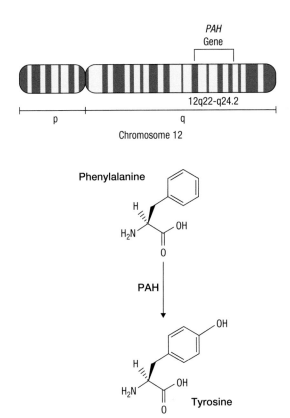

Figure 10.18 Genetic and molecular structure of PKU.

PAH, phenylalanine hydroxylase. ; *PKU, phenylketonuria.*

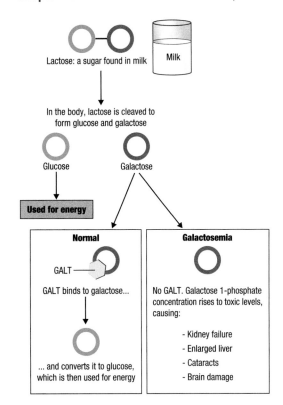

Figure 10.19 Normal lactose metabolism versus galactosemia.

GALT, gut-associated lymphoid tissue.

long-term disabilities. Life-span implications include intellectual impairment, speech and language deficits, apraxia/dyspraxia and dysarthria, motor disorders, and transient cataracts. Females with galactosemia may develop primary ovarian insufficiency. In addition, adolescents with galactosemia are at a higher risk for altered social function, often reporting difficulty coping with the disease process and maintaining compliance with the prescribed medical diet (Varela-Lema et al., 2016).

Organic Acidemias

Maple Syrup Urine Disease. Maple syrup urine disease (MSUD) is an autosomal recessive error of branched-chain amino acid catabolism, caused by mutations in the *BCKDHA, BCKDHB,* and *DBT* genes. Rarely, MSUD manifests as a result of mutations in the *DLD* gene. Globally, classic type MSUD is diagnosed in one of every 185,000 newborns (NIH, 2018c). However, the incidence of MSUD within the United States is particularly noteworthy within the Mennonite population, commonly located within Lancaster County, Pennsylvania. An estimated one of every 176 newborns in Lancaster, Pennsylvania, is affected by MSUD. Worldwide, the incidence of MSUD among Mennonites

is one of every 380 newborns (National Center for Biotechnology Information, 1998).

Valine, leucine, and isoleucine are three essential amino acids with branched side chains. This protein complex is commonly found in infant formulas and certain table foods (soy products, meats, fish, dairy products, and legumes). Normally, the enzyme complexes BCDHA, BCKDH, and DBT are involved in the stepwise catabolism of valine, leucine, and isoleucine. MSUD involves a disruption or dysfunction of one or more of the necessary enzyme complexes, which results in toxic accumulation of these three essential amino acids and failed synthesis of glutamate. Glutamate is a CNS neurotransmitter, serving a key role in cognition, memory, and learning.

Five phenotypes of MSUD are reported in the literature (Table 10.7). Clinical manifestations of classic and intermediate MSUD present in the neonatal period, with the maple syrup urine odor noted as the most common manifestation of the disease process. Other clinical manifestations include irritability, feeding difficulties, CNS disturbances, and lethargy.

Life-span implications of MSUD are directly related to elevated leucine levels and low circulating glutamate. Persistently elevated leucine levels are associated with

TABLE 10.7 Five Phenotypes of Maple Syrup Urine Disease			
MSUD Type	**Gene Involvement**	**Onset of Symptoms**	**Common Clinical Manifestations**
Classic	*BCKDHA; BCKDHB; DBT*	Neonatal period	*Neonatal period*: Maple syrup urine fragrance, irritability, feeding difficulties, lethargy, periodic apnea, opisthotonus *Infancy*: Nausea, anorexia, dystonia, ataxia *Childhood and beyond*: Intellectual impairment, sleep and mood disturbances, focal dystonia, ataxia
Intermediate Type 1	*BCKDHA; BCKDHB; DBT*	Varies across the life span	*Neonatal period*: Maple syrup urine fragrance *Infancy and beyond*: Feeding difficulties, poor linear growth, developmental delay
Intermediate Type 2	*BCKDHA; BCKDHB; DBT*	Varies across the life span	Stress-mediated encephalopathy
Thiamine-Responsive	*DBT*	Varies across the life span	Same as intermediate manifestations
E3-Deficient	*DLD*	Neonatal period or beyond	*Neurologic*: Hypotonia, lethargy, seizures, spasticity, emesis, hepatomegaly, poor linear growth/failure to thrive, developmental delays *Hepatic*: Nausea, emesis, hepatomegaly, hepatic encephalopathy

BCKDHA, branched chain keto acid dehydrogenase E1, alpha polypeptide; BCKDHB, branched chain keto acid dehydrogenase E1 subunit beta; DBT, dihydrolipoamide branched chain transacylase E2; DLD, dihydrolipoamide dehydrogenase.

Source: Blackburn, P. R., Gass, J. M., Vairo, F. P. E., Farnham, K. M., Atwal, H. K., Macklin, S., . . . Atwal, P. S. (2017). Maple syrup urine disease: Mechanisms and management. The Application of Clinical Genetics, 10, 57–66. doi:10.2147/TACG.S125962.

altered water homeostasis within subcortical gray matter, encephalopathic syndrome, and associated neurologic dysfunction (Blackburn et al., 2017). Low circulating glutamate levels are associated with neuropsychiatric disorders of cognition, attention, and mood as well as intellectual impairment (Muelly et al., 2013).

Congenital Hypothyroidism. Congenital hypothyroidism (CH) is an autosomal recessive genetic disorder. The incidence of CH in the United States is estimated at one of every 2,000 to 4,000 newborns, with the global incidence of CH on the rise due to the widespread adoption of rigorous newborn screening requirements and increased survivability of extremely premature infants (NIH, 2018a). Premature infants and infants of Hispanic or Asian descent are among those at a heightened risk for CH.

Two types of CH are known. Thyroid dysgenesis is the most common type of CH (85%) and involves either the absence, hypoplastic development, or abnormal positioning of the gland. The exact cause of thyroid dysgenesis is unknown; however, the *PAX8* and *TSHR* genes are both implicated with this genetic disorder and interrupt the normal genesis of the thyroid gland during fetal development. Thyroid dyshormonogenesis is the second type of CH and involves a normal or enlarged thyroid gland (goiter) and associated decreased or absent synthesis of thyroid hormone. This inborn error of thyroid hormone biosynthesis occurs in up to

10% to 15% of all cases of CH. The *DUOX2*, *SLC5A5*, thyroglobulin (*TG*), and *TPO* genes undergo aberrant mutations, stunting or blocking the synthesis of thyroid hormone. The result is abnormally low circulating thyroid hormone levels, which may be permanent and require lifelong hormone replacement, or transient with recovery to normal hormone synthesis within the first few years of life (Figure 10.20; NIH, 2018a; Wassner & Brown, 2015).

The clinical presentation of CH may be nondescript and subtle. Common clinical manifestations of CH during the neonatal period and into infancy include large-for-gestational-age (LGA) status, a hoarse cry, decreased activity, fatigue with increased sleep interval, feeding difficulties, irregular stooling patterns, and prolonged physiologic hyperbilirubinemia lasting in excess of 3 weeks. Physical features that should increase the index of suspicion for CH include hypotonia, enlarged fontanelles (due to a lack of thyroid hormone production and resultant decreased bone maturation), facial edema, macroglossia, and the presence of abdominal distension with a coexisting umbilical hernia. CH can be associated with trisomy 21; midline defects, including cleft palate, cardiac and genitourinary malformations; and liver hemangiomas (Wassner, 2017).

It is particularly important for practicing clinicians to appreciate the significance of performing a second metabolic screening test after the first month of life among premature infants, as TSH synthesis may be delayed until the third week of postnatal life, thereby providing a false negative result on the initial newborn screen (Wassner & Brown, 2015).

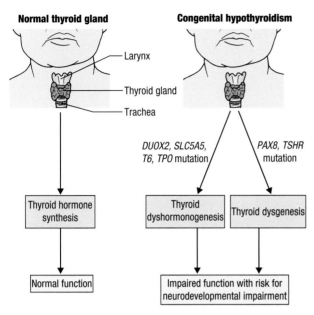

Figure 10.20 Normal thyroid function versus congenital hypothyroidism.

TPO, thyroperoxidase.

Life-span implications are primarily focused on neuro-developmental delays. CH is the leading cause for intellectual impairment within the United States and on a global level. IQ and timing of diagnosis with subsequent treatment are inversely related; earlier identification is advantageous to affected infants and families.

MATERNAL HEALTH INFLUENCES

The maternal endocrine system undergoes significant changes prenatally to support the pregnancy and the developing fetus. Alterations in these changes lead to maternal and fetal complications (Frise & Williamson, 2013). A myriad of maternal health issues can implicate fetal endocrine development as several hormones, minerals, and proteins are known to cross the placenta (Table 10.8). Disruptions in placental phosphate transfer observed with maternal preeclampsia, chorioamnionitis, and placental infections increase the risk for interuterine growth restriction and the acquisition of rickets. Maternal thyroid disorders and maternal diabetes are two additional common maternal disease states that can negatively affect the developing metabolic and endocrine system. Both disease processes are discussed in this section of the chapter. Additional maternal disorders that affect the developing fetal endocrine system are summarized in Table 10.9.

TABLE 10.8 Maternal Hormones That Cross the Placenta and Their Influence on the Developing Fetus

Organ	Physiologic Influence
Adrenal	• *Glucocorticoids*: Increased deoxycorticosterone, CBG, ACTH, and free cortisol leading to physiologic hypercortisolism • *Mineralocorticoids*: Stimulation of the RAA system leading to increased plasma volume
Pancreas	• Diabetogenic state due to placental-hormone-inducing insulin resistance • Maternal pancreatic dysfunction induces GDM
Parathyroid	• Ionized calcium values are normal; intestinal calcium absorption increases; calcium is transferred to the fetus
Pituitary	• *Anterior*: Proliferation of prolactin-producing cells; increased growth hormone • *Posterior*: Increased oxytocin and AVP; decreased serum sodium causes decreased osmolality requiring adjustment of osmoreceptors for thirst sensation and release of ADH
Thyroid	• Increased TBG leading to higher levels of T3/T4 • Relative iodine deficiency due to transplacental transfer to the fetus

ACTH, adrenocorticotropic hormone; ADH, antidiuretic hormone; AVP, arginine vasopressin; CBG, corticosteroid binding globulin; GDM, gestational diabetes mellitus; RAA, renin–angiotensin–aldosterone; TBG, thyroxine binding globulin; T3, triiodothyronine; T4, thyroxine.

Source: Soma-Pillary, P., Nelson-Piercy, C., Tolppanen, H., & Mebazaa, A. (2016). Physiological changes in pregnancy. *Cardiovascular Journal of Africa, 27*(2), 89–94.

TABLE 10.9 Maternal Endocrine Disorders and Their Effect on the Developing Fetus

Organ	Abnormality	Effect(s)
Adrenal	Cushing syndrome	Hypercortisolemia: weight gain, fatigue, glucose intolerance, hypertension
	Conn syndrome (primary hyperaldosteronism)	Hypokalemia, hypertension, proteinuria, placental abruption, preterm delivery
	Adrenal insufficiency	N&V, weight loss, hyperpigmentation, weakness, hyponatremia, hypoglycemia
	Congenital adrenal hyperplasia	Virilization, salt wasting, adult hirsutism, menstrual irregularity, subfertility, PIH, GDM
	Pheochromocytoma	Hypertension, placental insufficiency, placental abruption
Parathyroid	Hyperparathyroidism	Hypertension, preeclampsia, maternal mortality secondary to pancreatitis, maternal and fetal mortality secondary to hypercalcemic crisis
Pituitary	Prolactinoma	Reduced GRH: Infertility Maternal visual disturbances
	Acromegaly	PIH, GDM
	Pituitary insufficiency	Miscarriage; stillbirth
	Lymphocytic hypophysitis	ACTH deficiency
	Diabetes insipidus	Worsening of symptoms secondary to increased placental production of vasopressin
Thyroid	Hypothyroidism	Lethargy, weight gain, constipation, cold intolerance, bradycardia, amenorrhea, infertility, miscarriage, anemia, preeclampsia, LBW infant
	Hyperthyroidism	Infertility, miscarriage, preterm delivery, fetal growth restriction, fetal hyperthyroidism, goiter

ACTH, adrenocorticotropic hormone; GDM, gestational diabetes mellitus; GRH, gonadotropin-releasing hormone; LBW, low birth weight; N&V, nausea, vomiting; PIH, pregnancy-induced hypertension.

Source: Adapted from Frise, C. J., & Williamson, C. (2013). Endocrine disease in pregnancy. *Clinical Medicine: The Journal of the Royal College of Physicians, 13*(2), 176–181.doi:10.7861/clinmedicine.13-2-176

Maternal Thyroid Disease

The developing fetus relies heavily on maternal production of thyroid hormones during the first few months of pregnancy, as these hormones are crucial for normal brain development. Thyroid hormones can cross the placenta, and as such fetal growth and development can be negatively implicated by maternal thyroid disease.

Hypothyroidism. Hypothyroidism involves the underproduction of circulating thyroid hormone. This disorder can develop prior to or during pregnancy. Hypothyroidism is a relatively common problem among women of reproductive age, with a reported incidence ranging from 4% to 10% (Ozdemir et al., 2013). Risk factors for women include nutrient deficiencies and food sensitivities, adrenal dysfunction, and bacterial and viral infections.

Hashimoto's Thyroiditis. With Hashimoto's thyroiditis, antithyroid antibodies cross the placenta, causing decreased fetal circulating TSH and elevated T_4 levels. Significant fetal and maternal mortality risks are associated with persistently abnormal circulating thyroid hormone levels, including spontaneous abortion, intrauterine fetal demise, and maternal morbidity and mortality risks. Fetal manifestations to maternally acquired Hashimoto's thyroiditis include arrhythmias and decreased cardiac output secondary to prolonged TSH suppression. Both manifestations require emergent delivery (Tudosa et al., 2010).

Early establishment of maternal euthyroid status significantly reduces the risks for immediate and long-term maternal and fetal/neonatal complications. With proper medical management, it is possible to carry a fetus to term without severe complications (Tudosa et al, 2010). Postnatal manifestations of maternal Hashimoto thyroiditis include congenital anomalies, acidosis, tachycardia, pulmonary hypertension, reduced cardiac output, and the onset of a congenital hypothyroid state. Life-span implications associated with poorly controlled maternal thyroid hormone levels include low IQ and impaired psychomotor development (Gleason & Devaskar, 2012).

Hyperthyroidism. Hyperthyroidism involves overproduction of circulating thyroid hormone. This disorder can develop prior to or during pregnancy. The incidence of maternal hyperthyroidism during pregnancy is 0.1% to 2.7%, although the incidence of transient disease states is 1.5% to 2.5% (van der Kaay, Wasserman, & Palmert, 2016). Women incur a fourfold higher risk for developing hyperthyroid disease as compared to men.

Graves' Disease. Graves' disease is the most common cause of maternal hyperthyroidism. The pathogenesis of Graves' disease involves autoimmunity to TSH receptors. Antibodies bind to the TSH receptors, activating them and stimulating overproduction of thyroid hormone. These TSH-stimulating receptor antibodies can cross the placenta, and as such, may facilitate fetal hyperthyroidism (after 20 weeks of gestation).

Generally speaking, medically managed hyperthyroidism does not complicate pregnancy. Fetal manifestations of poorly controlled maternal thyroid hormone levels include tachycardia, heart failure with nonimmune hydrops, interuterine growth retardation, preterm birth, and advanced skeletal maturation and craniosynostosis (van der Kaay et al., 2016). Thyroid storm, a life-threatening complication of hyperthyroidism, is rarely reported yet associated with maternal fever, dehydration, diarrhea, cardiac dysrhythmias, shock, and maternal and fetal death (Gleason & Devaskar, 2012).

Maternal Diabetes

Maternal diabetes is a metabolic disease resulting from defects in insulin secretion and/or insulin action that causes a hyperglycemic state. The World Health Organization offers three major classifications for diabetes: type 1, type 2, and gestational diabetes. Other rarer forms of diabetes are reported and involve impaired glucose tolerance and fasting hyperglycemia (World Health Organization, 2017).

Gestational diabetes mellitus (GDM), or glucose intolerance during pregnancy, affects up to 14% of all pregnancies in the United States and globally, approximately 20.9 million pregnancies (Melchior, Kurch-Bek, & Mund, 2017; Ornoy et al., 2015; Vambergue & Fajardy, 2011). Onset of GDM typically occurs in the second trimester. The etiology for GDM is rather poorly understood, yet it is accepted that GDM primarily occurs as a result of deficient pancreatic ß-cell responses to hyperglycemia, which promotes increased insulin resistance and decreased insulin sensitivity (Daher, 2015). The increased accumulation

of adipose tissue among women with GDM may also be associated with increased circulating inflammatory mediators (C-reactive protein, IL-6, and TNF-α), which may contribute to the pathogenesis of GDM.

Prolonged hyperglycemia has a significant impact on both maternal and fetal well-being. Consequences to the pregnant woman include cardiovascular disease and dysfunction as well as organ failure. Fetal sequela includes macrosomia; microsomia; defects of the cardiovascular, vascular, renal, gastrointestinal, and neurological systems; and death (Vambergue & Fajardy, 2011).

COMMON PROBLEMS WITH IMPLICATIONS ACROSS THE LIFE SPAN

Many problems associated with the metabolic and endocrine system are genetically inherited (see the section "Genetic Influences: Inborn Errors of Metabolism"). The syndrome of inappropriate antidiuretic hormone (SIADH), adrenal insufficiency, and osteopenia of prematurity are three commonly *acquired* problems that affect normal metabolic and endocrine function.

Syndrome of Inappropriate Antidiuretic Hormone

SIADH is the most frequent cause of hyponatremia; it involves the inappropriate secretion of ADH in the presence of euvolemia. Hyponatremia affects approximately 25% of hospitalized children (Reid-Adam, 2013). Risk factors for SIADH include adrenal insufficiency, hypoxia and acidosis, pain, stress, marked elevation of lipids, hypothyroidism, medications, and infection (Table 10.10). In addition, genetic mutations triggering SIADH have been reported (Verbalis et al., 2013).

In the blood, solutes suspended in plasma constitute the density of the solution, also known as *serum osmolality*. The normal serum osmolality is 260 mOsm/L to 320 mOsm/L. The major contributor to the serum solute load is sodium, which contributes approximately 280 mOsm/L of the total value. The normal range for serum sodium is 135 mEq/L to 145 mEq/L. When values fall below this range, hyponatremia is present. *Hypo*natremia may occur from a low sodium intake, body losses such as sweating or diarrhea, the inability of the renal tubule to reabsorb sodium from the filtrate, or an overabundance of free water that results in a dilutional state. *Hyper*natremia results from high amounts of sodium intake, poor intake of free water, or losses of body water as seen with renal or gastrointestinal abnormalities.

ADH, also known as *vasopressin*, is a polypeptide hormone produced by the hypothalamus and stored in and released from the posterior pituitary gland. ADH controls water conservation; a paucity of ADH permits water removal to maintain the normal serum osmolality. In

TABLE 10.10 Common Risk Factors for SIADH

Body System	Risk Factor
CNS	Cerebral trauma
	Maternal renal loss of magnesium with glycosuria*
	Fetal macrosomia*
	Hypothermia
	Pain/stress
	Encephalitis
	Hydrocephalus
	Intraventricular hemorrhage
Cardiovascular	Early termination of placental calcium transfer
	Acute blood loss
	Urinary calcium loss secondary to immature renal function
	Patent ductus arteriosus*
	Inadequate calcium intake enterally or intravenously
Pulmonary	Hypoxia/asphyxia
	Acidosis
	Atelectasis
	Air leak syndrome
Endocrine	Adrenal insufficiency
	Hyperlipidemia
	Hypothyroidism
	Improper enteral formula, high phosphorus, or cow's milk (seven times the phosphorus of breast milk)
	Low production of PTH secondary to hypomagnesemia triggered by insufficient circulating vitamin D
Immune	Infection (meningitis, respiratory syncytial virus, pneumonia)
	22q11.2 deletion (DiGeorge syndrome)
Other	Diuretic use (e.g., furosemide)

*NOTE: Maternal renal loss of magnesium with glycosuria causes fetal hypomagnesemia and the inability to synthesize sufficient PTH. Surgical ligation of patent ductus arteriosus may increase the risk for onset of SIADH. Diuretic use is associated with natriuresis. Fetal macrosomia may lead to premature birth and delivery complications The administration of any drug with tubular toxicity risks increases the likelihood for development of SIADH.

PTH, parathyroid hormone; SIADH, syndrome of inappropriate secretion of antidiuretic hormone.

Sources: Kim, Y.-J., Lee, J. A., Oh, S., Choi, C. W., Kim, E.-K., Kim, H.-S., … Choi, J.-H. (2015). Risk factors for late-onset hyponatremia and its influence on neonatal outcomes in preterm infants. *Journal of Korean Medical Science, 30*(4), 456–462. doi:10.3346/jkms.2015.30.4.456; Kliegman, R., Stanton, B., St Geme, J. W., & Schor, N. F. (Eds.). (2016). *Nelson textbook of pediatrics* (20th ed.). Philadelphia, PA: Elsevier.

normal conditions, triggers for ADH release include hypo-volemia, hypotension, angiotensin II, and an increase in serum osmolality. Hypovolemia stimulates baroreceptors in the major vessels, namely the aorta and carotid arteries, as well as within the left atrium. This activates the renin-angiotensin-aldosterone cascade, which leads to vasoconstriction. Simultaneously, when osmoreceptors in the brain detect a rising serum osmolarity, signals are transmitted to the posterior pituitary to release ADH, which conserves body water. These mechanisms serve to maintain homeostasis by providing an adequate vascular volume at normal pressure and control serum osmolality within a normal range. On release from the posterior pituitary, ADH is transported via the vascular system to the renal tubule. ADH binds with receptors on principal cells of the collecting ducts of the renal tubule. Principal cells then place aquaporins, small apertures that allow water to move by diffusion from the filtrate out toward the high solute milieu surrounding the renal tubule, in the renal medulla portion of the kidney. This salvaging of water permits an increase in vascular volume and pressure and helps reestablish a normal range of serum osmolality.

In abnormal conditions, vasopressin (ADH) is released in excess. This is SIADH. This abnormality leads to water retention and, subsequently, to dilution of electrolytes, particularly sodium since it is the most abundant intravascular electrolyte. SIADH thereby manifests as oliguria, free water retention, decreased serum sodium concentration and osmolality, increased urine concentration, and weight gain with edema. It is essential that the APN recognize that despite the low serum sodium concentrations, total body sodium concentrations are normal. The increase in total body water (edema with weight gain) causes a dilutional hyponatremic state.

Life-span implications of SIADH are correlated with early identification, management, and treatment. Delayed recognition of decreasing serum osmolality can increase the risk for cerebral edema and herniation. Alternatively, overzealous correction of hyponatremia can precipitate severe and long-term neurologic dysfunction.

Acquired Adrenal Insufficiency

Adrenal insufficiency (AI) can be an inherited steroidogenesis defect (congenital adrenal hyperplasia or congenital adrenal hypoplasia; see Chapter 11); a result of an injury to the hypothalamus or pituitary gland during fetal development (central adrenal insufficiency aka *ACTH* or *CRH deficiency*); a result of a hemorrhage within the adrenal gland, hypothalamus, or pituitary; or an acquired insufficiency. The acquired form of AI typically manifests during the postnatal period, often as a result of prolonged, supraphysiologic corticosteroid therapy. In addition, an immature HPA axis may be a root cause for AI, in particular among infants born at less than or equal to 30 weeks gestation (Auron & Raissouni, 2015; Quintos & Boney, 2010, Witt, 1999). Precursors for acute AI are summarized in Table 10.11.

TABLE 10.11 Common Stressors (Precursors) for Acute Adrenal Insufficiency

Body System	Risk Factor
CNS	Hypoxia
	Immature HPA axis
Pulmonary	Prolonged, supraphysiologic corticosteroid replacement therapy with or without abrupt cessation
Endocrine	ACTH unresponsiveness
	Congenital adrenal hyperplasia*
	Adrenal hypoplasia
	Adrenal hemorrhage*
Immune	Sepsis*
Other	Gestational age ≤ 30 weeks, low birth weight, prolonged maternal steroid administration

*NOTE: All risk factors noted above affect serum cortisol concentrations during the first few weeks of life. Congenital adrenal hyperplasia may be of the 21-hydroxylase, 11-hydroxylase, 3-β-hydroxylase, 17-hydroxylase, or lipoid type. Adrenal hemorrhage may occur secondary to birth injury, asphyxia, sepsis, or disseminated intravascular coagulation. Sepsis may occur secondary to fungal or viral etiologies.

CNS, central nervous system; HPA, hypothalamic–pituitary–adrenal axis.

Source: Adapted from Witt, C. L. (1999). Adrenal insufficiency in the term and preterm neonate. *Neonatal Network, 18*(5), 21–28. doi:10.1891/0730-0832.18.5.21

In cases of HPA axis immaturity, premature infants exposed to internal or environmental stressors exhibit normal to elevated ACTH synthesis and secretion with suboptimal cortisol synthesis and secretion. Etiologies include an immature neurologic response to stress, adrenal immaturity to ACTH stimulation, and reduced enzymatic precursors necessary for cortisol synthesis and secretion. Of note, one particulary important precursor is 3-β-hydroxysteroid dehydrogenase (3-β-HSD). 3-β-HSD is essential for the biosynthesis of many hormonal steroids, including glucocorticoids and mineralocorticoids. Specific to AI, decreased levels of this enzymatic precursor are associated with a reduced ability to synthesize cortisol. Low cortisol levels are detected by the hypothalamus, which secretes CRH to the pituitary, which thereby secretes ACTH. ACTH levels continue to rise relative to low cortisol; however, the adrenal gland fails to synthesize and secrete cortisol (Figure 10.21).

In cases of prolonged exposure to corticosteroids, an abnormal suppression of endogenous corticosteroid (ACTH) production is observed during the fight-or-flight response to an internal or environmental stressor. Decreased ACTH secretion occurs, which suppresses the HPA axis and causes insufficient cortisol synthesis and resultant hypotension refractory to volume or vasopressors (Auron & Raissouni, 2015; Quintos & Boney, 2010).

The early clinical presentation may be ill-defined during early manifestations of the disease process. Poor feeding and emesis are common. Biochemical indicators include hyponatremia, hyperkalemia, hypoglycemia, and ketonuria (Auron & Raissouni, 2015). AI is considered a life-threatening condition associated with a high risk for mortality when left untreated. Among medically managed infants, life-span implications are associated with complications of corticosteroid therapy. Neurodevelopmental and gastrointestinal consequences, including lower mental developmental index (MDI) and Bayley infant developmental scores, in addition to spontaneous intestinal perforation, have been reported (Quintos & Boney, 2010).

Osteopenia of Prematurity

Osteopenia of prematurity (OoP; rickets) is an acquired metabolic bone disease characterized by deficient bone mineralization and subsequent loss of bone mass. The precise incidence of OoP is rarely quantified in the literature, due to variability in screening and diagnostic methods. It is widely accepted that OoP is inversely proportional to gestational age, with infants weighing less than 1,500 g at birth at the highest risk for acquisition of the disease process. A prevalence of OoP among male newborns is reported. Risk factors for OoP are summarized in Table 10.12.

Bone mineralization peaks during the third trimester; it is estimated that 80% of all calcium and phosphate accumulation occurs at this time (Groh-Wargo, Thompson, Cox,

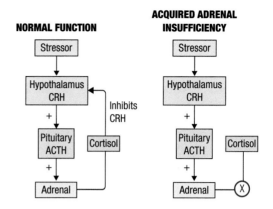

Figure 10.21 Normal adrenal feedback loop as compared to acquired adrenal insufficiency. The image depicts normal function compared to the interrupted feedback loop noted with acquired adrenal sufficiency.

ACTH, adrenocorticotropic hormone; CRH, corticotropin-releasing hormone.

& Academy of Nutrition and Dietetics. Pediatric Nutrition Practice Group, 2016). During this time, the fetal skeleton requires ample transfer of calcium, phosphorus, vitamin D, and protein. In fact, third trimester circulating calcium and phosphorus levels are approximately 20% higher in the fetus than the pregnant woman, as each of these minerals (and protein) cross the placenta. Fetuses delivered at less than 34 weeks gestation are devoid of a full opportunity for phosphate and calcium accretion, and therefore are at higher risk for OoP (Rehman & Narchi, 2015).

Postnatally, premature infants are devoid of placentally supplied minerals (calcium and phosphate) necessary for optimal bone growth and development. Shortly after removal of the placental blood supply, the premature infant's parathyroid gland detects low circulating calcium levels and synthesizes and secretes PTH. The secretion of PTH increases extracellular calcium concentrations, inhibits bone mineralization, and encourages osteoclast formation, which seeks to strip calcium from bones. During this time frame, the bones then undergo structural modifications, including widening of the internal cavity with rapid increases in bone length (Martin, Fanaroff, & Walsh, 2015). The chronic inhibition of bone mineralization over time increases the vulnerability to bone injury (rickets).

Consequences of OoP include mechanical fractures to the ribs and long bones. A longer birth hospitalization is common among infants with OoP. In addition, comorbidities, including periventricular leukomalacia, intraventricular hemorrhage, retinopathy of prematurity, persistent patent ductus arteriosus, and spontaneous intestinal perforation, have been reported. Life-span implications, in addition to the aforementioned neurodevelopmental consequences, include poor growth in infancy and throughout childhood (Moreira et al., 2014).

TABLE 10.12 Common Risk Factors for Osteopenia of Prematurity

Body System	Risk Factor
CNS	Cerebral pathology
	Neuromuscular disorders
Pulmonary	Acidosis
	Bronchopulmonary dysplasia
Gastrointestinal	Short gut syndrome
	Cholestatic jaundice
	Unsupplemented human-milk feedings
	Prolonged parenteral nutrition therapy
Immune	Sepsis
	Enterocolitis
Endocrine	Vitamin D deficiency
Other	Placental insufficiency*, prematurity (birth weight <1,500 g, <34 weeks gestation), male gender, prolonged periods of immobility, poor prenatal nutrition (maternal), methylxanthine administration, corticosteroid administration, loop diuretic administration

*NOTE: Chronic damage to the placenta (e.g., preeclampsia) is positively associated with intrauterine growth retardation and an increased risk for osteopenia of prematurity.

CNS, central nervous system.

Source: Gleason, C. A., & Devaskar, S. U. (Eds.). (2012). *Avery's diseases of the newborn* (9th ed.). Philadelphia, PA: Elsevier.

CONCLUSION

The metabolic and endocrine system is a network of organs, complex by way of its multiorgan involvement and innervation. The endocrine system functions to achieve and maintain homeostasis by responding and adapting to both internal and external events, by way of the synthesis of hormones that coordinate and control responses within cells, tissues, or organs within the body. Any failure in normal anatomic or functional development of these organ systems can result in developmental errors affecting growth, metabolism, fluid, and electrolyte balance; response to stress; reproduction; and influence on the immune system. Several problems associated with the metabolic and endocrine system are genetically inherited (IEM). New tests have expanded newborn metabolic screening to assess the newly born infant for 60 core and secondary conditions. Early detection permits treatment interventions decreasing morbidity and mortality.

ACKNOWLEDGMENT

The authors would like to thank Dr. Christie del Castillo-Hegyi for the contribution of the chapter podcast and Ms. Wanda Bradshaw for her support in the early development of this chapter.

LEARNING TOOLS AND RESOURCES

Podcast

 Neonatal Dehydration and Hypoglycemia

Christie del Castillo-Hegyi

Discussion Prompts

1. It is recommended that a second newborn screen be obtained when a baby is receiving adequate protein intake (~100 mL/kg/day) and when the baby is 2 to 4 weeks post birth. Discuss the rationale for these two parameters.
2. Insulin inhibits lipolysis and release of free fatty acids from adipose cells. Discuss the purpose for this action.
3. Infants of diabetic mothers (IDM) are at an increased risk for hypoglycemia. Discuss the factors that predispose the IDM infant to glucose dysregulation.

Advice From the Authors

"Never give up; each of us has our own individual way of learning. You have it within yourself to achieve whatever you put your mind to. Utilize several different learning techniques to help foster the learning process and to further reiterate the studied content. Think of learning as the spice of life."

–Stephanie M. Blake, DNP, APRN, NNP-BC

"When faced with complex phenomena, consider layering your approach to learning. I suggest mind-mapping while studying the written content, followed by testing your knowledge acquisition through application in the workplace. During preclinical semesters, this can be accomplished by 'talking through' concepts with other advanced practice providers. The teach-to-learn method is truly remarkable!"

–Amy J. Jnah, DNP, APRN, NNP-BC

"Always ask questions. The secret to success is to always improve your questions."

Deanna W. Adkins, MD

Mind Maps

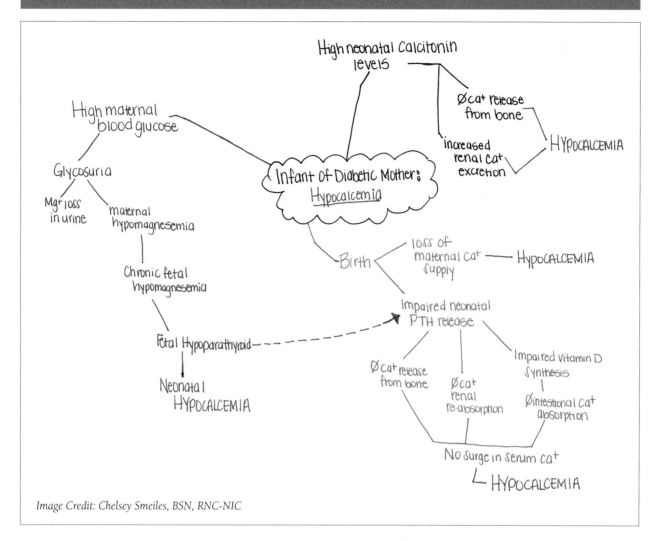

Image Credit: Chelsey Smeiles, BSN, RNC-NIC

Note: This mind map reflects one student's interpretation of a portion of one or more concepts addressed in this chapter. Readers should regard the mind maps woven throughout this textbook as examples of multi-sensory study tools that can be developed to encourage conceptual understanding. Readers are encouraged to develop their own unique mind maps in consultation with academic faculty or clinical preceptors.

TIMELINE OF ORGAN DEVELOPMENT

NOTE:	LEGEND
Placement of common problems is meant to offer visual/conceptual perspective on the timing of onset of these commonly reported malformations. Variation exists across the literature.	<22 – 27 6/7 weeks = extremely preterm 28 – 31 6/7 weeks = very preterm 32 – 36 6/7 weeks = late/moderate preterm 37 – 40 weeks = term

References

Adamkin, D. H. (2015). Metabolic screening and postnatal glucose homeostasis in the newborn. *Pediatric Clinics of North America, 62*(2), 385–409. doi:10.1016/j.pcl.2014.11.004

Adamkin, D. H. (2016). Neonatal hypoglycemia. *Seminars in Fetal and Neonatal Medicine, 22*(1), 36–41. doi:10.1016/j.siny.2016.08.007

Adamkin, D. H. & COMMITTEE ON THE FETUS AND NEWBORN. (2011). Clinical report–Postnatal glucose homeostasis in late-preterm and term infants. *Pediatrics, 127*(3), 575–579. doi: 10.1542/peds.2010–3851

Advisory Committee on Heritable Disorders in Newborns and Children. (n.d.). Recommended uniform screening panel. Retrieved from https://www.hrsa.gov/advisory-committees/heritable-disorders/rusp/index.html

American Association of Endocrine Surgeons. (2017a). Parathyroid gland. Retrieved from http://endocrinediseases.org/parathyroid/parathyroid_background.shtml

American Association of Endocrine Surgeon's Patient Education. (2017b). Thyroid gland. Retrieved from http://endocrinediseases.org/thyroid/thyroid_background.shtml

Auron, M., & Raissouni, N. (2015). Adrenal insufficiency. *Pediatrics in Review, 36*(3), 92–103. doi:10.1542/pir.36-3-92

Ballard, O., & Morrow, A. L. (2013). Human milk composition: Nutrients and bioactive factors. *Pediatric Clinics of North America, 60*(1), 49. doi: 10.1016/j.pcl.2012.10.00

Baynes, J. W. (2014). Carbohydrate storage and synthesis in liver and muscle. In J. W. Baynes & M. H. Dominiczak (Eds.), *Medical biochemistry* (4th ed., pp. 154–170). London, UK: Saunders.

Bilezikian, J. P., Marcus, R., Levine, M. A., Marcocci, C., Silverberg, S. J., & Potts, J. T., Jr. (Eds.). (2015). *The parathyroids: Basic and clinical concepts* (3rd ed.). London: Academic Press.

Blackburn, P. R., Gass, J. M., Vairo, F. P. E., Farnham, K. M., Atwal, H. K., Macklin, S., . . . Atwal, P. S. (2017). Maple syrup urine disease: Mechanisms and management. The Application of Clinical Genetics, 10, 57–66. doi:10.2147/TACG.S125962

Blaine, J., Chonchol, M., & Levi, M. (2014). Renal control of calcium, phosphate, and magnesium homeostasis. Clinical journal of the American Society of Nephrology : CJASN, 10(7), 1257–72.

Blaine, J., Chonchol, M., & Levi, M. (2015). Renal control of calcium, phosphate, and magnesium homeostasis. *Clinical Journal of the American Society of Nephrology, 10*(7), 1257–1272. doi:10.2215/CJN.09750913

Burlina, S., Dalfra, M. G., & Lapolla, A. (2017). Short- and long-term consequences for offspring exposed to maternal diabetes: A review. *Journal of Maternal, Fetal, and Neonatal Medicine, 16*, 1–8. Advance online publication. doi:10.1080/14767058.2017.1387893

Burns, C. M., Rutherford, M. A., Boardman, J. P., & Cowan, F. M. (2008). Patterns of cerebral injury and neurodevelopmental outcomes after symptomatic neonatal hypoglycemia. *Pediatrics, 122*(1), 65-74. doi:10.1542/peds.2007-2822

Cleary, M. A. (2015). Phenylketonuria. *Paediatrics and Child Health, 25*(3), 108–112. doi:10.1016/j.paed.2014.10.006

Cooper, A. R., Barnett, D., Gentles, E., Cairns, L., & Simpson, J. H. (2013). Macronutrient content of donor human breast milk.

Archives of Disease in Childhood: Fetal and Neonatal Edition, 98, F539–F541.doi:10.1136/archdischild-2013-304422

Cowett, R. M.(Ed.). (2012). *Principles of perinatal–neonatal metabolism* (2nd ed.). New York, NY: Springer.

Daher, S. (2015). Exploring the pathophysiology of gestational diabetes: Many questions still unanswered. *Placenta, 36*(4), 476. doi:10.1016/j.placenta.2015.01.405

DeGroot, L. J., & Jameson, J. L. (2010). *Endocrinology: Adult and pediatric* (6th ed.). Philadelphia, PA: Saunders/Elsevier.

DeSisto, C. L., Kim, S. Y., & Sharma, A. J. (2014). Prevalence estimates of gestational diabetes mellitus in the United States, Pregnancy Risk Assessment Monitoring System (PRAMS), 2007–2010. *Preventing Chronic Disease, 11*, 130415. doi:10.5888/pcd11.130415

Divall, S. A. & Merjaneh, L. (2018). Developmental Endocrinology. In C. A. Gleason & S. E. Juul (Eds.), *Avery's diseases of the newborn* (10th ed., pp. 1324–1332). Philadelphia, PA: Elsevier.

Feher, J. J. (2017). *Quantitative human physiology* (2nd ed.). London, UK: Academic Press.

Felsenfeld, A. J., & Levine, B. S. (2015). Calcitonin, the forgotten hormone: Does it deserve to be forgotten? *Clinical Kidney Journal, 8*(2), 180–187. doi:10.1093/ckj/sfv011

Ferber, S. G., Als, H., McAnulty, G., Peretz, H., & Zisapel, N. (2011). Melatonin and mental capacities in newborn infants. Journal of Pediatrics, 159(1), 99–103.e1. doi:10.1016/j.jpeds.2010.12.032

Frise, C. J., & Williamson, C. (2013). Endocrine disease in pregnancy. *Clinical Medicine: The Journal of the Royal College of Physicians, 13*(2), 176–181. doi:10.7861/clinmedicine.13-2-176

Gidrewicz, D. A., & Fenton, T. R. (2014). A systematic review and meta-analysis of the nutrient content of preterm and term breast milk. *BMC Pediatrics, 14*(1), 216. doi:10.1186/1471-2431-14-216

Gleason, C. A., & Devaskar, S. U.(Eds.). (2012). *Avery's diseases of the newborn* (9th ed.). Philadelphia, PA: Elsevier.

Gouyon, J. B., Iacobelli, S., Ferdynus, C., & Bonsante, F. (2012). Neonatal problems of late and moderate preterm infants. *Seminars in Fetal and Neonatal Medicine, 17*(3), 146–152.doi:10.1016/j.siny.2012.01.015

Groh-Wargo, S., Thompson, M., Cox, J. H., & Academy of Nutrition and Dietetics. Pediatric Nutrition Practice Group (Eds.). (2016). *Academy of Nutrition and Dietetics pocket guide to neonatal nutrition* (2nd ed.). Chicago, IL: Academy of Nutrition and Dietetics.

Hay W., Jr., Adamkin, D., Harding, J., & Hawdon, J. (2018). The postnatal glucose concentration nadir is not abnormal and does not need to be treated. *Neonatology, 114*(2), 163. doi:10.1159/000489552

Hester, S. N., Hustead, D. S., Mackey, A. D., Singhal, A., & Marriage, B. J. (2012). Is the macronutrient intake of formula-fed infants greater than breast-fed infants in early infancy? *Journal of Nutrition and Metabolism, 2012*, 891201–13. doi:10.1155/2012/891201

Hill, M. A. (n.d.). Embryology: Embryonic development. Retrieved from https://embryology.med.unsw.edu.au/embryology/index.php/Embryonic_Development

Hill, M. A. (n.d.-b). Embryology: Endocrine–adrenal development. Retrieved from https://embryology.med.unsw.edu.au/embryology/index.php/Endocrine_-_Adrenal_Development

Hill, M. A. (n.d.-c). Embryology: Endocrine–hypothalamus development. Retrieved from https://embryology.med.unsw.edu.au/embryology/index.php/Endocrine_-_Hypothalamus_Development

Hill, M. A. (n.d.-d). Embryology: Endocrine–pancreas development. Retrieved from https://embryology.med.unsw.edu.au/embryology/index.php/Endocrine_-_Pancreas_Development

Hill, M. A. (n.d.-e). Embryology: Endocrine–pineal development. Retrieved from https://embryology.med.unsw.edu.au/embryology/index.php/Endocrine_-_Pineal_Development

Hill, M. A. (n.d.-f). Embryology: Endocrine–pituitary development. Retrieved from https://embryology.med.unsw.edu.au/embryology/index.php/Endocrine_-_Pituitary_Development

Hill, M. A. (n.d.-g). Embryology. Endocrine–thyroid development. Retrieved from https://embryology.med.unsw.edu.au/embryology/index.php/Endocrine_-_Thyroid_Development

Jahnen-Dechent, W., & Ketteler, M. (2012). Magnesium basics. Clinical Kidney Journal, 5(Suppl. 1), i3–i14. doi:10.1093/ndtplus/sfr163

Jenness, R. (1979). The composition of human milk. Seminars in Perinatology, 3(3), 225–239.

Kaiser, J. R., Bai, S., Gibson, N., Holland, G., Lin, T. M., Swearingen, C. J., … ElHassan, N. O. (2015). Association between transient newborn hypoglycemia and fourth-grade achievement test proficiency: A population-based study. JAMA Pediatrics, 169(10), 913–921. doi:10.1001/jamapediatrics.2015.1631

Kalhan, S., & Parimi, P. (2000). Gluconeogenesis in the fetus and neonate. Seminars in Perinatology, 24(2), 94–106. doi:10.1053/sp.2000.6360

Kaludjerovic, J., & Ward, W. E. (2012). The interplay between estrogen and fetal adrenal cortex. Journal of Nutrition and Metabolism, 2012, 1–12. doi:10.1155/2012/837901

Kansra, A. R. (2018). Hypoglycemia. In R. Kliegman, P. Lye, B. Bordini, H. Toth, & D. Basel (Eds.), Nelson pediatric symptom-based diagnosis (pp. 811–823.e1). Philadelphia, PA: Elsevier.

Khetan, S. K. (2014). Mechanisms of endocrine system function. (pp. 29–50). Hoboken, NJ: John Wiley & Sons. doi:10.1002/9781118891094.ch2

Kim, G., Nandi-Munshi, D., & DiBlasi, C. C. (2018). Disorders of the thyroid gland. In C. A. Gleason & S. E. Juul (Eds.), Avery's diseases of the newborn (10th ed., pp. 1388-1402). Philadelphia, PA: Elsevier.

Kim, Y.-J., Lee, J. A., Oh, S., Choi, C. W., Kim, E.-K., Kim, H.-S., … Choi, J.-H. (2015). Risk factors for late-onset hyponatremia and its influence on neonatal outcomes in preterm infants. Journal of Korean Medical Science, 30(4), 456–462.doi:10.3346/jkms.2015.30.4.456

Kinnala, A., Rikalainen, H., Lapinleimu, H., Parkkola, R., Kormano, M., & Kero, P. (1999). Cerebral magnetic resonance imaging and ultrasonography findings after neonatal hypoglycemia. Pediatrics, 103(4), 724-729. doi:10.1542/peds.103.4.724

Kliegman, R., Stanton, B., St Geme, J. W., & Schor, N. F., (Eds.). (2016). Nelson textbook of pediatrics (20th ed.). Philadelphia, PA: Elsevier.

Koutcherov, Y., Mai, J. K., Ashwell, K. W. S., & Paxinos, G. (2002). Organization of human hypothalamus in fetal development. Journal of Comparative Neurology, 446(4), 301–324. doi:10.1002/cne.10175

Long, S., & Romani, A. M. (2014). Role of cellular magnesium in human diseases. Austin Journal of Nutrition and Food Sciences, 2(10), 1051.Retrieved from http://austinpublishinggroup.com/nutrition-food-sciences/fulltext/ajnfs-v2-id1051.php

Loughead, J. L., Mimouni, F., & Tsang, R. C. (1988). Serum ionized calcium concentrations in normal neonates. American Journal of Diseases of Children, 142(5), 516–518. doi:10.1001/archpedi.1988.02150050054030

Macchi, M. M., & Bruce, J. N. (2004). Human pineal physiology and functional significance of melatonin. Frontiers in Neuroendocrinology, 25(3), 177–195. doi:10.1016/j.yfrne.2004.08.001

Martin, R. J., Fanaroff, A. A., & Walsh, M. C. (2015). Fanaroff and Martin's neonatal–perinatal medicine: Diseases of the fetus and infant (10th ed.). Philadelphia, PA: Elsevier/Saunders.

McGowan, J. E. (1999). Neonatal hypoglycemia. Pediatrics in Review, 20(7), 6–15. doi:10.1542/pir.20-7-e6

McKinlay, C. J. D., Alsweiler, J. M., Anstice, N. S., Burakevych, N., Chakraborty, A., Chase, J. G., … Harding, J. E. (2017). Association of neonatal glycemia with neurodevelopmental outcomes at 4.5 years. JAMA Pediatrics, 171(10), 972-983. doi:10.1001/jamapediatrics.2017.1579

Melchior, H., Kurch-Bek, D., & Mund, M. (2017). The prevalence of gestational diabetes: Aopulation-based analysis of a nationwide screening program. Deutsches Ärzteblatt International, 114(24), 412–418. doi: 10.3238/arztebl.2017.0412

Melmed, S. (Ed.).(2017). The pituitary (4th ed.). San Diego, CA: Elsevier/Academic Press.

Melmed, S., Polonsky, K. S., Larsen, P. R., & Kronenberg, H. (Eds.).(2016). Williams textbook of endocrinology (13th ed.). Philadelphia, PA: Elsevier.

Merritt, J. L. & Gallagher, R. C. (2017). Inborn errors of carbohydrate, ammonia, amino acid, and organic acid metabolism. In C. A. Gleason & S. E. Juul (Eds.), Avery's diseases of the newborn (10th ed., pp. 230-252). Philadelphia, PA:

Molina, P. E. (2013). Endocrine physiology (4th ed.). New York, NY: McGraw-Hill Medical.

Moreira, A., Swischuk, L., Malloy, M., Mudd, D., Blanco, C., & Geary, C. (2014). Parathyroid hormone as a marker for metabolic bone disease of prematurity. Journal of Perinatology: Official Journal of the California Perinatal Association, 34(10), 787–791. doi:10.1038/jp.2014.97

Muelly, E. R., Moore, G. J., Bunce, S. C., Mack, J., Bigler, D. C., Morton, D. H., & Strauss, K. A. (2013). Biochemical correlates of neuropsychiatric illness in maple syrup urine disease. Journal of Clinical Investigation, 123(4), 1809–1820. doi:10.1172/JCI67217

Namgung, R. & Tsang, R. C. (2017). Neonatal calcium, phosphorus, and magnesium homeostasis. (pp. 296–312). In R. A. Polin, H. S. Abrams, & D. H. Rowtich (Eds.). Fetal and neonatal physiology (5th ed). Philadelphia, PA: Elsevier.

National Center for Biotechnology Information. (1998). Genes and disease: Maple syrup urine disease [Internet]. Bethesda, MD: Author Retrieved from https://www.ncbi.nlm.nih.gov/books/NBK22214

National Institutes of Health. (2018a). Genetics home reference: Congenital hypothyroidism. Retrieved from https://ghr.nlm.nih.gov/condition/congenital-hypothyroidism#statistics

National Institutes of Health. (2018b). Genetics home reference: Galactosemia. Retrieved from https://ghr.nlm.nih.gov/condition/galactosemia#statistics

National Institutes of Health. (2018c). Genetics home reference: Maple syrup urine disease. Retrieved from https://ghr.nlm.nih.gov/condition/maple-syrup-urine-disease#statistics

National Institutes of Health. (2018d). Genetics home reference: Phenylketonuria. Retrieved from https://ghr.nlm.nih.gov/condition/phenylketonuria

Neal, J. M. (2016). *How the endocrine system works* (2nd ed.). Hoboken, NJ: Wiley Blackwell.

Nelson, D. L.&, Cox, M. M. (2017). *Lehninger principles of biochemistry* (7th ed.). New York, NY: W. H. Freeman.

Neville, M. C., Keller, R., Seacat, J., Lutes, V., Neifert, M., Casey, C., … Archer, P. (1988). Studies in human lactation: Milk volumes in lactating women during the onset of lactation and full lactation. *American Journal of Clinical Nutrition, 48*(6), 1375–1386. doi:10.1093/ajcn/48.6.1375

Ornoy, A., Reece, E. A., Pavlinkova, G., Kappen, C., & Miller, R. K. (2015). Effect of maternal diabetes on the embryo, fetus, and children: Congenital anomalies, genetic and epigenetic changes and developmental outcomes. *Birth Defects Research Part C: Embryo Today: Reviews, 105*(1), 53–72. doi:10.1002/bdrc.21090

Ozdemir, H., Akman, I., Coskun, S., Demirel, U., Turan, S., Bereket, A., … Ozek, E. (2013). Maternal thyroid dysfunction and neonatal thyroid problems. *International Journal of Endocrinology, 2013*, 1–6. doi:10.1155/2013/987843

Pfaff, D. W., & Joëls, M.(Eds.). (2017). *Hormones, brain, and behavior* (3rd ed.). Amsterdam, The Netherlands: Elsevier/Academic Press.

Polin, R. A., Abman, S. H., Rowitch, D. H., Benitz, W. E., & Fox, W. W.(Eds.). (2017). *Fetal and neonatal physiology* (5th ed.). Philadelphia, PA: Elsevier.

Quintos, J. B., & Boney, C. M. (2010). Transient adrenal insufficiency in the premature newborn. *Current Opinions in Endocrinology, Diabetes, and Obesity, 17*(1), 8–12. doi:10.1097/MED.0b013e32833363cc

Rehman, M. U., & Narchi, H. (2015). Metabolic bone disease in the preterm infant: Current state and future directions. *World Journal of Methodology, 5*(3), 115–121. doi:10.5662/wjm.v5.i3.115

Reid-Adam, J. (2013). Hyponatremia. Pediatrics in Review, 34(9), 417–419. doi:10.1542/pir.34-9-417

Roberts, M. F., & Kruchten, A. E. (2016). *Receptor biology* (1st ed.). Weinheim, Germany: Wiley-VCH Verlag GmbH & Co.

Rozance, P. J., & Rosenberg, A. A. (2017). The neonate. In S. G. Gabbe, J. R. Niebyl, J. L. Simpson, M. B. Landon, H. L. Galan, E. R. M. Jauniaux, . . . W. A. Grobman (Ed.s), *Obstetrics: Normal and problem pregnancies* (7th ed., pp. 468–498). Philadelphia, PA: Elsevier/Saunders.

Sapsford, A. & Smith, C. (2016). Enteral nutrition. (pp. 76–124). In S. Groh-Wargo, M. Thompson, & J. H Cox (Eds). *Pocket guide to neonatal nutrition.* (2nd Ed). USA: Academy of Nutrition and Dietetics.

Sargis, M. R. (2014a). An overview of the pineal gland: Maintaining circadian rhythm. Retrieved from http://www.endocrineweb.com/endocrinology/overview-pineal-gland

Sargis, M. R. (2014b). An overview of the pituitary gland: The endocrine system's Master gland. Retrieved from https://www.endocrineweb.com/endocrinology/overview-pituitary-gland

Sargis, M. R. (2015a). An overview of the adrenal gland: Beyond fight or flight. Retrieved from https://www.endocrineweb.com/endocrinology/overview-adrenal-glands

Sargis, M. R. (2015b). An overview of the pancreas. Retrieved from http://www.endocrineweb.com/endocrinology/overview-pancreas

Sargis, M. R. (2015c). An overview of the parathyroid: The calcium gland that helps keep bones healthy. Retrieved from https://www.endocrineweb.com/endocrinology/overview-parathyroid

Sargis, M. R. (2016). About the endocrine system: Endocrine glands and hormones. Retrieved from https://www.endocrineweb.com/endocrinology/about-endocrine-system

Soma-Pillary, P., Nelson-Piercy, C., Tolppanen, H., & Mebazaa, A. (2016). Physiological changes in pregnancy. *Cardiovascular Journal of Africa, 27*(2), 89–94. doi:10.5830/CVJA-2016-021

Sperling, M. A. (2016). Hypoglycemia. In R. M. Kliegman, B. Stanton, J. W. St Geme, & N. F Schor, (Eds.), *Nelson textbook of pediatrics* (20th ed. pp. 773–788). Philadelphia, PA: Elsevier.

Stanley, C. A., Anday, E. K., Baker, L., & Delivoria-Papadopolous, M. (1979). Metabolic fuel and hormone responses to fasting in newborn infants. *Pediatrics, 64*(5), 613–619. Retrieved from http://pediatrics.aappublications.org/content/64/5/613?download=true

Stokowski, L. (2015). Endocrine disorders. In T. M. Verklan & M. Walden (Eds.), *Core curriculum for neonatal intensive care nursing* (5th ed., pp. 632–665) St. Louis, MO: Elseiver.

Tam, E. W. Y., Haeusslein, L. A., Bonifacio, S. L., Glass, H. C., Rogers, E. E., Jeremy, R. J., … Ferriero, D. M. (2012). Hypoglycemia is associated with increased risk for brain injury and adverse neurodevelopmental outcome in neonates at risk for encephalopathy. *Journal of Pediatrics, 161*(1), 88–93. doi:10.1016/j.jpeds.2011.12.047

Thornton, Paul S., MB, BCh, Stanley, C. A., MD, De Leon, Diva D., MD, MSCE, Harris, D., PhD, Haymond, M. W., MD, Hussain, Khalid, MD, MPH, . . . Pediatric Endocrine Society. (2015). Recommendations from the pediatric endocrine society for evaluation and Management of persistent hypoglycemia in neonates, infants, and Children. *Journal of Pediatrics, the, 167*(2), 238–245. doi:10.1016/j.jpeds.2015.03.057

Thurecn, P. J., & Hay, W. W. (2006). *Neonatal nutrition and metabolism* (2nd ed.). New York, NY: Cambridge University Press.

Tin, W., Brunskill, G., Kelly, T., & Fritz, S. (2012). 15-year follow-up of recurrent "hypoglycemia" in preterm infants. *Pediatrics, 130*(6), e1497-e1503. doi:10.1542/peds.2012-0776

Tudosa, R., Vartej, P., Horhoianu, I., Ghica, C., Mateescu, S., & Dumitrache, I. (2010). Maternal and fetal complications of the hypothyroidism-related pregnancy. *Mædica, 5*(2), 116–123. Retrieved from https://www.ncbi.nlm.nih.gov/pmc/articles/PMC3150006/

Vambergue, A., & Fajardy, I. (2011). Consequences of gestational and pregestational diabetes on placental function and birth weight. *World Journal of Diabetes, 2*(11), 196–203. doi:10.4239/wjd.v2.i11.196

van der Kaay, D. C., Wasserman, J. D., & Palmert, M. R. (2016). Management of neonates born to mothers with Graves' disease. *Pediatrics, 137*(4. doi:10.1542/peds.2015-1878

Varela-Lema, L., Paz-Valinas, L., Atienza-Merino, G., Zubizarreta-Alberdi, R., Villares, R. V., & López-García, M. (2016). Appropriateness of newborn screening for classic galactosaemia: Asystematic review. *Journal of Inherited Metabolic Disease, 39*(5), 633–649. doi:10.1007/s10545-016-9936-y

Verbalis, J. G., Goldsmith, S. R., Greenberg, A., Korzelius, C., Schrier, R. W., Sterns, R. H., & Thompson, C. J. (2013). Diagnosis, evaluation, and treatment of hyponatremia: Expert panel recommendations. *American Journal of Medicine, 126*(10, Suppl. 1), S1–S42. doi:10.1016/j.amjmed.2013.07.006

Volpe, J. J. (Ed.). (2018). Volpe's neurology of the newborn (6th ed.). Philadelphia, PA: Elsevier.

Walker, R. W., & Goran, M. I. (2015). Laboratory determined sugar content and composition of commercial infant formulas, baby foods and common grocery items targeted to children. Nutrients, 7(7), 5850-5867. doi:10.3390/nu7075254

Wassner, A. J. (2017). Congenital hypothyroidism. Clinics in Perinatology, 45(1), 1–18. doi:10.1016/j.clp.2017.10.004

Wassner, A. J., & Brown, R. S. (2015). Congenital hypothyroidism: recent advances. *Current Opinion in Endocrinology, Diabetes, and Obesity, 22*(5), 407.–412. doi:10.1097/MED.0000000000000181

Weinstein, D. A., Steuerwald, U., De Souza, C. F. M., & Derks, T. G. J. (2018). Inborn Errors of Metabolism with Hypoglycemia Glycogen Storage Diseases and Inherited Disorders of Gluconeogenesis: Glycogen Storage Diseases and Inherited Disorders of Gluconeogenesis. *Pediatric clinics of North America, 65*(2), 247–265. doi: 10.1016/j.pcl.2017.11.005

Wickström, R., Skiöld, B., Petersson, G., Stephansson, O., & Altman, M. (2018). Moderate neonatal hypoglycemia and adverse neurological development at 2-6 years of age. *European Journal of Epidemiology, 33*(10), 1011–1020. doi:10.1007/s10654-018-0425-5

Witt, C. L. (1999). Adrenal insufficiency in the term and preterm neonate. *Neonatal Network, 18*(5), 21–28. doi:10.1891/0730-0832.18.5.21

World Health Organization. (2017, November). Diabetes fact sheet. Retrieved from http://www.who.int/mediacentre/factsheets/fs312/en/

11

THE REPRODUCTIVE SYSTEM

Amy Bieda, Mary Terhaar, and Mary Elaine Patrinos

LEARNING OBJECTIVES

After completing this chapter, the reader should be able to:

- Understand normal reproductive system development.
- Analyze the physiologic function of the fetal and neonatal reproductive system.
- Discuss common inherited disorders and their effect on fetal and neonatal reproductive system development and function.
- Identify maternal health issues that have a potential impact on fetal and postnatal reproductive system development and function.
- Evaluate common disorders that affect the reproductive system and their implications across the life span.

INTRODUCTION

The development of the reproductive system is a complex process. Differentiation of sex progresses through discrete stages following in a sequence from genetic to gonadal, hormonal, phenotypic, and psychological development (Makiyan, 2016). Fertilization determines the genetic sex. Over the next 14 weeks, through the integrated action of genetic codes, hormones, and the nervous system, sexual differentiation occurs as the human moves from zygote to embryo to fetus. The observable physical properties of a fetus (phenotype) also include physical and psychological development over time. Adverse events from fertilization through fetal development can result in abnormalities in genetic makeup, sexual differentiation, and external genitalia. This chapter discusses normal physiologic development with an emphasis on hormones that contribute to sexual differentiation and development of internal and external genitalia. Also included is an overview of disorders of sexual development.

TIMELINE OF ORGAN DEVELOPMENT

Gonads are reproductive glands that produce mature germ cells, either male or female, and carry a haploid chromosome set, capable of initiating formation of a new individual. Fetal development of gonads begins in an undifferentiated state and progresses to development of specialized male or female organ systems capable of differentiated functions as a direct result of exposure to sex hormones. This development includes formation of the gonads, genital ducts, and external genitals from undifferentiated primordial structures within the embryo into adapted structures that meet the functional needs of the two sexes.

In the male fetus, gonads differentiate into testes and the duct system becomes the efferent ductules of the testes, the duct of the epididymis, the ductus deferens, the seminal vesicles, and the largest portion of the urethra. External genitalia become specialized to form the penis and scrotum. In the female fetus, gonads differentiate into the ovaries and the duct system becomes the fallopian tubes, uterus, and the upper third of the vagina. External genitalia become specialized to form the clitoris, labia majora and minora, vulva, and mons pubis.

This developmental process begins at fertilization with the determination of genetic sex as either male (XY) or female (XX). This differentiation of sex marks the end of the sex-indifferent or undifferentiated stage. In total, fetal and gonadal development progress through four phases:

- Sex indifferent or bipotential gonad
- Differentiation of gonadal sex
- Differentiation of somatic sex
- Differentiation of neuroendocrine sex

DEVELOPMENTAL PHYSIOLOGY

The Sex-Indifferent, Bipotential Gonad

Regardless of chromosomal sex as female (46 XX) or male (46 XY), the embryo and early fetus are sex-indifferent and have the potential to develop into either sex. For both sexes, gonadal development begins in an undifferentiated state. During week 4 of gestation, irrespective of sex, primordial germ cells arise from the mesonephros to form the genital ridge, the somatic precursor of gonads. The genital ridge forms next to the developing kidney. Two transcription-factor genes are essential for human genital ridge development: Wilms tumor 1 (*WT1*) and steroidogenic factor 1 (*SF1*; Wilhelm & Koopman, 2006).

Early gonads arise in pairs on day 10.5 of gestation (Wilhelm & Koopman, 2006), from the ventromedial surface of the intermediate mesoderm. They align on either side of the embryo and line the coelomic cavity between the limb buds during the first half of development (Wilhelm, Palmer, & Koopman, 2007). This development is triggered by the *SRY* gene.

SRY Gene. The *SRY* gene is located on the short arm of the Y chromosome and is the testis-determining factor. The gene produces sex-determining region Y protein, a transcription factor that binds to a specific region of DNA and helps control activity of specific genes. It results in the production of hormones that guide male sexual differentiation and development. If there is absence or dysfunction of the *SRY* gene, ovaries develop.

SRY encodes the transcription factor that is a member of the high-mobility group (HMG)-box family of DNA-binding proteins. *SRY* binds to *SF1* and together they bind to a specific region of the *SOX9* enhancer and activate the *SOX9* gene that is expressed in Sertoli cells (Kashimada & Koopman, 2010). The expression timing and pattern of *SRY* begins at day 41 of gestation and reaches its peak at day 44 of gestation, then decreases to low levels up until week 18 of gestation (Hanley et al., 2000).

SOX9 Gene. Both *SRY* and *SOX9* support cell lineage precursors with differentiation of these cells into Sertoli cells. *SOX9* expression starts at day 41 of gestation and continues to approximately 18 weeks of gestation (Hanley et al., 2000). The protein encoded by the *SOX9* gene is a transcription factor that binds to DNA and activates other genes, including blocking the gene pathway leading to the differentiation of ovarian cells (Kashimada & Koopman, 2010). There are two other essential products of *SOX9* upregulation. These products are prostaglandin D2 (PGD2) and fibroblast growth factor 9 (FGF9). PGD2 recruits cells of the supporting cell lineage in order to ensure enough Sertoli cells are provided for normal testis development (Wilhelm et al., 2007). FGF9 promotes reproduction of Sertoli cell precursors (Brennan & Capel, 2004).

DAX1 Gene. The *DAX1* gene is another gene required for sex determination. *DAX1* is located on the X chromosome and is upregulated by *WT1* and *SF1*. *DAX1* expression occurs prior to *SRY* and remains in Sertoli cells throughout the sex determination period (Hanley et al., 2000). *DAX1* is expressed in both ovarian and testicular tissue, but downregulates the effectiveness of *SRY*. Overexpression of *DAX1* in XY individuals may result in sex reversal (Blecher & Erickson, 2007). A summary is presented in Table 11.1.

Differentiation of Gonadal Sex

The bipotential gonad, or genital ridge (urogenital ridge), proliferates from coelomic epithelium. The external genitalia for both sexes are derived from the urogenital sinus, genital tubercle, genital swellings, and genital folds. The differentiation of the genital ridge into the testis, with the formation of Sertoli cells, occurs in the presence of the Y chromosome. *SRY* is detected in the genital ridge soon after its formation. The primordial germ cells, which originate in the epiblast, migrate through the primitive streak to the posterior body wall of the yolk sac and then move into the mesenchyme of the genital ridge. The epithelium of the genital ridge proliferates and the cells enter the underlying mesenchyme. Under the influence of *SOX9*, primitive sex cords develop in the genital ridge and become enlarged and more defined. The cords are embedded within the surface of the coelomic epithelium. The indifferent gonad now consists of an external cortex and an internal medulla and resides in the Wolffian body.

When differentiation of the sex cords occurs, they are separated from the germinal epithelium. The tunica vaginalis is the outer layer that surrounds the testis and the tunica albuginea, a dense layer of connective tissue, divides the testis cords from the epithelium surface. The

TABLE 11.1 Developmental Physiology: Bipotential Gonad

Primordial germ cells form the genital ridge	Pronephros: Anterior region
	Mesonephros: Central region
	Metanephros: Posterior region
SRY gene	Located on the short arm of the Y chromosome
	Determines testis formation
SOX9 gene	Blocks differentiation of ovarian cells
	Precursor of prostaglandin D2
	Precursor of fibroblast growth factor 9
DAX1 gene	Located on the X chromosome
	Upregulated by *WT1* and *SF1*
	Remains in Sertoli cells through sex determination
	Expressed in ovarian and testicular tissue
	Overexpression can result in sex reversal

SF1, steroidogenic factor; *WT1*; Wilms tumor 1.

tunica albuginea ultimately attaches to the rete testis. The tunica albuginea thickens at the posterior margin of the testis and forms the mediastinum testis, which is a mass of fibrous tissue that is continuous externally with the tunica albuginea. The outer portion of the sex cords becomes the seminiferous tubules. The spaces between the seminiferous tubules are occupied by highly vascularized connective tissue containing fibroblasts, macrophages, and Leydig cells. Each seminiferous tubule forms a loop and connects to the rete testes. Fetal Leydig cells begin developing shortly after the differentiation of the testis cords with production of testosterone to impact sexual differentiation of the genital ducts and external genitalia.

Testis Differentiation

Peritubular Myoid Cells. Peritubular myoid cells are thought to migrate from the mesonephros and form a single layer of flattened cells that surround the Sertoli cells. Their main functions include providing structural support of the forming testis cords (Wilhelm & Koopman, 2006), in conjunction with Sertoli cells, and stimulating movement of mature sperm through the seminiferous tubules to the seminal vesicles. Peritubular myoid cells may represent the only cell type in the testis for which no

corresponding cell type has been identified in the ovary (Wilhelm et al., 2007).

Leydig Cells. Development of Leydig cells in humans occurs during embryonic and fetal development, as well as during puberty. Leydig cell androgen production begins in embryonic life and is critical for intrauterine masculinization of the male fetus genital tract and brain, and continues until birth, at which time it decreases. The second increase of Leydig cells occurs at 2 months of age and then the cells remain dormant until the third surge occurs, when adult Leydig cells arise at puberty (S. Griswold & Behringer, 2009).

Fetal Leydig cells are thought to originate in the mesonephric or coelomic epithelium and develop outside the testicular cord in the testes. From week 6 of gestation, the Leydig cells (also known as *interstitial cells*) secrete testosterone. A rapid rise in production is noted between weeks 14 and 16 of gestation, when the cells comprise more than 50% the volume of the fetal testis.

The function of the Leydig cells is to respond to the luteinizing hormone (LH) secreted from the pituitary gland. The LH, which is released from the hypothalamus via the gonadotropin-releasing hormone (GnRH), is responsible for stimulating testosterone production from the Leydig cells in the testes. This acts as a negative feedback on the pituitary to suppress or modulate further LH secretion. The LH binds to the cell surface receptors on the Leydig cells, activating the synthesis and secretion of androgens: testosterone, androstenedione, and dehydroepiandrosterone. Some testosterone is converted into dihydrotestosterone (DHT), which influences the development of the penis, scrotum, and prostate.

Sertoli Cells. During week 7 of gestation, Sertoli cells (sustentacular cells) differentiate in the testis and organize to form the testis cords, surrounding the incoming germ cells in the center of the cords and expressing *SOX9* (Wilhelm et al., 2007). The cords form loops in the mesenchymal region of the developing testis and are connected to the rete testis located in the hilum of the testicle.

Sertoli cells are the supporting cells for germ cells. These cells are important in establishing testis vasculature and inducing differentiation of peritubular myoid cells and fetal Leydig cells. The function of the Sertoli cells is controlled by the follicle-stimulating hormone (FSH) via the hypothalamus, which secretes GnRH. FSH stimulates the Sertoli cells to produce androgen-binding protein (ABG) and the anti-Müllerian hormone (AMH). ABG is a protein that binds to testosterone and keeps it concentrated within the seminiferous tubules so that spermatogenesis can progress. AMH is a glycoprotein and is responsible for the regression of Müllerian ducts in male fetuses; it is the first hormone secreted by the Sertoli cells.

Blood–Testis Barrier. The specialized junctions of the Sertoli cells create a barrier separating the testes from the normal circulation and testicular tubules. The barrier restricts fluids from entering or exiting the lumen (Mital, Hinton, & Dufour, 2011). The blood-testis barrier only allows secretion from Sertoli cells to enter the lumen of the seminiferous tubules. However, the primary function of this barrier is to provide an environment for germ cell development and maturation. A summary is provided in Table 11.2 and Figure 11.1.

TABLE 11.2 Developmental Physiology: Testis Differentiation	
Peritubular myoid cells	Migrate from the mesonephros
	Form a single layer surrounding the Sertoli cells
	Provide structural support for formation of testis cords
	Contribute to movement of mature sperm cells through seminiferous tubules
	May be the only cells in the testis lacking a corresponding cell type in the ovaries
Leydig cells	Originate in the mesonephros
	Begins in embryonic stage
	In utero androgen production essential for masculinization
	Key to fetal genital track development
	Key to fetal brain development
	Increases in second month; more than half the volume of testis
	Respond to LH secreted by the pituitary and stimulate testosterone production
	Secrete testosterone in weeks 14–16
	Activates synthesis and secretion of androgens
	A portion is converted to dihydrotestosterone and influences development of penis, scrotum, and prostate
	Third surge in adulthood
Sertoli cells	Differentiate in week 7 within the testis
	Form the testis cords in the mesenchymal region
	Express *SOX9*
	Cords form loops
	Act as support for germ cells
	Key to formation of testis vasculature
	Induce differentiation of peritubular myoid cells & fetal Leydig cells
	Function controlled by FSH and GnRH
	Produces ABG, which binds to testosterone and retains it in the seminiferous tubules
	Produces AMH responsible for regression of Müllerian ducts
Blood–testis barrier	Junction of Sertoli cells
	Forms barrier between systemic circulation and that of the testis
	Provides environment for germ cell development and maturation

ABG, androgen-binding hormone; AMH, anti-Müllerian hormone; FSH, follicle-stimulating hormone; GnRH, gonadotropin-releasing hormone; LH, luteinizing hormone.

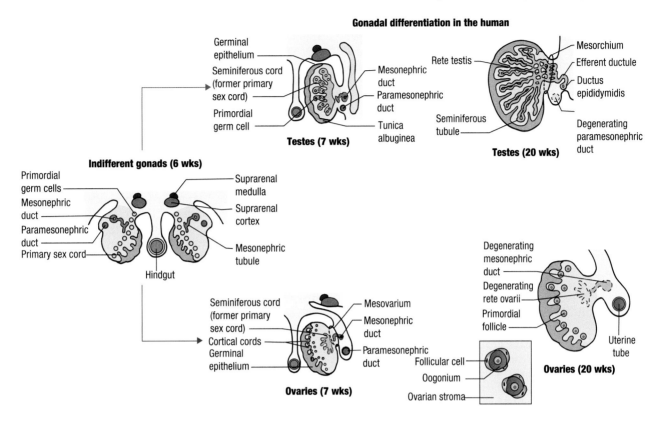

Figure 11.1 Overview of gonadal development.

Development of the Ovary

The development of the ovary occurs more slowly than the development of the testis. Ovarian development is very complex and not well understood. The common belief that females are the "default sex" has been challenged since the early 2000s with the discovery of genes that stimulate ovary development and prevent testicular development (Ainsworth, 2015).

The primordial germ cells arise from the yolk sac and migrate through the primitive gut to incorporate into the extracellular matrix of the dorsal mesentery and then cluster on the outer half of the genital ridge. If the primordial germ cells do not migrate, streak gonads (gonadal dysgenesis) develop; in these circumstances, the ovary is replaced by functionless tissue. In embryos with the XX sex chromosome, the cortex differentiates into an ovary and the medulla regresses. The primary sex cords, which are in the medullary region of the ovary, develop from the gonadal ridge but are not prominent in the female gonad and develop from the mesonephros into the rete ovarii, which eventually degenerates and disappears.

After the primordial germ cells reach the ovary, they proliferate in vast number through mitosis and are called *oogonia* (primordial female sex cells). Research indicates that this occurs under the influence of retinoic acid (Childs, Cowan, Kinnell, Anderson, & Saunders, 2011; M. Griswold, Hogarth, Bowles, & Koopman, 2012; Le Bouffant et al., 2010). During this time the oogonia divide, forming germ-cell nests. These nests are partitioned into ovigerous cords that are open to the surface of the ovary. Ovigerous cords consist of a cluster of primordial germ cells surrounded by somatic cells (Nef et al., 2005). No oogonia form postnatally and many of them degenerate before birth through apoptosis.

The first stage of folliculogenesis occurs during week 10 of gestation, when the oogonia undergo meiosis, enlarge, and develop into oocytes. During this same time frame, somatic cells develop into the follicular epithelial granulosa cells (Maheshwari & Fowler, 2008). Granulosa cells can have specific names depending on their location within the follicle. They may derive from the mesonephros (primitive sex cords), the coelomic epithelium (the secondary sex cords), or from ovarian mesenchyme (Maheshwari & Fowler, 2008).

One oocyte is surrounded by a single layer of flat pregranulosa cells (Pepling, 2012), which become primordial follicles. Primordial follicles contain the germinal vesicle oocytes, which are actually oocyte nuclei at this stage of development (Virant-Klun, 2015). Primordial follicles are found on the edge of the cortex and medulla as well as in the internal cortex (Maheshwari & Fowler, 2008). It is estimated that the ovaries contain approximately 5 to

7 million primordial follicles. The majority of primordial follicles undergo atresia mediated by programmed cell death or apoptosis (Markström, Svensson, Shao, Svanberg, & Billig, 2002). Atresia occurs at every stage of follicular development.

The tunica albuginea, which forms at the corticomedullary junction of the ovary, contains the majority of oocytes. The majority of oocytes degenerate across fetal development and the entire volume of oocytes is determined at birth. The primordial follicles enter the diplotene stage of prophase 1, which lasts until puberty (onset of ovulation; Figure 11.2).

The molecular regulation of early ovarian development is not well understood. There are several genes that are directly linked to ovarian development and research by Nef and colleagues (2005) indicate that gene expression in ovarian development is detected as early as postcoital day 11.5 of gestation (Nef et al., 2005). At least 1,000 female-specific genes have been identified, but for the purpose of this chapter, we discuss four gene markers that have been studied in humans.

DAX1 Gene. DAX1 plays a complex role in the downregulation of the AMH, leading to Müllerian duct development and internal female differentiation. Elevated levels of this hormone are associated with sex reversal in XY chromosomes in mouse models; this is thought to be repression of transcription factor SOX9 (Lalli, Melner, Stocco, & Sassone-Corsi, 1998). The loss of DAX1 function is

associated with X-linked congenital adrenal hypoplasia (Suntharalingham, Buonocore, Duncan, & Achermann, 2015).

FOX12. FOX12 is a female-specific marker of the Forkhead box transcription factor (FOX) family and has been evolutionarily conserved. This marker is expressed in the supporting cells of the XX gonad as early as day 12.5 of gestation. In vivo, FOX12 represses testis differentiation through repression of the SOX9 cis-regulatory sequence of TESCO (testis-specific enhancer core element). Cis-regulatory sequences of TESCO are areas of noncoding DNA important to the understanding of gene regulatory mechanisms. The majority of research, done in mice, has demonstrated that deletion of FOX12 causes ovarian dysgenesis and infertility; therefore, it may be a primary female-determining gene (Dupont, Krust, Gansmuller, Chambon, & Mark, 2000).

WNT4 and FST1. The absence of SRY in the XX gonad releases WNT4 expression. WNT4 also upregulates DAX1, which antagonizes SF1 and thereby inhibits steroidogenic enzymes. Recent evidence has demonstrated that the signaling pathway of WNT4 may be a multigene signaling pathway. FST1 (follistatin) acts downstream of WNT4 to impede the formation of the coelomic vessel in the male gonad and also maintains survival of the germ cells in the cortical region of the ovary (Yao et al., 2004). A summary is presented in Table 11.3.

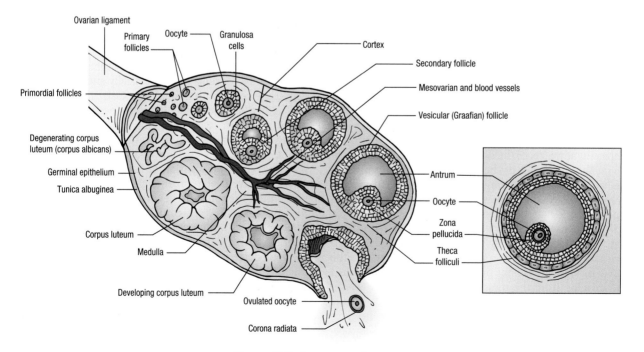

Figure 11.2 Oogenesis in the ovary.

Sexual Duct Systems

Although gonads are sex determined at the end of week 7 of gestation, reproductive ducts are still indifferent. Male (Wolffian) external genitalia originate from the mesonephric ducts, whereas female (Müllerian) external genitalia originate from the paramesonephric ducts. The mesonephric tubules grow into the gonadal ridge and are connected to the mesonephric duct. The paramesonephric duct invaginates into the coelomic epithelium. By the end of week 8 of gestation, the embryo has an undifferentiated gonadal primordium and two embryonic duct systems (Sobel, Zhu, & Imperato-McGinley, 2004).

Differentiation of the Male Duct System. After the gonads have differentiated into testes, the secretion of testicular hormones is required to develop the sexual duct system in the male. The Müllerian-inhibiting substance (MIH) belongs to the transforming growth factor-β (TGFβ) superfamily. MIH is expressed in Sertoli cells and causes

TABLE 11.3 Developmental Physiology: Ovarian Development	
Oogenesis	Primordial germ cell arises from the yolk sac to cluster on the outer half of the genital ridge
	Primary sex cords in the medullary region arise from the gonadal ridge
	Cells proliferate under the influence of retinoic acid to form oogonia
	Oogonia divide to form germ cells
	Germ cells cluster into nests
	Nests partition to form ovigerous cells that are surrounded by somatic cells
	Five to seven million primordial follicles form and situate at the inner cortex, the outer edge of the cortex, and medulla
	Most follicles will die by apoptosis
	Atresia occurs at every stage of development
	Tunica albuginea, containing the majority of oocytes, forms
DAX1 gene	Complex role in downregulation of anti-Müllerian hormone
	Contributes to Müllerian duct formation
	Contributes to female differentiation
	Elevated levels associated with sex reversal in XY mouse models
	Loss associated with X-linked congenital adrenal hypoplasia
FOX12 gene	Forkhead box transcription factor
	Female-specific marker
	Expressed as early as day 12 postcoitus
	Represses testis differentiation by suppressing *SOX9*
WNT4	Expressed in the absence of *SRY* in the XX gonad
	Upregulates *DAX1*
	Antagonizes *SFI*
FST1	Acts downstream to *WNT4* to impede formation of coelomic vessel in male gonads
	Maintains survival of germ cells in the ovary

FST, follistatin.

regression of the Müllerian (paramesonephric) ducts by week 9 of gestation. In the Leydig cells, the LH initiates the production of pregnenolone, which is converted to DHEA (dehydroepiandrosterone) and then to testosterone. This promotes development of the Wolffian (mesonephric) ducts. The Wolffian ducts then differentiate to form the ductus deferens and urethra as well as the male accessory sex glands: the seminal vesicle, prostate, and bulbourethral gland (Cowper's gland). The formation of the accessory sex glands in the male depends on androgenic stimulation.

Differentiation of the Female Duct System. Two mesenchymal projections border the cloacal membrane laterally; these are the paired primordia of the genital tubercle. The cloacal fold surrounds the cloacal membrane and prolongs the genital tubercle; on either side of the cloacal folds are the genital swellings. The cloacal membrane divides into the urogenital membrane anteriorly and the anal membrane posteriorly. During week 9 of gestation, the urogenital membrane dissipates and the phallic segment of the urogenital sinus opens to the exterior.

The Müllerian ducts develop laterally to the Wolffian ducts. In the absence of male hormones, the Wolffian ducts degenerate and the Müllerian ducts are retained and differentiate into the Fallopian tubes (oviducts), uterus, and vagina. The caudal end of the Müllerian ducts form the Müllerian tubercle at the dorsal wall of the urogenital sinus. The Müllerian tubercle is destroyed and becomes the vaginal plate. By weeks 16 to 18 of gestation, the central core breaks down to form the vaginal lumen. The upper two thirds of the vagina is formed by the Müllerian tubercle, whereas the lower third of the vagina is formed by the urogenital sinus.

The role of steroids in female development has not been determined. The ovary does not produce steroids during embryogenesis and the female reproductive tract is independent of gonadal secretions. A summary is presented in Table 11.4.

Development of External Genitalia

Although the sex of the embryo is genetically determined at fertilization, the morphological characteristics of normal male and female external genitalia remain undifferentiated until week 7 of development. If the sexual determination of the zygote is male, masculinization occurs through physical growth and fusion. The development of the external genitalia cannot be accomplished without DHT, an essential androgenic hormone. It is derived from testosterone via the action of the enzyme 5-alpha-reductase (Sajjad, 2010). Without DHT present, the external genitalia will be female.

Male External Genitalia. Inguinal-canal development provides the testes with the ability to migrate to the labioscrotal swellings. The gubernaculum starts to develop during week 6 of gestation and is the primary structure in testicular descent. This process is regulated by insulin-like 3 (INLS-3), which is secreted by the Leydig cells (Nation,

Balic, Southwell, Newgreen, & Hutson, 2009). The gubernaculum, attached to the caudal end of the testis, descends on each side from the lower poles of the gonads and migrates from the abdominal wall to the internal inguinal ring (Favorito, Costa, Julio-Junior, & Sampaio, 2014), where it innervates the cremaster muscle and then across the pubic region to the scrotum (Hughes & Acerini, 2008). Migration occurs as the abdominal cavity and the pelvic region enlarge.

The processus vaginalis, an invagination of the peritoneum, develops ventral to the gubernaculum and pushes through the lower abdominal wall using the path formed by the gubernaculum. The processus vaginalis carries layers of the abdominal wall, which covers the testes and spermatic cord. The mesonephric duct develops into the epididymis. At 26 to 36 weeks of gestation, the epididymis enters the processus vaginalis prior to the testis. The epididymis and testis descend into the scrotum and fuse with the posterior layers of the scrotum to prevent the testis from rotating. At 37 to 40 weeks of gestation, the processus vaginalis closes, preventing communication between the peritoneum and the inguinal canal or scrotum.

During this phase of sexual development, the genital tubercle elongates to form a phallus, which pulls the urethral folds forward to form the lateral walls of the urethral groove, resulting in the penile portion of the male urethra. The growth of the phallus is dependent on DHT and testosterone. At the base of the urethral groove, ectoderm grows toward the penile urethra. Originating in the endoderm, the epithelial lining of the groove forms the urethral plate. The two urethral folds close over the urethral plate, which does not reach the glans. Ectoderm cells from the tip of the glans penetrate inward and form an epithelial cord known as the *glandular epithelial plate*. When this plate splits, it forms the glandular urethra on the ventral part of the glans. The movement of the urethral opening to the tip of the glans forming the external urethral meatus occurs as a result of the closing of the groove in the glans. The labioscrotal folds fuse at midline to form the scrotal raphe (Shulman, Palmert, & Wherrett, 2015).

Female External Genitalia. Without androgen influence on the development of external female genitalia, the genital tubercle remains small and differentiates into the body and glans of the clitoris. The urogenital sinus remains open with the urethra opening anteriorly and the vagina posteriorly, within the vestibular portion of the urogenital sinus. The majority of the labioscrotal swelling remains unfused and becomes the labia majora. The labioscrotal folds fuse anteriorly to form the mons pubis and posteriorly to form the posterior labial commissure. The urethral folds fuse posteriorly to form the frenulum of the labia minora. The urethral folds that do not fuse become the labia minora. The accessory glands of female genitalia include the Skene or lesser vestibular glands and the urethral glands. All arise from the urogenital sinus. The Bartholin glands (greater vestibular glands) are located on the right and left side of the vaginal vestibule. A summary is presented in Table 11.5 and Figure 11.3.

TABLE 11.4 Developmental Physiology: Duct Systems

Male	Gonads differentiate into testis.
	Testosterone signals development of male duct system.
	Müllerian-inhibiting hormone is expressed from Sertoli cells.
	MIH leads to regression of Müllerian ducts by week 9.
	LH in Leydig cells produces pregnenolone.
	Pregnenolone converts first to DHEA and then to testosterone.
	Testosterone promotes development of Wolffian ducts.
	Wolffian ducts form the ductus deferens, urethra, and male sex glands.
	Seminal vesicle, prostate, and bulbourethral glands develop dependent on stimulation by androgen.
Female	Two mesenchymal projections border the cloacal membrane.
	Cloacal fold extends the genital tubercle.
	Cloacal membrane forms urogenital membrane anteriorly.
	Cloacal membrane forms anal membrane posteriorly.
	Phallic segment opens to the urogenital sinus at week 9.
	Müllerian duct develops lateral to the Wolffian.
	Wolffian duct degenerates in the absence of male hormones.
	Müllerian ducts differentiate into fallopian tubes.
	Caudal end of Müllerian duct forms dorsal wall of urogenital sinus.
	Müllerian tubercle degenerates to form vaginal plate.
	Central core breaks down at weeks 16–18 to form vagina.
	Upper vagina formed by Müllerian tubercle & lower formed from sinus.

DHEA, dehydroepiandrosterone; LH, luteinizing hormone; MIH, Müllerian-inhibiting hormone.

TABLE 11.5 Developmental Physiology: External Genitalia

Male testis	Inguinal canal provides path for testis migration.
	Gubernaculum provides structure for testicular descent and development begins in week 6.
	INLS-3 secreted by Leydig cells, regulates descent.
	Gubernaculum migrates from abdominal wall to inguinal ring.
	Gubernaculum then innervates the cremaster muscle and scrotum.
	Processus vaginalis follows the path of the gubernaculum, carrying layers of the abdominal wall to cover the testis and spermatic cord.
	Epididymis enters the processus vaginalis and then joins the testes to descend into and fuse with the walls of the scrotum at week 26.
	Processus vaginalis closes at weeks 37–40.

(continued)

TABLE 11.5 Developmental Physiology: External Genitalia (*continued*)

Male phallus	Genital tubercle elongates to form phallus.
	Urethra is pulled forward to form lateral walls of urethral groove.
	DHT and testosterone influence formation of the phallus.
	Ectoderm grows from the base toward the penile urethra.
	Endothelial lining originates in the endoderm and forms the epithelial lining of the urethral plate.
	Ectoderm cells from the glans move inward to form the epithelial cord and plate.
	Plate splits to form the urethra and ventral glans.
	Opening of the urethra moves to the tip of the glans forming the urinary meatus and closing the groove of the glans.
	Labiosacral fold fuses at midline.
Female external genitalia	Absence of androgen leads to small genital tubercle, which differentiates into the body and glans of the clitoris.
	Labia minora urethral folds become one.
	Labiosacral folds become labia majora.
	Labiosacral folds join anteriorly to form mons pubis.
	Labiosacral folds join posteriorly to form labial commissure.
	Skene, lesser vestibular, urethral, and Bartholin's glans form.

DHT, dihydrotestosterone; INLS-3, insulin-like substance;

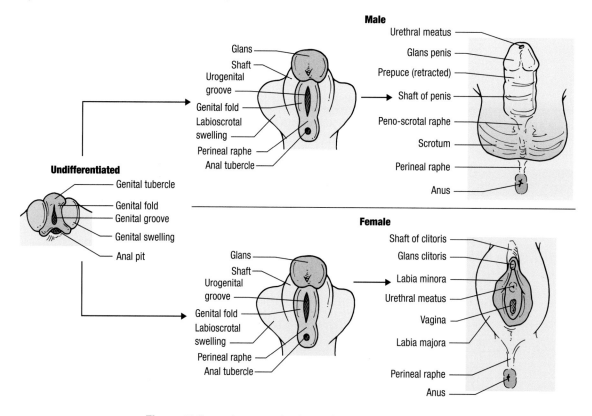

Figure 11.3 Development of male and female external genitalia.

COMMON PROBLEMS WITH IMPLICATIONS ACROSS THE LIFE SPAN

Variations in development of gonads and sex that present at birth impose lifelong implications. In 2005, an international consensus group on intersex disorders proposed the term *disorders of sex development* to describe the conditions. Subsequently, advocates proposed *sex development* as a more fitting label, because it accommodates identity rather than exclusively medical criteria. Both can be referred to as *DSD*, which comprise a variety of patterns of atypical development (Meyer-Bahlburg, 2017). This set of disorders consists of a variety of conditions characterized by complex interactions between multiple organ systems and psychological development that affect individuals in varying degrees and have long-lasting impact (Van Batavia & Kolon, 2016). These DSDs can be classified by karyotype (47XXY, 45XO/46XY, 46XX/46XY, and a few other variations), phenotype, or gonadal histology (Figure 11.4; Hughes, Houk, Ahmed, & Lee, 2006).

For the purpose of linking genetic, gonadal, and somatic sex development to interconnected body systems, a few of the more prevalent intersex conditions are highlighted in the final section of this chapter. These conditions are Turner syndrome (TS), Klinefelter syndrome (KS), complete androgen insensitivity syndrome, and congenital adrenal hyperplasia.

Intersex (Ambiguous Genitalia)

Intersex refers to a set of atypical patterns of development involving both internal and external genitalia. Labeled in the past as *ambiguous genitalia*, these conditions lead to questions about gender assignment and long-term management. Such variations occur once in every 1,500 to 2,000 births in the United States (Davis & Preves, 2017; Sax, 2002). The root cause of intersex is dysfunctional androgen activity, commonly androgen insensitivity syndrome, or AIS. Individuals with AIS will develop testicular dysgenesis and exhibit either female external genitalia or ambiguous genitalia as a result of incomplete masculinization. In some cases, gonads will develop ovotesticular gonads composed of both ovarian tissue and testicles joined together end to end via the primordial tubular and ductal structures. A summary is presented in Table 11.6.

Turner Syndrome (Female)

TS is characterized by a single X chromosome and found in one of 2,500 female births (National Institutes of Health [NIH], 2018c). Among the most common forms of aneuploidy, individuals with TS have short stature, sexual infantilism, and a variety of malformations, including webbing of the neck, widening between nipples, a low hairline on the neck, brown nevi on

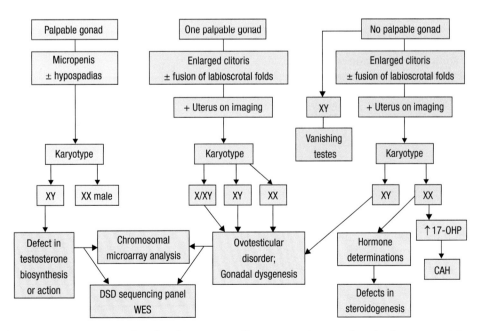

Figure 11.4 Infant with ambiguous genitalia. This decision tree offers a practical approach to the diagnosis and determination of the pathogenesis of ambiguous genitalia.
Source: Yatsenko, S. A., & Witchel, S. F. (2017). Genetic approach to ambiguous genitalia and disorders of sex development: What clinicians need to know. *Seminars in Perinatology, 41,* 232–243. doi:10.1053/j.semperi.2017.03.016

TABLE 11.6 Intersex	
Incidence	One in every 1,500–2,000 live births in the United States
Etiology	Androgen dysfunction or insensitivity
Impact	Testicular dysgenesis and incomplete masculinization
Presentation	Either female or ambiguous external genitalia

the skin, elbow deformities, short metacarpals, small fingernails, and lymphedema in hands and feet (Oliveira et al., 2009). Individuals with TS may also present with a shield-shaped chest, horseshoe-shaped kidney, and coarctation of the aorta (Pennington et al., 1985). Undifferentiated gonads are a hallmark of the disorder. Both external and internal genitals are female, but the breasts are small and underdeveloped, as are the uterus and ovaries; primary amenorrhea is common (Oliveira et al., 2009).

Approximately 99% of all embryos with the pure 45X karyotype die in utero. However, mosaicism is higher among live-born fetuses with TS than among aborted fetuses, and is considered necessary for survival and the source of variability in presentation (Hassold, Benham, & Leppert, 1988; Held et al., 1992). Risk for gonadal tumors results from abnormal gonadogenesis (Verp & Simpson, 1987). Gonadoblastoma is one such tumor, which despite its benign presentation can transform into more invasive tumors. For this reason, careful monitoring is required.

Individuals with TS also face increased risk for catastrophic aortic dissection. Among 85 reported cases, more than half of the dissections presented in women below the age of 30. No additional risk factors were identified in 21% of the cases. Congenital heart disease was reported in 69% of the cases, and among these 54% were hypertensive, although blood pressure measurements were unavailable (Carlson & Silberbach, 2007). A summary is presented in Table 11.7.

Klinefelter Syndrome (Male)

KS, also known as *47,XXY* or *XXY*, is characterized by hypergonadotropic hypogonadism. The most common sex-chromosome-linked DSD in males, KS presents as often as one in 500 to 1,000 live births (NIH, 2018b). Individuals with KS face greater risk for all-cause mortality (40%) as well as cardiovascular risk, present with subclinical cardiovascular abnormalities, and perform poorly during exercise stress testing (Salzano et al., 2016). As well as issues with cognitive development, individuals with KS have a higher prevalence of metabolic syndrome, insulin resistance, and type 2 diabetes (Salzano et al., 2016).

Individuals with KS are trapped in a cycle of hypogonadism, increasing body fat, failing carbohydrate

TABLE 11.7 Turner's Syndrome (Female)	
Incidence	One in every 2,000 live female births
Etiology	Single X chromosome
Impact	99% embryos die in utero
	Mosaicism common in live-born fetus may be necessary for survival
Long-term outcomes	Gonadal tumors may develop (benign and/or invasive)
	Congenital heart disease in 69% of cases
	Essential hypertension
	Risk for aortic dissection
Presentation	Short stature
	Sexual infantilism
	Webbing of neck
	Widening between nipples
	Hairline low on neck
	Brown nevi
	Elbow deformities
	Short metacarpals
	Small fingernails
	Lymphedema in hands and feet
	Shield-shaped chest
	Horseshoe-shaped kidney
	Coarctation of the aorta
	Undifferentiated gonads
	Female internal and external gonads; underdeveloped breasts, uterus, and ovaries
	Primary amenorrhea

metabolism, insulin resistance, suppressed testosterone production, and progressive hypogonadism. In theory, supplemental testosterone can break the cycle and may reduce levels of C-reactive protein associated with persistent inflammation. However, robust data are not yet available to support this practice (Salzano et al., 2016).

Individuals with KS face increased risk for both thromboembolic and stasis events. Mesenteric venous thrombosis, arterial infarction, and ischemic injury are more common than in the general population adjusted for age (Campbell, Newton, & Price, 1980; Campbell & Price, 1981; Rouffy et al., 1973).

The cardiovascular function is also altered by the hypogonadism of KS. Shortened QTC intervals are common. It is interesting to note that the alteration is more pronounced in KS patients taking testosterone replacements as compared to those who do not (Jørgensen et al., 2015). This introduces the hypothesis that individuals with KS may be protected against the cardiovascular danger of low testosterone identified across males more broadly in the general population (Salzano et al., 2016). A summary is presented in Table 11.8.

Complete Androgen Insensitivity Syndrome

Complete androgen insensitivity syndrome (CAIS) refers to a condition in which affected individuals are nonresponsive to male sex hormones (androgens). Androgen insensitivity syndrome is differentiated according to the degree of genital masculinization. CAIS is only significant when it occurs in genetic males and is reported among two to five of every 100,000 individuals (Hughes & Deeb, 2006; NIH, 2018a). Due to the unresponsiveness to male hormones, there is no masculinization of male genitalia. Genetic male individuals affected by CAIS will have female external phenotypic development despite the presence of a Y chromosome; they may have a separate urethral and vaginal orifice. Individuals may have sparse axilla and pubic hair. Breast development may occur due to conversion of excessive testosterone to estrogen. Females have primary amenorrhea and are diagnosed with CAIS during puberty. A summary is presented in Table 11.9.

Congenital Adrenal Hyperplasia

Congenital adrenal hyperplasia (CAH) is a group of autosomal recessive genetic disorders with varying phenotypic presentations. This defect results from a deficiency in reduced activity of one of the five crucial enzymes required for cortisol and aldosterone biosynthesis (from cholesterol) in the adrenal cortex. In approximately 95% of cases of CAH, the genetic defect affects the enzyme 21-hydroxylase (21-OH), which is a cytochrome P450 enzyme. The gene for 21-OH is found on chromosome 6 and is known as *CYP21A2* (Online Mendelian Inheritance in Man, 2018). CAH is the most common cause of ambiguous genitalia in the newborn, affecting one in 15,000 newborns (NIH, 2018d; Shulman et al., 2015). Nonclassic

TABLE 11.8 Klinefelter's Syndrome (Male)	
Incidence	One in 660 live births
Etiology	47,XXY
Impact	Hypergonadotropic hypogonadism
Presentation & long-term outcomes	Increased risk for mortality from all causes (40%)
	Subclinical cardiovascular abnormalities
	Issues with cognitive development
	Metabolic syndrome
	Insulin resistance
	Persistent inflammatory processes
	Increasing body fat
	Failing carbohydrate metabolism
	Suppressed testosterone production
	Progressive hypogonadism
	Thromboembolic events
	Vascular stasis
	Arterial infarction and ischemic injury

TABLE 11.9 Complete Androgen Insensitivity (Male)	
Incidence	One in every 1,500–2,000 live births in the United States
Etiology	Unresponsive to male sex hormones
Impact	No masculinization of male genitalia
Presentation	Genetic males present with female external phenotype
	Sparse axillary and pubic hair
	Breasts may develop
	Primary amenorrhea in individuals thought to be female

disease is reported among one in 1,000 individuals (NIH, 2018d).

The basic pathophysiology of this condition involves the decrease of cortisol synthesis resulting in hyperplasia of the adrenal cortex due to (a) continuous stimulation by ACTH and (b) an overproduction of androgens that are shunted into other metabolic pathways. These androgens can cause virilization of female genitalia and possible salt-wasting due to decreased production of deoxycorticosterone and aldosterone.

The enzyme 21-hydroxylase (21-OH) is required to make cortisol, which is needed to keep glucose levels normal. Newborns with CAH may present with hypoglycemia. The salt-wasting form of CAH occurs when infants do not produce enough aldosterone and lose excess salt and water to the urine. Electrolyte imbalance, hypotension, shock, and cardiovascular collapse from adrenal crisis may result if not recognized and treated promptly.

Female infants may be recognized at birth due to atypical external genitalia, but have normal internal genitalia. Male infants may appear phenotypically normal with symptoms appearing 1 to 4 weeks after birth. Newborn metabolic screening is performed across the United States for 21-OH deficiency to facilitate the early identification of infants at risk for developing life-threatening adrenal crisis. In addition, early identification prevents affected female infants with ambiguous genitalia from receiving an incorrect sex assignment (Levine, 2000). A summary is presented in Table 11.10.

CONCLUSION

Sex hormones, which are primarily androgens, are produced in small amounts; this process begins during early embryonic development and extends across the life span. The formation of the accessory sex glands in the male depends on androgenic stimulation. Females rely on androgen secretion for normal development of genitalia. An error in genetic, gonadal, ductal, or genital development, as a result of dysfunctional androgen activity, may result in a disorder of sexual differentiation. Turner syndrome involves normal ovarian differentiation until the early fetal period of development, when degeneration and atresia of the primordial ovarian follicles occurs. These infants exhibit normal Müllerian duct development, absent Wolffian ducts, and phenotypically female external genitalia with bilateral streak gonads. Many affected infants manifest with impaired lymphatic drainage and cardiac anomalies. KS typically manifests during puberty with persistently small testes and impaired spermatogenesis. CAH is a group of autosomal recessive disorders that occurs as the result of impaired cortisol synthesis, most often due to 21-hydroxylase deficiency, an enzyme responsible for the conversion of cholesterol to cortisol

TABLE 11.10 Congenital Adrenal Hyperplasia	
Incidence	One in every 12,000–15,000 live births
Etiology	Autosomal recessive disease; gene is found on chromosome 6 (CYP21A2)
Impact	Virilization of female genitalia with incorrect sexual assignment
	Periods of adrenal crisis
Long-term outcomes	Decreased fertility in women
	Short stature
	Severe acne
	Early puberty changes, as early as 3–4 years of age
Presentation	**Classic CAH** (salt-wasting): Vomiting, diarrhea, dehydration, low blood pressure, weight loss, hyponatremia, poor feeding, metabolic acidosis
	Classic CAH (simple virilizing form): Ambiguous genitalia, fused labia, enlarged clitoris, adrenal crisis
	Nonclassic CAH: Variable symptoms with milder effects *Males and females*: Rapid growth during childhood, early puberty, hirsutism, severe acne *Males only*: Small testicles, enlarged penis, early facial hair *Females only*: Irregular menses, infertility, behavior becomes masculinized

CAH, congenital adrenal hyperplasia.

and aldosterone. CAH is the most common cause for ambiguous genitalia among females, and, depending on its severity, females may manifest with a simple virilizing form of CAH or a more severe salt-wasting form of the disease. Clinically, term males with bilateral impalpable gonads and infants who present with ambiguous genitalia must be considered positive for CAH until proven otherwise. An understanding of normal sexual differentiation and the more common disorders of sexual differentiation that may manifest during the birth hospitalization or early childhood is essential. Clinicians must remain vigilant and prioritize the early identification, diagnosis, and treatment of these disorders, and, in some cases, offer timely counseling and psychosocial support for family members.

LEARNING TOOLS AND RESOURCES

Podcast

 Congenital Adrenal Hyperplasia/21-Hydroxylase Deficiency

Andrea N. Trembath

Discussion Prompts

1. Contrast the concepts of development and differentiation.
2. What is meant by the bipotential gonad?
3. Describe the function of estrogen and progesterone.
4. Explain the function of the *SRY* gene.
5. Explain the function of the *SOX9* gene in the male.
6. Explain the function of the *DAX1* gene in the male.
7. Describe the genital ridge and its significance for fetal gonadal sex.
8. Discuss what is meant by the notion that female is the default sex.
9. What is the function of the *DAX1* gene in female development?
10. What is the function of the *FOX12* gene in female development?
11. How do *WNT4* & *FST1* influence female development?
12. Explain the differences between the sexes with respect to ductal system differentiation.
13. When is the sex of the embryo genetically determined?

Advice From the Authors

 "Comprehensive assessment, consistent communication, and transparency from all members of the healthcare team are essential in a family's adaptation to a diagnosis related to abnormal fetal development of the reproductive system."

–Amy Bieda, PhD, APRN, PNP-BC, NNP-BC

 "This is an area of science where knowledge is changing at a brisk pace. Use the content presented here as a scaffolding and always return to the most recent literature to refresh your knowledge."

–Mary Terhaar, DNSc, RN, ANEF, FAAN

 "A disorder of sex development in the newborn is considered a medical and psychosocial emergency that requires immediate attention and disclosure to the parents. Designation of sex assignment in the electronic medical record and in all forms of communication with the family and between healthcare team members is to be avoided. The infant should be referred to as 'baby' until appropriate."

–Mary Elaine Patrinos, MD

Mind Map

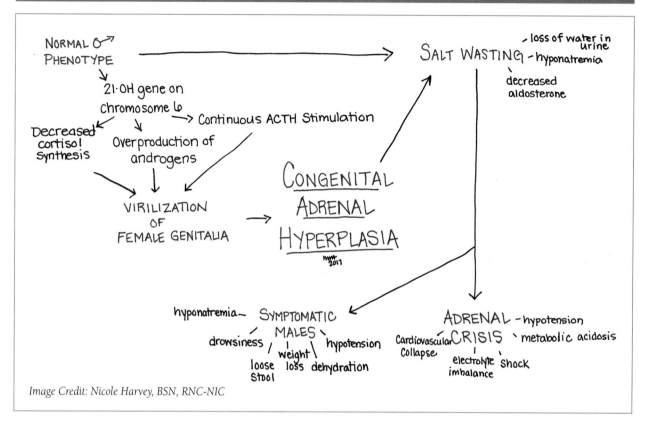

Image Credit: Nicole Harvey, BSN, RNC-NIC

Note: This mind map reflects one student's interpretation of a portion of one or more concepts addressed in this chapter. Readers should regard the mind maps woven throughout this textbook as examples of multi-sensory study tools that can be developed to encourage conceptual understanding. Readers are encouraged to develop their own unique mind maps in consultation with academic faculty or clinical preceptors.

TIMELINE OF ORGAN DEVELOPMENT

NOTE:	LEGEND
Placement of common problems is meant to offer visual/conceptual perspective on the timing of onset of these commonly reported malformations. Variation exists across the literature.	<22 – 27 6/7 weeks = extremely preterm 28 – 31 6/7 weeks = very preterm 32 – 36 6/7 weeks = late/moderate preterm 37 – 40 weeks = term

References

Ainsworth, C. (2015). Sex redefined. *Nature, 518,* 288–291. doi:10.1038/518288a

Blecher, S., & Erickson, R. (2007). Genetics of sexual development: A new paradigm. *American Journal of Medical Genetics: Part A, 143A*(24), 3054–3068. doi:10.1002/ajmg.a.32037

Brennan, J., & Capel, B. (2004). One tissue, two fates: Molecular genetic events that underlie testis versus ovary development. *Nature Reviews Genetics, 5,* 509–521. doi:10.1038/nrg1381

Campbell, W. A., Newton, M. S., & Price W. H. (1980). Hypostatic leg ulceration and Klinefelter's syndrome. *Journal of Mental Deficiency Research, 24,* 115–117. doi:10.1111/j.1365-2788.1980.tb00064.x

Campbell, W. A., & Price, W. H. (1981). Venous thromboembolic disease in Klinefelter's syndrome. *Clinical Genetics, 19,* 275–280. doi:10.1111/j.1399-0004.1981.tb00709.x

Carlson, M., & Silberback, M. (2007). Dissection of the aorta in Turner syndrome: Two new cases and review of 85 cases in the literature. *Journal of Medical Genetics, 44,* 745–749. doi:10.1136/jmg.2007.052019

Childs, A., Cowan, G., Kinnell, A., Anderson, R., & Saunders, P. (2011). Retinoic acid signaling and the control of meiotic entry in the human fetal gonad. *PLoS One, 6*(6), e20249. doi:10.1371/journal.pone.0020249

Davis, G., & Preves, S. (2017). Intersex and the social construction of sex. *Contexts, 16*(1), 80. doi:10.1177/1536504217696082

Dupont, S., Krust, A., Gansmuller, A., Dierich, P., Chambon, P., & Mark, M. (2000). Effect of single and compound knockouts of estrogen receptor α (ERα) and β (ERβ) on mouse reproductive phenotypes. *Development, 127*(19), 4277–4291. Retrieved from http://dev.biologists.org/content/develop/127/19/4277.full.pdf

Favorito, L., Costa, S., Julio-Junior, H., & Sampaio, F. (2014). The importance of the gubernaculum in testicular migration during the human fetal period. *International Brazilian Journal of Urology, 40*(6), 722–729. doi:10.1590/S1677-5538.IBJU.2014.06.02

Griswold, M., Hogarth, C., Bowles, J., & Koopman, P. (2012). Initiating meiosis: The case for retinoic acid. *Biology of Reproduction, 86*(2), 1–7. doi:10.1095/biolreprod.111.096610

Griswold, S., & Behringer, R. (2009). Fetal Leydig cell origin and development. *Sexual Development, 3*(1), 1–15. doi:10.1159/000200077

Hanley, N., Hagan, D., Clement-Jones, M., Ball, S., Strachan, T., Salas-Cortés, L., … Wilson, D. (2000). *SRY, SOX9* and *DAX1* expression patterns during human sex determination and gonadal development. *Mechanisms of Development, 91*(1–2), 403–407. doi:10.1016/S0925-4773(99)00307-X

Hassold, T., Benham, F., & Leppert, M. (1988). Cytogenetic and molecular analysis of sex-chromosome monosomy. *American Journal of Human Genetics, 42*(4), 534–541. Retrieved from https://www.ncbi.nlm.nih.gov/pmc/articles/PMC1715233/pdf/ajhg00127-0010.pdf

Held, K. R., Kerber, S., Kaminsky, E., Singh, S., Goetz, P., Seemanova, E., & Goedde, H. W. (1992). Mosaicism in 45, X Turner syndrome: Does survival in early pregnancy depend on the presence of two sex chromosomes? *Human Genetics, 88*(3), 288–294. doi:10.1007/BF00197261

Hughes, I., & Acerini, C. (2008). Factors controlling testis descent. *European Journal of Endocrinology, 159* (Suppl. 1), s75–s82. doi:10.1530/EJE-08-0458

Hughes, I., & Deeb, A. (2006). Androgen resistance. *Best Practices and Research Clinical Endocrinology and Metabolism, 4,* 577–598. doi:10.1016/j.beem.2006.11.003

Hughes, I. A., Houk, C., Ahmed, S. F., & Lee, P. A. (2006). Consensus statement on management of intersex disorders. *Archives of Diseases in Children, 91*(7), 554–563. doi:10.1136/adc.2006.098319

Jørgensen, I. N., Skakkebæk, A., Andersen, N. H., Pedersen, L. N., Hougaard, D. M., Bojesen, A., … Gravholt, C. H. (2015). Short QTc interval in males with Klinefelter syndrome—Influence of CAG repeat length, body composition, and testosterone replacement therapy. *Pacing and Clinical Electrophysiology, 38,* 472–482. doi:10.1111/pace.12580

Kashimada, K., & Koopman, P. (2010). SRY: The master switch in mammalian sex determination. *Development, 137,* 3921–3930. doi:10.1242/dev.048983

Lalli, E., Melner, M. H., Stocco, D. M., & Sassone-Corsi, P. (1998). DAX-1 blocks steroid production at multiple levels. *Endocrinology, 139*(10), 4237–4243. doi:10.1210/endo.139.10.6217

Le Bouffant, R., Guerquin, M., Duquenne, C., Frydman, N., Coffigny, H., Rouiller-Fabre, V., … Livera, G. (2010). Meiosis initiation in the human ovary requires intrinsic retinoic acid synthesis. *Human Reproduction, 25,* 2579–2590. doi:10.1093/humrep/deq195

Levine, L. (2000). Congenital adrenal hyperplasia. *Pediatrics in Review, 21*(5), 159–170. doi:10.1542/pir.21-5-159

Maheshwari, A., & Fowler, P. A. (2008). Primordial follicular assembly in humans-revisited. *Zygote, 16*(4), 285–296. doi:10.1017/S0967199408004802

Makiyan, Z. (2016). Studies of gonadal sex differentiation. *Organogenesis, 12*(1), 42–51. doi:10.1080/15476278.2016.1145318

Markström, E., Svensson, E., Shao, R., Svanberg, B., & Billig, H. (2002). Survival factors regulating ovarian apoptosis-dependence on follicle differentiation. *Reproduction, 123*(1), 23–30. Retrieved from https://rep.bioscientifica.com/view/journals/rep/123/1/23.xml?rskey=x2TV2d&result=1

Meyer-Bahlburg, H. F. L. (2017). Intersex care development: Current priorities. *LGBT Health, 4*(2), 77–80. doi:10.1089/lgbt.2017.0021

Mital, P., Hinton, B., & Dufour, J. (2011). The blood–testis and blood–epididymis barriers are more than just their tight junctions. *Biology of Reproduction, 84,* 851–858. doi:10.1095/biolreprod.110.087452

Nation, T., Balic, A., Southwell, B., Newgreen, D., & Hutson, J. (2009). The hormonal control of testicular descent. *Pediatric Endocrinology Review, 7*(1), 22–31.

National Institutes of Health. (2018a). Genetics home reference: Androgen insensitivity syndrome. Retrieved from https://ghr.nlm.nih.gov/condition/androgen-insensitivity-syndrome

National Institutes of Health. (2018b). Genetics home reference: Klinefelter syndrome. Retrieved from https://ghr.nlm.nih.gov/condition/klinefelter-syndrome#statistics

National Institutes of Health. (2018c). Genetics home reference: Turner syndrome. Retrieved from https://ghr.nlm.nih.gov/condition/turner-syndrome#statistics

National Institutes of Health. (2018d). Genetics home reference: 21-hydroxylase deficiency. Retrieved from https://ghr.nlm.nih.gov/condition/21-hydroxylase-deficiency

Nef, S., Schaad, O., Stallings, N. R., Cederroth, C. R., Pitetti, J.-L., Schaer, G., … Vassalli, J.-D. (2005). Gene expression during sex determination reveals a robust female genetic program at the onset of ovarian development. *Developmental Biology, 287*(2), 361–377. doi:10.1016/j.ydbio.2005.09.008

Oliveira, R. M., Verreschi, I., Lipay, M. V., Eça, L., Guedes, A., & Bianco, B. (2009). Y chromosome in Turner syndrome: Review of the literature. *Sao Paulo Medical Journal, 127*(6), 1–11. doi:10.1590/S1516-31802009000600010

Online Mendelian Inheritance in Man. (2018). #201910 adrenal hyperplasia, congenital, due to 21-hydroxylase deficiency. Retrieved from http://www.omim.org/entry/201910

Pennington, B. F., Heaton, R. K., Karzmark, P., Pendleton, M. G., Lehman, R., & Shucard, D. W. (1985). The neuropsychological phenotype in Turner syndrome. *Cortex, 21,* 391–404. doi:10.1016/S0010-9452(85)80004-6

Pepling, M. E. (2012). Follicular assembly: Mechanisms of action. *Reproduction, 143*(2), 139–149. doi:10.1530/REP-11-0299

Rouffy, J., Pestel, M., Cortot, A., Sikorav, H., Michaux, A., & Julien, R. (1973). Klinefelter's syndrome, endogenous hypertriglyceridemia, and arteriopathy of the lower limbs. Apropos of a case. *Annales de Médecine Interne, 124,* 201–206.

Sajjad, Y. (2010). Development of the genital ducts and external genitalia in the early human embryo. *Journal of Obstetrics and Gynaecology Research, 6*(5), 929-937. doi: 10.1111/j.1447-0756.2010.01272.x

Salzano, A., Acropinto, M., Marra, A., Bobbio, E., Esposito, D., Accardo, G., … Cittadini, A. (2016). Klinefelter syndrome, cardiovascular system, and thromboembolic disease: Review of the literature and clinical perspectives. *European Journal of Endocrinology, 175*(1), R27–R40. doi:10.1530/EJE-15-1025

Sax, L. (2002). How common is intersex? A response to Anne Fausto-Sterling. *Journal of Sex Research, 39*(3), 174–178. doi:10.1080/00224490209552139.

Shulman, R., Palmert, M., & Wherrett, D. (2015). Metabolic and endocrine disorders. In R. Martin, A. Fanaroff, & M. Walsh (Eds.), *Fanaroff & Martin's neonatal–perinatal medicine: Diseases of the fetus and infant* (10th ed., pp. 1584–1590). Philadelphia, PA: Elsevier/Saunders.

Sobel, V., Zhu, Y., & Imperato-McGinley, J. (2004). Fetal hormones and sexual differentiation. *Obstetrical and Gynecological Clinics of North America, 31,* 837–856. doi:10.1016/j.ogc.2004.08.005

Suntharalingham, J., Buonocore, F., Duncan, J., & Achermann, J. (2015). DAX-1 (NR0B1) and steroidogenic factor-1 (SF-1, NR5A1) in human disease. *Best Practices and Research Clinical Endocrinology and Metabolism, 29*(4), 607–619. doi:10.1016/j.beem.2015.07.004

Van Batavia, J. P., & Kolon, T. F. (2016). Fertility in disorders of sex development: A review. *Journal of Pediatric Urology, 12*(6), 418–425. doi:10.1016/j.jpurol.2016.09.015

Verp, M. S., & Simpson, J. L. (1987). Abnormal sexual differentiation and neoplasia. *Cancer Genetics & Cytogenetics, 25*(2), 191–218. doi:10.1016/0165-4608(87)90180-4

Virant-Klun, I. (2015). Postnatal oogenesis in humans: A review of recent findings. *Stem Cells and Cloning: Advances in Application, 8,* 49–60. doi:10.2147/SCCAA.S32650

Wilhelm, D., Hiramatsu, R., Mizusaki, H., Widjaja, L., Combes, A., Kanai, Y., & Koopman, P. (2007). SOX9 regulates prostaglandin D synthase gene transcription *in vivo* to ensure testis development. *Journal of Biological Chemistry, 282*(14), 10553–10560. doi:10.1074/jbc.M609578200

Wilhelm, D., & Koopman, P. (2006). The making of maleness: Towards an integrated view of male sexual development. *Nature Reviews Genetics, 7,* 620–631. doi:10.1038/nrg1903

Wilhelm, D., Palmer, S., & Koopman, P. (2007). Sex determination and gonadal development in mammals. *Physiological Review, 87,* 1–28. doi:10.1152/physrev.00009.2006

Yao, H., Matzuk, M., Jorgez, C., Menke, D., Page, D., Swain, A., & Capel, B. (2004). *Follistatin* operates downstream of *Wnt4* in mammalian ovary organogenesis. *Developmental Dynamics, 230*(2), 210–215. doi:10.1002/dvdy.20042

Yatsenko, S. A., & Witchel, S. F. (2017). Genetic approach to ambiguous genitalia and disorders of sex development: What clinicians need to know. *Seminars in Perinatology, 41,* 232–243. doi:10.1053/j.semperi.2017.03.016

12

THE SKIN

Leigh Ann Cates-McGlinn, Rebecca Chuffo Davila,
Marty Visscher, and Vivek Narendran

LEARNING OBJECTIVES

After completing this chapter, the reader should be able to:

- Understand normal skin development.
- Analyze the physiologic function of the fetal and neonatal skin.
- Discuss common inherited disorders and their effect on fetal and neonatal skin development and function.
- Identify maternal health issues that have a potential impact on fetal and postnatal skin development and function.
- Evaluate common disorders that affect the skin and their implications across the life span.

INTRODUCTION

The skin, or integumentary system, is the largest organ in the body. It modulates multiple functions, including protection, sensation, metabolic functions, and thermoregulation. It does so by forming a physical barrier to the environment, harmful microorganisms, ultraviolet radiation, toxic agents, and mechanical injuries. The skin functions as a conduit for sensation and a metabolic organ that allows or limits the transmission of passage of water, electrolytes, and various substances as well as energy stored as fat and the synthesis of vitamin D. The skin is critical to thermoregulatory homeostasis and impacts the maintenance of euthermia through an intricate process of capillary dilatation and restriction, as well as the regulation of moisture. This chapter reviews embryologic development, lists the primary functions, explores the anatomic layers and their physiologic functions, discusses genetic influences, and outlines common neonatal skin problems.

TIMELINE OF ORGAN DEVELOPMENT

The skin is embryologically derived from two separate origins. The epidermis, or the superficial layer, originates from the ectoderm, whereas the deeper layer, known as the *dermis*, arises from the mesenchyme (Sadler, 2015). The following is an overview of embryologic development of the skin and its derivatives. It is important to remember that studying the details of skin-layer-specific maturation with the use of visual aids may create the false perception of spaciousness. Rather, we encourage students and clinicians to be mindful of the fact that the five major layers of the skin are tightly connected and account for, on average, 0.9 mm (premature infants) to 1.2 mm (term infants) of depth (Bolender & Kaplan, 2017).

Epidermis

Embryonic Period. The epidermis arises from the embryonic ectoderm (neural crest; Figure 12.1). During week 4 of gestation, a single layer of ectodermal cells appears. Between weeks 4 and 6 of gestation, these cells stratify into peridermal (outermost) and basal (innermost) layers (Bolender & Kaplan, 2017; Carlson, 2014; Moore, Persaud, & Torchia, 2016). The periderm protects the developing epidermis from amniotic fluid and manages glucose uptake. The periderm thereby begins a cyclic process of cellular generation, keratinization, and exfoliation. Simultaneously, the lower basal layer begins synthesizing skin cells (Moore et al., 2016). Around week 4, the sebaceous glands begin to form and mammary ridges begin to appear. Melanocytes start appearing in the basal layer from weeks 5 to 8 of gestation. The ectodermal cells begin to form ridges around week 6 and, by week 8, as epidermal mammary ridges begin to disappear.

Fetal Period. The early fetal period is marked by epidermal differentiation into a three-layered structure, which begins between weeks 8 and 11 of gestation. Proliferation and maturation of basal layer keratinocytes proliferate to form the spinous cell layer between the basal layer and the periderm (Figure 12.2). The lowest basal layer (stratum germinativum) increases production of cells and assumes the role of germinal matrix for cellular synthesis. The rapid synthesis and upward migration of new skin cells exceeds the turnover rate of normally expiring peridermal cells and gives rise to an intermediate skin layer (Bolognia, Schaffer, & Cerroni, 2018). Periderm, spinous cells (two layers), basal cells, desmosomes, hair follicles, and hair bulb mesenchymal cells of the hair bulb appear between weeks 12 and 16 of gestation. There are six to eight basal layers for each periderm layer, and the upper spinous cells flatten from weeks 14 to 17 of gestation (Visscher & Narendran, 2014).

Basal layer cellular proliferation also projects in a downward direction, toward the deeper mesenchyme (dermis). This gives rise to epidermal ridges, or invaginations, that resemble U-shaped curves. By week 15 of gestation, these ridges give rise to touch pads and grooves at the hands and feet (Moore et al., 2016). These grooves develop curves and whorls by week 35 of gestation, bestowing a unique fingerprint to the infant; abnormal matriculation of the pads and grooves are commonly observed among individuals with trisomy 21 (Moore et al., 2016).

By week 16 to 23 of gestation, the five epidermal layers are evident (Table 12.1). These layers are both thick and thin, uniquely equipped with a complement of follicles, arrector muscles, sebaceous glands, and sweat glands (Table 12.2; Moore et al., 2016; Sadler, 2015). Polygon-shaped cells, composed of keratin, appear in the interfollicular regions and hair follicles. At 18 to 19 weeks of gestation, the stratum corneum (SC) can be seen around the hair follicle. By week 21, it can be seen along the hair canal. This demonstrates the important role of the hair follicle in epidermal barrier development. The terminally differentiated outermost layer, or SC, can be seen at week 23, but may be only a few layers thick. Periderm is no longer observed around week 23. By week 26, the epidermis is fully keratinized, composed of (a) one basal layer, (b) two to three spinous layers, (c) a granular layer containing keratohyalin granules, and (d) five to six layers of SC. The interfollicular epidermis cornifies programmatically from head (initially, week 23) to toe and dorsal–ventral (week 25, abdomen) across the developing infant (Visscher & Narendran, 2014). Cornification of the appendages and trunk usually begins between weeks 24 and 26 of gestation and continues throughout gestation. The time for complete maturation of the neonatal epidermal barrier, to achieve structure and function comparable to adults, is currently unknown (Visscher & Narendran, 2014).

Dermis and Hypodermis

Embryonic Period. The origin of the dermis is shared between the neural crest and mesoderm (Carlson, 2014). Dermal mesenchyme that comprise the face and scalp arise from the neural crest. Dermal mesenchyme of the

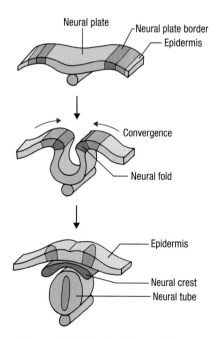

Figure 12.1 Origin of the epidermis.

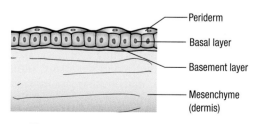

Figure 12.2 Early layers of the epidermis.

TABLE 12.1 The Epidermis

Epidermal Sublayer	Composition and Function	Visual Description
Corneum *Outermost layer*	• *Composition*: On average, 16 layers composed of nonviable cells known as corneocytes consisting of water-retaining keratin proteins and a highly structured cell envelope to provide strength. • *Function*: Barrier to external agents and transepidermal water loss and containing antimicrobial proteins.	
Granulosum and lucidum	• *Composition*: Consists of 3–5 cell layers with the lucindum present only in skin of palms and soles; keratinocytes at this stage contain keratohyalin granules • *Function*: Keratohyalin granule proteins aggregate keratin proteins and move the cells toward the stratum corneum	
Spinosum	• *Composition*: 8–10 layers of keratinocytes with tonofibrils and Langerhans cells • *Function*: Formation of keratinocytes begins here; keratins are synthesized; intermediate filaments form to strengthen cells and connect to desmosomes; initiates cell-mediated immune response	
Basal *Deepest layer*	• *Composition*: Single germinal cell layer of proliferating and stem keratinocytes and melanocytes (pigment cells) • *Function*: Melanocytes produce melanin pigmentation to protect the living cells from solar radiation damage	

NOTE: This information is based on normal adult skin values. Comparable data for premature and full-term infant skin is currently incomplete.

Sources: Carlson, B. M. (2014). *Human embryology and developmental biology* (5th ed., pp. 156–192). Philadelphia, PA: Elsevier/Saunders; Leung, A., Balaji, S., & Keswani, S. G. (2013). Biology and function of fetal and pediatric skin. *Facial Plastic Surgery Clinics of North America*, 21(1), 1–6. doi:10.1016/j.fsc.2012.10.001; Moore, K. L., Persaud, T. V. N., & Torchia, M. G. (2016). Integumentary system. *The developing human: Clinically oriented embryology* (10th ed., pp. 437–455). Philadelphia, PA: Elsevier.

back arises from the embryonic somite. In addition, the dermal mesenchyme associated with the appendages and trunk (ventral) arise from the lateral plate mesoderm. No rationale for this phenomenon exists. Primitive dermal cells can be seen during the latter end of the embryonic period of development (week 8 of gestation); however, they are not active until the early fetal period of development (Figure 12.3).

TABLE 12.2 Features of Epidermal Skin Thickness

	Thick Skin Layer (*Hands, Feet*)	Thin Skin Layer (*All Areas Except Hands and Feet*)
Follicles	NO	YES
Arrector Muscles	NO	YES
Sebaceous Glands	NO	YES
Sweat Glands	YES	YES

Source: Moore, K. L., Persaud, T. V. N., & Torchia, M. G. (2016). *The developing human: Clinically oriented embryology* (10th ed., pp. 437–455). Philadelphia, PA.: Elsevier.

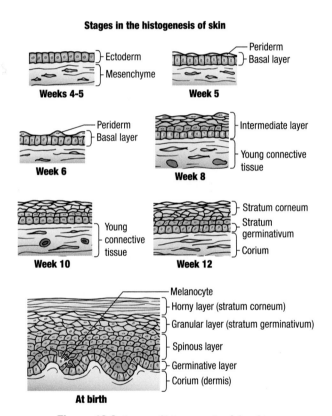

Figure 12.3 Stages of histogenesis of the skin.

Fetal Period. Proliferation commences early into the fetal period, as the dermis subdivides into its two primary layers, the (a) dermal papillae and (b) reticular layer. Although the previously described epidermal cells invade the topmost layer of the dermis, creating epidermal ridges, the dermis reciprocates by developing rounded, fingerlike extensions (papillae) that project upward and into the epidermal ridges. This marks the genesis of the *dermal papillae* (papillary layer), the most superficial layer of the dermis. Papillae permit the proliferation of primitive blood vessels and the matriculation

of afferent sensory nerves. This process of vascular proliferation directs the differentiation of primitive capillaries into arterioles and arteries, whereas others become veins (Table 12.3). The *reticular layer*, which lies below the papillary layer, thereby begins to form. Collagen fibers arranged in parallel ranks and lymphatic meshes, which drain into larger lymphatic vessels, comprise this layer of the dermis.

Evidence of the hypodermis can be seen between weeks 7 and 9 of gestation, as distinct from the dermis. Fibroblasts, adipose cells, and macrophages comprise this layer of the skin and have been observed using electron microscopes beginning with week 22 of gestation (Bolognia et al., 2018; Schoenwolf, Bleyl, Brauer, & Francis-West, 2015). From this period through birth, the dermis shifts from a well-hydrated and cellular-dense structure to a thicker, more fibrous structure (Bolognia et al., 2018).

Hair

Embryonic Period. Hair is derived from the surface ectoderm (Carlson, 2014). In fact, dermal-to-epidermal signaling is responsible for follicle formation. The dermis modulates a process of epidermal thickening, which forms hair placode cells within the basal layer of the epidermis. These placodes are observed by the end of week 11 of gestation and participate in the formation of the dermal papillary layer (Bolender & Kaplan, 2017). The placodes interact with genes, including Sonic hedgehog (*SHH*), wingless type (*WNT*), bone morphogenic proteins (*BMPs*), and fibroblast growth factor (*FGF*), which signals further downward movement and differentiation. This movement pushes the placodes deeper while carving a canal for the future expression of hairs.

Fetal Period. By week 12 of gestation, the keratinocytes of the placode reach the dermis and the germinal matrix and hair formation is established. Peripheral cells along

TABLE 12.3 The Dermis and Hypodermis

Dermal Sublayer	Composition and Function	Visual Description
Papillary	• *Composition*: Vasculature and afferent nerves • *Function*: Renders vascular and sensory (afferent) nervous innervation	
Reticular	• *Composition*: Collagen fibers, lymphatic meshes • *Function*: Contain loosely organized collagen fibers	
Hypodermis	• *Location*: Innermost layer of the skin • *Composition*: Fibroblasts, adipose cells and collagen fibers, and macrophages • *Function*: Insulation and shock absorption; renders vascular and sensory (afferent) nervous innervation	

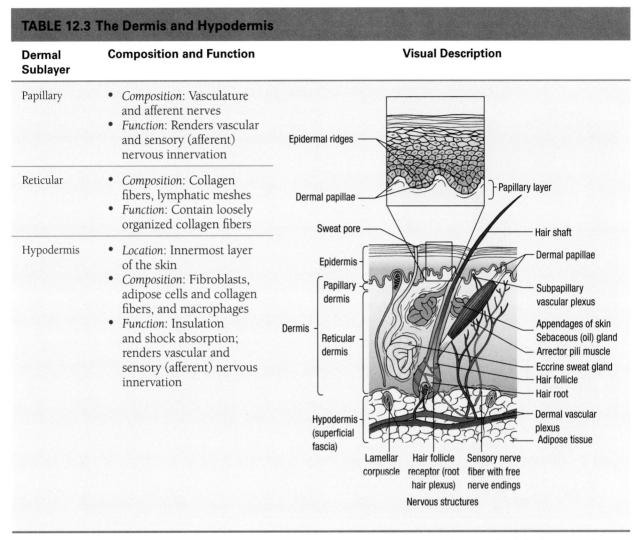

Source: Vandergriff, T. W. (2018). Anatomy and physiology. In J. Bolognia, J. V. Schaffer, & L. Cerroni (Eds.), *Dermatology* (4th ed., pp. 44–55). Philadelphia, PA: Elsevier.

the hair shaft take on a cuboidal shape and give rise to the epithelial hair sheath. This hair sheath bulges, allowing innervation of arrector pili muscles and sebaceous glands. By week 14 of gestation, the base of the follicle is properly situated within the papillary layer. The hair canal is fully formed by week 21 of gestation (Bolender & Kaplan, 2017). The proliferation of hair begins as cells are pushed upward by the arrector muscles, keratinized, and expressed. In fact, contraction of the arrector muscles elicits the "goose bump" response (Moore et al., 2016).

Hair first appears on the surface of the fetus, in particular along the regions of the eyebrow and upper lip. The majority of body hair is visible by week 20 of gestation. Over time, several cycles of hair proliferation and shedding occur during intrauterine development;

hair that is shed can be found within the amniotic fluid (Bolender & Kaplan, 2017; Moore et al., 2016). The first fine and downy hair that appears along the embryo's body, and is particularly abundant among premature infants, is termed *lanugo* (Table 12.4; Sadler, 2015).

Nails

The nails are derived from the surface ectoderm (Carlson, 2014). The fingernails are first to develop, beginning during early fetal development (weeks 9 and 10 of gestation) as thickenings in the epidermal layer (Bolender & Kaplan, 2017; Moore et al., 2016). The toenails follow in a similar fashion and begin matriculating within 4 weeks of the fingernails (Moore et al., 2016).

TABLE 12.4 The Hair and Glands

Visual Description	Hair and Glands	Primary Function
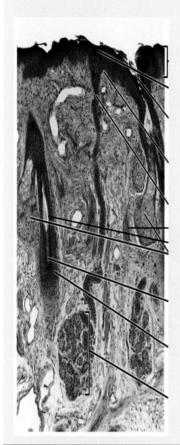	Epidermis Sweat pore Hair follicle Dermis Duct of eccrine gland Arrector pili Hair sheath Sebaceous glands Hair shaft Dermal papillae (hair root) Eccrine gland	• The *epidermis* is the outermost layer of the skin. • The *sweat pore* is an opening through which sweat emerges on the surface of the skin (not functional in neonates). • Each hair is made of a hair shaft, hair sheath, and root. The *hair shaft* contains the keratinized fibers that appear as a single hair. The *hair sheath* surrounds the hair shaft and connects to the sebaceous glands. The body's hair serves to protect the skin. • The *duct of the eccrine gland* is a conduit through which sweat rises from the eccrine gland to the surface of the skin (not fully functional in neonates). • Connected to each hair is a tiny muscle known as the *arrector pili* muscle that contracts in response to cool temperatures or emotions, such as fear, causing the hair to stand on end. • The *sebaceous glands* are attached to each hair and secrete an oily sebum. This lipid-based substance functions to provide an epidermal permeability barrier as well as structure and differentiation, signal skin-specific hormones, transport antioxidants to the skin's surface, and offer protection from ultraviolet radiation. • The *hair root*, or *dermal papilla*, is fed by tiny blood vessels and is responsible for thermoregulation. • The *eccrine glands* are found over a majority of the body and are secretory glands that are under psychological and thermal control through sympathetic (cholinergic) nerve fibers. Eccrine glands secrete sweat containing chloride, lactic acid, fatty acids, urea, glycoproteins, and mucopolysaccharides.

Source: Vandergriff, T. W. (2018). Anatomy and physiology. In J. Bolognia, J. V. Schaffer, & L. Cerroni. (Eds.). *Dermatology* (4th ed., pp. 44–55). Philadelphia, PA: Elsevier.

Nails reach the fingertips by 32 weeks of gestation and the distal edges of the toes by week 36 of gestation (Moore et al., 2016; Sadler, 2015).

Glands

The glands (sebaceous, sweat, apocrine, mammary, lacrimal, and salivary) are derived from the surface ectoderm (Carlson, 2014). The skin contains several types of glands, including sebaceous, sweat, and mammary glands. Each has a distinct developmental timeline, location, and function.

Sebaceous Glands. Sebaceous glands are found only where hair grows and are directly connected to the hair's sheath. These are, at first, solid, hemispherical protuberances on the posterior surfaces of the hair pegs.

The sebaceous glands are formed from the epidermal cells and begin to develop between weeks 13 and 14 of gestation (Niemann & Horsley, 2012). Sebaceous glands are well developed and generally large at term. Yet, after birth, the size rapidly diminishes, and only after puberty do they once again enlarge to become functional.

Sweat Glands. There are two primary types of sweat glands: eccrine and apocrine; each type of gland is located within the dermal layer. Eccrine glands reside over most of the body, with the exception of the lips and external ear canals, and are derived as buds from the basal layer of the epidermis (Cui & Schlessinger, 2015). These glands begin to form between weeks 28 (palmoplantar region) and 35 (rest of body) of gestation (Cui & Schlessinger, 2015). Apocrine glands reside within the axillae and external genitalia (Sadler, 2015). These glands form during early adolescence, commensurate with the onset of puberty.

Mammary Glands. Mammary glands are adapted sweat glands that first appear during week 4 of gestation as bilateral buds of thickened epidermis (Moore et al., 2016). These buds are commonly referred to as *mammary ridges* or *crests*. By the end of week 5 of gestation, the mammary crests penetrate the underlying mesenchyme and form 16 to 24 sprouts, which give rise to the mammary buds. Mammary buds undergo a progressive process of canalization and form lactiferous ducts. By term, up to 20 lobes of breast tissue have formed, each affixed with one lactiferous duct (Javed & Lteif, 2013; Moore et al., 2016; Sadler, 2015). Further differentiation of the buds gives rise to the glands, located at the tips of each mammary bud. The glands are well established by week 24 of gestation and breast tissue is evident on physical examination (Javed & Lteif, 2013). Although the term neonate is affixed with lactiferous ducts at birth, the breasts are devoid of milk-releasing alveoli.

Nipples

Nipple formation also begins during late fetal development. The epidermis invaginates within the pectoral region at the fourth intercostal space on the chest region, forming a pit. Abnormal positioning yields supernumerary nipples, which are observed in 2% to 5% of newborns (Javed & Lteif, 2013). These pits give rise to each nipple, which often remain below the level of the epidermis for several weeks into postnatal life. During this time, connective tissue infiltrates the surrounding area and raises the nipple to a position above the level of the epidermis. During puberty, females will undergo progressive breast development, whereas male breasts remain in their primitive form across the life span (Moore et al., 2016).

DEVELOPMENTAL PHYSIOLOGY

The skin, or integumentary system, is the largest organ in the body and serves multiple functions, including barrier protection, thermoregulation, sensation, and metabolic functions. Through its anatomic construct and physiologic function, the skin resists infection and offers immunosurveillance, an acid mantle, antioxidant function, and protection from ultraviolet light (Visscher, Adam, Brink, & Odio, 2015). We offer a discussion of the core functions of the skin, which serves as an expansion of core concepts discussed within Chapter 9.

Barrier Protection

The epidermal barrier forms as a result of a well-orchestrated progression that culminates in the formation of flattened, cornified keratinocytes. The keratinocytes are imbedded within a sophisticated bilayer lipid matrix, connected together by specialized structures called *desmosomes*. This outermost barrier provides protection from chemicals and irritants as well as physical dangers and mechanical trauma (Mancini & Lawley, 2015). At birth, this role becomes immediately crucial, as the fetus transitions from the hospitable environment provided by the womb to a cold, dry, and microorganism-filled atmosphere (Hoath & Shah, 2017).

Skin barrier function is typically effective among infants born at or beyond 37 weeks of gestation, yet immature among infants born at less than 37 weeks of gestation. As with other organ systems, skin barrier function increases with advancing gestational age (GA). Well-developed skin is affixed with a thick epidermis and SC; these layers offer physical barrier function (Mancini & Lawley, 2015). In contrast, the skin of premature infants is affixed with fewer cornified layers, resulting in reduced barrier function, an increased risk for the penetration of exogenous materials and pathogens, transepidermal water loss (TEWL), and mechanical injuries (skin tears; Visscher et al., 2015). TEWL decreases with maturation of the SC, which among premature infants occurs between 2 to 9 weeks postnatal age; complete acid mantle formation may require additional months. Time required for epidermal maturation among infants less than 28 weeks GA is unknown (Visscher & Narendran, 2014).

Thermoregulation

The skin also participates in postnatal thermoregulation, a function that was unnecessary before birth and largely performed by the placenta. Maintaining optimal body core temperature (37°C or 98°F–99°F), or thermoregulation, involves balancing heat loss and production. The majority of thermoreceptors are located at the face, neck, and shoulder region; activation elicits a thermoregulatory response that involves increased caloric expenditures. Thermoregulatory function is modulated through a complex series of neurogenic, myogenic, and metabolic processes; collectively, these processes regulate vasomotor tone within the dermis. Neurogenic and myogenic processes trigger the constriction or expansion of blood vessels. This controls blood flow and determines whether heat is dispelled or conserved.

Heat production, or *thermogenesis*, is modulated through oxidative metabolism as regulated by the thyroid gland, nonshivering thermogenesis, muscle flexion, and peripheral vasoconstriction. Oxidative metabolism involves the mobilization of glucose, fats, and proteins. Nonshivering thermogenesis involves the metabolism of brown fat; this offers limited thermogenesis as brown fat accounts for approximately 4% to 10% of total adipose tissue among term infants (Mancini & Lawley, 2015). Premature infants possess reduced brown fat and glycogen stores. In fact, brown adipose tissue is often not generated until 26 to 30 weeks of gestation. In addition, premature infants possess a reduced capacity to remain in a flexed position (to prevent heat loss through increased surface area exposure to colder temperatures), as well as reduced ability to mobilize existing brown adipose tissue.

Thermolysis refers to the loss of heat. Infants born at less than 38 weeks of gestation are at increased risk for heat loss. Heat loss can occur by way of (a) conduction, (b) convection, (c) radiation, and (d) evaporation. *Conduction* involves heat lost through direct contact with a cold surface, such as a cold blanket or neonatal scale. *Convection* involves heat lost from cooler air flowing over the body's surface, such as from an air-conditioning vent. *Radiation* is electromagnetic heat lost from heat radiating toward a cooler surface, which does not come into direct contact with the neonates' skin. Examples include a cold exterior window or the walls of an isolette. *Evaporation* is the final mechanism of heat loss and can be the result of bathing, birth, and sweating. Evaporation involves heat lost through wet skin.

Neurosensory Function

Skin contains both somatic sensory and sympathetic autonomic nerve fibers (Figure 12.4). These fibers function to innervate with arrector pili muscles, cutaneous blood vessels, and sweat glands. They serve as receptors for touch, pain, temperature, itch, and mechanical stimuli (Mancini & Lawley, 2015). Each stimulus provides the brain with afferent information that the brain translates into an efferent response. At the level of the skin, responses may include "goose bumps" or mottling. Thus, evidence of central nervous system maturation and responses to stimuli at the skin depend on sensory input received during the immediate postnatal period (Hoath & Shah, 2017).

Glandular Function

As mentioned earlier, the skin contains glands, including apocrine, eccrine, mammary, and sebaceous glands. The apocrine glands are secretory glands found within the face, axilla, and pubic region. These glands open solely into hair follicles, develop during puberty, and are under thermal control by way of sympathetic (adrenergic) nerve fibers (Schaller & Plewig, 2018). Sweat, a by-product of the apocrine glands, is composed of lipids, proteins, and pheromones. Typically, once children reach puberty, the bacterial breakdown of sweat produces foul odors.

The eccrine glands are also sweat glands and are found throughout the body. The highest density of eccrine glands is noted in the palms of the hands and soles of the feet. Eccrine sweat glands are composed of a secretory coil and a duct (located in the lower dermis), as well as subcutaneous tissue. Components of eccrine sweat include water, sodium, chloride, potassium, urea, lactate, ammonia, antimicrobial peptides, cytokines, and immunoglobulins (Schaller & Plewig, 2018). *Eccrine glands* are innervated by the sympathetic nervous system. Pharmacologic stimulation or emotional or thermal stress stimulates the secretion of acetylcholine, which activates eccrine activity (Mancini & Lawley, 2015). Among neonates, eccrine activity manifests as thermal

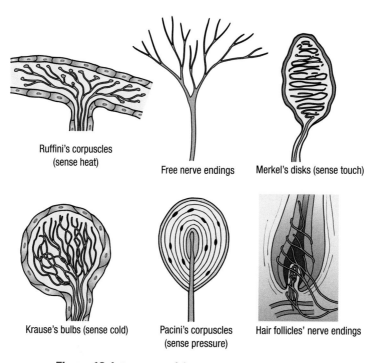

Ruffini's corpuscles (sense heat)

Free nerve endings

Merkel's disks (sense touch)

Krause's bulbs (sense cold)

Pacini's corpuscles (sense pressure)

Hair follicles' nerve endings

Figure 12.4 Depiction of the cutaneous nerve endings.

and emotional sweating. The core temperature required to induce neonatal sweating is approximately 37.2°C (Mancini & Lawley, 2015). This is typically immature among premature neonates and is a process that matures over time among all neonates. *Mammary glands* are found in the breast tissue. These glands have no secretory tissue at birth. At puberty, increased circulating estrogen and progesterone stimulate the lactiferous ducts to form alveoli and secretory cells primarily for milk production (Sadler, 2015). *Sebaceous glands* are numerous at birth. During fetal development, secretions from the sebaceous glands contribute to vernix formation. This early sebaceous gland activity is modulated by maternal hormonal (androgen) influences. After birth, maternal hormone concentrations wane; however, residual hormonal influence may trigger continued sebaceous activity, which manifests as scalp flaking, or cradle cap. Once this transient phenomenon subsides, physiologic function of the sebaceous glands is not observed until puberty.

Vernix

During the last trimester vernix caseosa, a whiteish paste-like substance, begins to coat fetal skin from head to toe and back to front (Visscher et al., 2015). The cells in vernix may originate from the hair follicles, suggesting that vernix is "extruded" out through the hair shaft onto the skin surface initially around the hair and spreading over the entire surface as gestation progresses (Sadler, 2015). Vernix is primarily composed of sebaceous gland secretions and desquamated SC cells and provides physical protection from maceration by amniotic fluid and enzymes due to its hydrophobic lipids. Vernix also influences the antimicrobial function of the skin by (a) lowering the pH of the skin's surface, and (b) providing hydration and lipids for further formation of the cutaneous layers (Visscher et al., 2015). Each of these aforementioned functions is enhanced by allowing vernix to remain in place at least 6 hours after birth (Visscher et al., 2015). Clinicians are encouraged to delay the first postnatal bath, as appropriate.

Histological Function

Although an investigation into cell-mediated skin function of the skin may seem like a daunting task, it is particularly significant for the neonatal clinician. Neonates, specifically premature neonates, depend on their skin for barrier protection against surface pathogens. In order to achieve this functional status, certain cells must matriculate into the epidermis.

Skin Coloration. Beginning with the second month of gestational development, primitive epidermal neural crest cells migrate from the dermis into the epidermis. This stimulates the synthesis of melanocytes. Under the influence of *WNT* signaling pathways, skin pigment granules are synthesized. These processes modulate melanin production and skin coloring, which is known to be influenced by ethnicity (Moore et al., 2016). Darker skin coloration is associated with earlier production of melanocytes and an increased number of pigment granules per cell (Carlson, 2014; Moore et al., 2016).

Immune Response. Toward the end of the first trimester, Langerhans cells migrate from the bone marrow to the stratum germinativum. These cells participate in cell-mediated immune responses to pathogens that persistently attempt to penetrate the skin barrier. The quantity of Langerhans cells increases across gestational development, with the most significant amount of proliferation noted during the third trimester. As such, infants born prematurely are often affixed with a significantly reduced number of Langerhans cells, which reduces the skin's ability to protect the body from antigens (Carlson, 2014).

GENETIC INFLUENCES

There are certain hereditary disorders that manifest with noteworthy dermatologic aberrations. Here, we review some common genetic disorders and their associated dermatologic findings.

Noonan Syndrome

Noonan syndrome is one of a group of related autosomal dominant inherited disorders, collectively known as the *RASopathies* caused by a mutation in the genes of the RAS/MAPK pathway. In addition to Noonan syndrome, the RASopathies include cardiofaciocutaneous syndrome, Costello syndrome, neurofibromatosis 1, and Legius syndrome. Noonan syndrome affects one in every 1,000 to 2,500 births (National Institutes of Health [NIH], 2018c; Roberts, Allanson, Tartaglia, & Gelb, 2013). Heterozygous mutations in the genes affect the *RAS/MAPK* (mitogen-activated protein kinase) signaling pathway, most commonly isolated at the *PTPN11* gene (75%). This disrupts normal cellular proliferation, differentiation, and migration (Bertola et al., 2014). Common skin-related manifestations include a deep groove at the philtrum, webbing of the skin of the neck, and a low posterior hairline. Abnormal synthesis and secretion of growth hormone may implicate the aforementioned manifestations, as well as stunt overall growth and development.

Neurofibromatosis (Type 1)

Neurofibromatosis type 1 (NF1) is the more common form of autosomal dominant neurofibromatosis, with an estimated incidence of one in every 3,000 to 4,000 individuals (Paulus, Koronowska, & Fölster-Holst, 2017; NIH, 2018b). Germline mutations in the *NF1* gene (involved in the RAS/MAPK pathway) overstimulate the RAS signaling activity, which alters normal keratinocyte differentiation (Peltonen, Kallionpää, & Peltonen, 2017). Therefore, although NF1 is commonly characterized by the growth of tumors on the nerves, this disease can also affect the skin. Common skin-related manifestations include cutaneous neurofibromas, café-au-lait lesions (infancy), freckles (childhood), and palpable neurofibromas (noncancerous tumors) that manifest under the skin; these tumors often present in adulthood.

Waardenburg Syndrome

Waardenburg syndrome is an autosomal dominant auditory-pigmentary syndrome. The incidence is estimated at one in every 40,000 individuals (NIH, 2018e). Mutations in several genes, including *PAX3*, *EDN3*, *EDNRB*, and *SOX10*, impose alterations in melanocyte production. Four types of Waardenburg syndrome are reported; type 1 and 2 are associated with alterations to skin and hair pigmentation. Skin-related manifestations include a white forelock and cutaneous hypochromia. The clinical picture is quite striking. It is interesting to note that 2% to 5% of all cases of congenital hearing loss are also attributed to Waardenburg syndrome (type 1 and 2; NIH, 2018e).

Localized Hypotrichosis

Localized autosomal recessive hypotrichosis is characterized by sparse hair on the scalp beginning in infancy. The global incidence is unknown; however, an incidence of one in every 10,000 individuals is reported among Japanese infants, as this condition prevails among the Japanese population (NIH, 2018a). Males and females are equally affected. Mutations in the *LIPH*, *LPAR6*, and *DSG4* genes alter the normal synthesis and proliferation of the hair and also may contribute to epidermal dysfunction. Common skin-related manifestations of hypotrichosis may include erythema, pruritis, or coarse, dry skin. At birth, scalp hair ranges from sparse and tightly curled whorls of hair to thin hair, which typically gradually decreases as the infant ages. A decreased complement of eyebrows, eyelashes, and axillary hair has also been reported (Basit, Khan, & Ahmad, 2015).

Sturge–Weber Syndrome

Sturge–Weber syndrome is a congenital neurocutaneous disorder that affects one in every 20,000 to 50,000 individuals (NIH, 2018d). It commonly manifests during infancy as a triad of three classic features: (a) port-wine stains, usually located to the cutaneous distribution of the first branch of the trigeminal nerve; (b) a leptomeningeal venous malformation; and (c) glaucoma (Jnah, Newberry, & Robertson, 2017). Life-span implications do not relate to the skin. Rather, affected individuals may suffer visual disturbances (associated with choroidal hemangiomas), intellectual disabilities (secondary to seizures or leptomeningeal angiomas), and hemiparesis (NIH, 2018d).

Epidermolysis Bullosa

Epidermolysis bullosa (EB) refers to a group of heterogeneous diseases that may affect the epidermis, dermal–epidermal junction, and dermis (Jnah et al., 2017; Moore et al., 2016). Current evidence suggests that EB affects 19.6 per 1 million individuals (Fine, 2016). The four major types of EB are (a) EB simplex (most common; 1/30,000–50,000 infants), (b) junctional EB, (c) dystrophic EB, and (d) Kindler syndrome (rarest; 250 cases worldwide); at least 39 subtypes have been reported (Table 12.5; Fine & Mellerio, 2018). At present, 14 distinct structural genes representing more than 1,000 different mutations are linked etiologically to EB and affect at least 19 different structural proteins (Fine & Mellerio, 2018; Gonzalez, 2013). The degree (severity) of gene mutation directly affects protein synthesis and disease severity.

In 2014, seeking to foster continuity in the use of nomenclature and diagnostics, the National Epidermolysis Bullosa Registry proposed a revised classification system. Patients are currently classified by major type of EB, phenotype (severity and distribution of lesions), mode of transmission, site of cleavage, protein involvement, gene involvement, and type of mutation. Terminology used to describe disease distribution and severity would be limited to *localized*, *generalized other*, and *generalized severe*, as opposed to prior use of vague eponyms (Fine et al., 2014).

Clinical manifestations vary in the newborn period; however, *skin fragility and blistering are consistent findings across all types and subtypes of EB* (Figure 12.5). EB simplex usually manifests with small and localized blisters. Junctional and dystrophic EB, most notably the recessive forms, involve deeper blisters that may implicate a larger surface area (Jnah et al., 2017). Blisters are termed

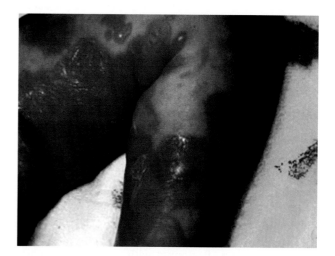

Figure 12.5 Denudation and erosion as a result of blistering in an infant with epidermolysis bullosa.

Source: Antaya, R. J., & Robinson, D. M. (2010). Blisters and pustules in the newborn. *Pediatric Annals, 39,* 635–645. doi:10.3928/00904481-20100922-01

TABLE 12.5 Epidermolysis Bullosa: Inheritance Pattern, Level of Skin Cleavage, and Affected Proteins

	Inheritance Pattern	Level of Skin Cleavage	Common Proteins
EB simplex	Autosomal dominant[a]	Intraepidermal (*basal and basal epidermis*)	Keratins 5 and 14 Plectin Dystonin Plakophillin-1 Desmoplakin
Junctional EB	Autosomal recessive	Intralamina lucida (*basement membrane*)	Laminin-332 Collagen XVII α6β64 integrin
Dystrophic EB	Autosomal dominant *and* Autosomal recessive	Sublamina densa (*dermis*)	Collagen VII
Kindler syndrome	Autosomal recessive	Multiple points	Kindlin-1

[a]Most forms of EB simplex are autosomal dominant, with the exception of suprabasilar types and forms with muscular dystrophy or pyloric atresia.

EB, epidermolysis bullosa.

Source: Gonzalez, M. E. (2013). Evaluation and treatment of the newborn with epidermolysis bullosa. *Seminars in Perinatology, 37,* 32–39. doi:10.1053/j.semperi.2012.11.004

a *congenital localized absence of skin (CLAS)*; the classic appearance is a red, shiny blister with clearly defined margins (Fine & Mellerio, 2018). Infants who do not manifest with intrauterine-acquired blisters will develop them in the postnatal period, often secondary to friction imposed during the birth process. Blisters are composed of serous or hemorrhagic fluid; many heal without scarring, yet the breach in the skin barrier increases the risk for nosocomial infection during the birth hospitalization and later bacterial infections. Other consequences of EB include transepidermal water loss and fluid and electrolyte imbalances.

The care of EB extends across the life span and may involve rigorous and frequent dressing changes, rehospitalizations, recurrent infections, dehydration, or poor nutrition secondary to oral or esophageal blistering. Activity restrictions are common in order to reduce high-friction blistering. Affected children and adults are at risk for psychosocial disturbances due to disfigurement (Adni, Martin, & Mudge, 2012).

MATERNAL HEALTH INFLUENCES

Maternal health issues can influence fetal skin development and function. In particular, maternal autoimmune disorders, infectious diseases, and nutritional deficits can implicate fetal and neonatal skin. We discuss the effect of maternal lupus infection and nutritional deficits on the developing skin. The effect of maternal viral infections, when acquired by the fetus or neonate, is presented later in this chapter.

Maternal Systemic Lupus Erythematosus and the Fetus and Neonate

Mothers with anti-Ro/SSA and/or anti-La/SSB antibodies are at increased risk for giving birth to infants with neonatal lupus, an autoimmune disease that occurs in approximately 10% of infants whose mothers test positive for systemic lupus erythematosus (SLE). Common clinical manifestations of neonatal lupus include dermatologic, cardiac, and hepatic abnormalities (Bermas & Smith, 2018). Specific to the skin, cutaneous lesions may present at birth, but often appear within the first few weeks of life. Erythematous or polycystic plaques appear mainly on the scalp, neck, or face, but similar plaques may appear on the trunk or extremities. This dermatitis resembles the rash of subacute cutaneous lupus erythematosus rather than the malar rash of SLE. Periorbital erythema, referred to as *raccoon eye* or *owl eye*, is a very common characteristic (Figure 12.6). Bullous lesions may be seen on the soles of the feet. Besides the dermatologic signs, the most serious complication of neonatal lupus that all clinicians should be mindful of is complete heart block (Lun Hon & Leung, 2012). Children with neonatal lupus have an excellent long-term outcome when only skin lesions are present. The cutaneous lesions usually disappear by 6 months of age (Lun Hon & Leung, 2012).

Maternal Nutritional Deficits

Biotin Deficiency. Biotin deficiency is a rare nutritional disorder, more often observed in poorly developed countries. Biotin is a water-soluble vitamin, generally classified as a B-complex vitamin. Genetic disorders, such as biotinidase deficiency, multiple carboxylase deficiency, and holocarboxylase synthetase deficiency, can lead to

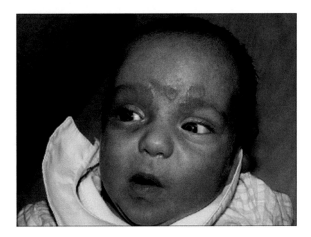

Figure 12.6 Cutaneous neonatal lupus erythematosus.

NOTE: "Racoon eye" appearance is noted over the right periorbital area. Customary erythematous annular plaques are seen over the glabella, along with central atrophy.

Source: Jaka, A., Zubizarreta, J., Ormaechea, N., & Tuneu, A. (2012). Cutaneous neonatal lupus erythematosus. *Indian Journal of Dermatology Venereology & Leprology, 78*(6), 775. Retrieved from http://www.ijdvl.com/text.asp?2012/78/6/775/102396

inborn or late-onset forms of biotin deficiency (National Organization of Rare Disorders, 2017). In all cases, dietary, genetic, or otherwise, supplementation with biotin is the primary method of treatment.

Pregnancy alters biotin catabolism and, despite a regular biotin intake, approximately 50% of pregnant women in the United States are recognized as marginally biotin deficient (Zempleni, Wijeratne, & Hassan, 2009). Signs and symptoms of neonatal biotin deficiency include red, patchy rashes near the mouth (erythematous periorofacial macular rash), fine and brittle hair, alopecia, anemia, birth defects, seborrheic dermatitis, and fungal infections. Fortunately, biotin supplements are readily available within the United States, and when prenatal care is pursued and continued throughout pregnancy, biotin deficiency is typically averted.

COMMON PROBLEMS WITH IMPLICATIONS ACROSS THE LIFE SPAN

The skin is a critical interface between the body and environment. This layer differentiates between "self" and "nonself." In fact, maternal–infant bonding is, in large part, a complex dynamic interaction between skin surfaces. Cutaneous characteristics are routinely used as determinants of gestational age. Pathologic processes visible on the skin surface range from general signs of systemic

TABLE 12.6 Common Dermatological Terms

	Brief Description	Examples of Association(s)	Primary or Secondary
Cicatricial	Fibrous and contracted scar tissue	Congenital VZV	Primary
Crusted ulcerations	Crusted skin lesions composed of dried exudate (blood, pus, or other serous or serosanguinous fluid) found on the epidermal layer of the skin	Trauma, viral/infectious etiologies, genetic or congenital syndromes, or vascular or other malformations	Secondary
Erythema	Redness of the skin that can occur in one or more locations and cover a small to large volume of surface area of the skin	Erythema toxicum, periumbilical erythema (omphalitis or funisitis), erythema multiforme, and staphylococcal scalded skin syndrome	Secondary
Exanthem	Widespread rash	Toxoplasmosis, HSV	Primary
Fissures	Linear breaches at the skin surface, resulting in an often painful separation of the epidermal layer	Keratodermas, eczema	Secondary
Scaling	Heaping of the stratum corneum with resultant shedding upon exfoliation	Ichthyosis, seborrheic dermatitis	Secondary
Scarring	Permanent, fibrotic alteration in skin integrity incurred as a result of trauma or tissue injury	Congenitally acquired infections, epidermolysis bullosa, infantile acne	Secondary

HSV, herpes simplex virus; VZV, varicella zoster virus.

Source: Jnah, A., Newberry, D., & Bell Robertson, T. (2017). Dermatology cases. In S. Bellini & M.J. Beaulieu (Eds.), *Neonatal advanced practice nursing: A case-based approach* (pp. 217–218). New York: Springer.

dysfunction to clinical evidence of specific diseases. Table 12.6 presents a list of common dermatology-specific terms and associated definitions. Readers should refer to this table while studying the common problems described in this final section of the chapter.

Transient Cutaneous Lesions

A number of benign and transient skin lesions are commonly observed in a normal newborn nursery population. It is important for the clinician to distinguish such transient lesions from cutaneous manifestations associated with life-threatening diseases. A precise description of primary and secondary skin cutaneous lesions forms the basis for understanding the skin pathology. Tables 12.7 and 12.8 describe the basic lesional morphology of infant skin with associated clinical exemplars.

Acrocyanosis. Acrocyanosis is one of the most common and typically transient cutaneous blood flow abnormalities,

caused by reduced capillary reperfusion to the hands and feet. Reduced perfusion may be secondary to vasomotor immaturity, or caused by vasoconstriction secondary to cold temperatures (Maguiness & Garzon, 2015). Common clinical manifestations include a bluish color to the hands and feet. Because this phenomenon commonly self-resolves within 24 to 48 hours after birth and is not typically a primary or sole indicator of a congenital heart lesion, it is considered a benign finding (Jnah et al., 2017).

Sebaceous Gland Hyperplasia and Milia. These two conditions are presented in a side-by-side manner because they are easily confused in the clinical setting. Sebaceous gland hyperplasia is reported in approximately 20% to 40% of well-appearing newborns, with recent reports indicating occurrences of 89% (Haveri & Inamadar, 2014). The enlarged glands manifest secondary to increased sebum secretion at birth, likely due to maternal levels of the androgen dehydroepiandrosterone (via the placenta; Brzezinski & Chiriac, 2015). Defining

TABLE 12.7 Primary Cutaneous Lesions

Type	Description	Clinical Examples
Abscess	Same as a pustule but >1 cm in size	Pyodermas
Bulla	Same as a vesicle but >1 cm in size	Sucking blisters Epidermolysis bullosa Bullous impetigo
Nodule	A circumscribed, elevated, solid lesion with depth, up to 2 cm in size	Neuroblastoma
Macule	A circumscribed, flat lesion with color change, up to 1 cm in size; by definition, they are not palpable	Café-au-lait spots Capillary ectasias
Papule	A circumscribed, elevated, solid lesion, <1 cm in size; elevation may be accentuated with oblique lighting	Milia
Patch	Same as macule but >1 cm in size	Mongolian spots Nevus simplex
Plaque	A circumscribed, elevated, plateau-like, solid lesion, >1 cm in size	Nevus sebaceous
Pustule	A circumscribed, elevated lesion filled within purulent fluid, <1 cm in size	Neonatal pustular melanosis Erythema toxicum neonatorum Infantile acropustulosis
Tumor	Same as a nodule but >2 cm in size	Hemangioma Rhabdomyosarcoma
Vesicle	A circumscribed, elevated, fluid-filled lesion up to 1 cm in size	Herpes simplex virus Varicella zoster virus Miliaria crystalline
Wheal	A circumscribed, elevated, edematous, often evanescent lesion, caused by accumulation of fluid within the dermis	Urticaria Bite reactions Drug eruptions

Source: Modified from Yan, A. C., Kim, H. J. & Honig P. J., (2015). Lesional morphology and assessment. In L. F. Eichenfield, I. J. Frieden, E. F. Mathes, & A. L. Zaenglein (Eds.), *Neonatal and infant dermatology* (3rd ed., pp. 24–35). Philadelphia, PA: Elsevier Saunders.

TABLE 12.8 Secondary Cutaneous Lesions*

Type	Description	Clinical Examples
Atrophy	Localized diminution of skin. *Epidermal atrophy* results in a translucent epidermis with increased wrinkling, whereas *dermal atrophy* results in depression of the skin with retained skin markings. Use of topical steroids can result in epidermal atrophy, whereas intralesional steroids may result in dermal atrophy.	Aplasia cutis congenita Intrauterine scarring Focal dermal hypoplasia
Crust	Results from dried exudates overlying an impaired epidermis. Can be composed of serum, blood, or pus.	Epidermolysis bullosa Impetigo
Erosion	Intraepithelial loss of epidermis. Heals without scarring.	Herpes simplex
Fissure	Linear, often painful break within the skin surface, as a result of excessive xerosis.	Inherited keratodermas Eczema (hands, feet)
Lichenification	Thickening of the epidermis with exaggeration of normal skin markings caused by chronic scratching or rubbing.	Sucking blister Atopic dermatitis
Scale	Results from increased shedding or accumulation of stratum corneum as a result of abnormal keratinization and exfoliation. Can be subdivided further into pityriasiform (branny, delicate), psoriasiform (thick, white, and adherent), and ichthyosiform (fish scale–like).	Ichthyoses Postmaturity desquamation Seborrheic dermatitis
Scar	Permanent fibrotic skin changes that develop as a consequence of tissue injury. In utero scarring can occur as a result of certain infections or amniocentesis or postnatally from a variety of external factors.	Congenital varicella Aplasia cutis congenita
Ulcer	Full-thickness loss of the epidermis with damage into the dermis. Will heal with scarring.	Ulcerated hemangiomas Aplasia cutis congenita

*Lesions arise as characteristic modifications of primary lesions through environmental interaction (e.g., drying) or subject interaction (e.g., scratching).

Source: Modified from Yan, A. C., Kim, H. J., & Honig P. J. (2015). Lesional morphology and assessment. In L. F. Eichenfield, I. J. Frieden, E. F. Mathes, & A. L. Zaenglein (Eds.), *Neonatal and infant dermatology* (3rd ed., pp. 24–35). Philadelphia, PA: Elsevier Saunders.

characteristics include yellow-white papules with swelling of the sebaceous glands (Figure 12.7). These papules are often clustered together into small groupings, often located on the nose or midface region (Lucky, 2015).

On the contrary, milia are characterized as white cysts measuring approximately 1 mm in diameter. Milia are typically scattered over the cheeks, forehead, nose, and nasolabial folds. They may be few or numerous, but they frequently occur in clusters. Because all of these cysts exfoliate or involute spontaneously within the first few weeks of life, they are considered a benign finding.

Pigmentary Abnormalities

The melanocyte system of the newborn skin usually is not mature at birth. As a result, all babies, regardless of racial pigmentation, may look lighter than their parents at birth. Within the first few weeks, pigmentation becomes more evident because melanin production has been stimulated by exposure to the postnatal environment.

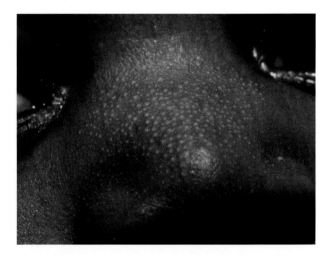

Figure 12.7 Sebaceous gland hyperplasia.

Source: Image appears with permission of VisualDx.

Albinism. Albinism (e.g., complete albinism, oculocutaneous albinism), which occurs in all races, has an incidence of one per 17,000 individuals in the United States; the phenotypic picture is caused by an autosomal recessive gene. Several forms of this disorder have been delineated, including albinism type 1 and type 2 (Chan & Tay, 2015).

The biochemical defect responsible for oculocutaneous albinism type 1 is a deficiency of tyrosinase, the enzyme responsible for converting tyrosine to dopamine, an early step in the formulation of melanin. Structurally, the melanosomes appear to be normal. In oculocutaneous albinism type 2, however, mutations in the *OCA2* gene affect function of a melanosomal protein. Both conditions reduce melanin synthesis and yield reduced pigmentation.

Clinical manifestations include markedly reduced skin pigment, yellow or white hair, pink pupils, gray irises, photophobia, and cutaneous photosensitivity. Among African American infants, the skin may be tan, the hair may have a yellow or orange color, and freckles can appear upon exposure to light (Wright, Norval, & Hertle, 2015). Over the lifetime, reduced pigmentation and associated increased susceptibility to ultraviolet radiation can result in elastosis, actinic keratoses, and skin cancers including squamous cell carcinoma, basal cell carcinoma, and melanoma (Figure 12.8).

Café-au-Lait Macules. Café-au-lait macules are flat, pigmented macules with distinct borders that may be present in the newborn infant. The macules are light brown in Caucasians and dark brown in African Americans (Marcoux et al., 2011). Lesions are commonly seen on the trunk in older children, and over the buttocks in newborns (Price & Marghoob, 2015; Figure 12.9).

The pathogenesis involves an accumulation of melanin within the epidermis. Because the macules may be associated with several syndromes, including neurofibromatosis type 1, Leopard syndrome, Russell–Silver syndrome, and tuberous sclerosis, a differential diagnosis is recommended based on size and number (single versus multiple; Taieb, Ezzedine, & Morice-Picard, 2014). *Lesions that are larger than 0.5 cm in diameter and more than six in number, especially when accompanied by "freckling" in the flexures, strongly suggest neurofibromatosis, a disorder characterized by mutations of the* NF1 *gene.* The *NF1* gene makes neurofibromin, a protein that regulates cell growth and prevents tumor formation. In neurofibromatosis, neurofibromin is deficient, thereby allowing tumors to grow along nerves in various locations. Patients with tuberous sclerosis also may have café-au-lait spots that are identical in appearance to those of neurofibromatosis, but they are usually accompanied by white macules.

Clinical manifestations may include axillary freckles, which actually represent tiny café-au-lait macules. Café-au-lait spots are usually the first cutaneous lesions to appear in a patient with neurofibromatosis, but additional genetic and clinical investigations are required to establish a diagnosis. Café-au-lait macules may change size, and even increase over the first few years of life, but they do not spontaneously resolve. Because these skin lesions persist, they may be cosmetically problematic as the child ages. Lesions associated with neurofibromatosis incur additional life-span issues addressed in prior chapters of this textbook, which include neurological or cognitive difficulties and/or tumor formation.

Congenital Melanocytic Nevi, Small to Intermediate. Congenital melanocytic (pigmented) nevi present at birth or within the first few months of life. Small nevi (<1.5 cm) are seen in 1% to 2% of newborns and intermediate nevi (1.5 to 20 cm) in 0.6% (Price & Marghoob, 2015). These skin lesions are believed to arise due to mutations in *NRAS* and *BRAF* genes. The mutations provoke an abnormal proliferation of cells with a melanocytic phenotype, which nest together in the epidermis; at least three melanocytic cells touch the dermis or other tissues (Roh, Eliades, Gupta, & Tsao, 2015). Clinical manifestations of small nevi are flat and light- to dark- brown lesions, often with variegated color or speckling and an accentuated epidermal surface ridge pattern. These lesions vary in site, size, and number, but most often are solitary. Melanocytic nevi may be malignant and should be monitored diligently from birth through adulthood (Figure 12.10A).

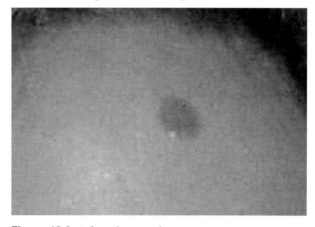

Figure 12.9 Café-au-lait macules.

Source: Bellini, S., & Beaulieu, M. J. (Eds.). (2017). *Neonatal advanced practice nursing: A case-based learning approach.* New York, NY: Springer Publishing.

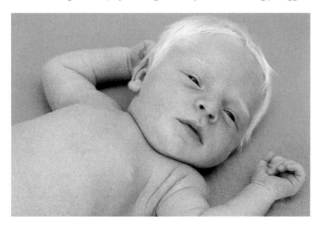

Figure 12.8 Albinism.

Congenital Melanocytic Nevi, Large. The occurrence of large nevi is less than 0.02%. The giant (>20 cm) nevus is associated with a lifetime risk for malignant transformation, and melanoma is estimated to occur in 6% to 8% of affected individuals (Price & Marghoob, 2015). The onset of melanoma in utero has been reported. These nevi may occupy 15% to 35% of the body surface, most commonly involving the trunk. The pigmentation often is variegated from light brown to black. The affected skin may be smooth, nodular, or leathery in consistency. Prominent hypertrichosis is often present. Almost invariably, numerous satellite nevi coexist elsewhere on the body. Leptomeningeal melanocytosis has been documented in some of these patients, and this complication may manifest as seizures. Because of the significant incidence of malignant transformation, the hideous deformity, and the intense pruritus that may accompany them, it is desirable, when feasible, to excise these lesions surgically as soon as possible (Figure 12.10B).

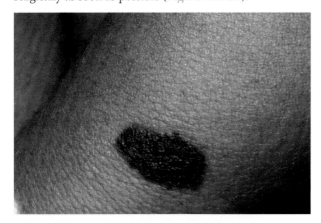

(A)

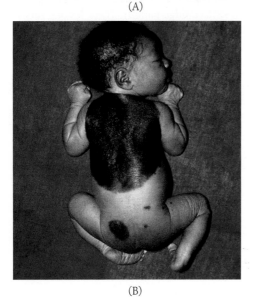

(B)

Figure 12.10 Congenital melanocytic nevi: (A) small to intermediate; (B) large.

Source: (A) Image appears with permission of VisualDx.

Nevus Anemicus. Nevus anemicus is a congenital vascular anomaly that occurs in about 1% to 2% of individuals, and typically yields lesions that measure 5 to 10 cm in diameter (Kolb & Krishnamurthy, 2017). These lesions present as permanently pale, mottled lesions located on the trunk. The cause is believed to be secondary to a heightened response to the effects of catecholamines (adrenaline noradrenaline). For that reason, the nevus is best characterized as a pharmacologic abnormality, rather than an anatomic one. The lesions appear hypopigmented, but contain normal amounts of pigment. Pallor results from increased local reactivity to catecholamines, which provokes vasoconstriction and subsequent pallor. When rubbed, the lesion does not redden like the surrounding skin. These lesions do not spontaneously resolve and, therefore, may impose cosmetic issues over time.

Pigmentary Lesions

Erythema Toxicum. Erythema toxicum is a benign and self-limited inflammatory reaction that usually manifests within the first 24 to 72 hours of life; new lesions may appear until 2 to 3 weeks of age (Monteagudo, Labandeira, Cabanillas, Acevedo, & Toribio, 2012). The disorder is more common among term than premature infants, which suggests that the inflammatory reaction requires mature skin. The pathogenesis involves skin reactions to elevated concentrations of IL-8, LI1, eotaxin, and psoriasin, further supporting the inflammatory etiology for this type of transient lesion (Monteagudo et al., 2012). Lesions may be firm, 1 mm to 3 mm in diameter, pale yellow to white, and manifest as papules or pustules that sit on an erythematous base resembling flea bites. They may also manifest as erythematous macules as large as 3 cm in diameter. Individual lesions are fleeting, often lasting only a matter of hours. They may be found on any area of the body, but only rarely to the palms and soles. They are asymptomatic with no related systemic involvement. A microscopic examination of a Wright- or

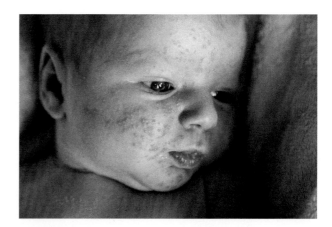

Figure 12.11 Erythema toxicum.

Source: © David Gee/Alamy Stock Photo

Giemsa-stained smear of the pustule contents will yield numerous eosinophils; Gram stains are negative for bacteria and cultures are sterile. Spontaneous resolution occurs in 6 days to 2 weeks (Figure 12.11).

Transient Neonatal Pustular Melanosis. Transient neonatal pustular melanosis is a distinctive eruption that consists of three types of lesions. First-stage lesions are small, superficial vesiculopustules with little or no surrounding erythema (Ghosh, 2015). These rapidly progress to the second stage, which consists of collarettes of scale or scale crust surrounding a hyperpigmented macule (third stage). All three types of lesions may be present at birth, but the macules are observed more frequently. The lesions may be profuse or sparse and occur on most body surfaces, including the palms, soles, and scalp. Sites of predilection are the forehead, submental area, anterior neck, and lower back. The pathophysiology is not well understood. Cultures and Gram stains of smears prepared from intact pustules are typically devoid of organisms; however, increased neutrophil counts have been observed (Reginatto, Muller, Peruzzo, & Cestari, 2017). Pustules typically disappear within 48 hours of onset, whereas the hyperpigmented macules may persist for as long as 3 months. The disorder is benign and transient (Figure 12.12).

Harlequin Color Change. Harlequin color change is a transient phenomenon observed in the immediate neonatal period, commonly noticed among low-birth-weight infants. The pathophysiology is attributed to a temporary imbalance in the autonomic regulatory mechanism of the cutaneous vessels; there are no accompanying vital sign changes (Figure 12.13; Khemani, Ali, Karim, & Yezdan, 2017). The dependent side of the body becomes intensely red, the upper side pales, and a sharp, vertical line of demarcation appears down the trunk (midline). The episodes can be observed during the first 3 weeks of life and are of no pathologic significance.

Miliaria. Miliaria is a skin eruption that results from eccrine sweat duct obstruction. This leads to sweat retention (Engür, Türkmen, & Şavk, 2013; Hölzle & Kligman, 1978). Three clinical presentations are observed: (a) superficial thin-walled vesicles without inflammation (i.e., miliaria crystalline); (b) small, erythematous, grouped papules (i.e., miliaria rubra); and (c) nonerythematous pustules (i.e., miliaria pustulosis). The eruption most frequently develops in the intertriginous areas and over the face and scalp. It is exacerbated by exposure to a warm and humid environment. Rapid resolution occurs when the infant is placed in a cooler environment. A Wright-stained smear of vesicular lesions demonstrates only few squamous cells or lymphocytes. In a seminal controlled study, *Staphylococcus epidermidis* produced miliaria but *S. hameolyticus, S. hominis, S. cohnii, S. saprophyticus,* and *S. simulans* did not (Mowad, McGinley, Foglia, & Leyden, 1995). The condition resolves spontaneously (Figure 12.14).

Mongolian Spot. The most frequently encountered pigmented lesion is the Mongolian spot (dermal melanosis), which occurs in 90% to 100% of African American and Asian infants, 50% in Hispanic infants, and less frequently (less than 10%) among Caucasian infants (Gupta & Thappa, 2013). The pathophysiology relates to the excessive accumulation and delayed disappearance of melanocytes in varying numbers. Although most of these lesions are found in the lumbosacral area, they can occur at other sites. The pigmentation is macular and gray-blue, lacks a sharp border, and may span a diameter of 10 cm or more. Most of these lesions gradually disappear during the first

Figure 12.13 Harlequin color change.

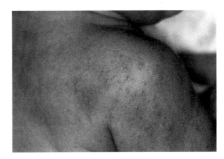

Figure 12.14 Miliaria.

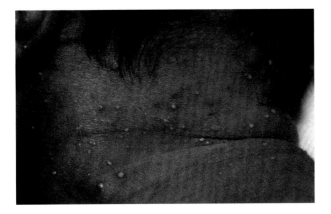

Figure 12.12 Transient neonatal pustular melanosis.

few years of life, but aberrant lesions in unusual sites are more likely to persist. There is some indication that they are associated with metabolism disorders or neurocristopathies (Figure 12.15).

Neonatal Acne. Neonatal acne occurs in up to 20% of newborns, and is more common among males (Yeo & Ormerod, 2014). Increased sebaceous secretions, secondary to maternal and neonatal androgens, and colonization of the sebaceous glands by the yeast *Malassezia furfur* are implicated in its pathogenesis (Friedlander, Baldwin, Mancini, Yan, & Eichenfeld, 2011).

Neonatal acne presents as small, red papules and pustules on the face, usually within the first weeks of life. Unlike in adolescence, comedones and cysts are usually absent. The lesions are asymptomatic and resolve spontaneously without scarring over several weeks. The clinical significance lies in differentiating this rash from infections, excluding virilization as its underlying cause, and potential implication of severe acne in adolescence.

Nevus Simplex (Salmon Patch). The nevus simplex (stork bite) is the most common neonatal cutaneous lesion, and is present in up to 80% of normal newborns (Kanada, Merin, Munden, & Friedlander, 2012). Stork bites manifest as a result of distended dermal capillaries and blanch when compressed. The lesions are transient and typically manifest within the first 72 hours of life (Reginatto, DeVilla, et al., 2017). Clinicians will commonly note their central location and symmetric presentation; lesions typically appear at the nape of the neck, eyelids, and glabella. In a prospective study of affected infants, most of the facial lesions had faded by 1 year of age, but those on the neck were more persistent

(Reginatto, DeVilla, et al., 2017). Surveys of adults confirm the persistence of the nuchal lesions in approximately 25% of affected individuals (Figure 12.16).

Disorders of Cornification: The Scaly Baby

The most common and benign cause for excessive scaling is attributed to physiologic desquamation (normal term infants) and dysmaturity (postmature and small-for-gestational-age infants), neither of which have long-term sequelae. Less common causes include the congenital ichthyoses and the ectodermal dysplasias, both of which are chronic, heritable disorders (Craiglow, 2013; Foley, Paller, & Irvine, 2015). In the normal infant with accentuated physiologic scaling and the dysmature infant,

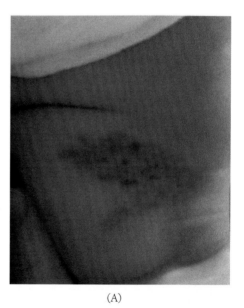

(A)

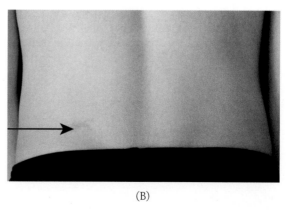

(B)

Figure 12.16 (A) Nevus simplex (salmon patch) on 2-month-old infant. (B) A faded salmon patch on a 13-year-old child.

Source: (A) Image courtesy of Elizabeth Carmac, MSN, NNP-BC; (B) image courtesy of Amy Jnah, DNP, NNP-BC.

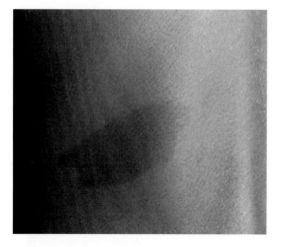

Figure 12.15 Mongolian spot.

Source: Bellini, S., & Beaulieu, M. J. (Eds.). (2017). Neonatal advanced practice nursing: A case-based learning approach. New York, NY: Springer Publishing.

desquamation is a transient phenomenon. The integument continues to serve its intended protective function. In contrast, the infant with congenital ichthyosis may exhibit impaired barrier function and incur a heightened risk for secondary infections.

Ichthyoses. *Ichthyosis* refers to a complex and often confusing plethora of conditions characterized by disorders of cornification with or without systemic symptoms (Craiglow, 2013; Foley et al., 2015). Ichthyosis is a genetic disorder, characterized by mutations in the genes that produce keratin (i.e., *KRT1, KRT2,* or *KRT10*), which disrupt normal skin barrier formation (Vahlquist, Fischer, & Törmä, 2018). The major clinical phenotypes in the newborn of ichthyoses are enumerated in the "Genetic Influences" section of this chapter (Figure 12.17). Clinical manifestations during the neonatal period include isolated scaling, scaling with erythroderma, a collodion membrane, or thickened plates of harlequin ichthyosis. Although rare, early recognition is critical. Ichthyosis compromises the skin barrier, which increases the risk for secondary infection and increased penetration of irritants.

Infectious Etiologies

Candidiasis. Candidiasis is an infection caused by *Candida*, a species of yeast. The incidence of confirmed cases ranges from 2% to 28% in U.S. NICUs (Benjamin et al., 2010). Among extremely premature infants (<1000 g), the incidence ranges from 4% to 8% and the mortality risk is 30% (Kelly, Benjamin, Daniel, & Smith, 2015). Fecal contamination is the usual source of the organism in candidal dermatitis. *Candida* species are commensal organisms commonly found in the gastrointestinal and female genital tracts. Roughly 33% of healthcare workers in NICUs test positive for *Candida* on routine surveillance cultures, and up to 40% of women are positive for *Candida* at the time of delivery (Filippidi et al., 2014).

Rarely, cutaneous candidiasis is congenitally acquired as a result of vertical (ascending) infection from a vaginal or cervical focus. Affected infants usually manifest with pustules to the palms and soles, and occasionally, nail dystrophy. Candidiasis in the first 4 weeks of life is more common, usually benign, and typically localized to the oral cavity (thrush) or diaper area (Figure 12.18A, B). The lesions of thrush are detectable as creamy-white patches of friable material on the buccal mucosa, gums, palate, and tongue. Early cutaneous lesions consist of erythematous papules and vesicopustules that become confluent, forming a moist, erosive, scaly dermatitis surrounded by satellite pustules.

In contrast to acquired cutaneous candidiasis, congenital candidiasis has lesions at nonflexural sites (K. Chen, Chien, Chen, & Chiu, 2016). Distinctive yellow-white papules on the umbilical cord and placenta represent

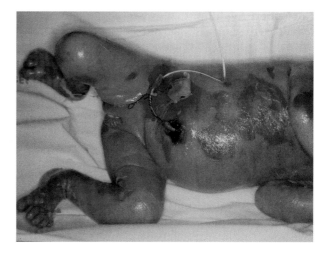

Figure 12.17 Ichthyoses.

Source: Waikato District Health Board/DermNet New Zealand

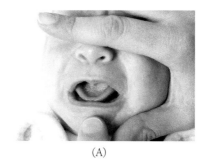

(A)

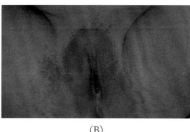

(B)

Figure 12.18 Candidiasis. (A) White, curd-like patch to the buccal mucosa, consistent with early stages of oral thrush. (B) Red, shiny rash with satellite lesions located within diaper region, consistent with candida diaper rash.

Sources: (A) Shutterstock/riopatuca; (B) Dr P. Marazzi/Science Source

Candida granulomas. *C. albicans* may be demonstrable on histologic examination of these tissues and may be cultured from the amniotic fluid. Although *Candida* infection is usually localized to skin, infants who weigh less than 1,500 g are at risk for systemic infections. Additional risk factors for disseminated candidiasis include central-line placement, invasive mechanical ventilation, broad-spectrum antibiotic exposure, and the provision of intravenous parenteral nutrition.

Congenital Syphilis. Congenital syphilis occurs as a result of vertical transmission of *Treponema pallidum*. Sixty percent of infants with congenital syphilis are asymptomatic at birth. Clinical manifestations include erythematous vesicles or bullae atop a polished base (macule with erythematous halo); lesions located on the palms and soles are pathognomonic (Figure 12.19; Tsimis & Sheffield, 2017). Skin lesions may be accompanied by hepatosplenomegaly, periostitis of long bones, snuffles, and iritis. If undiagnosed, the symptoms persist or worsen. Diagnosis is confirmed through nontreponemal antibody titers (Heston & Arnold, 2018).

Herpes Simplex Virus. Herpes simplex virus (HSV) infection is one of the most common causes for vesicular rashes in the neonatal period (Howard & Frieden, 2015). The virus may be acquired in utero or during the perinatal period. Intrauterine infection typically presents with vesicles at birth, or within the first 24 hours of life. An inconspicuous cutaneous lesion heralds the onset of severe systemic infection. The vesicular eruption may be widespread or even bullous, resembling epidermolysis bullosa (Figure 12.20). Vesicles may also present on the torso or buttocks, especially with a breech presentation. Rarely, congenital scars are present.

HSV infection acquired during the perinatal period is often limited to the skin, eyes, and mouth; disseminated infection is possible. Cutaneous lesions usually manifest during the second week of life, concurrent with or after nonspecific systemic signs and symptoms. Typically, the vesicles measure 1 mm to 3 mm in diameter and are usually noted on the scalp or face. Rarely, pustules, erosions, or oral ulcerations appear as isolated manifestations.

Staphylococcal Infection and Impetigo. Superficial skin infections caused by *Staphylococcus aureus* are a concern because of the increase in community acquired *Methicillin-resistant Staphylococcus aureus (MRSA)*. The *S. aureus* organism disrupts the host immune response by mechanisms that include isolation of host antibodies, the formation of a polysaccharide biofilm, and prevention of chemotaxis of leukocytes (Tong et al., 2015). Infections range from localized bullous impetigo to generalized cutaneous involvement with systemic illness. In contrast to congenital blistering diseases, which are often present at birth, skin infections with *S. aureus* usually develop after the first few days of life (Newnam, 2016). Lesions may be bullous, crusted, or pustular; typical lesions are small vesicles or pustules, or large, fragile bullae filled with clear, turbid, or purulent fluid. They rupture easily, leaving red, moist, denuded areas often with a superficial varnish-like crust (Figure 12.21 A, B; Nguyen, Wang, Eichenfield, & Barrio, 2016). Although they may develop anywhere on the body, the blisters and

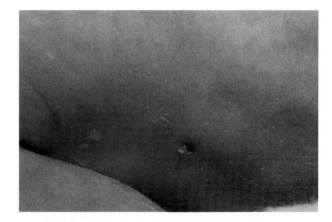

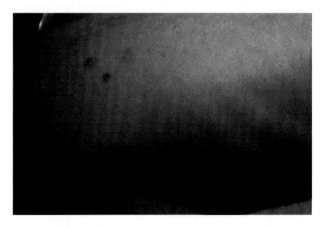

Figure 12.20 Herpes simplex virus.

Source: Bellini, S., & Beaulieu, M. J. (Eds.). (2017). Neonatal advanced practice nursing: A case-based learning approach. New York, NY: Springer Publishing.

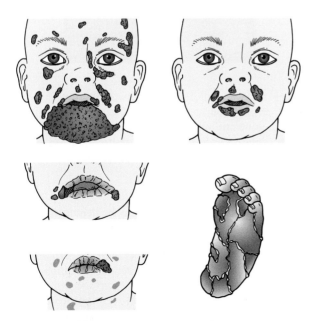

Figure 12.19 Congenital syphilis.

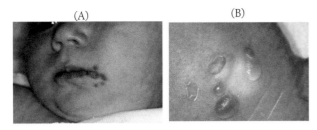

(A)   (B)

Figure 12.21 (A) Infant with perioral impetigo, an acute contagious staphylococcal or streptococcal skin disease that presents as vesicles or pustules, and yellowish crusts. (B) Bullish impetigo, a staphylococcal or streptococcal skin infection which begins as a red patch, followed by the formation of large and fragile pustules that join together and form crusty, yellow-colored blisters (bullae). May present around axilla or periumbilical area.

Sources: (A) ISM/MedicalImages.com; (B) © SPL/Science Source

pustules commonly occur on the diaper area, axillae, and periumbilical skin.

Staphylococcal Scalded Skin Syndrome. Staphylococcal scalded skin syndrome (SSSS) is a blistering skin disorder. Premature infants are at increased risk for SSSS due to a lack of maternal antitoxin antibodies. The infecting organism is *S. aureus*, usually a group 2 phage type, although other phage types occasionally have been incriminated. These organisms produce exotoxins (e.g., exfoliatin) that exert proteolytic activity on desmoglein-1, a molecule found within the desmosomes of keratinocytes responsible for the cutaneous manifestations (Hennigan & Riley, 2016). The release of the endotoxins (epidermolytic toxin A and B) provokes widespread epidermal necrolysis with severe bullous eruptions. The bullous eruptions usually present between days 3 and 7 of life. Denudation and blister formation characteristically occur after gentle rubbing of the skin, which is referred to as *Nikolsky's sign*. Histologic examination of the skin shows a striking absence of inflammatory infiltrate. Infants are typically febrile, irritable, and exhibit marked cutaneous tenderness. Crusting around the mouth and eyes results in atypical facies. Conjunctivitis is common, along with hyperemia of the mucous membranes, but oral ulcerations do not occur.

Vascular Anomalies: Vascular Malformations and Vascular Tumors

Arteriovenous Malformations. Arteriovenous malformations (AVMs) are a more aggressive type of simple malformation. They are composed of malformed arteries, veins, and capillaries; direct arteriovenous communications result in arteriovenous shunting (Wassef et al., 2015). The incidence is estimated to be 0.001% within northern European geographies. AVMs arise due to a mutation in the *RASA1* gene, which normally directs

cell proliferation and migration (Weitz et al., 2015). Lesions are large, red, warm, and painful and exhibit pulsations, thrills, or a bruit. Rarely, AVMs present as ulcerated and bleeding lesions or with high output congestive cardiac failure. AVMs may remain quiescent through early childhood, and display sudden growth at puberty or following a local trauma. A high recurrence risk is reported (Richter & Suen, 2010).

Epidermal Nevi. Epidermal nevi occur among one to three of every 1,000 newborns (Brandling-Bennett & Morel, 2010). *RAS* gene mutations have been implicated in the formation of this skin lesion, which provoke overgrowth of keratinocytes (Hafner et al., 2012; Prendiville, 2015). Variations in size, clinical appearance, histologic characteristics, and evolution are reported. Lesions occurring in sites normally rich in sebaceous glands (e.g., scalp) may appear similar to sebaceous nevi, whereas others found in areas where the epidermis is thick (e.g., elbow) appear wart-like.

The most common type of epidermal nevus in the newborn infant is the sebaceous nevus, a hairless, papillomatous, yellow or pink, slightly elevated plaque on the scalp, forehead, or face (Prendiville, 2015). These lesions have a characteristic oval or lancet shape. Because a significant incidence of basal cell epitheliomas occurs in these lesions after puberty, they should be surgically removed.

Hemangiomas. Hemangiomas are the most common soft tissue tumors of infancy, occurring in approximately 4% and 10% of infants and children, respectively (Kanada et al., 2012). These are benign vascular neoplasms that undergo rapid endothelial cell proliferation shortly after birth, stabilize, and then slowly involute with diminishing cellular activity and fibrous fatty deposition for up to 5 to 7 years (Shah et al., 2016).

Infantile hemangiomas (IH) are subclassified as focal, multifocal, segmental, and indeterminate, depending on their morphology, extent, or distribution (Wassef et al., 2015). IH are characterized by a growth phase, marked endothelial proliferation, and hypercellularity, followed by an involutional phase. IH that lie deeper in the skin are soft, warm masses with a slightly bluish discoloration. Frequently, IH have superficial and deep components. They range from a few millimeters to several centimeters in diameter and usually are solitary; up to 20% of infants display multiple lesions (Figure 12.22). Generally, superficial IH reach their maximal size by 6 to 8 months, but deep hemangiomas may proliferate for 12 to 14 months or, rarely, up to 2 years. MRI and ultrasonography are the preferred imaging methods and should be considered when lesions are detected on the scalp, orbits, airways, or are found in groups of five or more.

Despite the benign nature of most cutaneous hemangiomas, a significant number cause functional compromise or permanent disfigurement. Approximately 65% of hemangiomas are on the head and neck. Even with treatment, half

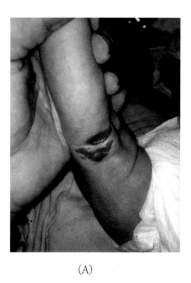

(A)

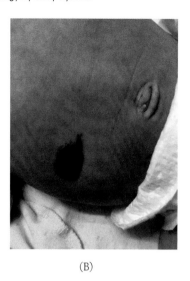

(B)

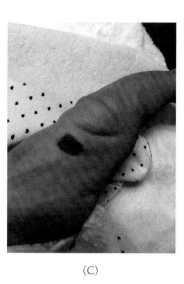

(C)

Figure 12.22 Images of a female newborn with five focal cutaneous hemangiomas (four shown here: [A] two lesions to the right leg; [B] lesion to the right abdomen; and [C] lesion to the left thigh). Further examination revealed normal thyroid function and an absence of associated hepatic hemangiomas.

of hemangiomas located on the lip, eyelid, nose, cheek, or glabella require surgical treatment (Brennan, Waner, & O, 2017). Nasal tip, lip, and parotid hemangiomas are notorious for slow involution, and very large superficial facial hemangiomas often leave disfiguring scarring. Ulceration, the most frequent complication, can be excruciatingly painful and carries the risk of infection, hemorrhage, and scarring. Occasionally, hemangiomas manifest as congenital ulcerations with only a very small rim of typical hemangioma, making the diagnosis difficult.

Periorbital hemangiomas and hemangiomas that involve the ear pose considerable risk to vision, hearing, and speech. Multiple cutaneous (i.e., diffuse hemangiomatosis) and large facial hemangiomas may be associated with visceral hemangiomas. Due to the potential for visceral hemangiomas, additional evaluations including ultrasounds and/or MRI may be warranted (Friedland, Ben Amitai, & Zvulunov, 2017; Reimer & Hoeger, 2016). Subglottic hemangiomas manifest with hoarseness and stridor, and progression to respiratory failure may be rapid. Approximately 50% of these infants have associated cutaneous hemangiomas. Any "noisy breathing" by an infant with a cutaneous hemangioma involving the chin, lips, mandibular region, and neck warrants direct visualization of the airway. Sixty percent of young infants with extensive facial hemangiomas in the "beard" distribution develop symptomatic airway hemangiomas.

The presence of an extensive cervicofacial hemangioma may indicate PHACE syndrome, where the hemangioma is associated with other anomalies; P = posterior fossa (possible abnormal structures in the brain, especially the cerebellum), H = hemangioma, A = arterial (possible brain artery abnormalities), C = cardiac (possible abnormalities of the great vessels of the heart), and E = eyes (possible eye anomalies). This syndrome has a marked female predominance (9:1) and is thought to represent a developmental field defect that occurs between weeks 8 and 10 of gestation. Lumbosacral hemangiomas may be markers for occult spinal dysraphism and anorectal and urogenital anomalies.

Congenital hemangiomas are relatively uncommon, present fully grown at birth, and either undergo rapid involution (RICH: rapidly involuting congenital hemangioma) or persist into adulthood (NICH: noninvoluting congenital hemangioma). Congenital hemangiomas that resolve rapidly often leave pronounced atrophic skin changes in their wake.

Most hemangiomas require "active nonintervention" coupled with a careful discussion of the natural history of the lesions and photographic documentation of involution (Blei & Guarini, 2014; T. S. Chen, Eichenfield, & Friedlander, 2013; Maguiness & Garzon, 2015). Up to 40% of children develop complications requiring intervention. Ulceration is the most common complication, but other problems include bleeding, airway or visual axis obstruction, cosmetic disfigurement, and high-output cardiac failure (Blei & Guarini, 2014; T. S. Chen et al., 2013; Maguiness & Garzon, 2015).

Kaposiform hemangioendothelioma (Kasabach–Merritt phenomenon), a complication of a rapidly enlarging vascular lesion, is characterized by hemolytic anemia, thrombocytopenia, and coagulopathy. These massive tumors are usually a deep red-blue color, firm, grow rapidly, have no sex predilection, tend to proliferate for a longer period (2 to 5 years), and have a different histologic pattern than other hemangiomas.

Most patients with Kasabach–Merritt phenomenon manifest with proliferative vascular tumors, usually kaposiform hemangioendotheliomas or tufted angiomas (Maguiness & Garzon, 2015). The Kasabach–Merritt phenomenon carries a significant mortality risk.

Lymphangiomas. Lymphangiomas are congenital hamartomatous malformations composed of dilated lymph channels that are lined by normal lymphatic endothelium (Maguiness & Garzon, 2015). Fetal skin and subcutaneous tissues are involved in this malformation that affects 1.1 to 5.3 of every 10,000 births (Ersoy, Oztas, Saridogan, Ozler, & Danisman, 2016). These malformations may be observed prenatally via ultrasound, may be superficial or deep, and are often associated with anomalies of the regional lymphatic vessels (Figure 12.23).

Milroy primary congenital lymphedema may present at birth and often affects the dorsal aspects of the feet. This autosomal dominant condition arises from a congenital dysgenesis of the lymphatic microvessels secondary to mutation in the *FLT4* (*VEGFR3*) gene. This condition is rarely associated with significant complications.

Simple and deep lymphangiomas, as well as cystic hygromas, may present at birth or during infancy. Simple lymphangiomas appear as solitary, skin-colored, dermal or subcutaneous nodules. After trauma, they may exude serous fluid. On occasion, these lesions have been associated with more extensive lymphatic involvement. Alternatively, deep lymphangiomas are more diffuse and consist of large, cystic dilations of lymphatics in the dermis, subcutaneous tissue, and intermuscular septa. Cystic hygroma is a benign, multilocular tumor usually found in the neck region. These tumors tend to increase in size.

Lymphangioma circumscriptum is probably the most common type of lymphangioma and may be present at birth or appear in early childhood. Areas of predilection are the oral mucosa, proximal limbs, and flexures. This malformation consists of clustered, small, thick-walled vesicles resembling frog spawn; it is often skin colored but may have a red or purple cast because of the presence of blood mixed with lymph in the vesicles.

Port-Wine Stain. Port-wine stains are capillary malformations that are almost always present at birth and should be considered permanent developmental defects (Maguiness & Garzon, 2015). They occur in 0.3% of neonates (Bae, Ng, & Geronemus, 2016). These lesions may span a few millimeters in diameter or cover extensive areas, but facial lesions are the most common (Figure 12.24). They do not proliferate after birth, but may appear to increase in size with the growth of the child. Port-wine stains are sharply demarcated and flat during infancy, but with time develop a pebbly or slightly thickened surface and frequently darken. Most port-wine stains occur as isolated defects; occasionally, these lesions may be associated with ocular defects or certain vascular malformation syndromes.

Inflammatory Diseases of the Skin

Several inflammatory skin conditions may occur in the neonate. Irritant contact dermatitis and seborrheic dermatitis are the most frequently encountered (Cordoro & Schulman, 2015; Tom & Eichenfield, 2015). They may be difficult to distinguish because their clinical features have a significant degree of overlap.

Irritant Contact Dermatitis. Primary irritant contact dermatitis (as opposed to allergic contact dermatitis) is probably the most common exogenous cause for

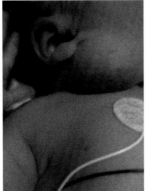

Figure 12.23 Lymphatic malformation ("cystic hygroma") present at birth.

Source: Bellini, S., & Beaulieu, M. J. (Eds.). (2017). *Neonatal advanced practice nursing: A case-based learning approach.* New York, NY: Springer Publishing.

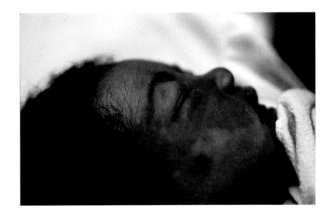

Figure 12.24 Port wine nevus.

Source: Clark, D. A. (2000). *Atlas of Neonatology.* Philadelphia, PA: Saunders.

dermatitis in the newborn. Irritant contact dermatitis is generally a result of penetration of external agents, or iatrogenic causes, via a damaged or underdeveloped SC. External agents may disrupt the SC barrier by way of hydration or alteration of the lipid bilayer structure. Irritants penetrate into the epidermis causing inflammation, cytokine release, and acceleration of barrier repair (Visscher et al., 2015). The distribution of the eruption varies somewhat, depending on the precipitating agent. The principal irritants in diaper dermatitis are fecal enzymes, skin maceration, friction, high pH, and prolonged contact with urine and feces (Figure 12.25; Atherton, 2016). Detergent bubble bath, antiseptic proprietary agents, and soap zealously used to clean the perianal area may cause acute eczematous diaper dermatitis, which may become generalized. Obtaining precise information about what has been applied to the skin and how it has been applied is imperative in making an accurate diagnosis.

Seborrheic Dermatitis. Seborrheic dermatitis affects as many as 10% of neonates. It typically occurs on the scalp but may develop on the face, neck, and in the diaper area (Cohen, 2017). Seborrheic dermatitis is characterized by greasy, nonpruritic scaling associated with patchy redness, fissuring, and occasional weeping, usually involving the scalp, ears, axillary, and perineal folds (Figure 12.26). The yeast *Malassezia* is believed to contribute to the pathophysiology. There is controversy about whether seborrheic dermatitis is a distinct entity or presages the advent of atopic dermatitis. Some infants never progress beyond the seborrheic phase of the dermatitis, which in its classic form rarely is seen in the first month of life. Cradle cap is a minor variant of seborrheic dermatitis.

Other Skin Disorders

Sucking Blisters. Sucking blisters present in 0.4% of neonates (Aydin, Hakan, Zenciroglu, & Demirol, 2013). They are benign, fluid-filled erosions on the skin surface secondary to in utero fetal sucking maneuvers. Episodic or short-term sucking produces a soft and fluid-filled blister, whereas chronic sucking may increase the likelihood for postnatal calluses (Figure 12.27). Asymmetric or irregular borders are common and, unlike infectious blisters, these are often limited to one blister in a specific location. As such, these blisters often present on the hands, lips, or inside the mouth (Bruckner & O'Regan, 2015).

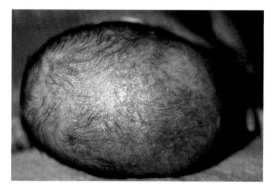

Figure 12.26 Infant with scales on the scalp, consistent with seborrheic dermatitis. ("cradle cap")

Source: Biophoto Associates/Science Source

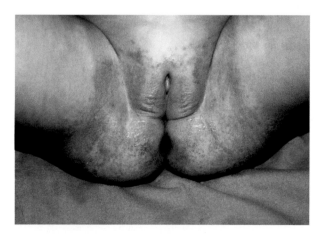

Figure 12.25 Irritant contact dermatitis.

Source: © Dr. Ken Greer/Visuals Unlimited, Inc.

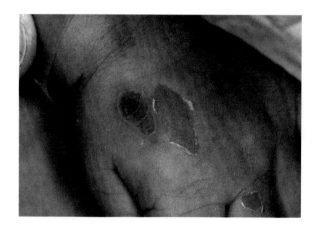

Figure 12.27 Evidence of sucking blister to left hand, which presented at birth.

Source: Image appears with permission of VisualDx

CONCLUSION

The skin is the largest organ in the body and plays vital roles in protection, thermoregulation, and communication with the environment. Understanding its embryologic origins is important. Genetic and maternal influences should be explored. Finally, accurate visual diagnosis is key to uncovering neonatal skin conditions.

ACKNOWLEDGMENT

The editors would like to thank Drs. Rani Delaney, Melissa Bauserman, Lauren Fraser and Ms. Maryellen Lane for their contribution of the chapter podcast.

LEARNING TOOLS AND RESOURCES

Podcast

 Neonatal Skin and Innate Immunity: Differences Between the Term and Preterm Infant

Rani Delaney, Lauren Fraser, Maryellen Lane, and Melissa Bauserman

Discussion Prompts

1. Discuss the purpose and derivatives of vernix. How might the presence or absence of vernix implicate newborn skin?
2. Identify and discuss the major issues for the premature infant as a result of underdeveloped skin.
3. What is the most common neonatal skin condition? Correlate the etiology with your understanding of the physiology of the skin.
4. Describe the difference between a vascular malformation and a vascular tumor in neonates.
5. Describe the causes and appearance of Candida infections.

Advice From the Authors

"You are learning to be a neonatal detective. Your patients cannot tell you what is wrong. You must seek out the clues through assessment, diagnostics, labs, thorough history, and chart review. Pathophysiology is the bedrock of understanding diseases, syndromes, and congenital abnormalities. If you can understand the pathogenesis of your patient's disorder(s), then moving forward to diagnosis and treatment will be more seamless. Use the keen observation skills you have developed as a bedside nurse. Assessment is primarily observation. Gather information as you walk up to the bedside and begin your differential diagnosis list from there."

–Leigh Ann Cates-McGlinn, PhD, APRN, NNP-BC, RRT-NPS, CHSE

"This book is very unique in that it will help the learner in various didactic methods. Not all of us learn at the same pace or in a certain way. This textbook is structured to assist the student learner to understand concepts in various ways and to enhance your learning. The book will not only help you in understanding neonatal concepts in order to pass certification, but will also assist you in becoming a lifelong learner."

–Rebecca Chuffo Davila, DNP, APRN, NNP-BC, FAANP

"A keen understanding of the structure and function of the epidermal barrier is invaluable in evaluating, diagnosing, and determining the etiology of observed cutaneous conditions. As such, it forms the basis for treatment planning. Many neonatal skin 'conditions' have common features. A differential approach to diagnosis is warranted. Conditions, such as irritant contact dermatitis, may occur as a result of standard infant care practices, for example, use of tapes and adhesives, and may be exacerbated in prematurely born infants. Strategies to minimize iatrogenic effects are necessary."

—Marty Visscher, PhD, MEd, CPI

"It is crucial to familiarize and understand the skin-specific basic lesion (morphology) and its associated definition. This will help with accurate description of the lesion, which will assist you in making the correct differential diagnosis. Remember that the common, benign, and transient lesions occur more often than the severe pathological skin conditions. Ruling out infectious causes for the skin lesion is critical and a priority as you can avoid its widespread dissemination. The goal of treatment is to first do no harm or worsen the condition. Recognize and avoid all iatrogenic injuries."

—Vivek Narendran, MD, MRCP(UK), MBA

Mind Maps

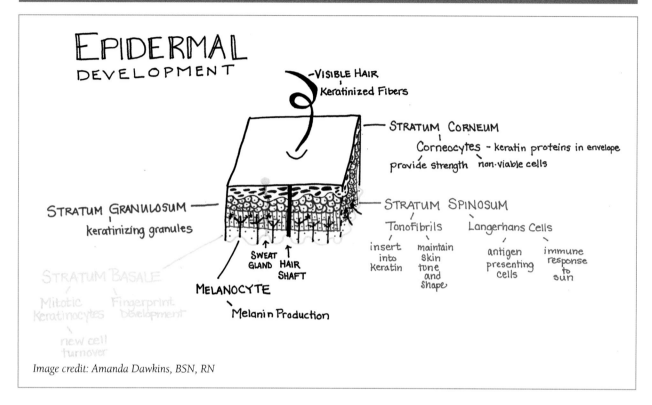

Image credit: Amanda Dawkins, BSN, RN

Note: This mind map reflects one student's interpretation of a portion of one or more concepts addressed in this chapter. Readers should regard the mind maps woven throughout this textbook as examples of multi-sensory study tools that can be developed to encourage conceptual understanding. Readers are encouraged to develop their own unique mind maps in consultation with academic faculty or clinical preceptors.

TIMELINE OF ORGAN DEVELOPMENT

NOTE:	LEGEND
Placement of common problems is meant to offer visual/conceptual perspective on the timing of onset of these commonly reported malformations. Variation exists across the literature.	<22 – 27 6/7 weeks = extremely preterm 28 – 31 6/7 weeks = very preterm 32 – 36 6/7 weeks = late/moderate preterm 37 – 40 weeks = term

References

Adni, T., Martin, K., & Mudge, E. (2012). The psychosocial impact of chronic wounds on patients with severe epidermolysis bullosa. *Journal of Wound Care, 21*(11), 528–538. doi:10.12968/jowc.2012.21.11.528

Antaya, R. J., & Robinson, D. M. (2010). Blisters and pustules in the newborn. *Pediatric Annuals, 39*, 635–645. doi:10.3928/00904481-20100922-01

Atherton, D. J. (2016). Understanding irritant napkin dermatitis. *International Journal of Dermatology, 55*, 7–9. doi:10.1111/ijd.13334

Aydin, M., Hakan, N., Zenciroglu, A., & Demirol, H. A. (2013). A rare location of sucking blister in newborn: The lips. *European Journal of Pediatrics, 172*(10), 1423–1424. doi:10.1007/s00431-013-2055-y

Bae, Y. C., Ng, E., & Geronemus, R. G. (2016). Successful treatment of two pediatric port wine stains in darker skin types using 595 nm laser. *Lasers in Surgery and Medicine, 48*(4), 339–342. doi:10.1002/lsm.22467

Basit, S., Khan, S., & Ahmad, W. (2015). Genetics of human isolated hereditary hair loss disorders: Genetics of hereditary hair loss disorders. *Clinical Genetics, 88*(3), 203–212. doi:10.1111/cge.12531

Benjamin, J., Daniel, K., Stoll, B. J., Gantz, M. G., Walsh, M. C., Sánchez, P. J., Das, A., . . . for the Eunice Kennedy Shriver National Institute of Child Health and Human Development Neonatal Research Network. (2010). Neonatal candidiasis: Epidemiology, risk factors, and clinical judgment. *Pediatrics, 126*(4), e865–e873. doi:10.1542/peds.2009-3412

Bermas, B. L., & Smith, N. A. (2018). Pregnancy in women with systemic lupus erythematosus. In M. Ramirez Curtis (Ed.), *UpToDate.* Retrieved from https://www.uptodate.com/contents/pregnancy-in-women-with-systemic-lupus-erythematosus

Bertola, D. R., Yamamoto, G. L., Almeida, T. F., Buscarilli, M., Jorge, A. A. L., Malaquias, A. C., . . . Pereira, A. C. (2014). Further evidence of the importance of RIT1 in Noonan syndrome. *American Journal of Medical Genetics Part A, 164*(11), 2952–2957. doi:10.1002/ajmg.a.36722

Blei, F., & Guarini, A. (2014). Current workup and therapy of infantile hemangiomas. *Clinics in Dermatology, 32*(4), 459–470. doi:10.1016/j.clindermatol.2014.02.001

Bolender, D. L., & Kaplan, S. (2017). Basic embryology. In R. A. Polin, S. H. Abman, D. H. Rowitch, W. E. Benitz, & W. W. Fox (Eds.), *Fetal and neonatal physiology* (5th ed., pp. 23–38). Philadelphia, PA: Elsevier.

Bolognia, J., Schaffer, J. V., & Cerroni, L. (Eds.). (2018). *Dermatology* (4th ed.). Philadelphia, PA: Elsevier.

Brandling-Bennett, H. A., & Morel, K. D. (2010). Epidermal nevi. *Pediatric Clinics of North America, 57*(5), 1177–1198. doi:10.1016/j.pcl.2010.07.004

Brennan, T. E., Waner, M., & O, T. M. (2017). The tissue expander effect in early surgical management of select focal infantile hemangiomas. *JAMA Facial Plastic Surgery, 19*(4), 282–286. doi:10.1001/jamafacial.2016.1991

Bruckner, A. L., & O'Regan, G. M. (2015). Inherited and acquired blistering diseases. In L. F. Eichenfield, I. J. Frieden, E. F. Mathes, & A. L. Zaenglein (Eds.), *Neonatal and infant dermatology* (3rd ed,. pp. 140–154). Philadelphia, PA: Elsevier Saunders.

Brzezinski, P., & Chiriac, A. (2015). Sebaceous hyperplasia in neonates and adults. *Our Dermatology Online, 6*(1), 107–108. doi:10.7241/ourd.20151.29

Carlson, B. M. (2014). Not an edited book, *Human embryology and developmental biology* (5th ed., pp. 156–192). Philadelphia, PA: Elsevier Saunders.

Chan, Y., & Tay, Y. (2015). Hypopigmentation disorders. In L. F. Eichenfield, I. J. Frieden, E. F. Mathes, & A. L. Zaenglein (Eds.), *Neonatal and infant dermatology* (3rd ed,. pp. 369–387). Philadelphia, PA: Elsevier Saunders.

Chen, K., Chien, M., Chen, C., & Chiu, H. (2016). Congenital cutaneous candidiasis. *BMJ Case Reports, 2016,* bcr2016216037. doi:10.1136/bcr-2016-216037

Chen, T. S., Eichenfield, L. F., & Friedlander, S. F. (2013). Infantile hemangiomas: An update on pathogenesis and therapy. *Pediatrics, 131*(1), 99–108. doi:10.1542/peds.2012-1128

Cohen, B. (2017). Differential diagnosis of diaper dermatitis. *Clinical Pediatrics, 56*(5 Suppl.), 16S–22S. doi:10.1177/0009922817706982

Cordoro, K., & Schulman, J. (2015). Papulosquamous & lichenoid disorders. In L. F. Eichenfield, I. J. Frieden, E. F. Mathes, & A. L. Zaenglein (Eds.), *Neonatal and infant dermatology* (3rd ed., pp. 233–244). Philadelphia, PA: Elsevier Saunders.

Craiglow, B. G. (2013). Ichthyosis in the newborn. *Seminars in Perinatology, 37*(1), 26–31. doi:10.1053/j.semperi.2012.11.001

Cui, C., & Schlessinger, D. (2015). Eccrine sweat gland development and sweat secretion. *Experimental Dermatology, 24*(9), 644–650. doi:10.1111/exd.12773

Engür, D., Türkmen, M. K., & Şavk, E. (2013). Widespread miliaria crystalline in a newborn with hypernatremic dehydration. *Pediatric Dermatology, 30*(6), e234–e235. doi:10.1111/pde.12055

Ersoy, A. O., Oztas, E., Saridogan, E., Ozler, S., & Danisman, N. (2016). An unusual origin of fetal lymphangioma filling right axilla. *Journal of Clinical and Diagnostic Research, 10*(3), QD09–QD11. doi:10.7860/JCDR/2016/18516.7513

Filippidi, A., Galanakis, E., Maraki, S., Galani, I., Drogari-Apiranthitou, M., Kalmanti, M., . . . Samonis, G. (2014). The effect of maternal flora on candida colonisation in the neonate. *Mycoses, 57*(1), 43–48. doi:10.1111/myc.12100

Fine, J. (2016). Epidemiology of inherited epidermolysis bullosa based on incidence and prevalence estimates from the national epidermolysis bullosa registry. *JAMA Dermatology, 152*(11), 1231–1238. doi:10.1001/jamadermatol.2016.2473

Fine, J., Bruckner-Tuderman, L., Eady, R. A. J., Bauer, E. A., Bauer, J. W., Has, C., . . . Zambruno, G. (2014). Inherited epidermolysis bullosa: Updated recommendations on diagnosis and classification. *Journal of the American Academy of Dermatology, 70*(6), 1103–1126. doi:10.1016/j.jaad.2014.01.903

Fine, J.-D., & Mellerio, J. E. (2018). Epidermolysis bullosa. In J. L. Bolognia, J. V. Schaffer, & L. Cerroni (Eds.), *Dermatology* (4th ed., pp. 538–553). Philadelphia, PA: Elsevier Saunders.

Foley, C. C., Paller, A. S., & Irvine, A. D. (2015). Disorders of cornification (ichthyosis). In L. F. Eichenfield, I. J Frieden, E. F. Mathes, & A L. Zaenglein (Eds.), *Neonatal and infant dermatology* (3rd ed., pp. 281–302). Philadelphia, PA: Elsevier Saunders.

Friedlander, S. F., Baldwin, H. E., Mancini, A. J., Yan, A. C., & Eichenfield, L. F. (2011). The acne continuum: An age-based approach to therapy. *Seminars in cutaneous medicine and surgery, 30*(3 Suppl.), S6–S11. doi:10.1016/j.sder.2011.07.002

Friedland, R., Ben Amitai, D., & Zvulunovs, A. (2017). Screening for brain involvement in infants with multifocal cutaneous infantile hemangiomas. *Dermatology, 233*(6), 435–440. doi:10.1159/000484598

Ghosh, S. (2015). Neonatal pustular dermatosis: An overview. *Indian Journal of Dermatology*, *60*(2), 211. doi:10.4103/0019-5154.152558

Gonzalez, M. E. (2013). Evaluation and treatment of the newborn with epidermolysis bullosa. *Seminars in Perinatology*, *37*(1), 32–39. doi:10.1053/j.semperi.2012.11.004

Gupta, D., & Thappa, D. M. (2013). Mongolian spots: How important are they? *World Journal of Clinical Cases*, *1*(8), 230–232. doi:10.12998/wjcc.v1.i8.230

Hafner, C., Toll, A., Gantner, S., Mauerer, A., Lurkin, I., Acquadro, F., . . . Real, F. X. (2012). Keratinocytic epidermal nevi are associated with mosaic *RAS* mutations. *Journal of Medical Genetics*, *49*(4), 249. doi:10.1136/jmedgenet-2011-100637

Haveri, F. T. T. S, & Inamadar, A. C. (2014). A cross-sectional prospective study of cutaneous lesions in newborn. *ISRN Dermatology*, *2014*, 1–8. doi:10.1155/2014/360590

Hennigan, K., & Riley, C. (2016). Staphylococcal scalded skin syndrome: A case review. *Neonatal Network*, *35*(1), 8–12. doi:10.1891/0730-0832.35.1.8

Heston, S., & Arnold, S. (2018). Syphilis in children. *Infectious Disease Clinics*, *32*(1), 129–144. doi:10.1016/j.idc.2017.11.007

Hoath, S. B., & Shah, K. N. (2017). Physiologic development of the skin. In R. A. Polin, S. H. Abman, D. H. Rowitch, W. E. Benitz, & W. W. Fox (Eds.), *Fetal and neonatal physiology* (5th ed., pp. 498–514). Philadelphia, PA: Elsevier.

Hölzle, E., & Kligman, A. M. (1978). The pathogenesis of miliaria rubra: Role of the resident microflora. *British Journal of Dermatology*, *99*(2), 117–137. doi:10.1111/j.1365-2133.1978.tb01973.x

Howard, R., & Frieden, I. (2015). Vesicles, pustules, bullae, erosions, and ulceration. In L. F. Eichenfield, I. J. Frieden, E. F. Mathes, & A. L. Zaenglein (Eds.), *Neonatal and infant dermatology* (3rd ed., pp. 111–139). Philadelphia, PA: Elsevier Saunders.

Jaka, A., Zubizarreta, J., Ormaechea, N., & Tuneu, A. (2012). Cutaneous neonatal lupus erythematosus. *Indian Journal of Dermatology Venereology & Leprology*, *78*(6), 775. Retrieved from http://www.ijdvl.com/text.asp?2012/78/6/775/102396

Javed, A., & Lteif, A. (2013). Development of the human breast. *Seminars in Plastic Surgery*, *27*(1), 5–12. doi:10.1055/s-0033-1343989

Jnah, A. J., Newberry, D., & Robertson, T. (2017). Dermatology cases. In S. Bellini & M. Beaulieu (Eds.), *Neonatal advanced practice nursing: A case-based learning approach* (pp. 213–254). New York, NY: Springer Publishing.

Kanada, K. N., Merin, M. R., Munden, A., & Friedlander, S. F. (2012). A prospective study of cutaneous findings in newborns in the United States: Correlation with race, ethnicity, and gestational status using updated classification and nomenclature. *Journal of Pediatrics*, *161*(2), 240. doi:10.1016/j.jpeds.2012.02.052

Kelly, M. S., Benjamin, J., Daniel, K., & Smith, P. B. (2015). The epidemiology and diagnosis of invasive candidiasis among premature infants. *Clinics in Perinatology*, *42*(1), 105–117. doi:10.1016/j.clp.2014.10.008

Khemani, S., Ali, S. B., Karim, S., & Yezdan, M. A. (2017). Harlequin colour change. *Journal of the College of Physicians Surgeons Pakistan*, *27*(9), S127–S128. Retrieved from https://www.jcpsp.pk/archive/2017/SS_Sep2017/25.pdf

Kolb, L., & Krishnamurthy, K. (2017). Nevus anemicus. Retrieved from https://www.ncbi.nlm.nih.gov/books/NBK459139

Leung, A., Balaji, S., & Keswani, S. G. (2013). Biology and function of fetal and pediatric skin. *Facial Plastic Surgery Clinics of North America*, *21*(1), 1–6. doi:10.1016/j.fsc.2012.10.001

Lucky, A. W. (2015). Transient benign cutaneous lesions of the newborn. In L. F. Eichenfield, I. J. Frieden, E. F. Mathes, & A. L. Zaenglein (Eds.), *Neonatal and infant dermatology* (3rd ed., pp. 65–76). Philadelphia, PA: Elsevier Saunders.

Lun Hon, K., & Leung, A. K. C. (2012). Neonatal lupus erythematosus. *Autoimmune Diseases*, *2012*, 1–6. doi:10.1155/2012/301274

Maguiness, S., & Garzon, M. (2015). Vascular malformations. In L. F. Eichenfield, I. J. Frieden, E. F. Mathes, & A. L. Zaenglein (Eds.), *Neonatal and infant dermatology* (3rd ed., pp. 352–368). Philadelphia, PA: Elsevier Saunders.

Mancini, A. J., & Lawley, L. P. (2015). Structure and function of newborn skin. In L. F. Eichenfield, I. J. Frieden, E. F. Mathes, & A. L. Zaenglein (Eds.), *Neonatal and infant dermatology* (3rd ed., pp. 14–23). Philadelphia, PA: Elsevier Saunders.

Marcoux, D. A., Durán-McKinster, C., Baselga, E., Morelli, J., Thieu, K., & Tsao, H. (2011). Pigmentary abnormalities. In L. Schachner & R. Hansen (Eds.), *Pediatric dermatology* (4th ed., pp. 700–746). Philadelphia, PA: Elsevier Saunders.

Monteagudo, B., Labandeira, J., Cabanillas, M., Acevedo, A., & Toribio, J. (2012). Prospective study of erythema toxicum neonatorum: Epidemiology and predisposing factors. *Pediatric Dermatology*, *29*(2), 166–168. doi:10.1111/j.1525-1470.2011.01536.x

Moore, K. L., Persaud, T. V. N., & Torchia, M. G. (2016). *The developing human: Clinically oriented embryology* (10th ed., pp. 437–455). Philadelphia, PA: Elsevier.

Mowad, C. M., McGinley, K. J., Foglia, A., & Leyden, J. J. (1995). The role of extracellular polysaccharide substance produced by *Staphylococcus epidermidis* in miliaria. *Journal of the American Academy of Dermatology*, *33*(5), 729–733. doi:10.1016/0190-9622(95)91809-4

National Institutes of Health. (2018a). Genetics home reference: Autosomal recessive hypotrichosis. Retrieved from https://ghr.nlm.nih.gov/condition/autosomal-recessive-hypotrichosis#genes

National Institutes of Health. (2018b). Genetics home reference: Neurofibromatosis type 1. Retrieved from https://ghr.nlm.nih.gov/condition/neurofibromatosis-type-1#statistics

National Institutes of Health. (2018c). Genetics home reference: Noonan syndrome. Retrieved from https://ghr.nlm.nih.gov/condition/noonan-syndrome

National Institutes of Health. (2018d). Genetics home reference: Sturge-Weber syndrome. Retrieved from https://ghr.nlm.nih.gov/condition/sturge-weber-syndrome#statistics

National Institutes of Health. (2018e). Genetics home reference: Waardenburg syndrome. Retrieved from https://ghr.nlm.nih.gov/condition/waardenburg-syndrome#statistics

National Organization of Rare Disorders. (2017). Rare diseases. Retrieved from https://rarediseases.org

Newnam, K. M. (2016). Surveillance and isolation of methicillin-resistant *Staphylococcus aureus* colonization in the neonatal intensive care unit. *Advances in Neonatal Care*, *16*(4), 298–307. doi:10.1097/ANC.0000000000000312

Nguyen, T. A., Wang, A. S., Eichenfield, L. F., & Barrio, V. (2016). "EB, or not EB?" Neonatal desquamative impetigo in a degloving pattern. *Pediatric Dermatology, 33*(2), e147–e148. doi:10.1111/pde.12766s

Niemann, C., & Horsley, V. (2012). Development and homeostasis of the sebaceous gland. *Seminars in Cell & Developmental Biology, 23*(8), 928–936. doi:10.1016/j.semcdb.2012.08.010

Paulus, S., Koronowska, S., & Fölster-Holst, R. (2017). Association between juvenile myelomonocytic leukemia, juvenile xanthogranulomas and neurofibromatosis type 1: Case report and review of the literature. *Pediatric Dermatology, 34*(2), 114–118. doi:10.1111/pde.13064

Peltonen, S., Kallionpää, R. A., & Peltonen, J. (2017). Neurofibromatosis type 1 (NF1) gene: Beyond café au lait spots and dermal neurofibromas. *Experimental Dermatology, 26*(7), 645–648. doi:10.1111/exd.13212

Prendiville, J. (2015). Lumps, bumps, and hamartomas. In L. F. Eichenfield, I. J. Frieden, E. F. Mathes, & A. L. Zaenglein (Eds.), *Neonatal and infant dermatology* (3rd ed., pp. 422–442). Philadelphia, PA: Elsevier Saunders.

Price, H., & Marghoob, A. (2015). Disorders of hyperpigmentation and melanocytes. In L. F. Eichenfield, I. J. Frieden, E. F. Mathes, & A. L. Zaenglein (Eds.), *Neonatal and infant dermatology* (3rd ed., pp. 388–409). Philadelphia, PA: Elsevier Saunders.

Reginatto, F. P., DeVilla, D., Muller, F. M., Peruzzo, J., Peres, L. P., Steglich, R. B., & Cestari, T. F. (2017). Prevalence and characterization of neonatal skin disorders in the first 72 h of life. *Jornal de Pediatria, 93*(3), 238–245. doi:10.1016/j.jped.2016.06.010

Reginatto, F. P., Muller, F. M., Peruzzo, J., & Cestari, T. F. (2017). Epidemiology and predisposing factors for erythema toxicum neonatorum and transient neonatal pustular: A multicenter study. *Pediatric Dermatology, 34*(4), 422–426. doi:10.1111/pde.13179

Reimer, A., & Hoeger, P. H. (2016). Lesion morphology in multifocal infantile hemangiomas. *Pediatric Dermatology, 33*(6), 621–626. doi:10.1111/pde.12956

Richter, G. T., & Suen, J. Y. (2010). Clinical course of arteriovenous malformations of the head and neck: A case series. *Otolaryngology—Head and Neck Surgery, 142*(2), 184–190. doi:10.1016/j.otohns.2009.10.023

Roberts, A. E., Allanson, J. E., Tartaglia, M., & Gelb, B. D. (2013). Noonan syndrome. *Lancet, 381*(9863), 333–342. doi:10.1016/S0140-6736(12)61023-X

Roh, M. R., Eliades, P., Gupta, S., & Tsao, H. (2015). Genetics of melanocytic nevi. *Pigment Cell & Melanoma Research, 28*(6), 661–672. doi:10.1111/pcmr.12412

Sadler, T. W. (2015). *Langman's medical embryology* (13th ed.). Philadelphia, PA: Lippincott, Williams & Wilkins.

Schaller, M., & Plewig, G. (2018). Structure and function of eccrine, apocrine, and sebaceous glands. In J. Bolognia, J. V. Schaffer, & L. Cerroni. (Eds.), *Dermatology* (4th ed., pp. 580–587). Philadelphia, PA: Elsevier.

Schoenwolf, G. C., Bleyl, S. B., Brauer, P. R., & Francis-West, P. H. (2015). *Larsen's human embryology* (5th ed., pp. 155–171). Philadelphia, PA: Churchill Livingstone

Shah, S. D., Baselga, E., McCuaig, C., Pope, E., Coulie, J., Boon, L. M., . . . Frieden, I. J. (2016). Rebound growth of infantile hemangiomas after propranolol therapy. *Pediatrics, 137*(4), e20151754. doi:10.1542/peds.2015-1754

Taieb, A., Ezzedine, K., & Morice-Picard, F. (2014). Diagnosis of some common and uncommon hyperpigmentation disorders in children. *Dermatlogica Sinica, 32*, 211–216. doi:10.1016/j.dsi.2014.08.001

Tom, W. L., & Eichenfield, L. F. (2015). Eczematous disorders. In L. F. Eichenfield, I. J. Frieden, E. F. Mathes, & A. L. Zaenglein (Eds.), *Neonatal and infant dermatology* (3rd ed., pp. 216–232). Philadelphia, PA: Elsevier Saunders.

Tong, S. Y. C., Davis, J. S., Eichenberger, E., Holland, T. L., Fowler, J., & Vance, G. (2015). *Staphylococcus aureus* infections: Epidemiology, pathophysiology, clinical manifestations, and management. *Clinical Microbiology Reviews, 28*(3), 603–661. doi:10.1128/CMR.00134-14

Tsimis, M. E., & Sheffield, J. S. (2017). Update on syphilis and pregnancy. *Birth Defects Research, 109*(5), 347–352. doi:10.1002/bdra.23562

Vahlquist, A., Fischer, J., & Törmä, H. (2018). Inherited nonsyndromic ichthyoses: An update on pathophysiology, diagnosis and treatment. *American Journal of Clinical Dermatology, 19*(1), 51–66. doi:10.1007/s40257-017-0313-x

Vandergriff, T. W. (2018). Anatomy and physiology. In J. Bolognia, J. V. Schaffer, & L. Cerroni (Eds.), *Dermatology* (4th ed., pp. 44–55). Philadelphia, PA: Elsevier.

Visscher, M. O., Adam, R., Brink, S., & Odio, M. (2015). Newborn infant skin: Physiology, development and care. *Clinics in Dermatology, 33*(3), 271–280. doi:10.1016/j.clindermatol.2014.12.003

Visscher, M. O., & Narendran, V. (2014). The ontogeny of skin. *Advances in Wound Care, 3*(4), 291–303. doi:10.1089/wound.2013.0467

Wassef, M., Blei, F., Adams, D., Alomari, A., Baselga, E., Berenstein, A., . . . on behalf of the ISSVA Board and Scientific Committee. (2015). Vascular anomalies classification: Recommendations from the International Society for the Study of Vascular Anomalies. *Pediatrics, 136*(1), e203–e214. doi:10.1542/peds.2014-3673

Weitz, N. A., Lauren, C. T., Behr, G. G., Wu, J. K., Kandel, J. J., Meyers, P. M., . . . Garzon, M. C. (2015). Clinical spectrum of capillary malformation–arteriovenous malformation syndrome presenting to a pediatric dermatology practice: A retrospective study. *Pediatric Dermatology, 32*(1), 76–84. doi:10.1111/pde.12384

Wright, C. Y., Norval, M., & Hertle, R. W. (2015). Oculocutaneous albinism in Sub-Saharan Africa: Adverse sun-associated health effects and photoprotection. *Photochemistry and Photobiology, 91*(1), 27–32. doi:10.1111/php.12359

Yan, A. C., Kim, H. J., Honig, P. J. (2015). Lesional morphology and assessment. In L. F. Eichenfield, I. J. Frieden, E. F. Mathes, & A. L. Zaenglein (Eds.), *Neonatal and infant dermatology* (3rd ed.). Philadelphia, PA: Elsevier Saunders.

Yeo, L., & Ormerod, A. D. (2014). Treatment of acne in children. *American Journal of Clinical Dermatology, 15*(2), 77–86. doi:10.1007/s40257-013-0057-1

Zempleni, J., Wijeratne, S. S. K., & Hassan, Y. I. (2009). Biotin. *BioFactors, 35*(1), 36–46. doi:10.1002/biof.8

13

THE EYES

Desi M. Newberry, Debbie Fraser, Sofia Aliaga, and Bill Diehl-Jones

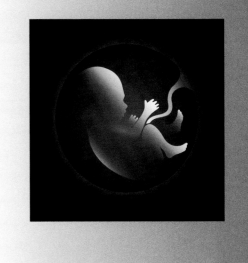

LEARNING OBJECTIVES

After completing this chapter, the reader should be able to:

- Understand normal ocular development.
- Analyze the physiologic function of the fetal and neonatal ocular system.
- Discuss common inherited disorders and their effect on fetal and neonatal ocular system development and function.
- Identify maternal health conditions that have a potential impact on fetal and postnatal ocular system development and function.
- Evaluate common disorders that affect the ocular system and their implications across the life span.

INTRODUCTION

The human eyes allow us to see the world as we know it. The human fetus can detect light as early as 16 weeks of gestation. Term infants exhibit farsightedness at birth with eye function developing rapidly over the first 6 months of life. At term, the eye is 70% of its adult size, and by age 3, the cornea and eyeball measure 95% of adult diameter (Martin, Fanaroff & Walsh, 2015). Full ocular maturity, both in size and visual acuity, is achieved by 7 years of age. Maturation of the eyes can be affected by abnormal visual conditions early in life, prematurity, and poor nutrition, among others. The development of the human eye may also be affected by various genetic conditions, infectious diseases, and maternal substance abuse. Furthermore, retinopathy of prematurity (ROP) represents the leading cause of blindness in developed countries. In this chapter, we review the embryology, developmental physiology, and genetic and maternal health influences on the human eyes. In addition, a relevant discussion of common eye problems, including ROP, and the potential implications of these problems across the life span are presented.

TIMELINE OF ORGAN DEVELOPMENT

Eye development involves a complex and interconnected morphologic differentiation and maturation. Most primitive eye structures arise at the same time, during the early embryonic period, while the fetal and postnatal periods primarily involve structural and functional maturation. Note that as you progress through this section of the chapter, our use of plurality accounts for the bilateral development of structures which comprise each individual eye.

Eye structures arise from the neuroectoderm, surface ectoderm, mesoderm, and neural crest cells, and this miraculous process begins during week 3 of gestation (Table 13.1; Moore, Persaud, & Torchia, 2016). During this time, the neural folds approximate and fuse, which creates the forebrain. During the process of folding and

TABLE 13.1 Summary of Embryologic Origins of Eye Structures

Mesoderm	Neural Crest Cells	Ectoderm	
		Neural	**Surface**
• Extraocular muscle cells	• Corneal endothelium	• Neural retina	• Lens
• Vascular endothelia	• Trabecular meshwork	• Epithelium: Retinal pigment	• Corneal epithelium
• Schlemm's canal endothelium	• Stroma: Iris	• Epithelium: Ciliary body	• Conjunctival epithelium
	• Stroma: Cornea	• Epithelium: Posterior iris	• Caruncle
	• Stroma: Ciliary bodies	• Pupillary muscles	• Eyelid epidermis
	• Choroid		• Eyelid cilia
	• Sclera		• Epithelium of adnexal glands
	• Episclera		• Epithelium of nasolacrimal duct
	• Ciliary muscle		• Lacrimal gland
	• Perivascular connective tissue and smooth muscle cells		
	• Meninges of optic nerve		
	• Orbital cartilage and bone		
	• Connective tissue of extrinsic ocular muscles		
	• Secondary vitreous		
	• Zonules		

Sources: From Moore, K. L., Persaud, T. V. N., & Torchia, M. G. (2016). *The developing human* (10th ed., pp. 417–436). Philadelphia, PA: Elsevier; Schoenwolf, G. C., Bleyl, S. B., Brauer, P. R., & Francis-West, P. H. (2015). *Larsen's human embryology* (5th ed.). Philadelphia, PA: Churchill Livingstone.

fusion, optic sulci (grooves) protrude at the cranial end of the neural folds and give rise to the optic vesicles (primitive eyes; Figure 13.1). These primitive optic vesicles undergo two concurrent and critical processes, invagination and stimulation of the surface ectoderm, which ultimately give rise to the major structures and vasculature of the eye (Schoenwolf, Bleyl, Brauer, & Francis-West, 2015).

Invagination

The process of invagination (folding inward) begins during week 6 of gestation. The distal ends of the optic vesicles increase in size and invaginate, giving rise to the primitive optic cups (future retina and iris) and optic stalks. Fissures, or grooves, develop on the ventral sides of both structures, which give rise to the optic disks and the primitive vascular supply. The outer mesenchyme surrounding the optic cups differentiates into the choroid (vascular layer which lies between the retina and sclera) and scleral (opaque, fibrous outer layer of the eye) layers.

Primitive vascular supply to the retina is established by week 15 to 16 of gestation. This primitive vascular supply includes the hyaloid artery and vein (future central retinal artery and vein). The hyaloid artery will nourish the retina and lens during early development, while the hyaloid vein offers venous outflow (Figure 13.2). Later, the choroid will supply the outer retina, whereas the opthalamic artery and its branches, including the central retinal artery and long

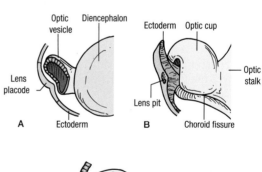

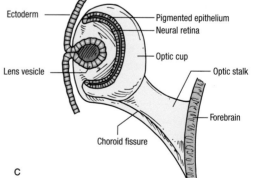

Figure 13.1 Early eye formation.

posterior and anterior ciliary arteries, will supply the inner retina. These vessels are derivatives of the internal carotid artery

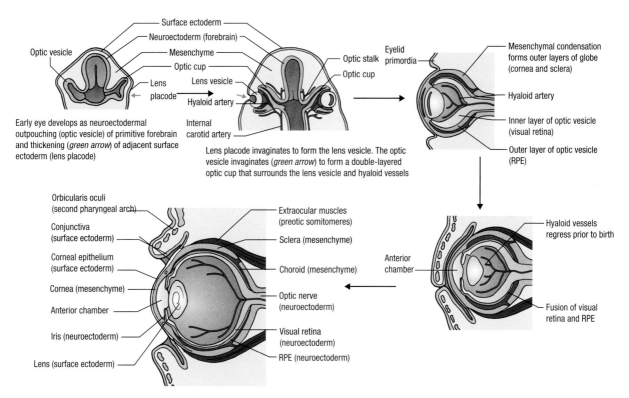

Figure 13.2 The eye and adnexa.

RPE, retinal pigment epithelium

(a portion of the Circle of Willis), which receives its arterial supply from the right and left brachiocephalic arteries, branches of the ascending aorta. The central retinal vein will modulate venous outflow to the superior, then inferior opthalamic vein, which then drains into the internal jugular vein and superior vena cava, and finally into the right atrium.

Formation of the Retina

During week 5 of gestation, the walls of the optic cup give rise to each retina. This primordial retina begins as a two-layered structure, transiently separated by an intraretinal space. The outermost layer is the pigmented layer (not to be confused with the pigmented layer of the iris which dictates eye coloration), while the inner layer is the neural retina. As morphologic development continues, the two retinal layers fuse and the intraretinal space is obliterated. The neural retina continues to differentiate and develop a neuroepithelium. The cells within the neuroepithelium give rise to the photoreceptors (rods and cones) and neurons (retinal ganglion cells). Ganglion cells thereby grow toward the optic stalk (optic nerve). Photoreceptor cells, primarily responsible for the process of light transduction, begin their differentiation during week 25 of gestation (Moore et al., 2016).

The processes of vasculogenesis (the differentiation of precursor cells into the primitive vascular network) and angiogenesis (growth of new capillaries) support the growth and differentiation of the retina (Hughes, Yang, &

Chan-Ling, 2000). Prior to week 15, a rudimentary vascular supply is apparent. By week 25 of gestation, angiogenesis increases and vascular density in the incipient fovea (a small depression in the retina where acuity is highest) is notably increased (Figure 13.3; Hughes et al., 2000). Retinal vascularization is complete by 36 to 40 weeks of gestation (González, Stahl, Hellström, & Smith, 2017).

Formation of the Iris

The iris, which arises and develops between weeks 4 and 7 of gestation, forms from the outer wall of the optic cup. Over time, the iris evolves into a covering over the lens of the eye. Two major layers comprise the iris and include the pigmented epithelium (outermost layer) and stroma (supporting tissue; Table 13.2). The iris functions to control light input through the pupil and therefore influences the image quality delivered to the retina (Nischler et al., 2013). Definitive coloration is established between 6 and 10 months of postnatal life and depends upon distribution of melanin. Genetic inheritance patterns influence melanin distribution. Genes located on chromosome 15, in particular the *OCA2* and *HERC2* genes, modulate the synthesis and expression P protein, which influence the production of melanin. Similar to skin tone, the amount of melanin located in the pigmented epithelium or stroma influences eye coloration. Reduced production of P protein results in lighter (blue) colored eyes, whereas an increased quantity

Figure 13.3 Retinal scan.

TABLE 13.2 Eye Coloration	
Eye Color	**Melanin Pigmentation**
Albino	Minimal to none
Blue	Low
Green/hazel	Moderate
Dark brown	High

Source: From Moore, K. L., Persaud, T. V. N., & Torchia, M. G. (2016). *The developing human* (10th ed., pp. 417–436). Philadelphia, PA: Elsevier.

of melanin is associated with darker (brown) colored eyes. While it is uncommon for brown-eyed parents to have blue-eyed children, it is not impossible. Therefore, neonatal advanced practice nurses should exercise caution when opining on definitive eye coloration, as genetic variations can give rise to unexpected results.

Formation of the Optic Nerve

As previously discussed, during week 4 of gestation, the distal ends of the optic vesicles increase in size and invaginate, giving rise to the primitive optic cups and optic stalks. The optic stalks exist as hollow tubules and arise from the fusion of retinal fissures (grooves). The tubules are progressively infiltrated by retinal ganglion cells from the neural retina (innermost layer). By week 8 of gestation, axons extend off the ganglion cells and extend through the optic stalk, connecting the neural retina to the brain. These ganglion clog and permanently obliterate the hollow interior of the optic stalk, thereby converting it to the optic nerve. The optic nerve becomes covered within three layers of myelin. The outermost layer arises from the dura mater and is fibrous in construct. The middle layer originates from the arachnoid

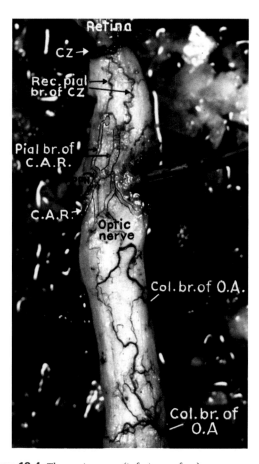

Figure 13.4 The optic nerve (inferior surface)

Source: Singh, S., & Dass, R. (1960). The central artery of the retina II. A study of its distribution and anastomoses. *British Journal of Ophthalmology, 44,* 280–299. Retrieved from https://bjo.bmj.com/content/bjophthalmol/44/5/280.full.pdf. Used with permission from BMJ Publishing Group Ltd.

mater and is relatively thin when compared to the outer layer. Last, the interior layer originates from the pia mater and is a densely vascular layer, which provides blood supply to the optic nerve from the opthalmic artery (main blood supply), a branch of the internal carotid artery. The first branch of the opthalmic artery is the central artery and vein, the main blood supply for the retina (Figure 13.4).

Lens Formation

Optic vesicles also induce the formation of the lens placodes (primitive lens of each eye). The surface ectoderm undergoes a process of folding and separates, forming these hollow lens vesicles (lens placodes). These primitive lenses fold inward, forming pits (lens pits). Over time, these lens pits fuse together and form the lens vesicles. The lens vesicles give rise to the lens of the eye, as well as the cornea. Maternal infections, such as rubella, or the development of inborn errors of metabolism can derange lens formation. For example, maternal rubella infection, in particular during weeks 4 and 7 of gestation, can predispose the developing eyes to cataracts. Postnatally, untreated galactosemia leads to high levels of circulating galactose, which can damage the lens and lead to cataract formation; treatment of the inborn error of metabolism facilitates resolution of the cataracts (Moore et al., 2016).

Cornea, Ciliary Bodies, Iris, and Pupil

By week 8 of gestation, the stromal layer of the developing cornea appears between the two corneal layers. The cornea evolves into the transparent covering of the iris, pupil, and anterior chamber of the eye. Ciliary bodies and muscles arise during this time. Ciliary bodies are highly vascularized structures that synthesize and secrete aqueous humor, a watery and transparent fluid primarily composed of amino acids and glucose. The aqueous humor travels from the ciliary epithelium to the anterior chamber of the eye to nourish the cornea, iris, and mature lens, as well as maintain homeostatic intraocular pressures. Any disruption to this pathway can lead to the development of congenital glaucoma.

The lens of the eye is essentially suspended by the ciliary muscle, which modulates focusing. Parasympathetic and sympathetic neurons innervate the ciliary muscle during early embryogenesis. Once mature, parasympathetic stimulation causes constriction and sympathetic stimulation causes relaxation of the ciliary muscle.

Support Structures

Eyelids. By week 6 of gestation, the surface ectoderm and mesenchyme fold to create the primitive eyelids and conjunctival sac, a space between the corneas and eyelids. The lids thereby remain fused until months 5 to 7 of gestation.

Nasolacrimal Glands. Nasolacrimal glands arise from within the conjunctival sacs and undergo a progressive maturational process until approximately week 6 of postnatal life (Schoenwolf et al., 2015). The lacrimal gland is located behind the lateral aspect of the upper eyelid and, when mature, functions to lubricate, cleanse, and protect the eye (Figure 13.5; Gosling, Harris, Humpherson, Whitmore, & Willan, 2016; Moore et al., 2016). Small ducts carry tear fluid into the conjunctiva and then medially across the surface of the cornea. Tears thereby enter the lacrimal punctum (superior and inferior) and drain into the nasal cavity via the nasolacrimal duct and nasolacrimal canal (Gosling et al., 2016; Moore et al., 2016; Schoenwolf et al., 2015).

Eyelashes. A double row of eyelashes is usually present by 28 to 32 weeks of gestation. The eyelashes cover the edge of the eyelids along with associated sebaceous glands. Medially, the eyelashes end at the lacrimal punctum, which describe the structures inside the eye that function to collect tears from the lacrimal glands (Gosling et al., 2016).

Ocular Orbit. The bony walls of the orbit separate its contents from the cranial fossa, ethmoidal air cells and nasal cavity, maxillary sinus, temporal fossa, and lateral surface of the face (Figure 13.6; Gosling et al., 2016). The orbit contains the eye globe, extraocular muscles, fat, vasculature, cranial nerves (CNs), and lacrimal gland (Burns, Iyer, Robinson, & Chapman, 2013; Gosling et al., 2016). The fascia bulbi (or vagina bulbi) is the fascial sheath that allows for eye movement. It is attached to the eye at the corneal edge by suspensory ligaments (Gosling et al., 2016). The sclera is a tough structure that supports the inner structures of the eye (Schoenwolf et al., 2015). The six muscles (four recti, two obliques, and the levator palpebrae superioris) that control eye movement pierce the fascia to connect to the eye. These muscles are controlled by three CNs: the (a) oculomotor (III) nerve, (b) trochlear (IV) nerve, and (c) abducens (VI) nerve. The optic nerve, the fourth significant nerve affecting eye function, is composed of nerve fibers from the ganglion cell layer of the retina. *The optic nerve conveys visual sensation.*

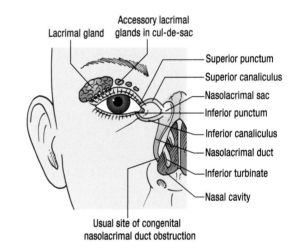

Figure 13.5 The nasolacimal gland

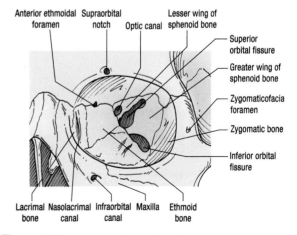

Figure 13.6 Anatomy of the orbit (left eye).

Source: Adapted from Gosling, J. A., Harris, P. F., Humpherson, J. R., Whitmore, I., & Willan, P. L. T. (2016). *Human anatomy: Color atlas and textbook* (6th ed.). New York, NY: Elsevier.

DEVELOPMENTAL PHYSIOLOGY

Sensory Innervation to the Eye

Recall that the eyes are innervated by several CNs and each modulates a specific process. Cranial nerve II transmits visual information, whereas CNs III, IV, VI, and VII modulate ocular motor function. CN V (trigeminal nerve) holds the unique role of transmitting sensory information from the eye to the cranial structures and is the focus of this section of the chapter.

As you may recall from Chapter 3, neurons within the cerebral cortex and other areas of the brain work collaboratively (in circuits). The neurons transmit information received via afferent (input) pathways and orchestrate responses via efferent (motor output) pathways. Afferent pathways are either somatic or visceral and, as such, involve the CNs. This is particularly important when considering organs, such as the eyes, because they are richly innervated with somatic (sensory) nerve fibers. Sensory nerve receptors, located at the tips of second-order nerve fibers, are in abundance at the cornea, iris, sclera, and conjunctiva. Therefore, these structures are particularly sensitive to pain, temperature, and touch. It is interesting to note that the cornea consists of 400% more sensory nerve fibers than other tissues and structures (Ueno et al., 2012).

Three types of sensory receptors innervate the eye. *Mechanoreceptors* sense mechanical irritants (ocular contact with foreign bodies or other mechanical forces) and modulate a localized pain response. *Polymodal receptors* also sense mechanical irritants, as well as chemical and thermal (heat) irritants, and perpetuate the pain response even after the acute injury phase has passed (Belmonte, Acosta, Merayo-Lloves, & Gallar, 2015; McMahon, Koltzenburg, Tracey, & Turk, 2013). *Cold receptors* sense reductions in corneal surface temperature.

The introduction of any mechanical, thermal, or chemical stimuli (irritant) to the corneal surface activates the corresponding second-order neuron. Nerve impulses (often pain impulses) travel along afferent pathways and to the central nervous system (Figure 13.7). Once the sensory input has been processed within the brain, an efferent motor or autonomic response is returned from the brain to the eye in the form of motor and autonomic responses. Typical responses include blinking and tearing; both seek to protect the eye as well as raise ocular surface temperature (Meng & Kurose, 2013).

Retinal Function: The Rods and Cones

The human eye contains two types of photoreceptor cells, rods and cones, which are located in the neural retina. These highly specialized neurons are responsible for transducing light into electrical signals, which, in turn, provides the sensory input for vision throughout the diurnal cycle of illumination (Chalupa & Werner, 2014; MacLeish & Makino, 2011). This process, called *phototransduction*, is achieved through a series of biochemical processes stimulated by light and results in decreased ongoing release of neurotransmitters at the synapse. In essence, light enters the eye, comes into contact with rhodopsin (a photosensitive chemical contained in rods), and, as a result of chemical reactions, sends electrical impulses to the brain where it is interpreted as light (Gross & Wensel, 2011; Purves, Augustine, Fitzpatrick, Hall, LaMantia, & White 2012).

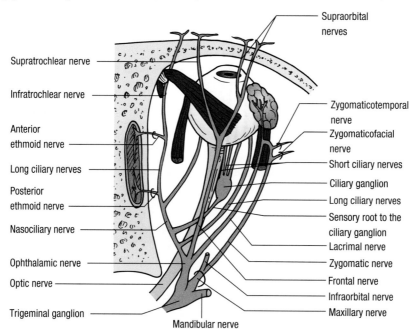

Figure 13.7 Trigeminal nerve branches with the ocular orbit.

There are approximately 6.5 million cones in the human eye. Three main types of cones are observed: include S-cones ("blue cones"), M-cones ("green cones"), and L-cones ("red cones"). A high concentration of cones is found in the macula, providing sharp, detailed vision (Wu, 2011). Cones are responsible for photopic vision (vision in well-lit conditions), color vision, and detail. As such, cones function best in bright illumination and are relatively unresponsive in low light (Wu, 2011).

There are approximately 120 million rods in the human eye. Rods are responsible for scotopic vision (vision in dim light) and do not differentiate colors. Rhodopsin enables vision in low-light conditions. Rods have a limited sensitivity over a narrow range of light intensities; the benefit of this is a decreased metabolic demand (Chalupa & Werner, 2014; Lamb, 2011).

Adaptation to Light

Light itself is integral to functional maturation of synaptic function within the inner retina (Chalupa & Werner, 2014). Light adaptation is the ability of the visual system to adjust between light and dark. This ability matures quickly among infants born after 35 weeks' gestation, but is functionally immature among infants 30 to 35 weeks' gestation and absent among infants <30 weeks' gestation (Ikeda, Ishikawa, Shimizu, Asakawa & Goseki, 2015; Lamb, 2011).

Rods are primarily responsible for visual adaptation (image-forming systems and pupillary reflex) in dimly lit areas. Cones remain responsible for visual adaptation in well-lit areas. The combined effort of both systems, in low lighting, is termed mesopic vision and is evident among infants >35 weeks' gestation (Chalupa & Werner, 2014; Lamb, 2011). The pupillary (blink-to-light) reflex is mediated by these photoreceptor cells (rods and cones) and implicated by pupillary size. Reduced ocular and corneal diameter, which is commonly noted among infants <38 weeks' gestation, corresponds with reduced pupillary size. In fact, infants born at less than 30 weeks of gestation typically exhibit no blink-to-light reflex and only primitive image-forming systems, due to pupillary and retinal immaturity (Ikeda et al., 2015).

Visual Milestones

The fetus is able to detect light as early as 16 weeks of gestation (Gardner, Carter, Enzman Hines, & Hernandez, 2016; Martin et al., 2015). By week 26, the fetal eye is affixed with most histological features of the mature eye; visual milestones are evident beginning with week 30 of gestation.

The first visual milestone to appear is the pupillary light reflex. This reflex is noted at 30 weeks of gestation and involves a reduction in pupillary diameter with lid closure in response to light stimulation (Gardner et al., 2016; Martin et al., 2015). The preterm neonate is able to focus and track objects, and has a preference for patterns by 33 to 34 weeks of gestation (Madan & Good, 2005). Vestibular rotations, or the doll's eye maneuver, in which

the eyes deviate to the opposite direction when the head is quickly rotated from side to side, are well developed at 34 weeks of gestation (Gardner et al., 2016).

At term, infants are farsighted (objects nearby are blurry) and have the ability to respond to light (Moore et al., 2016). The visual field is typically limited to approximately 8 to 10 inches, with estimated visual acuity of 20/400 (Gleason & Juul, 2018). Patterned stimuli are preferred over uniform brightness (Norcia, 2011). This is likely due to functional immaturity of vision processing centers in the brain, which improves over time. Visual fixation, conjugate horizontal gaze, and optokinetic nystagmus are also well developed at birth (Martin et al., 2015). Visual fixation is the maintenance of visual gaze on a single location. The ability to move the eyes together horizontally refers to *conjugate horizontal gaze*. Optokinetic nystagmus is the ability to follow moving objects while keeping the head still.

Preterm and term infants are born into a state of functional immaturity; as such, the first few months of postnatal life are regarded as a critical period for visual development. The blink response to a visual threat, color vision (the ability to discern different wavelengths of light), stereopsis (depth perception), and ocular alignment (normal eye alignment) rapidly develop during the first 6 months of life (Lambert & Lyons, 2017). Additional developments in the first 6 months include visual following, accommodation, conjugate vertical gaze, fusional convergence, and differentiation of fovea and iris stromal (the front fibrovascular layer of the iris) pigmentation (Martin et al., 2015). *Visual following* involves the ability to control where eyes are aimed, whereas *accommodation* refers to the ability to maintain clear focus as the distance of an object varies. The ability to move the eyes together vertically refers to *conjugate vertical gaze*. *Fusional convergence* is the ability of the two eyes to perceive one single image.

The eye is considered to be mature, both in size and visual acuity, by 7 years of age. Color perception and accommodation, as well as visual acuity, are considered equal to that of the adult eye by this time. As a result, advanced practice nurses must recognize the importance of early identification and treatment of ocular disorders as a critical means to optimize eye health across the life span.

GENETIC INFLUENCES

There are a number of genetic conditions that are accompanied by ocular abnormalities. Conditions, such as trisomy 13, 18, and 21, as well as Turner syndrome, are more common, whereas others are quite rare. Additional inherited disorders affecting the ocular system are provided in Table 13.3.

Chromosomal Abnormalities

Trisomy 21. Trisomy 21, or Down syndrome, is the most common inherited disorder and is slightly more common in males than females. This syndrome affects a total of one in 800 births, with an increased incidence of one in 25 to

TABLE 13.3 Other Inherited Disorders of the Eyes

- Apert syndrome
- Congenital stromal corneal dystrophy
- Crouzon syndrome
- Focal dermal hypoplasia
- Fraser syndrome
- Graves' disease
- Marfan syndrome
- Moebius syndrome
- Ocular albinism
- Renal coloboma syndrome
- Sjögren syndrome
- Zellweger syndrome

Note: A more comprehensive list is provided by the National Institute of Health, Genetic and Rare Diseases Information Center.

300 births reported among pregnant women over the age of 35 (Jones, Jones, & Del Campo, 2013; National Institutes of Health [NIH], 2018b). There are a number of ocular findings common to trisomy 21. Epicanthal folds, an extra layer of skin that covers the inner canthus (corner) of the eye, are a classic feature of this disorder, as are upturned palpebral fissures. Other findings include refractive errors, usually myopia (70%), lens opacities (59%), nystagmus (35%), strabismus (45%), blepharitis, glaucoma, Brushfield's spots (speckling or nodules on the iris), and adult-onset cataracts (30%–60%; Jones et al., 2013; Orge & Grigorian, 2015). Long-term visual outcome is dependent on the degree of myopia and the impact of cataracts.

Trisomy 13. Trisomy 13, or Patau syndrome, affects an estimated one in 16,000 live births (National Organization for Rare Disorders, 2007). Survival beyond the neonatal period is rare. Trisomy 13 may be the result of a spontaneous mutation (66%) or the result of autosomal dominant inheritance (33%; National Library of Medicine [NLM], 2018b). Rarely, mosaic trisomy 13 can occur and, in those cases, the severity of the disorder will depend on the number and type of cells that have the extra chromosome (Genetic and Rare Diseases Information Center [GARD], 2016a). Ocular involvement in trisomy 13 is common (90%) and includes microphthalmia, cataracts, colobomas of the iris and retina, persistent fetal vasculature, persistent tunica vasculosa lentis, and retinal dysplasia (Lueder, 2006; Madan-Khetarpal & Arnold, 2018). Additional findings include short/slanted palpebral fissures, ptosis, and hypertelorism (Orge & Grigorian, 2015).

Trisomy 18. Trisomy 18, or Edwards syndrome, occurs in one in 5,000 to 8,000 live births, and carries a 90% to 95% mortality rate within the first year of life (Lal, 2016; NIH, 2018f). This disorder usually results from a spontaneous mutation and approximately 80% of affected infants are female (GARD, 2015). Ocular abnormalities include

epicanthal folds, hypertelorism, gliosis, retinal folds, hypopigmentation, dysplasia, and areas of hemorrhage (Lim et al., 2010).

Turner Syndrome. As the result of a spontaneous error, girls with Turner syndrome have an absent set of genes on the short arm of one X chromosome (Daniel, 2018). The global incidence is one in every 2,500 females (NIH, 2018g). The karyotype in Turner syndrome is usually 45 X; however, approximately 15% of affected individuals have a mosaic form of the syndrome resulting in a variable expression of typical findings (Madan-Khetarpal & Arnold, 2018). Ocular findings are present in 35% of cases of Turner syndrome and include ptosis, strabismus, amblyopia, cataracts, and red-green color blindness. Some individuals may also have epicanthal folds (Daniel, 2018). Visual impairment will depend on the severity of the refractive error.

Craniofacial Syndromes

Craniosynostosis. Craniosynostosis involves the premature fusion of one or more of the cranial sutures. Craniosynostosis affects approximately one in 2,500 newborns when associated with a syndrome; nonsyndromic craniosynostosis affects approximately one per 1,000 live births (Garza & Khosla, 2012; Steinbacher & Bartlett, 2013). Ocular findings include amblyopia (reduced vision in the affected eye) related to strabismus, anisometropia (in which eyes have unequal refractive power), ametropia (nearsightedness or farsightedness), astigmatism (blurred vision caused by irregular shaped cornea or lens), and optic neuropathy (damage to the optic nerve) caused by craniocerebral alterations, hydrocephalus, and obstructive sleep apnea (Nischal, 2014). Small orbits increase the risk for globe subluxation and drying of the cornea results from exposure (Orge & Grigorian, 2015). The impact of craniosynostosis on long-term visual outcome is dependent on the underlying cause of the disorder as well as the severity of cranial malformation (Steinbacher & Bartlett, 2013).

Hemifacial Microsomia. Underdevelopment of the lower portion of the face is sometimes referred to as *first and second brachial arch syndrome*, or *lateral facial dysplasia*. The etiology is unknown and usually occurs with no family history. Ocular findings include anopthalmia (missing eye), microphthalmia (rare), coloboma of the upper eyelid or iris, and vertical displacement of the orbit (Heike, Luquettti, & Hing, 2014). Other findings include minor fissure abnormalities and orbital lipodermoids (a collection of adipose tissue found on the conjunctiva; Orge & Grigorian, 2015).

Gene Mutations

11p Abnormalities. WAGR syndrome (**W**ilms tumor, **a**niridia, **g**enitourinary abnormalities, and **r**ange of developmental delays) results from a deletion on the short arm of chromosome 11 (Orge & Grigorian, 2015). This syndrome is rare, occurring in one in 500,000 to 1 million individuals (NIH, 2018i). Most cases result from a de novo mutation although, rarely, a family history is present. Aniridia (absence of the iris) occurs in 80% to 99% of cases. Other ocular abnormalities include aplasia or hypoplasia of the iris (GARD, 2018b). Life-span implications include cataract formation, glaucoma, and corneal opacification (Hingorani & Moore, 2013).

Syndromes

Pierre Robin Sequence. Pierre Robin sequence (PRS) is characterized by micrognathia, glossoptosis, and airway obstruction (Breugem & Courtemanche, 2010). The reported prevalence of this disorder ranges from one in 2,000 to 3,000 live births; isolated PRS affects one in every 8,500 to 14,000 individuals (Kaufman et al., 2016; NIH, 2018d). Of infants diagnosed with PRS, approximately 37% have Stickler syndrome, an inherited disorder that involves mutations in the *COL2A1* and *COL11A1* genes. These genes normally modulate the formation of collagen and the vitreous humor within the eyes. Ocular manifestations include congenital high myopia (eyeball is very long from front to back), nearsightedness, cataracts, and glaucoma; an increased risk for retinal detachment is reported (Robin, Moran, & Ala-Kokko, 2017). Visual outcomes are dependent on treatment of refractive errors and management of retinal detachment.

Waardenburg Syndrome. Waardenberg syndrome (WS) is a group of genetic disorders that result in congenital sensorineural hearing loss, as well as the loss of eye, hair, and skin pigmentation (Chen et al., 2017; Waardenberg, 1951). There is an estimated prevalence of one in every 40,000 individuals, and the syndrome is classified into four different subtypes (NIH, 2018h). Mutations in the *WS1*, *WS4*, or *PAX3* genes disrupt melanocyte development and lead to abnormal eye pigmentation, as well as abnormal skin and hair pigmentation. Other ocular findings include dystopia canthorum, a lateral displacement of the inner canthum of the eyes (GARD, 2016b). Vision is usually normal in WS.

Cornelia de Lange Syndrome. Cornelia de Lange syndrome (CdLS) is a genetic condition resulting from mutations in the *NIPBL* (65%), *SMC1A*, *SMC3*, *HDAC8*, or *RAD21* (5%) genes. Experts estimate that CdLS affects one in every 10,000 to 30,000 newborns (NIH, 2018a). Most cases are de novo mutations; however, both autosomal dominant and x-linked inheritance patterns have been described (GARD, 2018a). Ocular findings include long eyelashes and a brushed-on appearance to the arch of the eyebrows (Madan-Khetarpal & Arnold, 2018). In addition, myopia, blepharitis (inflammation of the eyelids at the base of the eyelashes), nasolacrimal duct obstruction, and ptosis can occur (GARD, 2018a).

CHARGE Syndrome. CHARGE is an acronym for coloboma of the retina, heart abnormalities, choanal atresia, retarded growth and mental development, genital hypoplasia, and ear anomalies (Madan-Khetarpal & Arnold, 2018).

CHARGE occurs in one in 8,500 to 10,000 newborns (NLM, 2018a) and, in more than 50% of cases, is the result of mutations in the *CHD7* gene. Most cases of CHARGE result from de novo mutations; some are autosomal dominant disorders. Ocular findings include coloboma and microphthalmia (GARD, 2017a). Facial palsies associated with CHARGE syndrome may result in corneal scarring. Retinal detachment has also been reported (Tegay, 2018).

Neurocutaneous Disorders (Phakomatosis)

Neurofibromatosis Type 1. Neurofibromatosis type 1 (NF1) is an autosomal dominant hamartomatous disorder reported to affect one in 3,000 to 4,000 people (NIH, 2018c). In neonates, the presence of *six or more café-au-lait patches* should raise the index of suspicion for NF1 (Patterson, 2016). Ocular findings include pigmented iris hamartomas (Lisch nodules), retinal hamartomas, and optic nerve gliomas. Symptoms of an optic glioma include optic atrophy and vision loss, pain, and bulging of the eye (Islam & Roach, 2016). Life-span implications include the risk for cataract formation as early as during the teenage years (GARD, 2017c).

Sturge–Weber Syndrome. Sturge–Weber syndrome (SWS), a neurocutaneous disorder occurring in one in every 20,000 to 50,000 births, is characterized by port-wine stains of the upper trigeminal region of the face and underlying vascular malformations of the eye and leptomeninges (Greene, Taber, Ball, Padwa, & Mulliken, 2009; NIH, 2018e). SWS is caused by a spontaneous mutation in the *GNAQ* gene (Shirley et al., 2013). Glaucoma and vascular malformations of the conjunctiva, choroid retina, and sclera occur in SWS, with glaucoma being the most common finding (Satpathy, 2018). According to a seminal study of adults with SWS, the onset of glaucoma ranges from birth to 41 years of age (Sujansky & Conradi, 1995).

Tuberous Sclerosis Complex. Tuberous sclerosis complex (TSC) is a multisystem genetic disorder occurring in one in 6,000 individuals (NLM, 2018c). TSC has an autosomal dominant pattern of inheritance and affects males and females equally. Mutations in the *TSC1* or *TSC2* genes provoke the pathogenesis of *TSC* and clinical manifestations (NLM, 2018c). Retinal tumors occur in up to 53% of patients with tuberous sclerosis. These small gray-white infiltrating tumors are classified as astrocytic hamartomas and are usually slow growing and benign. Retinal detachment leading to blindness and vitreous seeding has been reported (Cruess & Sharma, 2018).

X-Linked Disorders

Norrie Disease. Norrie disease, an X-linked, recessive disorder, results from a mutation on the *NDP* gene on chromosome Xp11.4. The incidence is unknown. Norrie disease involves incomplete retinal vascularization, retinal dysgenesis, and incomplete regression of primary hyaloid structures. Bilateral retinal detachment is common and may be present at birth; the detachment manifests as a white pupil. Infantile symptoms include leukocoria (white pupillary reflex), iris atrophy, retrolental fibroplasia (excessive fibrous tissue behind the lens of the eye), vitreous hemorrhage, dysplastic retinae, retinal folds, and retinal detachments. The disease may progress to cataract, glaucoma, retinal schisis, and/or atrophy of the globe (Hartnett, 2014; Orge & Grigorian, 2015). Males affected by Norrie are considered legally blind and have no light perception.

Recessive Disorders

Leber Congenital Amaurosis. Leber congenital amaurosis (LCA) occurs in two to three per 100,000 newborns, and accounts for 10% to 18% of congenital blindness (Nelson & Olitsky, 2013). LCA is an autosomal recessive condition due to a mutation in the *CKBI* gene. LCA presents with poor vision, mainly attributed to poor light perception, nystagmus, and poor papillary reactions. Children with this condition often rub their eyes excessively, known as *blindism behavior*. Nystagmus presents after a few months and severe visual impairment develops during infancy (Hartnett, 2014; Orge & Gregorian, 2015).

MATERNAL HEALTH INFLUENCES
. . . .
Ocular Manifestations of Intrauterine Infections

Neonatal eyes can be affected by any of the TORCH (toxoplasmosis, other agents, rubella, cytomegalovirus (CMV), and herpes simplex) infections and can be transmitted via the placenta or via contact in the birth canal (Orge & Grigorian, 2015). The TORCH infections represent a preventable cause of childhood blindness. Infections occurring in the first 2 to 8 weeks of fetal life, representing organogenesis, are concerning for the development of the eyes. The most common ocular manifestation of congenital or prenatal infection is chorioretinal scaring (Teär Fahnehjelm, Olsson, Fahnehjelm, Lewensohn-Fuchs, & Karltorp, 2015). The sequelae of prenatal infections can result from teratogenesis in the form of cell death, cell growth alteration, or chromosomal damage.

Toxoplasmosis. The fetus is susceptible to infection with *Toxoplasma gondii* throughout gestation, during the first trimester (25%), second trimester (75%), and up until the last few weeks of pregnancy (>90%; Fraser & Diehl-Jones, 2015; Mets & Chhabra, 2008). Infections at earlier gestational ages are generally more severe, and greater than 80% of affected premature infants develop either learning or visual disabilities (Mets & Chhabra, 2008; Russell-Eggitt & Lightman, 1992).

Approximately one in 1,000 women will seroconvert during pregnancy with fetal transmission risk of 19% to 50% (Fraser & Diehl-Jones, 2015). The wide range of transmission rates may be dependent on the timing of maternal treatment with fetuses of mothers receiving treatment earlier

demonstrating significantly lower transmission rates (Peyron et al., 2017). Of the infected infants, 80% to 90% are symptomatic at birth (Fraser & Diehl-Jones, 2015). A delay of 8 weeks between maternal seroconversion and initiation of treatment has been identified as a risk factor for retinochoroiditis in the first 2 years of life in infants treated for congenital toxoplasmosis (Kieffer et al., 2008). In a 10-year follow-up study of children with congenital toxoplasmosis in France, 30% had at least one ocular manifestation with approximately 20% demonstrating vision loss (Wallon et al., 2014).

Neonatal and recurrent ophthalmologic findings are seen with congenital toxoplasmosis. *Chorioretinitis is the most common presenting manifestation at birth* and can present with leukocoria (Fraser & Diehl-Jones, 2015; Kodjikian et al., 2006; Mets & Chhabra, 2008; Remington, Klein, Wilson, Nizet, & Maldonado, 2011; Russell-Eggitt & Lightman, 1992). Neonatal and recurring manifestations include necrotizing chorioretinitis and associated retinal vasculitis resulting in chorioretinal scars (Orge & Gregarian, 2015). Recurrent infection can result in worsening visual outcomes. Inflammation in the tissues caused by cysts results in the damage seen. Associated pathologies, including strabismus, microphthalmia, microcornea, cataract, retinitis, vitritis, phthisis, retinal detachment, optic nerve atrophy, nystagmus, choroidal neovascularization, and glaucoma, occur more often in patients with chorioretinitis and frequently contribute to impaired visual function (Kodjikian et al., 2006; Mets & Chhabra, 2008; Park & Nam, 2013; Remington et al., 2011). Visual loss is a problem noted in long-term survivors.

Congenital Rubella Syndrome. Congenital rubella syndrome is now rare since the implementation of routine vaccination for rubella in 1969. Ocular insults related to congenital rubella syndrome are dependent on the timing of maternal infection (Fraser & Diehl-Jones, 2015). The incidence of congenital defects is highest in the first 11 weeks of gestation (70%), lower between weeks 12 and 20 (30%) of gestation, and nonexistent thereafter (Remington et al., 2011). Exposure during the first 2 months of gestation is associated with cataracts and glaucoma as maximum blood supply to the lens occurs between 2 and 11 weeks of gestation, whereas retinopathy is associated with exposure during the first 5 months (Mets & Chhabra, 2008; Russell-Eggitt & Lightman, 1992).

Common ocular findings in congenital rubella syndrome include microphthalmia, corneal haze, cataract, glaucoma, uveitis, and, most common, "salt and pepper" retinopathy (Jivraj, Rudnisky, Tambe, Tipple, & Tennant, 2014; Remington et al., 2011). Cataracts and retinopathy are the two most common ocular manifestations of congenital rubella and are often bilateral. Cataracts occur in approximately 30% of cases and are associated with the greatest risk for visual loss (Fraser & Diehl-Jones, 2015; Orge & Gregarian, 2015). Visual impairment is not generally associated with retinopathy unless neovascularization develops (Tamayo et al., 2013). Other reported ophthalmologic associations include dacryostenosis, edema to the cornea, keratoconus, iris hypoplasia, iris coloboma, aniso-coria, posterior synechiae, persistent pupillary membrane, mesodermal dysgenesis, optic atrophy, nystagmus, and strabismus (Mets & Chhabra, 2008).

Cytomegalovirus. Cytomegalovirus (CMV) transmission can occur transplacentally, via the birth canal or postnatally through breast milk or transfusion of CMV-positive blood transfusion (Coats, Demmler, Paysse, Du, & Libby, 2000). CMV is the most common congenital viral infection, occurring in 0.2% to 2.2% of all newborns (Fraser & Diehl-Jones, 2015; Remington et al., 2011). Primary maternal CMV infection carries a 24% to 75% risk for fetal infection, whereas transplacental infection is associated with a 24% risk for fetal infection during the first trimester (Pass & Anderson, 2014). The relative risk increases with advancing trimesters of pregnancy; recurrent infections are less likely to affect the fetus and are reported in 1% to 2.2% of cases (Bonalumi, Trapanese, Santamaria, D'Emidio, & Mobili, 2011). Symptomatic infection may be more likely in those exposed in the first half of pregnancy.

Infants are rarely symptomatic at birth and ocular involvement is rare but can include chorioretinitis, keratitis, cataract, conjunctivitis, microphthalmos, strabismus, cortical blindness, anterior chamber malformations with glaucoma, retinal necrosis and calcification, blindness, optic disk malformations, and optic atrophy (Fraser & Diehl-Jones, 2015; Orge & Gregorian, 2015; Remington et al., 2011). Chorioretinitis is the most common finding, present in 10% to 21% of symptomatic patients, and is evidenced by chorioretinal scars. Cortical visual impairment and optic atrophy are the most common etiology for common visual impairment in symptomatic patients. Asymptomatic patients rarely have visual impairments.

Herpes Simplex Virus. Congenital herpes simplex virus (HSV) can be acquired in utero, intrapartum, or postnatally. Passage through the birth canal is the most common method of acquisition of congenital HSV (86% of cases) with type 2 most commonly responsible (Orge & Gregorian, 2015). Intrauterine infection is rare and estimated at one in 100,000 births or three of every 100 infected infants (Marquez, Levy, Munoz, & Palazzi, 2011; Remington et al., 2011).

Congenital infection with HSV is associated with blepharoconjunctivitis, keratitis, iritis, chorioretinitis with vitritis, corneal dendrites and ulcers, cataracts, optic atrophy, and bilateral macular scars without other ocular signs (Marquez et al., 2011; Orge & Gregorian, 2015; Ramasubramanian & Johnston, 2011; Remington et al., 2011). Lid, conjunctival, and corneal lesions may occur with acute ocular involvement. Timing of conjunctivitis onset is usually 0 to 14 days of age, but retinitis may not be noted until over 1 month of age. Late ocular sequelae of congenital HSV infection include cortical blindness, cortical visual loss, squint, chorioretinal scars, optic atrophy, corneal scarring, and cataract. Keratoconjunctivitis may lead to chorioretinitis, cataracts, and retinal detachment.

Syphilis. Most cases of congenital syphilis are transmitted vertically during the prenatal period but can also occur perinatally and postnatally. The likelihood of vertical transmission increases with advancing gestational age and with early maternal stages of syphilis rather than late latent infections. Approximately 33% of infants are asymptomatic at birth, but develop signs and symptoms later in life (Remington et al., 2011).

Neonatal ocular manifestations of congenital syphilis are rare and include chorioretinitis; eyelid skin rash; orbital and intraocular inflammation; interstitial keratitis; CN involvement; "salt and pepper" fundus; uveitis; glaucoma; cataract; and central visual pathway involvement, including optic nerve atrophy and pupillomotor disturbances (Orge & Gregorian, 2015; Remington et al., 2011). Chancres of the eyelid are rare. Keratitis is seen in untreated children over 5 years old who present with acute photophobia, lacrimation, corneal edema, and iritis.

Human Immunodeficiency Virus. Transmission of HIV can occur prenatally, perinatally, or postnatally through breastfeeding. In the United States, perinatal HIV transmission rates have decreased to 2% or less due to universal HIV testing, antiretroviral treatment during pregnancy, and avoidance of breastfeeding in HIV-positive mothers. Without intervention, the vertical transmission rate is estimated at 25% to 30%. Infants with congenital HIV are often asymptomatic at birth; if present, symptoms are generally nonspecific and subtle (Remington et al., 2011).

Ocular findings, mainly chorioretinitis, are generally associated with concurrent infections, including HSV, CMV, and toxoplasmosis (Orge & Gregorian, 2015; Remington et al., 2011). Loss of vision is low unless complicated by a concurrent infection.

Ocular Manifestations of Maternal Substance Abuse

The fetal eyes are not immune to the effects of maternal substance abuse. Substances, such as alcohol, cocaine, and tobacco, all have been associated with teratogenic effects on the developing eyes.

Fetal Alcohol Syndrome. The incidence of fetal alcohol syndrome (FAS) ranges between 0.2 to seven per every 1,000 live births in the United States (Centers for Disease Control and Prevention, 2002; O'Leary et al., 2015). The exact mechanism for the teratogenic effects of alcohol on the embryogenic eye are not known, but may be related to the effects of ethyl alcohol or acetaldehyde, its metabolite. The type of insult may determine the timing of exposure, with insults to the optic nerve beginning at week 6 of gestation through birth and retinal vascularization beginning after week 16 of gestation. Environmental factors, genetics, timing of exposure, and dose may all play a part in and help explain the variation in the ophthalmologic expression of FAS (Vernescu, Adams, & Courage, 2012).

Ocular findings associated with FAS include refractive errors, strabismus, anterior segment abnormalities, cataracts, ptosis, long eyelashes, telecanthus, and optic nerve hypoplasia (ONH; Miller et al., 1984). Studies report approximately 25% to 48% of infants manifest with accompanying ONH; these estimates may be falsely inflated due to limited sample sizes (Garcia-Filion & Borchert, 2013).

Cocaine. Cocaine use is often associated with polysubstance abuse and it is therefore difficult to tease out the effects of cocaine alone. Ocular manifestations associated with prenatal exposure to cocaine have not changed over the past several decades and include optic nerve abnormalities/atrophy, delayed visual maturation, and prolonged eyelid edema (Good, Ferriero, Golabi, & Kobori, 1992; Peragallo, Biousse, & Newman, 2013). In a study of 55 children prenatally exposed to cocaine, strabismus was significantly higher in the cocaine-exposed group in comparison to 100 controls when comparing full-birth-weight infants ($p < 0.05$). However, these differences did not persist in low-birth-weight infants. ROP, although rare, was also associated with prenatal cocaine exposure in the same study (Peragallo et al., 2013).

Tobacco. Prepregnancy smoking rates range from 2.6% to 32.9% within the United States, smoking at any time during pregnancy is reported among 8.4% of pregnant women, and third-trimester smoking is reported in approximately 10.9% of pregnant women (Curtin & Matthews, 2016).

Prenatal exposure to cigarette smoking is a risk factor for the esotropia and exotropia type of strabismus, refractive errors, and ROP. The ROP association is significant for progression to stages 3 or 4 disease (see the section "Retinopathy of Prematurity" later in the chapter). This is likely secondary to fetal retinal and intraocular muscle sensitivity. A dose-dependent relationship between smoking and ocular disturbances in infancy and childhood has been reported; however, further research is indicated (Fernandes, Yang, Li, & Cheikh Ismail, 2015).

COMMON PROBLEMS WITH IMPLICATIONS ACROSS THE LIFE SPAN

Early detection and treatment of congenital eye disorders is critical to optimize vision development. Although congenital eye disorders can be isolated, they are often part of a broader genetic syndrome and frequently accompany brain malformations. The timing of embryonic insult determines the type of eye abnormalities; disruption of the optic field occurs in the earliest embryonic stage, and includes anophthalmia, whereas abnormalities of various components of the eye occur in later embryonic stages, and include microphthalmia (Figure 13.8) and coloboma (Schoenwolf et al., 2015). Several common ocular problems are discussed in this section of the chapter.

Congenital Dacryostenosis

Congenital dacryostenosis involves narrowing or obstruction of the nasolacrimal duct (Figure 13.9). This defect affects approximately 20% of newborns (Orge & Gregorian, 2015; Zitelli, McIntire, & Nowalk, 2018). The obstruction causes a stagnant pool of tears in the lacrimal sac that leads to chronic or recurrent inflammation, or dacryocystitis. Massage of the lacrimal duct results in resolution of the blockage in more than 50% of cases. No common long-term complications are reported (Hussein, Miller, & Steinkuller, 2014).

Primary Congenital Glaucoma

Congenital glaucoma is a primary cause for blindness in children. This condition involves uncontrolled ocular pressure. The incidence of congenital glaucoma is one in 10,000 to 20,000 infants. A male prevalence is observed, as males account for approximately 65% of all cases of congenital glaucoma.

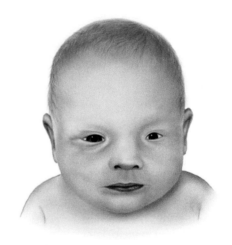

Figure 13.8 Microphthalmia.

Source: Centers for Disease Control and Prevention. (2015). Facts about anophthalmia/microphthalmia. Retrieved from https://www.cdc.gov/ncbddd/birthdefects/anophthalmia-microphthalmia.html

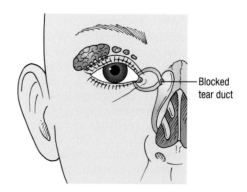

Blocked tear duct

Figure 13.9 Congenital dacryostenosis.

Three subtypes of primary congenital glaucoma affect children: congenital glaucoma (the focus of this discussion), infantile glaucoma (1 to 3 years of age at onset), and juvenile glaucoma (4 years to adulthood; Aponte, Diehl, & Mohney, 2010). Most cases are a result of spontaneous mutation; however, some reports suggest an autosomal recessive or polygenic inheritance pattern account for onset of the disease process. Secondary glaucoma is the result of a spontaneous mutation or a manifestation of a genetic disorder such as SWS. Last, acquired glaucoma occurs in an otherwise healthy eye due to pharmacologic treatment, trauma, surgery, or inflammation (Aponte et al., 2010).

The pathogenesis of congenital glaucoma involves an obstruction to aqueous flow that increases intraocular pressure. The obstruction may occur secondary to trabeculodysgenesis, or angle maldevelopment. The iris abnormally inserts into the surface of the trabeculum in two possible ways: (a) flat insertion at or anterior to the scleral spur, or (b) concave insertion with the plane of the iris posterior to the scleral spur. Alternatively, the pathogenesis may involve uncontrolled ocular pressure secondary to drainage abnormalities (Figure 13.10).

Common clinical manifestations include a cloudy cornea and progressive myopia. A corneal diameter of greater than 12 mm (enlarged cornea) with corneal haze, tearing, blepharospasm, and photophobia should raise suspicion for congenital glaucoma (Mansoor, Mansoor, & Ahmed, 2016; Orge & Gregorian, 2015). An enlarged eye should raise concern for later infantile glaucoma, which needs to be treated quickly to preserve visual development.

Life-span implications are primarily associated with untreated glaucoma. Photophobia with loss of vision may occur due to stretching of the eye from increased intraocular pressure. The age at onset and time to diagnosis will affect visual outcome (Orge & Gregorian, 2015). Delayed diagnosis after 1 year of age is associated with poor visual acuity across the life span; congenital glaucoma accounts for 0.01% to 0.04% of all cases of blindness (Mansoor et al., 2016).

Colobomas

Colobomas are one of the most common congenital abnormalities of the eyelid and/or structures of the eye, occurring in approximately one in every 10,000 newborns. A coloboma is a defect in structure and can occur in the eyelid or structures of the eye, including the iris, lens, retina or optic nerve.

Eyelid colobomas range from partial-thickness to full-thickness defects (Olitsky et al., 2016). The extent of the defect can range from a small notch on the lid border to involvement of the entire length of the lid. The pathogenesis of eyelid colobomas involves failed closure of the optic fissure. The etiology is unknown, but may be a result of adhesion failure of lid folds resulting in lack of growth or the effect of amniotic bands; epigenetic influences; or environmental factors, including alcohol consumption during pregnancy (Orge & Gregorian, 2015).

Eyelid colobomas may prevent complete lid closure and manifest with exposure of the cornea. This leads to thickening, opacification, infection, ulceration, and/or perforation of the exposed cornea.

Colobomas involving the lower aspect of the iris create a "keyhole" appearance of the pupil (Figure 13.11). Defects involving the pupil typically do not derange vision; however, visual difficulties, including refractive errors and light sensitivity, occur when the retina, optic nerve, or macula is involved (Mansoor et al., 2016; Orge & Gregorian, 2015).

Lens Abnormalities

Congenital Cataracts. Similar to congenital glaucoma, congenital cataracts are a major cause for blindness during the childhood years. The incidence of congenital cataracts

Normal aqueous flow

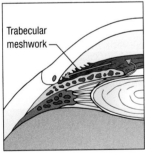

Obstructed aqueous flow

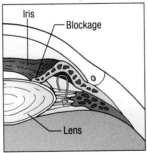

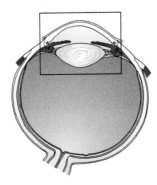

Figure 13.10 Normal and abnormal iris insertion with congenital glaucoma.

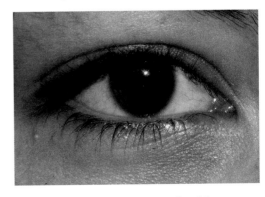

Figure 13.11 "Keyhole" appearance with coloboma.

is three per 10,000 live births (Mansoor et al., 2016). Cataracts can have a hereditary, chromosomal, metabolic, traumatic, or infectious etiology (Mansoor et al., 2016; Orge & Gregorian, 2015; Schoenwolf et al., 2015). The majority (70%) of cataracts are isolated disorders, whereas approximately 8% to 25% of all cataracts are inherited and 15% are a manifestation of a complex syndrome such as neurofibromatosis (Yi, Yun, Li, Xu, & Pan, 2011).

Congenital cataracts involve an opacity or abnormality within the structure of the lens that clouds its appearance. Clinical manifestations of cataracts are dependent on the timing during organogenesis. Insults occurring early in embryogenesis result in opacification in the center of the lens (Figure 13.12). Insults occurring later in fetal development cause the emergence of ring-like opacifications surrounded by central and peripheral clear zones. Alternatively, recent damage results in peripheral opacifications near the surface of the lens. Congenital or infantile cataracts may be subtle and likewise overlooked. In these cases, diagnosis is rendered secondary to abnormal loss of visual function or white pupillary reflex. Presenting symptoms include absent red reflex, nystagmus, and inability to fix and follow.

Congenital and infantile cataracts account for 10% of childhood blindness worldwide (Orge & Gregorian, 2015). Prognosis for vision is poorer when only one eye is involved. Visual prognosis is improved if treatment is initiated before 2 months of age (Mansoor et al., 2016).

Optic Nerve Hypoplasia

Optic nerve hypoplasia (ONH), the most common congenital disk anomaly, involves an abnormally small, underdeveloped optic nerve with decreased nerve axons (Figure 13.13). ONH occurs in approximately 15% to 25% of infants and experts posit that this once rare disease is on the rise (Kaur, Jain, Sodhi, Rastogi, & Kamlesh, 2013). There are no genetic correlations; this disease is only known to be sporadic. No gender prevalence is reported.

The pathogenesis of ONH involves an interruption in normal embryonic and fetal development between weeks 6 and 16 of gestation. Experts posit that this disrupted development occurs secondary to failure of ganglion cells, a malformed chiasm, or due to abnormal stretching of the optic nerves (Kaur et al., 2013). A sporadic genetic alteration or intrauterine shock (see Chapter 1) may explain ONH. Other risk factors are summarized in Table 13.4.

Clinical manifestations are usually subtle in the newborn period and through early childhood. Unless other hypothalamic dysfunction is noted during early childhood, the defect is typically identified in early childhood with the onset of routine clinical ophthalmic examinations. This defect manifests with a gray or pale optic nerve head. In addition, the optic disk may be bordered by a yellowish, mottled parapapillary halo surrounded by an increase or decrease in pigmentation. An altered pupillary light reflex may be evident. Visual acuity may be decreased (Kaur et al., 2013).

Prognosis ranges from 20/20 vision to no light perception; visual-evoked responses range from normal to fully extinguished. ONH is associated with astigmatism, nystagmus, amblyopia, and visual field and associated nerve fiber bundle defects (Al-Mohtaseb & Foroozan, 2012; Orge & Gregorian, 2015).

Retinoblastoma

Retinoblastoma is the most common intraocular tumor in children, accounting for 11% of all pediatric tumors diagnosed within the first year of life. It occurs at a rate of approximately one case per 15,000 to 20,000 live births (Rao, Goldstein, & Tu, 2014). These neoplasms arise within the developing retina as a result of a mutation in both alleles of the *RB1*, or retinoblastoma tumor suppressor gene, on chromosome 13 (Mendoza & Grossniklaus, 2015; Ortiz & Dunkel, 2016). The majority (75%) of cases are nonhereditary and unilateral. The remainder of retinoblastomas are inherited or a result of gene mutation, and typically affect

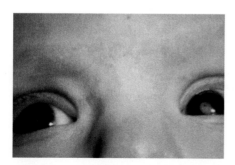

Figure 13.12 Congenital cataracts. This photograph shows congenital cataracts in a child's eyes secondary to congenital rubella syndrome.

Source: Centers for Disease Control and Prevention. (1976). Public health image library, ID #4284. Retrieved from https://phil.cdc.gov/Details.aspx?pid=4284

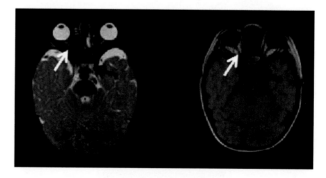

Figure 13.13 Optic nerve hypoplasia. Arrows denote optic nerve fiber thinning.

Source: Pensiero, S., Cecchini, P., Michieletto, P., Pelizzo, G., Madonia, M., & Parentin, F. (2011). Congenital aplasia of the optic chiasm and esophageal atresia: A case report. *Journal of Medical Case Reports, 5*, 335. doi:10.1186/1752-1947-5-335

TABLE 13.4 Common Risk Factors for Optic Nerve Hypoplasia

Maternal	Fetal
• Addictive behaviors (smoking, recreational drugs, alcohol) • Anemia • Cytomegalovirus infection • Depression • Gestational diabetes • Metabolic disorder • Young primigravida	• Low birth weight • Intrauterine growth restriction • Prematurity • Twin–twin transfusion syndrome

NOTE: Metabolic conditions may include hypothyroidism, hypocortisolism, panhypopituitarism, diabetes insipidus, and hyperprolactinemia.

Source: From Kaur, S., Jain, S., Sodhi, H. B. S., Rastogi, A., & Kamlesh.(2013). Optic nerve hypoplasia. *Oman Journal of Ophthalmology, 6*(2), 77–82. doi:10.4103/0974-620X.116622

both eyes. Retinoblastoma usually presents in children less than 5 years of age with leukocoria or strabismus.

The pathogenesis of retinoblastoma involves tumor formation near the photoreceptors and subsequent extension into the vitreous cavity of the eye. The tumor manifests as a flesh-like, heterogeneous structure that rapidly proliferates and fills the posterior chamber of the eye (Figure 13.14). The tumor often invades the choroid, providing ample vascular supply and margin for expansion. Metastasis into the sclera and orbit, ciliary body and lymph nodes, or optic nerve and intracranial cavity has been reported.

Clinical manifestations during infancy are often noticed by way of photographs. Parents or caregivers may observe leukocoria, or a white-colored reflection from the retina. Other clinical manifestations include strabismus and glaucoma, which present with advanced cases of retinoblastoma secondary to tumor size and increased intraocular pressure (Orkin et al., 2015). On average, children with bilateral disease present 9 months earlier than those with unilateral disease. Life-span implications are contingent on the type and severity of retinoblastoma; cases that involve metastasis into intracranial structures are associated with high mortality (Orkin et al., 2015).

Rhabdomyosarcoma

Rhabdomyosarcoma (RMS), a soft-tissue sarcoma, is the most common orbit malignancy in children. The mean age of onset is 6 to 8 years. Most cases of RMS are not familial, but rather are the result of sporadic mutations and epigenetic influences causing hypermethylation of genes tasked with coding proteins for skeletal muscle development.

RMS has two subtypes: the more common embryonal type that is less aggressive and the less common but more aggressive alveolar type. Common ocular manifestations of RMS include proptosis and diplopia. Ocular tumors, including but not limited to RMS, often demonstrate rapid proliferation causing bulging and displacement of the affected eye (Figure 13.15). Hemorrhage, pain, and excessive tearing may also be

Figure 13.14 Retinoblastoma. Gross appearance of leukocoria (A) with an enucleated eye; (B) maximally dilated pupil shows large retinoblastoma filling the posterior chamber, vitreous seeds, and retinal detachment.

Source: Rodriguez-Galindo, C., Orbach, D. B., & VanderVeen, D. (2015). Retinoblastoma. *Pediatric Clinics of North America, 62*(1), 201–223. doi:10.1016/j.pcl.2014.09.014

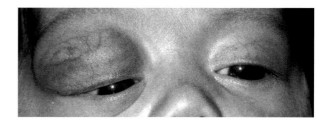

Figure 13.15 Orbital mass in small child (rhabdomyosarcoma is most common).

Source: Goddard, K. (Ed.). (2008). Ophthalmology for the oncologist. *Pediatric Oncology Education Materials.* Retrieved from http://www.pedsoncologyeducation.com/OpthalmologyProptosis.asp

present (Rao et al., 2014). Life-span implications of embryonal RMS involve age of onset and metastasis to the lungs. Failure-free survival, or the length of time a treated infant or child survives without disease progression, is estimated at 57% for those diagnosed during infancy, 81% for children diagnosed between age 1 and 9 years, and 67% for those diagnosed after age 10 (Orkin et al., 2015).

Neuroblastoma

Neuroblastoma is a common solid tumor found in infants and children and arises from neural crest cells. It is the most common cancer in children; approximately 7% of all pediatric cancers are attributed to neuroblastoma. Risk factors include autosomal dominant inheritance as well as Turner syndrome; Noonan syndrome; neuro-cardio-facial syndromes, including Costello syndrome; and overgrowth disorders such as Beckwith–Weidemann syndrome (Orkin et al., 2015). Epigenetic factors may implicate the formation of a neuroblastoma, as deficient methylation has been associated with the onset of non-Wilms tumors.

The pathogenesis of neuroblastoma is poorly understood. However, similar to other ocular tumors, neuroblastomas are thought to arise secondary to epigenetic influences causing abnormal proliferation of embryonal cells. Tumors present as small, blue-colored, dense cellular masses. Tumors may appear anywhere that involves sympathetic innervation, including the orbit, neck, chest, pelvis, and abdomen. Similar to RMS, orbital symptoms include bulging of the eye and bruising around the eyes (Rao et al., 2014). A 5-year survival rate of 50% is reported for those diagnosed with the metastatic form of the disease (Orkin et al., 2015).

Strabismus

Strabismus, a neuromuscular abnormality, presents as the misalignment of gaze and is a result of abnormal extraocular muscles or their innervation (Schoenwolf et al., 2015). Strabismus can occur as horizontal deviations, esodeviations or exodeviations, or rarely, vertical deviations. Strabismus can be either concomitant, with deviation the same regardless of gaze position, or incomitant, variable deviation as gaze is shifted up, down, or to the side (Orge & Gregorian, 2015).

The most common infantile forms of concomitant strabismus include congenital exotropia, early intermittent exotropia, congenital/infantile esotropia, early accommodative esotropia, and sensory esotropia. Accommodative esotropia occurs secondary to exaggerated accommodative efforts, whereas sensory strabismus is due to vision loss in one or both eyes (Orge & Gregorian, 2015).

Impaired globe movements secondary to muscle restriction or weakness result in noncomitant strabismus. Etiologies for noncomitant strabismus include fractures, orbital tumors, CN palsies, and congenital myasthenia gravis (Orge & Gregorian, 2015).

Two situations occur that can confuse the diagnosis of strabismus. Pseudostrabismus can present as esotropia and exotropia. A large nasal bridge and prominent epicanthal folds can create the appearance of pseudoesotropia (Figure 13.16). In addition, immaturity of foveal fixation and binocularity and the establishment of firm control of eye movement can also create a small misalignment of one or both eyes (Orge & Gregorian, 2015).

Figure 13.16 Pseudoestropia.

Pseudostrabismus is self-limiting and presents no long-term visual deficits. True strabismus requires early corrective surgery (within 4–6 months) after correction of refractive errors and any associated amblyopia in order to improve binocular cooperation (Orge & Gregorian, 2015).

Nystagmus

Nystagmus, involuntary eye movements, usually present as rapid, rhythmic, and repetitious movements. This disorder affects four of every 10,000 live births (Lambert & Lyons, 2017). Risk factors include sensory abnormalities and diseases, including albinism, achromatopsia, and congenital cataracts.

The pathogenesis of nystagmus is not well understood. Clinical manifestations include periods of slow and rapid eye movements. Essentially, infants are unable to hold a gaze; slow eye movements evolve into rapid fluttering movements away from an initial focal point (Lambert & Lyons, 2017). The fluttering movements permit refocusing of the eye to the focal point. Lifespan implications are significant and include visual degeneration, psychosocial dysfunction secondary to altered self-image, and driving limitations among older adolescents.

Amblyopia

Often called *lazy eye*, amblyopia is the reduction in vision from abnormal visual development during infancy and early childhood. For at least the past decade, amblyopia has been regarded as the most common cause of monocular vision loss in children and young adults (Doshi & Rodriguez, 2007; Lambert & Lyons, 2017). The incidence is estimated at 1% to 5%, with approximately 12 million children affected by uncorrected amblyopia (World Health Organization, n.d.). Risk factors include prematurity, low birth weight, visual deprivation through early childhood, family history of amblyopia, and strabismus (Chou, Dana, & Bougatsos, 2011).

Amblyopia likely results secondary to strabismus (ocular misalignment is the most common risk factor), anisometropia (uncorrected refractive errors between both eyes), opacities (cataracts), or visual deprivation (often caused by eyelid drooping; Chou et al., 2011). More specific, refractive amblyopia results from two types of refractive errors: Anisometropic amblyopia occurs when there is an unequal refractive error that prevents the normal fusing of an image seen by each eye; more common, bilateral hyperopia (farsightedness) also causes refractive amblyopia. Deprivation amblyopia results from blocked visual axis information received by the retina during a critical period of eye development.

The most notable clinical manifestation in young children is eye rubbing observed secondary to abnormal processing of visual images, secondary to loss of visual acuity. On exam, the cornea, lens, retina, and optic disk appear normal.

Early childhood life-span implications include difficulty with participation in athletics, psychosocial dysfunction secondary to teasing from peers, and altered depth perception. Although the incidence is reported to be less than 2%, vision loss in the affected eye can significantly impair visual acuity and potentially precede blindness (Chou et al., 2011).

Blindness

Loss of vision in the neonatal population can result from a number of causes, including congenital abnormalities affecting the optic nerve or brain, genetic syndromes, trauma, infection, hypoxia, and ROP. In developed countries, cerebral visual impairment and optic nerve abnormalities are the most common causes of severe visual impairment. Retinopathy, glaucoma, cataracts, and injury are the most common preventable causes of blindness in developed countries (Solebo, Teoh, & Rahi, 2017).

Neonatal Conjunctivitis

Ophthalmia neonatorum, conjunctivitis occurring in the first month of life, is most commonly the result of infection with *Staphylococcus aureus, Staphylococcus epidermidis, Streptococcus pneumoniae,* or *Moraxella catarrhalis*

(Richards & Guzman-Cottrill, 2010). Infections caused by *Chlamydia trachomatis, Neisseria gonorrhea,* or HSV can be acquired through the birth canal.

Chlamydia trachomatis. Conjunctivitis caused by maternal *Chlamydia trachomatis* infection usually presents at 5 to 14 days after birth with edema, erythema of the conjunctiva, and copious thin watery discharge that progresses to mucopurulent drainage (Richards & Guzman-Cottrill, 2010). Untreated maternal chlamydia infection results in 30% to 40% of exposed neonates developing conjunctivitis.

Neisseria gonorrhea. Conjunctivitis caused by *Neisseria gonorrhea* usually presents within 24 to 48 hours of birth with severe eyelid and conjunctival edema and profuse purulent discharge. *N. gonorrhea* may cause a more serious infection than conjunctivitis through penetration of the corneal epithelium, resulting in corneal perforation if untreated.

Herpes Simplex Virus. Conjunctivitis caused by HSV typically presents between days 6 to 10 of postnatal age and may be the only sign of HSV skin, eye, and mouth disease. Symptoms of HSV conjunctivitis include serous or serosanginous discharge. Classic vesicular lesions may be noted along the eyelid margin, but are not always present (Richards & Guzman-Cottrill, 2010).

Viral Conjunctivitis. Viral conjunctivitis is less common in the neonatal population compared to older children. The most common cause of this self-limiting condition is adenovirus (Richard & Guzman-Cottrill, 2010).

Chemical Conjunctivitis. Chemical conjunctivitis can occur following instillation of medication. Silver nitrate was a common cause of redness and eye discharge in newborns. Chemical irritation is less common following instillation of erythromycin ointment.

Ocular Trauma

Eye-related birth injuries are more common with operative deliveries and include orbital fracture and corneal lacerations. Subconjunctival and retinal hemorrhages are common with precipitous or vacuum-assisted delivery, or when the umbilical cord is wrapped tightly around the neck. Owing to the protective bony prominence surrounding the eye, traumatic eye injury is relatively uncommon in neonates. Retinal hemorrhages increase the risk of visual impairment if the optic nerve is involved (Akangire & Carter, 2016). A focal globular hemorrhage at the posterior pole of the eye, as well as severe retinal hemorrhage, is associated with shaken baby syndrome. Severe hemorrhage may involve the covering (sheath) of the optic nerve. Shaken baby syndrome should be considered among infants who present with the aforementioned findings.

Retinopathy of Prematurity

ROP, first reported in 1942 and labeled *retrolental fibro-plasia (RLF)*, was the consequence of supplemental oxygen use. Oxygen therapy inhibited normal retinal vascular proliferation among premature infants, leading to retinal detachment, and, in some cases, blindness (Terry, 1942). In the 1950s, as awareness of causative factors for ROP increased, the supplemental use of oxygen became more restrictive; this practice extends into modern times. Although the judicious use of oxygen has led to a decrease in the incidence of ROP, an optimum saturation range remains unknown (Sun, Hellström, & Smith, 2015). Efforts to narrow the oxygenation saturation (SaO_2) range endorsed by the American Academy of Pediatrics (85%–95%) so as to reduce ROP and avoid a consequential increase in mortality have been subject to debate.

The incidence of ROP is highest among premature infants born at less than 28 weeks of gestation. The incidence has increased due to increased survival of infants at lower gestational ages. This is balanced somewhat by the proliferation of neonatal intensive care (Sun et al., 2015). In the United States, 1,300 infants suffer vision loss and 500 infants experience severe visual impairment due to ROP each year (Asano & Dray, 2014). ROP remains the leading cause of blindness in developed countries (Asano & Dray, 2014).

The primary risk factors for ROP include prematurity, low birth weight, and postnatal oxygen exposure. The use of supplemental oxygen increases damaging reactive oxygen species (ROS). Premature infants have fewer antioxidants to counteract the ROS; the result is endothelial cell damage, apoptosis, and capillary constriction (Asano & Dray, 2014). Infants born at <33 weeks of gestation exhibit decreased circulating growth factors, which contribute to an increased risk for ROP. Hyperglycemia and insulin use have also been implicated in the incidence of ROP (Sun et al., 2015). Secondary risk factors in the development of ROP include hyperoxia, apnea, sepsis, blood transfusions, antioxidant deficiency, and patent ductus arteriosus (Table 13.5; Shah et al., 2016).

Blood vessels that supply the retina begin to develop at the optic disk at 15 to 16 weeks of gestation; this process is stimulated by the release of vascular endothelial growth factor (VEGF) and insulin growth factor (IGF-1). The retinal vasculature moves in a predictable pattern from the optic nerve to the periphery; at 36 and 40 weeks of gestation the vessels reach the nasal and temporal edge of the retina, respectively (Asano & Dray, 2014). In utero, VEGF controls the proliferation of the retinal vasculature as well as its regression. However, premature birth halts the proliferation of the retinal vasculature and the normal, physiologic expression of VEGF. This predisposes the premature infant to abnormal retinal development.

Phase-1 ROP. The development of ROP is explained as a series of two sequential phases. Phase-1 ROP encompasses the cessation of normal growth of blood vessels, which occurs at birth. As a result, VGEF and IGF-1 levels drop. Concurrent with the onset of phase 1, and in the immediate window after birth, is a brief and possibly subtle period of postnatal hypoxia, as the infant adjusts to extrauterine life. This elicits significant upregulation of VEGF with a slower increase in IGF-1 concentrations. Subsequently, and throughout the early postnatal period, any exposure to physiologic stressors, including illness, stress, or persistent fluctuations in oxygen levels, can encourage additional abnormal downregulation and upregulation of VEGF concentrations. Abnormally high saturation levels (in comparison to normal intrauterine $paO_2 < 50$ mmHg) downregulate VEGF and favor vasoobliteration, whereas periods of hypoxia upregulate VEGF and encourage abnormal vasoproliferation.

Phase-2 ROP. Phase-2 ROP involves one of two possible pathways: spontaneous regression of ROP, or progression to pathologic proliferative retinopathy. Spontaneous regression involves the return of VEGF levels to normal, physiologic concentrations. This facilitates normal, progressive retinal vascularization and marks the resolution of ROP.

Alternatively, pathologic proliferation is modulated by markedly elevated increases in factors, including VEGF, erythropoietin (EPO), IGF-1, and long-chain polyunsaturated fatty acids (LCPUFA; Eldweik & Mantagos, 2016). Recall that VEGF and EPO are oxygen-regulated angiogenic growth factors. IGF-1 is essential for normal growth of blood vessels (among other tissues), and omega LCPUFA is crucial for retinal development (Sun et al., 2015). The end result is a retina that is metabolically active, yet poorly vascularized. Neovascularization provides poor oxygenation to the retina, leading to disease progression and the potential for retinal detachment and blindness.

Classification of ROP. ROP is classified according to the International Classification of Retinopathy of Prematurity (ICROP) by zone, extent of disease severity, and stage. ROP begins with the cessation of normal retinal neuronal and vascular development. Vessel growth may become pathologic and result in neovascularization (pathologic vessel growth) of the retina.

TABLE 13.5 Common Risk Factors for Retinopathy of Prematurity

- Prematurity
- Supplemental use of oxygen
- Low birth weight
- Hyperglycemia and insulin use
- Apnea
- Sepsis
- Blood transfusions
- Antioxidant deficiency
- Patent ductus arteriosus

ROP zone, or location, of the disease is distinguished by dividing the retina into three concentric areas centered on the optic disk. The more posterior (earlier zone) the disease occurs, the more severe the disease. There are three zones used to describe the location of progressive vascular development. Zone 1 is the most posterior zone, defined by a circle around the optic nerve head. Zone 1 represents the most immature vascularization; as such, zone 1 is considered the area of most concern and is associated with increased disease severity (Shah et al., 2016). Zone 2 consists of a concentric circle around zone 1 and is twice the radius of zone 1. Zone 2 extends to the ora serrata nasally. Zone 3 encompasses the remaining crescent-shaped retina and extends to the temporal side (Table 13.6; González et al., 2017; Sharma & VanderVeen, 2017).

The extent of disease is expressed as clock hours of retinal involvement. The clock hours are separated into 30-degree segments. For advance practice nurses, the temporal side of the right eye corresponds with 3 o'clock, whereas the temporal side of the left eye corresponds with 9 o'clock.

Furthermore, ROP is divided into five stages (Table 13.7). Stages 1 to 3 describe increasing degrees of abnormal blood vessel growth. Stage 1 consists of a flat demarcation line at the junction of the vascular and avascular retina. Stage 2 involves a slightly elevated ridge of fibrovascular tissue. In Stage 3, the vessels grow into the vitrea (clear jelly that fills the eyeball) and may be severe enough to cause partial (stage 4) or complete (stage 5) retinal detachment (Sharma & VanderVeen, 2017; Sun et al., 2015). *Plus disease* describes venous dilation and arterial tortuosity that increase the risk for retinal detachment (Sharma & VanderVeen, 2017; Sun et al., 2015). Plus disease is evidence of active and progressive disease. Aggressive posterior ROP (AP ROP) is an additional classification used to describe a more severe retinopathy. AP ROP involves a very marked neovascularization in addition to plus disease and can progress very quickly to stage 5 ROP and blindness (González et al., 2017; Sharma & VanderVeen, 2017).

ROP regresses spontaneously in over 90% of cases; the remaining cases require treatment to avoid negative sequelae (Asano & Dray, 2014). Stage 1 or stage 2 ROP is considered mild and is likely to resolve spontaneously. Even with spontaneous regression of mild ROP, neural deficits are possible and include loss of photoreceptor function (Sun et al., 2015). Premature infants with stage 1 or stage 2 ROP have only a slightly increased risk for optical conditions, including myopia/hyperopia, strabismus, and amblyopia, in comparison to their full-term counterparts. Stage 4 and stage 5 ROP carry a poor prognosis; when untreated, retinal detachment leads to blindness. ROP that develops in the most immature zone 1 is associated with poor prognosis. Onset of ROP in zone 2 is more likely to resolve spontaneously and achieve good prognosis. Preterm infants who do not develop ROP by 36 to 42 weeks postmenstrual age are at low risk for the development of ROP (Sun et al., 2015).

CONCLUSION

Embryologic development of the eye begins at 4 weeks of gestation. Sensory innervation of the eye is mediated by several CNs to allow a response, usually blinking or tearing, to pain and temperature. Sensory input—the transduction of light into electrical signals—is provided by the photoreceptor cells (rods and cones). The development of visual milestones begins at 16 weeks of gestation and continues on throughout early childhood. Factors, such as abnormal visual conditions, prematurity, and poor nutrition, can affect the physiologic maturation of the eyes. Genetic aberrations, intrauterine infections, and maternal substance abuse all have associated ocular sequelae, whereas ROP remains a leading cause of blindness. The prompt identification and treatment of common eye problems is essential to optimize visual development.

TABLE 13.6 Zones of Retinopathy of Prematurity	
Zones	**Visual Description**
Zone 1: Twice the radius from optic nerve to macula (fovea centralis) **Zone 2:** Nasal edge of zone 1 to temporal equator **Zone 3:** Residual crescent anterior to zone 2	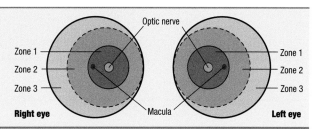

Source: Drawing courtesy of Amanda Smith, MSN, NNP-BC

TABLE 13.7 Stages of Retinopathy of Prematurity

Stage	Definition	Visual Description	Life-Span Implications
1	**Line of demarcation** separates avascular and vascularized portions of the retina	Lens; Avascular retina; Demarcation line; Vascular retina	Likely to resolve spontaneously, loss of photoreceptor cell function possible, slightly increased risk for myopia/hyperopia, strabismus, and amblyopia
2	The line of demarcation develops into fibrous **ridge** of tissue, often with small tuffs of new blood vessels	Demarcation line widens and thickens, forming a ridge	Likely to resolve spontaneously, loss of photoreceptor cell function possible, slightly increased risk for myopia/hyperopia, strabismus, and amblyopia
3	Ridge of blood vessel development extends, demonstrating **extraretinal fibrovascular proliferation** beyond the retina and into the vitreous humor	Extraretinal fibrovascular proliferation	May be severe enough to cause partial (stage 4) or complete (stage 5) retinal detachment and blindness
4	**Partial retinal detachment**	Fibrous material attaches to zonule and to lens; Subtotal retinal detachment	Poor prognosis; when untreated, retinal detachment leads to blindness
5	**Total retinal detachment**	Fluid in eye cannot drain: glaucoma; Dense fibroplasia; Totally detached retina	Poor prognosis; when untreated, retinal detachment leads to blindness

LEARNING TOOLS AND RESOURCES

Podcasts

 #1: Visual Input; #2: ROP; #3- The Red Reflex

Desi M. Newberry, Debbie Fraser, Sofia Aliaga, Bill Diehl-Jones, and Amy J. Jnah

Discussion Prompts

1. Review the timeline of visual milestones in the premature and term neonate. What milestones should you expect for each gestational age?

2. What are the most common causes of conjunctivitis? Differentiate the most common causes based on symptoms and timing of symptoms.

3. Discuss the timing of ROP development in relation to screening recommendations. Why do we screen when we do? Which zone/stage combination is most concerning?

Advice From the Authors

"My advice while studying the eye content is to try to think of sample test questions while you are reading the content. When studying, try to answer discussion prompts without referring back to the text. Try to explain concepts in your own words to demonstrate understanding of the content."

–Desi M. Newberry, DNP, APRN, NNP-BC

"Clinical pearl—practice, practice, practice with the ophthalmoscope. Determine the best setting for your vision by focusing on a freckle or spot on your hand or eye. Once you know the appropriate setting you won't have to manipulate the settings. I am a green 6 and can set that on the device before I begin to examine a neonate. Once you are set it's time to practice. When an infant needs a routine discharge eye exam we are usually looking to ensure that the red reflex is present. This helps to rule out cataracts and retinoblastoma. Make note of the eye structures, beginning with eyebrows, lashes, and then the eye itself. The more normal eyes you see the more readily you will be able to identify abnormalities."

–Debbie Fraser, MN, RNC-NIC

"As with other organ systems, use embryological timelines to understand disease states. For example, if you create a timeline for retinal vascular development you will be able to better understand and remember the risk for ROP and severity of ROP in the premature newborn of varying gestational ages."

–Sofia Aliaga, MD, MPH

"I taught Optometry students for several years, and when confronted with a large volume of information, my advice to those students was to always focus first on the major concepts and ideas. After mastering those, one has a framework on which to organize some of the minutiae. I think the same principle applies here. For example, the timelines are meant to provide a temporal framework for major developmental events; once one has internalized those, some of the finer details will become more easily mastered."

–Bill Diehl-Jones, PhD, BScN, RN

Mind Map

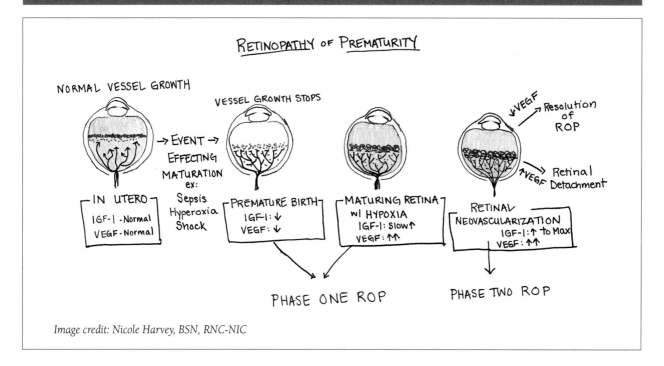

RETINOPATHY OF PREMATURITY

NORMAL VESSEL GROWTH

VESSEL GROWTH STOPS

→ EVENT →
EFFECTING
MATURATION
ex:
Sepsis
Hyperoxia
Shock

↓VEGF → Resolution of ROP

↑VEGF → Retinal Detachment

IN UTERO
IGF-1 - Normal
VEGF - Normal

PREMATURE BIRTH
IGF-1: ↓
VEGF: ↓

MATURING RETINA
w/ HYPOXIA
IGF-1: Slow↑
VEGF: ↑↑

RETINAL
NEOVASCULARIZATION
IGF-1: ↑ to Max
VEGF: ↑↑

PHASE ONE ROP

PHASE TWO ROP

Image credit: Nicole Harvey, BSN, RNC-NIC

Note: This mind map reflects one student's interpretation of a portion of one or more concepts addressed in this chapter. Readers should regard the mind maps woven throughout this textbook as examples of multi-sensory study tools that can be developed to encourage conceptual understanding. Readers are encouraged to develop their own unique mind maps in consultation with academic faculty or clinical preceptors.

TIMELINE OF ORGAN DEVELOPMENT

NOTE:
Placement of common problems is meant to offer visual/conceptual perspective on the timing of onset of these commonly reported malformations. Variation exists across the literature.

LEGEND
<22 – 27 6/7 weeks = extremely preterm
28 – 31 6/7 weeks = very preterm
32 – 36 6/7 weeks = late/moderate preterm
37 – 40 weeks = term

References

Akangire, G., & Carter, B. (2016). Birth injuries in neonates. *Pediatrics in Review*, 37(11), 451–462. doi:10.1542/pir.2015-0125

Al-Mohtaseb, Z., & Foroozan, R. (2012). Congenital optic disc anomalies. *International Ophthalmology Clinics*, 52(3), 1–16. doi:10.1097/IIO.0b013e31825a1166

Aponte, E. P., Diehl, N., & Mohney, B. G. (2010). Incidence and clinical characteristics of childhood glaucoma: A population-based study. *Archives of Ophthalmology*, 128(4), 478–482. doi:10.1001/archophthalmol.2010.41

Asano, M. K., & Dray, P. B. (2014). Retinopathy of prematurity. *Disease-a-Month*, 60(6), 282–291. doi:10.1016/j.disamonth.2014.03.009

Belmonte, C., Acosta, M. C., Merayo-Lloves, J., & Gallar, J. (2015). What causes eye pain? *Current Ophthalmology Reports*, 3(2), 111–121. doi:10.1007/s40135-015-0073-9

Bonalumi, S., Trapanese, A., Santamaria, A., D'Emidio, L., & Mobili, L. (2011). Cytomegalovirus infection in pregnancy: Review of the literature. *Journal of Prenatal Medicine*, 5(1), 1–8. Retrieved from https://www.prenatalmedicine.com/common/php/portiere.php?ID=433479ca1d65d5b8d134f10b39369625

Breugem, C. C., & Courtemanche, D. J. (2010). Robin sequence: Clearing nosologic confusion. *Cleft Palate–Craniofacial Journal*, 47(2), 197–200. doi:10.1597/08-061_1

Burns, N. S., Iyer, R. S., Robinson, A., & Chapman, T. (2013). Diagnostic imaging of fetal and pediatric orbital abnormalities. *American Journal of Roentgenology*, 201(6), W797–W808. doi:10.2214/AJR.13.10949

Centers for Disease Control and Prevention. (1976). Public health image library, ID #4284. Retrieved from https://phil.cdc.gov/Details.aspx?pid=4284

Centers for Disease Control and Prevention. (2002). Fetal alcohol syndrome—Alaska, Arizona, Colorado, and New York, 1995–1997. *Morbidity Mortality and Weekly Report*, 51(20), 433–435. Retrieved from https://www.cdc.gov/mmwr/preview/mmwrhtml/mm5120a2.htm

Centers for Disease Control and Prevention. (2015). Facts about anophthalmia/microphthalmia. Retrieved from https://www.cdc.gov/ncbddd/birthdefects/anophthalmia-microphthalmia.html

Chalupa, L. M., & Werner, J. S. (Eds.). (2014). *The new visual neurosciences*. Cambridge, MA: MIT Press.

Chen, D., Zhao, N., Wang, J., Li, Z., Wu, C., Fu, J., & Xiao, H. (2017). Whole-exome sequencing analysis of Waardenburg syndrome in a Chinese family. *Human Genome Variation*, 4. doi:10.1038/hgv.2017.27

Chou, R., Dana, T., & Bougatsos, C. (2011). *Screening for visual impairment in children ages 1–5 years: Systematic review to update the 2004 U.S. Preventive Services Task Force recommendation*. Rockville, MD: Agency for Healthcare Research and Quality.

Coats, D. K., Demmler, G. J., Paysse, E. A., Du, L. T., Libby, C., & the Congenital Longitudinal Study Group. (2000). Ophthalmologic findings in children with congenital cytomegalovirus infection. *Journal of American Association for Pediatric Ophthalmology and Strabismus*, 4(2), 110–116. doi:10.1067/mpa.2000.103870

Cruess, A., & Sharma, S. (2018). Tuberous sclerosis and the eye. In A. Schachat (Ed.), *Ryan's retina* (6th ed., pp. 2438–2445). Philadelphia, PA: Elsevier.

Curtin, S. C., & Matthews, T. J. (2016). Smoking prevalence and cessation before and during pregnancy: Data from the birth certificate, 2014. *National Vital Statistics Reports*, 65(1), 1–13. Retrieved from https://www.cdc.gov/nchs/data/nvsr/nvsr65/nvsr65_01.pdf

Daniel, M. S. (2018). Turner syndrome. In L. O. Rohena (Ed.), *Medscape*. Retrieved from https://emedicine.medscape.com/article/949681-overview

Doshi, N. R., & Rodriguez, M. L. (2007). Amblyopia. *American Family Physician*, 75(3), 361–367. Retrieved from https://www.aafp.org/afp/2007/0201/p361.html

Eldweik, L., & Mantagos, I. S. (2016). Role of VEGF inhibition in the treatment of retinopathy of prematurity. *Seminars in Ophthalmology*, 31, 163–168. doi:10.3109/08820538.2015.1114847

Fernandes, M., Yang, X., Li, J. Y., & Cheikh Ismail, L. (2015). Smoking during pregnancy and vision difficulties in children: A systematic review. *Acta Ophthalmologica*, 93(3), 213–223. doi:10.1111/aos.12627

Fraser, D., & Diehl-Jones, W. (2015). Ophthalmologic and auditory disorders. In M. T. Verklan & M. Walden (Eds.), *Core curriculum for neonatal intensive care nursing* (5th ed., pp. 813–831). St. Louis, MO: Elsevier Saunders.

Friel, J., Diehl-Jones, B., Cockell, K., Chiu, A., Rabanni, R., Davies, S., & Roberts, L. (2011). Evidence of oxidative stress in relation to feeding type during early life in premature infants. *Pediatric Research*, 69, 160–164. doi:10.1203/PDR.0b013e3182042a07

Garcia-Filion, P., & Borchert, M. (2013). Optic nerve hypoplasia syndrome: A review of the epidemiology and clinical associations. *Current Treatment Options in Neurology*, 15(1), 78–89. doi:10.1007/s11940-012-0209-2

Gardner, S. L., Carter, B. S., Enzman Hines, M., & Hernandez, J. A. (Eds.). (2016). *Merenstein & Gardner's handbook of neonatal intensive care* (8th ed.). St. Louis, MO: Elsevier.

Garza, R. M., & Khosla, R. K. (2012). Nonsyndromic craniosynostosis. *Seminars in Plastic Surgery*, 26(2), 53–63. doi:10.1055/s-0032-1320063

Genetic and Rare Diseases Information Center. (2015). Trisomy 18. Retrieved from https://rarediseases.info.nih.gov/diseases/6321/trisomy-18

Genetic and Rare Diseases Information Center. (2016a). Trisomy 13. Retrieved from https://rarediseases.info.nih.gov/diseases/7341/trisomy-13

Genetic and Rare Diseases Information Center. (2016b). Waardenburg syndrome. Retrieved from https://rarediseases.info.nih.gov/diseases/5525/waardenburg-syndrome

Genetic and Rare Disease Information Center. (2017a). CHARGE syndrome. Retrieved from https://rarediseases.info.nih.gov/diseases/29/charge-syndrome

Genetic and Rare Disease Information Center. (2017b). Leber congenital amaurosis. Retrieved from https://rarediseases.info.nih.gov/diseases/634/leber-congenital-amurosis

Genetic and Rare Disease Information Center. (2017c). Neurofibromatosis. Retrieved from https://rarediseases.info.nih.gov/diseases/10420/neurofibromatosis

Genetic and Rare Diseases Information Center. (2018a). Cornelia de Lange syndrome. Retrieved from https://rarediseases.info.nih.gov/diseases/10109/cornelia-de-lange-syndrome

Genetic and Rare Diseases Information Center. (2018b). WAGR syndrome. Retrieved from https://rarediseases.info.nih.gov/diseases/5528/wagr-syndrome

Gleason, C. A., & Juul, S. E. (Eds.). (2018). *Avery's diseases of the newborn* (10th ed.). Philadelphia, PA: Elsevier.

Goddard, K. (Ed.). (2008). Ophthalmology for the oncologist. *Pediatric Oncology Education Materials.* Retrieved from http://www.pedsoncologyeducation.com/OpthalmologyProptosis.asp

González, E., Stahl, A., Hellström, A., & Smith, L. E. H. (2017). Pathophysiology of retinopathy of prematurity. In R. A. Polin, S. H. Abman, D. H. Rowitch, W. E. Benitz, & W. W. Fox (Eds.), *Fetal and neonatal physiology* (5th ed., pp. 1681–1686). Philadelphia, PA: Elsevier.

Good, W. V., Ferriero, D. M., Golabi, M., & Kobori, J. A. (1992). Abnormalities of the visual system in infants exposed to cocaine. *Ophthalmology, 99*(3), 341–346. doi:10.1016/S0161-6420(92)31967-0

Gosling, J. A., Harris, P. F., Humpherson, J. R., Whitmore, I., & Willan, P. L. T. (2016). *Human anatomy: Color atlas and textbook* (6th ed.). New York, NY: Elsevier.

Greene, A. K., Taber, S. F., Ball, K. L., Padwa, B. L., & Mulliken, J. B. (2009). Sturge–Weber syndrome: Soft-tissue and skeletal overgrowth. *Journal of Craniofacial Surgery, 20,* 617–621. doi:10.1097/SCS.0b013e318192988e

Gross, A. K., & Wensel, T.G. (2011). Biochemical cascade of phototransduction. In L. A. Levin, S. F. E. Nilsson, J. Ver Hoeve, & S. M. Wu (Eds.), *Adler's physiology of the eye* (11th ed., pp. 394–410). Edinburgh, Scotland: Saunders/Elsevier.

Hartnett, M. E. (Ed.). (2014). *Pediatric retina* (2nd ed.). Philadelphia, PA: Lippencott, Williams, & Wilkins.

Heike, C. L., Luquetti, D. V., & Hing, A. V. (2014). Craniofacial microsomia overview. *GeneReviews.* Retrieved from http://www.ncbi.nlm.nih.gov/books/NBK5199

Hingorani, M., & Moore, A. (2013). *PAX6*-related aniridia. *GeneReviews.* Retrieved from https://www.ncbi.nlm.nih.gov/books/NBK1360

Hughes, S., Yang, H., & Chan-Ling, T. (2000). Vascularization of the human fetal retina: Roles of vasculogenesis and angiogenesis. *Retinal Cell Biology, 41,* 1217–1228. Retrieved from https://iovs.arvojournals.org/article.aspx?articleid=2123358

Hussein, M., Miller, A. M., & Steinkuller, P. G. (2014). Ocular infections. In J. Cherry, G. Demmler-Harrison, S. Kaplan, W. J. Steinbach, & P. J. Hotez (Eds.), *Feigin and Cherry's textbook of pediatric infectious diseases* (7th ed., pp. 794–822). Philadelphia, PA: Elsevier.

Ikeda, T., Ishikawa, H., Shimizu, K., Asakawa, K., & Goseki, T. (2015). Pupillary size and light reflex in premature infants. *Neuro-Ophthalmology, 39*(4), 175–178. doi:10.3109/01658107.2015.1055363

Islam, M. P., & Roach, E. S. (2016). Neurocutaneous syndromes. In R. B. Daroff, J. Jankovic, J. C. Mazziotta, & S. L. Pomeroy (Eds.), *Bradley's neurology in clinical practice* (7th ed., pp. 1538–1562). Philadelphia, PA: Elsevier.

Jivraj, I., Rudnisky, C. J., Tambe, E., Tipple, G., & Tennant, M. T. S. (2014). Identification of ocular and auditory manifestations of congenital rubella syndrome in Mbingo. *International Journal of Telemedicine and Applications, 2014,* 1–5. doi:10.1155/2014/981312

Jones, K. L., Jones, M. C., & Del Campo, C. M. (2013). *Smith's recognizable patterns of human malformation* (7th ed.). Philadelphia, PA: Elsevier.

Kaufman, M. G., Cassady, C. I., Hyman, C. H., Lee, W., Watcha, M. F., Hippard, H. K., . . . Buchanan, E. P. (2016). Prenatal identification of Pierre Robin sequence: A review of the literature and look towards the future. *Fetal Diagnosis and Therapy, 39*(2), 81–89. doi:10.1159/000380948

Kaur, S., Jain, S., Sodhi, H. B. S., Rastogi, A., & Kamlesh. (2013). Optic nerve hypoplasia. *Oman Journal of Ophthalmology, 6*(2), 77–82. doi:10.4103/0974-620X.116622

Kieffer, F., Wallon, M., Garcia, P., Thulliez, P., Peyron, F., & Franck, J. (2008). Risk factors for retinochoroiditis during the first 2 years of life in infants with treated congenital toxoplasmosis. *Pedaitric Infectious Disease, 27*(1), 27–32. doi:10.1097/INF.0b013e318134286d

Kodjikian, L., Wallon, M., Fleury, J., Denis, P., Binquet, C., Peyron, F., & Garweg, J. G. (2006). Ocular manifestations in congenital toxoplasmosis. *Graefe's Archive for Clinical and Experimental Ophthalmology, 244,* 14–21. doi:10.1007/s00417-005-1164-3

Lal, M. K. (2016). Trisomy 18. In L. O. Rohena (Ed.), *Medscape.* Retrieved from https://emedicine.medscape.com/article/943463-overview

Lamb, T. D. (2011). Light adaptation in photoreceptors. In L. A. Levin, S. F. E. Nilsson, J. Ver Hoeve, & S. M. Wu (Eds.), *Adler's physiology of the eye* (11th ed., pp. 429–442). Edinburgh, Scotland: Saunders/Elsevier.

Lambert, S. R., & Lyons, C. J. (Eds.). (2017). *Taylor & Hoyt's pediatric ophthalmology and strabismus* (5th ed.). New York: Elsevier.

Lim, F.-F., Ng, Y.-Y., Hu, J.-M., Chen, S.-J., Su, P.-H., & Chen, J.-Y. (2010). Ocular findings in a case of trisomy 18 with variant of Dandy-Walker syndrome. *Pediatrics Neonatology, 51*(5), 292–295. doi:10.1016/S1875-9572(10)60056-3

Lueder, G. (2006). Clinical ocular abnormalities in infants with trisomy 13. *American Journal of Ophthalmology, 141*(6), 1057–1060. doi:10.1016/j.ajo.2005.12.048

MacLeish, P. R., & Makino, C. L. (2011). Photoresponses of rods and cones. In L. A. Levin, S. F. E. Nilsson, J. Ver Hoeve, & S. M. Wu (Eds.), *Adler's physiology of the eye* (11th ed., pp. 411–428). Edinburgh, Scotland: Saunders/Elsevier.

Madan, A., & Good, W. V. (2005). Preterm birth and the visual system. *NeoReviews, 6*(3), e153–e159. doi:10.1542/neo.6-3-e153

Madan-Khetarpal, S., & Arnold, G. (2018). Genetic disorders and dysmorphic conditions. In B. J. Zitelli, S. C McIntire, & A. J. Nowalk (Eds.), *Zitelli and Davis' atlas of pediatric physical diagnosis* (7th ed., pp. 1–43). Philadelphia, PA: Elsevier.

Mansoor, N., Mansoor, T., & Ahmed, M. (2016). Eye pathologies in neonates. *International Journal of Ophthalmology, 9*(12), 1832–1838. doi:10.18240/ijo.2016.12.22

Marquez, L., Levy, M. L., Munoz, F. M., & Palazzi, D. L. (2011). A report of three cases and review of intrauterine herpes simplex virus infection. *Pediatric Infectious Disease Journal, 30*(2), 153–157. doi:10.1097/INF.0b013e3181f55a5c

Martin, R. J., Fanaroff, A. A., & Walsh, M. C. (Eds.). (2015). *Fanaroff and Martin's neonatal–perinatal medicine: Diseases of the fetus and infant* (10th ed.). Philadelphia, PA: Saunders/Elsevier.

McMahon, S. B., Koltzenburg, M., Tracey, I., & Turk, D. C. (Eds.). (2013). *Wall and Melzack's textbook of pain* (6th ed.). Philadelphia, PA: Elsevier/Saunders.

Mendoza, P. R., & Grossniklaus, H. E. (2015). The biology of retinoblastoma. *Progress in Molecular Biology and Translational Science, 134,* 503–516. doi:10.1016/bs.pmbts.2015.06.012

Meng, I. D., & Kurose, M. (2013). The role of corneal afferent neurons in regulating tears under normal and dry eye conditions. *Experimental Eye Research, 117,* 79–87. doi:10.1016/j.exer.2013.08.011

Mets, M. B., & Chhabra, M. S. (2008). Eye manifestations of intrauterine infections and their impact on childhood blindness. *Survey of Ophthalmology, 53*(2), 95–111. doi:10.1016/j.survophthal.2007.12.003

Miller, M. T., Epstein, R. J., Sugar, J., Pinchoff, B. S., Sugar, A., Gammon, A., . . . Israel, J. (1984). Anterior segment anomalies associated with the fetal alcohol syndrome. *Journal of Pediatric Ophthalmology and Strabismus, 21*(1), 8–18 doi:10.3928/0191-3913-19840101-04.

Moore, K. L., Persaud, T. V. N., & Torchia, M. G. (2016). *The developing human* (10th ed., pp. 417–436). Philadelphia, PA: Elsevier.

National Institutes of Health. (2018a). Genetics home reference: Cornelia de Lange syndrome. Retrieved from https://ghr.nlm.nih.gov/condition/cornelia-de-lange-syndrome#inheritance

National Institutes of Health. (2018b). Genetics home reference: Down syndrome. Retrieved from https://ghr.nlm.nih.gov/condition/down-syndrome#statistics

National Institutes of Health. (2018c). Genetics home reference: Neurofibromatosis type 1. Retrieved from https://ghr.nlm.nih.gov/condition/neurofibromatosis-type-1#statistics

National Institutes of Health. (2018d). Genetics home reference: Pierre Robin sequence. Retrieved from https://ghr.nlm.nih.gov/condition/isolated-pierre-robin-sequence#statistics

National Institutes of Health. (2018e). Genetics home reference: Sturge–Weber syndrome. Retrieved from https://ghr.nlm.nih.gov/condition/sturge-weber-syndrome#statistics

National Institutes of Health. (2018f). Genetics home reference: Trisomy 18. Retrieved from https://ghr.nlm.nih.gov/condition/trisomy-18#statistics

National Institutes of Health. (2018g). Genetics home reference: Turner syndrome. Retrieved from https://ghr.nlm.nih.gov/condition/turner-syndrome#statistics

National Institutes of Health. (2018h). Genetics home reference: Waardenburg syndrome. Retrieved from https://ghr.nlm.nih.gov/condition/waardenburg-syndrome#statistics

National Institutes of Health. (2018i). Genetics home reference: WAGR syndrome. Retrieved from https://ghr.nlm.nih.gov/condition/wagr-syndrome#statistics

National Library of Medicine. (2018a). CHARGE syndrome. Retrieved from https://ghr.nlm.nih.gov/condition/charge-syndrome

National Library of Medicine. (2018b). Trisomy 13. Retrieved from https://ghr.nlm.nih.gov/condition/trisomy-13

National Library of Medicine. (2018c). Tuberous sclerosis complex. Retrieved from https://ghr.nlm.nih.gov/condition/tuberous-sclerosis-complex

National Organization for Rare Disorders. (2007). Trisomy 13 syndrome. Retrieved from https://rarediseases.org/rare-diseases/trisomy-13-syndrome

Nelson, L. B., & Olitsky, S. E. (2013). *Harley's pediatric opthamology.* (6th ed). Philadelphia, PA: Lippincott, Williams & Wilkins.

Nischal, K. K. (2014). Visual surveillance in craniosynostoses. *American Orthoptic Journal, 64*(1), 24–31. doi:10.3368/aoj.64.1.24

Nischler, C., Michael, R., Wintersteller, C., Marvan, P., van Rijn, L. J., Coppens, J. E., . . . Grabner, G. (2013). Iris color and visual functions. *Graefe's Archives of Clinical and Experimental Ophthalmology, 251*(1), 195–202. doi:10.1007/s00417-012-2006-8

Norcia, A. M. (2011). Development of vision in infancy. In L. A. Levin, S. F. E. Nilsson, J. Ver Hoeve, & S. M. Wu (Eds.), *Adler's physiology of the eye* (11th ed., pp. 713–724). Edinburgh, Scotland: Saunders/Elsevier.

O'Leary, L. A., Ortiz, L., Montgomery, A., Fox, D. J., Cunniff, C., Ruttenber, M., . . . & Meaney, J. F. (2015). Methods for surveillance of fetal alcohol syndrome: The Fetal Alcohol Syndrome Surveillance Network II (FASSNetII)—Arizona, Colorado, New York, 2009–2014. *Birth Defects Research Part A: Clinical and Molecular Teratology, 103*(3), 196–202. doi:10.1002/bdra.23335

Olitsky, S. E., Hug, D., Plummer, L. S., Stahl, E. D., Ariss, M. M., & Lindquist, T. P. (2016). Abnormalities of pupil and iris. In R. M. Kliegman, B. F. Stanton, J. W. St Geme, & N. F. Schor (Eds.), *Nelson textbook of pediatrics* (20th ed., pp. 3023–3025). Philadelphia, PA: Elsevier.

Orge, F. H., & Grigorian, F. (2015). Examination and common problems of the neonatal eye. In R. J. Martin, A. A. Fanaroff, & M. C. Walsh (Eds.), *Fanaroff and Martin's neonatal–perinatal medicine* (10th ed., Vol. 103, pp. 1734–1766). Philadelphia, PA: Saunders/Elsevier.

Orkin, S. H., Nathan, D. G., Ginsburg, D., Look, A. T., Fisher, D. E., & Lux, S. (Eds.). (2015). *Nathan and Oski's hematology and oncology of infancy and childhood* (8th ed.). Philadelphia, PA: Saunders.

Ortiz, M. V., & Dunkel, I. J. (2016). Retinoblastoma. *Journal of Child Neurology, 31*(2), 227–236. doi:10.1177/0883073815587943

Park, Y. H., & Nam, H. W. (2013). Clinical features and treatment of ocular toxoplasmosis. *Korean Journal of Parasitology, 51*(4), 393–399. doi:10.3347/kjp.2013.51.4.393

Pass, R. F., & Anderson, B. (2014). Mother-to-child transmission of cytomegalovirus and prevention of congenital infection. *Journal of the Pediatric Infectious Diseases Society, 3*(Suppl. 1), S2–S6. doi:10.1093/jpids/piu069

Patterson, J. (2016). *Weedon's skin pathology* (4th ed.). Philadelphia, PA: Elsevier.

Pensiero, S., Cecchini, P., Michieletto, P., Pelizzo, G., Madonia, M., & Parentin, F. (2011). Congenital aplasia of the optic chiasm and esophageal atresia: A case report. *Journal of Medical Case Reports, 5*, 335. doi:10.1186/1752-1947-5-335

Peragallo, J., Biousse, V., & Newman, N. J. (2013). Ocular manifestations of drug and alcohol abuse. *Current Opinion in Ophthalmology, 24*(6), 566–573. doi:10.1097/ICU.0b013e3283654db2

Peyron, F., McLeod, R., Ajzenberg, D., Contopoulos-Ioannidid, D., Kieffer, F., Mandelbrot, L., . . .Montoya, J. G. (2017). Congenital toxoplasmosis in France and the United States: One parasite, two diverging approaches. *PLoS Neglected Tropical Diseases, 11*(2), 1–6. doi:10.1371/journal.pntd.0005222

Purves, D., Augustine, G. J., Fitzpatrick, D., Hall, W. C., LaMantia, A.-S., & White, L. E. (Eds.). (2012). *Neuroscience* (5th ed.). Sunderland, MA: Sinauer Associates.

Ramasubramanian, A., & Johnston, S. (2011). Neonatal eye disorders requiring ophthalmology consultation. *NeoReviews, 12*(4), e216–e222. doi:10.1542/neo.12-4-e216

Rao, N. K., Goldstein, M. H., & Tu, E. Y. (2014). Dry eye. In M. Yanoff & J. S. Duker (Eds.), *Ophthalmology* (4th ed., pp. 274–279). Philadelphia, PA: Elsevier Saunders.

Remington, J. S., Klein, J. O., Wilson, C. B., Nizet, V., & Maldonado, Y. A. (Eds.). (2011). *Infectious diseases of the fetus and newborn infant* (7th ed.). Philadelphia, PA: Elsevier Saunders.

Richards, A., & Guzman-Cottrill, J. A. (2010). Conjunctivitis. *Pediatrics in Review, 31*(5), 196–208.

Robin, N. H., Moran, R. T., & Ala-Kokko, L. (2017). Stickler syndrome. *GeneReviews.* Retrieved from https://www.ncbi.nlm.nih.gov/books/NBK1302

Rodriguez-Galindo, C., Orbach, D. B., & VanderVeen, D. (2015). Retinoblastoma. *Pediatric Clinics of North America, 62*(1), 201–223. doi:10.1016/j.pcl.2014.09.014

Russell-Eggitt, I., & Lightman, S. (1992). Intrauterine infection and the eye. *Eye, 6,* 205–210. doi:10.1038/eye.1992.40

Satpathy, R. (2018). Sturge-Weber syndrome. In F. Ferri (Ed.), *Ferri's clinical advisor* (p. 1222.e2). Philadelphia, PA: Elsevier.

Schoenwolf, G. C., Bleyl, S. B., Brauer, P. R., & Francis-West, P. H. (2015). *Larsen's human embryology* (5th ed.). Philadelphia, PA: Churchill Livingstone.

Shah, P. K., Prabhu, V., Karandikar, S. S., Ranjan, R., Narendran, V., & Kalpana, N. (2016). Retinopathy of prematurity: Past, present and future. *World Journal of Clinical Pediatrics, 5*(1), 35–46. doi:10.5409/wjcp.v5.i1.35

Sharma, M., & VanderVeen, D. K. (2017). Identification and treatment of retinopathy of prematurity: Update 2017. *NeoReviews, 18*(2), e84–e90. doi:10.1542/neo.18-2-e84

Shirley, M. D., Tang, H., Gallione, C. J., Baugher, J. D., Frelin, L. P., Cohen, B., . . . & Pevsner, J. (2013). Sturge–Weber syndrome and port-wine stains caused by somatic mutation in GNAQ. *New England Journal of Medicine, 368*(21), 1971–1979. doi: 10.1056/NEJMoa1213507

Singh, S., & Dass, R. (1960). The central artery of the retina II. A study of its distribution and anastomoses. *British Journal of Ophthalmology, 44,* 280–299. Retrieved from https://bjo.bmj.com/content/bjophthalmol/44/5/280.full.pdf

Solebo, A. L., Teoh, L., & Rahi, J. (2017). Epidemiology of blindness in children. *Archives of Disease in Childhood, 102*(9), 853–857. doi:10.1136/archdischild-2016-310532

Steinbacher, D. M., & Bartlett, S. P. (2013). Nonsyndromic craniosynostosis. In P. C. Neligan (Ed.), *Plastic surgery* (3rd ed., Vol. 3, pp. 749–760). Philadelphia, PA: Elsevier.

Sujansky, E., & Conradi, S. (1995). Outcome of Sturge–Weber syndrome in 52 adults. *American Journal of Medical Genetics Part A, 57*(1), 35–45. doi:10.1002/ajmg.1320570110

Sun, Y., Hellström, A., & Smith, L. E. H. (2015). Retinopathy of prematurity. In R. J. Martin, A. A. Fanaroff, & M. C. Walsh (Eds.), *Fanaroff and Martin's neonatal–perinatal medicine: Diseases of the fetus and infant* (10th ed., pp. 1767–1774). Philadelphia, PA: Elsevier/ Saunders.

Tamayo, M. L., Garcia, N., Bermúdez Rey, M. C., Morales, L., Flórez, S., Varón, C., & Gelvez, N. (2013). The importance of fundus eye testing in rubella-induced deafness. *International Journal of Pediatric Otorhinolaryngology, 77*(9), 1536–1540. doi:10.1016/j.ijporl.2013.06.028

Teär Fahnehjelm, K., Olsson, M., Fahnehjelm, C., Lewensohn-Fuchs, I., & Karltorp, E. (2015). Chorioretinal scars and visual deprivation are common in children with cochlear implants after congenital cytomegalovirus infection. *Acta Paediatrica, 104*(7), 693–700. doi:10.1111/apa.12988

Tegay, D. H. (2018). CHARGE syndrome. In M. Descartes (Ed.), *Medscape.* Retrieved from https://emedicine.medscape.com/article/942350-overview

Terry, T. L. (1942). Fibroblastic overgrowth of persistent tunica vasculosa lentis in infants born prematurely: II. Report of cases—Clinical aspects. *Transactions of the American Ophthalmological Society, 40,* 262–284. Retrieved from https://www.ncbi.nlm.nih.gov/pmc/articles/PMC1315050/pdf/taos00059-0283.pdf

Ueno, H., Ferrari, G., Hattori, T., Saban, D. R., Katikireddy, K. R., Chauhan, S. K., & Dana, R. (2012). Dependence of corneal stem/progenitor cells on ocular surface innervation. *Investigative Ophthalmology & Visual Science, 53*(2), 867–872. doi:10.1167/iovs.11-8438

Vernescu, R. M., Adams, R. J., & Courage, M. L. (2012). Children with fetal alcohol spectrum disorder show an amblyopia-like pattern of vision deficit: Vision in children with FASD. *Developmental Medicine & Child Neurology, 54*(6), 557–562. doi:10.1111/j.1469-8749.2012.04254.x

Waardenburg, P. J. (1951). A new syndrome combining developmental anomalies of the eyelids, eyebrows and nose root with pigmentary anomalies of the iris and head hair and with congenital deafness. *American Journal of Human Genetics, 3*(3), 195–253. Retrieved from https://www.ncbi.nlm.nih.gov/pmc/articles/PMC1716407/pdf/ajhg00426-0007.pdf

Wallon, M., Garweg, J. G., Abrahamowicz, M., Cornu, C., Vinault, S., Quantin, C., . . . Binquet, C. (2014). Ophthalmic outcomes of congenital toxoplasmosis followed until adolescence. *Pediatrics, 133*(3), e601–e608. doi:10.1542/peds.2013-2153

World Health Organization. (n.d.). Prevention of blindness and vision impairment. Retrieved from http://www.who.int/blindness/partnerships/vision2020/en

Wu, S. M. (2011). Signal processing in the outer retina. In L. A. Levin, S. F. E. Nilsson, J. Ver Hoeve, & S. M. Wu (Eds.), *Adler's physiology of the eye* (11th ed., pp. 459–470). Edinburgh, Scotland: Saunders/Elsevier.

Yi, J., Yun, J., Li, Z. K., Xu, C. T., & Pan, B. R. (2011). Epidemiology and molecular genetics of congenital cataracts. *International Journal of Ophthalmology, 4*(4), 422–432. doi:10.3980/j.issn.2222-3959.2011.04.20

Zitelli, B. J., McIntire, S., & Nowalk, A. J. (Eds.). (2018). *Zitelli and Davis' atlas of pediatric physical diagnosis* (7th ed.). Philadelphia, PA: Saunders/Elsevier.

III

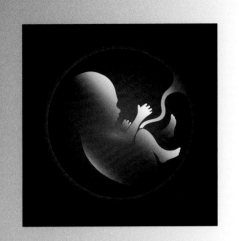

TRANSITION TO EXTRAUTERINE LIFE

14

DELIVERY METHODS

Amy R. Koehn, Melody Norris Waller, and Evelyn Stephenson

LEARNING OBJECTIVES

After completing this chapter, the reader should be able to:
- Review the role of cardiovascular development in overall fetal growth and development.
- Review the changes that take place from fetal to neonatal circulation.
- List three factors that influence the neonate's transition to extrauterine life.
- Identify maternal and fetal indications for and implications of an emergent cesarean delivery.
- Identify maternal and fetal indications for and implications of an operative vaginal delivery.
- Recognize common contraindications for spontaneous and operative vaginal deliveries.
- Differentiate among risk factors, pathophysiology, clinical findings, and long-term effects of common birth injuries in neonates.
- Identify appropriate means to assess for common birth injuries in neonates.

INTRODUCTION

The transition from placenta-dependent to postnatal life is a complex and vulnerable period for all newborns. All organ systems must quickly adjust to postnatal life; however, the establishment of placenta-independent cardiovascular and respiratory function is the most immediate and necessary adaptation, and contingent upon the first postnatal breath. Extrauterine adaptation is influenced by epigenetic, genetic, chronic maternal health, prenatal, and intrapartum-related complications, as well as the gestational age of the fetus at the time of delivery. In fact, a fetus subject to acute or prolonged interruptions in uterine blood flow is at increased risk for a pathological transition to extrauterine life and neurologic morbidity. In addition, the delivery method may implicate the transition to extrauterine life, and in some circumstances injure the fetus. Neonatal advanced practice nurses (APNs) are expected to recognize maternal, fetal, and intrapartum risk factors that increase the likelihood for an altered transition to extrauterine life. These risk assessments help ensure that proper personnel are immediately available during and after the birth process, to reduce the high burden of neonatal mortality and morbidity.

THE BIOLOGY OF BIRTH

Placental and fetal circulation have been described in prior chapters as a means to establish understanding of the genesis of fetal blood flow and its function during intrauterine development; however, use of a spiral curriculum is essential to promote knowledge acquisition and retention. Therefore, we present an abbreviated review of normal placental and fetal circulation, followed by a discussion of the biology of labor, circulatory transition to extrauterine life, and common factors that may compromise fetal blood flow, oxygenation, and an otherwise healthy transition to life outside the womb.

Placental and Fetal Circulation

Recall from Chapter 2 that blood flows into the uterus by way of the uterine arteries. Once within the uterus, blood flow continues into the intervillous spaces (IVS), where it is preferentially directed toward the chorionic plate, or "roof," of the placenta. From here, blood flow readily transfers between the maternal and fetal circulations by way of the placenta and umbilical blood vessels. Placental transfer involves bidirectional movements of gases, nutrients, waste materials, drugs, and other substances; filtration occurs at the placenta (Morton & Brodsky, 2016).

Recall from Chapters 4 and 5 that fetal circulation occurs in a circuit. Although the heart technically marks the starting point for fetal circulation, beginning a review of circulation at the umbilical vein, the point of entry of freshly oxygenated blood into the fetal circulation, is often ideal for student learners (Figure 14.1; Kiserud & Haugen, 2017). The umbilical vein carries approximately 40% of total cardiac output; the majority (50%) of blood flow passes through the ductus venosus, with the remainder left to support liver growth. The fact that the liver is the first organ to receive freshly oxygenated blood from the placental circuit highlights its importance in fetal development. Blood then passes into the inferior vena cava (IVC) and into the right atrium. Once in the right atrium, the majority of blood flow will travel across the foramen ovale and into the left atrium and left ventricle and finally out to the brain and peripheral tissues by way of the aorta. This preferential streaming of oxygenated blood ensures the brain and myocardium are well supplied (Fineman & Clyman, 2014; Kiserud & Haugen, 2017).

Deoxygenated blood returning to the heart from the systemic circulation, by way of the superior vena cava and the coronary system, is deposited in the right atrium. This blood flow is preferentially diverted into the right ventricle, rather than the left atrium, into the pulmonary artery, and either shunts across the ductus arteriosus, rejoining the blood flow in the aorta, or travels on to the lungs, providing nutrients to the developing lung tissue. Blood that traverses the ductus arteriosus subsequently enters the descending aorta, in order to perfuse the lower body organs, and eventually reaches the placenta where it undergoes reoxygenation (Figure 14.2; Fineman & Clyman, 2014).

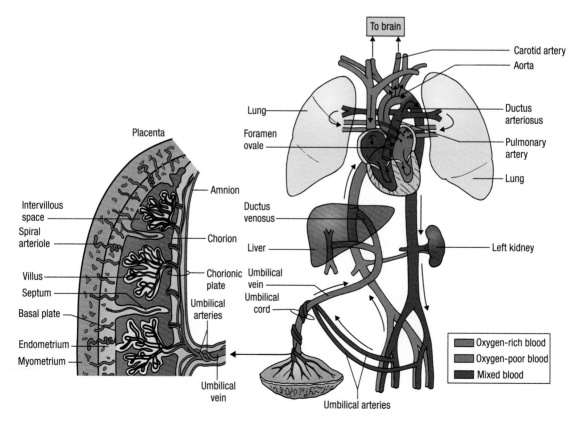

Figure 14.1 Anatomy of maternal-fetal circulatory pathway.

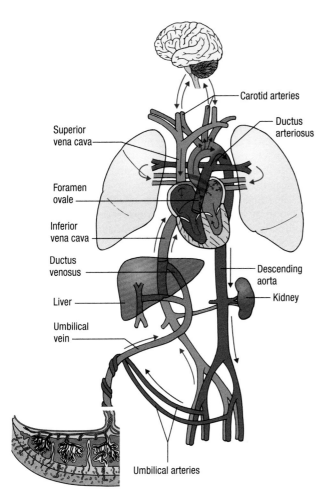

Figure 14.2 Directional blood flow within fetal circulation.

Labels: Carotid arteries; Ductus arteriosus; Superior vena cava; Foramen ovale; Inferior vena cava; Ductus venosus; Liver; Umbilical vein; Descending aorta; Kidney; Umbilical arteries

Placental and Fetal Circulation During Labor

Human labor integrates a complex set of changes within the uterus and fetal membranes that occur over a period of days to weeks. Changes include an increase in prostaglandin synthesis, an increased uptake of oxytocin receptors, fetal influence on placental steroid hormone production, and secretion of multiple hormones that stimulate prostaglandin synthesis. The interplay of these physiological and hormonal changes is termed a *parturition cascade*.

Labor can alter normal placental and fetal blood flow. The onset of labor and subsequent contractions of the uterine wall compress the myometrium and the umbilical vessels. During normal labor, intrauterine pressures do not compromise gas exchange within the placenta and do not endanger the fetus. However, changes in placental resistance can reduce placental blood flow and favor hypoxemia and/or ischemia. Recall that flow within the umbilical circuit is determined by cardiac force (blood pressure and kinetic energy) as well as vascular resistance

(geometry and viscosity; Kiserud & Haugen, 2017). Fetuses subjected to altered vascular resistance and decreased blood flow will likely show intolerance of labor and require expedited delivery (Marsal, 2017).

TRANSITION TO EXTRAUTERINE LIFE

Cardiovascular Transition to Postnatal Life

Once the umbilical cord is clamped, the low resistance placental circuit is disrupted, resulting in increasing systemic pressure (Rozance & Rosenberg, 2017). Increased systemic pressure thereby increases pressure within the left atrium and blood flow coming from the lungs. Once the left atrial pressure is higher than the right atrial pressure, the septum primum closes (Morton & Brodsky, 2016). These two processes reverse the fetal right-to-left shunt through the ductus arteriosus to the postnatal left-to-right shunt through the pulmonary circuit (Rozance & Rosenberg, 2017). Along with this shunt reversal, changes in cardiac preload and afterload occur. The removal of the elevated pulmonary pressures allows significant increase in pulmonary blood flow and initiation of gas exchange. Concurrently, a sudden increase in systemic vascular resistance (SVR) leads to increased left ventricular afterload (McNamara & El-Khuffash, 2017) as the left ventricle, which previously pumped blood only to the upper part of the body and brain, must now deliver the entire cardiac output systemically (about 350 mL/kg/min, a twofold increase compared to fetal cardiovascular function; Bernstein, 2016).

During the transition from fetal to neonatal circulation, SVR has a greater impact on blood pressure than blood flow. Rises in SVR lead to a rapid increase in cerebral blood flow; the increase in brain oxygenation occurs faster compared to other vital organs (Morton & Brodsky, 2016).

Delayed Cord Clamping. When considering the dramatic changes that occur with the clamping of the cord at delivery, a discussion of the impact of delayed cord clamping is warranted. Historically, clamping of an umbilical cord occurred within a few seconds after birth; however, current evidence indicates that delaying cord clamping for 30 to 60 seconds after birth is advantageous to the newborn. Benefits to term infants include increased hemoglobin levels after birth and iron stores in early infancy. Premature infants benefit from a more gradual transition, increased red cell volume (increased circulating blood volume), and decreased risk for IVH and NEC (American College of Obstetricians and Gynecologists [ACOG], 2017b; Rozance & Rosenberg, 2017).

A more gradual transition may be the result of allowing neonates to breathe and establish pulmonary blood flow before the cord is clamped. Studies show rapid cord clamping results in acute increases in SVR and arterial blood pressures, which disrupt pressure-passive organs, most notably in the brain. Delaying cord clamping may result in less fluctuation in blood pressure and cardiac output (McNamara & El-Khuffash, 2017). It has been shown that the timing of cord clamping is important to the initiation of lung ventilation, and that initiation of ventilation before cord clamping decreases pulmonary vascular resistance and increases pulmonary blood flow. Both avoid rapid increases in impedance and blood pressure seen during routine clamping (Kiserud & Haugen, 2017). Table 14.1 distinguishes between the advantages and disadvantages of delayed cord clamping between term and preterm neonates.

Pulmonary Transition to Postnatal Life

The most critical step in accomplishing the transition from intrauterine to extrauterine life is the conversion of the lung from a fluid-filled to air-filled organ capable of gas exchange. Multiple processes must occur for this to happen and include the aeration of the lungs, establishment of pulmonary circulation, ventilation of the lung parenchyma, and diffusion of oxygen and carbon dioxide through capillary membranes (Rozance & Rosenberg, 2017).

Prior to the onset of labor, the pulmonary epithelium actively secretes fluid into the lung to support and promote tissue development. With the onset of labor, the tissues change from fluid production to fluid absorption, using active transport to draw fluid into the interstitium and to allow for gas (air) to fill the lungs. Increased oxygenation after birth helps to maintain this fluid-absorbing process as well as the increase in pressure gradient caused

by the negative pressure of the first breath. Therefore, effective clearance of lung fluid not only decreases PVR but also increases plasma volume during the first hours after birth (Morton & Brodsky, 2016).

The first breath induces forced expansion of the lungs. Concurrently, increasing arterial oxygen levels and synthesis of endothelium-derived relaxing factor acutely lower the PVR (Rozance & Rosenberg, 2017). As a result, right ventricular output is now redirected into the pulmonary circulation (Bernstein, 2016). Surfactant secretion by the lung parenchyma, stimulated initially by labor, reduces the surface tension of the liquid–air interface lining the lungs. Reduction of surface tension allows for lung inflation at lower pressures (Morton & Brodsky, 2016). Comparisons between fetal and neonatal circulations are demonstrated in Figure 14.3.

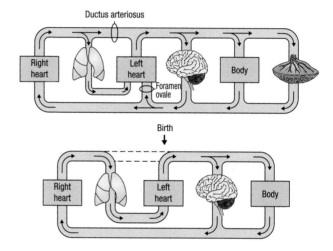

Figure 14.3 Comparison of fetal (parallel) with adult (series) circulation.

TABLE 14.1 Comparisons in Delayed Cord Clamping Between Term and Preterm Neonates

Preterm Neonates	Term Neonates
Benefits	**Benefits**
• Reduced need for transfusion	• Increased hemoglobin and hematocrit
• Improved blood pressure	• Reduced risk for iron deficiency anemia in the first year
• Decreased use of inotropes	• Potential for improved neurodevelopmental outcomes
• Decreased rate of sepsis	**Risks**
• Reduced risk of intraventricular hemorrhage	• Increased risk for phototherapy
Risks	• Hyperviscosity syndrome (IDM)
• Delay in initial steps of neonatal resuscitation	• Cardiac overload (infants with CHD)
• Risk for hypothermia	

CHD, congenital heart disease; IDM, infant of a diabetic mother.

Source: Adapted from Martin, R. J., Fanaroff, A. A., & Walsh, M.C. (Eds.). (2006). *Faranoff and Martin's neonatal–perinatal medicine: Diseases of the fetus and infant* (8th ed., p. 277). Philadelphia, PA: Elsevier-Mosby.

TRANSITIONAL ISSUES WITH PREMATURITY

In 2013, the ACOG Committee on Obstetric Practice and the Society for Maternal–Fetal Medicine (SMFM) introduced a vocabulary of terms associated with gestational age. These are proposed to reduce variation and increase consistency in practices. *Early term* is used to designate those neonates born between 37 0/7 and 38 6/7 weeks of gestation, and *full term* identifies those neonates born between 39 0/7 and 40 6/7 weeks of gestation. Neonates born between 41 0/7 and 41 6/7 weeks of gestation are labeled *later term*. Finally, the *postterm* neonate is one born after 42 0/7 weeks of gestation (ACOG & SMFM, 2013b).

Neonates born prior to 37 0/7 weeks of gestation are considered preterm; however, terminology used to classify subgroups of preterm neonates varies and definitions are not well articulated. Neonates born between 34 0/7 and 36 6/7 weeks are often regarded as *late preterm* (Engle, 2006). Neonates born between 32 0/7 and 33 6/7 weeks may be termed *moderately* preterm, whereas neonates born between 28 0/7 and 31 6/7 weeks may be termed *very* preterm. Neonates born less than 28 weeks of gestation are considered *extremely* preterm (Figure 14.4; World Health Organization [WHO], 2018a).

Between 1983 and 2004, the birth rate for preterm neonates (those born prior to 37 0/7 weeks' gestation) rose from 9.6% to 12.5%; three major theories have been proposed as to the reason for this. First, there is improved gestational dating through the use of early ultrasound. Second, there is continued delivery of multifetal pregnancies related to assisted reproductive technologies. Finally, maternal health risks may mandate the early delivery of a fetus (Greenberg, Narendran, Schibler, Warner, & Haberman, 2014). For example, premature or prolonged rupture of membranes often involves the administration of maternal antibiotics and tocolytics. These medications can negatively impact the neonate (Greenberg et al., 2014). Antibiotic use during pregnancy can increase risk for spontaneous abortions, congenital malformations, and even childhood otitis media (Muanda, Sheehy, & Bérard, 2017a, 2017b; Pedersen, Stokholm, Thorsen, Mora-Jenses, & Bisgaard, 2017). Maternal tocolytic use is associated with transient postnatal respiratory depression (Swanson & Kinkin, 2015).

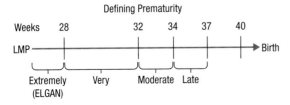

Figure 14.4 Timeline of prematurity.

ELGAN, extremely-low-gestational-age newborn; LMP, last menstrual period.

The transition to extrauterine life and associated mortality and morbidity risks for preterm neonates are inversely related to gestational age at birth. The risk for poor outcomes, defined as *death* or *lifelong handicap*, is higher in lower gestational ages. Preterm birth is associated with increased risk of morbidity with virtually each body system. For example, bleeding can occur in the fragile germinal matrix in the brain and precipitate an intraventricular hemorrhage (IVH), the lungs can become chronically damaged from artificial ventilator support and predispose the premature neonate to bronchopulmonary dysplasia (BPD), or damage to the intestinal mucosa can increase the risk for necrotizing enterocolitis (NEC). Furthermore, the preterm neonate is wholly at risk for infection throughout their time in the hospital, which can lead to other comorbidities (Greenberg et al., 2014).

MATERNAL HEALTH INFLUENCES

Placenta Previa

Placenta previa, a condition of abnormal placentation in which the internal cervical os is completely or nearly covered by placental tissue, is often characterized by its classic symptom of painless vaginal bleeding. The incidence is estimated at four per 1,000 live births.

The strongest risk factor for placenta previa is a prior caesarean delivery. It is theorized that uterine scarring may impact both implantation and placentation, indicating failed decidualization (Jauniaux, Bhide, & Wright, 2017). Other risk factors include advanced maternal age (>35 years), increasing parity, maternal race (Asian race is at highest risk), use of cigarettes, cocaine use, and repeated fertility treatments. Placenta previa is also more likely to occur with multiple-gestation pregnancies versus singletons (Cresswell, Ronsmans, Calvert, & Filippi, 2013; Francois & Foley, 2017; Oyelese & Smulian, 2006; Walfisch & Sheiner, 2016).

Placenta previa can be classified as complete or marginal (Figure 14.5). Complete placenta previa is diagnosed when the internal opening of the cervix or internal cervical os is entirely covered by the placenta. However, in cases in which the placenta does not cover the cervical os, but is attached within 2 to 3 cm from the opening, the condition is categorized as marginal placenta previa. Though no longer recommended for use, a third classification of low-lying placenta previa was a category used to describe cases in which an accurate determination regarding placental location could not be confirmed. Use of this term is no longer recommended due largely to difficulty validating the need for cesarean delivery (Cresswell et al., 2013).

The pathogenesis relates to thinning of the uterine wall that normally occurs during the third trimester. Typically, placental implantation will take place in the fundus, as opposed to implantation occurring in the lower segment, as seen with placenta previa. When this occurs, thinning continues at the site of implantation, causing interruption in placental

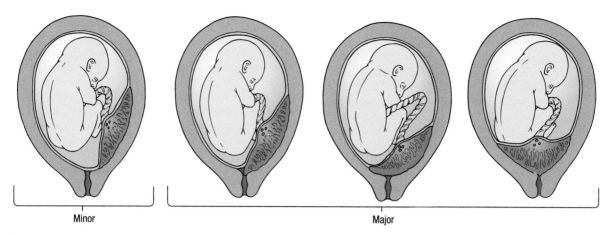

Figure 14.5 Placenta previa. Classification into "major" and "minor" placenta previa depends on the distance of the placenta from the internal os. It is also important to note whether the placenta is anterior or posterior, as cesarean section is more difficult through an anterior placenta.

attachment as the uterus prepares for labor. As a result, hemorrhage may occur and persist from the inability of the thin-walled uterus to constrict bleeding vessels. This may create a cycle of bleeding that stimulates uterine contractions, which are followed by continued bleeding. As labor progresses and causes cervical change in the form of dilation and effacement, the potential for hemorrhage increases from continued separation of the placenta from the uterine wall (Oyelese & Smulian, 2006; Walfisch & Sheiner, 2016).

Classic manifestations include painless vaginal bleeding after 20 weeks of gestation. The absence of pain with bleeding aids in differentiating this diagnosis from other conditions of abnormal placentation, such as abruptio placenta (Walfisch & Sheiner, 2016).

The effect of placenta previa on future pregnancies depends on the severity of intervention necessary to control the complications of previa at delivery. Intrapartum hemorrhages may require blood transfusions or even an emergency hysterectomy. As advanced maternal age is a risk, subsequent years between pregnancy may affect the maternal risks associated with placenta previa, as is the continued use of nicotine and/or illicit drugs (Gurol-Urganci et al., 2011).

Abruptio Placentae/Placental Abruption

Abruptio placentae, a condition of abnormal placentation, occurs when separation of the placenta takes place prior to childbirth (Figure 14.6). Abruptio placentae is reported in approximately 1% of all pregnancies both in the United States and worldwide. This condition, also known as *placental abruption*, involves separation of a normally implanted placenta from the uterus and typically takes place in the third trimester of pregnancy, but may be diagnosed any time after 20 weeks of gestation. The separation of the placenta from the uterine wall often occurs as a result of bleeding, which has great

potential to develop into a life-threatening hemorrhage (Ananth et al., 2016).

Several factors are thought to predispose or precipitate risk for development of abruptio placentae. These commonly range from, though are not limited to, (a) previous abruption, (b) maternal hypertension, (c) cigarette smoking, (d) cocaine use, (e) advanced maternal age, (f) multiparity, and (g) abdominal trauma. The risk of perinatal death occurring as a result of abruptio placentae is largely dependent on gestational age. Recent literature reveals that up to 60% of abruptions occur prior to 37 weeks' gestation (Ananth et al., 2016).

The pathogenesis involves rupture of maternal or fetal–placental vessels located in the decidua basalis. The accumulation of blood from hemorrhage acts to separate layers of the decidua from the maternal side of the placenta. Further separation may ensue from the formation of a decidual hematoma. As a result, placental tissue in the detached area is destroyed and unable to facilitate gas exchange, provide nutrients, or eliminate waste, each of which may contribute to fetal compromise (Ananth et al., 2016; Tikkanen et al., 2013).

Common clinical manifestations include vaginal bleeding, uterine contractions, abdominal or back pain, and uterine tenderness. The uterus may also be rigid or board-like on palpation. Many women may report experiencing decreased fetal movement, a symptom indicative of fetal compromise. Further fetal assessment may reveal the presence of nonreassuring fetal heart rate (FHR) patterns.

The recurrence risk (with future pregnancies) after one affected pregnancy is estimated at 5% to 15%, and 20% to 25% with additional pregnancies. When an abruption is associated with a fetal demise there is a 7% chance of a repeat outcome in future pregnancies (Francois & Foley, 2017). Perinatal death depends on the severity of placental separation and maternal distress. Fetal morbidities are largely related to hypoxemia, asphyxia, and prematurity.

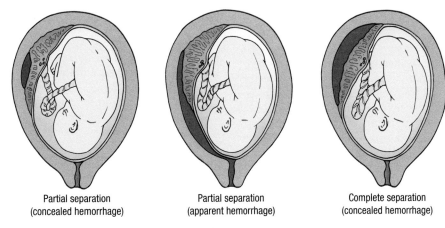

Partial separation
(concealed hemorrhage)

Partial separation
(apparent hemorrhage)

Complete separation
(concealed hemorrhage)

Figure 14.6 Abruptio placentae.

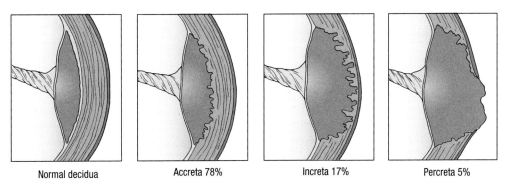

Normal decidua

Accreta 78%

Increta 17%

Percreta 5%

Figure 14.7 Placenta accreta, increta, and percreta.

Placenta Accreta, Increta, and Percreta

Placenta accreta is a condition involving superficial placental attachment to the uterine myometrium; it is a serious complication that can occur with placenta previa (Figure 14.7).

The incidence of placenta accreta has increased in recent years, occurring in nearly one in 730 deliveries, due to the overall increase in cesarean delivery, a significant risk factor for development of the condition. Both placenta increta and percreta occur at significantly lower rates than accreta, noted to occur in 17% and 5% of conditions of abnormal placentation, respectively (Cunningham et al., 2018; Oyelese & Smulian, 2006).

Although implantation typically takes place in decidua, with conditions of morbidly adherent placenta, which also include placenta increta and percreta, implantation extends into the uterine wall or surrounding organs. Increta occurs when the placenta penetrates the myometrium, whereas percreta involves placental penetration that extends through the myometrium to the uterine serosa. Placental attachment with percreta may also involve organs, including the bladder or rectum (Cunningham et al., 2018; Oyelese & Smulian, 2006).

Placenta accreta is strongly associated with any intervention that alters the uterine endometrial–myometrial integrity. The most common cause of these alterations occurs as a result of cesarean delivery. Over the last 50 years, concurrent with the increase in cesarean deliveries, there has been an estimated tenfold increase in the instance of placenta accreta (Jauniaux & Bhide, 2017).

The pathogenesis is well understood. As placenta accreta involves a partial or complete absence of decidua basalis, the absence results in direct attachment or invasion of placental villi into the myometrium. Severity is determined by the degree of villous invasion into the placenta. When the villi adhere to the myometrium without invading it, placenta accreta, also known as placenta accreta vera, occurs. Placenta increta occurs when the villi invade the myometrium; placenta percreta occurs when the villi invade or penetrate the uterine serosa (Jauniaux & Bhide, 2017).

Clinical manifestations in undiagnosed cases include severe hemorrhage accompanied by unsuccessful manual removal of the placenta. Once the fetus is delivered, the placenta is unable to separate from the uterine wall or surrounding organs, leading to profuse bleeding and shock.

There is general agreement, despite limited data, that women who suffer a placenta accreta and go on to conceive additional children incur a higher risk for adverse outcomes, including a recurrent placenta previa, uterine rupture, and peripartum hysterectomy (Jauniaux et al., 2017). Complications from uterine rupture and obstetric or antepartum hemorrhage can be critical for both the mother and fetus. Hemorrhage that occurs as a result of conditions related to abnormal placentation have great potential to alter uteroplacental circulation, thus reducing fetal oxygen supply. This gives rise to a non-reassuring fetal heart pattern, which is identified by way of cardiotocography (electronic fetal monitoring). When maternal and/or fetal compromise arise from conditions causing obstetric hemorrhage, emergent cesarean delivery may be carried out in an effort to optimize birth outcomes (ACOG & SMFM, 2013a).

When compared to vaginal or planned cesarean births, emergent cesarean delivery has been linked to increased risks for negative maternal or fetal outcomes, including complications from anesthetic administration and accidental fetal injury. However, the fundamental consideration regarding the decision to deliver in emergency situations is achieving an optimal outcome in the resolution of maternal and/or fetal threats to safety and reduction of morbidity and mortality (ACOG & SMFM, 2013a; ACOG, SMFM, Caughey, Cahill, Guise, & Rouse, 2014).

Chorioamnionitis

Intraamniotic infection, or chorioamnionitis (CA), is a perinatal condition characterized by inflammation of the placenta, decidua, amniotic fluid, fetal membranes, or fetus (ACOG, Heine, Puopolo, Beigi, Silverman, & El-Sayed 2017; Ericson & Laughon, 2015). Acute clinical CA is estimated to implicate 2% to 5% of all deliveries (ACOG, 2017a; J. Martin, Hamilton, Osterman, Driscoll, & Matthews, 2017). Comparatively, histological CA is estimated to affect between 10% and 15% of term and 40% and 70% of premature deliveries (J. Martin et al., 2017; Tita & Andrews, 2010). It is estimated that women diagnosed with CA are 40% more likely to have a cesarean delivery, despite the mounting data that expediting delivery following antibiotic treatment for clinical CA is not correlated with reduced maternal or neonatal morbidity (Bommarito, Gross, Willers, Fraser, & Olsen, 2016).

Establishing an understanding of the differences between acute clinical and histologic CA is important for the neonatal advanced practice clinician (Table 14.2). Once an obstetric care provider has diagnosed CA, it is his or her duty to communicate that finding to the neonatal advanced practice clinician to promote early identification, diagnosis, and treatment of the at-risk neonate (ACOG, 2017a). Risk factors for CA are provided in Table 14.3. Of note, neonatal sepsis risk models consider maternal group B *Streptococcus* colonization and peak intrapartum maternal temperature significant factors for predicting sepsis risk among term and premature neonates.

TABLE 14.2 Diagnostic Criterion for Chorioamnionitis

Category of Intraamniotic Infection	Criterion
Isolated maternal fever[a]	One of the following must be present: • Single oral temperature ≥39°C • Persistent oral temperature 38°–38.9°C for >30 minutes
Suspected intraamniotic infection	Intrapartum fever *and* one of the following must be present: • Leukocytosis • Purulent cervical drainage • Fetal tachycardia
Confirmed intraamniotic infection[b]	One of the following must be present: • Positive amniotic fluid test result (Gram stain or fluid culture) • Positive placental histology result indicating either infection or inflammation

NOTE: [a]Isolated maternal fever, with or without infection, is associated with poor short-term and long-term neonatal outcomes.
[b]Denotes the only objective method for diagnosing CA.

CA, chorioamnionitis.

Source: American College of Obstetricians and Gynecologists, Heine, R. P., Puopolo, K. M., Beigi, R., Silverman, N. S., & El-Sayed, Y. Y. (2017). ACOG Committee Opinion No. 2: Intrapartum management of intraamniotic infections. Retrieved from https://www.acog.org/-/media/Committee-Opinions/Committee-on-Obstetric-Practice/co712.pdf?dmc=1&ts=20170811T1344408044

TABLE 14.3 Proposed Risk Factors for Intraamniotic Infection

Risk Factor

Genital tract pathogens (GBS, sexually transmitted infections)

GBS bacteriuria

Intrapartum internal uterine and fetal monitoring devices

Multiple intrapartum maternal digital examinations

Meconium stained amniotic fluid

Low parity

NOTE: ACOG emphasizes that these risk factors may not be independently associated with chorioamnionitis, but rather a consequence of prolonged rupture of membranes and duration of labor

GBS, group B Streptococcus.

Sources: American College of Obstetricians and Gynecologists, Heine, R. P., Puopolo, K. M., Beigi, R., Silverman, N. S., & El-Sayed, Y. Y. (2017). ACOG Committee Opinion No. 712: Intrapartum management of intraamniotic infection. Retrieved from https://www.acog.org/-/media/Committee-Opinions/Committee-on-Obstetric-Practice/co712.pdf?dmc=1&ts=20170811T1344408044; Martin, R. J., Fanaroff, A. A., & Walsh, M. C. (Eds.). (2015). *Fanaroff and Martin's neonatal–perinatal medicine: Diseases of the fetus and infant* (10th ed.). Philadelphia, PA: Elsevier/Saunders.

The pathogenesis of CA most commonly involves vertical, or ascending, transmission of polymicrobial organisms through the vaginal canal (Ericson & Laughon, 2015). With acute CA, loss of the mucus plug removes a functional (antimicrobial) and mechanical barrier. Pathogens thereby enter the intrauterine space and invade the gestational membranes (maternal decidua and fetal chorion and amnion). It is widely accepted that invasion of the maternal decidua precedes that of the fetal membranes. The introduction of pathogens to the gestational membranes invokes a proinflammatory response. When inflammation is present, CA disrupts normal placental transfer of nutrients, as well as placental barriers that protect the fetus (Greenberg et al., 2014). The inflammatory response involves the activation of transcription factors, cytokines, and the release of prostaglandins and metalloproteases. In aggregate, this cascade facilitates weakening and invasion of the maternal decidua, followed by invasion of the fetal chorion and amnionic cavity (Anders, Gaddy, Doster, & Aronoff, 2017; R. J. Martin et al., 2015).

Life-span implications to the neonate point to a contentious relationship among CA, BPD, and cerebral palsy (Greenberg et al., 2014). A recent population-based epidemiologic investigation of BPD and histologic CA among premature neonates found no relationship between cases of confirmed histologic CA and BPD following premature labor with or without prolonged rupture of membranes,

whereas alternative publications offer opposing conclusions (Maisonneuve et al., 2017). The risk for cerebral palsy secondary to CA is estimated at two per every 1,000 live births, with premature neonates among those with a particularly heightened risk (Oskoui, Coutinho, Dykeman, Jetté, & Pringsheim, 2013).

Obstetric Hemorrhage

Obstetric hemorrhage may be defined as excessive uterine or vaginal bleeding that exceeds 1,000 mL, which occurs during the antepartum or postpartum period (ACOG, 2017a). Obstetric hemorrhage is one of the leading causes of maternal morbidity and mortality throughout the world, accounting for 11.5% of all pregnancy-related deaths in the United States between 2011 and 2014 (Centers for Disease Control and Prevention [CDC], 2018). Comparatively, *antepartum hemorrhage* is characterized by bleeding that occurs after 20 weeks gestation, often attributed to placenta previa, abruptio placenta, or other conditions of abnormal placentation (accreta, increta; Fan et al., 2017; Francois & Foley, 2017). Postpartum hemorrhage involves bleeding that occurs during the immediate postpartum period and through 12 weeks after delivery, often caused by uterine atony (most common), lacerations or trauma, and inherited bleeding disorders (Paidas et al., 2011). Risk factors for postpartum hemorrhage are provided in Table 14.4.

Recall that significant hemodynamic changes occur during pregnancy, the first of these being an increase in the woman's plasma volume. Pregnant women also increase their red blood cell (RBC) mass by an expected 20% to 30%. The maternal cardiac output increases by 30% to 50% to manage the increased volume and increased baseline heart rate. Concurrently, SVR falls. Finally, fibrinogen and the majority of procoagulant blood factors, most notably factors VII, VIII,

TABLE 14.4 Risk Factors for Postpartum Hemorrhage

Prior history of hemorrhage

Fetal macrosomia

Maternal inherited bleeding disorders

Multiple gestation

Prolonged labor >12 hours

Induction of labor

Maternal obesity

Advanced maternal age

Low parity

Source: Paidas, M. J., Hossain, N., Shamsi, T., Rodger, M. A., Langhoff-Rose, J., & Lockwood, C. J. (2011). *Hemostasis and thrombosis in obstetrics & gynecology*. Chichester, UK: Wiley-Blackwell.

TABLE 14.5 Common Causes for Postpartum Hemorrhage and Associated Pathogenesis	
Cause	**Pathogenesis**
Uterine atony	Failed contraction and retraction of uterine myometrial fibers
Lacerations or trauma	Increased regional blood supply
Inherited bleeding disorders	Delayed or impaired hemostasis

Sources: Giordano, R., Cacciatore, A., Cignini, P., Vigna, R., & Romano, M. (2010). Antepartum haemorrhage. *Journal of Prenatal Medicine*, 4(1), 12–16. Retrieved from https://www.prenatalmedicine.com/common/php/portierc.php?ID=0aaa4ed18afc2b83676696fe1290dfcf; Paidas, M. J., Hossain, N., Shamsi, T., Rodger, M. A., Langhoff-Rose, J. & Lockwood, C. J. (2011). *Hemostasis and thrombosis in obstetrics & gynecology*. Chichester, UK: Wiley-Blackwell.

X, and von Willebrand factor, increase during pregnancy. Under normal circumstances, suppression of clot busting and a state of hypercoagulability arises. Although these systemic changes are vital for maternal hemodynamic stability during pregnancy, the combination also facilitates a rapid decompensation during an obstetric hemorrhage (Francois & Foley, 2017; Key, Makris, & Lillicrap, 2017). Table 14.5 lists the most common causes for postpartum hemorrhage with their likely pathogenesis (Giordano, Cacciatore, Cignini, Vigna, & Romano, 2010).

When a maternal hemorrhage occurs, the body's arterial and venous compartments vasoconstrict, but can only compensate with up to 20% of total volume loss. With massive hemorrhage, cardiovascular collapse occurs, as cardiac output falls due to decreased preload, leading to poor end-organ perfusion. Shock and acidosis thereby ensue and, if left uncorrected, will result in maternal, and possibly fetal, demise (Francois & Foley, 2017). The long-term effects to the liveborn neonate subject to an obstetric hemorrhage are dictated by its etiology and severity.

DELIVERY METHODS

The ACOG and the SMFM have long discouraged nonindicated delivery before 39 weeks of gestation. The reason for this long-standing principle is that the neonatal risks of late-preterm (34 0/7–36 6/7 weeks of gestation) and early-term (37 0/7–38 6/7 weeks of gestation) births are well established (ACOG, 2017a). Delivery methods include planned vaginal delivery, operative vaginal delivery, elective cesarean delivery without labor, cesarean delivery with trial of labor, and emergency cesarean delivery.

Vaginal Delivery

Vaginal deliveries, including planned and operative vaginal deliveries, account for approximately 67.9% of all deliveries within the United States (CDC, 2017). Planned vaginal births are associated with fewer postpartum risks, including a lower incidence of postpartum hemorrhage, blood transfusions, procedural complications, infection, and anesthesia-related complications (ACOG, 2017a). Neonatal benefits include earlier onset of breastfeeding, with reductions in rates of iatrogenic prematurity, hypothermia, hypoglycemia, retained fetal lung fluid, and other causes for respiratory distress during the immediate postnatal period. Finally, the mother–neonate dyad often benefits from earlier initiation of breastfeeding practices and incurs a shorter length of stay (ACOG, 2017a; Ditzenberger, 2013; R. J. Martin et al., 2015). Contraindications to a planned vaginal delivery may include, but are not limited to, multiple gestation; fetal malposition; maternal disease states, such as obesity and diabetes mellitus; or other safety issues. One particular mechanical complication that precludes a vaginal birth is umbilical cord prolapse, which may present at any time during the intrapartum period and warrants a cesarean delivery.

Umbilical Cord Prolapse. Prolapse of the umbilical cord has been noted to occur in 0.6% of all births within the United States (Gibbons, O'Herlihy, & Murphy, 2014). The prolapse may be described as overt or occult (Figure 14.8). An overt prolapse occurs when the umbilical cord is positioned in front of the presenting fetal part. An occult prolapse occurs when the cord is positioned adjacent to the presenting part. Both conditions can lead to umbilical cord compression or occlusion and resultant fetal hypoxia (Royal College of Obstetricians and Gynaecologists, 2014).

Risk factors include malpresentation, prematurity, polyhydramnios, or having a long umbilical cord. In addition, the implementation of various obstetric interventions is known to increase risk of cord prolapse. These interventions include amniotomy (particularly when the presenting part is unengaged), induction of labor, and amnioinfusion, among others (Gibbons et al., 2014).

The pathogenesis is well understood. Umbilical cord prolapse is typically seen when the presenting fetal part is unengaged or has not yet entered into the pelvic inlet. The condition is thought to occur as a result of the increased force produced by the flow of amniotic fluid entering the lower uterine segment, which happens to be free from the presenting part of the fetus during rupture of membranes.

Clinical manifestations include the sudden onset of moderate to severe variable decelerations. Severe, prolonged bradycardia may also rapidly occur in women previously noted to have a reassuring or category I FHR tracing. Often changes in FHR patterns are identified soon after the rupture of membranes or other associated obstetric procedures. In addition, palpation of an overt cord

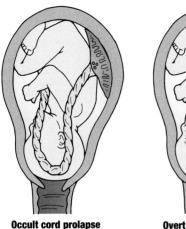 

Occult cord prolapse　　　**Overt cord prolapse**

Figure 14.8 Umbilical cord prolapse.

prolapse during bimanual vaginal exam has been reported, although rare (Gibbons et al., 2014). Neonatal life-span implications related to prolapse of the umbilical cord are largely dependent on the severity and duration of cord compression.

Operative Vaginal Delivery. Operative vaginal deliveries involve the use of obstetric instruments to expedite delivery in cases of maternal or fetal compromise. In 2015, vacuum-assisted deliveries accounted for 3.14% of all vaginal births, whereas forceps accounted for 0.56%, a decline from prior years (CDC, 2017).

Certain criteria must be met to qualify for an operative-vaginal delivery. Criteria include: (a) complete cervical dilation, (b) rupture of membranes, (c) engagement of the fetal head, and (d) an empty maternal bladder. Contraindications include extreme prematurity, demineralizing disease, bleeding disorders, unengaged head, or malpresentation (ACOG, 2015).

Although operative vaginal delivery can be electively used to reduce fetal exposure to abnormal labor patterns or threats of compromise, the procedure is only indicated for use when it can be implemented both efficiently and effectively. Indications include inappropriate duration of the second phase of labor, nonreassuring FHR pattern, or when Valsalva maneuvers or other maternal pushing techniques are contraindicated. Although many cases of obstetric hemorrhage require cesarean delivery, some women with abruptio placentae may deliver vaginally depending on the severity of abruption and/or blood loss. In cases of fetal compromise or acidemia denoted by category III FHR tracings, operative vaginal delivery may be indicated when birth is imminent. In addition, operative vaginal delivery may also be permitted with marginal placenta previa. Under both circumstances, if vaginal birth with assistance is not possible, cesarean delivery is suggested (Palatnik et al., 2016).

Forceps-assisted delivery. Forceps are instruments in which blades are used to apply traction to the fetal head in an effort to facilitate vaginal delivery. A variety of types are available and are selected based on fetal position, station (level of fetal head in relation to maternal ischial spine) or descent, and size of the fetal head or maternal pelvis. On application, the forceps should be used to grasp the fetal head while using a pulling force during uterine contractions to expedite fetal descent. The forceps should be removed prior to entrance of the largest transverse diameter of the fetal head through the vaginal canal. After this time, delivery of the fetal head should be able to occur without assistance (Aiken, Aiken, Brockelsby, & Scott, 2014).

The ACOG (2015) classifies forceps deliveries based on fetal station and rotation, a denotation characterizing degrees of difficulty associated with the procedure. The classification includes outlet forceps, low forceps, and midforceps. Low-forceps deliveries are typically deemed uncomplicated for both mother and the fetus, whereas midforceps deliveries tend to present greater risk for injury and are recommended to implement with caution (ACOG, 2015).

Vacuum-assisted delivery. Vacuum extraction is another mode of operative vaginal delivery that may be considered as an alternative to using forceps. The procedure involves use of a cup attached to a handle for traction and a suction device or pump that operates to create a vacuum. Instruments used for vacuum extraction vary in design and allow a vacuum to be created manually or to be generated using electrical suction. Use of these devices requires a technique that involves accurate placement of the cup onto the fetal head with application of suction and traction. Suction is typically applied with traction and not applied at pressures measuring greater than 600 mmHg. Traction should be exerted simultaneously with uterine contractions and/or maternal pushing efforts and directed along the pelvic curve to assist in guiding the fetal head through the birth canal (Ghidini, Stewart, Pezzullo, & Locatelli, 2017).

Neonatal life-span implications are largely dependent on skill or proficiency of the provider conducting the procedure. Vacuum-associated birth injuries may involve bruising, lacerations, external ocular trauma, cephalohematoma, and a brachial plexus injury. Rare, life-threatening complications include intracranial hemorrhage or IVH. In rare instances, death may occur (Ghidini et al., 2017; Palatnik et al., 2016).

Cesarean Delivery

Cesarean delivery accounts for more than 1 million major operations performed in the United States annually and is the most common major surgical procedure undertaken around the world. In the United States in 2015, 32% of all births involved cesarean deliveries, marking a steady decline from 2012, yet alarmingly high compared to the 5% rate of cesarean deliveries reported in 1960 (CDC, 2017; Martin et al., 2017). Factors that contribute to the overall high rate of cesarean deliveries include (a) failed induction of labor; (b) fetal malpresentation; (c) maternal disease (i.e., obesity, diabetes mellitus); and (d) maternal request/preference (Figure 14.9; ACOG et al., 2014; Berghella, Mackeen, & Jauniaux, 2017; J. Martin et al., 2017).

For some women, symptoms may arise during the antepartum or intrapartum period that can only be resolved through cesarean delivery. The presentation of such symptoms supports the need for birth using the invasive, surgical procedure (Dahlke et al., 2013; Lothian, 2014). Medically indicated cesarean deliveries may be warranted for fetal well-being, maternal health, or maternal–fetal indications (ACOG, 2014; Lothian, 2014).

Fetal indications are recognized by nonreassuring heart rate patterns that may indicate developing fetal acidosis. Maternal health indications warranting cesarean delivery can be considered medical or mechanical in nature. In order of frequency, the most common maternal–fetal risks warranting cesarean delivery include fetal cephalopelvic disproportion (CPD) or shoulder dystocia, prior cesarean delivery, nonreassuring FHR patterns, and fetal malpresentations (Berghella et al., 2017). Other examples include Marfan syndrome or cases in which the avoidance of intracranial pressure (ICP) is indicated. Maternal–fetal indications describe conditions that would pose a threat to the life of both the mother and fetus should attempts for a vaginal delivery continue. Abruptio placenta is a common example of this.

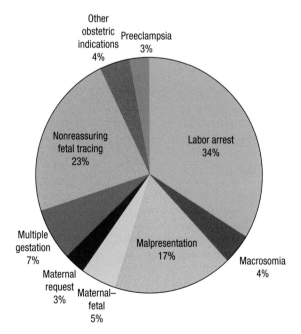

Figure 14.9 Indications for primary cesarean delivery.

Source: Data adapted from American College of Obstetricians and Gynecologists, Society for Maternal–Fetal Medicine, Caughey, A. B., Cahill, A. G., Guise, J.-M., & Rouse, D. J. (2014). Safe prevention of the primary cesarean delivery. *American Journal of Obstetrics & Gynecology, 123,* 693–711. doi:10.1016/j.ajog.2014.01.026

When conditions compromise maternal or fetal well-being during childbirth, the decision must be made by healthcare providers to determine the urgency of delivery. Intrapartum cesarean delivery classified as emergent should be carried out immediately if presenting conditions pose life-threatening risks to the mother or fetus (Veltman, 2017). Recommendations endorsed by the ACOG (2017) and the American Academy of Pediatrics (AAP) suggest that in these circumstances, a 30-minute decision-to-incision interval be observed (ACOG et al., 2016; Schauberger & Chauhan, 2009).

Classifying the Fetal Heart Rate. Categories for classification of the FHR are based on definitions of normal cardiotocography (CTG). Normal CTG is defined as a baseline FHR between 110 bpm and 160 bpm and moderate FHR variability (variation in FHR baseline) ranging between 6 and 25 bpm (ACOG, 2017a).

Using the three-tiered system, normal baseline FHR and variability are classified as category I and indicative of normal fetal acid–base balance. Category II findings are considered to be indeterminate, as FHR monitor readings in this category are interpreted as not demonstrating findings that can be considered as category I or III. This category is characterized by bradycardia, tachycardia, minimal or absent variability, variable decelerations, or late decelerations occurring with moderate FHR variability. Although this categorization should be closely evaluated, additional surveillance and/or monitoring tools should be implemented to further evaluate fetal health and determine the need for prompt delivery (ACOG, 2017a).

Last, category III FHR monitoring tracings are determinant of abnormal fetal acid–base balance and require prompt intervention to resolve compromising fetal patterns. Examples of compromising fetal patterns include absent FHR variability occurring with persistent bradycardia, late, or variable decelerations. Prompt interventions may include maternal oxygen administration, position changes, discontinuation of oxytocic agents, or treatment of maternal hypotension and/or uterine tachysystole (ACOG, 2014, 2017a).

Currently, a three-tier classification system is used for FHR monitoring; however, a revised five-tier system has been proposed to ensure early recognition of the at-risk fetus and expedited delivery (ACOG, 2014, 2017a; Gamboa et al., 2017). Research conducted by Gamboa et al. (2017) reveals that the recently revised five-tier system demonstrated greater interobserver agreement when used to determine the presence of neonatal acidemia. A recent study compared interobserver agreement with the three-tier and five-tier systems. The three-tier system showed greater sensitivity and lower specificity in detecting neonatal acidemia and severe metabolic acidemia, compared with the five-tier system. The author noted interobserver agreement was moderate for both systems, as both systems demonstrated comparable predictive ability for detecting fetal acidemia (Table 14.6; Gamboa et al., 2017).

TABLE 14.6 Comparison of FHR Evaluative Systems

Three-Tiered System	Five-Tiered System
Category 1 Tracings strongly predictive of normal fetal acid–base status; may be monitored in a routine manner and no specific action is required.	**Green** No acidemia; very low risk of evolution; no indications for delivery
Category 2 Tracings are not predictive of abnormal fetal acid–base status; tracings require evaluation and continued surveillance and reevaluation, taking into account the entire associated clinical circumstances.	**Blue** No central fetal acidemia (oxygenation); low risk of evolution; begin preparations for delivery
Category 3 Tracings are associated with abnormal fetal acid–base status at the time of observation. Category III FHR tracings require prompt evaluation. If a category III tracing does not resolve with conservative intervention measures, delivery should be undertaken.	**Yellow** No central fetal acidemia, but FHR pattern suggests intermittent reductions in O_2, which may result in fetal O_2 debt; moderate risk of evolution; begin preparations for delivery and increase surveillance
	Orange Fetus potentially on verge of decompensation; high risk of evolution; prepare for urgent delivery
	Red Evidence of actual or impending damaging fetal asphyxia; at highest possible evolution; deliver emergently

FHR, fetal heart rate.

Nonreassuring Fetal Heart Status. During labor and childbirth, regularly occurring uterine contractions may cause transient disruptions in fetal oxygenation. These disruptions are often well tolerated by the fetus through compensatory responses that are dependent on maternal respiration, circulation, and placental perfusion. Compensatory responses include a redistribution of blood flow and adjustment to anaerobic metabolism, which prioritizes oxygenation to the vital organs (fetal heart and brain) and is essential in preserving their function (Ugwumadu, 2014; Yli & Kjellmer, 2016).

Prolonged periods of fetal hypoxia or acidosis may lead to a decreased FHR and reduction in gross body movements, a rescue effort to reserve minimally available oxygen stores for the vital organs (ACOG, 2014). Although these compensatory mechanisms are often successful in the prevention of sequalae associated with fetal asphyxia, much of this success is dependent on overall fetal and placental health and available stores of glycogen, in addition to the occurrence and severity of hypoxic episodes (Yli & Kjellmer, 2016).

The pathogenesis of the shift from normal to nonreassuring FHT relates to decreases in placental blood flow and reduced gas exchange. Over time, the fetal compensatory mechanisms fail to maintain homeostasis, which manifests as alterations in heart rate patterns and/or fetal movements (ACOG, 2014). Failed recognition of this decompensatory cascade promulgates a prolonged state of fetal asphyxia, which can contribute to untoward outcomes, including neurological or cognitive impairment, hypoxic–ischemic injury, and intellectual disability (Ugwumadu, 2014; Yli & Kjellmer, 2016).

Use of Anesthesia. Anesthesia used for cesarean delivery must be safely administered with goals to not only provide comfort for the mother, but also in a manner that ensures fetal well-being. Regional anesthesia is typically used with planned cesarean deliveries. During emergent situations, maternal or fetal well-being may require the provision of general anesthesia.

Regional anesthesia may be administered by way of spinal, epidural, or combined spinal–epidural anesthesia, given as a single injection or continuous infusion. Medications include local anesthetics, intrathecal or epidural opioids, and other adjuvants that may comprise adrenergic agonists. Following placement of regional anesthetic using either technique, fetal assessment should be conducted until the desired sensory level is achieved. Fetal bradycardia is the most commonly reported adverse effect of maternally administered regional anesthesia yet occurs in relatively few (8%) cases. In addition, transient decreases in the baseline FHR have been reported.

General anesthesia may be indicated for emergent cesarean delivery when timing is paramount to ensure a safe and effective maternal or fetal outcome. Other indications for general anesthesia include maternal anticoagulant use, hypovolemia, or noted infection at epidural or spinal anesthesia placement sites, though women with systemic bacterial or viral infection may receive regional anesthesia in the absence of other contraindications (American Society of Anesthesiologists Task Force on Obstetric Anesthesia and the Society for Obstetric Anesthesia and Perinatology, 2016). Fetal risks associated with general anesthesia focus primarily on fetal hypoxia. The threat of fetal hypoxia occurs as a result of alterations in umbilical cord and uteroplacental blood flow, thereby decreasing oxygen delivery to the fetus. As such, the ACOG recommends prompt initiation of the cesarean delivery with a maximum window of 90 seconds between uterine incision and delivery of the neonate. Prolonged fetal exposure to general anesthesia and adjunct medications may manifest as postnatal respiratory depression. In such cases, a neonatal resuscitation team, which includes an advanced practice clinician who holds practice, prescriptive, and procedural permissions specific to advanced airway management, should be immediately available to assess the neonate's well-being and facilitate an optimal transition to extrauterine life.

Procedural Risks. Accidental fetal lacerations are the most common cesarean-related procedural injury, reported in approximately 78% of all cases (ACOG et al., 2014). Most lacerations are mild and occur on the scalp or face but can occur on the extremities (Figure 14.10; Carrapato, Ferreira, & Wataganara, 2017). Although the risk for injury with cesarean delivery is typically low, these injuries are most commonly seen when membranes are ruptured prior to delivery or in emergent situations. Preventative strategies include moving the uterine wall or removing abdominal retractors prior to making the uterine incision (Dahlke et al., 2013).

(A)   (B)

Figure 14.10   (A) Fetal laceration after cesarean section with application of steristrip adhesive. (B) Same laceration at 12 years of age. Laceration is now wider and longer (approximately 10cm in length).

Source: Gajjar, K., & Spencer, C. (2009). Fetal laceration injury during cesarean section and its long-term sequelae: A case report. *American Journal of Obstetrics & Gynecology, 201*(4), e5–e7. doi:10.1016/j.ajog.2009.07.055

BIRTH INJURIES AND IMPLICATIONS ACROSS THE LIFE SPAN

The ultimate goal of labor and delivery is to have a healthy baby and mother. Unfortunately, this outcome is not always achieved. A *birth injury* is defined as an injury to the neonate during the birth process (Hurst, 2015). Birth injuries run a spectrum from mild and self-limiting to so severe they result in the death of the neonate. They are classified by location or etiology. Birth injuries often are a result of a difficult or prolonged delivery process (Parsons, Seay, & Jacobson, 2016). The risk of birth injuries increases with fetal prematurity, macrosomia, and in cases of malpresentation such as breech, transverse, and face or brow positioning and shoulder dystocia (Mangurten, Puppala, & Prazad, 2015; R. J. Martin et al., 2015). Maternal conditions that increase the risk of birth injuries are a contracted pelvis, cephalopelvic disproportion, and prolonged or precipitous labor (Mangurten et al., 2015). Instruments, such as fetal scalp electrodes, forceps, and vacuum extractors, are also associated with an increase in birth injuries (Mangurten et al., 2015).

Assessment is the first step in the diagnosis and treatment of any birth injury. A general assessment for location and size of bruises (ecchymosis), edema, hematomas, cuts, lacerations, and abrasions should be done in the first minutes of life. The neonate's posture and tone will give an indication of possible palsy, paralysis, or central nervous system damage. Therefore, it is particularly important to note and to determine the cause of any lack of flexion or asymmetrical movements. Vertex and breech are the most common birth presentations, so it is important to inspect the head and genital areas carefully.

Edema and bruising of the eyes are some of the most common birth traumas noted on the face. The edema usually subsides in the first 2 to 3 days of life without intervention (Mangurten et al., 2015). Subconjunctival hemorrhages may be seen after a normal uncomplicated delivery or after a prolonged or difficult second stage of labor. Bright-red patches on the bulbar conjunctiva are caused by obstruction to venous return by uterine contractions. This redness on the sclera usually resolves in a week to 10 days without intervention or long-term sequelae (Mangurten et al., 2015).

Careful inspection of male and female genitals for edema and patency of the urethra is necessary. If the urethra is obstructed, temporary hydronephrosis may occur. Bladder and voiding assessment are necessary to ensure the passage of urine is unobstructed. An edematous scrotum should be evaluated for hematomas and testicular torsion, which can be performed using Doppler ultrasonography. Testicular torsion interrupts blood flow and can lead to asymmetry of size. A comprehensive list of birth injuries with associated risk factors is presented in Table 14.7.

TABLE 14.7 Common Birth Injuries With Associated Risk Factors

Birth Injury	Risk Factors	Incidence
Injuries to the Head and Neck		
Extracranial hemorrhages		
• Caput succedaneum	Prolonged labor, primiparous mothers, vacuum-assisted delivery, large baby, small maternal pelvis	Common
• Cephalohematoma	Prolonged labor, primiparous mothers, forceps- or vacuum-assisted delivery, large baby, small maternal pelvis	Common
• Subgaleal hemorrhage	Prolonged labor, primiparous mothers, forceps, vacuum-assisted delivery with traction applied, large baby, small maternal pelvis	Uncommon
Intracranial hemorrhages		
• Intracerebellar hemorrhage	Preterm, difficult delivery	Uncommon
• Subdural hemorrhage	Prolonged labor, forceps, vacuum-assisted delivery	Uncommon
• Subarachnoid hemorrhage	Prolonged labor, forceps, vacuum-assisted delivery	Common
Skull fracture	Prolonged labor, primiparous mothers, difficult labor, vacuum extraction, forceps	Common
Facial palsy	Fetal position, prolonged labor, forceps, large baby, small maternal pelvis, increased pressure from maternal sacral promontory	Common
Vocal cord paralysis	Fetal malpresentation, breech, large baby, small maternal pelvis	Rare
Injuries to the Shoulders, Chest, and Other Bones		
Clavicular fracture	Large baby, small maternal pelvis, shoulder dystocia, breech	Common
Brachial plexus injuries	Fetal malpresentation, breech, increased traction on presenting part during delivery, large baby, small maternal pelvis	
• Erb's palsy		Common
• Klumpke's palsy		Rare
• Erb–Duchenne–Klumpke Paralysis		Uncommon
Phrenic nerve paralysis	Fetal malpresentation, breech, increased traction on presenting part during delivery, large baby, small maternal pelvis	Uncommon
Humerus fracture	Fetal malpresentation, breech, large baby, small maternal pelvis	Rare
Femur fracture	Breech	Rare
Injuries to the Abdomen		
Rupture of the liver	Breech, large baby, small maternal pelvis	Rare
Rupture of the spleen	Breech, large baby, small maternal pelvis	Rare
Rupture of the adrenal glands	Breech, large baby, small maternal pelvis	Rare

Injuries to the Head and Neck

Caput Succedaneum. Caput succedaneum is the most common extracranial scalp injury and is characterized by soft tissue swelling, usually of the presenting part of the scalp (Figure 14.11). Incidence increases to 10% to 20% in deliveries that are vacuum assisted (Volpe, 2018).

The injury is due to hemorrhagic edema superficial to the periosteum of the scalp causing discoloration at the site. Due to the pressure of the cervix on the presenting part, usually the scalp, venous and lymph flow are restricted, resulting in edema. Serum and/or blood accumulation results in the noted scalp edema.

Caput succedaneum edema is present at birth and usually does not grow in size after delivery. The edema is not bound by suture lines, has poorly defined borders, and can shift toward dependent positions. Pitting occurs with pressure, and ecchymosis, petechiae, or purpura may or may not be present. Differential diagnosis includes cephalohematoma. Caput succedaneum usually resolves in 24 to 72 hours, and there are no known long-term consequences. However, when caput succedaneum is accompanied by a skin laceration, there is the potential for infection and the possibility of scarring of the scalp, resulting in a lack of hair growth in the affected area.

Cephalohematoma. *Cephalohematoma* is a collection of blood caught between the periosteum and cranium and is classified as an extracranial scalp injury, occurring in approximately 0.4% to 2.5% of live births (Mangurten et al., 2015). This injury on the presenting part of the fetal head is usually a result of birth trauma seen in forceps- or vacuum-assisted deliveries.

The bleeding of a cephalohematoma results from ruptured blood vessels that run from the skull to the periosteum. This rupture is thought to be caused by the external dragging forces of the forceps or vacuum device over the parietal or occipital bones, which are the most common skull bones involved (Volpe, 2018). Due to the bleeding that occurs as a result of trauma, cephalohematomas tend to be unilateral and may not be obvious in the early hours after birth if caput succedaneum is present. Generally, cephalohematomas develop over the first 24 to 72 hours after delivery.

Cephalohematomas will develop and enlarge over the first 2 to 3 days of life and will usually resolve by 1 to 3 months of life. They are firm to palpation and have defined fixed borders. Diagnosis is made by assessment of the trauma site, as they do not cross suture lines, which is a key feature in distinguishing them from caput succedaneum. If the neonate has accompanying poor tone, decreased activity, or feeding difficulty, a detailed neurological assessment is necessary. Skull x-rays or CT scans may be necessary to determine the full extent of the injury. Cephalohematomas may have associated linear skull fractures (Mangurten et al., 2015; Parsons et al., 2016). As resolution takes place, the cephalohematoma site may become soft and fluctuant to palpation. A calcified ring or knot may develop and require up to 6 months to resolve. If the hematoma is large, the neonate will need close monitoring and to determine whether treatment for hyperbilirubinemia and/or anemia is necessary. An uncomplicated cephalohematoma heals with no long-term sequelae.

Subgaleal Hemorrhage. Subgaleal hemorrhage is the most serious extracranial birth injury. The incidence of subgaleal hemorrhage increases with instrumentation such as vacuum-assisted deliveries (Mangurten et al., 2015). It is believed that the damage is secondary to the traction applied during a vacuum-assisted delivery.

The venous ruptures are the result of the external compressing and dragging forces of vacuum-assisted delivery. A subgaleal hemorrhage occurs when blood collects in

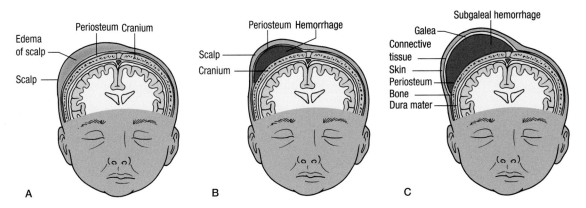

Figure 14.11 (A) Caput succedaneum. (B) Cephalohematoma. (C) Subgaleal hemorrhage.

the subaponeurotic space after the rupture of one or more emissary veins (Volpe, 2018). The aponeurotic space is located above the periosteum, where no barrier exists to limit or to stop bleeding. The subgaleal space can hold approximately 240 mL to 260 mL of blood. With neonatal blood volume estimated to be 80 mL/kg to 90 mL/kg, this approximates the total blood volume of a 3-kg neonate (Fasano, Said, & Luban, 2017).

The subgaleal hemorrhage presents with an enlarging mass that crosses suture lines and fontanelles. The lesion is ballotable and firm but fluctuant to palpation. The scalp mass is not fixed, has poorly defined margins, and moves easily with dependent positioning. Swelling can occur from the orbital ridge to behind the ears and down the nape of the neck. It is worth noting this is an area that could be covered by a stocking cap and thereby go unassessed.

The delivery history is important to appreciate as part of the initial assessment of a neonate with subgaleal hemorrhage. The neonate may appear well at birth with good Apgar scores; however, as bleeding progresses and intravascular blood volume decreases, the neonate will show symptoms of hypovolemic shock, including increased heart rate, pallor, delayed capillary refill, decreased tone, decreased blood pressure, and increasing respiratory distress. Assessing serial hematocrits may be helpful in both diagnosis and management. X-rays may identify skull fractures; however, CT scans will show the extent of epicranial blood. The primary goal of treatment is restoration of blood volume using packed RBCs and augmentation of clotting through the use of fresh frozen plasma (FFP) and/or cryoprecipitate. Disseminated intravascular coagulation (DIC) and multiple-organ failure contribute to the high mortality rate.

Subgaleal hemorrhage has a high morbidity and mortality rate due to the potential for massive blood loss. Hypoxia as a result of blood loss may lead to increased morbidity and mortality as well. If alterations to the hemodynamics of the neonate are minimized, the impact may be small and result in an overall good outcome. If significant hemodynamic instability arises, there is a potential for long-term neurodevelopmental impairment (Shah & Wusthoff, 2016).

Intracerebellar Hemorrhage. Intracerebellar hemorrhage (ICH) is bleeding within the cerebellum. Preterm neonates born at less than 1,500 grams or less than 32 weeks gestation have the highest occurrence at 15% to 25% (Volpe, 2018).

ICH may result from primary bleeding or as a result of the extension of subarachnoid or intraventricular bleeding into the cerebellar tissues (Limperopoulos, du Plessis, & Volpe, 2018). An ICH is most commonly associated with four mechanisms: (a) trauma to the posterior fossa resulting in rupture of the cerebellar bridging veins or the occipital sinuses, (b) venous infarction, (c) primary cerebellar hemisphere or vermis hemorrhages, or (d) supratentorial IVH and subarachnoid hemorrhage (SAH). The majority of ICH in term neonates is related to birth trauma (Limperopoulos et al., 2018).

Common symptoms are unexplained motor agitation, respiratory compromise, and apnea and may be associated with brainstem compression secondary to intracerebral hemorrhage. Other symptoms of ICH include bradycardia and lateral eye deviation. Neonates with ICH require close neurologic and neurodevelopmental assessment. Term neonate outcomes are more reassuring compared to preterm neonates with ICH. Life-span implications for ICH include possible long-term neurodevelopmental deficits (Limperopoulos et al., 2018).

Subdural Hemorrhage. A subdural hemorrhage (SDH) is an accumulation of blood between the arachnoid and dura membranes. Incidence of SDH is relatively uncommon, affecting up to only 10% of live births (Limperopoulos et al., 2018). Only in rare cases does an SDH become serious. Occurrence is more common among term versus preterm neonates as an SDH is typically related to labor-and-delivery events.

An SDH results from tearing of the bridging veins of the subdural compartments. Excessive pressure may produce shear forces resulting in tears in the dura, falx cerebri, falx tentorium, or other associated venous sinuses. Skull fractures may accompany the SDH. The resulting blood collection may cause acute symptoms of increased ICP or form a hematoma evolving into a chronic subdural hematoma. The subdural hematoma results in fluid accumulation and increased ICP.

Many neonates may be asymptomatic; however, clinical symptoms may include lethargy, irritability, and asymmetric hypotonia of the upper and lower extremities on the opposing side of the SDH (Limperopoulos et al., 2018). Low-birth-weight neonates may present with focal seizures. Increased ICP manifests as bulging fontanelle, deviated eye movement, excessive emesis, poor feeding, and increased frontal–occipital head circumference measurements. The third cranial nerve may be impacted ipsilateral to the SDH.

Outcomes of SDH vary widely from no long-term impact to early death. Most long-term neurologic sequelae depend on associated comorbidities. Comorbidities of concern are birth asphyxia, prematurity, infection, or hypoxic–ischemic injury. Early death may occur from substantial shear tearing of the affected veins. Neonates with a significant SDH can have mortality rates as high as 45% (Limperopoulos et al., 2018). The majority of SDHs in neonates have limited effect, produce few if any clinical findings, and result in good outcomes overall.

Subarachnoid Hemorrhage. SAH is an accumulation of blood in the subarachnoid space (between the pia mater and arachnoid mater). The pia mater is the innermost membrane enveloping the brain and spinal cord. It is very delicate and thin and adheres tightly to the surface of the brain and spinal cord (Volpe, 2018). Between the arachnoid and pia mater, in the subarachnoid space, the cerebral spinal fluid (CSF) circulates. A small SAH can be common. The majority of SAHs are venous in origin and rarely arterial. SAHs may be primary or secondary: Primary SAH most often results from birth-related complications or instrument-assisted deliveries, whereas secondary SAH may result from extension of another type of bleed such as subdural or cerebellar hemorrhage, bleeding disorders, or a hypoxic event. The SAH is the second most common type of ICH in the term neonate (Limperopoulos et al., 2018).

An SAH is typically asymptomatic in the term neonate, but when symptoms do present they are usually lethargy or irritability and eventually possible seizures by day 2 or 3 of age (Limperopoulos et al., 2018). The neonate with an SAH may appear "well with seizures" beginning as late as the second day of age. CT scans will be necessary to exclude other forms of intracranial bleeding. Blood will be present in the CSF when a lumbar puncture is performed. Of the neonates who exhibit seizures, 90% will have normal follow-up (Volpe, 2018).

Overall outcomes of SAH are generally good. With early diagnosis and control of seizures, if they occur, minimal or no neurologic impairments will exist (Shah & Wusthoff, 2016). Isolated, primary SAH is typically uncomplicated. Long-term complications are limited for those neonates with seizures that resolve prior to discharge (Limperopoulos et al., 2018). Long-term neurodevelopmental outcomes are worsened by comorbidities, such as prematurity, hypoxic birth injury, and birth trauma.

Skull Fracture. Skull fractures are linear or depressed, usually without loss of bone continuity. Linear skull fractures may go undetected without an x-ray. Skull fracture is uncommon in the neonate as the bones are not calcified, which is the feature allowing for pliability during delivery. Fractures are most often associated with the use of a forceps during delivery.

Most fractures are linear in nature and result from compression of the skull during delivery. Depressed fractures, which are those that have an indentation and may be without loss of bony continuity, may be accompanied by caput succedaneum and cephalohematoma. They are usually visible and palpable indentations are seen on the scalp.

Unless intracranial injury is present, skull fractures are typically asymptomatic. If neurologic signs are present, intracranial injury should be suspected and evaluated. Skull fractures are often without complication or sequelae unless a leptomeningeal cyst develops (Mangurten et al., 2015).

Facial Palsy. Facial palsy results from compression of the facial nerve (Figure 14.12). This compression most often takes place with the use of forceps, but can also occur spontaneously due to prolonged pressure applied from the maternal sacral promontory. Compression may occur near the stylomastoid foramen or along the nerve course to the ramus of the mandible. Volpe (2018) reports that facial nerve injury is the most common form of perinatal nerve trauma.

There are two main types of paralysis, central facial paralysis and peripheral paralysis, which are expressions of the trauma related to hemorrhage or edema of the nerve sheath. Central facial paralysis is a spastic paralysis and peripheral paralysis is a flaccid paralysis. When central facial paralysis is noted, the lower half of the contralateral side of the face will be affected. Peripheral paralysis will involve the entire side of the face. The differential diagnosis includes Möbius syndrome (nuclear agenesis) and congenital absence or hypoplasia of the depressor muscle.

The face will appear asymmetrical and drooping at the corner of the mouth will be present. When the neonate cries, asymmetrical facial movement will be noted. This assessment can be made at birth or may not be recognized until the second or third day of life. Depending on the amount of eye involvement, care must be taken to protect the cornea of the eye. Most facial palsies resolve spontaneously without intervention in a few days. Complete recovery may take several weeks or months. The extent

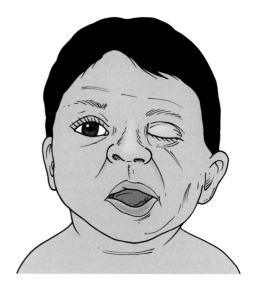

Figure 14.12 Facial paralysis.

of nerve excitability is a good predictor of recovery and long-term prognosis.

Vocal Cord Paralysis. Vocal cord paralysis occurs when too much traction is placed on the head during a breech or vaginal delivery. Unilateral paralysis occurs when the recurrent laryngeal branch of the vagus nerve is injured. When peripheral trauma occurs, bilateral paralysis involving both recurrent laryngeal nerves may be noted. Bilateral paralysis is more frequently seen in conjunction with a central nervous system insult. Twenty percent of vocal cord paralysis can be attributed to Chiari type 2 malformations (Darras & Volpe, 2018).

Neonates who have unilateral paralysis may be asymptomatic when at rest; however, with crying they will demonstrate hoarseness and mild inspiratory stridor, and additional difficulty in feeding may be noted. Bilateral paralysis results in more severe respiratory symptoms such as difficulty maintaining respirations, retractions, stridor, and cyanosis. Differential diagnosis will include congenital laryngeal malformations. To establish a diagnosis, direct or flexible laryngoscopy is necessary.

Unilateral vocal palsy most often resolves within the first 6 weeks of life without treatment or intervention. Bilateral paralysis may require establishing an airway, usually by tracheal intubation, and subsequent tracheostomies are needed in some patients (Mangurten et al., 2015). Return of functionality of the vocal cords will vary by time and degree; it may take months or years for complete recovery.

Injuries to the Shoulders, Chest, and Other Bones

Clavicular Fracture. The clavicle is the neonatal bone most often fractured during delivery (Figure 14.13). Clavicle fractures occur in two to seven per 1,000 live births (Liu & Thompson, 2015). A greenstick fracture is the most common type; however, complete fractures can occur.

A clavicle fracture may occur with difficult delivery of the neonatal shoulders, which can occur with vertex and breech deliveries. Forceful manipulation of arms and shoulders during delivery increases the risk of fracturing the clavicle. The greatest risk for injuries of the shoulders and chest occur with prematurity, macrosomia, and breech presentation, especially if the arms are extended above the neonate's head. Risk is also increased with maternal conditions such as cephalopelvic disproportion.

A greenstick fracture may not be evident until a callus has formed, creating a palpable knot on the clavicle, as late as 7 to 10 days after birth. Crepitus, tenderness, and

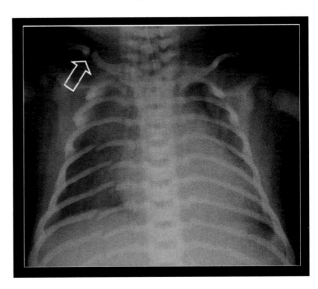

Figure 14.13 Fractured clavicle (arrow).

Source: van Rijn, R. R., Bilo, R., & Robben, S. G. (2008). Birth-related mid-posterior rib fractures in neonates: A report of three cases (and a possible fourth case) and a review of the literature. *Pediatric Radiology, 39*(1), 30–34. doi:10.1007/s00247-008-1035-2 Reprinted with permission.

irregularity may be present on palpation. Differential diagnosis will include a humerus fracture, brachial palsy, and congenital pseudoarthrosis of the clavicle, and diagnosis is made with an x-ray. The neonate demonstrates irritability with arm manipulation of the affected side or if positioned with pressure on the injured shoulder.

Brachial Plexus Injuries. Brachial plexus injury occurs when excessive stretching of the brachial plexus occurs during delivery. The brachial plexus includes spinal nerves cervical 5 through thoracic 1 (Figure 14.14). This injury results when lateral traction is placed on the shoulder during vertex deliveries or the head in breech deliveries. Forceful manipulation of the shoulders and arms during a vertex or breech delivery, especially in conjunction with prolonged labor, shoulder dystocia, and malpresentation, increase the risk of this injury.

The brachial plexus will present in one of three forms based on the level of nerve injury: (a) Erb's palsy, (b) Klumpke's palsy, or (c) Erb–Duchenne–Klumpke paralysis. A number of brachial plexus injuries will have phrenic nerve injury if C4 is affected (Parsons et al., 2016). Brachial plexus injury is characterized by decreased tone and movement in the affected shoulder and arm, based on the level of the injury.

Erb's palsy. Erb's palsy or upper arm paralysis accounts for 90% of brachial plexus injuries (Volpe, 2008). The nerves involved are C5 to C7. Erb's palsy presents with

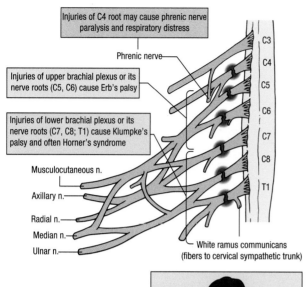

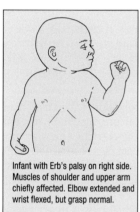

Infant with Erb's palsy on right side. Muscles of shoulder and upper arm chiefly affected. Elbow extended and wrist flexed, but grasp normal.

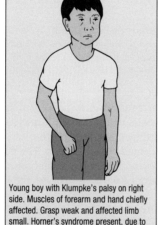

Young boy with Klumpke's palsy on right side. Muscles of forearm and hand chiefly affected. Grasp weak and affected limb small. Horner's syndrome present, due to interruption of fibers to cervical sympathetic trunk.

Figure 14.14 Brachial plexus and cervical nerve injuries at birth.

the shoulder and upper arm paralyzed with the Moro, bicep, and radial reflexes being decreased or absent on the affected side. The grasp reflex is present. A waiter's-tip position is often noted with the elbow extended, arm pronation, and wrist flexion. The arm is abducted and internally rotated.

Klumpke's palsy. Klumpke paralysis involves the muscles of the lower arm and hand and is extremely rare. Swelling occurs in the shoulder and supraclavicular fossa with C8 to T1 involvement. Horner syndrome (ptosis, miosis, and enophthalmos) is noted with T1 involvement. The hand is paralyzed and may have a claw-like appearance. The grasp reflex is absent with Klumpke's paralysis. The triceps reflex will also be decreased or absent.

Erb–Duchenne–Klumpke paralysis. Erb–Duchenne–Klumpke paralysis is more common than Klumpke paralysis alone. The presentation is a combination of Erb's palsy and Klumpke paralysis. The entire arm is flaccid and the Moro and grasp reflex are both absent (Figure 14.15).

Phrenic Nerve Paralysis. Phrenic nerve paralysis occurs when cervical nerves 3, 4, and 5 are overstretched during a traumatic delivery that results in the tearing of the nerve sheath with edema and hemorrhage. The greatest potential for occurrence is during a difficult breech delivery. It can occur in isolation but has an 80% to 90% association with brachial plexus injuries (Volpe, 2018).

The neonate with phrenic nerve paralysis will present with respiratory distress as the diaphragm's function is compromised. The neonate may have irregular labored respirations with cyanosis, tachypnea, hypoxemia, hypercapnia, and acidosis. Diagnosis is best made with ultrasonography to completely assess the function of the diaphragm and the presence of an elevated hemidiaphragm and paradoxical movement on the affected side during respiration. Therefore, if positive pressure ventilation is being used for the treatment of the respiratory distress, chest x-rays will not be helpful. Life-span implications for birth injuries to the shoulder and chest are summarized in Table 14.8.

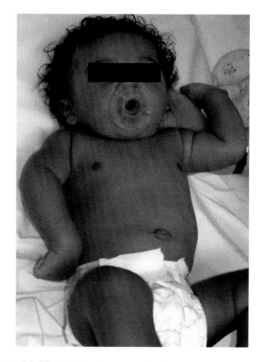

Figure 14.15 Erb–Duchenne paralysis.

Source: Perry, S. E., Hockenberry, M. J., Lowdermilk, D. L., & Wilson, D. (2014). *Maternal child nursing care* (5th ed.). St. Louis, MO: Elsevier.

TABLE 14.8 Birth Injuries to the Shoulder and Chest: Life-Span Implications

Injury	Expected Trajectory	Life-Span Implication
Clavicle fracture	Heal without difficulty	Full recovery
Brachial plexus injury	Long-term sequelae will depend on nerve injury	Expect full recovery
Erb's palsy	Injury caused by edema and hemorrhage will have less sequelae than those in which avulsion of the nerve from the spinal cord has occurred	Full recovery occurs in 88% by 4 months of age
Klumpke paralysis	Recovery is generally spontaneous	Recovery occurs gradually over the first year of life
Erb–Duchenne–Klumpke paralysis	Supportive treatment with passive range of motion and splints to prevent contractures	Return of function in approximately 93% with conservative treatment
Phrenic nerve paralysis	Oxygen and ventilator support may be necessary	10%–15% mortality rate; without prolonged respiratory support, most will recover in 6–12 months

Humerus Fracture. The humerus is the second most commonly fractured bone after the clavicle. Separations of the proximal humeral epiphysis or fractures are infrequently seen after difficult deliveries. The risk factors for this injury are the same as for the fracture of the clavicle and brachial plexus injury.

Extended arms and direct pressure on the humerus are the underlying cause of the injury. Greenstick fractures are the most common. Pain, swelling, and crepitus may be found on assessment. A depressed or absent Moro reflex will be noted in the affected arm. Proper immobilization and alignment while healing should result in minimal to no long-term impairment.

Femur Fracture. Femur fractures are the most common lower extremity fracture. The fracture occurs when a leg of a breech presentation is pulled down or the thigh is improperly held during the delivery of the shoulders and arms. The break usually occurs in the upper half or third of the bone. The thigh will show a malformation with a swollen and discolored area. Decreased movement and cries of pain with passive movement will be noted on the affected leg. Complete healing without shortening of the limb is expected.

Injuries to the Abdomen

Rupture of the Liver. Injuries and lacerations to the liver, spleen, adrenals, and kidneys are uncommon. Traumatic handling due to difficult deliveries increases the potential of injury. The injury is caused by rupturing or bruising the organ. Subcapsular hematomas are frequently seen. Of the

abdominal organs, the liver is the most frequently injured during delivery, at an injury rate of 0.9% to 9.6%. Injuries to the abdomen occur most often after increased manual pressure during a difficult delivery. Large neonates, neonates of diabetic mothers, neonates with hepatomegaly, and breech presentation are all at risk for injuries (Mangurten et al., 2015).

With liver trauma, the neonate may appear normal after birth for the first 1 to 3 days, or symptoms may be nonspecific such as poor feeding, tachypnea, tachycardia, jaundice, and lethargy. Decreasing hematocrit and hemoglobin levels may be indicative of blood loss. If a neonate presents with pallor, abdominal distention, anemia, or shock with any of the previously mentioned risk factors and without evidence of external blood loss, the possibility of intraabdominal organ laceration and/or injury should be explored. With early diagnosis and prompt interventions, a positive long-term prognosis can be accomplished (Mangurten et al., 2015).

Rupture of the Spleen. The spleen is injured much less frequently than the liver. Enlarged spleens, such as those found with congenital syphilis, increase the risk of rupture. Expedient diagnosis is necessary due to the potential fulminant shock that can occur. With early diagnosis and prompt interventions, long-term prognosis can be very good for neonates with spleen injuries (Mangurten et al., 2015).

Rupture of the Adrenal Glands. Adrenal and kidney trauma are the least frequent of the abdominal injuries.

As with other injuries to the abdomen, traumatic handling due to difficult deliveries increases the potential of injury. Placental hemorrhage, hypoxia, and hemorrhagic disease of the newborn are additional risk factors for adrenal hemorrhage.

The injury is caused by rupturing or bruising the organ. When the adrenal damage occurs, symptoms may vary based on the extent of the hemorrhage. Fever, tachypnea, pallor, cyanosis of the lips and fingertips, discoloration over the flanks, and purpura are classic findings. Vomiting, diarrhea, dehydration, irritability, and hypoglycemia uremia may be additional findings.

Adrenal function should be evaluated by an adrenocorticotropic hormone stimulation test. With early diagnosis and prompt interventions, long-term prognosis can be very good for neonates with adrenal injuries (Mangurten et al., 2015).

Hypoxic–Ischemic Injury

Birth asphyxia is the third-most prevalent contributor to the global burden of disease and death within the neonatal period, surpassed only by prematurity and low birth weight, and infection (WHO, 2018b). Birth asphyxia may give way to hypoxic–ischemic injury, which involves abnormal neurologic behavior in the neonate following perinatal hypoxia–ischemia. This type of birth injury has been classically termed *hypoxic-ischemic encephalopathy*, perinatal hypoxia–ischemia, or asphyxia neonatorum. Of late, the term *peripartum neonatal encephalopathy (NE)* has gained favor as a more inclusive description of relevant clinical manifestations that result from disordered brain function, including but not limited to difficulty with maintaining respiration, depressed tone and reflexes, stupor, and often seizures (Inder & Volpe, 2018; Kurinczuk, White-Koning, & Badawi, 2010). The global incidence of NE is two to five per every 1,000 live births; up to 56% of these injuries occur during the intrapartum period (Inder & Volpe, 2018; Nelson et al., 2012). Risk factors are summarized in Table 14.9.

Many experts, including Kinney and Volpe (2018), recommend beginning the study of hypoxic–ischemic injury with a review of key terms and associated definitions. Neonatal APNs should take time to study and establish familiarity with the following terms before progressing to an investigation of the pathogenesis, manifestations, and outcomes of hypoxic-ischemic injury. *Hypoxia* denotes a partial or complete lack of oxygen within the blood. *Ischemia* describes a reduction or cessation of blood flow to the brain, which compromises both oxygen and glucose delivery. Hypoxia and ischemia can both result from the larger problem of perinatal asphyxia. *Asphyxia*, the Greek word for *suffocation*, denotes the condition in which the supply of oxygen through the placenta and/or umbilical cord is interrupted. In other words, *asphyxia* refers to aberrations in cerebral blood flow, which often occur secondary to hypercarbia-induced cerebral vasodilation (Inder & Volpe, 2018). Interruption of oxygen leads to anaerobic glycolysis, lactic acid, and resultant metabolic acidosis (Groenendaal & DeVries, 2015).

Pathophysiology: Primary and Secondary Energy Failure. The response to a hypoxic–ischemic event begins after the causative insult has finished, not at its onset (Kinney & Volpe, 2018). Diminished blood supply to the brain occurs as a result of myocardial dysfunction and failed cerebral autoregulation, in conjunction with (or just prior to) diminished delivery of oxygen to the brain. The subsequent pathogenesis is best described as a series of two phases of energy failure. A decrease in cerebral blood flow occurs and blood is preferentially redistributed to the deeper structures of the brain (brainstem, ganglia, and cerebellum) at the expense of the cortex and watershed areas. The body's response occurs in two phases.

During the *primary phase of energy failure*, ischemia causes a depletion of energy metabolites and glucose to the brain. This promulgates anaerobic metabolism as well as the accumulation of extracellular glutamate. Excess

---

TABLE 14.9 Risk Factors for Hypoxic–Ischemic Injury

• Impaired placental gas transfer secondary to acute placental or umbilical cord accidents (e.g., abruptio placentae, cord prolapse, arrest of descent during labor, forceps-assisted delivery, or failed external cephalic version) • Respiratory dysfunction (e.g., persistent apnea at birth, severe respiratory distress)	• Cardiovascular dysfunction (e.g., persistent right-to-left [fetal] shunting across ductus arteriosus) • Failed cerebral autoregulation • Cardiovascular dysfunction (e.g., persistent left-to-right shunting across ductus arteriosus) • Sepsis

NOTE: Maternal infections, obesity, hypertension, and metabolic disorders are also etiologies for neonatal encephalopathy.

Source: Inder, T., & Volpe, J. (2018). Hypoxic–ischemic injury in the term infant: Clinical–neurological features, diagnosis, imaging, prognosis, therapy. In J. Volpe, T. Inder, B. Darras, L. de Vries, A. du Plessis, J. Neil, & J. Perlman (Eds.), *Volpe's neurology of the newborn* (6th ed., pp. 510–563). Philadelphia, PA: Elsevier.

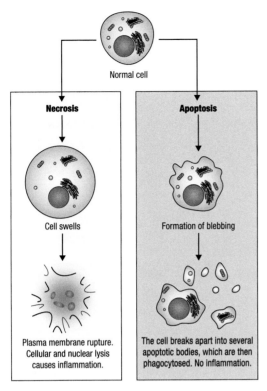

Figure 14.16 Cell apoptosis and necrosis: defining factors.

extracellular glutamate triggers a neuroexcitatory cascade, which, in combination with failure of the Na+/K+ adenosine triphosphatase (ATPase) pump, permits a destructive influx of sodium, chloride, water, and calcium into the cells. Free radicals and nitric oxide are formed, which in aggregate lead to cytotoxic edema and resultant cellular necrosis. During the process of cell necrosis, the cell ruptures, which releases inflammatory mediators (interleukin [IL]-1, IL-6, and tumor necrosis factor alpha [TNFa]; Figure 14.16). These factors are responsible for early damage to the white matter.

During the *secondary phase of energy failure*, increased levels of inflammatory mediators (IL-1, IL-6, and TNFa) respond to the site of injury. A perturbed level of oxidant stress and free radical release continues. In addition, an abundance of glutamate (neuroexcitatory amino acids) is noted. Secondary cytotoxic edema occurs, which increases the rate of cell death and often leads to seizure activity, a nefarious indicator of significant white (and gray) matter injury. In aggregate, these factors promote apoptotic cell death. Figure 14.17 summarizes the characteristic timeline of events involved with neonatal hypoxic–ischemic injury.

Clinical Manifestations. The timing, degree, and duration of impaired cerebral infusion and hypoxia impact the severity of brain injury in term newborns (Table 14.10). Term neonates are depressed at birth

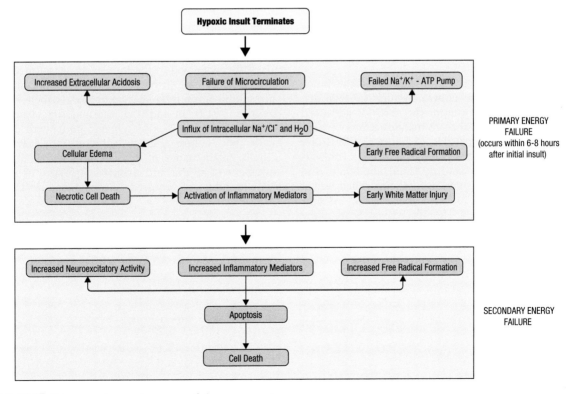

Figure 14.17 Primary and secondary energy failure: an overview.

ATP, adenosine triphosphate.

TABLE 14.10 Clinical Features of HIE			
Birth to 12 Hours	**12–24 Hours**	**24–72 Hours**	**After 72 Hours**
• Depressed level of consciousness: Usually deep stupor or coma • Ventilatory disturbance: "Periodic" breathing or respiratory failure • Intact pupillary responses • Intact oculomotor responses • Hypotonia, minimal movement > hypertonia • Seizures	• Variable change in level of alertness • More seizures • Apneic spells • Jitteriness • Weakness of proximal limbs, upper > lower (full term); hemiparesis (full term); lower limbs (premature)	• Stupor or coma • Respiratory arrest • Brainstem, oculomotor, and pupillary disturbances	• Persistent, yet diminishing stupor • Disturbed sucking, swallowing, gag, and tongue movements • Hypotonia > hypertonia • Weakness • Proximal limbs, upper > lower • Hemiparesis

HIE, hypoxic–ischemic encephalopathy.

Source: Adapted from McAdams, R., & Traudt, C. (2018). Brain injury in the term infant. In C. Gleason & S. Juul (Eds.), *Avery's diseases of the newborn* (10th ed., pp. 897–909). Philadelphia, PA: Elsevier.

and display clinical symptomology consistent with neurologic injury. These infants typically require advanced neonatal resuscitation, including chest compressions, thereby resulting in low Apgar scores. An Agpar score less than 5 at 5 minutes and 10 minutes of life, as well as an umbilical artery pH of less than 7.0 and/or a base deficit greater than or equal to 12 to 15 mmoL/L, are strong indicators of an acute peripartum event (McAdams & Traudt, 2018).

Therefore, three factors should increase the index of suspicion for hypoxic–ischemic injury: (a) fetal distress, (b) low Apgar scoring or the need for advanced neonatal resuscitation, and (c) manifestations of neurologic injury within the first 24 hours of life (Inder & Volpe, 2018). The peripartum neurologic presentation is categorized by severity (mild, moderate, and severe), commonly measured using the modified Sarnat staging system (Table 14.11). Other scoring systems are available, including the Thompson scale, Score of the Ibero-American Society of Neonatology (SIBEN) scale, and the National Institute of Child Health and Human Development (NICHD) scale. The SIBEN and NICHD scales are limited to use within the first 6 hours of life and are useful for research (randomization) purposes. Although an exploration into each scoring method is beyond the scope of this textbook, we encourage clinicians who indirectly or directly participate in research initiatives to take time to compare and contrast the study-specific scoring tool with available alternatives.

It is common for affected neonates to manifest with neurologic impairment paired with at least one other indicator of major organ dysfunction. Therefore, cardiovascular, liver, and kidney dysfunction are commonly observed among affected neonates. Impaired myocardial contractility leads to a significant reduction in cardiac output, hypotension, and impairment of blood flow to other organs. Transient elevation in liver enzymes and impaired coagulation is to be expected; both are considered transient, reversible problems. DIC is well recognized and is related to the low levels of factor XIII and alterations to the thrombin–antithrombin complexes and soluble fibrin monomer complexes (Groenendaal & DeVries, 2015). In addition, the majority of neonates who experience hypoxic–ischemic injury will develop acute renal failure, due to decreased renal perfusion. Careful maintenance of fluid balance with daily measurement of serum and urine electrolytes, as well as daily weights, is required (Groenendaal & DeVries, 2015).

Neuropathological Features. Although neuropathological features of hypoxic–ischemic injury vary with gestational age, certain basic lesions can be identified, and these lesions provide the framework for clinical discussion.

Selective neuronal necrosis. Selective neuronal necrosis refers to necrosis of neurons in a characteristic and generally widespread distribution, and is the most common variety of injury observed in neonatal hypoxic–ischemic injury. The appearance of neuronal injuries depends on the severity and timing of the insult and the

TABLE 14.11 Clinical Staging of Hypoxic-Ischemic Encephalopathy

	Stage 1 (Mild)	Stage 2 (Moderate)	Stage 3 (Severe)
Consciousness	Hyperalert	Lethargic or obtunded	Stupor or coma
Activity	Normal	Decreased	Absent
Neuromuscular control			
• Muscle tone	Normal	Mild hypotonia	Flaccid
• Posture	Mild distal flexion	Strong distal flexion	Intermittent decerebration
• Stretch reflexes	Overactive	Overactive	Decreased or absent
Primitive reflexes			
• Suck	Weak	Weak or absent	Absent
• Moro	Strong	Weak, incomplete	Absent
• Tonic neck	Slight	Strong	Absent
Autonomic function			
• Pupils	Dilated	Constricted	Variable, unequal
• Heart rate	Tachycardia	Bradycardia	Variable
Seizures	None	Common	Uncommon

Source: Adapted from McAdams, R., & Traudt, C. (2018). Brain injury in the term infant. In C. Gleason & S. Juul (Eds.), *Avery's diseases of the newborn* (10th ed., pp. 897–909). Philadelphia, PA: Elsevier.

gestational age of the neonate. As the name implies, the site of injury is the neuron. Oligodendrocytes exhibit some of the same sensitivity to hypoxia and hypoglycemia as do the neurons; however, the astrocytes are not affected. Temporal features of neuronal changes in the brain are well documented and include eosinophilia, condensation or fragmentation of nuclei, and cell swelling with observed breakdown of nuclear and plasma membranes. These early stages are followed in several days by overt signs of necrosis, and then macrophages consume the necrotic debris, and a glial mat forms. This mat will form over several weeks. In severe cases, lesions may result in cavity formations (Kinney & Volpe, 2018).

Parasagittal cerebral injury. The parasagittal cerebral injury, also called a *watershed infarct*, refers to lesions of the cerebral cortex and subcortical white matter. The injury is characterized by necrosis of the cortex and the immediately subjacent white matter and is seen in 40% to 60% of asphyxiated neonates. The posterior aspects of the cerebral hemispheres are more affected than the

anterior areas due to disturbances in cerebral perfusion. The injury is usually bilateral and symmetrical although small differences between the spheres may exist. The precise pathological evaluation of parasagittal cerebral injury is not known, although the factors underlying the propensity of the parasagittal region to ischemia have been identified. The susceptibility relates to the parasagittal vascular anatomical factors and cerebral ischemia with a pressure-passive state of the cerebral circulation (Kinney & Volpe, 2018).

Cerebral white matter injury. For the term neonate who experiences hypoxic–ischemic injury, the predominant injury is to the cerebral white matter (Kinney & Volpe, 2018). White matter injury is usually more predominant in the posterior aspects of the brain than the anterior and affects both periventricular and central white matter. The damage to white matter crosses a spectrum from "focal necrotic/cystic" to "nonnecrotic/noncystic" disease. Focal necrotic/cystic disease is the most severe form and is demonstrated by large focal necrotic lesions that evolve to cysts that are evident on ultrasonography. Less severe are the focal necrotic/non-cystic lesions that do not evolve into cysts. The non-necrotic/noncystic injuries' lesions are either absent or too small to be picked up by neuroimaging. Questions remain as to the clinical significance and lifetime impact of these different types of injuries; however, researchers do agree that subsequent disturbances to white matter development will likely become apparent by term-equivalent age and beyond (Kinney & Volpe, 2018).

Life-Span Implications. Cognitive impairment with or without cerebral palsy, seizure disorders, a notable weakening and/or spasticity of all extremities, visual impairments, and death are reported among affected neonates. In fact, the presence of seizures increases the risk for neurological sequelae by as much as 40-fold. Clinicians must also recognize that mild injury may lead to no long-term consequences, whereas those with moderate to severe hypoxic–ischemic injury have exhibited long-term neurodevelopmental and cognitive deficits (Inder & Volpe, 2018; McAdams & Traudt, 2018). The aforementioned Sarnat and Thompson scales, in conjunction with MRI findings, offer clinicians the ability to discuss prognostics with family members.

CONCLUSION

Multiple angiogenic factors must align and coordinate in order to result in a circulatory system involving coordination of both maternal and fetal components. The fetal heart begins to beat during early embryologic development, and subsequent vascular development is crucial for other organ placement and formation. Maternal health prior to and in the early stages of pregnancy can have a significant impact on fetal development. Transition from fetal to neonatal circulation is a crucial time for the newborn and can be heavily influenced again by maternal health and also by mode of delivery. Delays or complications to delivery impact the cardiopulmonary transition and result in neonatal disease. Birth injuries can also occur as a result of the mode of delivery and carry long-term neurologic, orthopedic, and dermatologic system implications. Should a worst-case scenario arise, the neonatal APN requires a communication skill set in order to communicate with the family in an empathetic manner. Pearls and pitfalls to communicating difficult information, as well as information on palliation, hospice, and a discussion of parental bereavement, follows in Chapter 15.

LEARNING TOOLS AND RESOURCES

Podcast

 Transition to Extrauterine Life

Janice L. Wilson and Jennifer Fitzgerald

Discussion Prompts

1. Discuss how economic investment in comprehensive maternal healthcare could prevent elevated costs associated with maternal disease states and neonatal morbidities, including prematurity.
2. Discuss how indications of fetal health status should or should not impact the decision to proceed with vaginal versus operative delivery.
3. You are performing a newborn exam on a 3.9 kg 2-hour-old neonate. In your assessment you find the right arm is not flexed and there is an absent Moro reflex on the right side; the left side shows a normal expected response. Discuss the possible etiology for this finding, what other assessments will need to be made, possible long-term outcomes, and the conversation that will occur with the parents.
4. You are counseling a family that is attempting to lay blame for their 4-hour-old neonate having experienced a hypoxic–ischemic injury during a forceps-assisted delivery that failed and required an emergency cesarean section. The parents are convinced that their child will have permanent, long-term brain damage and claim they asked for the cesarean early in the birth process and were denied. How do you answer their challenges and concerns?

Advice From the Authors

"Learning is never-ending. Be willing, always, to admit you don't know everything, but be proactive in seeking the answers. In doing so, you will likely discover more questions; such is the cycle."

–Amy R. Koehn, PhD, APRN, NNP-BC

"In your quest to acquire knowledge, know why your work is important! Always keep this in mind during the learning process. While your recognition of significance may shift, always try to learn what will most positively influence your future and the future of others."

–Melody Norris Waller, PhD, RN

"Graduate education is not a hobby. Learning is a lifelong process that is exciting, invigorating, stimulating, and hard work. You will get out of your education what you put into it, so your learning is up to you. Your patients and families will thank you for your diligence and persistence."

–Evelyn Stephenson, DNP, APRN, NNP-BC, RNC-NIC, CHSE

References

Aiken, C. E., Aiken, A. R., Brockelsby, J. C., & Scott, J. G. (2014). Factors influencing the likelihood of instrumental delivery success. *Obstetrics & Gynecology, 123*(4), 796–803. doi:10.1097/AOG.0000000000000188

American College of Obstetricians and Gynecologists. (2014). Practice Bulletin No. 145: Antepartum fetal surveillance. *Obstetrics & Gynecology, 124*(1), 182–192. doi:10.1097/01.AOG.0000451759.90082.7b

American College of Obstetricians and Gynecologists. (2015). Practice Bulletin No. 154 summary: Operative vaginal delivery. *Obstetrics & Gynecology, 126*(5), 1118–1119. doi:10.1097/AOG.0000000000001142

American College of Obstetricians & Gynecologists. (2017a). ACOG Practice Bulletin No. 106: Intrapartum fetal heart rate monitoring: Nomenclature, interpretation, and general management principles. *Obstetrics & Gynecology, 114*(1), 192–202. doi:10.1097/AOG.0b013e3181aef106

American College of Obstetricians & Gynecologists. (2017b). Committee Opinion No. 684: Delayed umbilical cord clamping after birth. Retrieved from https://www.acog.org/Clinical-Guidance-and-Publications/Committee-Opinions/Committee-on-Obstetric-Practice/Delayed-Umbilical-Cord-Clamping-After-Birth

American College of Obstetricians & Gynecologists, & Society for Maternal–Fetal Medicine. (2013a). Committee Opinion No. 560: Medically indicated late-preterm and early-term deliveries. *Obstetrics & Gynecology, 121*(4), 908–910. doi:10.1097/01.AOG.0000428648.75548.00

American College of Obstetricians & Gynecologists, & Society for Maternal–Fetal Medicine. (2013b). Committee Opinion No. 579: Definition of term pregnancy. *Obstetrics & Gynecology, 122*(5), 1139–1140. doi:10.1097/01.AOG.0000437385.88715.4a

American Congress of Obstetricians & Gynecologists, Society for Maternal–Fetal Medicine, Caughey, A. B., Cahill, A. G., Guise, J.-M., & Rouse, D. J. (2014). Safe prevention of the primary cesarean delivery. *American Journal of Obstetrics & Gynecology, 210*(3), 179–193. doi:10.1016/j.ajog.2014.01.026

American College of Obstetricians & Gynecologists, Heine, R. P., Puopolo, K. M., Beigi, R., Silverman, N. S., & El-Sayed, Y. Y. (2017). ACOG Committee Opinion No. 712: Intrapartum management of intraamniotic infections. Retrieved from https://www.acog.org/-/media/Committee-Opinions/Committee-on-Obstetric-Practice/co712.pdf?dmc=1&ts=20170811T1344408044

American Society of Anesthesiologists Task Force on Obstetric Anesthesia, & Society for Obstetric Anesthesia and Perinatology. (2016). Practice guidelines for obstetric anesthesia: An updated report. *Anesthesiology, 124*(2), 270–300. doi:10.1097/ALN.0000000000000935

Ananth, C. V., Lavery, J. A., Vintzileos, A. M., Skupski, D. W., Varner, M., Saade, G., . . . Wright, J. D. (2016). Severe placental abruption: Clinical definition and associations with maternal complications. *American Journal of Obstetrics & Gynecology, 214*(2), 272.e1–272.e9. doi:10.1016/j.ajog.2015.09.069

Anders, A. P., Gaddy, J. A., Doster, R. S., & Aronoff, D. M. (2017). Current concepts in maternal–fetal immunology: Recognition and response to microbial pathogens by decidual stromal cells. *American Journal of Reproductive Immunology,* 77(3), e12623. doi:10.1111/aji.12623

Berghella, V., Mackeen, A., & Jauniaux, E. (2017). Cesarean delivery. In S. Gabbee, J. Niebyl, J. Simpson, M. Landon, H. Galan, E. Jauniaux, . . . W. Grobman (Eds.), *Obstetrics: Normal and problem pregnancies* (7th ed., pp. 425–443). Philadelphia, PA: Elsevier.

Bernstein, D. (2016). The fetal to neonatal circulatory transition. In R. M. Kliegman, B. F. Stanton, J. W. St Geme, & N. F. Schor (Eds.), *Nelson textbook of pediatrics* (20th ed., pp. 2161–2162). Philadelphia, PA: Elsevier.

Bommarito, K. M., Gross, G. A., Willers, D. M., Fraser, V. J., & Olsen, M. A. (2016). The effect of clinical chorioamnionitis on cesarean delivery in the United States. *Health Services Research,* 51(5), 1879–1895. doi:10.1111/1475-6773.12447

Carrapato, M. R. G., Ferreira, A. M., & Wataganara, T. (2017). Cesarean section: The pediatricians' views. *Journal of Maternal-Fetal & Neonatal Medicine,* 30(17), 2081–2085. doi:10.1080/14767058.2016.1237496

Centers for Disease Control and Prevention. (2018). Pregnancy mortality surveillance system. Retrieved from https://www.cdc.gov/reproductivehealth/maternalinfanthealth/pmss.html

Centers for Disease Control and Prevention. (2017). Births–method of delivery. Retrieved from https://www.cdc.gov/nchs/fastats/delivery.htm

Cresswell, J. A., Ronsmans, C., Calvert, C., & Filippi, V. (2013). Prevalence of placenta praevia by world region: A systematic review and meta-analysis. *Tropical Medicine & International Health,* 18(6), 712–724. doi:10.1111/tmi.12100

Cunningham, F. G., Leveno, K. J., Bloom, S. L., Dashe, J. S., Hoffman, B. L., Casey, B. M., & Spong, C. Y. (Eds.). (2018). *Williams obstetrics* (25th ed., pp. 755–802). New York, NY: McGraw-Hill.

Dahlke, J. D., Mendez-Figueroa, H., Rouse, D. J., Berghella, V., Baxter, J. K., & Chauhan, S. P. (2013). Evidence-based surgery for cesarean delivery: An updated systematic review. *American Journal of Obstetrics & Gynecology,* 209(4), 294–306. doi:10.1016/j.ajog.2013.02.043

Darras, B., & Volpe, J. (2018). Muscle involvement and restricted disorders. In J. Volpe, T. Inder, B. Darras, L. de Vries, A. du Plessis, J. Neil, & J. Perlman (Eds.), *Volpe's neurology of the newborn* (6th ed., pp. 922–970). Philadelphia, PA: Elsevier.

Ditzenberger, G. (2015) Nutritional management. In M. T. Verklan & M. Walden (Eds.), *Core curriculum for neonatal intensive care nursing* (5th ed., pp. 172–196). St. Louis, MO. Elsevier.

Engle, W. A. (2006). A recommendation for the definition of "late preterm" (near-term) and the birth weight–gestational age classification system. *Seminars in Perinatology,* 30(1), 2–7. doi:10.1053/j.semperi. 2006.01.007

Ericson, J., & Laughon, M. (2015). Chorioamnionitis: Implications for the neonate. *Clinics in Perinatology,* 42(1), 155–165. doi:10.1016/j.clp.2014.10.011

Fan, D., Wu, S., Liu, L., Xia, Q., Wang, W., Guo, X., & Liu, Z. (2017). Prevalence of antepartum hemorrhage in women with placenta previa: A systematic review and meta-analysis. *Science Reports,* 7, 40320. doi:10.1038/srep40320

Fasano, R., Said, M., & Luban, N. (2015). Blood component therapy for the neonate. In R. Martin, A. Fanaroff, & M. Walsh (Eds.), *Fanaroff and Martin's neonatal–perinatal medicine: Diseases of the fetus and infant* (10th ed., pp. 1344–1361). Philadelphia, PA: Elsevier.

Fineman, J., & Clyman, R. (2014). Fetal cardiovascular physiology. In R. Creasy, R. Resnik, J. Iams, C. Lockwood, T. Moore, & M. Greene (Eds.), *Creasy and Resnik's maternal–fetal medicine: Principles and practice* (7th ed., pp. 146–154). Philadelphia, PA: Elsevier.

Francois, K., & Foley, M. (2017). Antepartum and postpartum hemorrhage. In S. Gabbee, J. Niebyl, J. Simpson, M. Landon, H. Galan, E. Jauniaux, . . . W. Grobman (Eds.), *Obstetrics: Normal and problem pregnancies* (7th ed., pp. 395–424). Philadelphia, PA: Elsevier.

Gajjar, K., & Spencer, C. (2009). Fetal laceration injury during cesarean section and its long-term sequelae: A case report. *American Journal of Obstetrics & Gynecology,* 201(4), e5–e7. doi:10.1016/j.ajog.

Gamboa, S., Giménexz, O., Mancho, J., Moros, M., Sada, J., & Mateo, S. (2017). Diagnostic accuracy of the FIGO and the 5-tier fetal heart rate classifications systems in the detection of neonatal acidemia. *American Journal of Perinatology,* 34, 508–514. doi:10.1055/s-0036-1593810

Ghidini, A., Stewart, D., Pezzullo, J. C., & Locatelli, A. (2017). Neonatal complications in vacuum-assisted vaginal delivery: Are they associated with number of pulls, cup detachments, and duration of vacuum application? *Archives of Gynecology and Obstetrics,* 295(1), 67–73. doi:10.1007/s00404-016-4206-7

Gibbons, C., O'Herlihy, C., & Murphy, J. F. (2014). Umbilical cord prolapse–Changing patterns and improved outcomes: A retrospective cohort study. *BJOG: An International Journal of Obstetrics & Gynaecology,* 121(13), 1705–1708. doi:10.1111/1471-0528.12890

Giordano, R., Cacciatore, A., Cignini, P., Vigna, R., & Romano, M. (2010). Antepartum haemorrhage. *Journal of Prenatal Medicine,* 4(1), 12–16. Retrieved from https://www.prenatalmedicine.com/common/php/portiere.php?ID=0aaa4ed18afc2b83676696fe1290dfcf

Greenberg, J., Narendran, V., Schibler, K., Warner, B., & Haberman, B. (2014). Neonatal morbidities of prenatal and perinatal origin. In R. Creasy, R. Resnik, J. Iams, C. Lockwood, T. Moore, & M. Greene (Eds.), *Creasy and Resnik's maternal–fetal medicine: Principles and practice* (7th ed., pp. 1215–1239). Philadelphia, PA: Elsevier.

Groenendaal, F., & DeVries, L. (2015). Hypoxic–ischemic encephalopathy. In R. Martin, A. Fanaroff, & M. Walsh (Eds.), *Fanaroff and Martin's neonatal–perinatal medicine: Diseases of the fetus and infant* (10th ed., pp. 926–942). Philadelphia, PA: Elsevier.

Gurol-Urganci, I., Cromwell, D., Edozien, L., Smith, G., Onwere, C., Mahmood, T., . . . van der Meulen, J. (2011). Risk of placenta previa in second birth after first birth cesarean section: A population-based study and meta-analysis. *BMC Pregnancy and Childbirth,* 11, 95. doi:10.1186/1471-2393-11-95

Hurst, H. (2015). Antepartum-intrapartum complications. In M. T. Verklan & M. Walden (Eds.), *Core curriculum for neonatal intensive care nursing* (5th ed., pp. 21–42). St. Louis, MO: Elsevier.

Inder, T., & Volpe, J. (2018). Hypoxic–ischemic injury in the term infant: Clinical–neurological features, diagnosis, imaging, prognosis, therapy. In J. Volpe, T. Inder, B. Darras, L. de Vries, A. du Plessis, J. Neil, & J. Perlman (Eds.), *Volpe's neurology of the newborn* (6th ed., pp. 510–563). Philadelphia, PA: Elsevier.

Jauniaux, E., & Bhide, A. (2017). Prenatal ultrasound diagnosis and outcome of placenta previa accreta after cesarean delivery: A systematic review and meta-analysis. *American Journal of Obstetrics & Gynecology*, 217(1), 27–36. doi:10.1016/ .jajog.2017.02.050

Jauniaux, E., Bhide, A., & Wright, J. (2017). Placenta accreta. In S. Gabbee, J. Niebyl, J. Simpson, M. Landon, H. Galan, E. Jauniaux, D. Driscoll, . . . W. Grobman (Eds.), *Obstetrics: Normal and problem pregnancies* (7th ed., pp. 456–466). Philadelphia, PA: Elsevier.

Key, N., Makris, M., & Lillicrap, D. (Eds.). (2017). *Practical hemostasis and thrombosis* (3rd ed.). Hoboken, NJ: John Wiley.

Kinney, H., & Volpe, J. (2018). Hypoxic–ischemic injury in the term infant: Neuropathology. In J. Volpe, T. Inder, B. Darras, L. de Vries, A. du Plessis, J. Neil, & J. Perlman (Eds.), *Volpe's neurology of the newborn* (6th ed., pp. 484–499). Philadelphia, PA: Elsevier.

Kiserud, T., & Haugen G. (2017). Umbilical circulation. In R. Polin, S. Abman, D. Rowitch, W. Benitz, & W. Fox (Eds.), *Fetal and neonatal physiology* (5th ed., pp. 599–610). New York, NY: Elsevier.

Kurinczuk, J., White-Koning, M., & Badawi, N. (2010). Epidemiology of neonatal encephalopathy and hypoxic–ischaemic encephalopathy. *Early Human Development*, 86, 329–338. doi:10.1016/j.earlhumdev.2010.05.010

Limperopoulos, C., du Plessis, A., & Volpe, J. (2018). Cerebellar hemorrhage. In J. Volpe, T. Inder, B. Darras, L. de Vries, A. du Plessis, J. Neil, & J. Perlman (Eds.), *Volpe's neurology of the newborn* (6th ed., pp. 623–636). Philadelphia, PA: Elsevier.

Liu R., & Thompson, G. (2015). Musculoskeletal disorders. In R. Martin, A. Fanaroff, & M. Walsh (Eds.), *Fanaroff and Martin's neonatal–perinatal medicine: Diseases of the fetus and infant* (10th ed., pp. 407–435). Philadelphia, PA: Elsevier.

Lothian, J. A. (2014). Safe prevention of the primary cesarean delivery: ACOG and SMFM change the game. *Journal of Perinatal Education*, 23(3), 115–118. doi:10.1891/1058-1243.23.3.115

Maisonneuve, E., Lorthe, E., Torchin, H., Subtil, D., Marret, S., Ancel, P., & Kayem, G. (2017). 335: Impact of chorioamnionitis on neurodevelopmental outcomes and mortality at 2 years in premature infants after preterm labour or preterm premature rupture of membranes. *American Journal of Obstetrics and Gynecology*, 216(1), S203. doi:10.1016/ j.ajog.2016.11.593

Martin, R. J., Fanaroff, A. A., & Walsh, M. C. (Eds.). (2006). *Faranoff and Martin's neonatal–perinatal medicine: Diseases of the fetus and infant* (8th ed.). Philadelphia, PA: Elsevier-Mosby.

Martin, R. J., Fanaroff, A. A., & Walsh, M. C. (Eds.). (2015). *Fanaroff and Martin's neonatal–perinatal medicine: Diseases of the fetus and infant* (10th ed.). Philadelphia, PA: Elsevier/Saunders.

Marsal, K. (2017). Fetal and placental circulation during labor. In R. Polin, S. Abman, D. Rowitch, W. Benitz, & W. Fox (Eds.), *Fetal and neonatal physiology* (5th ed., pp. 611–618) New York, NY: Elsevier.

Martin, J., Hamilton, B., Osterman, M., Driscoll, A., & Mathews, T. (2017). Births: Final data for 2015. *National Vital Statistics Reports*, 66(1), 1–70. Retrieved from https://www.cdc.gov/ nchs/data/nvsr/nvsr66/nvsr66_01.pdf

Mangurten, H., Puppala, B., & Prazad, P. (2015). Birth injuries. In R. Martin, A. Fanaroff, & M. Walsh (Eds.), *Fanaroff and Martin's neonatal–perinatal medicine: Diseases of the fetus and infant* (10th ed., pp. 407–435). Philadelphia, PA: Elsevier.

McAdams, R., & Traudt, C. (2018). Brain injury in the term infant. In C. Gleason & S. Juul (Eds.), *Avery's diseases of the newborn* (10th ed., pp. 897–909). Philadelphia, PA: Elsevier.

McNamara, P., & El-Khuffash, A. (2017). Oxygen transport and delivery. In R. Polin, S. Abman, D. Rowitch, W. Benitz, & W. Fox (Eds.), *Fetal and neonatal physiology* (5th ed., pp. 724–736). New York, NY: Elsevier.

Morton, S., & Brodsky, D. (2016). Fetal physiology and the transition to extrauterine life. *Clinics in Perinatology*, 43, 395–407. doi:10.1016/j.clp.2016.04.001

Muanda, F., Sheehy, O., & Bérard, A. (2017a). Use of antibiotics during pregnancy and risk of spontaneous abortion. *Canadian Medical Association Journal*, 189(17), E625–E633. doi:10.1503/cmaj.161020

Muanda, F., Sheehy, O., & Bérard, A. (2017b). Use of antibiotics during pregnancy and the risk of major congenital malformations: A population based cohort study. *British Journal of Clinical Pharmacology*, 83(11), 2557–2571. doi:10.1111/bcp.13364

Nelson, K. B., Bingham, P., Edwards, E. M., Horbar, J. D., Kenny, M. J., Inder, T., ... Soll, R. F. (2012). Antecedents of neonatal encephalopathy in the Vermont Oxford Network Encephalopathy Registry. *Pediatrics*, 130(5), 878–886. doi:10.1542/peds.2012-0714

Oskoui, M., Coutinho, F., Dykeman, J., Jetté, N., & Pringsheim, T. (2013). An update on the prevalence of cerebral palsy: A systematic review and meta-analysis. *Developmental Medicine & Child Neurology*, 55(6), 509–519. doi:10.1111/dmcn.12080

Oyelese, Y., & Smulian, J. C. (2006). Placenta previa, placenta accreta, and vasa previa. *Obstetrics & Gynecology*, 107(4), 927–941. doi:10.1097/01.AOG.0000207559.15715.98

Paidas, M. J., Hossain, N., Shamsi, T., Rodger, M. A., Langhoff-Rose, J., & Lockwood, C. J. (Eds.). (2011). *Hemostasis and thrombosis in obstetrics & gynecology*. Chichester, UK: Wiley-Blackwell.

Palatnik, A., Grobman, W. A., Hellendag, M. G., Janetos, T. M., Gossett, D. R., & Miller, E. S. (2016). Predictors of failed operative vaginal delivery in a contemporary obstetric cohort. *Obstetrics & Gynecology*, 127(3), 501–506. doi:10.1097/ AOG.0000000000001273

Parsons, J. A., Seay, A. R , & Jacobson M. (2016). Neurologic disorders. In S. Gardner, B. Carter, M. Enzman Hines, & J. Hernández (Eds.), *Merenstein & Gardner's handbook of neonatal intensive care* (8th ed., pp. 727–762). St. Louis, MO: Elsevier.

Pedersen, T., Stokholm, J., Thorsen, J., Mora-Jenses, A., & Bisgaard, H. (2017). Antibiotics in pregnancy increases children's risk of otitis media and ventilation tubes. *Journal of Pediatrics*, 183(4), 153–158. doi:10.1016/j.jpeds.2016.12.046

Perry, S. E., Hockenberry, M. J., Lowdermilk, D. L., & Wilson, D. (2014). *Maternal child nursing care* (5th ed.). St. Louis, MO: Elsevier.

Royal College of Obstetricians and Gynaecologists. (2014). Umbilical cord prolapse (Green-top Guideline No. 50) Retrieved from https://www.rcog.org.uk/globalassets/ documents/guidelines/gtg-50-umbilicalcordprolapse-2014.pdf

Rozance, P., & Rosenberg, A. (2017). The neonate. In S. Gabbee, J. Niebyl, J. Simpson, M. Landon, H. Galan, E. Jauniaux, ... W. Grobman (Eds.), *Obstetrics: Normal and problem pregnancies* (7th ed., pp. 468–496). Philadelphia, PA: Elsevier.

Schauberger, C. W., & Chauhan, S. P. (2009). Emergency cesarean section and the 30-minute rule: Definitions. *American Journal of Perinatology*, 26(3), 221–226. doi:10.1055/s-0028-1103033

Shah, N., & Wusthoff, C. (2016). Intracranial hemorrhage in the neonate. *Neonatal Network*, 35(2), 67–71. doi:10.1891/0730-0832.35.2.67

Swanson, J., & Kinkin, R. (2015). Transition from fetus to newborn. *Pediatric Clinics of North America, 62,* 329–343. doi:10.1016/j.pcl.2014.11.002

Tikkanen, M., Luukkaala, T., Gissler, M., Ritvanen, A., Ylikorkala, O., Paavonen, J., ... Metsäranta, M. (2013). Decreasing perinatal mortality in placental abruption. *Acta Obstetricia et Gynecologica Scandinavica, 92*(3), 298–305. doi:10.1111/aogs.12030

Tita, A., & Andrews, W. (2010). Diagnosis and management of clinical chorioamnionitis. *Clinics in Perinatology, 37*(2), 339–354. doi:10.1016/j.clp.2010.02.003

Ugwumadu, A. (2014). Are we (mis)guided by current guidelines on intrapartum fetal heart rate monitoring? Case for a more physiological approach to interpretation. *BJOG: An International Journal of Obstetrics & Gynaecology, 121*(9), 1063–1070. doi:10.1111/1471-0528.12900

van Rijn, R. R., Bilo, R., & Robben, S. G. (2008). Birth-related mid-posterior rib fractures in neonates: A report of three cases (and a possible fourth case) and a review of the literature. *Pediatric Radiology, 39*(1), 30–34. doi:10.1007/s00247-008-1035-2

Veltman, L. (2017). The "6 A's": A risk manager's guide to emergency cesarean delivery. *Journal of Healthcare Risk Management, 36*(4), 19–24. doi:10.1002/jhrm.21269

Volpe, J. (2018). Injuries of extracranial, cranial, intracranial, spinal cord, and peripheral nervous system structures. In J. Volpe, T. Inder, B. Darras, L. de Vries, A. du Plessis, ... J. Perlman (Eds.), *Volpe's neurology of the newborn* (6th ed., pp. 1093-1123). Philadelphia, PA: Elsevier.

Walfisch, A., & Sheiner, E. (2016). Placenta previa and immediate outcome of the term offspring. *Archives of Gynecology and Obstetrics, 294*(4), 739–744. doi:10.1007/s00404-016-4044-7

World Health Organization. (2018a). Newborns: Reducing mortality. Retrieved from http://www.who.int/mediacentre/factsheets/fs333/en

World Health Organization. (2018b). Preterm birth. Retrieved from http://www.who.int/mediacentre/factsheets/fs363/en

Yli, B., & Kjellmer, I. (2016). Pathophysiology of foetal oxygenation and cell damage during labour. *Best Practice and Research Clinical Obstetrics and Gynaecology, 30,* 9–21. doi:10.1016/j.bpobgyn.2015.05.004

15

DIFFICULT CONVERSATIONS

Ana Arias-Oliveras, Molly F. May, Courtney Komar,
Meghan Bjerke, and Wendy J. Sturtz

LEARNING OBJECTIVES

After completing this chapter, the reader should be able to:
- Determine important aspects of critical conversations with parents and families.
- Discuss palliative care recommendations for infants and families.
- Identify challenges at the end of life and with limiting life-sustaining medical interventions.
- Apply best practices for communicating with parents to provide holistic, family-centered care for high-risk infants.

INTRODUCTION

The beauty of life is inseparable from its fragility. As highlighted in Chapter 14, several factors may disrupt the birth process and result in the delivery of premature, critically ill, or terminally ill infants. Current data indicates that the infant mortality rate is 5.9 per 1,000 live births (Centers for Disease Control and Prevention [CDC], 2018). Birth defects, prematurity, birth complications, and intrapartum-related events are the leading causes

for infant death (CDC, 2018; World Health Organization [WHO], 2018). These circumstances call on neonatal clinicians to coordinate and facilitate difficult conversations with family members.

These difficult conversations may begin during the intrapartum period, the immediate postnatal period, or at any time throughout the birth hospitalization. Unanticipated emergencies that result in premature birth or birth injuries often involve impromptu and complicated discussions with family members prior to the establishment of a trusted relationship between the family and neonatal team. This can be particularly stress provoking for clinicians as well as family members, who are simultaneously dealing with the pain and fatigue associated with labor and delivery.

This chapter is provided to call attention to common factors that affect difficult conversations with family members. This content should not be considered all-inclusive, but rather a stimulus for further theoretical and clinical discussions as well as simulation-based training within graduate and postgraduate training programs. Clinicians and graduate faculty must recognize that critical to any successful communication is awareness and anticipatory planning, along with the ability to convey complex information in a manner understood by the recipient. The opportunity to rehearse information sharing, in particular, information involving complex pathophysiologic problems with moderate to high mortality or morbidity risks, helps rising advanced practice nurses (APNs) and other clinicians develop basic skills to take forward into the clinical arena.

PREPARING FOR DIFFICULT CONVERSATIONS

Death within the first 28 days of life accounts for approximately 46% of all deaths among children less than 5 years of age (WHO, 2018). Infants born prematurely and those with birth defects are particularly vulnerable and, as a result, difficult conversations and decisions fill neonatal intensive care units (NICU) on a daily basis. Factors that influence the delivery of bad news to families include (a) lack of requisite provider education, (b) clinician attitudes, and (c) paternalism.

Clinician Education

Professional standards and guidelines for teamwork and communication training are lacking among graduate and postgraduate curricula (American College of Graduate Medical Education, 2017; National Organization of Nurse Practitioner Faculties, 2013, 2017). As many as 79% of neonatal nurse practitioner students and 41% of neonatology fellows receive no didactic or clinical education and training on communicating difficult or bad news to family members. A paucity of standards and professional guidelines for graduate medical and nursing programs, limited information sharing, and limited availability of continuing education training programs (many of which are considered home-grown programs within healthcare systems) contributes to this problem (Boss, Urban, Barnett, & Arnold, 2013; Botwinski, 2010).

As a result of education gaps, experts report that 43% to 90% of perinatal–neonatal clinicians have "never" or "rarely" received any formal continuing-education training in the delivery of bad news to families of critically ill or terminally ill infants (Boss et al., 2013; Botwinski, 2010; Daboval, Ferretti, & Moore, 2014). This paucity of graduate-level and continuing-education training can encourage feelings of discomfort among providers and erode the effectiveness of these difficult conversations (Daboval et al., 2014).

Clinician Attitudes

Discussions regarding the resuscitation of infants with high mortality risk, the withholding or withdrawal of life support, and do-not-resuscitate (DNR) orders tend to provoke fear among ill-prepared clinicians. Clinicians report fear of being blamed, feeling unprepared to answer questions from parents, and fear of embarrassment associated with losing their composure during these difficult conversations (Bell, Bivoleanu, Stamatin, & Stoicescu, 2014; Boss et al., 2013; Botwinski, 2010; Cortezzo, Sanders, Brownell, & Moss, 2013, 2015; El Sayed, Chan, McAllister, & Hellmann, 2013; McAdams, Erdenebileg, Batra, & Gerelmaa, 2012; Murakami et al., 2015). Recent studies indicate that between 51% and 90% of neonatologists feel "not very" or "not at all" comfortable when speaking with parents about resuscitation at birth of an infant with a small chance of survival, and 50% and 82% feel "not very" or "not at all" comfortable with discussing withdrawal of life support with families of infants with a poor prognosis (Bell et al., 2014; El Sayed et al., 2013; McAdams et al., 2012). According to other data, merely 35.1% of neonatologists feel confident in their communication skills during end-of-life discussions (Cortezzo et al., 2015). Experienced neonatal nurse practitioners also report insecurities with finding a balance between removing all hope and giving false hope to parents and communicating bad news to parents; additional data are needed to quantify perceptions among neonatal APNs and to develop quality-improvement processes to properly educate and equip all clinicians for these difficult conversations (Botwinski, 2010).

Paternalism

Discomfort with initiating difficult conversations, a genuine desire to reduce emotional burden among family members, or authoritarian personality traits may tempt providers to shield parents from bad news; this manifests as paternalistic behavior. For example, treatment decisions may be ordered prior to consultation with family members in the hope that pathologic aberrations can be corrected and parents protected from additional emotional burden. In other circumstances, prognostic uncertainty may leave clinicians unsure of what information to provide parents and when to deliver that information, for fear that premature information sharing may dampen the parents' hope that their child will overcome acute illnesses (Strong, 1984; Vasli, Dehghan-Nayeri, Borim-Nezhad, & Vedadhir, 2015). Others argue that self-serving attitudes may be the fertile soil for the onset of paternalistic behaviors (Butts & Rich, 2016). Regardless, paternalism risks a violation of parental autonomy and shared decision making. Several reports indicate that families recognize when information is purposefully or otherwise omitted from conversations and subsequently experience moral distress (Caeymaex et al., 2013; Daboval & Shidler, 2014; de Boer, van Blijderveen, van Dijk, Duivenvoorden, & Williams, 2012; Janvier, Barrington, & Farlow, 2014; Pasarón, 2013).

APNs are encouraged to maintain a spirit of transparency with families, permitting and encouraging bidirectional conversations and shared decision making. Thoughtful consideration of cultural and spiritual needs is essential to ensure that parents are properly integrated as valued and participatory members of the healthcare team.

DISCUSSIONS OF VIABILITY AND FUTILITY

Although the majority of difficult conversations occur within the NICU unit, it is not uncommon for the neonatal APN to be summoned to the labor and delivery unit, to speak to the parents of a fetus deemed at high risk for death or disability. It is likely that the neonatal APN will function as one part of a multidisciplinary group of specialists who offer their perspective on prognostics and implications for the family unit. These perinatal consultations help parents develop an understanding and expectation of their fetus's early experience outside of the womb. In circumstances in which a fetus meets or challenges the cusp of viability, perinatal consultations offer parents the ability to determine the extent of resuscitation they are comfortable with, or their desire to forego invasive life-saving procedures in exchange for the ability to hold and bond with their infant (Davies, Inglis, Jardine, & Koorts, 2012).

Viability

Periviable birth is defined by the American Academy of Pediatrics (2007) and the American College of Obstetricians and Gynecologists (ACOG) as a "delivery occurring between 20 0/7 weeks to 25 6/7 weeks" (ACOG, & Society for Maternal–Fetal Medicine [SMFM] 2017, p. e188). The most recent data point to survival rates of 5% to 6% among infants born less than 23 weeks of gestation (ACOG & SMFM, 2017). Initiating or withholding aggressive cardiopulmonary resuscitation among infants near the limit of viability is a nagging ethical dilemma; significant variability in hospital preferences, policies, and practices exist across the United States (Rysavy et al., 2015). Although factors such as gender, administration of antenatal steroids, and singleton versus multiple gestation affect outcomes, the most common factors used to predict outcomes are birth weight and gestational age (Raju, Mercer, Burchfield, & Joseph, 2014; Seri & Evans, 2008). Due to the extensive range of severity of outcomes associated with periviable birth, the AAP and ACOG recommend that healthcare providers and families partner in discussions of viability, taking into consideration the parents' preferences as well as survival rates and morbidity data (ACOG & SMFM, 2017; Rysavy et al., 2015).

Futility

Is it possible to identify a patient who is "too sick to benefit" from medical interventions? Similarly, is it possible to identify an objective, working definition of medical futility that is generally accepted across the healthcare system? Historically, the definition of futility was limited to a physician's personal or shared value judgments, or his or her review of 100 prior cases to which the treatment rendered was proven to be useless (Schneiderman, Jecker, & Jonsen, 1990). This definition was thereby expanded to include the synergy of the aforementioned criterion in addition to qualitative and physiologic evidence of futility (Youngner, 1988). However, after decades of subsequent and contentious medical, ethical, and legal debate and a persistent lack of consensus, the American Medical Association (AMA) Council on Ethical and Judicial Affairs (2016) concluded that no single universal definition can be discerned and applied in all circumstances. In fact, anencephaly and brain death may be the only two diagnoses widely accepted as futile, as a 0% chance for conscious existence occurs in these circumstances. Circumstances are unique and, as a result, the AMA suggests that clinicians seek to understand the patient or family's values and goals when discerning medical futility (AMA, 2016). The AMA recommendations are summarized in Table 15.1.

Rendering the conclusion that medical treatment is futile is particularly difficult within intensive care units, which offer complex life-saving medical therapies for the sickest of all subpopulations, from premature infants to geriatric patients (Courtwright, 2012). Technological advancements span from interventional surgeries to repair congenital defects thought to be incompatible with life to extreme postnatal life-saving maneuvers, such as extracorporeal membrane oxygenation. These developments stretch the margin between good outcomes and death and likewise blur the ability for providers and families to discern between life-sustaining and futile medical treatments.

Life-sustaining medical treatments (LSMT) have historically described all interventions used to prolong the life of an infant (AAP Committee on Bioethics, 1994). This has not changed over the years, as the most recent AAP Policy Statement continues to define LSMT as medical interventions that extend the life of a patient (Weise, Okun, Carter, & Christian, 2017). The "best interest" standard typically guides the initiation of LSMT and likewise helps to discern when to forego LSMT. Balancing treatment burden versus benefit contributes to this decision-making process. The AAP publicly supports the withholding or withdrawing of treatments, when associated risks outweigh the projected benefits (Diekema & Botkin, 2009; Porta & Frader, 2007; Weise et al., 2017). According to the AAP, intensive care is indicated if survival is likely and severe morbidity risks are low. On the contrary, intensive care is not indicated when early death or survival with severe morbidities is very likely. Situations may arise that traverse both categories. In these situations, the prognosis may be uncertain but is likely to be very poor and survival may be associated with a diminished quality of life for the child. In these cases, parental values and goals should guide the treatment decisions (Weise et al., 2017).

TABLE 15.1 American Medical Association Recommendations for Determining Medical Futility	
Recommendations for Providers	**Recommendations for Health Policy**
• Discuss with the patient the individual's goals for care, including desired quality of life, and seek to clarify misunderstandings. Include the patient's surrogate in the conversation if possible, even when the patient retains decision-making capacity. • Reassure the patient (and/or surrogate) that medically appropriate interventions, including appropriate symptom management, will be provided unless the patient declines particular interventions (or the surrogate does so on behalf of a patient who lacks capacity). • Negotiate a mutually agreed-on plan of care consistent with the patient's goals and with sound clinical judgment. • Seek assistance from an ethics committee or other appropriate institutional resource if the patient (or surrogate) continues to request care that the physician judges not to be medically appropriate, respecting the patient's right to appeal when review does not support the request. • Seek to transfer care to another physician or another institution willing to provide the desired care in the rare event that disagreement cannot be resolved through available mechanisms, in keeping with ethics guidance. If transfer is not possible, the physician is under no ethical obligation to offer the intervention.	• Acknowledges the need to make context-sensitive judgments about care for individual patients. • Supports physicians in exercising their best professional judgment. • Takes into account community and institutional standards for care. • Uses scientifically sound measures of function or outcome. • Ensures consistency and due process in the event of disagreement over whether an intervention should be provided.

Source: From American Medical Association. (2016). *Chapter 5: Opinions on caring for patients at the end of life.* Retrieved from https://www.ama-assn.org/sites/default/files/media-browser/code-of-medical-ethics-chapter-5.pdf

Two categories of LSMT apply to the neonatal intensive care environment: (a) medically provided fluids and nutrition and (b) respiratory support (Diekema & Botkin, 2009; Weise et al., 2017). Of the two, forgoing artificial nutrition and hydration (FANH) is the most controversial. A paucity of data exists that addresses the long-standing concerns for a potential prolonged death secondary to dehydration. In addition, limited educational resources exist for healthcare professionals struggling with personal or group perceptions of FANH (Rapoport, Shaheed, Newman, Rugg, & Steele, 2013).

Clinicians are encouraged to explore the parents' understanding of the infant's diagnosis, prognosis, and medical treatment plan, as well as their values and goals for their infant. One may initiate this assessment by asking the following questions: "What is your understanding of [insert infant's name]'s medical condition?" or "Please share with me how others have explained [insert infant's name]'s condition or status?" Provide a moment of silence after divulging information for the family to process what has been discussed. Family members may

require clarification of information provided or they may request additional details related to their infant's prognosis. Clinicians may conclude that all available medical treatments offer zero probability of achieving a favorable clinical outcome and no spiritual or physical benefit, yet parents may disagree. Discussions of quality of life, clarifying misunderstandings, and providing careful reassurance that suffering will be avoided are essential to maintaining trust between all parties and to avert futility disputes (Leland, Torke, Wocial, & Helft, 2017). Futility disputes are a primary cause for failed communication and trust between families and clinicians. In fact, data suggest that as many as 50% to 80% of conversations involving treatment decisions of critically ill pediatric and adult patients involve disagreements between family members and clinicians (Leland et al., 2017). Data are lacking specific to families of hospitalized neonates and chronically ill infants who experienced prolonged birth hospitalizations.

Clinicians should avoid instilling false hope during difficult conversations, as this could erode trust and prolong the parents' grieving process. Finally, clinicians must recognize that an ongoing assessment of parental perceptions is crucial to maintaining trust and situational awareness during end-of-life situations. Parental perspectives and emotional, spiritual, or informational needs may shift during the grieving process; a purposeful and holistic integration of family support services is recommended.

Parental Perspectives

Life-threatening illnesses can provoke anxiety and stress, reducing a parent's ability to comprehend complex information provided at one time. In this state of mind, parents often ask questions multiple times, perhaps not to seek different answers, but rather to seek clarification in understanding their infant's current state (Brooten et al., 2013). A preexisting awareness of common parental perspectives of difficult conversations can help clinicians anticipate and prepare talking points, accordingly.

Three common themes describe parental needs during difficult conversations: (a) accurate, honest, and consistent communication from clinicians, expressed in terminology that is easily understood; (b) the ability to participate in choosing medical treatments for their infant; and (c) consistent clinician-driven expressions of empathy, compassion, and respect for their infant and family (Branchett & Stretton, 2012; Brooten et al., 2013; Izatt, 2008; Rosenthal & Nolan, 2013; Sadeghi, Hasanpour, & Heidarzadeh, 2016). Pearls and pitfalls of clinician-to-parent communications are summarized in Table 15.2.

DISCUSSIONS OF END-OF-LIFE CARE

Difficult conversations often involve palliation and end-of-life care. The National Association of Neonatal Nurses (NANN) considers palliative and end-of-life care integral aspects of care of the terminally ill infant (NANN, 2015). Palliative care coexists with curative care to improve the patient's quality of life. End-of-life care supports a peaceful, dignified death for the infant and the provision of support to the family and healthcare providers (NANN, 2015).

Perinatal Palliative Care

The WHO (n.d.) defines *pediatric palliative care* as a model of care that focuses on enhancing quality of life for children and families facing life-threatening illnesses. Palliation focuses on the alleviation of suffering through total care of the mind, body, and spirit (WHO, n.d.). Although the philosophy of palliative care is often associated with the dying process, it is considered multidimensional care that confronts infant suffering and optimizes both life and death, while providing intense family support (Catlin & Carter, 2002; Conway-Orgel & Edlund, 2015; Kenner, Press, & Ryan, 2015). Advancements in healthcare technology, as well as therapeutic modalities, have led to increasing survival of many infants who may not have survived previously; these infants may likely benefit from palliation (Bhatia, 2006; Currie et al., 2016).

Perinatal palliative care (PPC) focuses on prenatal diagnosis and prognosis of life-threatening diseases with collaborative birth planning, to ensure family goals and wishes are honored (Bhatia, 2006; Kukora, Gollehon, & Laventhal, 2017). When a pregnancy or fetal outcome is grave or uncertain, PPC provides an extension of additional support for expecting parents and their families above usual obstetric care that focuses on emotional, sociocultural, and spiritual support (Limbo et al., 2017). Once the life-limiting diagnosis has been determined, or a poor or uncertain prognosis is predicted and shared with the family, a holistic assessment of the family's global needs is pursued. Exploring these unique family characteristics and values allows the creation of an individualized plan of care aligned with the parents' goals. Discussion points for perinatal providers are summarized in Table 15.3.

TABLE 15.2 Information Sharing With Parents: Pearls and Pitfalls	
Communication Pearls	**Communication Pitfalls**
• Accurate, honest, and consistent communication between providers and parents, expressed in terminology that is easily understood • Communications that enable parental decision making • Consistent provider-driven expressions of empathy, compassion, and respect for the infant and family	• Inconsistent, ineffective, or selective information sharing from clinicians to parents • Disputes or conflicts between clinicians and parents • Communications that limit or exclude parental decision making • Insensitive, desensitized, or nonsupportive communications from clinicians to parents

Postnatal Palliative Care

Postnatal palliative care begins after delivery. This may be a continuation of prenatal palliative care or a new care pathway. There are three generally agreed upon categories of infants who benefit from postnatal palliative care: infants (a) with life-limiting or life-threatening congenital anomalies, (b) born at the limits of viability, and (c) with overwhelming illness deemed unresponsive to life-sustaining interventions. Palliative care is intended to guide the family toward death without fear, isolation, or a sense of abandonment (Carter, 2016). Clinicians should prioritize the establishment of an individualized plan of care that is developed in consultation with the family. Parents must be afforded the right to advocate on behalf of their child and partner with medical providers when the burden of care outweighs benefit (Catlin, 2011; Currie et al., 2016). Clear communication must prevail throughout the planning process, as well as once the palliative care plan is established. Frequent and cyclic reassessment of the family's goals and wishes is indicated thereafter and should be provided using specially trained interdisciplinary team members, including pastoral care services, social work, case management, and, in cases in which language barriers risk clear communication between clinicians and families, hospital translators (Feudtner, 2007; Kenner, Press, & Ryan, 2015). The development of this individualized plan of care calls on clinicians to display critical decision making and problem solving, identify interventions necessary to provide holistic care to the family unit, and make logistical decisions differentiated to the environment in which palliation is rendered (Table 15.4).

The transition from curative efforts to palliative care can be contentious. In some situations, discordance may arise among clinicians, families, or both (Catlin, 2011). Disagreements typically occur with discussions of the threshold for cessation of curative efforts. Both clinicians and family members report feelings of moral distress with these conversations (Catlin, 2011; Currie et al., 2016). In fact, a lack of certainty specific to outcomes of life-limiting conditions, extreme prematurity, and among infants with congenital anomalies may cause clinicians (or families) to consider pivoting away from perceivably difficult discussions of PPC. A tandem approach to PPC may be appropriate in these circumstances. The tandem approach offers opportunity for the simultaneous provision of curative and palliative care; a steady increase in palliation occurs with a concurrent decrease in aggressive medical interventions (Carter, 2017; Feudtner, 2007).

TABLE 15.3 Palliative Care Discussions: Suggested Priorities for Clinicians

- Address the fetus or neonate using the designated first name, if available.
- Assess parental understanding of the life-threatening diagnosis.
- Identify family member(s) who assume decision-making responsibility.
- Determine the family's spiritual, social, or cultural needs.
- Discuss support services (e.g., pastoral care, baptism, photography, etc.) and identify family goals and wishes.
- Assess individual parental and collective family coping.

Source: Adapted from Fanaroff, J. M. (2015). Medical ethics in neonatal care. In R. J. Martin, A. A. Fanaroff, & M. C. Walsh (Eds.), *Fanaroff & Martin's neonatal–perinatal medicine* (10th ed., pp. 24–40). St Louis, MO: Elsevier; Janvier, A., Barrington, K., & Farlow, B. (2014). Communication with parents concerning withholding and withdrawing of life-sustaining interventions in neonatology. *Seminars in Perinatology, 38,* 38–46. doi:10.1053/j.semperi.2013.07.007

TABLE 15.4. Key Priorities and Goals With Postnatal Palliative Care

Clinician Priorities	Unique Goals
Problem solving and decision making	• Identify any conflicts among all parties involved (family, nurses, and providers). • Establish family goals and hopes for their child. • Reassess goals if there is a change in condition. • Communicate family goals to the interdisciplinary team. • Maintain consistency in communicating status, prognosis, and overall care of the child. • Discuss all reasonable options of care.
Interventions	• Multidimensional: Improve the quality of life and minimize suffering for patients, family members, and clinical staff. • Holistic, multifaceted approach to ensure the needs of the patient and family are met (e.g., physical, emotional, spiritual, sociocultural, etc.).
Logistics	• Provide high-quality services in various settings, including the hospital and home-consulting services.

Hospice

The National Hospice and Palliative Care Organization defines *hospice care* as "the model for quality, compassionate care for people facing a life-limiting illness" (Friebert & Williams, 2015, p. 1). As such, hospice care is a specialized component of palliative care, used in conjunction with, but not in the absence of, palliation. Pediatric palliative care teams and hospice care teams function as collaborative partners to provide an integrated, holistic model of care to serve the needs of children with life-limiting conditions and their families (AAP, 2013; Friebert & Williams, 2015). These teams are typically composed of physicians, APNs, clinical nurses, pastoral care providers, and a social worker or case manager. This type of care team develops an individualized care plan for pain management and a specialized, integrated medical care based on the goals of treatment, in preparation for the transition to home (Friebert & Williams, 2015). The AAP policy statement on pediatric palliative care and hospice care is summarized in Table 15.5.

TABLE 15.5 Core Commitments of Hospice
• Provides patient-centered care with family engagement
• Respects and partners with patients and families
• Pursues care that is high quality, readily accessible, and equitable
• Provides care across the age spectrum and life span that is integrated into the continuum of care
• Ensures that all clinicians can provide basic palliative care and consult PPC–PHC specialists in a timely manner
• Improves care through research and quality-improvement efforts

Source: American Academy of Pediatrics Section on Hospice and Palliative Medicine, & Committee on Hospital Care. (2013). Pediatric palliative care and hospice care commitments, guidelines, and recommendations. *Pediatrics, 132*(5), 966–972. doi:10.1542/peds.2013-2731

BEREAVEMENT

Births are heralded with great celebration, anticipatory joy, hopes, and dreams (Kendall & Guo, 2008). The loss of a baby, whether anticipated or unexpected, can cause traumatic grief (Cacciatore, 2016). Feelings of loss of the baby, oneself, parental role, or womanhood and safety may be expressed (Côté-Arsenault & Denney-Koelsch, 2016). Grief is felt by siblings, extended family, and friends. It is essential to understand grieving as a natural process linked with death and dying. Clinicians should facilitate a collaborative and interprofessional approach to supporting family members throughout the grief process. In most circumstances, grief leads to acceptance of the loss.

Kübler-Ross and Kessler (2005) describe five behaviors, or emotional states, that are often exhibited during the grieving process (Table 15.6). According to

TABLE 15.6. Kübler-Ross Stages of Grief	
Stage	**Key Characteristics**
Denial	• Characterized by feelings of disbelief; stunned after receiving bad news. • This stage may take a few hours to a few weeks. • The individual may compartmentalize the loss or may have outbursts of anger and intense distress.
Anger	• Once the individual is aware of the significance of the loss he or she can move onward. • In some cultures, it is prohibited to express anger in a social context. • This may lead to depression and a sense of guilt. "Why me?" "Is this my fault?" • Anger may be expressed toward any member of the healthcare team. • If this stage is prolonged, it may inhibit continuation into the subsequent stages.
Bargaining	• This stage may last a few months or even a few years. • Can be observed with the initial stage of denial. The individual may bargain with God, or another spiritual/religious deity.
Depression	• The initial acceptance of the loss may trigger depressive episodes. • Social interactions with friends and family may cease or be limited. • Significant variability in the duration of this stage.
Acceptance	• Completes the grieving process. • Separation of life's meaning from the lost relationship.

Source: Adapted from Kübler-Ross, E., & Kessler, D. (2005). *On grief and grieving: Finding the meaning of grief through the five stages of loss.* New York, NY: Scribner.

Kübler-Ross and Kessler (2005), grieving is an individualized, asynchronous, and progressive experience that may span several months to years; a lock-step methodology to grieving is not supported in the literature, nor suggested here. Clinicians must acknowledge that reactions to a loss are variable and may be influenced by past experiences, values, and cultural or social influences (Gardner & Dickey, 2011). Clinicians should assess for risk factors that may exacerbate grieving, which may include a pre-existing psychiatric disorder, symptoms of poor health, or altered health literacy. In these circumstances, mental health services or other specialized services may be indicated.

COMMUNICATION TOOLS FOR CLINICIANS

Above all, the delivery of bad news should be conveyed in an empathetic manner to allow for a meaningful exchange between the clinicians and families. Families will always remember the clinician who communicates well; alternatively, they will be hard pressed to forgive a clinician who communicates poorly (Hollyday & Buonocore, 2015). Clinicians should be mindful of fluctuating emotions among parents or family members; mood fluctuations are normal and important to the grieving process (Cacciatore, 2016).

The use of a mnemonic tool is a practical method to guide novice clinicians through difficult conversations. Mnemonics tend to make long-term memories easily retrievable and recognizable, and allow clinicians to focus on empathetic, clear communications with families. Three mnemonics used to guide difficult conversations within the NICU and pediatric and oncology units are the SOBPIE, SPIKES, and ABCDE methods (Table 15.7).

SOBPIE

Janvier, Barrington, and Farlow (2014) developed the SOBPIE (situation, opinions and options, basic human interactions, parental concerns, information, and emotion) method to facilitate emotionally delicate discussions in the NICU in a compassionate and respectful manner. This method enables clinicians to personalize their difficult interactions with parents in a manner that includes a discussion of emotions, regrets, hope, quality of life, resiliency, and relationships; each person is respected as unique and individuality is accepted (Janvier et al., 2014). *Situation* refers to the determination of terminal illness or survivability. *Options and opinions* refer to purposeful identification and bracketing of provider biases with the identification of treatment options that can be presented to the parents. *Basic human interaction* is, as its name implies, genuine interaction that values each person as a unique sum of the whole team of decision makers. Information relates to the provision of balanced information (risks and benefits) to the parents. Finally, *emotion* refers to the purposeful provision of sensitive, respectful communications that address parental emotional, psychosocial, or grieving needs (Janvier et al., 2014).

TABLE 15.7. Mnemonic Guides for Difficult Conversations

Author	Mnemonic Device
Janvier, Barrington, & Farlow (2014)	• **S**ituational awareness • **O**pinions and **O**ptions • **B**asic human interactions • **P**arental concerns • **I**nformational needs • **E**motional responses
Baile et al. (2000)	• **S**et the stage • **P**atient/family perception • **I**nvitation—Asks the family whether they are ready and how much they would like to know • **K**nowledge—Educate the family about the medical situation • **E**xplore and empathize with emotions • **S**ummarize the strategy and next steps and decision points
Rabow & McPhee (1999)	• **A**dvanced preparation • **B**uilding a therapeutic environment and relationship • **C**ommunicating well • **D**ealing with patient and family reactions • **E**ncouraging and validating emotions

SPIKES

Baile and colleagues' (2000) SPIKES strategy was originally developed for use by oncologists. The SPIKES (setting the stage, perceptions, invitation, knowledge, exploring emotions, summarizing) strategy offers a step-by-step framework for clinicians relaying bad news. This method is particularly helpful when (a) procuring patient information, (b) relaying troublesome or ominous clinical information to parents, (c) offering emotional aid to patients and family members, and (d) encouraging collaboration when devising a plan of care.

ABCDE

Rabow and McPhee's (1999) **ABCDE** communication model was originally designed for use in the adult population after Rabow and McPhee, internal medicine physicians, recognized the lack of formal training clinicians receive in the skill of conveying bad news. **A**dvanced preparation cues clinicians to prepare for questions that may arise during the difficult conversation, to ensure the ability to meet the parents' informational and educational needs. **B**uilding a therapeutic environment relates to securing a safe, confidential environment where parents can speak candidly and without fear of retaliation or judgment. **C**ommunicating well reminds clinicians that parents desire transparency and open communication channels; reinforcing this priority during difficult conversations is essential. **D**ealing with patient and family reactions to bad news reminds clinicians to appraise the response to information sharing, which may be exhibited differently among family members; using interdisciplinary support services, including social work and pastoral care, may help families who struggle with grief. Finally, **e**ncouraging and validating parental emotions is most critical and essential; rigidity in the face of complexity is toxic (Rabow & McPhee, 1999).

CONCLUSION

Transmission of information is not the only goal of interpersonal communication. Good communication forms the foundation of trust between healthcare providers and families (Hollyday & Buonocore, 2015). Effective communication is the making of a human connection and can serve as the foundation for a relationship to form over time. These interactions are not limited to words, but also caring gestures and interactions based on a sincere desire to seek to understand families and value their point of view. Listening and eliciting information are necessary and vital activities for the neonatal APN to tailor methods of communication to parents and families in ways that are helpful and meaningful to them. Developing an individualized, holistic care plan for each patient and family is essential to enhancing the parent–interdisciplinary team relationship. Parents will have a sense of autonomy and be active participants in the care rendered for their child.

LEARNING TOOLS AND RESOURCES

Podcasts

 Difficult Conversations

Anna Arias-Oliveras and Wendy J. Sturtz

Discussion Prompts

Scenario: You are taking care of baby A. A. born at 22 6/7 weeks gestation and now 4 days old. The head ultrasound reveals that the infant has sustained bilateral grade 4 intraventricular hemorrhage. Currently, A. A. is on a conventional ventilator receiving parenteral nutrition via a peripherally inserted central catheter line and enteral feeds of donor breast milk (1 mL every 6 hours). Vital signs have been stable within the last 24 hours. His parents are anxiously awaiting the results of the head ultrasound and have asked whether you may provide them with information.

1. As a member of the interdisciplinary team who will participate in the delivery of the ultrasound results, what special considerations should be addressed? Which are a priority?
2. The parents would like to continue with the current medical plan without any limitations to care. On day of life 7, A. A. became critically ill, requiring aggressive resuscitative interventions. Once A. A. is stabilized, a discussion with the family is warranted. Taking into consideration the best-interest standard, who is best to determine futility and who is best to define the quality of life for A. A.? With the current advancements in neonatal intensive care, should all medical interventions continue to be offered?
3. As an APN, what information is crucial in supporting this family through the grieving process? Consider cultural, social, spiritual, and religious aspects in setting goals with this family.

Advice From the Authors

"As you read through each section, reflect on past experiences with a particular family, mother, and patient. There is a large spectrum to the degree of loss. This may be a term infant transferred to the NICU for a sepsis evaluation, prematurity, an infant born with congenital anomalies, unexpected diagnosis such as sexual differentiation, etc. What role did you take during the hospital stay? Any difficulties conveying information or words of encouragement? Use the tools provided in this chapter to enhance your experiences with a family."

—Ana Arias-Oliveras, MSN, CRNP, NNP-BC

"As a neonatal advanced practice nurse, you will work closely with your obstetric and pediatric colleagues to provide comprehensive care to mothers, babies, and families. It is critical to think about what stressors and risk factors exist that are important for you to be aware of as you become the primary advanced practice caretaker for the infant in the NICU. The evolution of life in the NICU as a family unit is multifactorial and being a nurse practitioner gives you the unique role to be able to be a bridge among families, nursing staff, and the medical team. This is essential for all families that have had their birth and newborn experience interrupted by admission to the NICU and a great opportunity for all caregivers to come together in understanding and empathy."

—Molly F. May, MSN, CRNP, NNP-BC

"For many parents and families, the NICU is terrifying new territory, especially when their baby is given a poor prognosis. In those circumstances, advanced practice providers need to deliver bad news to families. As a student or novice advanced practice provider, take every opportunity to listen in on these conversations. This will help you to not only grow and develop your own words when holding difficult discussions, but also your confidence. Lastly, always remember to show empathy and compassion when interacting with families."

—Courtney Komar, MSN, APRN, NNP-BC

"Sharing sad or scary news is never easy, but as a neonatal nurse practitioner (NNP) student or a novice nurse practitioner it can be overwhelmingly difficult. I have found the value of listening and connecting with families to be helpful, both as a bedside nurse and an NNP student. I ask myself, 'How would I want someone to convey this information to me? How would I feel in this moment, if I were a parent to this baby?' Take your knowledge and feelings to heart and never forget to empathize with the family, no matter how small, simple, or complex the problem may seem."

—Meghan Bjerke, MSN, APRN, NNP-BC

"Apply information learned in this chapter to 'real world' experiences. Seek out the topics discussed in this chapter in ongoing patient and family encounters, explore varied presentations and implications in your patients, practice communication frameworks or new language, and incorporate clinical pearls in patient encounters. Create a relevant narrative or reflect on a patient's presentation and history using new information—this 'storytelling' contributes to a deeper understanding of concepts. Recall past personal or patient experiences that relate to newly acquired knowledge and skills. Both reflection on past experiences as well as heightened awareness as you approach new learning opportunities are important components of your education."

—Wendy J. Sturtz, MD

References

American Academy of Pediatrics Committee on Bioethics (1994). Guidelines on forgoing life-sustaining medical treatment. *Pediatrics, 93*(3), 532–536. Retrieved from http://pediatrics. aappublications.org/content/pediatrics/93/3/532.full.pdf

American Academy of Pediatrics Committee on Fetus and Newborn. (2007). Noninitiation or withdrawal of intensive care for high-risk newborns. *Pediatrics, 119*(2), 401–403. doi:10.1542/peds.2006-3180

American Academy of Pediatrics Section on Hospice and Palliative Medicine, & Committee on Hospital Care. (2013). Pediatric palliative care and hospice care commitments, guidelines and recommendations. *Pediatrics, 132*, 966–972. doi:10.1542/peds.2013-2731

American College of Graduate Medical Education. (2017). ACGME program requirements for graduate medical education in pediatrics. Retrieved from https://www.acgme. org/Portals/0/PFAssets/ProgramRequirements/320_pediatrics_2017-07-01.pdf

American College of Obstetricians and Gynecologists, & Society for Maternal–Fetal Medicine. (2017). Obstetric Care Consensus: Periviable birth. *Obstetrics & Gynecology, 130*(4), e187–e199. Retrieved from https://www.acog.org/-/media/Obstetric-Care-Consensus-Series/occ006.pdf?dmc=1&ts=20180129T0128313960.

American Medical Association. (2016). *Chapter 5: Opinions on caring for patients at the end of life.* Retrieved from https://www.ama-assn.org/sites/default/files/media-browser/code-of-medical-ethics-chapter-5.pdf

Annas, G. J. (1991). Determining the fate of gestational mothers. *Women's Health Issue, 1*(3), 158–160. Retrieved from https://www.whijournal.com/article/S1049-3867(05)80124-0/pdf

Baile, W. F., Buckman, R., Lenzi, R., Glober, G., Beale, E. A., & Kudelka, A. P. (2000). SPIKES—A six-step protocol for delivering bad news: Application to the patient with cancer. *The Oncologist, 5*(4), 302–311 doi:10.1634/theoncologist.5-4-302

Bell, E., Bivoleanu, A., Stamatin, M., & Stoicescu, S. (2014). Physician attitudes in Romania toward withholding and withdrawal of intensive care for infants with very poor prognosis. *American Journal of Perinatology, 31*(6), 477–482. doi:10.1055/s-0033-1353440

Bhatia, J. (2006). Palliative care in the fetus and newborn. *Journal of Perinatology, 26*(Suppl. 1), S24–S26. doi:10.1038/sj.jp.7211468

Boss, R. D., Urban, A., Barnett, M. D., & Arnold, R. M. (2013). Neonatal Critical Care Communication (NC3): Training NICU physicians and nurse practitioners. *Journal of Perinatology, 33*(8), 642–646. doi:10.1038/jp.2013.22

Botwinski, C. (2010). NNP education in neonatal end-of-life care: A needs assessment. *American Journal of Maternal/Child Nursing, 35*(5), 286–292. doi:10.1097/NMC.0b013e3181e62440

Branchett, K., & Stretton, J. (2012). Neonatal palliative and end of life care: What parents want from professionals. *Journal of Neonatal Nursing, 18*(2), 40–44. doi:10.1016/j.jnn.2012.01.009

Brooten, D., Youngblut, J. M., Seagrave, L., Caicedo, C., Hawthorne, D., Hidalgo, I., & Roche, R. (2013). Parent's perceptions of health care providers actions around child ICU death: What helped, what did not. *American Journal of Hospice and Palliative Medicine, 30*(1), 40–49. doi:10.1177/1049909112444301

Butts, J. B., & Rich, K. L. (2016). *Nursing ethics: Across the curriculum and into practice* (4th ed.). Burlington, MA: Jones & Bartlett Learning.

Cacciatore, J. (2016). When the unthinkable happens: A mindfulness approach to perinatal and pediatric death. In B. P. Black, P. M. Wright, & R. K. Limbo (Eds.), *Perinatal and pediatric bereavement in nursing and other health professions* (pp. 97–110). New York, NY: Springer Publishing.

Caeymaex, L., Jousselme, C., Vasilescu, C., Danan, C., Falissard, B., Bourrat, M., … Speranza, M. (2013). Perceived role in end-of-life decision making in the NICU affects long-term parental grief response. *Archives of Disease in Childhood: Fetal and Neonatal Edition, 98*(1), F26–F31. doi:10.1136/archdischild-2011-301548

Carter, B. S. (2016). More than medication: Perinatal palliative care. *Acta Pædiatrica, 105*(11), 1255–1256. doi:10.1111/apa.13529

Carter, B. S. (2017). Liminality in pediatric palliative care. *American Journal of Hospice and Palliative Medicine, 34*(4), 297–300. doi:10.1177/1049909116629758

Catlin, A. (2011). Transition from curative efforts to purely palliative care for neonates: Does physiology matter? *Advances in Neonatal Care, 11*(3), 216–222. doi:10.1097/ANC.0b013e31821be411

Catlin, A., & Carter, B. (2002). Creation of a neonatal end-of-life palliative care protocol. *Journal of Perinatology, 22*(3), 184–195. doi:10.1038/sj.jp.7210687

Centers for Disease Control and Prevention. (2018). Infant mortality. Retrieved from https://www.cdc.gov/reproductive-health/maternalinfanthealth/infantmortality.htm

Chandra, A., Martinez, G. M., Mosher, W. D., Abma, J. C., & Jones, J. (2005). Fertility, family planning, and reproductive health of U.S. women: Data from the 2002 National Survey of Family Growth. Hyattsville, MD: National Center for Health Statistics. Retrieved from https://www.cdc.gov/nchs/data/series/sr_23/sr23_025.pdf

Conway-Orgel, M., & Edlund, B. J. (2015). Challenges in change: The perils and pitfalls of implementing a palliative care program in the neonatal intensive care unit. *Journal of Hospice & Palliative Nursing, 17*(3), 206–212. doi: 10.1097/NJH.0000000000000150

Cortezzo, D. E., Sanders, M. R., Brownell, E., & Moss, K. (2013). Neonatologists' perspectives of palliative and end-of-life care in neonatal intensive care units. *Journal of Perinatology, 33*(9), 731–735. doi:10.1038/jp.2013.38

Cortezzo, D. E., Sanders, M. R., Brownell, E., & Moss, K. (2015). End-of-life care in the neonatal intensive care unit: Experiences of staff and parents. *American Journal of Perinatology, 32*(8), 713–724. doi:10.1055/s-0034-1395475

Cote-Arsenault, D., & Denney-Koelsch, E. (2016). "Have no regrets:" Parents' experiences and developmental tasks in pregnancy with a lethal fetal diagnosis. *Social Science and Medicine, 154*, 100–109. doi:10.1016/j.socscimed.2016.02.033

Courtwright, A. (2012). Who is "too sick to benefit?" *Hastings Center Report, 42*(4), 41–47. doi:10.1002/hast.51

Currie, E. R., Christian, B. J., Hinds, P., Perna, S., Robinson, P., Day, P., & Meneses, K. (2016). Parent perspectives of neonatal intensive care at end-of-life. *Journal of Pediatric Nursing, 31*, 478–489. doi:10.1016/j.pedn.2016.03.023

Daboval, T., Ferretti, E., & Moore, G. P. (2014). Innovative holistic teaching in a Canadian neonatal perinatal residency program. *Hastings Center Report, 44*(6), 21–25. doi:10.1002/hast.384

Daboval, T., & Shidler, S. (2014). Ethical framework for shared decision making in the neonatal intensive care unit: Communicative ethics. *Paediatrics & Child Health, 19*(6), 302–304. doi:10.1093/pch/19.6.302.

Davies, M., Inglis, G., Jardine, L., & Koorts, P. (2012). *Antenatal consults: A guide for neonatologists and paediatricians*. Sydney, Australia: Elsevier.

de Boer, J., van Blijderveen, G., van Dijk, G., Duivenvoorden, H. J., & Williams, M. (2012). Implementing structured, multiprofessional medical ethical decision-making in a neonatal intensive care unit. *Journal of Medical Ethics, 38*(10), 596–601. doi:10.1136/medethics-2011-100250

Diekema, D. S., & Botkin, J. R. (2009). Forgoing medically provided nutrition and hydration in children. *Pediatrics, 124*(2), 813–822. doi:10.1542/peds.2009-1299

El Sayed, M. F., Chan, M., McAllister, M., & Hellmann, J. (2013). End-of-life care in Toronto neonatal intensive care units: Challenges for physician trainees. *Archives of Disease in Childhood: Fetal and Neonatal Edition, 98*(6), F528–F533. doi:10.1136/archdischild-2012-303000

Gardner, S. L., & Dickey, L. A. (2011). Grief and perinatal loss. In S. L. Gardner, B. S. Carter, M. Enzman-Hines, & J. Hernandez (Eds.), *Merenstein & Gardner's handbook of neonatal intensive care* (7th ed., pp. 898–937). St. Louis, MO: Mosby.

Fanaroff, J. M. (2015). Medical ethics in neonatal care. In R. J. Martin, A. A. Fanaroff, & M. C. Walsh (Eds.), *Fanaroff & Martin's neonatal–perinatal medicine* (10th ed., pp. 24–40). St. Louis, MO: Elsevier.

Feudtner, C. (2007). Collaborative communication in pediatric palliative care: A foundation for problem-solving and decision-making. *Pediatric Clinics of North America, 54*(5), 583–607. doi:10.1016/j.pcl.2007.07.008

Friebert, S., & Williams, C. (2015). *NHPCO's facts and figures: Pediatric palliative and hospice care in America*. Alexandria, VA: National Hospice and Palliative Care Organization. Retrieved from https://www.nhpco.org/sites/default/files/public/quality/Pediatric_Facts-Figures.pdf

Hollyday, S., & Buonocore, D. (2015). Breaking bad news and discussion goals of care in the intensive care unit. *AACN Advanced Critical Care, 26*(2), 131–141. doi:10.1097/NCI.0000000000000082

Izatt, S. (2008). Educational perspectives. *NeoReviews, 9*(8), e321–e325. doi:10.1542/neo.9-8-e321

Janvier, A., Barrington, K., & Farlow, B. (2014). Communication with parents concerning withholding or withdrawing of life-sustaining interventions in neonatology. *Seminars in Perinatology, 38*(1), 38–46. doi:10.1053/j.semperi.2013.07.007

Kendall, A., & Guo, W. (2008). Evidence-based neonatal bereavement care. *Newborn and Infant Nursing Reviews, 8*(3), 131–135. doi:10.1053/j.nainr.2008.06.011

Kenner, C., Press, J., & Ryan, D. (2015). Recommendations for palliative and bereavement care in the NICU: A family-centered integrative approach. *Journal of Perinatology, 35* (Suppl. 1), S19–S23. doi:10.1038/jp.2015.145.

Kübler-Ross, E., & Kessler, D. (2005) *On grief and grieving: Finding the meaning of grief through the five stages of loss*. New York, NY: Scribner.

Kukora, S., Gollehon, N., & Laventhal, N. (2017). Antenatal palliative care consultation: Implications for decision-making and perinatal outcomes in a single-centre experience. *Archives of Disease in Childhood: Fetal and Neonatal Edition, 102*(1), F12–F16. doi:10.1136/archdischild-2016-311027

Leland, B. D., Torke, A. M., Wocial, L. D., & Helft, P. R. (2017). Futility disputes: A review of the literature and proposed model for dispute navigation through trust building. *Journal of Intensive Care Medicine, 32*(9), 523–527. doi:10.1177/0885066616666001

Limbo, R., Brandon, D., Côté-Arsenault, D., Kavanaugh, K., Kuebelbeck, A., & Wool, C. (2017). Perinatal palliative care as an essential element of childbearing choices. *Nursing Outlook, 65*(1), 123–125. doi:10.1016/j.outlook.2016.12.003

McAdams, R. M., Erdenebileg, A., Batra, M., & Gerelmaa, Z. (2012). Attitudes of healthcare providers towards non-initiation and withdrawal of neonatal resuscitation for preterm infants in Mongolia. *Journal of Health, Population and Nutrition, 30*(3), 346–352. doi:10.3329/jhpn.v30i3.12298

Mercer, B. M. (2017). Periviable birth and the shifting limit of viability. *Clinics in Perinatology, 44*, 283–286. doi:10.1016/j.clp.2017.02.002

Murakami, M., Yokoo, K., Ozawa, M., Fujimoto, S., Funaba, Y., & Hattori, M. (2015). Development of a neonatal end-of-life care education program for NICU nurses in Japan. *Journal of Obstetric, Gynecologic, & Neonatal Nursing, 44*(4), 481–491. doi:10.1111/1552-6909.12569

National Association of Neonatal Nurses. (2015). Palliative and end-of-life care for newborns and infants: Position statement #3063. Retrieved from http://nann.org/uploads/About/PositionPDFS/1.4.5_Palliative%20and%20End%20of%20Life%20Care%20for%20Newborns%20and%20Infants.pdf

National Consensus Project for Quality Palliative Care. (2013). *Clinical practice guidelines for quality palliative care* (3rd ed.). Retrieved from https://www.nationalcoalitionhpc.org/ncp-guidelines-2013

National Organization of Nurse Practitioner Faculties. (2013). *Population-focused nurse practitioner competencies*. Retrieved from https://cdn.ymaws.com/www.nonpf.org/resource/resmgr/competencies/populationfocusnpcomps2013.pdf

National Organization of Nurse Practitioner Faculties. (2017). *Nurse practitioner core competencies content*. Retrieved from http://c.ymcdn.com/sites/www.nonpf.org/resource/resmgr/competencies/2017_NPCoreComps_with_Curric.pdf

Pasarón, R. (2013). Neonatal bioethical perspectives: Practice considerations. *Neonatal Network, 32*(3), 184–192. doi:10.1891/0730-0832.32.3.184

Porta, N., & Frader, J. (2007). Withholding hydration and nutrition in newborns. *Theoretical Medicine and Bioethics, 28*(5), 443–451. doi:10.1007/s11017-007-9049-6

Rabow, M. W., & McPhee, S. J. (1999). Beyond breaking bad news: How to help patients who suffer. *Western Journal of Medicine, 171*(4), 260–263.

Raju, T. N. K., Mercer, B. M., Burchfield, D. J., & Joseph, J. G. F., Jr. (2014). Periviable birth: Executive summary of a joint workshop by the Eunice Kennedy Shriver National Institute of Child Health and Human Development, Society for Maternal-Fetal Medicine, American Academy of Pediatrics, and American College of Obstetricians and Gynecologists. *Obstetrics and Gynecology, 123*(5), 1083–1096. doi:10.1097/AOG.0000000000000243

Rapoport, A., Shaheed, J., Newman, C., Rugg, M., & Steele, R. (2013). Parental perceptions of forgoing artificial nutrition and hydration during end-of-life care. *Pediatrics, 131*(5), 861–869. doi:10.1542/peds.2012-1916

Rosenthal, S. A., & Nolan, M. T. (2013). A meta-ethnography and theory of parental ethical decision making in the neonatal intensive care unit. *Journal of Obstetric, Gynecologic, & Neonatal Nursing, 42*(4), 492–502. doi:10.1111/1552-6909.12222

Rysavy, M. A., Li, L., Bell, E. F., Das, A., Hintz, S. R., Stoll, B. J., … Higgins, R. D. (2015). Between-hospital variation in treatment and outcomes in extremely preterm infants. *New England Journal of Medicine, 372*(19), 1801–1811. doi:10.1056/NEJMoa1410689

Sadeghi, N., Hasanpour, M., & Heidarzadeh, M. (2016). Information and communication needs of parents in infant end-of-life: A qualitative study. *Iranian Red Crescent Medical Journal, 18*(6), e25665. doi:10.5812/ircmj.25665

Schneiderman, L. J., Jecker, N. S., & Jonsen, A. R. (1990). Medical futility: Its meaning and ethical implications. *Annals of Internal Medicine, 112*(12), 949. doi:10.7326/0003-4819-112-12-949

Seri, I., & Evans, J. (2008). Limits of viability: Definition of the gray zone. *Journal of Perinatology, 28*(Suppl. 1), S4–S8. doi:10.1038/jp.2008.42

Strong, C. (1984). Paternalism in the neonatal intensive care unit. *Theoretical Medicine, 5*(1), 105–116. doi:10.1007/BF00489250

Tibballs, J. (2007). Legal basis for ethical withholding and withdrawing life-sustaining medical treatment from infants and children. *Journal of Paediatrics and Child Health, 43*(4), 230–236. doi:10.1111/j.1440-1754.2007.01028.x

Vasli, P., Dehghan-Nayeri, N., Borim-Nezhad, L., & Vedadhir, A. (2015). Dominance of paternalism in family-centered care in the pediatric intensive care unit (PICU): An ethnographic study. *Issues in Comprehensive Pediatric Nursing, 38*(2), 118–135. doi:10.3109/01460862.2015.1035464

Weise, K. L., Okun, A. L., Carter, B. S., & Christian, C. W. (2017). Guidance on forgoing life-sustaining medical treatment. *Pediatrics, 140*(3), e20171905. doi:10.1542/peds.2017-1905.

Wool, C., Côté-Arsenault, D., Black B. P., Denney-Koelsch, E., Kim, S., & Kavanaugh, K. (2016). Provision of services in perinatal palliative care: A multicenter survey in the United States. *Journal of Palliative Medicine. 19*(3), 279–285. doi:10.1089/jpm.2015.0266

World Health Organization. (n.d.). WHO definition of palliative care. Retrieved from http://www.who.int/cancer/palliative/definition/en

World Health Organization. (2018). Newborns: Reducing mortality. Retrieved from http://www.who.int/mediacentre/factsheets/fs333/en

Youngner, S. J. (1988). Who defines futility? *Journal of the American Medical Association, 260*(14), 2094–2095. doi:10.1001/jama.1988.03410140106033

INDEX